The
ENCYCLOPEDIA
of
MICROSCOPY

Edited by

GEORGE L. CLARK

Research Professor of Analytical Chemistry, Emeritus,
University of Illinois, Urbana, Illinois

REINHOLD PUBLISHING CORPORATION, *NEW YORK*

CHAPMAN & HALL, LTD., *LONDON*

Printed in the United States of America by
THE WAVERLY PRESS, INC., BALTIMORE, MD.

CONTRIBUTING AUTHORS

A

KENNETH W. ANDREWS
The United Steel Companies Ltd., England

B

ALBERT V. BAEZ
Harvey Mudd College
THOMAS F. BATES
Pennsylvania State University
JOHN H. BENDER
Los Alamos Scientific Laboratory
JAMES R. BENFORD
Bausch & Lomb, Inc.
C. G. BERGERON
University of Illinois
A. BERGSTRAND
Sabbatsbergs Hospital, Sweden
F. P. BOHATIRCHUK
University of Ottawa, Canada
W. BOLLMANN
Battelle Memorial Institute, Switzerland
WILLIAM. A. BONNER
Southwestern Medical School of the University of Texas
R. BORASKY
University of Illinois
D. E. BRADLEY
Associated Electrical Industries, England

C

RICHARD D. CADLE
Stanford Research Institute
GEORGE L. CLARK
University of Illinois
GERMAIN CROSSMON
Bausch & Lomb, Inc.

D

NORMAN L. DOCKUM
General Electric Company

FLOYD DUNN
University of Illinois
J. DYSON
Associated Electrical Industries, England
N. A. DYSON
University of Birmingham, England

E

WESLEY B. ESTILL
Sandia Corporation

F

M. L. FEENEY
University of California Medical Center
F. GORDON FOSTER
Bell Telephone Laboratories
JAMES A. FREEMAN
U. S. Public Health Service
WILLIAM J. FRY
University of Illinois
CHARLES C. FULTON
Department of Health, Education and Welfare

G

L. K. GARRON
University of California Medical Center
R. L. GREGORY
University of Cambridge, England

H

M. E. HAINE
Associated Electrical Industries, England
OLLE HALLÉN
University of Göteborg, Sweden
F. A. HAMM
Minnesota Mining and Manufacturing Company
BURTON L. HENKE
Pomona College

iii

Contributing Authors

L. L. Hundley
Southwestern Medical School of the University of Texas

I

Shinya Inoué
Dartmouth Medical School

J. Isings
Central Laboratory T. N. O., Holland

Kazuo Ito
Japan Electron Optics Laboratory Co., Ltd., Japan

J

William Johnson
The United Steel Companies Ltd., England

Raymond Jonnard
The Prudential Insurance Company of America

B. E. Juniper
Oxford University, England

K

Ernest H. Kalmus
University of California

P. M. Kelly
University of Cambridge, England

Charles J. Koester
American Optical Company

Motoi Kumai
University of Chicago

L

William R. Lasko
United Aircraft Corporation

Donald E. Laskowski
Armour Research Foundation of Illinois Institute of Technology

K. Little
Nuffield Department of Orthopedic Surgery, England

M

W. K. McEwen
University of California Medical Center

L. Marton
National Bureau of Standards

Ludwig J. Mayer
General Mills, Inc.

C. W. Melton
Battelle Memorial Institute

P. O'B. Montgomery
Southwestern Medical School of the University of Texas

Erwin Müller
Pennsylvania State University

Jean M. Mutchler
Linde Company

N

Joseph D. Nicol
Michigan State University

W. C. Nixon
University of Cambridge, England

J. Nutting
University of Cambridge, England

O

Ronald H. Ottewill
University of Cambridge, England

P

D. H. Page
British Paper and Board Industry Research Association, England

H. H. Pattee
Stanford University

Ong Sing Poen
Pomona College

R

Johannes A. G. Rhodin
Bellevue Medical Center

T. G. Rochow
American Cyanamid Company

George L. Royer
American Cyanamid Company

S

J. Salmon
Laboratoire de Biologie Vegetale I, France

iv

R. L. deC. H. SAUNDERS
Dalhousie University, Canada

C. M. SCHWARTZ
Battelle Memorial Institute

D. SCOTT
National Engineering Laboratory, Scotland

MICHAEL SEAL
University of Cambridge, England

K. C. A. SMITH
Pulp and Paper Research Institute of Canada, Canada

JOHN D. STEELY
Los Alamos Scientific Laboratory

T

J. H. TALBOT
Transvaal and Orange Free State Chamber of Commerce, Africa

V. J. TENNERY
Motorola Corporation

W

ERNEST E. WAHLSTROM
University of Colorado

MASARU WATANABE
Japan Electron Optics Laboratory Co., Ltd., Japan

ERWIN K. WEISE
University of Illinois

ALVAR P. WILSKA
University of Arizona

R. E. WRIGHT
Shell Chemical Company

PREFACE

With genuine pleasure and pride this "Encyclopedia of Microscopy" is presented as the fourth in a series of Reinhold contemporary, integrated compilations of rapidly developing areas of science, following the "Encyclopedia of Chemistry" (1957), the "Encyclopedia of Chemistry Supplement" (1958), and the "Encyclopedia of Spectroscopy" (December, 1960). Actually, "Spectroscopy" and "Microscopy" were planned, projected, assembled and edited concurrently as twin volumes, but of necessity there was an interval of a few months in publication of the two, or a slightly delayed birth, as it were, of the second twin.

These two great instrumental techniques, valuable in so many disciplines, are so intimately related and interwoven that the simultaneous development of encyclopedias was the most logical procedure. Even though microscopy as a science is about three centuries old and spectroscopy only one, the common background and origins are well exemplified in the respective historical articles by Professor E. K. Weise. It may not be surprising, then, that one Preface was written originally for both Encyclopedias. This has appeared already in "Spectroscopy," and it is hoped that users of this volume will have the opportunity to read this more extended introduction to the pair of volumes, as well as to browse in a kindred science.

The "Encyclopedia of Microscopy" is the fruit of the joint efforts of a truly international team of dedicated microscopists—English, Scotch, Canadian, South African, French, German, Swiss, Dutch, Swedish, Japanese and American—and it is this fact that gives such unique flavor, value and good will to the able and devoted coverage of a science which is as wide and boundless as the world itself.

This Encyclopedia, of course, is a mosaic of 26 kinds of microscopy, alphabetically arranged, and in most cases with numerous alphabetical subtopics under each. The numerous illustrations in this picture book—diagrams of all kinds, photographs of microscopes and related instruments, and the micrographs made with them—speak eloquently for themselves as superb art as well as science, heretofore unpublished in most cases. Carefully chosen lists of general and cross references, it is hoped, will add greatly to the value and usefulness of this volume to inquisitive students and laymen seeking information and illumination in this area which extends the powers of men's vision a millionfold or more, and to the experts who continue to build an ever-new science.

The Editor is indebted personally to all the eminent scientists throughout the world who have contributed vitally important advice and encouragement, as well as one or more articles based on experience and devotion in a specialized field. The entire list of authors presented in the front pages is indeed a Roll of Honor. Special mention is due to colleagues at the University of Illinois—Professors E. K. Weise of the Department of Mining and Metallurgical Engineering, and R. Borasky, Director of the Electron Microscope Laboratory; and to the two loyal and able secretaries serving consecutively, Mrs. Ruth Tuite (1958-9) and Mrs. Claretta Metzger (1959-60), with whose help the entire task of planning, organizing and editing has somehow been accomplished.

The patience, enduring faith, guidance and technical aid by the publishing staff, especially G. G. Hawley, Executive Editor, and Alberta Gordon, were indispensable factors in bringing both Encyclopedias to material fruition, and in looking ahead to new worlds of science to bring between the covers of future members of this series of encyclopedias. The deep personal challenge and satisfaction to the Editor upon becoming a Professor Emeritus may somehow be reflected in the last paragraph of the Preface to the "Encyclopedia of Spectroscopy."

GEORGE L. CLARK

Urbana, Illinois
January, 1961

CONTENTS

Contents

Autoradiography

AUTORADIOGRAPHY OF TISSUE*

This article discusses techniques used for autoradiography of human and animal tissues and, to a limited extent, plant tissues. Methods are outlined which will enable those relatively inexperienced in autoradiography to plan an experiment involving alpha, beta and gamma emitters and to proceed with the experiment confident of obtaining meaningful autoradiograms. A current bibliography for the period 1954 to 1959 is that of Johnston (1). Boyd (2) has cited numerous literature references. Foreign journals often carry detailed papers relating to autoradiography which should not be overlooked as a source of information.

The technique which produces an image on a photographic plate or film when radioactive material is opposed to it is called *autoradiography*. The result of the exposure of an emulsion to a radioactive specimen is called an *autoradiogram*. The autoradiogram supplies a graphic record of the sites of deposition of radioactive isotopes within or on a tissue and may be macroscopic, as in the case of plant leaves, or in some cases microscopic, at or below the cellular level. Autoradiography of tissues containing alpha, beta and gamma emitters may be performed.

Suggested Autoradiographic Techniques for Alpha Emitters; Plutonium

In industries where contamination of personnel with radioactive substances is pos-

* Work performed under Contract No. AT(45-1)-1350 between the Atomic Energy Commission and the General Electric Company.

sible, low level detection procedures are necessary. Plutonium, an alpha (5.14 Mev) emitting radionuclide with some gamma radiation and a 24,300 year half-life, may be used as an example to illustrate one autoradiographic technique by which either particulate or soluble material may be graphically localized.

A 24-hour sputum sample (3) from a person known to have inhaled plutonium was taken and fixed in 10% formalin, as was a human biopsy of skin removed from a puncture wound in the hand. The samples were dehydrated in "Cellosolve" (glycol monoethyl ether), cleared in xylene, and embedded in paraffin. Sections were cut and floated on a water bath, transferred by a clean slide to a crystallizing dish containing distilled water. Working under light filtered by a Wratten OA filter, a 5 μ NTA emulsion coated on a 1 x 3 inch slide with a thin gelatin protective "T" coat was slipped under the section. The excess water was drained on to filter paper; the slides were then placed in a light-tight plastic box made for this purpose. A small vial of a desiccant ($CaSO_4$) lightly closed with a cotton plug was added.

The appearance of the tracks from plutonium which was in solution is characterized in Figure 1 (a human sputum specimen), where individual alpha tracks proceed in a straight line. The appearance of the tracks in sputum when plutonium is in the particulate form is illustrated in Figure 2, in which alpha tracks arise from a central point, with some random single tracks in the field.

Thirty-three sections from the plutonium-

1

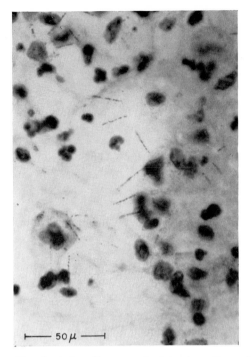

FIG. 1. Autoradiogram of stained section of human sputum illustrating diffuse alpha-track pattern of plutonium in solution. (*Courtesy Stain Technology*[3]).

determine the effect of radioiodine on the thyroid gland of grazing animals. The autoradiographic response of the thyroids of some of these animals is of interest.

Thyroid samples were routinely fixed in Bouin's solution for from 8 to 12 hours, followed by dehydration in "Cellosolve" and normal paraffin embedding. Adjacent sections were selected from the ribbons. One section was stained routinely with hematoxylin and eosin; the other was floated into a crystallizing dish containing distilled water, from which it was floated onto a slide bearing a 5 μ NTB emulsion plus a protective "T" coat. The slides, for animals which had received 100 μc I^{131} I.V. and which were sacrificed after 1 hour were then exposed for 5 days; the slides from animals receiving 100 μc I.V. in 0.9 % saline and sacrificed after 4 hours were exposed for 5½ days; and slides for ani-

contaminated skin biopsy (4) were autoradiographed by the above processing method. All of the two-hundred fifty individual skin sections were scanned in a thin window alpha detector. Radioanalysis showed that the entire skin biopsy specimen contained 0.0046 microcurie and the individual sections varied from 0 to 362 disintegrations per minute. The appearance of one autoradiogram of a human skin section is illustrated in Figure 3, in which alpha tracks may be seen arising from particles. In addition, random alpha tracks may be seen.

Suggested Autoradiographic Techniques for Beta Emitters; I^{131}, Ru^{106}, Sr^{90}, and P^{32}

I^{131}, with an eight day half-life, is predominantly a beta emitter with some gamma emission. It was administered to sheep in an acute and chronic feeding experiment (5) to

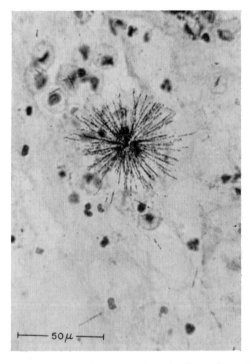

FIG. 2. Autoradiogram of stained section of human sputum illustrating star formation of alpha tracks originating from plutonium particle in central position. (*Courtesy Stain Technology*[3]).

The appearance of the autoradiograms of sheep thyroid tissue from animals administered 100 μc intravenously and sacrificed in 1 hour, illustrated in Figure 4, shows the grain response to be relatively uniform over both the colloidal areas and the epithelial cells. The colloidal area in animals administered 100 μc and sacrificed in 4 hours is shown in Figure 5. The grain distribution is more pronounced over many of the colloidal areas, indicating a variable uptake of I^{131} by the colloid in some of the follicles. For animals fed 5 μc a day for 129 days (Figure 6) there is an even distribution of grains over the colloidal areas in thyroid follicles which are greatly decreased in size from the normal. Areas showing no grain density indicate the edema surrounding the few remnant follicles that are present. The microfollicles register a limited grain density. Little or no interstitial tissue is present.

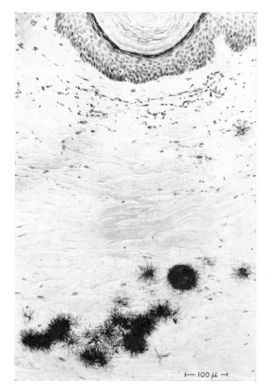

FIG. 3. Autoradiogram of human skin showing distribution of plutonium and alpha tracks approximately 800 μ beneath *stratum corneum*. Hematoxylin and eosin preparation. (*Courtesy Acta Radiologica*[4]).

mals which had received 5 μc per day for 129 days were exposed for 9 days. The last animal was sacrificed during gestation and had previously suckled its dam for 4 months. The dam had also been receiving 5 μc a day, so that some additional I^{131} was received by the lamb through the milk.

The autoradiograms were exposed in light-tight boxes containing "Drierite." The slides were warmed to room temperature and developed in D-19 at 18°C for 5 minutes, water rinsed and fixed in x-ray fixer for 30 minutes. They were water-washed and stained with hematoxylin and eosin. Sections that adhere to the emulsion can usually be stained satisfactorily, if the staining procedure is not prolonged to the point where overstaining of the emulsion is apparent.

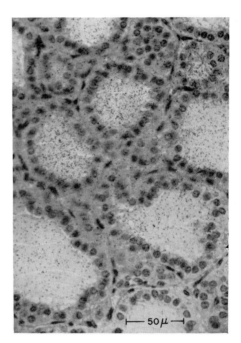

FIG. 4. Autoradiogram of hematoxylin and eosin stained sheep thyroid. Animal was administered 100 μc of I^{131} I.V. and sacrificed in one hour. Limited grain density increase over colloidal area and epithelial cells.

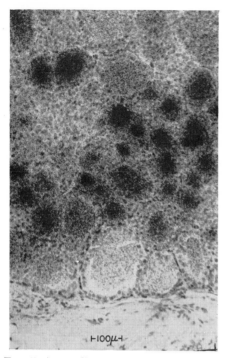

FIG. 5. Autoradiogram of sheep thyroid four hours following administration of 100 μc of I^{131}. Hematoxylin and eosin stain. Specific increase in grain density over various colloidal areas indicates variable uptake by the follicles.

It is important that the investigator be aware of the type of response to be expected after processing certain types of tissue and report the appearance of representative autoradiograms that are taken to illustrate the uptake of the radioisotope at selected times following administration. Specifically, the autoradiographic response in the thyroids of the experimental animals mentioned is that of single grains diffusely covering specified areas of the thyroid. Other types of emulsions will register the location of I^{131} as tracks rather than diffuse grains. Changes in the development procedures are necessary to register the I^{131} as tracks rather than grains.

It is interesting to compare at this point the autoradiographic response of Ru^{106}, another beta emitter having some gamma emission, and a half-life of one year. In this case the ruthenium was administered in an insoluble particulate form.

Ru^{106} particles were administered to mice by intravenous and intratracheal injection in 0.1 % aqueous dispersions of the wetting agent, Tween 80 (6). The animals were sacrificed after 100 to 420 days exposure to beta radiation. One experiment in autoradiographic quantitation was conducted on a single mouse into which 47 μc of Ru^{106} particles, ranging in size from 0.5 to 0.8 micron, were injected into the tail vein of the mouse. A portion of these particles lodged in the lungs of the animal. The lungs were excised after 100 days exposure and fixed in 70 % ethyl alcohol. Autoradiographic processing was standard, as outlined above. The result was a series of sections through the entire lung; one section was stained with orcein, one unstained autoradiogram fol-

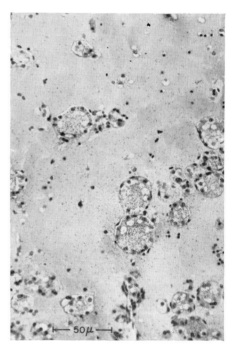

FIG. 6. Autoradiogram of sheep thyroid 129 days following administration of 5 μc of I^{131} per day. Negative grain density is apparent over areas of edema, with a limited uptake in the colloidal areas of the microfollicles.

lowed it, and this in turn was followed by a section stained by the Mallory method, to register connective tissue locations in relation to the "spot diameter" response of the unstained autoradiograms. A "spot diameter" is the grain response of the emulsion to a single radioactive particle. The staining sequence was followed through the entire lung. All of the sections were measured for Ru^{106} content on a mica window beta counter.

The insoluble ruthenium particles elicited a specific "spot diameter" response in the NTB emulsion. This was a well defined circular area of developed emulsion grains over the precise location of the deposited particles, as illustrated in Figure 7.

Knowing the total activity density for a specific slide, the activity density of a single particle was taken as proportional to the diameter of the darkened area of the emulsion. Thus, if a number of particles were present on a single slide, the total counting rate was compared with the sum of all of the darkened areas on that slide. Therefore, each particle could be assigned an activity density evaluation directly proportional to the size of the individual "spot diameter" measurement of the emulsion. The "spot diameter" darkenings of the grains of the emulsion varied in size and ranged from $8\,\mu$ to $170\,\mu$. A quantitative straight-line function exists between the sum of the spot diameters or a single-spot diameter and the total activity of each autoradiogram.

This particular technique provides a means of measuring the radioactivity of a single radioactive particle or many particles within tissue when the exposure, processing and development are standardized. The particles occur in a pattern of distribution such that the accumulated dose from nearby particles is sufficient to initiate fibrosis. By means of the serial sections stained specifically for connective tissue, and the autoradiograms, it is possible to reconstruct the tissue in depth and study the relationship

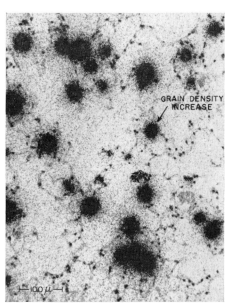

FIG. 7. Stained lung-autoradiogram preparation illustrating deposition of $Ru^{106}O_2$ particles with resultant spot diameter darkenings. (*Courtesy J. Biol. Phot. Assoc.*[16]).

of the fibrosis to the specific location of the deposited radioactive particles.

The autoradiographic technique for $Sr^{90}SO_4$ in lung tissue of mice, administered $1\,\mu c$ per animal by inhalation, is mentioned here for comparison with the foregoing methods.

Sections from lung tissue fixed in 80% ethyl alcohol were processed in a manner similar to lung tissue containing Ru^{106} particles (7). The film used in this case, however, was $25\,\mu$ No-Screen x-ray, single coated on 1 x 3 inch slides. These slides had a protective coating. As counting techniques indicated a low activity density for the sections, they were exposed for 8 weeks. The use of x-ray emulsion made it possible to register activity densities that were approaching the lower limits of detection by normal counting methods.

The autoradiogram of the lung section containing Sr^{90}, illustrated in Figure 8, shows both a diffuse and particulate response to the radioactive material. The adjacent his-

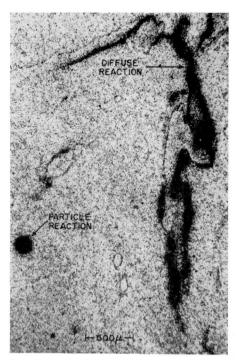

FIG. 8. Autoradiogram of lung section from chronic $Sr^{90}SO_4$ inhalation experiment. Particulate and diffuse distribution with heavy background grain density of x-ray emulsion visible. (*Courtesy J. Biol. Phot. Assoc.*[16]).

tological section is included, as Figure 9, for comparison purposes. A noticeable background of grains, larger than in the NTA and NTB emulsions, is observable. This is due in part to the 25 μ thickness of the x-ray emulsion and in part to the greater sensitivity. Even greater sensitivity could have been obtained had the film used been of the double coated type. However, the image rendered would have been more diffuse because the emulsion layers are coated on either side and separated by an acetate base. In this case detail has been sacrificed to record low activity density deposition of diffuse and particulate Sr^{90}.

The next example is that of a beta emitter, P^{32}, which has a 14.5 day half-life (8). A gross, fast survey method for the detection of P^{32} administered to rats by intraperitoneal injection of 2.5 μc per gram of body weight

is outlined. The rats were sacrificed 24 hours following administration of the P^{32} as $Na_2 \cdot HP^{32}O_4$.

The emulsion of choice in this case was 25 μ, single layer, No-Screen x-ray emulsion on 1 x 3 inch slides. Detail was sacrificed for rough localization of P^{32} by using an emulsion with a grain size varing from 3 to 5 μ. The increase in the sensitivity of the emulsion and the thickness insured a positive recording of the radioactive sites, with a minimum exposure period. Noticeable disadvantages with this technique are the large grain size which makes cellular autoradiography impossible. The extreme thickness of the emulsion makes illustration of the recorded data on the film difficult, except by macrographic methods.

Figure 10 is an autoradiogram of a rat ovary section from an animal sacrificed 24 hours following intraperitoneal administra-

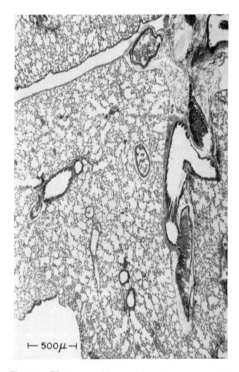

FIG. 9. Hematoxylin and eosin stained histological section adjacent to Fig. 8, for orientation purposes. (*Courtesy J. Biol. Phot. Assoc.*[16]).

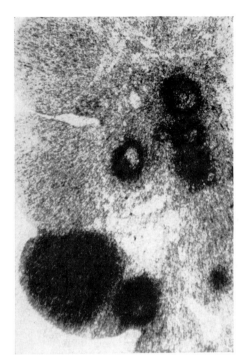

FIG. 10. Autoradiogram of rat ovary 24 hours after administration of 2.5 μc of P[32] per gram of rat. Concentrations of P[32] appear over cellular elements lining the follicular cavity, surrounding the ova and in some *corpora lutea*. (*Courtesy J. Biol. Phot. Assoc.*[16]).

The surface of the emulsion was then cleaned with absolute ethyl alcohol, to remove the impermeable layer. This method allows the fixing and staining of the tissues by means of all of the reagents commonly employed in histology, without any damage to the emulsion. The exposure of the tissue was for 24 hours at 2°C. The emulsions were processed by the Temperature Development Method. Good adhesion and minimum separation between specimen and emulsion are obtained, thus permitting reliable extrapolation of the electron tracks from P[32].

The Temperature Development Method of Dilworth, Occhialini and Payne, 1948, and Dilworth, Occhialini and Vermaesen, 1950, as modified by Guidotti, is worthy of specific mention. Essentially it consists of soaking the slides in distilled water for 30 to 40 minutes, beginning at room temperature, and

tion of P[32]. An increased grain density is noticeable in the area of three developing ova. The autoradiogram may be compared with the adjacent hematoxylin and eosin stained section in Figure 11.

In direct contrast with this gross survey method for the localization of P[32] is the extreme detail and precise localization obtained by Guidotti (9). Guidotti mounted paraffin sections, 2 to 4 μ thick, which were stained, dehydrated, and allowed to air dry. These were given a thin coating of 1 % "Plexiglas" solution in chloroform. The chloroform was allowed to evaporate completely in a dry atmosphere. An emulsion having a dried thickness of 100 to 150 microns, was prepared from Ilford G-5 type emulsion in gel form and glued to the section by means of a 15 % solution of shellac in absolute alcohol.

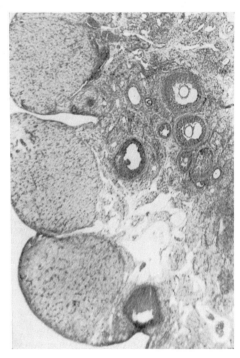

FIG. 11. Stained histological section adjacent to Fig. 10 of rat ovary 24 hours after administration of 2.5 μc of P[32] per gram of rat. Three developing ova are seen in central portion. (*Courtesy J. Biol. Phot. Assoc.*[16]).

then lowering the temperature gradually to about 4°C. The cold phase of development is for about 30 minutes. The developer used in this case was Amidol. The cold developer is poured off and the surface of the slides dried with filter paper. Warm slides to 22° to 24°C in a thermostatically controlled tank. The temperature of the warm stage must be chosen by trials. The slides are then placed in a stop bath of 0.2% acetic acid solution for about 30 to 40 minutes at 4°C. Fixation is at 4°C in a 40% sodium thiosulphate solution until the emulsion is clear. The emulsion is thoroughly washed at the low temperature and the emulsion allowed to dry slowly. The preparation is then capped with a thin coverslip.

One of the reasons for Guidotti's success with P[32] autoradiography is the varied temperature development allowing all layers of the emulsion to be penetrated by the developer; another is the thinness of the section, which is considerably less than most routine preparations. This allows the site of origin of the beta tracks to be more accurately located.

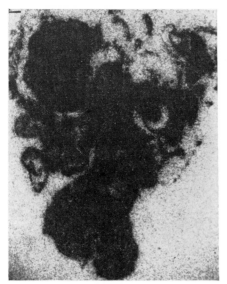

FIG. 12. Autoradiogram of rat ovary and adjacent tissue illustrating even diffuse distribution of Cs[137].

Cs[137], a beta and gamma emitter, with a half-life of 30 years, is an example of a water-soluble isotope that presents difficulties regarding methods for autoradiographic registration.

The usual fixing fluids leach Cs[137] from tissues as will any contact with water; therefore, a mixture of 80% acetone and 20% benzene was used as a fixative (10). This combination was decided upon after experimentation in which the leaching loss was determined by radiochemical analysis. There was a minimum cesium loss when this fixative was used. Tissues were then processed through "Cellosolve" and benzene and blocked in paraffin.

Since the sections could not be floated on water for transfer to the emulsion, sections were attached to the No-Screen x-ray emulsion by warming the slide until the emulsion became tacky, then the sections were attached by finger pressure. The slides were then exposed, the paraffin dissolved by immersion in xylene. The slides were run down to water from "Cellosolve" and the autoradiograms stained and the slides capped.

Figure 12 is an illustration of Cs[137] deposition in a rat ovary. It will be noted that there is a homogeneous distribution in the ovary and the surrounding tissue. There is no evidence of leaching into the emulsion area not covered by the tissue. Figure 13 is the adjacent section for histological comparison. Greater definition could have been obtained by using an NTB emulsion.

Limited Autoradiographic Techniques for Plant Tissue

An interesting experiment performed by Hungate et al. (11) involved exposure of plants to fallout from the experimental burning of an irradiated fuel element.

The fission products resulting from the burning of the fuel element were carried by the air to plants located downwind from the burning site. Later the plant leaves were exposed to double-coated Type KK industrial x-ray film. The gross autoradiographic result of this exposure of two plant leaves is illustrated in Figure 14. It will be noticed that there is a general darkening over the entire leaf with an increased density at its periphery. In addition, there are small black circular areas of increased grain density that are relatively indistinct. These circular areas of increased grain density suggest that some of the fission products were in the particulate form.

In order to substantiate the observation regarding specific deposition of particles, additional 1 x 3 inch plates coated with a 100 μ NTB[3] emulsion and a "T" coat were exposed to portions of the plant leaves for 4 days and developed in D-19 developer. These also demonstrated a particle response that was more detailed than that observed with the double-coated x-ray emulsion. The detailed microscopic particle response of fission material on plant leaves is illustrated in Figure 15. In this case the autoradio-

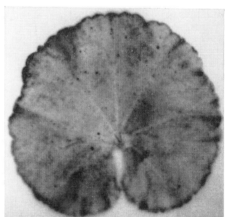

Fig. 14. Gross autoradiograms of plant leaves following exposure by air of the leaves to fission products. An over-all darkening with increased density at the periphery is noticed. Some small circular spot densities can be seen.

graphic technique demonstrated the presence of particles on leaves that was not detectable by routine counting procedures.

General Discussion

Up to this point practical problems involving autoradiography have been discussed. Many specific applications have been

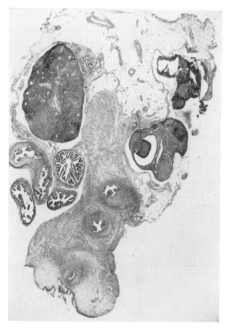

Fig. 13. Stained tissue section of ovary and related tissue adjacent to section used for autoradiography of Cs[137] in Fig. 12.

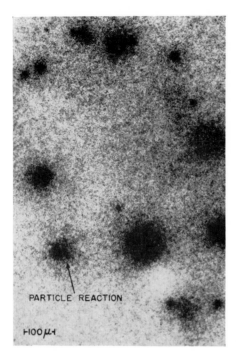

PARTICLE REACTION

⊢100 μ⊣

Fig. 15. Microscopic autoradiographic response of leaf exposed to fission products. Specific spot grain responses indicate that some of the material was in particulate form.

omitted. Among them is the classical work involving plutonium deposition in the bones of dogs administered plutonium. This is the excellent work of Jee (12) in which the results of autoradiographic methods involving hard bone are discussed in detail.

Autoradiographic techniques have been applied to electron microscopy. O'Brien and George (13) have examined sectioned yeast cells, previously suspended in a Po²¹⁰ solution. In this case the specimen grids were coated with the emulsion by touching them to a drop of diluted NTA emulsion. Borasky and Dockum (14) examined Pu²³⁹ particles contained in an aerosol sample collected on "Formvar" coated grids. The grids bearing the particles were chrome-shadowed and placed on "Lucite" plugs held upright in wells drilled in a metal block. A small wire loop was placed in diluted NTA gel emulsion and retracted, thus forming a very thin layer of emulsion. The loop bearing the emulsion was then lowered over the specimen grid and the loop retrieved by lifting the plug and withdrawing the loop from beneath the plug. The grids were exposed for 4 hours in a light-tight box when high activity specimens were examined. The emulsion-coated grids on the "Lucite" plugs were immersed in D-19 developer for 5 minutes, then washed in distilled water for one minute, after which they were fixed in liquid x-ray fixer for 3 minutes, washed and dried. The individual grains of the alpha tracks could be plainly seen when examined by an RCA EMU-2C electron microscope. The point of origin of the tracks was located by the shadow cast by the Pu²³⁹ particle.

George and Vogt (15), using unshadowed grids, examined plutonium particles collected on millipore filters, and prepared electron micrographs of selected areas of particles before and after autoradiography, thus differentiating radioactive from non-radioactive particles.

It is probable that small cubes of tissue of approximately 150 microns could be infiltrated in diluted gel emulsion long enough to penetrate the tissue. These small cubes could be exposed for the desired amount of time, developed by the Temperature Development Method, after which the cubes could be embedded in methacrylate and sectioned by ultra-thin sectioning methods. Selected areas of cells could be studied in relation to the developed grain deposition either by electron microscopy or by oil immersion phase microscopy, if mounted on a glass slide (16). This is an avenue that will lead the microscopist into cellular and subcellular autoradiography.

REFERENCES

1. Johnston, M. E., "A bibliography of biological applications of autoradiography, 1954 through 1957", UCRL-8400, 1958.

   Johnston, M. E., "A bibliography of biological applications of autoradiography, 1958 through 1959", UCRL-8901, 1959.

2. Boyd, G. A., "Autoradiography in biology and medicine", Academic Press, New York, 1955.

3. Dockum, N. L., Coleman, E. J., and Vogt, G. S., "Detection of plutonium contamination in humans by the autoradiographic method", *Stain Technology*, **33**(3), 137–142 (1958).

4. Dockum, N. L., and Case, A. C., "Autoradiographic analysis of plutonium deposition in human skin", *Acta Radiologica*, **50**, 559–64 (1958).

5. Marks, S., Dockum, N. L., and Bustad, L. K., "Histopathology of thyroid gland of sheep in prolonged administration of I[131]", *Am. J. Path.*, **33**, 219–250 (1957).

6. Dockum, N. L., and Healy, J. W., "Spot diameter method of quantitative autoradiography of ruthenium[106] particles in lung tissue", *Stain Technology*, **32**(5), 209–213 (1957).

7. Unpublished data, W. J. Bair.

8. Vogt, G. and Kawin, B., "Localization of radioelements in rat ovary", Document HW-53500, p. 120–123 (Unclassified), 1957.

9. Guidotti, G. and Levi Setti, R., "Autoradiography of tracks from beta particle emitters in tissues", *Stain Technology*, **31**, 57–65 (1956).

10. Unpublished data, N. L. Dockum.

11. Hungate, F. P., Uhler, R. L., Cline, J. F. and Stewart, J. D., "Decontamination of plants exposed to a simulated reactor burn", Document HW-63173 (Unclassified), 1959.

12. Jee, Webster S. S., Arnold, J. S., Mical, R., Lowe, M., Bird, B. and Twente, J. A. "The sequence of histopathologic bone changes in bones containing plutonium", p. 148–189. Univ. of Utah Radiobiology Laboratory Annual Progress Report, COO-218, 1959.

13. O'Brien, R. T., and George, L. A. II, "Preparation of autoradiograms for electron microscopy", *Nature*, **183**, 1461–1462 (1959).

14. Unpublished data, Borasky, R. and Dockum, N. L.

15. George, L. A. II, and Vogt, G. S., "Electron microscopy of autoradiographed radioactive particles", *Nature*, **184**, 1474–1475 (1959).

16. Dockum, N. L., Vogt, G. S., and Coleman, E. J., "Applications of autoradiography in biological research", *J. Biol. Phot. Assoc.*, **27**, 1–18 (1959).

Norman L. Dockum

SHADOW AUTORADIOGRAPHY

Shadow autoradiography is a technique that enables one to differentiate between radioactive and non-radioactive particles. The source of the particles may be suspensions or aerosols. The technique is described below.

Droplets of particle suspensions are placed on clean glass microscope slides, spread and allowed to dry. Aerosol particles may be collected directly on the glass substrate by gravity or by impaction methods. If the particles from aerosols are collected on membrane filters, the membrane filter is dissolved in a suitable volume of acetone and

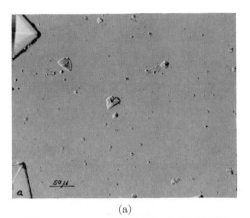

(a)

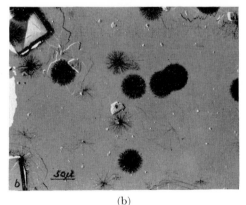

(b)

Fig. 1. Alpha emitters. Photomicrographs of chrome-shadowed particles before (a) and after (b) autoradiography. Alpha-emitting radioactive particles are those surrounded by star clusters of alpha tracks. (*Courtesy N. L. Dockum*).

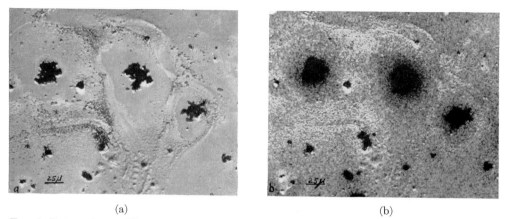

(a)   (b)

FIG. 2. Beta emitters. Photomicrographs of chrome-shadowed particles before (a) and after (b) autoradiography. Beta-emitting particles are covered by spots of dense granules. (*Courtesy of N. L. Dockum and R. Borasky, Nucleonics, 15, 110 1957*).

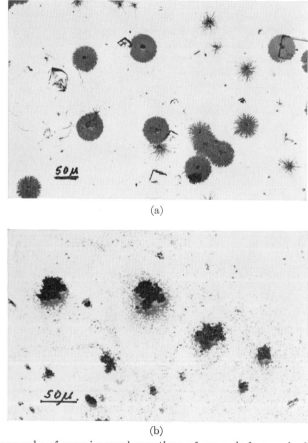

(a)

(b)

FIG. 3. Photomicrographs of superimposed negatives of areas before and after autoradiography. (a) Alpha-emitting particles. (b) Beta-emitting particles.

aliquots of the acetone suspension treated in the same manner as described above.

The glass slide containing the particles is shadowed with chromium at an acute angle (e.g. 30°) (1). The shadowed slide is next examined in the optical microscope and areas of interest are recorded by stage micrometer readings and by photomicrography.

Following the microscopic examination, a section of 5 micron nuclear track emulsion stripping film (e.g. NTA for alpha-emitting particles and NTB for beta-emitting particles) is floated over the sample and allowed to dry. The latter step is performed in a dark room using a series I Safelight filter. The slide bearing the particles and emulsion is placed in a light-tight box with a desiccant for a suitable standardized time for exposure at 3°C. The exposed slides are developed in D-19 developer for 5 minutes, washed, fixed, dehydrated and cleared, and a coverslip mounted over the emulsion. The slide is re-examined in the microscope and previously selected areas are photographed.

Alpha activity is manifested by star clusters of alpha tracks (cf. Fig. 1a and 1b). Beta activity is manifested by spots of dense granules (cf. Fig. 2a and 2b). Beta activity may be determined quantitatively by spot-diameter autoradiography (2).

The method for differentiating radioactive from non-radioactive particles is as follows. A sheet of tracing paper is placed over the photomicrographs or negatives of selected areas of the shadowed slide before autoradiography. Particle positions are noted with small circles. The tracing is next placed over the photomicrograph or negatives of the slide after autoradiography and activity centers noted with a check mark or cross. The tracing now has small circles representing non-radioactive particles and crosses or check marks denoting radioactive particles. Striking results are obtained by superimposing the negatives of the areas before and after autoradiography (cf. Figure 3). The physical characteristics of the particles are determined from the photomicrographs of selected areas on the shadowed slide before autoradiography.

REFERENCES

1. DEMPSTER, W. T., AND WILLIAMS, R. C., *Anat. Record*, **96,** 27 (1946).
2. DOCKUM, N. L. AND HEALY, T. W., *Stain Technology*, **32,** 209 (1957).
3. DOCKUM, N. L. AND BORASKY, R., *Nucleonics*, **15,** 110 (1957).

R. BORASKY

CHEMICAL MICROSCOPY

ALKALOIDS AND ALKALOIDAL-TYPE PRECIPITATION

An attempt is made in the article on Chemical Microcrystal Identifications to keep the discussion of practical work on a sufficiently general basis so that any analytical chemist concerned with identification may be able to see some application to his own work. If a consistent effort is made to use and develop this kind of chemical identification, it is usually best to work from tests that are already known and satisfactory in a restricted field, and to extend the coverage first to chemically related compounds, having the same or modified reagents, and by stages, systematically try to cover entirely different groups of compounds with other reagents and new crystal-producing reactions.

The traditional tests on the well-known alkaloids are made on aqueous solutions. About 80 substances, mostly natural alkaloids, or of natural origin although synthetically modified, have been studied repeatedly by different investigators for their reactions in such tests. Table 1 summarizes the data for 16 of these with the 11 reagents which give most of their major aqueous microcrystal tests.

These reagents are equally applicable to numerous other alkaloids. It is unfortunate that publication of the isolation of a new plant alkaloid is almost never accompanied by some individual or highly characteristic analytical test by which subsequent investi-

TABLE 1. SOME IMPORTANT MICROCRYSTAL TESTS FOR ALKALOIDS

	Iodine-KI	H_3BiI_6 rgt	K_2CdI_4	$HAuBr_4$ & HCl	$HAuCl_4$	$HAuCl_4$ & HCl	$HgCl_2$ (sl HCl)	H_2PtCl_6	Picric Acid	Na_2CO_3	$K_4Fe(CN)_6$ & HCl	Other
Caffeine	(c)	C	—	c	C	c	C	—	—	—	—	$HAuBr_4$
Ephedrine	a	C	—	a	(ac)	a	—	C	—	—	—	H_2PtI_6 rgt
Nicotine	c	c	ac	c	C	c	C	c	C	—	—	H_2PtBr_6
Aconitine	ac	ac	a	a	a	a	a	—	a	C	—	$HMnO_4$; $HClO_4$
Scopolamine	c	C	a	C	C	c	(a)	(ac)	ac		C	I-KI, 1:35
Hyoscyamine	C	C	a	c	C	c	c	a	C	(ac)	c	I-KI, 1:35; Br-HBr
Atropine	C	c	a	c	ac	C	(c)	(a)	c	ac	c	I-KI, 1:50; Br-HBr
Morphine	C(1)	C	C(2)	ac	a	a	(c)	(a)	a(c)	c	—	HCl-$HAuBr_4$ (HCl soln)
Codeine	C	c(a)	C	a	a	a	c	a	a(c)	(c)	—	HgI_2-NaCN & NaI (3)
Diacetyl-morphine (Heroin)	a	ac	ac	ac	a(c)	ac	C	C(4)	C	C	a	$HAuBr_4$ in (2 + 3) H_2SO_4
Meperidine	a	ac	a	ac	ac	c	ac	C	C	a	c	PbI_2 in K acetate soln
Procaine	ac	a(c)	a	C	a	C	c(a)	C	c(a)	(a)	(c)	H_2PtBr_6 ; Br-HBr
Cocaine	a	a	a	C	C	C	a	C(5)	c	c	c	H_2PtBr_6 ; PbI_2 in K acetate soln
Quinine	a	ac	a	ac	a(c)	c	ac	a	a	a(c)	C	Herapathite test; Na_2HPO_4 ; $HgCl_2$ & HCl (6)
Strychnine	c	a(c)	C	C	C	C	C	C	C	c	C	CrO_3 ; numerous others
Narcotine	a	a	a	a	a	a	a	a	a	C	a	K_2CrO_4 ; K acetate soln

a, amorphous precipitate, not crystallizing

c, crystals form, either directly or from an amorphous precipitate

a(c), amorphous precipitate, crystallization poor or uncertain

c(a), normally crystals but precipitate may remain amorphous

ac, discrepant reports, usually because of variations in reagents or because crystallization, while fairly certain, is quite slow

(a), (c), or (ac), amorphous precipitate or crystals may not form in most tests because of lack of sensitivity

—, no result

C, major crystal tests

1–6, Figures.

gators might distinguish it. When, in some study, alkaloids are isolated from plant material on a small scale, and are not among those commercially available, one usually finds that, even though the plant from which they came is known, and the alkaloids found are distinguished by analytical reactions, it is still impossible to tell which one if any corresponds to some previously studied alkaloid of that plant, without going through most of the original procedure. This necessitates a large quantity of material, obtaining

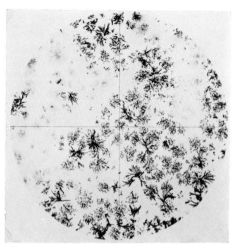

FIG. 3. A less-known alkaloidal crystal test: codeine with $HgI_2 \cdot NaCN$ and NaI (aqueous solutions).

FIG. 1. A well-known crystal test: morphine with iodine-KI (aqueous solutions).

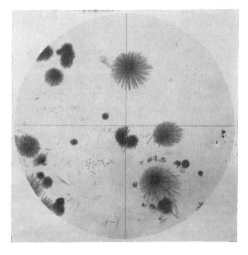

FIG. 4. A well-known crystal test: diacetylmorphine (heroin) with H_2PtCl_6 (aqueous solutions).

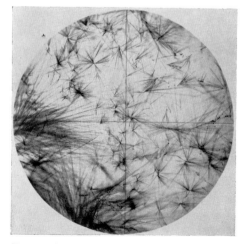

FIG. 2. A well-known crystal test: morphine with K_2CdI_4 (aqueous solutions).

melting-points, and analyzing for elementary composition, except in the rare event that a sample of the original isolate can be obtained for comparison. This kind of gap between research and application is very common.

Other Compounds with Aqueous Reagents. Alkaloids do not constitute a distinct chemical group. Their precipitation with the "general alkaloidal reagents" depends upon their being compounds of basic

15

FIG. 5. A well-known crystal test: cocaine with H_2PtCl_6 (aqueous solutions).

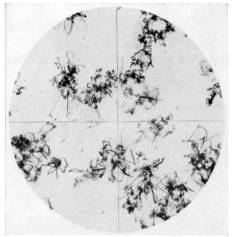

FIG. 6. A less-known alkaloidal crystal test: (2) quinine with mercuric chloride and HCl (aqueous solutions).

nitrogen, usually of a fairly high degree of complexity. There are now numerous drugs that are not considered alkaloids, but which have the same characteristics: they are nitrogen-bases, soluble in dilute acids, precipitated by exactly the same general reagents, and give characteristic crystals with certain of them (different ones, depending on the compound), just as the alkaloids do. Among these are the synthetic narcotics, local anesthetics, antihistamines, antimalarials, atro-

pine-like drugs and some kinds of tranquilizers. In some cases, whole classes of these drugs are recent introductions, and for all of them, the number in use has expanded greatly in recent years.

E. G. C. Clarke has given microcrystal and color tests for 101 alkaloids (including those synthetically modified), and for 156 of these other drugs (to the date of writing), with the same reagents.

Other classes of drugs which are amine bases are the sympathomimetics and central stimulants. Some of these also give good tests with the traditional aqueous reagents. Others, relatively simple in structure and often having hydroxyl groups, may be too water-soluble in their compounds for good tests in this way, and precipitation in phosphoric-acid solution is used.

Many different acidic and anionic reagents are available for basic compounds and it would seem that it should be equally possible to use basic reagents or cations to provide microcrystal tests for acidic compounds, at least those of some complexity. As a matter of fact, tests have been published for various acids using salts of silver, lead, copper, nickel, mercury, zinc, and palladium, usually in a solution made slightly basic with ammonia, pyridine, triethanolamine, or the like. Such tests are useful but as yet most of them hardly seem in the same class with the better alkaloidal tests, either for proving identity or in sensitivity, and much study to develop good tests is needed.

Aqueous Precipitation of the Free Substance. Many alkaloids are precipitated from acid solution by making the solution basic, or even, in the case of weak bases, by merely reducing the acid strength, for example with potassium acetate. Characteristic crystals are often produced and the tests also give chemical information merely by the fact of precipitation. The strength or weakness of the base is shown to some degree by the strength of the basic reagent required for sensitive precipitation. K_2CrO_4 may precipitate the chromate of a strong base but its really sensitive tests are those in which it acts as a basic group reagent for weak complex alkaloids.

Substances soluble in both strong aqueous acids and bases may be insoluble at some intermediate point. The method is obviously general and acidic substances may be precipitated from alkaline solution by ordinary acids. This is one way of obtaining crystal tests for barbiturates. While using various ways of separating the free substance for microcrystal tests, the chemical meaning of the reactions should always be noted.

Tests are also made on an acidic substance (which may be in fine particles, or amorphous, to start with) by dissolving it in NaOH solution, adding HCl in slight excess, and allowing the drop to evaporate to dryness. The reagents leave merely grains of NaCl, which are isotropic, and therefore invisible with crossed nicols; the acidic substance set free may crystallize, and may often be birefringent and easily seen, and then its refractive indices and other optical properties can be determined.

Halogen Reagents for Nitrogen Compounds in Aqueous Solutions. Bromine in water, or in HBr or NaBr solution, and iodine in KI or HI solution, are the reagents commonly used; iodine may also be used in HBr or NaBr solution. These are very general precipitants not only for the alkaloids but in general for amine compounds of any complexity. In a somewhat different type of reaction their use extends even to compounds in which the nitrogen no longer has appreciable basic properties.

The alkaloid-type reaction takes place in acid solution, or at least the alkaloid is combined with acid in a salt and itself acts as a cation. When an amine-derivative is predominantly acidic and is precipitated as an iodine compound in acid solution, it may not be clear whether the reaction should be attributed to residual basic qualities, or not. The related but anionic reaction is most clearly seen as a distinct type in neutral or slightly basic solution; occurs best with a high concentration of iodine. This type of reaction, which has not been explored nearly enough occurs with some barbiturates and with other compounds without appreciable basic properties, and also with some compounds that can react either as bases or acids, including the alkaloids caffeine, theobromine, theophylline, and colchicine, which give both the alkaloidal-type and the anionic-type of iodine precipitation. They all have acidic $\diagdown C = O \diagup$ groups.

Oxygen Acids. These may be divided into two kinds, complex and simple. The complex oxygen acids, phosphorituungstic, phosphorimolybdic, arsenimolybdic, silicotungstic, etc., are very general, precipitating from aqueous solution all the alkaloids and related compounds, and, generally speaking, potassium and the heavier alkali metals, ammonium and the simple amines, as well. As a rule they give crystals only with the simpler bases; most of their alkaloidal precipitates are amorphous. Phosphorimolybdic acid is, however, very useful for comparative precipitation. Instead of the absolute concentration of reactive substance, sensitivities may be reported in terms of the relative sensitivity compared with phosphorimolybdic acid. This is also important in classifying alkaloids by precipitation.

The simpler oxygen acids used as alkaloidal precipitants are perchloric, chromic, permanganic, etc., used either as free acid or alkali salt. Permanganate especially frequently reacts as an oxidizing reagent and is itself reduced, but it gives some excellent crystals with compounds not readily oxidized. Unlike the complex oxygen acids these compounds are not very general or sensitive as reagents, and so are chiefly useful with fairly complex bases which are easily precipitated. Chlorochromic acid, $HCrO_3Cl$, is more sensitive and general than CrO_3, but still gives similar precipitation and crystals.

Anionic Complexes of Central Metals. These reagents are commonly called "gold chloride", "platinum chloride", etc., and their precipitates are called "double salts", but actually the metals are in anionic complexes and the precipitating agents are really chlorauric acid, $HAuCl_4$, chloroplatinic acid, H_2PtCl_6, etc. Thus the reagents are given by those metals *and anions* which will form anionic complexes of this particular type, and the group might be subdivided either according to the metals or the simple anions concerned. The metals are central to the long periods of the periodic table; the anions are halogens (Cl^-, Br^-, I^-) and "pseudohalogens", such as CN^-, SCN^-, NO_2^-, N_3^-, etc.

The iodide reagents of bismuth and platinum are colored and so sensitive and general in aqueous solution that they are commonly used for spraying to bring out the spots of alkaloids or related compounds in paper chromatography.

The following table gives the reagents of greatest value for microcrystals, designated as R; other definite reagents within the scope of this table are indicated by a small r.

	Chloride	Bromide	Iodide	Cyanide
Gold (+3)	R	R	—	R
Platinum (+4)	R	R	R	R
Palladium (+2)	R	r		
Mercury (+2)	R	r	R	r
Cadmium (+2)	r	r	R	
Bismuth (+3)	r	r	R	

A "gold iodide" reagent is in use, made from HI and chlorauric acid, but the $HAuI_4$ immediately decomposes, and the chief effects seem to be due to iodine-HI, rather than any gold compound, with a few results due to an aurous iodide complex, a gold (+1) reagent.

The following might also be mentioned: chlorides (chloro-acids) of Fe, Zn, Sn (stannous and stannic), UO_2 (uranyl), and VO (vanadyl), which are most effective with a high content of HCl to form the chloro-acid; iodides of Pb, Sn (+2), Zn, and Ag, with alkali iodide; the complex cyanides of Fe, both ferro- and ferri-, and also nitroprusside; and complex thiocyanates of Pt, Hg, Sn (+2), Cd, Zn, Co (+2), Ni (+2), Mn (+2), and Cr (+3). Most precipitates with thiocyanate reagents do not crystallize very readily. A remarkable exception is reinecke salt, $NH_4Cr(NH_3)_2(SCN)_4$, which is very general and yet gives many crystals.

Double complexes are also possible; e.g., mercuric cyani-iodide or mercuric chloro-iodide, made by dissolving the insoluble HgI_2 in cyanide solution or in strong HCl, respectively.

On the whole this group is the most useful of all for microcrystal tests, and by using other strong acids besides HCl the use of these reagents may be extended over all compounds of basic nitrogen.

Simple Halides. These are useful with relatively complex bases, particularly iodide and thiocyanate, used as alkali salts.

Organic Reagents. The best reagent of this group is picric acid, and several others are highly nitrated compounds, e.g., styphnic and trinitrobenzoic acids. A few other kinds are known, e.g., sodium alizarin sulfonate. Sodium tetraphenyl-boron is a new type of reagent (in some ways allied to the complex oxygen acids), recently introduced, which is very useful for crystalline precipitates with free amines in volatility tests (without acidification), and quite sensitive to the lower amines in this way.

Reagents in Strong Acids. The study of strong acids as media for the precipitation of nitrogen-bases began with hydrochloric acid, which, because many of the precipitating agents are halides, often has special effects. Some reagents were already known which require a high content of HCl either to prevent precipitation of basic chloride (e.g., $SbCl_3$) or to form the chloro-acid (e.g., $FeCl_3$). These were more or less assimilated to the ordinary aqueous reagents; but some 20 or 25% of concentrated HCl in the reagent will profoundly affect the precipitation and crystal-forming properties of $HAuCl_3$, for example. Next, reagents made with concentrated HCl were tried; then instead of using only aqueous solutions of the substance tested, concentrated HCl was also used for this purpose. The value of other acids was later discovered. It became evident that instead of dissolving the substance tested in quite a number of different acids, it would be simpler to apply the reagents, in the various acids, directly to a little of the solid substance. This is now the method used, but precipitation from solution could be used. The precipitating agents are the same ones that have long been used in aqueous solution to precipitate alkaloids.

The acids proved to have very different effects. The ones chiefly used are diluted or syrupy (85–88%) H_3PO_4, diluted H_2SO_4, concentrated HCl, and (2 + 1) acetic acid. Concentrated H_2SO_4 would react with too many of the substances to be tested, and would decompose nearly all precipitating agents, but may be used up to (1 + 1) strength with chloride reagents, as strong as (2 + 3) with bromides, and up to (1 + 3) with iodides. Acetic acid may be used up to the glacial strength except that it then tends to creep and spread all over the slide, and for this reason (2 + 1) is usually the maximum strength employed.

Now it is found that the precipitation-effect is not greatly different in diluted H_2SO_4 or in concentrated HCl from that in plain water, only a little greater in diluted H_2SO_4 and a little less in concentrated HCl; and these acids are chiefly used, as media, to obtain certain crystallization effects not obtainable in plain water. The most surprising effects are obtained with phosphoric and acetic acids. The compounds formed by the precipitants with bases are immensely less soluble in H_3PO_4 than in water, and far more soluble in acetic acid than in water.

The reagents with acetic acid are therefore less general than others, and find their especial application with highly complex compounds, very easy to precipitate, particularly those that yield only amorphous precipitates in the conventional tests. Instead of having to study new precipitating agents which are less and less general in effect, we can simply try using acetic acid in the test-drop, as a medium for new, useful tests.

The effect of phosphoric acid in increasing the range of the tests is even more important. There are in fact three effects. One is the effect of a nonvolatile liquid medium in allowing a test to stand as long as may be desired for crystallization to occur. H_3PO_4 has no very strong tendency to absorb water, nor, when it is used already a little diluted, to dry out. It has no side effects corresponding to sulfonation, or to the withdrawal of water from the molecule of a dissolved substance, both often given by H_2SO_4 even when it is somewhat diluted. Another effect is that of any strong mineral acid in suppressing acidic qualities of amphoteric substances and enhancing their basic qualities. Third and especially important is the particular effect of phosphoric acid in increasing the insolubility of precipitates in it, as already mentioned.

The most useful of all the crystal-producing compounds are the chloro- and bromo-acids of gold and platinum, the iodide reagents of platinum and bismuth, and iodine-KI or iodine-HI. Among other advantages these are all colored, and crystals formed by them can be readily distinguished from original crystalline material, or from crystals, e.g., phosphates, formed simply by the acid used. They are compatible, with proper formulas, with all the acids mentioned, and extend the use of microcrystal tests for identification to all compounds of basic nitrogen. Phosphoric acid reagents in particular are used for relatively simple, and

19

feebly basic and partly acidic compounds, and those of high solubility in water.

Inorganic Precipitation with Reagents for Basic Nitrogen. Potassium and ammonium have similar solubilities for their salts, and so give similar precipitation reactions; and, in a more general view, the alkaloids and other compounds of basic nitrogen react much like the heavier alkali metals. Cesium (ion) is precipitated by most of the "alkaloidal" reagents and rubidium

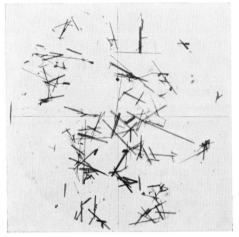

FIG. 7. Sodium bromaurate crystals. Na_2SO (solid) with $HAuBr_4$ in H_3PO_4.

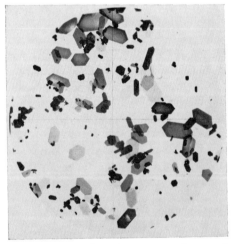

FIG. 8. Magnesium bromauraurate crystals $MgCl_2 \cdot 6H_2O$ (solid) with $HAuBr_4$ in H_3PO_4. (Photographed with red-sensitive plate.)

by perhaps a third of them, from aqueous solution. The most general of such reagents often precipitate ammonium and potassium; and conversely, a reagent used to precipitate potassium is worth trying as a general precipitant of nitrogenous bases.

Sodium ion is not precipitated from aqueous solution by the "alkaloidal" reagents, but in a medium of syrupy phosphoric acid the relationship of the lighter elements becomes apparent. Not only sodium, (Fig. 7) but even lithium, magnesium (Fig. 8), zinc, and cadmium, become more or less subject to such precipitation. Even the hydrogen compound verges on insolubility, and for example bromauric acid itself, $HAuBr_4$, will precipitate from H_3PO_4 solution with drying. These inorganic reactions have been studied very little, except the formation of bromaurates.

CHARLES C. FULTON

CHEMICAL MICROCRYSTAL IDENTIFICATIONS

The microscope should be used throughout chemistry; it is surely an obvious instrument (and not a new one) simply for taking a closer and better look at small things. Chemists should turn to it as naturally as to test-tubes or the bunsen burner, whenever it will help. It has applications requiring knowledge and study, too, particularly the polarizing microscope, which is by far the most valuable. Its especial use, discussed here, is in a basic branch of analytical chemistry—the making of identifications. This is a subsidiary science in its own right, not well explained by the vague general term "qualitative analysis". It is, of course, a part of qualitative analysis, as distinguished from quantitative, but it is a special part, in which we ought to use properties, tests, and reactions especially characteristic, or even specific for individual substances. Physical properties, although obtained by some general method, are often used when they can be accurately measured in such a way as to distinguish an individual compound even from those others that are closely related. Likewise, a chemical reaction may be general for a whole class of compounds, and yet we may be able to distinguish particular results. For example, a color reaction of phenols may give different colors with different phenols. The value of the microscope is to see different results given by different substances even in the same general precipitation reaction.

Chemical tests are mainly divided into two kinds—color tests and precipitation tests. Now the ordinary spectrophotometer (cf. Absorption Spectroscopy—Visible and Ultraviolet, in "Encyclopedia of Spectroscopy") may be regarded as giving not only a means of studying what might be called the "colorimetric" properties of a substance itself, but also, when a reagent is used, an enormous extension of the color tests of chemistry. Not only are comparisons and colorimetric readings made better, in the visible range, but also they are extended deep into the ultraviolet, where nothing at all could be seen with the unaided eye.

In a somewhat analogous way, the microscope enormously extends not merely the study of the form and crystal properties of a substance itself, but also the ordinary precipitation tests of chemistry, without changing their essential character as chemical reactions. Not only are details of the precipitate, when it is crystalline, seen better, and down to a smaller size, but with the polarizing microscope the observation of crystal characteristics is extended to things of an entirely different nature from those that can be seen with the unaided eye by ordinary light. Thus microscopic identifications by crystal forms and properties are at least potentially capable of extension from substances which are already crystalline to all substances that give precipitation reactions in ordinary chemistry, or indeed to those that give any kind of crystal-forming reaction.

The science of making chemical identifications is important in forensic chemistry (cf. Forensic Microscopy, p. 338), especially in law enforcement, because many legal cases involve questions of identity rather than quantity, as regards narcotics, poisons, potent drugs, adulterants, contaminants, substitutes, and so on, and such cases require exacting proof of the identity of the substances concerned. The uses are more general, however, for questions of chemical identity which can be answered in similar ways may arise in any field involving chemical substances. Usually too little attention is paid to the possibilities of microscopic chemistry, which may provide tests for very minute quantities, or such firm assurance of identity as to be the preferred method, when it can be used by anyone acquainted with it, regardless of the amount of substance available for tests.

Microcrystal tests are exceptionally good for court purposes, because they are as simple and direct as tests can be. In many cases, just looking at the crystals under the microscope enables the analyst to make the identification, and the things looked for are the characteristics of an actual, visible compound of the substance to be identified. It seems to be pretty generally realized that simple, direct tests are the best for forensic purposes. What sometimes seems to be overlooked or not realized as it should be, is that they are also best for chemical purposes.

In these microcrystal tests the polarizing microscope should by all means be used, and the relation to optical crystallography is, of course, close. Now optical crystallography, for which, in the field of mineralogy, the polarizing microscope was developed, is often an ideal means of identifying the crystal species, for any substance that is already present in microscopically sizable crystals or fragments of crystals, and in fair proportion in the material examined; and determination of refractive indices plays a large part. On the other hand, microscopic chemical identifications, which are the subject here, usually depend upon the formation of crystals by the action of a chemical reagent, which may even pick out the substance in a complex mixture for the analyst. Refractive indices are very seldom used, but optical-crystallographic properties which can be observed directly, without separating the crystals from the solution in which they are formed, are used, and therefore the polarizing microscope is needed. The two procedures go well together, but they are distinct. Figure 1 illustrates crystalline deposits examined between crossed nicols; the compound is aminotriazole. Figure 1b represents only 0.4 microgram in the deposit.

Other types of crystallization of a substance without a reagent can be seen in the photographs of d-, dl-, and $(d + dl)$-amphetamine hydrochloride and of NH_4Cl (see pages 67–69).

It should be noted that optical crystallography for substances already crystalline focuses upon the exact crystal species present, determined by such things as the acid with which a basic substance is combined, and even the proportion of molecules of water of crystallization, and sometimes the particular one of two or several polymorphic forms of the same substance, for these things often make major differences in the refractive indices and all the other crystal proper-

(a)

(b)

Fig. 1. Aminotriazole as seen with the polarizing microscope, between crossed nicols: (a) deposit from evaporated aqueous solution; (b) deposit of 0.4 microgram.

ties. In the microscopic chemical tests, on the other hand, one can test directly for a basic drug (e.g., morphine, or amphetamine) without necessarily being concerned with whether it is originally present as the sulfate or hydrochloride or in some other combination, and similarly for other kinds of substances.

Indeed, when a substance must be separated from a complex mixture, whether by extraction, chromatography, or some other means, its original state of combination is lost, and to use optical crystallography, or for that matter, to get a melting-point or x-ray diffraction pattern, it must be obtained in some kind of crystalline form. The greatest sensitivity, simplicity, and directness for any test requiring crystals exist if the crystals are obtained as some very insoluble compound which still crystallizes quite readily and in forms that are recognizable by direct inspection and observation. This is precisely the idea of the chemical microcrystal tests.

This subject is, therefore, a branch of chemistry. It involves the use of the microscope in making identifications by means of chemical reactions, especially precipitation reactions, yielding crystals. The optical crystallography used is limited and usually need not be of a specialized kind. In fact the chemistry used is not very unusual either, but naturally the reagents and reactions are selected as those especially useful in conjunction with the microscope. The science is to some extent a blend of chemistry and microscopy, but analysts should particularly keep in mind the chemical meaning of the tests, and development of the field will proceed along chemical lines. It is strange indeed that it has been so generally neglected by chemists, over a period of a hundred years.

Advantages and Disadvantages. The outstanding advantages of this kind of identification tests are:

(1) The high assurance with which microcrystal identifications can be made.

(2) The direct character of most of these tests.

(3) Their simplicity, convenience, and speed.

(4) Selectivity, in the sense of noninterference, or no great interference, by most impurities.

(5) High sensitivity, not necessarily in degree of dilution, but especially, with the aid of the microscope, in respect to amount of the substance for which the test is made.

In addition to various objections that are often made but have no very substantial basis, the main disadvantages are:

(1) The results are not readily classifiable.

(2) Applicability of coverage limited in organic chemistry.

(3) The general neglect.

When an identification is wanted for a chemical substance the identification should be specific. However, it is seldom reached by a single specific test, but usually as the only conclusion possible from two or more—commonly several—group tests or characteristic tests and properties. Often most of the chemical tests used are rather general, and are then supplemented with some physical measurement, often made on a derivative, to show differences between closely related compounds within the ascertained group, or provide final confirmation. The combined characteristics then become specific.

Much misunderstanding of the microcrystal tests seems to result from a failure to appreciate their chemical character. In a chemical microcrystal test we know, first of all, what reagent we used; and we know, or ought to know, what its chemical effects may be. We take a close look through the microscope at the crystals formed. Often we can recognize them immediately by their visible characteristics, assuming we have seen them before, and always remembering that we know what reagent was used.

The results are far more definite for individual compounds than in most chemical tests, but the procedure of identification is essentially the same, and these tests can well be used along with others, especially color tests for the spot-plate or designed for minute residues, or "spot tests" as developed by Feigl. However, the microcrystal tests are usually so highly characteristic, that two or three of them, even just using the ordinary microscope, and making comparisons, as necessary, with a known sample, will often make an identification certain, without necessarily having or obtaining any other type of information.

With the polarizing microscope the results are especially definite since a number of further observations can be made, even without removing the crystals from the solution in which they form. They do not have to be separated, washed, dried, recrystallized, and so forth, as for melting-point determinations and most other types of further tests, including refractive indices. All of the following are simply a matter of direct observation: not only the shape of the crystals, their grouping, color, size, and so on, but also birefringence, whether high, medium, low, or absent; whether extinction is inclined, and if so, the angle of extinction; in the case of colored crystals whether dichroism is present, and if so, the two different colors shown, and if the crystals are regularly elongated, the direction of dichroism (sign of absorption), and in the case of colorless elongate crystals, the sign of elongation. All these things can be observed without having to treat or prepare the crystals in any way, once they form in a solution.

Microcrystal tests are especially useful for distinguishing among closely related reactive compounds. Usually suitable tests can be found even to distinguish an isomer from the corresponding racemate, by completely different crystals. In fact, such tests have been used to identify d-amphetamine even in the presence of dl-amphetamine, and vice versa.

E. G. C. Clarke has shown how microcrystal tests can sometimes be used to distinguish microgram amounts of a d-isomer from the l-isomer, and without using an optically active reagent, which is another possibility. The question of identifying a d- or l-isomer is important in some cases now because the l-isomer of certain new synthetics is restricted as a narcotic while the d-isomer is also offered commercially as a different drug not subject to narcotic restrictions. The distinction is based on the fact that the racemate will give crystals in certain cases where a separate isomer will not. Besides knowing and having a suitable reagent, the analyst needs one known isomer, let us say the d-. If he mixes some of this with the suspected substance and it is l-, then he has the racemate and can get the appropriate crystals, but if the suspected substance is d- and he mixes d- with it, then of course he still cannot get crystals due to the racemate compound. If he has both known isomers for a cross-check, this kind of test can be completely certain.

The question about microcrystal tests so often asked, "what will they do on mixtures?"—reveals fundamental misunderstanding.

Most identification tests require that a substance to be identified be fairly pure. This is perhaps especially true of most physical and physicochemical tests, because they are so very general—melting-point tests, for example. A strictly chemical test or reaction, on the other hand, is bound to be selective in some degree, and will pick out a substance in the presence of all kinds of impurities except those that react with the same reagent, and occasionally even in the presence of compounds that react, but in a different way. A microcrystal test, where not merely the fact of a reaction, but crystals of a particular kind are looked for, cannot in general be expected to work on a complex of closely related, reactive compounds, although some tests that are remarkably searching, in this sense, are known. The application is often to a residue that has been separated as satisfactorily as possible from a mixture.

"Selective" is a term used in two different senses: a reagent may demonstrate that a compound belongs to a particular group, or it may actually pick out a reactive compound among others that are unreactive or that do not react as strongly or in the same way. Thus one kind of identity test may require an absolutely pure substance and be specific, or characteristic, or merely selective (in the first sense); while another type of test may not require great purity, and therefore when specific or characteristic for a compound may also be quite *selective* in the second sense, as well. The latter is very true of the chemical microcrystal tests.

These tests will work on mixtures with nonreactive material, with little or no interference, and can generally be applied directly to medicinal tablets, for example, in which a drug is mixed or diluted with material that is inert in the chemical reaction concerned. The reagent itself seeks out the particles or molecules of the substance that interests us, among particles and molecules of all sorts of other (nonreactive) substances. In the same way, these tests may be just the kind needed for extracts or isolates when it is not possible to get extremely high purity without risk of losing the little bit of material that is all that is available.

When procedures on a very small scale are combined with the use of the microscope, as is done by Clarke, a quite common sensitivity for a highly characteristic crystal test will be 2 or 3 hundredths of a microgram. Atropine gives tiny characteristic crystals with the right variety of iodine-KI reagent down to an aqueous dilution of 1 to 1,000,-000. Using a fair-sized ordinary drop of 0.04 ml the crystals can therefore be obtained with 0.04 microgram; by using a microdrop of 0.1 microliter (.0001 ml), the extreme sensitivity is .0001 microgram; or, as the crystals are hard to find at the extreme limit, the working sensitivity, using microdrops,

may be put at about .0004 microgram of atropine.

In general, however, the writer agrees with Chamot and Mason: "It is perhaps unfortunate that so much stress has been laid upon the sensitivity of microscopical crystal tests, both because their advantages of ease and directness are thereby obscured, and because the impression is given that they are appropriate only in case extremely minute amounts of material or low concentrations are to be dealt with." Sensitivities are important—sometimes very important, even absolutely essential in such a science as toxicology—but it does seem that when a microcrystal test is described in any detail, sensitivity is likely to be the one point seized on, in abstracts for example, to the exclusion of everything else. This degrades the microscopical crystal tests to the level of mere detection tests, which are often sensitive but very general, and worthless for identification whereas the purpose of the microcrystal tests is identification, whatever the amount of substance available. Their advantages are not only in ease and directness, as mentioned, but in providing highly characteristic and even specific identification tests, not mere detection. To the extent that sensitivity statements obscure this, they should be played down; at the same time it should be realized that the better microcrystal tests are exceedingly sensitive, and thus quite adequate for identification on almost any minute scale.

The statement is rather frequently encountered, that in general color tests are more sensitive than precipitation (or microcrystal) tests. This is both incorrect and fallacious. Some compounds give excellent color tests and few and poor precipitation tests, or none; others are just the reverse. Some compounds, e.g., morphine, are remarkable for both kinds, and in such cases they are likely to be of the same order of sensitivity, as a consultation of published statements in regard to morphine tests will show.

The sensitivities can be great for both, but they are usually due to different reactive radicals or atoms, sometimes both kinds present in the same molecule, as with morphine, and sometimes only the one or the other present for any known and useful tests. It would be almost as sensible for a chemist to cut off one hand, as to refuse to use one or the other kind, according to their merits in particular cases.

The preeminent radical for color tests is probably the phenolic hydroxyl. Even more preeminent for precipitation and microcrystal tests is the basic or partly basic nitrogen atom, no matter whether it is "primary", "secondary", or "tertiary", or whether it belongs to a straight chain of atoms, or is attached to a benzene ring, or is itself part of a ring. The chief counteractant to the precipitating effect of basic nitrogen is acidic oxygen, which shows why color tests may occasionally "oppose" crystal tests, i.e., the change of a molecule to include the preeminent radical for color tests may weaken and lessen the sensitivity of precipitation tests, especially for relatively simple compounds. Paradoxically, however, oxygen itself may be basic, in certain cases, and then forms oxonium salts, which are subject to precipitation tests.

While an identification may well be based on several results obtained separately by different disciplines, it is unfortunate that numerous researchers consider the form and obvious characteristics of crystals only as dressing for procedures resulting in micromelting points, refractive indices, or other numerical determinations. That is, they make the tests over in the usual pattern of organic confirmatory tests: formation of a derivative, isolation of the derivative and often its further purification (e.g., by recrystallization), and physical measurement of some characteristic of the isolated, purified derivative. Such procedures have been proposed even in the alkaloidal field, where the microcrystal tests are already best devel-oped. They are destructive alike to the speed, simplicity, ease, and directness of the microcrystal tests, in most cases without any concurrent gain, since the observation of characteristic crystals was already adequate to the purpose of identification. Much of the literature on the use of picric, styphnic, and picrolonic acids, reinecke salt, etc., is of this type.

A related erroneous idea sometimes encountered is that special measures should be taken to get the crystals as well-formed crystallographically as possible—whereas in fact, crystals ordinarily forming in characteristic distortions have far greater value. In most cases even procedures such as warming or adding alcohol are of value only when a particular compound is suspected that needs special measures to induce crystallization with a much-used reagent, and then a special reagent is usually better if one can be found that will readily give crystals without such measures.

Crystals given by a particular organic compound may be specific, that is, of a kind given by no other substance. Sometime objection is made to calling such tests specific, but on grounds that would prevent any tests ever being called specific: that not every possible substance has been tried, or even that some new compound might be discovered or synthesized sometime, that might be confused with the old one. To the writer it seems more reasonable to call a test specific if it is specific, so far as we know or can reasonably foresee, for our knowledge never can be infinite.

On the other hand, we should exercise considerable caution in designating a test as specific. The crystals are, in general, direct compounds of the substances for which the tests are made, and therefore in a particular case they are more or less different from those given by any other substance, just as each substance is, in itself, finally unique, if tests could be carried far enough to take in all its physical and chemical properties.

However, the question is whether the crystals in a particular case are sufficiently different from most others, or from all others, to be distinguished from them by informed direct observation. The writer is satisfied to call most of these crystal tests, even most of the very good ones, characteristic rather than specific; not only when we know of some definite resemblance but also whenever the crystals are some general type that might occur with some other compound, even if we do not yet know what it would be.

However, as an example of a specific test the intensely pleochroic crystals of herapathite, as a test for quinine, may be cited. These crystals of quinine iodosulfate (Fig. 2), produced by a suitable reagent, are recognizable at once and the test is so sensitive to quinine, and so insensitive to interference, that the writer has used it as a direct test for quinine in the diluted, adulterated, impure heroin mixtures of the illicit drug traffic. Of course, one almost never depends wholly upon any single test by itself, even if it is specific and the intense fluorescence of quinine sulfate solution in ultraviolet light, which is characteristic but not specific, is also easily observed.

Other cinchona alkaloids give highly char-

FIG. 3. Crystals produced by quinidine with Iodine-KI reagent C-3 or a similar reagent.

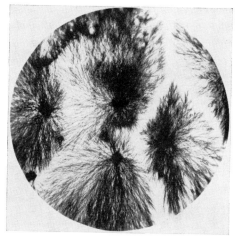

FIG. 4. Crystals produced by Cinchonidine with Iodine-KI reagent C-3 or a similar reagent.

acteristic, wholly different, iodosulfate crystals, with the same reagent used for quinine (Figs 3, 4, 5).

A strange objection is often made to crystal tests as, supposedly, a reason for not using them: that one substance with one reagent may give two or more different kinds of crystals. This undoubtedly happens, but, in the first place, it also happens with all other tests that depend on crystal form and properties, including melting points. As a difficulty it is very unlikely to be too serious

FIG. 2. Crystals of quinine iodosulfate (herapathite) (with polarized light). Iodine-KI reagent C-3 or a similar reagent.

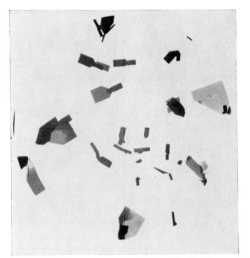

Fig. 5. Crystals produced by Cinchonine with Iodine-KI reagent C-3 or a similar reagent.

with microcrystal tests, because the crystals are not some that come to the analyst already formed under unknown conditions, but are formed under test conditions, and comparisons should be made with a known sample under as nearly as possible the same conditions.

Secondly, even if one crystal type was unexpectedly changed into another which was unknown to the analyst, this would presumably result in a failure to make the identification, but not in an erroneous identification. There is probably no way of testing known that may not sometimes fail to give a recognizable result because of some kind of interference with the usual test conditions. On the other hand, if both kinds of crystals are known, even if the reason for one changing into the other is not, the test is still good.

Finally, the objection is especially strange because in most cases, having two or more types of test-crystals is a positive advantage. If we can learn the reason for the change—and this is usually not very hard to do, and is known in many cases—then we have two tests instead of one, which together often provide enough evidence for identification in themselves. Or, the two kinds of crystals may occur in the same test, in which case

both types together characterize the substance, and the single test is all the more likely to be specific or very highly characteristic.

One crystal type is occasionally known to be changed to another by temperature or by stirring. However, the most common cause is a different concentration of the substance, especially relative to the precipitating agent in the test-drop. Particular advantage is taken of this in the new tests made by addition of a strongly acid reagent to a very little of the dry substance tested. A cover-glass is applied and this prevents the tested substance from diffusing equally through the test-drop. Thus the precipitation and crystallization take place at different concentrations in each single test even with only a minute amount of the substance. Therefore when a substance gives two or more completely different types of crystals at different concentrations, they are nearly always obtained in each single test, so that such tests are generally highly characteristic and may comparatively often be of specific rank.

For example, in one such test with an iodine-KI reagent in $HCl-H_3PO_4$, morphine gives four kinds of crystals (Fig. 6a), depending upon concentration: black needles,

Fig. 6a. Crystals given by extracted Morphine with Iodine-KI reagent M-2.

brown threads in rosettes, tiny rectangular orange-brown blades, and comparatively large brown to red square-cut and jagged birefringent plates. All four kinds can be obtained with only a few micrograms of morphine (in a small spot); the black needles are sensitive, with no special effort to reduce the scale, to 0.1 microgram. The test is extraordinarily resistant to interference, that is, the morphine need not have a high degree of purity to yield good crystals; in fact, the black needles and red plates have been obtained on a little dried poppy-juice (Papaver somniferum) without first separating the morphine from the other opium alkaloids or even purifying the alkaloids as such (Fig. 6b).

That specific tests are available for some substances is only one factor in deciding what tests to use in given circumstances. Even a very general reaction may be useful to prove the absence of a compound. For general identification work, reagents will be preferred which give many different characteristic results, rather than "tailor-made" reagents for a few specific results, particularly in using them before one has much idea what is present. Other important factors are sensitivity, and ease of obtaining crystals even when the substance is not quite pure. Some specific tests rank high in these ways also, but they do not necessarily go together. Regardless of other factors, there are always cases where what we want, when we can have it, is a test that, when successful, will prove the identity of the substance then and there, beyond doubt. This is possible with some microcrystal tests.

The very diverse nature of microcrystals is at the same time the strength and weakness of the method. The results are highly characteristic or specific, but they are hard to classify. Largely, this is due to the fact that the tests are not measurements; the results are not even directly numerical at all, and so they lack the automatic classification that numbers give. It is not that the tests are

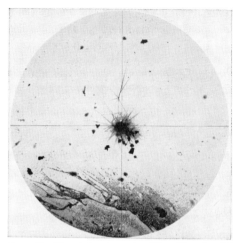

FIG. 6b. Crystals given by Morphine in dried juice from Popaver somniferum—no purification of the morphine, not even any separation of the alkaloids—with Iodine-KI reagent M-2.

good for only a few particular results: plenty of good results are obtainable. The difficulty is to have a way to look them up if they are not already familiar.

Possible solutions are being sought, now that the problem is becoming acute. Even if anyone wanted still to limit the scope of the tests to some 50 familiar alkaloids, it is not possible even in the drug field, for there is now a host of new drugs that react in the same way (by precipitation and crystal-forming reactions) with the same traditional reagents. Several different solutions of the classification problem are possible in principle, at least such that punched-card sorting would quickly lead one from results on an unknown back to the proper "known" if it had been previously studied and classified. However, at present, and probably for some time, the analyst has to rely largely on chemical classification, involving method of isolation, color reactions, precipitation reactions regarded chemically, and any other clues. Chemical evidence may reduce the number of compounds that have to be considered to something manageable, and then microcrystal tests will show exactly what the substance is, if "knowns" for comparisons are available. This goes well beyond using the tests as merely "confirmatory" of something already known or suspected, but even that is one of their useful functions.

The second real disadvantage listed above for these tests is the limited field of applicability, or lack of coverage outside a limited field. It has already been pointed out that the applicability is in fact not nearly so limited as generally supposed, but the disadvantage might be stated more accurately that tests have as yet been well worked out only for inorganic ions and the familiar alkaloids. The same reagents and procedures as for alkaloids can be used for a great many other drugs, e.g., antihistamines, and with some changes they can be extended over all derivatives of basic nitrogen, and even further, but certainly other types of organic precipitation have not been studied nearly enough, and in fact with the many new drugs the coverage is inadequate even for those giving tests with the traditional reagents.

Rather than any danger of making erroneous identifications, as seems to be feared by many (perhaps rightly in the case of the totally inexperienced), the bane of the experienced analyst is the finding of an occasional compound, in the line of work, which yields beautiful crystals, sometimes with several different reagents, but which, nevertheless, he still cannot identify. This is due much more to lack of study of the compounds than to the difficulty of looking up those already studied, because of lack of classification. The individual chemist or a single laboratory cannot possibly keep abreast of developments.

Both of the disadvantages just discussed are related to general neglect, which also has other features. The analyst must often train himself; he usually cannot obtain much instruction, or even textbooks, in this field. At the present time the writer does not even know of a good textbook for microcrystal tests for alkaloids that is now in print. The only good thing that can be said

about this state of affairs is that it should be a challenge and a stimulus to an analyst to promote application of the microscope to any problems of identification that occur in his own work.

It may be pointed out that these disadvantages, serious as they are in some cases, in no way interfere with the use of microcrystal tests by an analyst acquainted with them, in: (a) confirmatory tests, where tentative identification has been made, and comparison with a known sample is possible; (b) in proving the presence of a particular compound (here, if the compound sought turns out *not* to be present, the test may do more than most to show what *is* present); (c) in deciding, among a few alternatives, to which one an unknown corresponds: this is often possible by microscopic test-comparisons with the known alternatives even if nothing has been previously published or studied on these particular compounds; (d) in distinguishing between closely related compounds (including distinction of an isomer from the racemate, or even of the *d*- from the *l*-form, as previously explained); (e) in a larger and larger field of tests as the experience of the analyst grows.

Practical Work

As textbooks are nearly non-existent, some advice on practical work will be attempted. In the limited space it still must be rather general.

First, accustom oneself to the microscope by using it. Much analytical work will be helped enormously by preliminary microscopic observation of the material to be examined, either by reflected light (if it is opaque) or by transmitted light. This may, for example, show at the outset whether the material is a mixture or appears to be all one substance.

Then, bring the chemical work down to the level of convenience for microscopic observation. A precipitation test can be observed just as well with a drop of solution on a slide as with several ml in a test-tube, before using the microscope at all. Color tests on the spot-plate are a useful adjunct. Accustom oneself to working on some such scale, which will probably be found more convenient than the "usual" one, anyway.

Keep a polarizing microscope at hand, and use it. If a polarizing microscope cannot be used, polarizing attachments for the ordinary microscope are helpful, but are at best a poor makeshift. Observation of the microcrystal tests is almost always by transmitted light, although it would be possible to use reflected light in many cases. "Low Power" of 80–100 × is usually sufficient for the tests, at least for all the initial observations. If the crystals are very small, a higher power is then used.

Make a practice of looking at the result of a precipitation test microscopically, whether the textbook mentions crystals or not. For example, the iodoform test for ethyl alcohol is made quite definite for the product iodoform (although in any case it is not specific for ethanol) by microscopic observation, although textbooks often fail to mention this and may only refer to the odor.

Pictures that can be consulted are helpful in dealing with a test not yet familiar, and when time permits or the case is important enough the analyst should take them of his own results, as a reminder to himself and information to others.

There is a real art in taking photomicrographs of known crystals so that they will most plainly show the truly characteristic forms that should be looked for. Pictures for reference, however, valuable as they are, are no substitute for at least a little actual experience, and no substitute, either, for actual comparison of the results given by an unknown with those given by a known compound.

Most of the familiar tests, for organic as well as inorganic substances, are made with aqueous solutions. Usually the ordinary flat microscope slide is quite satisfactory. Com-

monly, a cover-glass is not used, unless or until examination by high power is wanted. The test is observed while evaporation takes place. This time can be prolonged by setting a petri-dish over the slide when it is not under immediate examination. Cavity slides are less convenient for focusing, but the evaporation is more gradual, and can be stopped by simply laying a slide over the one on which the test is made. Cavity slides are also more convenient for mixing three or four ordinary drops, in more complex tests.

The reagent drop may be added directly to the drop tested, or placed beside it on a plain slide and the two drops allowed to flow together. Reagent is usually added in about the same size drop as the solution tested. The actual concentration of substance tested is therefore reduced by about half in the test-drop, but it is customary to report the sensitivity or optimum concentration, etc., in terms of the solution tested, before it is mixed with reagent.

A full drop of water (let fall from a fairly wide opening) is about 0.05 ml. Use smaller rather than larger "drops", by touching the pipet to the slide and letting just a little flow out, by dropping from a narrow orifice, or by using a rod to transfer a drop. In most tests with no especial need to conserve material ordinary 1-ml pipets may be used for handling both the solutions to be tested and the reagents.

Not only crystals, but also amorphous precipitation, or absence of precipitation, are observed. Amorphous precipitates may be finely divided or curdy, or in drops, the latter often a prelude to the formation of large crystals. Crystals may form directly, or from an amorphous precipitate. As evaporation is usually not controlled, the time during which a test is observed is then only that required for the drop to dry up. Test-crystals often form around the edge, especially with dilute solutions, as the drop dries. The reagent itself may crystallize out when evaporation has gone far enough, and a reagent-blank should always be run in comparison with any test, until the analyst is thoroughly familiar with crystals or any other effect that may arise from the reagent alone.

Test solutions can be made up of weighed quantities in a few ml or less of water, or made right on the microscope slide. The analyst soon learns to judge the amount of substance needed, say about 0.2 mg if there is no need to conserve the substance, giving with an ordinary drop of about 0.04 ml a concentration of about 1:200, which is very good for many microcrystal tests, usually better than more concentrated. Most of the tests are best at concentrations between 1:100 and 1:5000 (0.4 mg to 8 γ in 0.04 ml); the very good ones still succeed at greater dilutions, requiring only a few micrograms even in an ordinary drop, and the tendency is always to study and use more and more sensitive tests.

The average analyst needs micro *tests* far more than "micro" procedures and equipment, aside from the microscope itself. It is often more convenient to carry out an extraction, for example, with ordinary equipment, and volumes of, say, 10 ml of solution and 5 or 10 ml of solvent at a time, for a few shake-outs, even if the amount of material is quite small and the final residue microscopic. Often, in fact, the analyst has to process quite large amounts of material to get an extremely minute residue. Chemistry has reached a stage where more and more sensitivity is wanted in tests, and they are almost never too sensitive if satisfactory in other respects.

A further long step downward can be taken when necessary, by using small droplets. If all the substance available will make only one small "macro" droplet of solution of, say, 0.01 ml, it will still be possible to try up to about 100 microcrystal tests, using microdrops of as little as 0.1 (mm)^3 or 0.1 microliter, each containing only 1 to 0.02 microgram of substance, to be within the best range for most tests. Thin solid rods (1

mm diameter) are used to make these micro-drops and add reagent (see Clarke).

To prevent too rapid evaporation a micro-test is made in a hanging drop. It may be put on an ordinary slide and inverted over a cavity slide. This procedure is also used for an ordinary small test-drop (say 0.01 ml), simply as a means of preventing or greatly slowing evaporation and the slide can be reinverted whenever rapid evaporation is desired. As an alternative to sealing-in, to be quite sure of preventing evaporation while the test stands, a drop of water, or better, a large "blank" test-drop, which will give virtually the same humidity as the hanging drop, can be put in the depression of the cavity slide. The enclosure technique also slows the evaporation of other substances besides water, e.g., iodine from solutions which have only a low content of iodide to hold it in solution.

With a standard "thin" slide (thickness not over 1 mm) the usual second power magnification (objective 20 or 21 ×, or 8 mm) can be used through the slide. If observation under still higher power is wanted, of course it is necessary to mix the test-drop on a cover-glass. In Clarke's technique the cover-glass is sealed in with 25 % gum-arabic solution to prevent its slipping and ensure only extremely slow evaporation. The seal may be made not quite complete at first if it is desired to allow a little evaporation (until precipitation occurs) before finally sealing. Square 25 mm cover glasses may be most convenient.

In new tests for basic substances in a medium of strong acid, a very small amount of solid material is put on a slide (finely powdered or in a thin deposit in one spot), a drop of reagent placed near it, and then a cover-glass, ordinarily of 18-mm size (round or square), is added so that the reagent flows over the solid. Or, the drop of reagent is put on the cover-glass, which is then inverted over the substance. The reagent consists of some precipitating compound in solution in a strong acid, most often syrupy H_3PO_4, $(2 + 3)$ H_2SO_4, concentrated HCl, or $(2 + 1)$ acetic acid—acids which give reagents of very different effects even with the same precipitating compound.

With a medium of strong phosphoric or sulfuric acid the drop cannot dry up, but its moisture content may gradually change on standing (generally increasing, sometimes considerably), depending on the humidity or dryness of the air. These tests are usually observed during only about two hours, so that ordinarily no special precautions are needed.

Small cover-glasses of 12-mm diameter are obtainable. A test made under this size can be inverted over a cavity slide, a procedure which will very nearly prevent any evaporation of a volatile acid or water, or changes due to humidity or dryness of the air. This is generally sufficient control for at least 24 hours without sealing-in. A further refinement is to put a drop of diluted sulfuric acid of a certain strength in the cavity of the lower slide, to regulate the humidity. H_2SO_4 $(45 + 55)$ will correspond pretty closely to a reagent of syrupy H_3PO_4; H_2SO_4 $(1 + 5)$ will provide controlled humidity; H_2SO_4 $(55 + 45)$ provides gentle drying for H_3PO_4 reagents.

Reagents in strong acids may also be added to aqueous solutions, or applied to solids in a form somewhat diluted with water, without a cover-glass. Then formation of a precipitate and crystallization may occur promptly, or only as the drop evaporates to a higher acid strength, particularly in using phosphoric acid. Sometimes drying in a desiccator may be useful, e.g., with $HAuCl_4$ in H_3PO_4, or a controlled humidity to allow drying just to a certain degree, or to prevent complete drying when the air is very dry, e.g., with the reagent H_3BiI_6 in $(1 + 7)$ H_2SO_4.

A hanging drop of reagent is also used in tests for volatile substances. This is more or less familiar in chemical and microcrystal tests for ammonia from ammonium salts, and as a test for urea when it is decomposed to ammonia by urease. Microcrystals tests in the hanging drop for the readily volatile d- and dl-amphetamine were perhaps first used by Griebel, with aqueous reagents. The material (e.g., a small amount of scrapings from a tablet containing an amphetamine salt), or its solution, is treated with dilute alkali on a cavity slide, and a hanging drop is inverted over it. There are now at least a dozen such sympathomimetic drugs regularly on the market, that are readily volatile, to be tested in this way, and others that are less readily volatile.

It is certainly not yet realized how far such tests can be extended, how many substances usually considered nonvolatile are in fact slightly volatile with water vapor even at room temperature and can be detected in a hanging drop with an exposure of, say, two hours, for example, l- and dl-ephedrine, and phenmetrazine. Gentle heat from above, e.g., from a desk lamp, may be used to shorten the time required, and may improve results, e.g., in the vaporization of pentylenetetrazol, but a longer exposure at room temperature is as good or better for most compounds.

On the acid side benzoic and salicylic acids may be mentioned as sufficiently volatile with water vapor for vaporization tests.

A hanging drop of an aqueous solution of reagent, above an aqueous solution on a cavity slide, does not dry up or expand unless considerable hygroscopic material is present in one solution, and a long exposure may be used. For basic vapors, a reagent in diluted H_3PO_4, $(1 + 4)$ to $(1 + 2)$, may be exposed for some two hours or more, with some increase in the size of the hanging drop due to absorption of water. The slide with the hanging drop is then reinverted to allow evaporation, even put in the desiccator if necessary, and tests can be obtained for a great many basic substances even if only slightly volatile.

A convenient purification as well as a test

for a volatile base is to catch the vapor in a hanging drop of dilute HCl (say 1% by volume of the concentrated acid), over an alkaline drop on a cavity slide. Then the slide with the hanging drop is reinverted and the drop allowed to dry up, leaving the hydrochloride of the volatile base. This solid hydrochloride may then be examined microscopically, if it crystallizes, or it may be tested with $HAuBr_4$ in H_3PO_4, or some other reagent of high acid content; or with this purification it may be simply dissolved in water for some test.

Some substances decompose in alkaline solution and give off a volatile base. For example, the drugs levarterenol, epinephrine, and isoproterenol, all diphenols and of similar uses, give off ammonia, methylamine, and isoproterenol give off ammonia, methylamine, and isopropylamine, respectively, and can be readily distinguished in this way, with a hanging drop of sodium tetraphenylboron solution. The assurance of the identity of the substance given off that is afforded by microcrystals raises these tests much above the usual chemical decomposition tests.

Still, a decomposition test is usually not the best, if a direct test is available. In showing contamination by rodent urine, instead of the indirect test for urea by decomposition with urease and detection of the ammonia evolved (a ubiquitous substance, and usually detected merely by its alkalinity, although microcrystals can be used here, too) a direct microcrystal test with xanthydrol can be used. In (2 + 1) acetic acid this is amazingly prompt and sensitive for an organic reaction, and results in crystals of a urea compound, dixanthylurea, which are observed directly, with obvious forensic and other advantages for the test. This is an example of the scattered microcrystal tests which are possible and depend on varied organic reactions.

If analysts, generally, would try to find microcrystal tests whenever this type would be the most advantageous way of identifying substances, many such tests undoubtedly will be found. However, the most familiar microcrystal tests at present are those for alkaloids and related substances, and related tests for other derivatives of basic nitrogen.

Criteria for Selecting the Best Identification Tests

(1) Highly characteristic crystals (which may be so by reason of two or more types occurring in the same test-drop, or for other reasons besides form); (2) Easily recognizable crystals; (3) Crystals forming very readily; (4) Crystals of the same type or types over a wide range of concentration or with widely different amounts of material (when direct addition is used); (5) Crystals reasonably stable; (6) Crystals not essentially changed by the presence of nonreactive material (e.g., tablet excipients); (7) Crystallization not prevented nor badly altered when impurities of other nitrogenous bases are present in quite minor amounts (experience with actual uses of the test affords the best information on this point); (8) High sensitivity; (9) Colored crystals are preferable (i.e., use of a colored precipitating compound); (10) The reagent by itself (blank test) should not give any possibly confusing crystals; (11) A permanent reagent is preferable; (12) A slow-evaporating or non-drying reagent is preferable; (13) A reagent of general usefulness for microcrystals is preferable, or alternatively (for some purposes) one that does not precipitate at all with most other alkaloids and amines; (14) Comparisons, both in general, and with the most closely related compounds available, should establish the meaning and value of the test for the particular substance.

Future Uses

It seems likely that for the near future the usefulness of microcrystal tests will remain chiefly in the drug field, as regards the substances tested, and in general in regulatory and law-enforcement work. Here, the highly individual character of the tests is much more an advantage than a defect. Here, highly characteristic and specific tests, the results of which can be photographed for possible introduction in court or in other proceedings, are welcomed. Here, it is a great advantage that the tests are simple and direct, and distinctions made on the basis of obvious, visible characteristics. The identifications clearly distinguish between closely related compounds, even between an isomer and the racemate, and by certain tests, between the d- and l-isomers; and this is just what is needed in the drug field and in forensic chemistry and related work.

In these applications the microcrystal tests are already used, and so too are color tests, of a kind with which the crystal tests form a natural partnership.

The classification of the microcrystal tests, to enhance and extend their usefulness, remains a problem. Compounds are only too likely to be met with occasionally, to which the tests are applicable but which still cannot be identified. This of course is due not merely to lack of classification, but is, at present, primarily because the tests for so many new drugs and other compounds have not been studied at all. However, this is a related aspect of the problem, for if a satisfactory system of classification is once worked out, the necessary experiments to find where all the compounds likely to be met with fit into the scheme are more likely to be made.

Whether a classification of crystal results should be primarily chemical, or morphological with the different reagents, or based simply on the fact of crystallization of each substance with certain reagents out of a standard list, there can be no reasonable doubt but that the science of microcrystal tests should be integrated with analytical chemistry, not pushed aside as a "specialty" nor even regarded as being more microscopy than chemistry.

The idea of using the microscope to make tests better for identification by simply looking at the different crystals formed in the usual precipitation reactions and other crystal-forming reactions of chemistry seems so sensible and also so obvious that it is hard to explain how it can be overlooked, as it usually seems to be. The idea develops normally in three stages:

(1) *Microscopic observation of chemical tests:* The microscope is used to distinguish the crystals occurring in chemical precipitation tests and other reactions, and thus to particularize them further; and the tests which are found especially characteristic are noted.

(2) *Microscopic study of microcrystal tests:* The tests thus found of especial value become in themselves the basis for identification, and the best reagents thus found are tried systematically on other, related compounds. In this stage, appreciation of the chemical nature of the tests sometimes almost disappears.

(3) *Chemical extension of microcrystal tests:* Chemical reagents and reactions are reconsidered and studied with the objective of improving microcrystal tests and extending them to new groups of compounds. As the tests come to cover a wider area in organic chemistry than simply "alkaloids", their chemical meaning in various cases becomes important.

The chemist needs the microscope, not only for primarily observational use, as in looking at the material he is dealing with, and as a convenient aid in all kinds of chemical procedures and research, for example, whenever he has a deposit or residue and merely wants to know whether it is crystalline or not. . . . He needs the polarizing microscope, not only as a means of identifying crystals of chemical substances by refractive indices and other properties shown by optical crystallography. . . . Most of all, in his own capacity of chemist, he needs it, as this article has tried to show, in analytical identification chemistry, as the prime means of making chemical tests more definite. The science of microcrystal tests is already useful now, especially in the drug field as well as in inorganic chemistry, but it needs to be fully integrated with analytical chemistry, and extended over all organic compounds that can give characteristic, identifying crystals in chemical reactions.

REFERENCES

1. STEPHENSON, CHARLES H., "Some Microchemical Tests for Alkaloids; including Chemical Tests of the Alkaloids Used," by C. E. Parker, Philadelphia and London, J. B. Lippincott Co., 1921.
2. KLEY, P. D. C. (a) BEHRENS-KLEY, "Mikrochemische Analyse," 1st part, (as 4th ed. of "Anleitung zur Mikrochemischen Analyse," by H. Behrens), Leipzig, Leopold Voss, 1921. (Inorganic). (b) BEHRENS-KLEY, "Organische Mikrochemische Analyse" (as 2nd ed. of "Anleitung zur Mikrochemischen Analyse der Wichtigsten Organischen Verbindungen," by H. Behrens), Leipzig, Leopold Voss, 1922.
3. AMELINK, F., "Schema zur mikrochemischen Identifikation von Alkaloiden; übersetzt von Marga Laur." (In German). Amsterdam, N.V.D.B. Centen's Uitgevers Maatschapij, 1934.
4. GEILMAN, W., "Bilder zur qualitativen Mikroanalyse anorganischer Stoffe," Leipzig, Leopold Voss, 1934. Republished by Authority of the Alien Property Custodian, by J. W. Edwards, lithoprinted by Edwards Brothers, Ann Arbor, Michigan, 1944.
5. ROSENTHALER, L., "Toxikologische Mikrochemie," Berlin, Gebrüder Borntraeger, 1935. Republished by Authority of the Alien Property Custodian, by J. W. Edwards, lithoprinted by Edwards Brothers, Ann Arbor, Michigan, 1946.
6. WAGENAAR, M., A series of articles on microchemical tests for particular alkaloids and related substances, (in Dutch), *Pharmaceutisch Weekblad voor Nederland*, **64-67** (1927-30); **70** (1933); **72-73** (1935-36).
7. HERZOG, ALOIS, "Mikroskopische Bilder für den Chemiker," Zeiss Nachrichten, 2 Folge, Heft 5, 149-81 (1938), and Heft 6, 183-215. (English summary at end of the volume.)
8. WHITMORE, W. F., AND WOOD, C. A., "Chemical Microscopy of Some Toxicologically Important Alkaloids," *Mikrochemie*, **27,** 249-334 (1939); "Scheme for the Microchemical Separation of Some Toxicologically Important Alkaloids," *Mikrochemie*, **28,** 1-13 (1940). (Both in English.)
9. CHAMOT, EMILE MONNIN, AND MASON, CLYDE WALTER, "Handbook of Chemical Microscopy, Volume II. Chemical Methods and Inorganic Qualitative Analysis," New York, John Wiley & Sons, 1940.
10. DUCLOUX, ENRIQUE HERRERO, "Notas Microquímicas sobre 'Doping'," Buenos Aires, Peuser Lda., 1943.
11. FULTON, CHARLES C. (1) Reagents: "The Precipitating Agents for Alkaloids," *Am. J. Pharmacy* (April, 1931); "New Precipitating Agents for Alkaloids and Amines," *Am. J. Pharm.*, (Feb. & Apr., 1940); "The Relation of Alkaloidal Chemistry to Inorganic, and the Use of Bromauric Acid as a Reagent for Inorganic Microcrystal Tests," *J. Am. Pharm. Assn.*, Scientific Edition, **31,** 177 (1942). (2) Classification by aqueous precipitation: "Alkaloids and Their Reagents," *Am. J. Pharm.* (May, 1939); for earlier, see *J. Association Official Agricultural Chemists*, **13,** 491 (1930). (3) Particular substances and development of new-type reagents: Atropine, *ibid.*, **12,** 312 (1929); Cocaine and Procaine, *Am. J. Pharm.* (July & Aug., 1933); Heroin (with G. D. Williams), *Am. J. Pharm.* (Sept., 1933); Morphine, *J. Lab. Clinical Medicine* (March, 1938); Cinchona alkaloids, *Ind. Eng. Chem., Anal. Edition*, **13,** 848 (1941); Morphine, Heroin, Dilaudid, Cocaine, in *American Journal of Police Science*, incorporated in *Journal of Criminal Law and Criminology*, **32,** 358-65 (1941); Methadone, Narceine, Thebaine, in United Nations document (mimeograph) E/CN.7/117, 14 April 1948, (also includes photomicrographs of the natural narcotine crystals of opium—see "Origin of Opium"), and Codeine in Add. 1 to this document, 22 Sept. 1948; Colchicine, *Jour. AOAC*, **41,** 756 (1958).
12. HARTSHORNE, N. H., AND STUART, A., "Crystals and the Polarizing Microscope," London, Edward A. Arnold & Co., (1943), 2nd ed. 1950. (Optical Crystallography.)
13. FARMILO, CHARLES G., LEVI, LEO; OESTREICHER, P. M. L.; AND ROSS, R. G. "Microcrystal and Colour Tests for the New Synthetic Narcotics," *Bulletin on Narcotics*, **4,** No. 4, 16-42 (1952).
14. CLARKE, E. G. C., AND WILLIAMS, MARGARET, "Microidentification of the Opium Alkaloids," *Bulletin on Narcotics*, **7,** No. 3-4,

33–42 (1955); "Microchemical Tests for the Identification of Alkaloids," *J. Pharmacy and Pharmacology*, **7**, 255–62 (1955).

15. CLARKE, E. G. C. (a) "Microchemical identification of Sugars as Osazones", *J. Physiology*, **135**, 28–9 P, from "Proceedings of the Physiological Society," December 1956. (b) In *J. Pharmacy and Pharmacology*, "Microchemical Identification": Local Anaesthetics, **8**, 202–6 (1956); Some Less common Alkaloids, **9**, 187–92 (1957); Antihistamines, **9**, 752–8 (1957); Antimalarials, **10**, 194–6 (1958). Atropine-Like Drugs, **11**, 629–36 (1959). "Microchemical Differentiation between Optical Isomers of N-Methylmorphinan Analgesics," **10**, 642–4 (1958). (c) "Microchemical identification of some modern analgesics," *Bulletin on Narcotics*, **11**, No. 1, 27–44 (1959).

CHARLES C. FULTON

FORMS OF MICROCRYSTALS

Descriptions and classifications of microchemical crystal forms have scarcely any relation to orthodox crystallography. What is needed is not a deduction of the crystal system—even if that were generally possible, which it is not—but simply a straightforward way of describing and classifying the forms just as they are seen as a result of the chemical test.

In the comprehensive study and classification of microcrystals, along with *form* goes *size*, and the latter is measurable. In the following classification of forms, however, the concern is not with the actual measured size, but only with considering, in relation to form, how many different measurements, of value to a description or classification, might be made on a particular type of crystal.

Crystals exist, of course, in three dimensions, but may *extend* significantly only in one direction, length, if they are fine needles, —or only in two, length and breadth, if they are plates or blades of negligible thickness. In the latter case, moreover, they may lie flat, especially if under a coverslip; so that such crystals, certainly as we see them, extend simply in two dimensions.

The number of dimensions subject to useful measurement will not (in general) be greater than the number of dimensions of extension, but may be smaller. In the case of a regular hexagonal plate, for example, only one measurement is needed to complete the description (so far as form and size go)—no matter whether we make it as the length of a side, or as a radius, or as the diameter from one vertex to the opposite one.

The writer uses the term "grain" for crystals which resemble the familiar grains of sand, salt, sugar, etc., as they appear under moderate magnification. The three dimensions of "extension" are essentially equal, so that only one measurement is needed (the diameter) to complete a description in a particular case.

These dimensional concepts give six classes; but there are two distinct kinds of crystals extending in three dimensions, each requiring two different measurements. They may best be taken as two separate classes (see table). It is also convenient to separate elongate or directional plates from blades. Together with a zero class for crystals of no significant dimensions (appearing as mere specks with the magnification usually used), this arrangement therefore provides nine classes in all (0–8) for the simple crystal forms. Distortions, contortions, and skeletons, as well as aggregates, should be referred to the corresponding simple forms.

Skeletonized crystals are here classed with the forms from which they are derived (which may occur along with them), rather than with the simple forms they may finally resemble in their parts. For example, some crystals vary from square plates to crosses. The flat, thin cross should still be assigned to the same class as regular plates although it might be described as having arms of blades.

Skeletonized forms can often be distinguished from aggregates by the birefringence. If a complex form extinguishes and brightens as a whole, it usually is basically

TABLE OF CRYSTAL FORMS

0   0–0   Specks; precipitate often amorphous-looking with birefringent specks seen with crossed nicols.

1   1–1   Needles (fine)
- distortions—hairs
- aggregates—fans, tufts, sheaves, bundles, rosettes, dendrites of needles; burs; wigs, spirals, balls of hairs

2   2–1   Plates essentially regular (triangles, squares, hexagons, octagons, disks)
- unformed or vague—precrystalline disks, smudge rosettes
- distortions—irregular but not definitely elongate plates, flakes
- skeletons—crosses, stars (formation all one crystal)

3   2–2   Elongate or Directional Plates (diamonds, rhomboids, elongate hexagons, etc.)
- skeletons—X's, flat nail shapes, flat combs, etc.
- twins—hourglass shapes, books, etc.
- aggregates—rosettes of plates; stepped or segmented plates; spears (built of diamonds)

4   2–2   Blades (thin flat forms with length considerably greater than breadth)
- distortions—irregular blades; splinters, ribbons
- skeletons—serrate and feathered blades
- aggregates—fans, sheaves, rosettes, dendrites of blades

5   3–1   Grains (cubes, polyhedra, pyramids, gems, kernels, sharply angular grains)
- unformed or shapeless—globes, globulites, spherulites; nuggets
- aggregates—granular clumps; sphero-rosettes of kernels; chains of grains

6   3–2   Rods, prisms; spindles, thick coarse needles,—(unimmeasurable cross-section)
- distortions—sticks, wires
- aggregates—fans, sheaves, rosettes, clusters, dendrites of rods, etc.

7   3–2   Regular Tablets (regular plates with thickness)
- distortions—tablets irregular but not definitely elongate
- skeletons—regular forms with thickness (e.g., crosses); regularly branching isotropic dendritic skeletons

8   3–3   Elongate Tablets and Bars
- with edges—chisels; thick ribbed blades
- skeletons—thick combs, ladders, etc.; dendritic anisotropic skeletons
- aggregates—clusters of bars; irregular multiformed dendrites

a single crystal, but if different parts brighten and extinguish independently, the whole must be composed of different simpler crystals growing from each other or from the same point.

The above table summarizes the suggested classification, including numerous kinds of distortions, skeletons, and aggregates. This is not a final answer to the problem, but shows that the many extremely diverse kinds of crystals can be grouped in a small number of classes, using primarily the two simple concepts of extension and measurement.

CHARLES C. FULTON

HISTORY

The microscope was invented between 1590 and 1609, and thus was available during the very beginning of scientific chemistry. Scientists of the 1700's used it to look at all sorts of small things, including natural crystals and such things of chemical nature. Some true chemists, as soon as there were any who deserved this name, used it, in an observational way, in their chemical researches.

True "chemical microscopy", although not then known by this name, began at least as early as 1742. In that year "The Microscope Made Easy", by Henry Baker, Fellow of the Royal Society and Member of the Society of Antiquaries of London, was published. Baker stated the following, under the chapter heading, "Of Salts in Mineral Waters":

"The Microscope may be of great Service to determine by ocular Examination, what kind of Salts our medicinal Springs are charged with, whence to form a Judgment in what Cases their Waters may be drank to Advantage." Five kinds of "fossile salts" were then enumerated.

Marggraf, in 1747, first published his research, which proved the presence of a true sugar in the beet, and thus laid the foundation of the German sugar industry. Despite his early date, he called himself and may truly be called a chemist (then "chymist"), and he used the microscope as a matter of course, as an aid in this research, remarking that little white crystals, looking like those of sugar, could be seen sprinkled over dried slices of the root, as a preliminary indication of the presence of sugar.

Another book by Baker, "Employment for the Microscope", was published in 1753. This work had two parts, of which Part I, containing 232 pages out of 442 for the book, had the title: "An Examination of Salts and Saline Substances, their Amazing Configurations and Crystals, as formed under the Eye of the Observer." His method was to prepare a saturated solution of a salt and then observe the formation of the crystals as a drop, spread out on a slide, began to dry up. There were 55 short chapters on different kinds of salts, and 9 plates out of 17 for the book illustrated their crystals. Not much was yet known about chemical composition, and Baker did not use reagents in his procedure. He was primarily a microscopist and such chemistry as he had was about as crude as it could be; but it may be pointed out that he preceded Raspail, often cited as having been "the first" or "earliest" in microchemistry, microscopical chemistry, or chemical microscopy, by 80 years; also he

preceded Emich, who still is often considered a pioneer, by over 150 years.

Chemistry became fully scientific in the late 1700's and in the early 1800's microscopic chemistry was still basically an observational science. Chemists examined rocks, sections of plants, any and all kinds of things under the microscope, as a means of learning something about their chemical constitution. By this time, they tried reagents on the things seen, to observe which parts or particles reacted and how. The reagents might be of any kind and in fact color reactions were perhaps most used. Crystals, certainly, were observed, as they had been by Baker and Marggraf, but they were still usually natural crystals, or crystals of common chemicals, or of substances isolated by some chemical process; as yet they were very seldom crystals formed in tests intended to produce them for diagnostic purposes. This microscopical chemistry, which was the original "microchemistry", was the chemistry of substances observed through the microscope.

Eminent chemists of this transitional time who used microscopic methods in some of their chemical researches included Wollaston in England and Döbereiner in Germany. Other chemists also used the microscope on occasion, chiefly to look at their material to be worked on; and they included some microscopically observed data in their writings. Thus Helwig notes that Hünefeld had included mention of the crystal forms of the alkaloids then known in a book of 1823.

Most emphatic of the early chemists in recommending the microscope for the uses just described, and indeed throughout chemistry, was F. V. Raspail, whose "Nouveau Système de Chimie Organique, Fondé sur des Méthodes Nouvelles d'Observation", was first published in Paris in 1833. Organic chemistry then and for some time still was the chemistry of living things, their constituents and products; Raspail may be called a biochemist in modern terms.

At about this time a new means of observing crystals microscopically was developed, that is, the polarizing microscope. Double refraction had been observed by Bartholinus as long ago as 1669, and about 1678 was partially explained by Huygens, who later in the century also made further observations bearing on polarization. The definitive discovery of polarized light is credited to Malus, over a hundred years later, in 1808. By 1811 it was completely explained in terms of light theory by Fresnel and by Arago. The optical crystallography of minerals was developed rapidly by Malus, Biot, and others, especially Sir David Brewster from 1811 to 1819 and later.

Brewster seldom referred to magnifying aids but used them as convenient; e.g., by mounting a plano-convex lens on a plate of tourmaline or agate as an analyzer, and even, on occasion, directing polarized light through a compound microscope. Sources of the polarized light were reflection (Malus' original observation), or oblique transmission through a set of plates of glass, as well as light transmitted through tourmaline, which has extreme dichroism. A black mirror could also be used to "analyze" by reflection; and also, as early as 1819, Brewster had discovered how to extinguish one of the images of calcareous spar, nearly perfecting the analyzer, and anticipating, in a way, Nicol's invention.

Nicol invented his remarkable prism in 1828. In 1834 (W.) H. F. Talbot made the polarizing microscope a definite instrument, and immediately applied it to chemical subjects. This was the same Talbot who became one of the founders of photography, and of modern archeology. Apparently chemists in general were not alert to utilize the new instrument, and only in recent years have they begun to borrow it back from the mineralogists.

J. B. Reade, another chemist, microscopist, and photographic discoverer, took photomicrographs in 1839. However, they were not the first, as stated by the "Dictionary of National Biography", for Talbot had already taken the first photomicrographs of history as early as 1835, and reported on his work in January 1839. Both men used the solar microscope, on which Reade made improvements. Talbot specifically called attention to the value of the photography for recording the appearance of microscopic, chemical crystallizations.

At least as early as 1838 toxicologists were concerned with how they might identify alkaloids, for obviously no drastic treatment could be used as in the separation of a mineral poison, and then there was the problem of distinguishing these poisons from harmless, possibly prevalent, natural bases. Already some suggestion had been made that microscopic distinctions might be possible, but in 1838 there was as yet little or no idea of using a reagent to produce crystals which could be seen microscopically to be different for different substances.

This idea, however, gradually appeared during the 1840's and 1850's. It was present, somewhat rudimentally, in some work of Thomas Anderson of Edinburgh, who described test-forms of some free alkaloids and their thiocyanates in 1848. A specific crystal test appeared in 1852–53, with Herapath's discovery of the remarkable quinine iodosulfate, and his own recommendation that the crystals could be formed in a drop of reagent as a test for quinine. Both of these were included in "The Micrographic Dictionary", by J. W. Griffith and Arthur Henfrey, first edition 1856. In 1859 Taylor, in the second edition of his toxicology, "On Poisons", gave seven different microcrystal tests for strychnine, and even made reference to the "polarizing properties" as helping to characterize the crystals, as well as giving some other microcrystal tests, including one for cyanide using crystals given by HCN vapor in a hanging drop of $AgNO_3$; but the microcrystal tests were not systematically developed.

The new science of microcrystal identification tests came of age in the 1860's. Perhaps it may be said that the idea had crystallized with the issuance of the prospectus of Wormley's book in the United States in 1861. This publication was delayed by the Civil War, and actually the honor of the first book of this science, at least the first findable by the writer, goes to Helwig, whose "Das Mikroskop in der Toxikologie" was published in Germany in 1864 and 1865. Chamot and Mason have also mentioned a similar book by Erhard, "Die giftige Alkaloide u. d. Ausmittelung auf Mikroskopischen Wege", 1866.

Wormley's great book, "Microchemistry of Poisons", was finally published in 1867 (1869). He gave attention to sensitivities and established the science on a firm basis. His book is a landmark; the tests are still good but, of course, the number of compounds covered has now become quite inadequate. A second edition was issued, without very much change, in 1885.

In those days, most poisons were inorganic or else natural plant alkaloids, and crystal tests were developed for both kinds. Later, such tests were extended over the whole field of inorganic chemistry, but their extension to other organic compounds besides the alkaloids has been very slow and meager.

Inorganic tests were further developed by Haushofer in "Mikroskopische Reaktionen" (1885), and by Klément and Rénard in "Reactions Microchimiques" (Brussels, 1886).

Behrens' outstanding work, with some publication as early as 1882, culminated near the end of the century in "Anleitung zur Mikrochemischen Analyse", 1895–97. He brought the inorganic part to a high level, and made a strong effort to develop the science throughout the organic field, with many examples of reactions and descriptions of crystals suitable for microscopic identification tests.

In spite of this, the majority of chemists even today think of such tests as suitable only for alkaloids, if they use them at all.

A new edition of Behrens' work, by Kley, in 1921–22, represented the fourth edition for the inorganic part, the second for the organic part.

The inorganic field has been developed further, and admirably, by Chamot and Mason, especially in volume II of the second edition of their "Handbook of Chemical Microscopy" (1940).

The work on alkaloids was carried on in excellent fashion by Stephenson, "Some Microchemical Tests for Alkaloids", 1921, and Amelink, "Schema zur mikrochemischen Identifikation von Alkaloiden", 1934. Amelink gave attention to just a few compounds besides alkaloids, reacting with the same reagents.

"Toxikologische Mikroanalyse", by Rosenthaler, 1935, included tests for various inorganic and other organic compounds as well as alkaloids and their modern analogs, and is very valuable although it often seems not too well based on the best preceding work. (It was reissued in the United States in 1946, and is still "in print".)

While Behrens was especially influential, "microchemistry" usually meant the use of the microscope in making chemical identifications, especially by means of reactions producing characteristic crystals. However, in the last 40 years, to most chemists the term "microchemistry" has come to mean merely small scale chemistry. Meanwhile the oldest type of microchemistry, i.e., the chemistry of things observed through the microscope, also survived and was further developed by botanist-chemists, Tunmann and Molisch in particular; it now includes considerable use of crystal-forming reagents, but is not limited to them.

Only the beginning of optical crystallography has been noted above, and no attempt has been made to trace the development of micro-sublimation, or micro-melting-points and the modern fusion microscopy.

Numerous studies giving microcrystal tests for various alkaloids and occasionally other compounds can be found in the periodical literature of the last century and this one. In 1932 and 1940 the present writer reviewed the field of "alkaloidal" reagents used for such tests, and began the work of extending them to cover all compounds of basic nitrogen.

In spite of the solid body of work on microcrystal tests cited above, and a considerable total of scattered work, largely on alkaloids, the general impression of past history, and certainly the present situation, is one of neglect. In most fields, the authors who have contributed to the development of microscopic chemistry are surprisingly outnumbered by those others who do not recognize any application of the microscope to that field at all.

This is most astonishing in toxicology, for here the science of crystal tests began. Helwig thought it strange that many toxicologists seemed unaware of the obvious advantages of the use of the microscope in their science, but this is still true nearly 100 years later, as published works show. The neglect is at least equally great elsewhere. In most colleges and universities, courses in qualitative analysis or analytical chemistry, whether inorganic or organic, usually do not even mention use of the microscope; if a query about it is made, it is passed off as a "specialty".

How has this neglect come about? Undoubtedly one factor is simply that the field underwent some development very early. It has often happened that a subject developed earliest is not developed best, for later researchers hesitate to work in a field already partly tilled.

A most important factor, however, has been the strangely long period through which chemistry has passed, during which only quantitative applications were considered to have any value at all. The microscope is not primarily a quantitative tool; this is one limitation on the tests. It has even happened that reagents already well-known and useful as alkaloidal precipitants for microcrystal tests were renamed "Wagner's reagent" and "Mayer's reagent", for example, for alleged quantitative uses almost devoid of value.

For three-quarters of a century or more it was the use of the microscope in chemistry, in one way or another, either purely observational, or a necessary aid in tests with crystal-producing reagents, that was commonly known as "microchemistry". Then, this name was appropriated for what is merely chemistry on a small scale, often not even on a "micro" scale at all; this new "microchemistry" had quantitative aspects, and by about the 1920's it was enthusiasically received. Emich himself spoke of the microscope as indispensable, and described numerous microcrystal tests, largely derived from Behrens, in his "Lehrbuch der Mikrochemie" (1911), endorsing also the use of optical crystallography; but since then the microscope seems to have been lost in the shuffle.

The use of microcrystal tests in the organic field never has disappeared among narcotic chemists, law-enforcement chemists in general, drug analysts, and others. At the present time E. G. C. Clarke in England is doing very effective work in extending the coverage of microcrystal tests, once again in toxicology. The flood of new drugs in recent years has vastly increased the demands and difficulties for reliable identification tests. The need of extended development of microcrystal tests was never greater than it is today.

CHARLES C. FULTON

MIXED FUSION ANALYSIS

Microscopic mixed fusion analysis consists of the microscopical observation of the melting and solidification behavior of mixtures of two or more fusible substances. Two main methods of mixture preparation are employed: the components may be thoroughly mixed physically or a contact preparation may be made. Melting and solidification phenomena are usually observed on preparations contained between a microscope slide and cover-glass; however, it is sometimes desirable to contain the mixture in a sealed micro-capillary tube.

Equipment. The equipment necessary for microscopic mixed fusion analysis is usually quite simple. Any microscope with magnification up to about 200× and capable of accommodating a hotstage is satisfactory. Some method for achieving polarized light is desirable; although this may be as simple as two pieces of "Polaroid" mounted to serve as a polarizer and an analyzer. For observations at various temperatures, a good hotstage is mandatory. Hotstages covering the range 30–350°C are commercially available as is a coldstage capable of functioning above −100°C. In addition, there are published in the literature designs for both hot and cold stages applicable at more extremes of temperature. Temperatures are measured either with a thermometer or a thermocouple. The commercial stages employ thermometers. Temperatures and heating rates are usually controlled with a variable resistor or a variable transformer. It is imperative that the temperature measuring devices be accurately calibrated with known melting point standards at a heating rate nearly identical with that at which an unknown is to be measured. Usually, a standard heating rate (such as 3°C/min) is selected and all calibration and melting point determinations are made at this heating rate. It is very helpful to have a good voltmeter in parallel with the hotstage heating element so that heating rates may be approximately adjusted to the desired value at any given temperature from predetermined stage characteristics.

A hotbar is a very useful adjunct to the hotstage microscope, especially for contact preparations. These devices are commercially available or may be constructed in the laboratory. However, it is possible to employ an alcohol lamp, a micro burner, or even a soldering iron to achieve the same ends. A micro sublimator for purification of compounds is also a useful item for microscopic mixed fusion analysis.

Contact Preparation Methods. Contact preparation methods rapidly yield information concerning the nature of the phase diagram of a two-component system. A more restricted definition of microscopic mixed fusion analysis would include only contact preparation methods. A contact preparation is made in the following fashion. A small amount of the higher melting component (A) is melted between a microscope slide and cover-glass so that, on solidification, approximately one half of the area of the cover-glass contains crystalline material. A small amount of the lower melting component (B) is then placed adjacent to the crystals of component (A) and in contact with the cover-glass. When the slide is warmed so that component (B) melts, the melt flows under the cover-glass and dissolves a portion of component (A). The entire preparation is then allowed to solidify. It is frequently desirable, in order to insure adequate mixing, to melt back the preparation so that most of the higher melting component is melted and then to allow the entire preparation to resolidify.

A concentration gradient, ranging from pure A on one side to pure B on the other side, exists in such a preparation. All intermediate compositions exist in some area of the zone of mixing. Microscopical observation of the mixing zone during the cooling process yields information concerning the nature of the phase diagram between A and B. If the system is simple eutectic, both components will crystallize rather rapidly until the crystal fronts reach the mixing zone. Crystal growth will then proceed at a greatly reduced rate. When the eutectic temperature is reached, fine grained crystals of eutectic composition will crystallize rapidly throughout the mixing zone. The appearance of a eutectic zone is quite characteristic and easily recognized once the observer is familiar with the phenomenon.

Molecular addition compound formation is readily observed in that a third solid phase may be seen to crystallize in the mixing zone of the two-component system. One or two eutectic zones are also observed, depending on whether the addition compound melts incongruently or congruently. The various types of solid solution are also readily detected on solidification of the melt. With solid solution, both component A and component B crystals are seen to grow through the mixing zone with a change in growth velocity but without the appearance of an area of eutectic composition or a molecular addition compound. If there is partial miscibility of liquid A and liquid B, the two liquid phases may be seen in the mixing zone.

Observations made during heating of a contact preparation serve to confirm the more rapidly obtained conclusions drawn from observations made on cooling. In addition, it is possible to measure the various melting points such as the eutectic temperatures, molecular compound melting points, maxima or minima in solid solution systems, and the melting points of the two starting components. The accuracy of such measurements is dependent on the accuracy of calibration of the hotstage and the care with which the proper heating rate is maintained.

Aside from the general determination of the type of phase diagram between two components and the determination of the significant temperatures, there are other applications of the contact preparation method. Identity or non-identity of an unknown compound and a suspect compound may be rapidly established both by observation on cooling and by observation on heating. If the two are identical, the growing crystal front will pass through the mixing zone without appreciable change in velocity as the preparation is cooled. The resultant solid crystals will appear homogeneous through the preparation and the polarization colors will be uniform. On heating, the entire preparation will melt at the same temperature as the two starting components. Small amounts of impurities modify the behavior only slightly. If the two components are not identical, there will normally be a marked depression of the melting point in the mixing zone.

Frequently, if a contact preparation between an unknown and an easily supercooled material such as thymol is allowed to digest on the hotbar, the unknown will develop well defined crystal faces in the mixing zone. It is then possible to measure accurately such quantities as profile angles, extinction angles, dichroisom, and refractive index relative to the melt for identification purposes. It is also sometimes possible, with the proper choice of second component, to nucleate unstable polymorphic forms of a given compound. This enables the investigation of polymorphic forms difficultly available or unattainable by other means.

An identification scheme based upon eutectic melting points has been published by the Koflers. Unknown compounds are subdivided into various restricted temperature ranges and two reagents are used for each temperature range. The eutectic temperature between the unknown and the two reagents, together with the refractive index of the melt determined by the Koflers glass powder method serves to identify the unknown compound. Over 1200 compounds have been so catalogued and either the contact preparation method or the method of mixtures may be used. In principle, this method may be applied to any fusible compound provided suitable reagents are chosen.

A different method of identification based upon molecular addition compound formation and applicable to aromatic compounds has been published by Laskowski, Grabar, and McCrone. A contact preparation between the reagent (2,4,7-trinitrofluorenone) and the unknown establishes if the unknown is of the class which forms addition compounds with the reagent. If an addition compound forms, the preparation is observed microscopically on heating. Identification is achieved on the basis of melting point of the unknown, the molecular addition compound, the eutectic between the reagent and the addition compound, and the eutectic between the addition compound and the unknown. Besides these four melting points the color of the addition compound is also observed. In several systems the addition compound was found to exist in two polymorphic forms, hence additional melting points are available for characterization. This method is rapid and is applicable to liquids as well as solids. It is also applicable if the addition compound melts incongruently.

The above identification scheme has been applied to alcohols by Laskowski and Adams. Although the alcohols do not generally form addition compounds, they may be converted to 2,4,6-trinitrobenzoates. The 2,4,6-trinitrobenzene grouping leads to addition compound formation with a variety of aromatic substances. Contact preparations were made between various trinitrobenzoate esters and both naphthalene and phenanthrene as reagents. Four significant temperatures (three if the addition compound melts incongruently) were obtained with each ester and each reagent. Satisfactory discrimination was achieved among all all of the alcohols investigated. The procedure of reacting a functional group with a suitable reagent so that the resultant derivative forms addition compounds with other reagents offers promise for wide applicability of this method of identification.

Method of Mixtures. Mixtures of known composition may be prepared by weighing the components together and grinding until a uniform composition is achieved. Since only small amounts of material are required for determination of a melting point with a hotstage microscope, it is possible to determine temperature-composition diagrams rapidly with a minimum expenditure of materials. The points of initial and final melting are easily determined microscopically. In addition it is frequently possible to observe polymorphic transitions in one or both of the starting components.

In such mixtures, it is also possible to determine microscopically the effect of composition and temperature on crystal growth velocity, nucleation rate, rate of nucleation and growth of unstable polymorphic forms, and the effect of added components on crystal habit. The method of mixtures is applicable to any number of components.

SELECTED REFERENCES

The literature on microscopic mixed fusion analysis as well as the various experimental techniques involved is covered extensively in the books by Kofler (1) and McCrone (2) and the review by Cecchini (3). Specific applications of mixed fusion analysis include the identification of aromatic compounds (4), the investigation of molecular compound formation (5), (6), isomorphic relations between organic compounds of sulfur and selenium (7), identification of alcohols (8), identification of fibers (9), effect of composition on crystal habit (10), and studies on crystal growth velocity (11).

Although this list of references is not intended to represent an exhaustive survey of the literature on microscopic mixed fusion analysis, it does serve to orient the reader in the general area.

1. Kofler, L., and Kofler, A., "Thermo-Mikro-Methoden zur Kennzeichnung Organischer Stoffe und Stoffgemisch," Wagner, Innsbruck, 1954.
2. McCrone, W. C. Jr., "Fusion Methods in Chemical Microscopy," Interscience Publishers, New York, 1957.
3. Cecchini, M. A., *Selecta Chimico*, **16,** 95 (1957).
4. Laskowski, D. E., Grabar, D. G., and McCrone, W. C. Jr., *Anal. Chem.*, **25,** 1400 (1953).
5. Fürst, H., and Praeger, K., *Chem. Tech.*, **11,** 653 (1958).
6. Laskowski, D. E., and McCrone, W. C. Jr., *Anal. Chem.*, **26,** 1497 (1954).

7. Cecchini, M. A., and Giesbrecht, E., *J. Org. Chem.*, **21**, 1217 (1956).
8. Laskowski, D. E., and Adams, O. W., *Anal. Chem.*, **31**, 148 (1959).
9. Grabar, D. G., and Haessly, R., *Anal. Chem.*, **28**, 1586 (1956).
10. Arceneax, C. J., *Anal. Chem.*, **27**, 970 (1955).
11. Gilpin, V., *J. Am. Chem. Soc.*, **70**, 208 (1948).

Donald E. Laskowski

NITROGEN-BONDED RADICALS: IDENTIFICATION

Most of the really excellent microcrystal tests known for organic compounds are due to basic nitrogen, but the crystals are so affected and modified by other elements and radicals, even quite separated from the nitrogen atom, and by the whole structure, that they identify the molecule of a specific substance as a whole. That they can do so is, in fact, their great value. However, sometimes it may be as well, and more convenient, to distinguish closely related compounds by precisely the points in which they differ. The difference may be in the radicals on a basic nitrogen atom, which volatilize while still attached to it in a deamination reaction. For example, the three USP drugs levarterenol, epinephrine, and isoproterenol, all diphenols and of similar uses, decompose spontaneously in alkaline solution to give off respectively, ammonia, methylamine, and isopropylamine, which can be distinguished readily by microcrystal tests in a hanging drop.

Still more important are cases where it is desired to learn the identity of radicals on the nitrogen atom as a step in analysis, either in identifying an unknown as something already known, or in formulating the structure of a compound whose precise constitution is not known. In either case there are of course chemical tests, such as those given by Feigl, for distinguishing primary, secondary, and tertiary amines; but the microcrystal tests are more definite and show exactly *what* radicals are attached to the nitrogen atom, provided the deamination reaction can be obtained. With many compounds, stable to alkali alone, alkaline oxidation with permanganate will cause deamination, the nitrogen carrying with it any simple carbon-hydrogen (non-oxygenated) radical attached to it, as it comes off.

For example, hydroxyamphetamine and methoxamine yield ammonia in this way, while phenylephrine and ephedrine yield methylamine (ephedrine volatilizes slowly unchanged, if not oxidized). Hordenine in the same way yields dimethylamine, choline yields trimethylamine, and N-ethyl-ephedrine yields methylethylamine. A test of an antibiotic, the exact structure of which was not known, showed that the amine coming off, either spontaneously from alkaline solution or more rapidly with alkaline oxidation, was unmistakably dimethylamine, showing that the nitrogen atom bore two methyl groups in the original compound.

Hanging-drop tests above an alkaline solution apply also, of course, to basic compounds that are themselves volatile. Also there are cases where an ester is soon hydrolyzed by alkali, and if basic nitrogen is present in the part that supplies the alcohol rather than the acid of the ester, the simpler basic compound resulting will very probably be volatile, as occurs with procaine and other synthetic anesthetics. Such decomposition compounds can be detected and identified by microcrystals in the hanging drop. However, the tests given below are suggested specifically for the simplest compounds resulting from deamination. The same tests are of course directly applicable to any minute amounts of the lower amines, whether formed by decomposition of a larger molecule or already individual compounds. The tests may be useful in several fields, e.g., botanical chemistry, as well as food and drug work.

Procedure. Stir a very little of the substance into a drop of 5 % NaOH in the depression of a cavity slide. Set a plain slide on the cavity slide and put on it, over the center of the cavity, a little droplet of sodium tetraphenylboron solution (1:20 in water); then invert this slide. Tetraphenylboron is extremely sensitive to ammonia and the lower amines, and if one of them is evolved, characteristic crystals form rapidly in the hanging drop. Examine them with a polarizing microscope with the slide in place, or transferred over an empty cavity to prevent further formation. In case of a mere trace of ammonia, compare with a blank test using the same reagents. Ammonia is so common from various causes, including contamination, and the tests so sensitive, that often its crystals are not very distinctive, as those of the lower amines are.

Usually a result appears within a few minutes, if at all. If there is no result in an hour or so, add a drop of 1 % $KMnO_4$ solution and invert over the cavity a fresh droplet of tetraphenylboron solution. Or better, if there is no shortage of material, run the test with oxidation at the same time as the one with alkali alone. The oxidation test may give a different result even when there is some evolution of a volatile base. Examine the crystals with the slide still inverted, over an empty cavity.

If either technique is effective for crystals apparently due to a lower amine, prepare another test. Use a hanging drop of simply 1 % of concentrated HCl in water. After an exposure which may be judged from the previous reaction, or up to about an hour, reinvert the slide and allow the drop to dry up (it may be put in a desiccator if hygroscopic). Examine the residue with a polarizing microscope and then test with one of the reagents suggested below, according to the identification or indication of the tetraphenylboron test.

Put a droplet of reagent on a small coverglass, then invert it upon the residue of hydrochloride. Examine the crystals, using a polarizing microscope, with magnifications of about 100 × and 200 ×, observing birefringence, dichroism if it occurs (as with diethylamine bromaurate), etc., as well as form. In the case of the red and brownish-yellow hexagonal crystals with dimethylamine (as well as the similar crystals, brownish-yellow only, with methylethylamine) it is surprisingly easy to get a good interference figure (a uniaxial cross), and determine the sign of the crystal (positive).

Working sensitivities, except for reagent 3, are of the order of hundredths of a microgram of the evolved amine captured in the hanging drop. Reagent 3, although less sensitive than was desired, can be used for highly characteristic crystals with as little as 4 or 5 micrograms of ethylamine. The alternative given for ethylamine, reagent 4, has the desired sensitivity, but has disadvantages due to the reagent itself, and because the crystals of the particular test are less easily distinguishable from others than is the case with the other recommended tests. The tests with reagent 5 can be obtained in the presence with NH_4Cl. (See table).

Compare results closely with the crystals given by knowns, until quite familiar with them.

Selection of a "best test" for ethylamine gave the most difficulty. Its test with $HAuBr_4$ in $2H_3PO_4 \cdot 1HBr$ was passed over at the time the table was drawn up, because good crystals form only at the periphery of precipitation. However, they are very characteristic, divided hexagons, quite different from the crystals of methylamine (or any others so far seen) with this reagent. $HAuBr_4$ in $2H_3PO_4 \cdot 1$(Acetic acid) also gives good results. These tests may be compared with the two that had been selected for the table.

Various examples of microcrystals of compounds are illustrated in Fig. 1 for NH_3, and Fig. 2 for methyl-, ethyl-, dimethyl- and trimethylamines.

Test for Ammonia with Formaldehyde. There should be no difficulty in identifying ammonia with certainty in the foregoing procedure, noting the small crystals

Recommended Tests

Structure	Base given off	Recommended reagent	Reagent No.
$-N$ with H, H	Ammonia	$HAuBr_4$ in H_3PO_4 , (20)	1
$-N$ with H, CH_3	Methylamine	$HAuBr_4$ in $2H_3PO_4 \cdot 1HBr$, (24)	2
$-N$ with H, C_2H_5	Ethylamine	$HAuBr_4$ in $9H_3PO_4 \cdot 2H_2O \cdot 15HBr$, (26) or H_2PtI_6 in diluted H_2SO_4 , (100)	3 4
$-N$ with CH_3, CH_3	Dimethylamine	Iodine-KI reagent B-1	5
$-N$ with CH_3, C_2H_5	Methylethylamine	Iodine-KI reagent B-1	5
$-N^+$ with CH_3, CH_3, CH_3	Trimethylamine	Iodine-KI reagent B-1	5
$-N$ with H, CH with CH_3, CH_3	Isopropylamine	$HAuBr_4$ in H_3PO_4 , (20)	1
$-N$ with C_2H_5, C_2H_5	Diethylamine	$HAuBr_4$ in H_3PO_4 , (20)	1

with tetraphenylboron, the characteristic isotropic crystallization of NH_4Cl, and the characteristic crystals with $HAuBr_4$ in H_3PO_4. However, a test especially for ammonia is desirable, as it is the commonest product.

Ammonia condenses very readily with formaldehyde to form methenamine (hexa-

FIG. 1a. Ammonium chloride isotropic crystallization (from water or dilute HCl). 66×.

FIG. 1c. NH_4Cl with $HAuBr_4$ in H_3PO_4, (20) crystals at periphery of precipitation, with a slightly moist reagent. 100×.

FIG. 1b. NH_4Cl deposit with $HAuBr_4$ in H_3PO_4, (20). 135×.

FIG. 2a. Methylamine (from epinephrine in volatility test with Na tetraphenylboron (1:20 in water), in hanging drop. 100×.

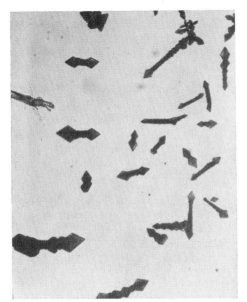

FIG. 2b. Ethylamine HCl with 1.3 HAuBr₄ in 9H₃PO₄·2H₂O·15HBr, (24), 135×.

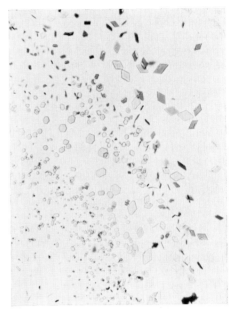

FIG. 2d. Dimethylamine HCl with iodine-KI reagent B-1. Yellow-brown diamonds and hexagons, fairly large at periphery of crystallization. Similar crystals are given by methylethylamine HCl, but only dimethylamine gives red hexagons forming among and from the little crystals (2e).

FIG. 2c. Ethylamine HCl with 1.8 H₂PtI₆ in diluted H₂SO₄ , (100). 100×.

FIG. 2e. Dimethylamine HCl with iodine-KI (5:80) in H₃PO₄ (2:1) (iodine-KI reagent B-1). (direct addition) 100×. Crystal red plates, forming from and among little brownish yellow plates or flakes.

methylenetetramine), (CH₂)₆N₄ . The low organic amines cannot give such a highly condensed product, and under the conditions specified here will hardly give more than trace reactions nevertheless they will inter-

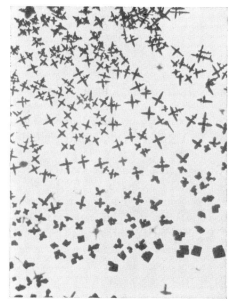

Fig. 2f. Trimethylamine HCl with iodine-KI (5:80) in H₃PO₄ (2:1) (iodine-KI reagent B-1). (direct addition), crystals black, opaque. 100×.

fere more or less with the ammonia reaction. The recommendation of the test, therefore, is still for cases where ammonia is the only product coming off, or at least the chief one.

Proceed as previously described, but instead of fixing the evolved ammonia with dilute HCl, use a hanging drop of neutral, 1% formaldehyde solution (0.1 ml of the usual concentrated formaldehyde, 37% by weight, diluted to 4 ml with water). After exposure above the alkaline solution, reinvert the hanging drop and allow it to dry. Methenamine gives branching isotropic crystallization, frequently with tripartite forms. Examine for a trace soon after drying, as it has a slight volatility. In a blank test there is at most a very slight deposit of trioxymethylene left from the formaldehyde solution itself, which usually does not show anything definite microscopically, and does not react in the following crystal tests.

To confirm methenamine, redissolve the deposit in a little droplet of water, add a droplet of iodine-KI solution (1:1 g in 100 ml), and preferably reinvert over a cavity containing a little crystal of iodine—this prevents evaporation of iodine from the test-drop, and the crystals can be examined at relative leisure. Characteristic birefringent crystals form at once.

Methenamine can also be confirmed with reagent 3 above, HAuBr₄ in 9H₃PO₄·2H₂O· 15HBr. Put a droplet of the reagent on a small cover-glass and invert on the dry residue. Allow a short time for the formation of characteristic crystals with a very small amount.

Of the lower amines, methylamine gives the most noticeable results, including minute microcrystals, but it could not possibly be confused with ammonia if more than a trace of the latter is concerned, or if the characteristic crystals are obtained and observed.

The formaldehyde test for ammonia, although confirmed by the usual sort of basic-nitrogen microcrystal tests, in the formation of methenamine illustrates the use of quite a different reaction for microscopical chemistry.

CHARLES C. FULTON

OBSERVING MICROCRYSTALS

To make full use of microcrystals, the chemist-analyst must learn to see and understand all the characteristics that may possibly distinguish them. In studying a particular test, not every detail descriptive of the crystals needs to be permanently recorded, but everything that can readily be observed should be observed, in deciding what is worth writing down for a formal description, and what should be the points of comparison to establish identity between known and unknown. Too often those who try such tests content themselves with a very superficial observation of the crystal forms alone. It is surprising how much can be done with such observations, often using merely the ordinary microscope; it is not nearly as bad as failing to use the microscope at all, but still a gross neglect of potentialities. The polarizing microscope is necessary, and this means a good instrument, not just "polarizing attachments", which are no more than a makeshift.

A magnification of about 100× is ordinarily used, and about 200× when a higher power seems advisable or necessary.

Looking at crystals through the microscope, the chief characteristics of form and aggregation immediately catch the eye. (See "Forms of Microcrystals", p. 37.) Size, not measured but rather loosely appreciated relative to other crystals commonly seen, is also obvious. Further things to observe will now be suggested.

Note how many dimensions of the crystals may be worth measuring. Note whether the crystals are fairly uniform, or show diversity within one type, or whether there are two or more distinct kinds. Look over the whole precipitate, if there are many crystals, to note how some forms develop from others. Thus disks or shapeless plates when more perfectly formed may be hexagons, or perhaps octagons. Squares and hexagons often skeletonize into 4- and 6-armed stars; oblongs and rhomboids into X-shapes. That the diamond shape is related to the hexagon is frequently evident; also diamonds may extend into daggers and spears. Often very irregular forms can be related to a fairly simple form. Regarding details of description, note particularly the *ends* of blades, rods, prisms, bars: whether square, slanting, pointed, incised, ragged. A number of points in regard to form have to be noted in connection with birefringence.

Usually the next step is to look at the crystals with crossed nicols. First, note the *degree* of birefringence. It will vary, of course, with the thickness of individual crystals, but very often the crystals of a precipitate will appear uniformly of much the same color, a weak gray, or gray-white, or bright white to yellow, in the first order, or, on the other hand, nearly all may show different brilliant interference colors mainly of a higher order. Even with crystals having a deep color of their own the birefringence may be expressed as dim, moderate, or bright. With crystals that are colorless or only lightly colored in themselves the place of an interference color in the first order can be specified as precisely as the uniformity of the crystals warrants; the order of higher colors can be determined with the quartz wedge.

Note, on more than one crystal, whether extinction is parallel to a principal side (or to the general direction of an irregular crystal), or bisects a principal angle, or is oblique.

The possibility of *measuring* an important angle, at least approximately, by using the revolving stage, should not be forgotten. This applies both to angles of form and to the angle of extinction.

Unless the angle of extinction is close to 45°, if the crystals are elongate, or directional at all, the sign of elongation is important, and finding it usually requires no more than pushing in the red plate and observing the result. With high-order interference colors it can usually be determined with the quartz wedge. All crystals can be put into four groups by the sign of elongation: +, −, ±, and indeterminate.

Birefringence often shows whether a complex form is all one crystal or an aggregate of several. X-shaped crystals are usually skeletons of a rhomboid or an oblong, along the diagonals. The direction of the acute angle shows the elongation of the parent form, regardless of distortions of the arms. (Fig 1.)

Colored crystals are nearly always due to a colored reagent, and to this extent the color does not distinguish the substance tested, but the color is more significant the more it differs from the usual color produced in crystals by the particular reagent. The color between crossed nicols is often significant. Some crystals are even known which do not extinguish completely but turn a different color at "extinction" positions.

Dichroism is common in crystals with

some colored reagents, giving not merely the fact of dichroism to distinguish certain substances, but two different colors to be observed and specified. Some crystals (mostly with iodine reagents) are pleochroic, with three extreme colors, and as seen on the slide usually show quite a variety of colors with polarized light, changing with rotation of the stage. Pleochroism is the general term (including dichroism), but as there are usually only two quite different colors, and moreover an individual crystal as it lies on the slide can only show two extreme colors with rotation of the stage, the writer prefers to use the term dichroism when it is applicable.

Dichroism can usually be noted merely by rotating the stage, but when it is feeble it may be necessary to test the extinction positions, which show the extreme colors, to observe it. A crystal is turned to extinction position between crossed nicols, then observed using only the polarizer or only the analyzer, then observed again in the next extinction position, at right angles. The change in color may be slight, or great; dichroic microcrystals are known with iodine reagents which change from slight yellowish to black, with bromauric acid which change from pale yellowish (sometimes appearing colorless) to deep bright red, with iodoplatinic acid which change from pink to dark blue, or from green to purplish red.

Note not only the two different colors, but also their orientation. The crystal is said to have a positive sign of absorption when the darker color is "lengthwise", negative when it is "crosswise". The sign of absorption, which also depends on elongation, nearly always agrees with the usual sign of elongation, when both can be observed.

Dichroic crystals often show a peculiar quality of c lor in ordinary light, and also show the deep dichroic color where they overlap at right angles. Pleochroic (trichroic) crystals may be recognizable even in ordinary light.

Observe the relation of various forms to

FIG. 1. *dl*-Amphetamine with $HAuCl_4$ in (1 + 2) H_3PO_4, applied directly to tablet material. Crossed nicols. 66×. The X-crystals show negative elongation.

birefringence. Hexagons may or may not show birefringence. When they do not show it, lying flat, there are often interspersed rods that do. Crystals appearing square or four-parted may be isotropic, or only some of them may show birefringence, in this case usually not very strong even when present (interference figures possible). All may show definite birefringence—even quite high—and may extinguish parallel to the crosshairs in some cases, or diagonally with crystals of a different kind. Thus crystals of the same form may be of quite different types when birefringence is also considered.

Examine for interference figures—this requires at least a 20 or 21× objective—when sizable, transparent crystals show only low or no birefringence, especially if in the latter case the crystals show birefringence when tilted, or some of them are more or less birefringent (tilt of the axes in the crystal), or are accompanied by other crystals (possibly of the same crystal system, but a different elongation) which are quite birefringent. Interference figures, while important in optical crystallography, have been very little used in microcrystal tests. In most cases it would be a waste of time to look for them, as they could not be found. On the other hand as soon as the analyst learns to recognize the kinds of crystals on which it may be possible to find them, they become an added diagnostic characteristic of value, and can often be obtained, even using the 20 or 21× objective, quite clearly on surprisingly small crystals (e.g., down to about 25 μ diameter, in the case mentioned in the previous article). Moreover, the sign of the crystal can then usually be obtained, as distinguished from the sign of elongation, which may or may not be the same, or the crystals may not be elongate. Some kinds of crystals will give only indistinct figures, and for test purposes it is not worth trying to see them.

A good example, but one seldom followed, was set by the Behrens-Kley text in stating actual *sizes* of microcrystals. No doubt merely saying small, medium, or large is often sufficient, and of course in a comparison one can instantly see whether the control crystals are of the same order of size as the crystals obtained with the sample. Moreover, one must often allow for change of size with various factors; dilution or stirring, for example, may cause diminution in size. However, if an ocular micrometer (kept in an extra ocular) has once been calibrated it certainly does not take long to use it, and the size of fairly uniform crystals under controlled conditions (i.e., in the test as usually made) can be a valuable and measured characteristic. Also the ratio of length to breadth of oblongs, for example, is then measured rather than estimated, and similar proportions for other shapes. These refinements may be reserved for important tests, but ought not to be completely neglected.

Refractive phenomena have been seldom noted in these tests. Measurement of refractive indices can be used in a few cases without invoking special procedures of filtration, purification, recrystallization, etc.; e.g., when a birefringent acidic substance is precipitated from dilute NaOH solution with HCl, and the drop then allowed to dry up. However, even this involves more than simply observing the crystals in the test-drop in which they form, the topic here.

Observation with an ordinary microscope which supplements the polarizing microscope is often useful, chiefly as a matter of convenience when it is troublesome to change objectives on the polarizing microscope because they are the type sliding on, while those on the ordinary microscope are on a turntable. Sometimes one wants to see what the crystals look like in ordinary light; the appearance of pleochroic or highly dichroic crystals is sometimes noteworthy.

Darkfield observation may also be used. Many kinds of crystals show up remarkably well, but there is not the distinction between crystals and non-crystals usually obtained with polarized light and crossed nicols. The role of darkfield therefore cannot be more than secondary. In fact, no vital distinctions (not seen otherwise) have been observed in this way. At present it is not particularly recommended, since to have a darkfield ready for immediate use still another microscope might be required. With a phase microscope both ordinary light and darkfield effects may be observed, but phase microscopy has not proved of value in these crystal examinations.

There is one other mode of observation of great advantage in a few cases, namely, use of incident light. This cannot supplant transmitted light, which is far more useful, but can supplement it. A light should be set up beside the microscope, which will throw a beam down on the stage; it is then no trouble at all to shut off the transmitted light and turn on the incident light. Usually the results are negative; that is, the crystals can

FIG. 2. Dihydromorphinone with H_2PtBr_6 in strong H_2SO_4, applied directly. These crystals are opaque; photographed by reflected light.

be seen much better by transmitted light and show no special phenomenon with incident light. However, there is added diagnostic value in crystals that show up well (especially on a dark background) or in an interesting way with incident light. (Fig. 2.)

Certainly not all these means of observing microcrystals will be used in routine tests, because then the analyst will be told or know from experience what to look for. However, he should know them all, and would do well to try them on new tests and in examining unknown crystals.

CHARLES C. FULTON

OPIUM, ORIGIN OF

One of the best tests for determining the origin of seized opium is simply examination of a smear between crossed nicols of the polarizing microscope, using a magnification of about 80-100× (and higher when desired).

Certain kinds of opium, notably Indian (Fig. 1a) and Iranian, are full of well-formed, highly birefringent, rod crystals, while other kinds, notably Turkish (Fig. 1b) and Yugoslav, contain much less crystalline material, and that mostly in the form of small shapeless or roundish particles. Often not even a single well-formed rod can be found in a smear of Turkish opium, while Indian opium contains a multitude of rod crystals. Still other kinds of opium, as Afghan (Fig. 1c), are intermediate between these types.

A small amount of the opium is treated with a drop of water and spread out on a slide. The water is primarily just a dispersing agent and the crystals can be seen floating in it. However, the examination is best made after the smear has dried up. With a strong light, the brown amorphous material is fairly transparent in a thin layer when dry. Alkali solution can be used to dissolve most of this other material, leaving the crystals, but generally this is not necessary.

The usual sort of examination of a crude drug with the ordinary microscope will disclose some of the large crystals in Indian or Iranian opium; in fact this distinction from Turkish opium was mentioned by The National Standard Dispensatory (Hare and others) in 1905, and Levine, in examining samples of seized opium for the U. S. Narcotics Bureau in 1945, used the crystal rods as one origin test, along with some others, for distinguishing Indian opium.

However, the crystals are not at all easy to see in any number with the ordinary microscope, or using only a polarizer, but spring brilliantly into view when the nicols are crossed. The present writer began using the polarizing test in 1947, also for the U. S. Narcotics Bureau, and showed the crystalline material to be narcotine, in work on methods for determining the origin of seized opium, which was later continued at United Nations, and which finally resulted in the U. N. Narcotics Laboratory now at Geneva.

The number and form of the crystals depend partly on the content of narcotine and partly on the physicochemical reaction of the other constituents. This one test, of

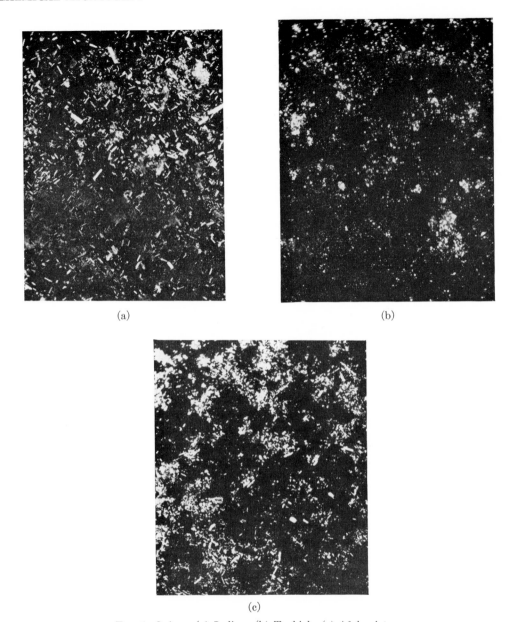

(a)

(b)

(c)

FIG. 1. Opium. (a) Indian; (b) Turkish; (c) Afghanistan.

course, is not sufficient by itself to prove a particular origin, but in conjunction with various chemical assays and ash analysis it is very useful. After years of study, it is still the easiest origin test to make, and at the same time one of the best.

CHARLES C. FULTON

PURPOSE

A fundamental error, which seems to be prevalent in modern "microchemistry", is the idea that the microscope has value in chemistry only as an adjunct to procedures on a small scale. Actually this is the least of its uses; and the early chemists, say from

200 to 100 years ago, who are cited for the beginnings of "microchemistry", were not, primarily, groping for small-scale procedures when they turned to the microscope. They had a much better appreciation of its real value.

The uses of the microscope in chemistry comprise at least the following:

(1) Taking a closer and better look at things, and observing their minute characteristics, regardless of the amount of material available.

(2) In particular, observing characteristics that cannot be seen at all with the unaided eye: for a century and a quarter now this has meant not merely characteristics too small to be seen by the unaided eye, but also those revealed by polarized light and an analyzer, plus compensators and the other fittings of the polarizing microscope. This use also does not depend on whether much or little material is available.

(3) Making identifications by microscopic observations and microcrystal tests, for which the microscope is essential, again regardless of the amount of material available.

(4) Using the microscope as an adjunct to procedures on a small scale.

These uses are not mutually exclusive or even distinct; they overlap greatly. There is no intention of saying here that the early chemists never thought of the fourth of the above uses: of course they did, but they had primarily in mind the other uses, which modern chemical science seems to have forgotten, and which most modern chemists disregard or overlook. When the early chemists turned to small-scale procedures it was, at least as often as not, to adapt them to microscopic observation, rather than the reverse, to adapt the microscope to small-scale chemistry.

All the uses apply both to the materials to be analyzed or studied, and to the results of chemical reactions, particularly the crystals resulting from chemical precipitations. The earliest uses of the microscope in chemistry were chiefly observational: noting the constituents in material to be analyzed, and making identifications by microscopic appearances existing in the material. The last use was later extended to identification of mineral crystals by their properties in polarized light, and now is gradually being applied in chemical science. About a hundred years ago, identification by means of chemical microcrystal tests was developed in some aspects, chiefly inorganic and alkaloidal, but the possibilities here were grossly neglected while chemistry "went quantitative", and still await anything like adequate development.

Charles C. Fulton

QUINOLINE AS A REAGENT

Quinoline is a useful reagent in chemical microscopy for detection of a number of cations and as a group reagent for the elements named below. Pure quinoline produces characteristic crystals with the solid chloride of any single one of the following: divalent cobalt, copper, iron, manganese, mercury, nickel, cadmium, calcium, and zinc, and monovalent copper. When more than one of these chlorides are present, mixed crystal formation may occur, so additional tests are needed for confirmation, but the mixed crystals formed are still a good indication of which cations are most probably present. When a cation which normally forms a colored product with quinoline is involved in mixed crystal formation with a cation which normally forms a colorless product, the resultant crystal generally shows the shape of the colorless specie and the color of the colored specie. When two cations which normally form colored products are involved, they may form off-colored crystals; heating will usually develop characteristics which resemble one of the components.

A drop of sample solution which has been converted to chlorides is evaporated on a slide; as the slide is removed from the source of heat, a coverglass from which a drop of quinoline is hanging is placed on the solids and when the slide has cooled the preparation is examined under a microscope. If larger, more euhedral crystals are desired, the slide may be gently warmed and then allowed to cool, but the cupric chloride-quinoline compound, if present, should be identified prior to this because its color is destroyed by heating. If the sample is a dry solid, it may be mounted in quinoline to establish the presence of the above-named cations as chlorides.

The characteristic crystals formed by quinoline with the metal chlorides are described below, grouped by color.

Yellow crystals indicate cuprous copper or ferrous iron. The copper compound appears as needles or rhomb-shaped plates and tablets; the iron compound appears as pleochroic (pale yellow to yellow) rectangular plates.

Blue crystals indicate cobalt, nickel, or cupric copper. The cobalt compound forms pleochroic (light blue to blue) rhomb-shaped or rectangular plates and tablets; the nickel compound forms pleochroic (violet to blue) blue-violet plates and tablets; the copper compound forms pleochroic (green to blue to blue-violet) crystals shaped like elongated hexagons or footballs.

Colorless, needle-like crystals indicate calcium or cadmium; these two are not readily differentiated from each other.

Colorless, well-defined crystals indicate manganese, mercury, or zinc. The manganese compound forms small elongated rectangular plates; the mercury compound forms pseudo-hexagonal plates; the zinc compound forms rhomb-shaped plates and tablets.

The chlorides of the less commonly encountered elements indium and thallium (thallous) also react with quinoline to yield colorless crystals. The indium compound forms diamond-shaped and rectangular plates; the thallium compound forms hexagonal, rhomb-shaped, and rectangular plates.

Primarily, quinoline serves as a group reagent; a positive test indicates that one (or more) of the above-named metal-chlorides is present and a negative test indicates absence of an appreciable quantity of any of them; under favorable conditions quinoline offers a specific test for these cations. When the sample is a solid, quinoline may distinguish these metal chlorides from their oxides, or sulfates, or free metals, and it simultaneously distinguishes the valence state in the cases of copper chlorides or iron chlorides.

J. M. MUTCHLER

REAGENTS FOR MICROCRYSTAL IDENTIFICATIONS

The reagents given here are primarily precipitants of organic compounds containing basic nitrogen. They include, but go far beyond, traditional alkaloidal reagents. A few give good inorganic tests for certain ions; a few extend to nitrogenous compounds that are almost completely acidic, such as the barbiturates.

Each of the outstanding *precipitating compounds*, $HAuBr_4$ for example, makes a number of quite different *reagents*, by the use of different solvent media, particularly:

(1) Syrupy H_3PO_4; diluted H_3PO_4,

(2) Diluted H_2SO_4 (up to $(1 + 1)$ for chlorides, $(2 + 3)$ for bromides, $(1 + 3)$ for iodides),

(3) Water; and aqueous solutions only slightly acid, or made acid only by the precipitating compound itself; sometimes even neutral, slightly basic, or alkaline,

(4) Concentrated HBr (40%); diluted HBr,

(5) Concentrated HCl (38%); diluted HCl,

(6) Acetic acid (usually diluted at least $(2 + 1)$ simply to prevent its spreading all over the slide).

These are given above in the order of de-

Chlorauric Acid (Gold Chloride) Reagents

(12) $HAuCl_4$ in H_3PO_4, $(1 + 2)H_3PO_4$, $(1 + 1)H_2SO_4$, water, conc. HCl, $(1 + 3)HCl$, or $(2 + 1)$ acetic acid, etc. 1 g $HAuCl_4 \cdot 3H_2O$ in 20 ml (usually) of the appropriate solvent; further dilution (60) with H_3PO_4, $(1 + 1)H_2SO_4$, concd HCl, or $(2 + 1)$ acetic acid may be used for tests of direct addition with easily precipitated compounds. In the traditional procedure, that is, simply in water and applied to aqueous solutions, $HAuCl_4$ is probably the best single reagent known for alkaloid-type compounds. $HAuCl_4$ in $(1 + 2)H_3PO_4$ is especially used in hanging drop tests for volatile bases and in direct addition to solids (salts of simple bases, etc.)—as well as for addition to aqueous solutions. No cover-glass is used and water is then allowed to evaporate from the test-drop if necessary for precipitation and crystallization.

Bismuth and Platinum Iodide Reagents

H_3BiI_6 and H_2PtI_6 are very general precipitants, so much so that they are the two precipitating agents most commonly used—though only in aqueous solution—for developing spots of alkaloid-type compounds in paper chromatography. (At this time the writer does not yet know of any paper-chromatographer who has used phosphoric acid, or even diluted sulfuric, to increase the generality and sensitivity of these reagents.)

Bismuth Iodide Reagents

An aqueous (strongly acid) H_3BiI_6 reagent is a traditional one from the last century; but as commonly made, it soon decomposes in part; then some effects are still due to the H_3BiI_6, but others to iodine-KI. Some users age their reagent for a time to obtain consistent results. Amelink even added iodine crystals to have a mixed reagent from the start. The reagents given here, however, depend upon H_3BiI_6 alone.

For crystal purposes, phosphoric acid has been difficult to use because colored crystals are likely to form due to the reagent itself. The use of BiI_3 and HI to make up the reagent has not as yet solved any important problems either, so the formulas given here simply employ a concentrated bismuth nitrate solution. The reagents have a bright orange color and are to be remade when they darken appreciably. This occurs very soon with $(1 + 7)H_2SO_4$, and too rapidly for convenience even with aqueous reagent, if no preservative is used. Sodium hypophosphite is here introduced as a preservative, which makes the reagents comparatively long-lasting.

Conc. $Bi(NO_3)_3$ soln: Dissolve 50 g bismuth subnitrate in 70 ml $(1 + 1)HNO_3$ and dilute to 100 ml with water.

(13) H_3BiI_6 in $(1 + 7)H_2SO_4$ or in water, etc.

(a) H_3BiI_6 in $(1 + 7)H_2SO_4$. KI 1.25 g, H_2O 2.0 ml, $(1 + 3)H_2SO_4$ 2.5 ml, conc. $Bi(NO_3)_3$ soln 0.5 ml, Na hypophosphite 0.05 g. Mix. Used especially for hanging-drop tests and direct-addition tests for sympathomimetics, etc.

(b) H_3BiI_6 (aqueous). Omit the diluted H_2SO_4, using simply 4.5 ml water. Used direct for theophylline and related compounds; also for addition to aqueous solutions (traditional). (0.04 g hypophosphite is enough.)

(c) Double strength H_3BiI_6 (aqueous) may sometimes be preferred. KI 2.25 g, Na hypophosphite 0.05 g, H_2O 4.0 ml, conc. $Bi(NO_3)_3$ soln 1 ml. Mix.

Platinic Iodide Reagents

1 g $H_2PtCl_6 \cdot 6H_2O$, with iodide, makes about 1.8 g H_2PtI_6.

(14) H_2PtI_6 with H_3PO_4, (A and B). Formulas for small dropping bottles.

(A) 1.8 H_2PtI_6 in $(2\frac{1}{2} + 1)H_3PO_4$, (250), with minimum NaI. Dissolve 0.04 g NaI in 0.5 ml H_2O; mix with 1.8 ml H_3PO_4, and add 0.2 ml of 1:20 aqueous platinic chloride solution (1 g $H_2PtCl_6 \cdot 6H_2O$ in 20 ml water). Keeps well for only about a week to a month at most; can be made up on half the above small scale.

(B) 1.8 H_2PtI_6 in $(4 + 1)H_3PO_4$, (250), high NaI. Dissolve 0.5 g NaI in 0.3 ml water, add 2.0 ml H_3PO_4 and 0.2 ml of 1:20 aqueous platinic chloride solution. Let stand about a day to develop good differentiation from (A). Keeps much better than the preceding, (A); in a few cases a rather old reagent even gives the best results for certain crystals.

Both of the above are among indispensable reagents for sympathomimetics, central stimulants, and other compounds which are of simple structure or partly acidic, not too easily precipitated.

(15) H_2PtI_6 *in diluted* H_2SO_4, *(100)*. H_2PtCl_6 soln (1:20 in water) 0.8 ml, $(1 + 3)$ H_2SO_4 3.2 ml, NaI 0.46 g. Preferably let stand at least 2 or 3 hours (or overnight) before use. Thereafter it slowly deteriorates, but can be used for a long time. The crystals it gives change to some extent with the age of the reagent. Also, the reagent itself deposits colored crystals as it partially dries, first around the edge of the cover-glass, where the solution is not covered. Used for ethylamine hydrochloride; uses not much explored.

(16) H_2PtI_6 *(acid aqueous)*. H_2PtCl_6 soln (1:20 in water) 4 ml, HCl 1 ml, NaI 1.25 g. If the HCl is omitted, the alkalinity of commercial NaI may cause precipitation. Only a little acid would be needed to overcome this, but Amelink indicates generally better results in an acid than in a "neutral" test-drop, anyway.

Platinic Bromide Reagents

(17) H_2PtBr_6 *in* H_3PO_4, *(1 + 3)*H_3PO_4, *(2 + 3)*H_2SO_4, *water, HBr, (1 + 3)HCl, or (2 + 1) acetic acid, etc.* $H_2PtCl_6 \cdot 6H_2O$ 1 g [makes about 1.3 g H_2PtBr_6]; HBr(40%) 2.5 ml, appropriate solvent to make 20 ml (usually). The aqueous reagent (which can

be made with NaBr instead of HBr) is excellent although strangely neglected in the past. New uses (hanging drop and direct, for sympathomimetics, etc.) especially concern H_2PtBr_6 in $(1 + 3)H_3PO_4$. The reagent with syrupy H_3PO_4 develops some precipitation in the bottle, but the clear supernatant solution can be used (rather than adding enough water to prevent precipitation).

(18) $H_2PtBrCl_5$ *in conc. HCl.* If the above formula is used with concentrated HCl for the solvent, even with twice as much HBr (not exceeding the molecular ratio of 1 HBr to 5 HCl), there is evidence—from microcrystals—that the precipitating compound is $H_2PtBrCl_5$. The four other possible Br-Cl combinations form in proportioned mixtures of the strong acids. They can be used by direct addition, for the particular effects; as originally worked out on morphine they were diluted to (60) with the strong acids and some water (up to one-fifth) for best results. Much dilution with water tends to give H_2PtBr_6, regardless of more HCl than HBr being present.

Platinum and Palladium Chlorides

(19) H_2PtCl_6 *in* H_3PO_4, *(1 + 3)*H_3PO_4, *(1 + 1)*H_2SO_4, *water, (1 + 3)HCl, etc.* 1 g $H_2PtCl_6 \cdot 6H_2O$ in 20 ml of the solvent. The aqueous reagent is of course the traditional one and very valuable. The reagent with $(1 + 3)H_3PO_4$ is particularly used in the hanging drop for *d*- and *dl*-amphetamine.

(20) H_2PdCl_4 *in* H_3PO_4, *or water, etc.* $PdCl_2 \cdot 2H_2O$ 1 g; conc. HCl 0.9 ml (in H_3PO_4) or 0.8 ml (in water, etc.); H_3PO_4, or water, etc. to make 20 ml. Aqueous or partly aqueous reagent may be made with NaCl 0.75 g, instead of the HCl (forming Na_2PdCl_4).

Tetraphenylboron and Reinecke Salt

(21) *Na tetraphenylboron*, 1 g in 20 ml water (not acidified). Used especially as a hanging drop; remarkable for its sensitivity

and crystals with ammonia and the lower amines.

(22) *Reinecke salt, $NH_4Cr(NH_3)_2(SCN)_4$*. A fresh, approximately saturated, aqueous solution is used. Stir a little of the compound into about 0.5 ml water at room temperature, to provide a few drops for use. Properties of the reagent begin to change within a few hours. Rosenthaler says that it is useless when the ferric salt test for thiocyanate ion can be obtained (red color). Some very interesting crystals with lower amines have been obtained with a still-effective reagent aged for a number of hours —e.g., overnight—but the writer does not know how to control these changes or stabilize any such intermediate stage. Gradually, in two or three days, effectiveness is completely lost.

Bromine-Bromide Reagents

Although various forms of bromine-bromide reagents should be possible and valuable (as with iodine-iodide), the difficulty of keeping any reagent without the bromine evaporating, and its disagreeable character, have so far prevented anything but a limited aqueous use.

(23) *Br in HBr solution; Br in NaBr solution*. HBr(40%) 10 ml, water 90 ml; or NaBr 5 g, water 100 ml. Saturate with bromine. Used for barbiturates, etc., as well as for basic compounds.

Other Reagents for Aqueous Tests

The following are added to aqueous solutions (usually of a salt of the base tested), unless otherwise stated.

Complex Oxygen Acids. (24) *Phosphoritungstic acid*. Obtainable commercially. 10 g in 100 ml water. Silicotungstic acid is used similarly.

(25) *Phosphorimolybdic acid with HNO_3*. 10 g of the commercial phosphomolybdic acid in 90 ml water and 10 ml concd HNO_3. Phosphorimolybdic acid has especial value as a standard for sensitivity determinations.

Formerly the reagent for this purpose was made with only a few drops HNO_3; but there is probably no sufficient reason to maintain a separate formula for it; the form with 10% HNO_3 may be better for crystals as well as being used for the following reagent.

(26) *Phosphorimolybdic acid with H_3PO_4*. A fresh solution of the commercial phosphomolybdic acid is decolorized immediately by H_3PO_4, but the preceding solution with HNO_3, after standing at least 6 weeks, is more stable. To 4 ml of the stabilized yellow phosphorimolybdic acid add 0.6 ml syrupy H_3PO_4 and mix. The solution should remain yellow for use (it will keep for a few days). Less sensitive but gives crystals (e.g., with narceine and atropine) which are unobtainable with the usual phosphorimolybdic acid solution.

Platinum and Mercury Thiocyanates. (27) $H_2Pt(SCN)_6$. $H_2PtCl_6 \cdot 6H_2O$ 1 g, water 20 ml, NaSCN 0.95 g. This hardly has outstanding importance for microcrystals so far, but probably is the best of the "normal" thiocyanates (i.e., aside from Reinecke salt); and the writer takes this opportunity of correcting a former statement that only about a third as much NaSCN need be used: the NaSCN must be sufficient to replace all six Cl atoms, or the reagent will precipitate on standing.

(28) $K_2Hg(SCN)_4$. Dissolve 3 g KSCN in 100 ml water and saturate with $Hg(SCN)_2$ (5 or 6 g required). This is an outstanding reagent for inorganic microcrystals of a number of cations, especially Zn, Cd, Cu, Co, and Au. It precipitates alkaloidal-type compounds but its value for this is minor.

Mercuric Iodide Reagents. (29) K_2HgI_4. Dissolve 2 g KI in 100 ml water and saturate with HgI_2 (nearly 3 g HgI_2 required). Only occasional value for crystals but much used for general tests of alkaloid-type precipitation.

(30) HgI_2 and HCl. Dilute 27 ml conc. HCl to 100 ml with water (makes an actual

10% HCl), then saturate with HgI_2 (does not take much). Used both for aqueous solutions and direct addition to the solid, for heroin, etc.

(31) $HgI_2 \cdot NaCN$ and NaI. Dissolve 0.5 g good NaCN in 100 ml water and saturate with HgI_2 (use $4\frac{1}{2}$ g). (This is a reagent in itself, and more sensitive, but the reagent with excess NaI is recommended more highly for crystals.) Filter the saturated solution and add 8 g NaI per 100 ml. Crystals with codeine, etc.

Cadmium and Lead Iodides. (32) K_2CdI_4. CdI_2 5 g, KI 4.5 g, water 100 ml.

(33) PbI_2 in K acetate solution. Dissolve 4 g lead acetate ($3H_2O$) and 30 g potassium acetate in water to make 100 ml, and add glacial acetic acid dropwise just to faint acidity to methyl red (reacts brown instead of yellow); then add 4.5 g KI.

Many crystals with both the above.

Mercuric Chloride Reagents. (34a) Simple $HgCl_2$ (5%) is commonly used but usually added to solutions containing dilute HCl, or the hydrochloride of the base, so that actually more or less of the following chloro-acid is present.

(b) $HHgCl_3$. $HgCl_2$ 5 g, concd HCl 1 ml, water 99 ml.

(c) $NaHgCl_3$. $HgCl_2$ 5 g, NaCl 0.75 g, water 100 ml.

(d) $HgCl_2$ & HCl. $HgCl_2$ 5 g, conc. HCl 15 ml, H_2O 85 ml. This is less sensitive; useful especially for quinine.

Ferric Chloride Reagents. (35a) $FeCl_3$ in HCl; H_3FeCl_6. $FeCl_3 \cdot 6H_2O$ 10 g, conc. HCl 100 ml. For addition to aqueous solutions (cocaine, methadone, etc.).

(b) H_3FeCl_6 for direct addition to solids: $FeCl_3 \cdot 6H_2O$ 10 g, concd HCl 17.5 ml, water to make 100 ml.

Organic Reagents. (36) Picric acid is outstanding.

(a) A saturated aqueous solution (about $1\frac{1}{2}$%). Many crystals. (b) A 0.2% aqueous solution. Picric acid crystals (10%) water) 0.2 g, water 100 ml. Cinchonine is an example of a base yielding crystals far more readily

with this dilute reagent than with the saturated. This weak solution may also be used for direct additions.

(c) Half-saturated Sodium Picrate. Precipitate sodium picrate from saturated picric acid solution with concentrated sodium acetate. Filter, then prepare a saturated solution of sodium picrate. Filter this from excess crystals and dilute with an equal volume of water. Crystals with bases are often obtained more readily than with the saturated acid.

(37) Other nitro-organic reagents. Styphnic acid (trinitroresorcin) and Trinitrobenzoic acid are used in saturated solutions.

Simple Oxygen Acids. (38) CrO_3 and $HCrO_3Cl$.

(a) 5% CrO_3. The chloroacid or its salt (following formulas) is more sensitive and better.

(b) $HCrO_3Cl$. Stock solution of 20 g CrO_3 in water to make 100 ml (this may be used as a concentrated CrO_3 reagent in itself). Reagent: 1 ml of foregoing stock solution plus 2 ml water and 1 ml concd HCl. Will keep for some time; slowly darkens.

(c) $NaCrO_3Cl$. Add 1 g NaCl to 4 ml of the 5% CrO_3. Keeps well.

(39) Perchloric acid. 5% solution of $HClO_4$ or $NaClO_4$.

(40) Permanganic acid oxidizes most alkaloids and other bases, but the stable crystalline permanganates are quite distinctive. Unfortunately reducing impurities can easily spoil a test.

(a) $KMnO_4$ 2 g in 100 ml water, with a few drops of syrupy H_3PO_4.

(b) $HMnO_4$ in dilute H_2SO_4, for direct addition. Use a stock solution of 1% $KMnO_4$. Reagent: 2 ml stock solution, 1 ml (1 + 3) H_2SO_4. Make up fresh for use. Used for cocaine, meperidine, methadone, etc.

Basic Reagents

Precipitation of the free base by addition of the reagent to a neutral or slightly acid solution of the salt of an alkaloid, etc.

(41a) 5% NaOH. Sometimes a concentrated solution is used.

(b) 5% Na_3PO_4. The alkalinity is about the same as for 5% Na_2CO_3, which is more often used, but effervesces when added to an acid solution.

(c) 5% K_2CrO_4. Precipitation of a chromate of a strong base is possible, but the principal use and value is as a basic group reagent for the weak alkaloids that are quite insoluble in water. It must, of course, be added to solutions that are only slightly acid, or, if strongly acid, the effect is that of $K_2Cr_2O_7$ (similar to CrO_3).

(d) Concentrated K acetate, 30 g in water to make 100 ml. For precipitation and crystals with very weak insoluble bases.

Cyanides

(42) *Gold Cyanide Reagent.* Dissolve 1 g $HAuCl_4 \cdot 3H_2O$ crystals in 20 ml water. Add 0.5 g NaCN a little at a time; if there is immediate precipitation add just enough NaCN to redissolve; otherwise 0.5 g should be the right amount. Makes a colorless solution, which sould not turn red litmus blue (if it does, acidify with acetic acid).

(43) *Platinum Cyanide Reagent.* Dissolve 1 g $H_2PtCl_6 \cdot 6H_2O$ in 18 ml water and add 1.5 g NaCN. Solution may warm up and become rather brown; if not, warm a little on the water bath until it just begins to darken, then cool. Cautiously acidify with 2 ml (1 + 3) H_2SO_4. There is usually a small amount of brown precipitate, apparently due to the reaction going a little too far, in part; this is removed by filtering either before or after acidifying. The solution is brown but not a dark brown.

(44) $H_4Fe(CN)_6$ *with* H_3PO_4. A stock solution is kept of 10 g $K_4Fe(CN)_6 \cdot 3H_2O$ in water to make 100 ml. Reagent: Mix 3.5 ml of the stock solution with 0.25 ml syrupy H_3PO_4. Has to be made fresh as it will not keep.

Simple Halides and Pseudohalides.

(45) 5% solutions of KI, NaSCN, $NaNO_2$. They are also used in concentrated solutions.

CHARLES C. FULTON

SYMPATHOMIMETICS AND CENTRAL STIMULANTS

Most of these are relatively simple compounds, compared with alkaloids (q.v.), and are not so readily precipitated. Some which have alcoholic and phenolic hydroxyl groups are not precipitated at all by the usual aqueous reagents, which are described in the article "Alkaloids and Alkaloidal-type Precipitation". The following 14 tests are se lected for tabulation in Table 1. Five reagents are applied directly to a very little of the solid, with addition of a cover-glass:

(1) 1.3 $HAuBr_4$ in H_3PO_4, (20)

(2) 1.3 $HAuBr_4$ in $2H_3PO_4 \cdot 1(2 + 3) \cdot H_2SO_4$, (90)

(3) 1.8 H_2PtI_6 in $(2\frac{1}{2} + 1)H_3PO_4$, (250), with minimum NaI

(4) 1.8 H_2PtI_6 in $(4 + 1)H_3PO_4$, (250), high NaI

(5) Iodine-HI-H_3PO_4 reagent.

Three reagents, which contain more water than the five above, are used in two tests each. They are applied to the solid without a cover-glass, and let stand for partial evaporation; they are also used as the reagent of a hanging drop, in volatility tests above an alkaline solution on a cavity slide. In the latter case the test-slide is in general reinverted after exposure to the vapor (of up to two hours), and evaporation to a higher content of the non-volatile acid then occurs.

(6, 7) H_3BiI_6 reagent in $(1 + 7)HC_2SO_4$; 6 direct application, (7), volatility test

(8, 9) $HAuCl_4$ in $(1 + 2)H_3PO_4$, (20)

(10, 11) 1.3 H_2PtBr_6 in $(1 + 3)H_3PO_4$, (20)

The two following reagents are also used for volatility tests (the first permitting reinversion, but the second only as a hanging drop):

(12) H_2PtCl_6 in $(1 + 3)H_3PO_4$, (20)

TABLE 1. CRYSTAL TESTS FOR SOME IMPORTANT SYMPATHOMIMETICS AND CENTRAL STIMULANTS
(Numbers in parentheses refer to Figures; symbols in text p. 69)

					Reagents										Notes
	1	2	3	4	5	6	(7)	8	(9)	10	(11)	(12)	(13)	(14)	
Group I:															
Phenylephrine	re	r	d	C	d	C	—	—(d)	—	d	—	—	—	—	1, let stand over (45 + 55) H_2SO_4; specific (1a)
Hydroxyamphetamine	C, C (1a, b)	r (e)	(c) C	C	C	C	—	dr	—	C	—	—	—	—	
Methoxamine	de	c	C	c	d	d	—	dr	—	C	—	—	—	—	
Naphazoline	c	C	a	d	d	/a(e)	—	C	—	/c	—	—	—	—	
Caffeine	c	C	c	c	c	c	—	c/C	—	c	—	—	—	—	Use $HAuBr_4$ in (1 + 3)HCl, (45)
Theobromine	c	C	C	C	C	c	—	/C	—	c	—	—	—	—	do.
Theophylline	C	C	c	C	c	c	—	C	—	C	—	—	—	—	do.
Group II:															
Levarterenol	d, r	r	C	C	C	d	c	dr	—/c	C	c	c	C	c	volatile base chiefly NH_3
l-Epinephrine	d, r	r	d	d	C	d	c	r	—/c	d	—/c	—/c	C	c	volatile base methylamine
Isoproterenol	r	r	d	C	C	d	c	r	—/c	—	—/C	—/c	C	C	volatile base isopropylamine
Nikethamide	C	C	c	c	c	C	C	c	(d)/c	—	—/(c)	c	c	C	volatile base mainly diethyl-amine
Group III:															
Pentylenetetrazol	C	C	C	C	d	c	(c)/c	dC	c	d	—	—	—	c	3, specific
Phenylpropanolamine	C	C	C	C	d	d	—/(e)	C	—/c	c	—/(c)	—	c	cdc	
l-Ephedrine	C	C (2a)	C	C	d	c/C	C	C	—/C	c	—/c	—	d	C	2, specific
dl-Ephedrine	C	C (2b)	C	c	d	/C	C	C	—/C	C	—/c	—	c	C	
Phenmetrazine	d, (c)	d	c	d (c)	C	d/c	C	C	d/C	C	c	e	(d)	d/c, (c)	5, specific
Group IV:															
d-Amphetamine	c	C	a (c)	c	d	c	c	C	C	/c	C	C	d	c	2, on tablets
dl-Amphetamine	c	C	a (c)	C	d	c	C	C (3a)	C	/c	C	C	c	c	2, on tablets. 4 with hydchl. vol. am.; specific
d-Methamphetamine	C	C	C	c	d	C	C	c	c	/c	C	c	(d)	C	
dl-Methamphetamine	C (3b)	C	C	c	d	c	C	c	c	/c	C	c	(d)	C	
Phenylpropylmethyl-amine	C	C	c	d	c	c	dc	c	c	C	/C	c	C	C	
Mephentermine	C	C	c	c	d	C	C	C	C	/c	C	c	c	c	
Propylhexedrine	d	d	C (5b)	d	d	c	c	d	d	/c	c	C	d	d	
Tuaminoheptane	C	C	c	c	d	c	c	c/C	c	/C	c	c	d	C	

(13) Sodium tetraphenylboron in water (1:20)

(14) Volatility tests are also made by catching the volatile amine (or amine of decomposition) in a hanging drop of dilute HCl (about 1% by volume of the concentrated acid) above a drop of alkaline solution on a cavity slide, then evaporating the HCl

FIG. 1a. Hydroxyamphetamine with HAuBr₄ in H₃PO₄ (20), red spindles (first formed), brown needles, orange-red platy crystals, formed with standing over (45 + 55) H₂SO₄ . 66×.

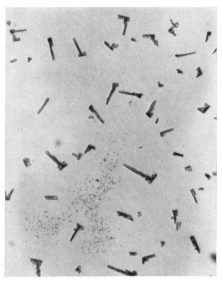

FIG. 2a. l-Ephedrine with 1.3 HAuBr₄ in 2H₃PO₄·1(2 + 3) H₂SO₄ , (90) "nail" crystals. 66×.

FIG. 1b. Hydroxyamphetamine with HAuBr₄ in H₃PO₄ (20), with humidity and standing. Large scarlet irregular and serrate blades. Small spots are blue-green crystals of metallic gold. 100×.

FIG. 2b. dl-Ephedrine with 1.3 HAuBr₄ in 2 H₃PO₄·1(2 + 3) H₂SO₄ , (90), red squares. 66×.

solution to dryness, and testing the solid hydrochloride of the volatile base with HAuBr₄ in H₃PO₄ . (Fig. 3a*)

The crystalline hydrochloride of a volatile amine can be examined microscopically before adding a reagent. If it is hygroscopic, and so fails to dry and crystallize in open air,

* See Fig. 1, p. 53.

FIG. 3b. dl-Methamphetamine with HAuBr₄ in H₃PO₄ , (20). 66×.

it can be inverted over a cavity which contains a drop of concentrated H₂SO₄ . Most of these residues are not especially distinctive in themselves, but as an exception, a mixture of d- and dl-amphetamine (used by some pharmaceutical manufacturers) leaves a hydrochloride residue altogether different from that of either d-amphetamine or dl-amphetamine alone. (Figs. 4a, b, c.)

In general, the tests are observed for only about two hours, although most of them can be allowed to stand much longer, preferably with humidity controlled, and occasionally with formation of valuable new test crystals.

The chemical meaning of the tests is noted: whether a test for a volatile amine is obtained, and if so whether it is the original compound or a decomposition product (especially likely with a diphenol). With phenols and diphenols the gold reagents give crystals of metallic gold by reduction, which when well-formed are hexagons and triangles, blue-green by transmitted light. This reduction may also be due to a double bond, as with isometheptene, one of the sympathomimetic drugs.

The compounds are classified into four groups:

I. no test for a volatile base.

FIG. 4a. Crystallization of d-amphetamine hydrochloride (volatility test), striate formation, with crossed nicols. 66×.

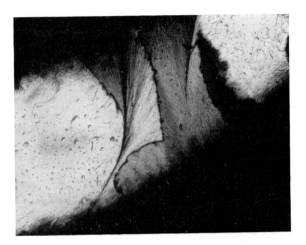

FIG. 4b. Crystallization of *dl*-amphetamine hydrochloride, (volatility test), "map formation", with crossed nicols. 66×.

FIG. 4c. Deposit of *d-* + *dl*-amphetamine hydrochloride. Volatility test, substance caught in a drop of dilute HCl and the drop evaporated, as seen with crossed Nicols. 66×.

II. a volatile base of decomposition is evolved.

III. at room temperature the substance shows only a slight volatility, unchanged.

IV. the substance is readily volatile with water vapor at room temperature.

In the table for sympathomimetics and central stimulants the following symbols are used:

—, no result

c, crystals are obtained

C, a major crystal test

a, amorphous

d, precipitate collects in drops which do not form crystals, or only after a considerable time

r, reduction occurs (crystals of metallic gold form). The reduction is sometimes fairly prompt and sometimes slow.

( ) parentheses indicate that the parenthetical result may not occur; usually used for (c) when, because of slow formation or lack of sensitivity, crystals may not be obtained.

/ change of conditions. In columns 6, 8, and 10, when direct addition of the reagent to the solid does not give good results (generally because of the instant formation of insoluble masses or coating), some of the substance is dissolved in a little water and the reagent added. The result is given following the /. In columns (7), (9), and (11), the result following the / is that noted after reinversion of the slide with the hanging drop, and at least partial evaporation of water from it.

In Fig. 5a, b, c are reproduced additional examples of microcrystals formed by compounds of this type (benzylephedrine, cyclopentamine, nylidrin) respectively, with HAu·Cl$_4$ in $(1 + 2)$H$_3$PO$_4$, H$_2$Pt I$_6$ in $(2\frac{1}{2} + 1)$·H$_3$PO$_4$ (minimum NaI), and 1.3 HAuBr$_4$ in 2H$_3$PO$_4$·1$(2 + 3)$H$_2$SO$_4$. Especially noteworthy are the "corkscrew" crystals of the first mentioned.

HAuBr$_4$ in H$_3$PO$_4$

Bromauric acid is the most generally useful of all amine precipitants. In phosphoric acid it appears to precipitate all nitrogenous compounds in which the nitrogen manifests any basic properties at all, external to the molecule. The restriction of the last four words applies only to a few "internal salts."

The only reagent that carries precipitation even further in some cases is iodine-KI (or HI) in H$_3$PO$_4$. It precipitates even some nitrogenous compounds that appear to be completely acidic (having an $>$NH group flanked by $>$C$=$O groups), as well as

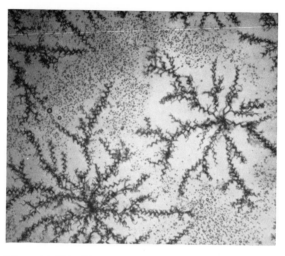

FIG. 5a. Benzylephedrine with HAuCl$_4$ $(1 + 2)$ H$_3$PO$_4$ added to aqueous solution of the salt. Extraordinary "corkscrew" crystals. With crossed nicols they resemble metal-turnings. 100×.

FIG. 5b. Cyclopentamine with H$_2$PtI$_6$ in $(2\frac{1}{2} + 1)$ H$_3$PO$_4$, minimum NaI. 66×. (Propylhexedrine gives similar crystals; test distinguishes those two from others.)

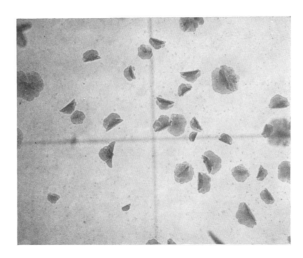

Fig. 5c. Nylidrin, 1.3 HAuBr₄ in 2H₃PO₄·1 (2 + 3) H₂SO₄ (90), on standing, with humidity. 100×.

amphoteric compounds (even when mainly acidic and only feebly basic) in which the strong H_3PO_4 brings out the basic character; this also occurs with bromauric acid in H_3PO_4. Iodine reagents are indispensable but not more so than bromauric acid; the iodine precipitates more often fail to crystallize, and different reagent-formulas are needed for them.

In general, the precipitates are not necessarily crystalline. With complex and definitely basic compounds, such as the alkaloids and antihistamines, the precipitates with $HAuBr_4$ in H_3PO_4, even when it is added to an aqueous solution, are far too insoluble for the best results. Such precipitates are usually amorphous or too minutely crystalline to have any value for microscopic crystal tests. On the other hand, compounds that are relatively simple but too water-soluble or too feebly basic, or both, to yield precipitates from an aqueous solution with reagents dissolved in water, will generally yield beautiful crystals with bromauric acid in a medium of phosphoric acid, although occasionally only drops are formed. The crystals show great differences from one compound to another, not only in their forms, but also in colors, birefringence, and dichroism. The reagent is added directly to the dry substance to be tested. Crystals of the bromaurate compound are easily distinguished from undissolved material, or any other crystals that may form, by their color.

The reagent also has a general use in determining whether any compound capable of this precipitation is present. A little powder from a tablet, for example, may be scattered thinly on a slide, a drop of the reagent and a cover-glass applied, and bromaurate crystals or precipitation looked for under the microscope immediately and after standing. In this direct addition there is some danger that a compound with too great bromaurate insolubility may not show up, because the insoluble precipitate may completely cover the surface of the material and prevent further solution. Therefore, some less sensitive reagents should also be tried, or the test tried on an aqueous or dilute acid solution of the substance, before concluding that no compound of basic nitrogen is present.

Precipitates may be due to other kinds of basic substances. These include:

(a) *Inorganic:* all the alkali metals, and magnesium and zinc, in particular, in the form of their salts, as well as ammonium and hydroxylamine.

71

(b) *Compounds of basic oxygen:* i.e., compounds of a certain complexity and capable of forming oxonium salts also react (for example coumarin). These are rare by comparison with the compounds of basic nitrogen, but in a general test it should be remembered that some organic bases do exist which do not contain nitrogen.

The reagent: Gold chloride crystals ($HAuCl_4 \cdot 3H_2O$) 1 g (makes about 1.3 g $HAuBr_4$); HBr (40%) 1.5 ml; H_2O 1.0 ml; syrupy (85–88%) H_3PO_4 to make 20 ml. This may be named in short, $HAuBr_4$ in H_3PO_4; or in more detail as 1.3 HAuBr in syrupy H_3PO_4, (20).

Excellent crystals for identification tests may be obtained with aminoacetic acid, betaine, glutamic acid, urea, acetamide, etc., as well as with many sympathomimetic drugs and other substances.

CHARLES C. FULTON

ELECTRON MICROSCOPY

AEROSOLS CONTAINING RADIOACTIVE PARTICLES

The electron microscope is an ideal tool for the analysis of aerosol particles. This pertains especially to particles with submicronic dimensions down to 0.002 micron (2×10^{-7} cm). Electronoscopic observations provide data on size, shape, aggregation tendencies and population density of the particles. In addition it may be possible to obtain electron diffraction data as a means for chemical identification (1). Correlation of electronoscopic observations with data obtained by other analytical methods makes possible a complete description of a particular aerosol. The purpose of this article is to describe the electron microscopic appearance of particles from aerosols containing $Sr^{90}SO_4$, $Ru^{106}O_2$, or $Pu^{239}O_2$.

Methods

Particles from the various aerosols were collected directly on "Formvar" coated electron microscope supporting grids or on membrane filters. In the latter case the particles had to be transferred to coated grids before observation in the electron microscope was possible. This was accomplished by a modified Kalmus technique (2). Each aerosol was represented by an appropriate number of specimen grids (minimum of six grids per aerosol) to provide a statistically valid sample of particles. All specimen grids used were preinspected for cleanliness, or pre-shadowed to delineate contaminations.

Screens representing the various aerosols were surveyed in the electron microscope and appropriate fields were photographed at magnifications of 2,000×, 6,500×, and/or 10,000×. The electron micrographs illustrating this report are photographic enlargements.

Size distribution data were obtained by measuring several hundred particles chosen at random on the prints representing the different samples. The particles were all measured in the same direction.

Observations and Discussion

Description of the Particles. *Strontium Sulfate.* The particles obtained from aerosols containing $Sr^{90}SO_4$ are characteristically in the form of needles. Typical examples are illustrated in Fig. 1. For the most part the needles occur in clusters. The dark cuboidal or spherical material noted in these micrographs may be undissolved membrane filter

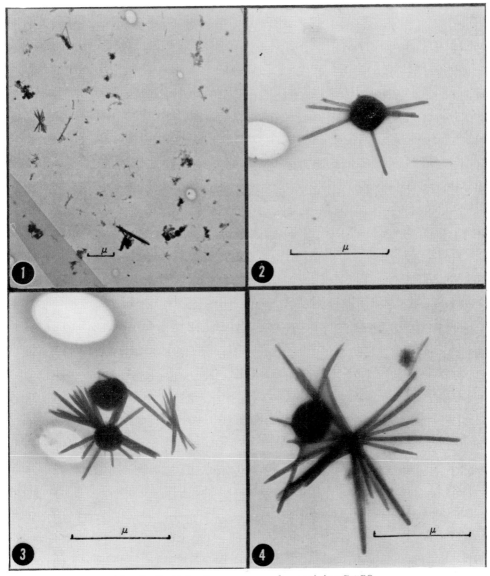

FIG. 1. Particles from an aerosol containing $Sr^{90}SO_4$.

1. Particles transferred from membrane filter to a "Formvar"-coated screen. 8500×. The broad gray band in the lower left corner is a common contaminant in this type of preparation. 2, 3 and 4. Selected fields illustrating particles collected directly on "Formvar"-coated screens. 25,000×.

from which the particles were transferred, or they may be small particles of Pluronics, a dispersing agent present in the aerosol generation suspension. The individual needles are rarely longer than 1 micron, or wider than 0.05 micron.

Ruthenium Dioxide. Particles obtained from aerosols containing $Ru^{106}O_2$ are illustrated in Fig. 2. The particles are characteristically three-dimensional chain aggregates, each aggregate consisting of many roughly spheroid unit particles. Ruthenium dioxide

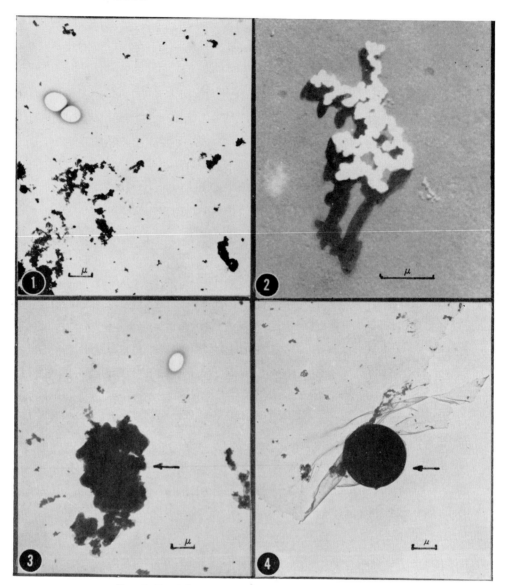

Fig. 2. Particles from an aerosol containing $Ru^{106}O_2$.

1. Particles transferred from membrane filter to a Formvar coated screen. 6,375×. The aggregate particles are slightly fused because of exposure to the electron beam in the electron microscope. 2. Three-dimensional chain aggregate particle. 14,450×. This preparation was shadowed with palladium. Negative print. Note the spheroid nature of the particles making up the aggregate. 3. and 4. The same field before and after prolonged exposure to the electron beam. 6,375×. The arrow in figure 3 points to a large aggregate particle. The arrow in figure 4 points to the same particle after it was exposed to the electron beam for 60 seconds. Such behavior is common for ruthenium dioxide particles. The aggregate particle is too large to dissipate the heat evolved by the impact of the electron beam on the specimen, and the melting point is low enough to cause fusion of the small particles into the resultant sphere.

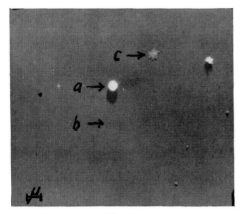

FIG. 3

The large particle (a) in Fig. 3 is about 0.65 μ across and about 0.65 μ high d/m = 0.38 if particle is PuO$_2$ with a S.G. 11.44. Particle (b) is approximately 0.05 μ. The aggregate particle (c) consists of a countless number of grains 0.05 μ and less. (About 4500×.)

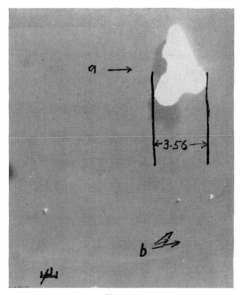

FIG. 4

In Figure 4, the large particle (a) appears to be made up of several cubes and a brick shaped particle. The volume of this particle can be approximated very roughly. Particles like these are frequently observed. This particle illustrates the discrepancy between actual or real volume and calculated volume based on a single linear measurement. The actual volume is roughly guessed to be about 7 μ^3. The calculated volume using the dimension shown is about 46 μ^3. If this particle

is sensitive to the electron beam, that is, when exposed to high beam intensity the agaggregates melt and fuse to form a single sphere. Large aggregates are more sensitive to the electron beam than small aggregates.

Plutonium Dioxide. Particles from Pu^{239}O$_2$ containing aerosols are characteristically cubic or brick shaped. These are illustrated in Figs. 3, 4, 5, 6, and 7. Unlike Sr^{90}SO$_4$ and Ru^{106}O$_2$ which occur predominantly as aggregate particles, Pu^{239}O$_2$ occurs predominantly as individual non-aggregated parti-

FIG. 5

Figure 5 shows a particle that appears to be almost a perfect cube approximately 0.4 μ on a side. Volume is therefore about 0.064 μ^3. Particles of this shape are commonly found in these samples. If this particle is PuO$_2$ (S.G. 11.44) the disintegration rate is about 0.09 d/m. The halo surrounding the particle is probably the remains of moisture that were associated with the particle. The round globule just outside the halo is an artifact—namely a bubble of carbon produced in shadow casting. (About 15,000×.)

FIG. 4.—*Continued*

represents a PuO$_2$ particle (S.G. = 11.44) the actual disintegration rate is somewhere near 10 d/m, whereas on a calculated basis the activity density would be about 62 d/m. This micrograph also illustrates the variation in particle size encountered in these samples. Compare particle (a) 3.55 μ across with particles labelled (b) 0.05 μ across. (About 4500×.)

Fig. 6

Figure 6 shows another characteristic shape (brick-shaped) of particles found in this sample. (About 15,000×.)

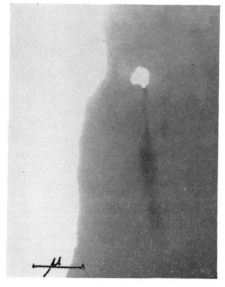

Fig. 7

In Figure 7 are shown particles that are observed occasionally. This particle is surrounded by a halo indicating moisture was associated with this particular particle. The particle is an aggregate of different sized particles standing one on another. The variation in width of the particle is manifested by the difference in width of the shadow. The widest portion of this particle is about 0.4 μ and its height is about 1.75 μ. (About 15,000×.)

cles. Aggregate particles of $Pu^{239}O_2$ rarely consist of more than 5 or 6 cubes.

The particles shown in Figures 3, 4, 5, 6, and 7 were collected directly on tungsten oxide and carbon preshadowed specimen screens. The specimens were shadowed again with chromium at a 30° angle before examination in the electron microscope. Double-shadowed particles therefore would indicate contaminants on the specimen grid prior to exposure to the aerosol.

Physical Data. Pertinent information on the physical characteristics of the particles from each of the aerosols is presented in Table 1 and Figure 8.

The data and observations presented above are very general in that they were based on measurements of 100 particles representing a single aerosol. However, analysis of other aerosols containing $Sr^{90}SO_4$, $Ru^{106} \cdot O_2$, or $Pu^{239}O_2$ gave similar results. Al-

TABLE 1. PHYSICAL CHARACTERISTICS OF PARTICLES FROM AEROSOLS CONTAINING $Sr^{90}SO_4$, $Ru^{106}O_2$, OR $Pu^{239}O_2$

Aerosol Contains	Size Range (μ)	Mean Size ± S.D. (μ)	Per Cent 0.5 μ or less	Remarks
$Sr^{90}SO_4$	0.05 − 1.30	0.38 ± 0.22	74	Particles are needles or needle clusters.
$Ru^{106}O_2$	<0.05 − 1.30	0.36 ± 0.29	75	Particles are three dimensional chain aggregates of small spheriod type particles.
$Pu^{239}O_2$	0.05 − 0.60	0.20 ± 0.09	99	Particles are cubic or brick-shaped

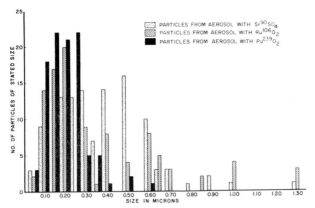

FIG. 8. Particle size distribution

though the size range and mean size for the particles from the different aerosols are similar, there are striking differences in shape and aggregation tendencies.

REFERENCES

1. KUMAI, MOTOI, "Encyclopedia of Microscopy," 1961.
2. BORASKY, R., AND MASTEL, B., *AEC R + D Report*, No. H.W. 46722 General Electric Co., Richland, Washington, 1956.
3. FITZGERALD, J. J. AND DETWILER, C. G., *KAPL-1088*, General Electric Co., Schenectady, New York, 1954.

R. BORASKY

BLOOD*

This method is designed to involve the least possible technical manipulation of the blood sample both before and after fixation. The sample was centrifuged to concentrate the buffy coat, thereby obtaining minimal contamination by erythrocytes. No anticoagulant or any other foreign substance was added to the blood prior to fixation.

About 6–7cc of blood was obtained by venipuncture either (a) by withdrawal with a 10cc syringe fitted with a 20-gauge needle

* (Excerpt of fixation, preparation, obtaining of, and microscopy of specimens taken from "Electron Microscopic Atlas of Normal and Leukemic Human Blood")

and transference to a 10cc Lusteroid centrifuge tube (International), precooled to 5–10° C; or (b) by needle drip directly into the tube. The syringe had been previously silicon-coated with Dow-Corning 200, 2 percent in CCl_4, by immersion and baking for $\frac{1}{2}$–1 hour at 450–550° C. The needle had been coated with 10 percent aqueous Armour Monocote [tris-(2-hydroxyethyldodecyl)-NH_4Cl] by immersion, draining, and air drying. The ice-cooled sample was then centrifuged at 1500 rpm for 15 minutes at 0° C (relative centrifugal force—265; International model PR-2, refrigerated, angle head centrifuge). The buffy coat was aspirated with a silicon-coated pipette and transferred to a glass tube containing 5cc of 1 percent Veronal-buffered (pH—7.4) OsO_4 at 5–10° C. It was fixed for $\frac{1}{2}$–1 hour, usually the former. Between the successive steps ($\frac{1}{2}$–1 hour) of fixation, dehydration, and methacrylate infiltration, the specimen was centrifuged for 1–1$\frac{1}{2}$ minutes at 1500 rpm (relative centrifugal force—385; Clay-Adams Safeguard centrifuge) in glass tubes (alcohol dissolves Lusteroid!). After each centrifugation the supernatant fluid was decanted, the next fluid added, and the tube manually agitated to produce a suspension. The last methacrylate suspension (6 parts *n*-butyl, 1 part methyl) was permitted to settle by gravity in 00 gelatin capsules for $\frac{1}{2}$–1 hour

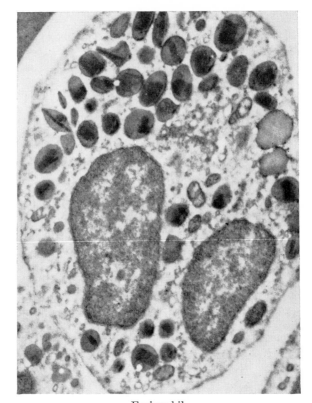

Eosinophil

Fig. 1. (a) Cell of normal blood

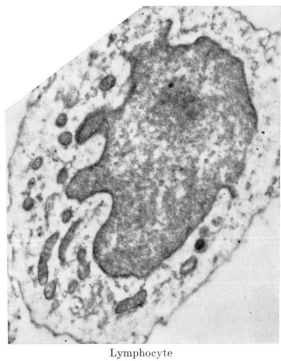

Lymphocyte

Fig. 1. (b) Cell of normal blood

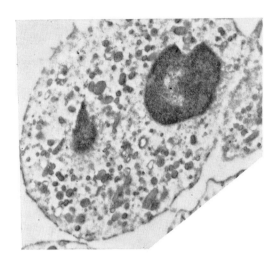

Neutrophil
← Fig. 1. (c) Cell of normal blood

Monocyte
↓ Fig. 2. Cell of normal blood

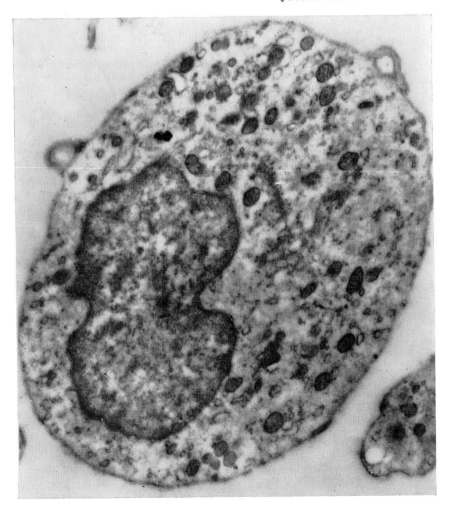

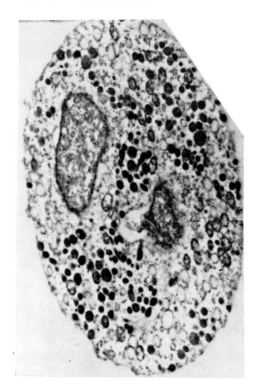

Neutrophilic Promyelocyte
FIG. 3. (a) Cell of granulocytic leukemia

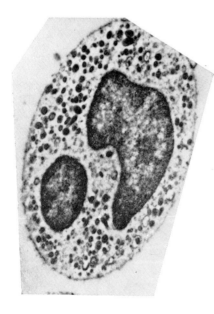

Neutrophilic metamyelocyte
FIG. 3. (b) Cell of granulocytic leukemia

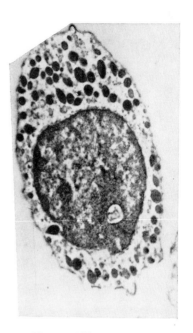

Neutrophilic myelocyte
FIG. 3. (c) Cell of granulocytic leukemia

to avoid close packing. This also eliminated bubble formation during polymerization, which was performed overnight at 47° C with dry heat in an oven. Sections were cut on a Porter-Blum ultramicrotome using a glass knife and were mounted on copper grids covered by Formvar or carbon membranes. Three RCA electron microscopes were used for viewing and photography—an EMU-2, an EML-1B, and an EMU-3. The micrographs were taken on 2 by 10 inch or 3¼ by 4 inch Kodak lantern-slide medium plates and were printed by projection enlargement. Neither the negatives nor prints were retouched.

JAMES A. FREEMAN

BOTANICAL APPLICATIONS

Introduction. The high resolution obtainable with the electron microscope permits it to be used to great advantage for a number of different problems in botanical

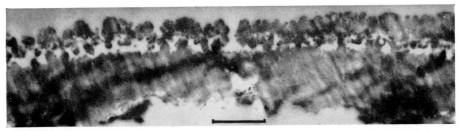

Fɪɢ. 1. Section through part of a pollen wall (acetolyzed and chlorinated) of *Rhododendron ponticum*, ×14,000. (*Afzelius, by courtesy of Grana Palynologica*)

research. The two main techniques employed have been thin sections and surface replicas, the former being particularly valuable in plant cytology where internal detail is of interest, and the latter being mainly applicable to taxonomic and morphological studies. In addition it is possible to obtain information in a number of particular cases using direct examination. The various results obtained in different fields of botany will be briefly described here.

Palynology. Pollen morphology has been fairly widely studied in the electron microscope. The results may be of interest in fields other than botany, for example, in studying the history of post-glacial flora by means of pollen analysis. In addition it may be of interest to those working on such problems as hay fever and asthma.

Two specimen preparation techniques, namely sectioning and replicas, provide different pictures of the sporoderm. Thin sections provide a great deal of information concerning its stratification, but in order to obtain a complete picture of the sporoderm of a given pollen grain it is desirable to have a knowledge of the surface topography in addition to sub-surface stratification. Earlier work on pollen grains was confined to the study of thin sections in the electron microscope (1, 2, 3).

It is difficult to prepare sections of pollen cell walls because they are extremely hard. However, advances in the technique of ultramicrotomy have permitted a considerable amount of information to be obtained in this way (4). The stratification of the sporoderm

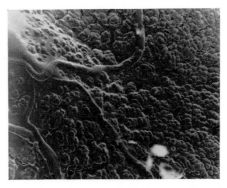

Fɪɢ. 2. Shadowed carbon replica of the surface of a fresh pollen grain of *Rhododendron ponticum*, ×7000.

is an extremely complex subject and cannot be discussed in detail here.

An interesting study of both sections and replicas of pollen grains has been carried out by Mühlethaler (5), who interprets electron micrographs of sections and carbon replicas (6) in terms of existing terminology on pollen morphology. An interesting comparison between the electron micrographs obtained by different authors of the same type of pollen grain is shown in Figures 1 and 2. Figure 1 shows a section through part of an acetolyzed and chlorinated pollen wall of *Rhododendron ponticum* (4), taken by Afzelius. This can be compared directly with the carbon replica of *Rhododendron ponticum* taken by the author and shown in Figure 2. It can be seen that the section shows indications of a surface structure which is similar in character to that revealed clearly in the replica.

The potentialities of the electron microscope compared with the light microscope in the study of pollen grains have been discussed by Bradley (7). For example, when studying pores, their outline can generally just be distinguished in the light microscope. With the electron microscope, however, the entire morphology is clearly resolved. A comparison between the pores of *Plantago media* and *Plantago lanceolata* is shown here. The pore of *P. media* (Figure 3) has a ragged outline and contains a number of irregularly scattered large protrusions; that of *P. lanceolata* is circular and completely different in form. This difference can just be detected in the light microscope, but the true structures cannot be resolved.

Surface replicas have indicated that the effect of the acetolyzation process on the sub-microscopic structure of the pollen grain surface is negligible. It might be expected that the use of powerful reagents such as those employed in acetolyzation would produce artefacts in the sporoderm. This is not the case with pollen grains studied in the light microscope and there appears to be no

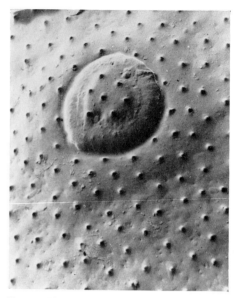

FIG. 4. Shadowed carbon replica of a fresh pollen grain of *Plantago lanceolata*, ×9000. (*Courtesy of the New Phytologist*)

noticeable effect at electron microscope levels of resolution.

An important problem in the study of pollen grains is the distinction between apparently identical grains of different species. If a separation of these species could be obtained it would be of considerable value in quaternary research. Preliminary electron microscope studies of *Cannabis* and *Humulus*, *Corylus* and *Myrica* have not produced the distinction hoped for. In the former case *Cannabis* and *Humulus* appeared identical in the electron microscope with regard to their surface structures. However some slight but definite structural distinction was found between *Corylus* and *Myrica* grains.

Rowley (8) has used both sectioning and surface replicas in an exhaustive study of the pollen wall in eleven species in the *Commelinaceae*. No basic differences were found in the structural elements making up the mature pollen wall; morphological variation at light microscope level was due to variations in the arrangement of these elements. Rowley also studied the develop-

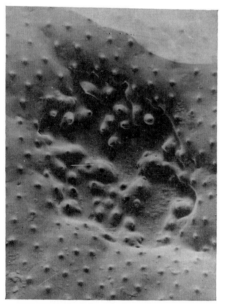

FIG. 3. Shadowed carbon replica of a fresh pollen grain of *Plantago media*, ×9000. (*Courtesy of the New Phytologist*)

ment of the pollen grain of *Tradescantia paludosa*. It is of considerable interest that he found that the basic form of exine sculpturing orginated very early in development. The intine was not recognizable until much later.

The entire structure of the sporoderm, both internal and external, can be fully elucidated by the judicious employment of replicas and thin sections.

Moss Spores. The spores of mosses and similar plants present a similar problem in replication and sectioning to pollen grains. Afzelius, Erdtman and Sjöstrand (3) have studied the fine structure of the outer part of the spore wall of *Lycopodium clavatum* using thin sections, the results indicating that the spore wall is divided into two layers, the outer being laminated and the inner granulated.

Moss spores have not been studied extensively, the only example being by Bradley (9), who shows electron micrographs of the surface structure of spores of *Atrichum undulatum* and *Dicranella heteromalla*. It seems that the value of studying such specimens in the electron microscope is somewhat limited.

Fungi. The direct examination of fungus spores of a number of different species was carried out by Gregory and Nixon (10). The spore structure is of interest in studies of asthma as is the case with pollen grains. Direct electron micrographs only provide a silhouette of the spores and little can be seen of their surface structure; the use of replicas, however, shows the surface structure clearly as in Figure 5.

An interesting application of the electron microscope using both surface replicas and sections has been carried out independently by two authors on the division of *Saccharomyces cerevisiae* (11, 12). The morphology of the different types of yeast bud scars and the mechanism of the division process was studied by replicas in the case of Bradley (12) and sections in the case of Agar and

Douglas (11), both authors independently reaching similar conclusions.

Algae. A group of algae which has been studied extensively in the electron microscope is that comprising the diatoms. So much work has been carried out that it is impossible to include more than a brief reference. Much of the work was done in the early days of electron microscopy, and several important contributions were made by Müller and Pasewaldt (13), Kolbe and Golz (14), Hustedt (15), and Hendey, Cushing and Ripley (16). The electron microscope is continually being used, generally as a taxonomic aid in studies of new species or populations.

The light microscope is fully adequate for distinguishing the diatom genera, and also for separating the great majority of species. However, the electron microscope permits a much fuller examination of the submicroscopic details of the silica valve and thus enables a far better understanding of the meaning of its finer visible features to be achieved. In addition, the hope is that it will provide useful information about the development of this fine structure.

The electron microscope has also been used in the study of one family and three genera of algae belonging to the *Chryso-*

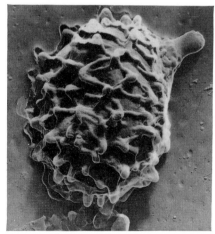

Fig. 5. Shadowed carbon replica of a spore of the fungus *Russula mairei*, ×9000.

83

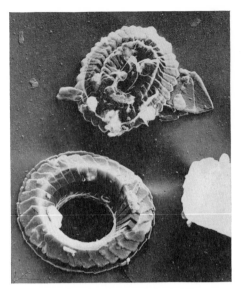

Fig. 6. Shadowed carbon replica of the calcite scales of a species of the family *Coccolithophoridaceae*, ×10,000.

phyceae. The first of these to be described here, *Coccolithophoridaceae*, is of wide interest since the unicellular organisms form minute calcite scales. These scales form sedimentary chalk deposits. They are deposited on the ocean bed after the cells have died and the protoplasm has disintegrated. There is a very large number of species in the family and classification is a difficult matter when the light microscope is used because of the limited resolution available. However, the electron microscope provides the increased resolution required for a full taxonomic study and as a result much useful information has been obtained which is of particular value to both botanists and palaeontologists.

As in many other cases, electron microscopy of the scales (coccoliths) requires a detailed terminology which is provided by Halldal and Markali (17). These authors give a comprehensive survey of a large number of species of the genus using direct examination in the electron microscope. Though much information can be gained by studying coccoliths directly, the results are much clearer if carbon replicas are prepared

(18). Figure 6 shows a carbon replica of the calcite scales and the full surface topography is clearly shown.

The remaining two genera studied in detail in the electron microscope are *Synura* and *Mallomonas*. These are closely related to the *Coccolithophoridaceae*, but the latter are marine organisms whereas the former are fresh-water organisms. *Synura* and *Mallomonas* are also unicellular and covered with scales, but these are generally much smaller and are composed of silica.

The genus *Synura* contains only a few species. These have been studied in detail in the electron microscope by Manton (19), Fott (20), Petersen and Hansen (21) and Harris and Bradley (22, 24). The latter two authors concentrated on their taxonomy using the electron microscope, but Manton studied internal morphology and employed thin sections.

The genus *Mallomonas* contains a much larger number of species, many of which have only been discovered recently. The electron microscope has been of great value as a taxonomic aid, since the classification of the genus depends almost entirely on the structure of the minute silica scales covering the organisms. Harris and Bradley (23, 24), also Harris (25), have studied the scales directly and used carbon replicas to show up their fine structure. Asmund used direct examination and has studied the occurrence of *Mallomonas* species in Danish ponds (26).

Although the cells of many *Mallomonas* species disintegrate when dried, most of them become sufficiently rigid after careful fixation to be studied complete in the electron microscope. Figure 7 shows a direct electron micrograph of a scale of a species of *Synura* and Figure 8 shows a carbon replica of a complete *Mallomonas*.

A small genus, *Chrysosphaerella*, about which relatively little is known, has also been studied in the electron microscope. It is rather similar to *Synura* and only consists of two or three species. The cells are also coated with silica scales and have long spines at-

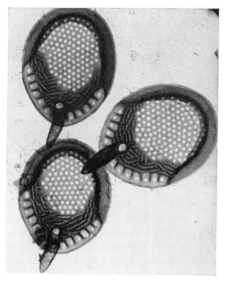

FIG. 7. Direct electron micrograph of scales of *Synura eichinulata*; the structure at the base of the spine is internal thickening, ×13,500.

tached to them. *Chrysosphaerella* is relatively uncommon compared with *Mallomonas* and *Synura*.

Petersen and Hansen (27) have studied some organisms associated with the surface of the water as opposed to those types of phyto-plankton which are free-swimming. By means of a special technique they were able to study single cells as they were situated on the water surface before drying.

Marine algae have been studied in detail by Parke, Manton and Clarke (28, 29) who used direct examination and sections. These authors are concerned mainly with the micro-anatomy and taxonomy of *Chryso-chromulina*. Their descriptions are extremely detailed and informative.

Manton and Clarke (30) have also given a detailed and interesting description of the spermatozoid of *Fucus serratus*. This interesting organism is shown in Figure 9. Manton and Clarke ascertained by comparing UV micrographs and electron micrographs that the body shrinks but does not alter its shape in the electron microscope. The function of the fine hairs on either side of the

front flagellum is not known. The proboscis, which is highly mobile in the living state, is a funnel-shaped membrane surrounding the front flagellum and attached to the body at the base. When dry, the organ is flattened and thirteen characteristic concentric thickenings can be seen. The study of the flagella is particularly interesting since the morphology can be compared with other flagella and cilia. Electron micrographs of the disintegrated front flagellum show it to be composed of eleven strands; in the rear flagellum there are only nine. It is interesting to note that fern cilia bear a close numerical relationship (31) yet there is no phyletic or

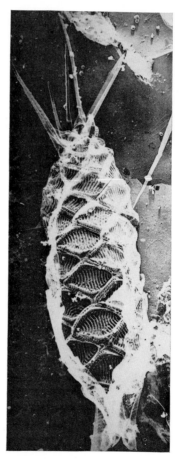

FIG. 8. Shadowed carbon replica of a complete cell of *Mallomonas coronata*, ×9000. (*Courtesy of Research*)

85

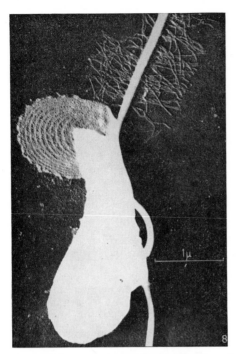

Fig. 9. Direct electron micrograph of a shadowed spermatozoid of *Fucus serratus*; the structure of the proboscis is particularly well shown,
×18,750. (*After Manton and Clarke, courtesy of the
Annals of Botany*)

structural relationship with brown algae.
Eleven strands can also be found in animals, for example, *Paramoecium* (32), the
sperms of domestic fowl and fish. The
prevalence of the number eleven suggests
some fundamental property in the geometric
relations of fibres.

Bacteriology. The electron microscope
has been used extensively in the study
of bacteria and related organisms. The development of the thin sectioning technique
has permitted bacteria to be sectioned and
internal structures to be examined in great
detail. In general the study of the surfaces
of bacteria using replica techniques is not
particularly rewarding, but in a few cases it
has been possible to obtain useful information in this way. The study of bacterial
cytology is a complicated and controversial
subject which cannot be described in any

detail here. Much of the controversy arises
from interpretations of electron micrographs
of thin sections of bacteria. The appearance
of sections of bacteria using different types
of embedding and staining techniques is
always at variance. The recent development
of the use of epoxy resins for embedding
specimens prior to sectioning (33) has indicated that some of the previous work using
methacrylate embedding materials is suspect. There is no doubt that the wealth of
information now available on this subject is
becoming much more co-ordinated.

The use of surface replicas in bacteriology
has generally been connected with taxonomic
studies such as in the case of the genus
Bacillus (34). Here it was shown that the
surface sculpturing of spores was different in
different species, so that once again the
electron microscope proved to be a valuable
taxonomic aid.

Plant Cytology. Plant cytology now
covers a wide field. The electron microscope has been used in the study of cell walls,
mitochondria, chromosomes and other cytoplasmic inclusions. The specimen techniques
required are variable, much of the work
being carried out using thin sections, but
direct examination and replicas of cell walls
have provided much information on their
structure. Detailed general reviews of the
electron microscopy of the plant cell have
been given by Mühlethaler (35) and Buvat
(36) and some of the more important findings
are described here.

The Cytoplasm. The structure of the
cytoplasm varies according to the fixing
agent and may appear as granular or in the
form of a fine network. It seems probable
that the reticulate structure does not correspond to the living state.

Studies of the distribution of the various
albumens and nucleic acids in the cytoplasm
have been attempted by forming heavy
metal complexes to act as specific electron
stains (37). Strugger (38) combined OsO_4
fixation with uranyl-acetate treatment and

was able to resolve sub-microscopic filament-like elements.

Plastids. These have received a great deal of attention, much work being carried out on their development (39, 40). The various stages in the development of the barley chloroplast are shown in Figure 10. Firstly (1) a proplastid develops in the leaf meri-

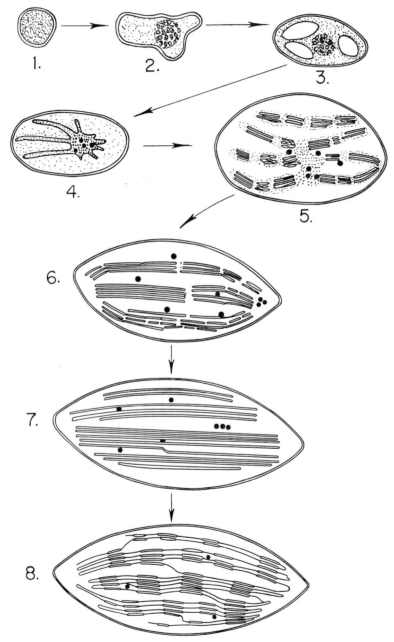

Fig. 10. A diagrammatic representation of the barley chloroplast (see text). (*After Diter von Wettstein, courtesy of Hereditas*)

87

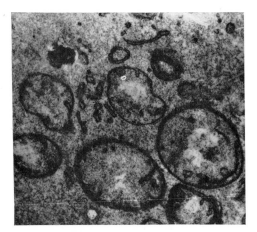

FIG. 11. Section through a proplastid from *Begonia*, ×25,000. (*By K. Mühlethaler*)

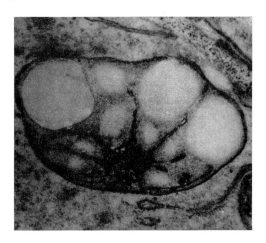

FIG. 12. Section through a further developed proplastid from *Begonia*, ×25,000. (*By K. Mühlethaler*)

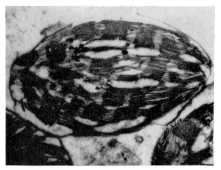

FIG. 13. Section through a chloroplast of *Elodea canadensis*, ×16,000. (*By K. Mühlethaler*)

stem. This shows more or less the same structure as the mitochondria. Next (2) the size increases and the plastid center, containing a tubular structure, is formed. Starch grains now appear (3), and then the material for the formation of the layer structure protrudes radially from the center (4). The starch breaks down (5) and the lamellae begin to form. They multiply by thickening and splitting until the continuous lamellar structure of the chloroplast (6) is formed by the fusion of short lengths. The resulting plastid is traversed by continuous double lamellae (7). Finally further splitting forms the grana of the fully differentiated chloroplast (8).

It is interesting to compare Figure 10 with the electron micrographs of Mühlethaler showing plastid development in *Begonia* and the chloroplast of *Elodea canadensis* (Figures 11–13). The proplastid from *Begonia* (Figure 11) is generally similar to the drawing of the barley proplastid (Figure 10) and the further development of the *Begonia* plastid (Figure 12) is like stage (4) of the description. The fully-differentiated chloroplast of *Elodea canadensis* (Figure 13) is also generally similar to that of barley. From this it may be inferred that the general pattern of chloroplast development is similar in different species.

It is not possible to study the structure of the chloroplast in detail here. The structure is generally similar in all plants, but there is much variation in the dimensions and spacings of the lamellae. The chloroplast is the site of photosynthesis, the chlorophyll being concentrated in the grana. The grana are distributed in the stroma which forms the body of the chloroplast.

The Nucleus. Sections through the nucleus show chromosomes in the despiralized condition and with good resolution a fine granular structure can be detected in the chromosomes and nuclear cytoplasm. However, the electron microscope has added little to our knowledge of chromosomes.

Mitochondria. The electron microscope shows that the mitochondria are fundamentally different morphologically from other cell particles. As in the case of animal mitochondria, those of plant cells show a double-membrane system. Within the mitochondrion are complex fine structures, the cristae mitochondriales, which consist of invaginations of the mitochondrial membrane reaching from one wall to the other. These structures are highly variable from cell to cell and between different species of plants. It is now known with reasonable certainty that the mitochondrion is the site of respiratory activity of the plant.

The Cell Wall. Many studies of the primary cell wall have been obtained by macerating the cells and reducing them to a very thin film. These thin films are in the form of sub-microscopic strands of cellulose which in turn can be split into even finer threads by means of such techniques as ultrasonic irradiation. The micro-fibrils obtained in this way are elementary in nature because they correspond to the crystalline micellar strands which can be detected by means of x-ray diffraction. It can be seen in Figure 14 that the micro-fibrils of the primary cell wall are interwoven to form a very dense network.

In the secondary cell wall which consists entirely of micro-fibrils of cellulose, the strands tend to lie parallel instead of in the form of a network as shown in Figure 15. In successive lamellae the orientation of the parallel fibrils is shifted.

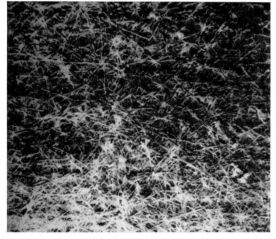

Fig. 14. Shadowed portion of primary cell wall *Valonia*, ×5500. (*After Steward and Mühlethaler, courtesy of the Annals of Botany*)

Fig. 15. Shadowed portion of secondary cell wall of *Valonia*, ×11,000. (*After Steward and Mühlethaler, courtesy of the Annals of Botany*)

Fig. 16. Pit membrane in a simple pit in the radicle of maize, ×15,000. (*After Mühlethaler, courtesy of Die Naturwissenschaften*)

It is possible to study changes in the primary cell wall structure during cell division. The manner in which the cellulose microfibrils are deposited can be examined. The secondary cell wall contains characteristic perforations known as pits. These pits have been studied extensively in the electron microscope and whereas optical evidence suggested that the pit membrane, which stretches across the perforation, acts as an impassable barrier, the electron microscope indicates that it is porous in nature (Figure 16).

Cell wall growth has been studied in detail in the onion root tip by Scott *et al.* (40).

Conclusion. The electron microscope is clearly very valuable in botanical research. It is extremely useful as a taxonomic aid, and much morphological information has been obtained in the field of plant cytology. It remains for these results to be correlated with biochemical investigations.

Acknowledgments. The author would like to thank the following for material and advice: Professor and Mrs. T. M. Harris, University of Reading; Dr. K. Mühlethaler, Eidgenossische Technische Hochschule, Zurich; and Dr. B. E. Juniper, University of Oxford; also Dr. T. E. Allibone, F.R.S., Director of the Research Laboratory, for permission to publish this article.

REFERENCES

1. FERNANDEZ-MORAN, H. AND DAHL, A. O., *Science* (Lancaster, Pa.) **116**, 465 (1952).
2. MÜHLETHALER, K., *Mikroskopie*, **8**, 103 (1953).
3. AFZELIUS, B. M., ERDTMAN, G., AND SJÖSTRAND, F. S., *Sv. Bot. Tidskr.*, **48**, 155 (1954).
4. AFZELIUS, B. M., *Grana Palynologica*, **1**, 22 (1956).
5. MÜHLETHALER, K., *Planta*, **46**, 1 (1955).
6. BRADLEY, D. E., *Brit. J. Appl. Phys.*, **5**, 96 (1954).
7. BRADLEY, D. E., *New Phytol.*, **57**, 226 (1958).
8. ROWLEY, J. R., *Grana Palynologica*, **2**, 3 (1959).
9. BRADLEY, D. E., *Mikroskopie*, **13**, 180 (1958).
10. GREGORY, P. H. AND NIXON, H. L., *Trans. Brit. Mycol. Soc.* **33**, 359 (1950).
11. AGAR, H. D. AND DOUGLAS, H. C., *J. Bacteriol.*, **70**, 427 (1955).
12. BRADLEY, D. E., *J. Roy. Micros. Soc.*, **75**, 254 (1956).
13. MÜLLER, H. O. AND PASEWALDT, C. W. A., *Naturwiss.*, **30** (1942).
14. KOLBE, R. W. AND GOLZ, E., *Ber. dtsch. bot. Ges.*, **61**, 91 (1943).
15. HUSTEDT, F., *Arch. hydrobiol. Plankt.*, **41**, 315 (1945).
16. HENDEY, N. I., CUSHING, D. H. AND RIPLEY, G. W., *J. Roy. Micros. Soc.*, **74**, 22 (1954).
17. HALLDAL, P. AND MARKALI, J., Avhandlinger Utgitt av Det Norske Videnskeps-Akademi, Oslo. Mat-Natruv. Klasse, No. 1 (1955).
18. BRADLEY, D. E., *J. Appl. Phys.*, **27**, 1399 (1956).

19. Manton, I., *Proc. Leeds Phil. Soc.*, **6**, 306 (1955).
20. Fott, B. and Ludvik, J., *Preslia*, **29**, 5 (1957).
21. Petersen, J. B. and Hansen, J. B., *Biol. Medd. Dan. Vid. Selsk.*, **23**, 1 (1956).
22. Harris, K. and Bradley, D. E., *Discovery*, **17**, 329 (1956).
23. Harris, K. and Bradley, D. E., *J. Roy. Micros. Soc.*, **76**, 37 (1957).
24. Harris, K. and Bradley, D. E., *J. gen. Microbiol.*, **18**, 71 (1958).
25. Harris, K., *J. gen. Microbiol.*, **19**, 55 (1958).
26. Asmund, B., *Dansk. Bot. Arkiv.*, **18**, 7 (1959).
27. Petersen, J. B. and Hansen, J. B., *Saertyk. Af. Bot. Tid.*, **54**, 93 (1958).
28. Parke, M., Manton, I. and Clarke, B., *J. Mar. Biol. Assn. U.K.*, **35**, 387 (1956).
29. Parke, M., Manton, I. and Clarke, B., *J. Mar. Biol. Assn. U.K.*, **37**, 209 (1958).
30. Manton, I. and Clarke, B., *Ann. Bot.*, **15**, 461 (1951).
31. Manton, I. and Clarke, B., *J. Exp. Bot.*, **ii**, 125 (1951).
32. Jackus, M. A. and Hall, C. E., *Biol. Bull.*, **91**, 141 (1946).
33. Glauert, A. M., *Nature*, **178**, 803 (1956).
34. Bradley, D. E. and Franklin, J. G., *J. Bacteriol.*, **76**, 618 (1958).
35. Mühlethaler, K., *Naturwiss.*, **44**, 204 (1957).
36. Buvat, R., *Ann. des Sci. Nat. Bot., 11th Series*, **19**, 121 (1958).
37. Lamb, W. G. P., Stuart-Webb, J., Bell, J. L. G., Bovey, R., and Danielli, J. F., *Exp. Cell Res.*, **4**, 159 (1953).
38. Strugger, S., *Naturwiss.*, **43**, 357 (1956).
39. Mühlethaler, K., Private communication.
40. Diter von Wettstein, *Hereditas*, **43**, 303 (1957).
41. Scott, F. M., Hanmer, K. C., Baker, E. and Bowler, E., *Amer. J. Bot.*, **43**, 313 (1956).

D. E. Bradley

CELL ULTRASTRUCTURE IN MAMMALS

The term "ultrastructure" refers to the fact that the cell structures accounted for here have been analyzed with the aid of the electron microscope. The finer details of cell structures cannot be resolved with the light or phase contrast microscopes and, therefore, have been considered as being beyond or *ultra* this level of resolution.

Methods

The techniques applied in modern electron microscopy are found elsewhere (electron microscopy: specimen preparations). It should be emphasized, however, that thin sectioning (section thickness about 100A) is required to permit the best resolution. Several specially designed microtomes are commercially available such as the Porter-Blum (U. S. A.), the Sjöstrand (LKB, Sweden), the Sitte (Reichert, Austria), the Moran (Leitz, Germany), the Hanstra (Philips, Holland). The microtome preferred by the author is the LKB Ultrotome (Sweden) which is the most recent and most superior in design.

The preservation of the tissue has been thoroughly worked out by Dr. Palade (U. S. A.) and Dr. Sjöstrand (Sweden). It is believed that any analysis of the cell ultrastructure today can be made without the risk of describing artifacts because so much is known about how various factors may influence the cell structures: the tonicity and acidity of the fixative, the temperature, post mortem changes, etc.

The contrast of the electron microscopic picture (electron micrograph) can be enhanced by applying special staining techniques, either during the fixation or dehydration periods or after sectioning. The fixative itself gives, however, quite sufficient contrast for most studies. The most commonly used is osmium tetroxide (often called osmic acid, although it is not an acid). After fixation, the specimen is dehydrated in graded alcohols and subsequently embedded in liquid plastics (usually a mixture of butyl and methyl methacrylates). The monomers are polymerized and the embedded tissue block is then ready to be sectioned.

Cell Shape

The general shape of cells varies from tissue to tissue (Fig. 1). This has been accurately analyzed with the light microscope and very little has been added to previous

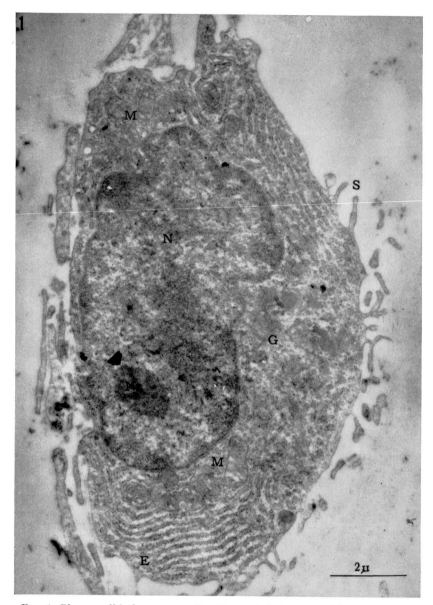

Fig. 1. Plasma cell in loose connective tissue of the human epididymis with most of the features present which usually are found in a mammalian cell: nucleus (N), nucleolus (Ne), Golgi zone (G), mitochondria (M), ergastoplasm (E). The cell is freely suspended in between the connective fibers and displays a number of surface extensions (S). Magnification 10,500×

descriptions by applying electron microscopy. However, the relationship between cells has been elucidated clearly. The old conception of cells being connected by intercellular bridges to a syncytium has been ruled out, as for example in the epidermis and in the heart muscle. Only in rapidly dividing cells, as for instance in the testis, can one find two or more cells interconnected at a certain stage of their differentiation.

Nucleus

As a rule, there is only one nucleus in each cell. The striated muscle cell is an exception and may contain several nuclei. A double-contoured membrane surrounds the nucleoplasm with a total thickness of about 250A (Fig. 3). Discontinuities have been demonstrated in the nuclear membrane, reminiscent of pores. There does not seem to be a free communication between the nucleoplasm and the cell cytoplasm, however, because the "pores" appear to be plugged by a dense substance of unknown nature. The structure of the nucleoplasm or chromatin is finely granulated. The granules have a diameter of about 250A and are clustered in a zone adjacent to the nuclear membrane but can, in addition, be seen distributed evenly throughout the nucleoplasm. The *nucleolus* represents a heavy aggregation of these granules (Fig. 1). Very little has been done so far on the ultrastructure of the chromosomes.

Centriole

The cell center or the centriole (centrosome) is located in the neighborhood of the nucleus, mostly within the Golgi zone of the cell. The centriole is a round or slightly elongated body with size and structure essentially similar to the basal body of the cilium (cross reference: ciliated epithelia) which represents a dense cortex and a lighter core. The cortex is composed of nine paired filaments and a matrix which embeds the filaments. The core is structureless (Fig. 2).

Plasma Membrane

The plasma membrane is the outermost limit of the cell. It has an average thickness of 70–100 A and stands out as a single dense line in the electron micrograph. It is composed of lipid and protein molecules, their mutual arrangement remaining unknown. It has been assumed that the dense line seen in the electron micrograph may represent the protein layer. The lipids would then be ar-

ranged in a layer outside the proteins. Also a mosaic arrangement of the lipid and protein molecules has been suggested. The apparent uncertainty is explained by the fact that very little is known about what structure is stained most intensely with osmium tetroxide—the proteins or the lipids.

Free Surface. The plasma membrane on the free surface of cells shows four types of differentiation—microvillus, brush border extension, stereocilium, and cilium.

Microvilli. The microvillus is essentially a short and thin projection of the cytoplasm which is covered by the plasma membrane. The microvillus does not contain any peculiar structures but a slightly dense ground substance. The free surface of most epithelial cells does display a varying number of microvilli with a great variation in length and thickness (Fig. 4). Supposedly, the microvilli have resorptive functions and certainly contribute to the increase of the cell surface.

Brush border extensions. The brush border extensions are longer than the microvilli, mostly thicker and occur in greater abundance. They all are of the same length and are found on the surface of the intestinal epithelial cells (Fig. 5) and on the proximal convoluted tubule cells of the nephron (cross reference: kidney ultrastructure). Similar structures (Fig. 8) are also seen in the efferent ducts of the testis (cross reference: ciliated epithelia ultrastructure). Although essentially representing extensions of the apical cell cytoplasm, the brush border extensions do contain some fine and dense striations oriented longitudinally, sometimes extending down into the apical cytoplasm below the level of their bases. Histochemical tests seem to prove that the enzyme alkaline phosphatase is associated with the brush border extensions.

Stereocilia. Stereocilia are longer and narrower than the brush border extensions, but the number of stereocilia on each cell is about identical with that of the brush border extensions. Each stereocilium contains three

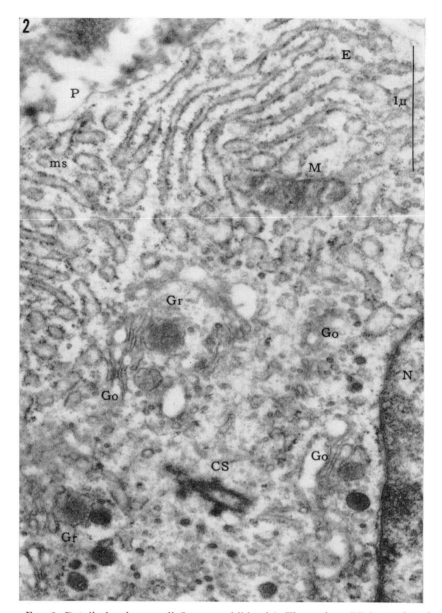

Fig. 2. Detail of a plasma cell (human epididymis). The nucleus (N) is enveloped by a triple-layered membrane. The Golgi Zone (Go) has both lamellar and vesicular components. In addition, dense large granules (Gr) are seen, each surrounded by a single membrane. In the center of the Golgi area is the centriole (CS) cut at an angle through its fibrillar components. Above the mitochondrion (M) is the ergastoplasm (granular endoplasmic reticulum) E, with its membrane bound flat cisternae and attached RNA granules. At ms the cisternae are more spherical. This shape is predominant after cell fractionation and centrifugation. These rounded structures then correspond to the microsome-fraction of the cell. The cell border is seen at P with some collagenous fibers in the interstitial space. Magnification 33,000×

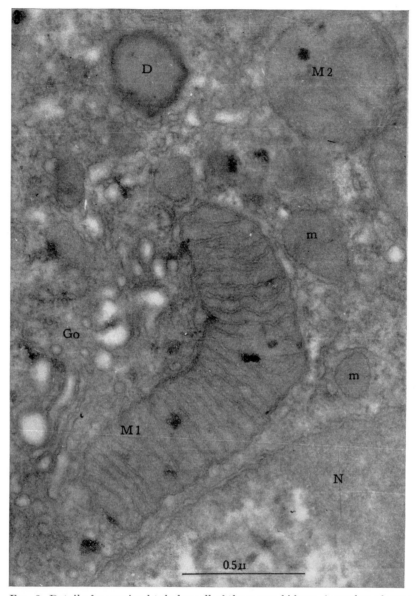

FIG. 3. Detail of a proximal tubular cell of the mouse kidney. A number of structures are seen which can be encountered in most mammalian cells. The nucleus (N) with its triple-layered envelop. Two mitochondria are present, one sectioned longitudinally (MI), the other cross cut (M2). In addition to several microbodies (m), Golgi membranes and vesicles (Go) a dense large body (D), may be seen. Magnification 67,000×

to five longitudinal fine filaments. In man, the stereocilia are found in the duct of the epididymis (Fig. 6). Their function is not clear because they do not have any contractibility. They seem to form an inter-

mediate stage between the ordinary brush border extensions and the cilia.

Cilia. The cilia are extremely long extensions of the apical cell cytoplasm. They are coarser than the stereocilia and display

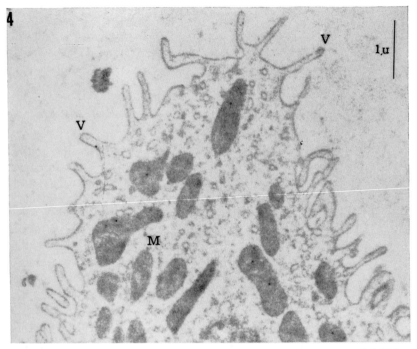

FIG. 4. Typical arrangement of microvilli (V) on the surface of an epithelial cell in the distal tubule of the mouse kidney. The microvilli are slender, short processes with seemingly poor rigidity, usually widely spaced. Mitochondria (M) are seen together with a few small vesicles in the apical cytoplasm. Magnification 15,000×

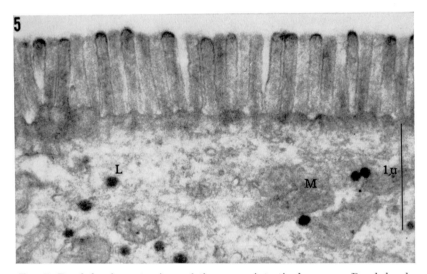

FIG. 5. Brush border extensions of the mouse intestinal mucosa. Brush borders are closely packed, rather rigid surface processes. They display a higher density than the microvilli. Some mitochondria (M) and several absorbed lipid droplets (L) are seen. Magnification 28,000×

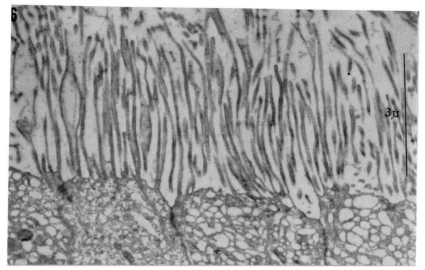

FIG. 6. Stereocilia on the surface of epithelial cells in the human ductus epididymis. The stereocilia are long and slender and lack basal bodies. They do not seem to have any mobility, but a few basal rootlets can be resolved. Magnification 10,800×

a peculiar inner structure of fine longitudinal filaments which are arranged in nine pairs peripherally and two single in the center (Fig. 7). The filaments are contractile and are all joined in the tip of the cilium and in the basal body below the cell surface (cross reference: ciliated epithelia ultrastructure).

Tubular invaginations. The free cell surface

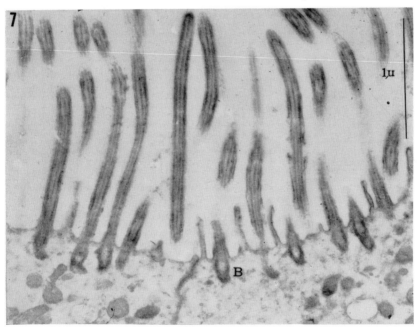

FIG. 7. Cilia on the surface of the cells of the rat trachea. Cilia are shorter and coarser than stereocilia and display distinct fine inner structures which terminate in the basal body (B). Magnification 31,500×

displays small tubular invaginations which penetrate about half a micron into the cell (Fig. 8). They are found mostly in cells with a high rate of fluid uptake. It has been assumed that they represent another means by which fluid and substances can be taken in by a cell without first penetrating the plasma membrane. Their activity has been compared with the uptake of water by an ameba (pinocytosis). The word "micropinocytosis" (or membrane flow) has been suggested, indicating that once the fluid or substance has been taken in by the microtubules, it can be entirely surrounded by the tubular membrane, forming a vesicle which can be transported elsewhere in the cell (cross reference: kidney ultrastructure, ciliated epithelia ultrastructure).

Cell Border. The plasma membrane which faces a neighboring cell is called cell border.

Lateral interdigitations. This portion of the plasma membrane frequently displays small lateral projections of the cell cytoplasm which penetrate into the cell in juxtaposition (Fig. 14). In some instances, the projections become quite numerous, as is the case between the cells of the ciliary epithelium of the eye or in the intestine. It was first believed that the lateral interdigitations helped in maintaining cell cohesion; however, it has been suggested recently that they rather are the result of a certain compression or expansion during different functional stages of the cells, much like what happens to the bellows of an accordion. The variation of volume does not occur in the cell itself to any large extent, but rather to the intercellular space, which is expanded by fluid from time to time. Cell cohesion is, on the other hand, definitely accomplished by two peculiar structures which are closely related to the cell border—the terminal bars and the desmosomes.

Terminal bars. The terminal bars are ring-like reinforcements of the cell border attached to the inner aspect of the plasma membrane close to the free surface of all epithelial cells (Fig. 8). In a sense, they are reminiscent of the coopering bands of a barrel, although located inside the barrel. The terminal bar of one cell is always located opposite a similar structure in a neighboring cell. Furthermore, the intervening space between the cells is filled with a denser structure and is smaller than usually recorded in other places, undoubtedly indicating the firmness by which the cells are attached.

Desmosomes. The desmosomes are in a section having almost the same appearance as the terminal bars. However, they represent only local points of attachment and are actually paired button-like structures with one "button" attached to the intracellular aspect of the plasma membrane of either cell (Fig. 8). In addition, the intercellular space between the two "buttons" is larger than in other places and is occupied by a substance of high density which frequently contains even denser structures of lamellated nature. The desmosomes are most abundant in the cells of the epidermis (Fig. 14) but are also found in other epithelial cells. Structures of identical appearance are also demonstrated in striated muscle and in the specific tissue of the heart (the impulse conducting system). Besides their adhesive function in these tissues, they probably also serve as points of less resistance across which the impulse of contraction can travel with much higher speed than elsewhere.

Basal Surface. The basal plasma membrane which faces the basement membrane is from time to time elaborately infolded.

Epithelial cells. This is particularly the case in the cells of the nephron, of the ciliary epithelium of the eye, and of the choroid plexus of the ventricles of the brain. The infoldings sometimes reach to the depth of half the cell and may also be seen interdigitating laterally with each other. Undoubtedly, they serve to increase the basal surface of the plasma membrane upon which enzymatic activity can more readily occur.

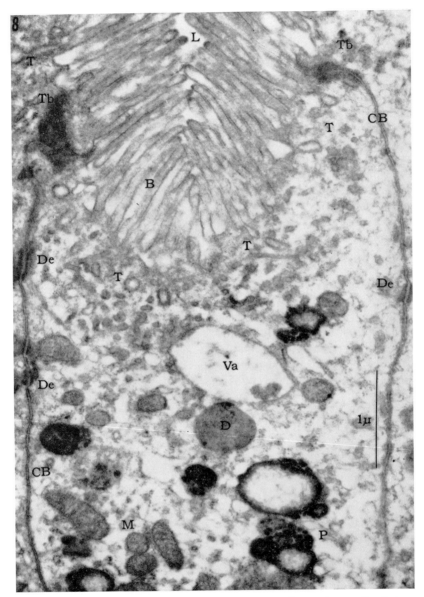

Fig. 8. Detail of epithelial cells of the human ductus efferens (connection between the testis and the epididymis). The surface of the cells is provided with brush border extensions (B) extending into the lumen (L) of the duct. Tubular invaginations (T) of the surface membrane descend into the upper part of the cells. The cell boundaries (CB) are held together by terminal bars (Tb) close to the surface, and by desmosomes (De) at lower levels. Except for mitochondria (M), these cells display large dense granules (D) as well as extremely osmiophilic bodies (P), some of which may represent pigments, others lipid granules. A large vacuole (Va) is seen in the center. Magnification 26,000×

Nerve cells. The extremely elongated cytoplasmic extension of a nerve cell is called the axon. The axon is covered by a number of Schwann cells along its course. It is the cytoplasm of the Schwann cell which wraps itself around the axon to form the myelin sheath. The axon and the myelin sheath together represent the nerve fiber. The main component of the myelin sheath is the plasma membrane of the Schwann cell which builds up the myelin sheath in a varying number of layers. It is, therefore, justifiable to consider the myelin sheath as being a specialized infolding of the plasma membrane of the Schwann cell.

Basement Membrane

The basement membrane forms the structure upon which most cells rest. It is a structureless layer with a thickness varying between 400 and 1000A (Fig. 13). According to histochemical tests, it does contain mucopolysaccharides but so far no peculiar ultrastructure has been detected in its homogeneous layer. The old conception of the basement membrane being a layer with a thickness of several microns in some tissues has been ruled out with the aid of the electron microscope. The thick basement membranes seen in the light microscope contain, in addition to the just described homogeneous layer, a number of fibrillar structures most of which are reticular fibers (Fig. 10) with some additional collagenous ones. It is not quite clear what kind of cell is responsible for the formation of the homogeneous basement membrane seen in the electron microscope. In some instances, it is surely laid down by fibroblasts and it should, therefore, be looked upon as being part of the connective tissue. However, sometimes no fibroblasts can be detected in adult tissue in connection with the basement membrane and it is, therefore, believed that other cells may have the ability of laying down this structure during their differentiation.

Cell Organelles

In the cell is recorded a number of organelles some of which are large and have a definite form—*mitochondria, microbodies, large granules,* and *pigments.* Other organelles have more flexible form—*Golgi apparatus, vesicles,* and *ergastoplasm* (rough surfaced endoplasmic reticulum). Within the homogeneous ground substance of the cytoplasm, as it was looked upon by means of light microscopy, structures have been detected with the electron microscope which are of rather small diameters, but which definitely should be listed among the cell organelles—*RNA-granules* and *glycogen granules.*

Mitochondria. The mitochondria are discrete bodies within the cell. They may vary in number, size, and shape, but their ultrastructure is remarkably unchanged from cell to cell and from tissue to tissue. In the light microscope, they can be selectively stained by Janus Green B, but even so, it is sometimes difficult to distinguish them from other granular structures in the cell. The mitochondria are surrounded by a double-contoured membrane, the thickness of which is in the neighborhood of 180 A. The matrix of each mitochondrion has a higher density than the surrounding cytoplasm. The matrix itself is homogeneous or slightly granulated. It is traversed by a varying number of double-contoured membranes (or cristae) which mostly are arranged parallel to each other. The inner mitochondrial membranes (or plates) with a thickness of roughly 150A are always connected with the mitochondrial capsule for some distance, but there is no open connection between the cytoplasm of the cell and the mitochondrial matrix (Fig. 3). Extremely electron-dense spherical bodies of different sizes are sometimes seen embedded in the mitochondrial matrix between the membranes. The mitochondria are the carriers of most cellular enzymes and one believes that the membranous structures of their interior represent either the enzymes proper or the surfaces upon which the enzymes and the metabolites interact.

Microbodies. The microbodies are spherical and usually smaller than the mitochondria. They are surrounded by a single membrane, about 50A thick. The matrix has the same appearance as that of the mitochondria but lacks the inner membranes of the latter (Fig. 3). They have been demonstrated so far only in kidney, liver, cortical adrenal cells, and in the delta cells of the endocrine portion of the pancreas. They may represent the precursors of mitochondria although this has not been convincingly proved. It is still a mystery how mitochondria develop. Some people believe they can arise *de novo* from the ground substance of the cytoplasm, where possibly the microbodies would constitute an intermediate stage. Others consider a splitting or budding of already existing mitochondria to be more likely, as is known to occur during cell mitosis.

Large Granules. The large granules encountered in cells of various tissues are usually very dense; this has led most investigators to believe that they contain lipids. They have, therefore, often been called cell lipid granules. However, the density varies from time to time and it is difficult to predict if this is due to a certain functional variation or if it mainly reflects a difference in structures. Most granules in cells represent a *secretory product* and as such will be dealt with below (Secretion). The remaining large granules are of two types —spherical granules and granules with irregular outlines. The *large spherical granules* are surrounded by a distinct single membrane and display a medium dense structureless matrix (Fig. 3). It is most likely that they represent end products of substances taken in by the cells by means of a micropinocytotic activity through the tubular

invaginations of the plasma membrane. By a certain metabolic process, the engulfed fluid, and therein dissolved substances, become concentrated and now appear as dense granules. This is surely the case with macrophages and has also been demonstrated in connection with uptake of proteins by the proximal convoluted cells of the nephron and of the intestinal cells. The granules with irregular outlines most likely represent *lipid granules* which the cell handles as part of its metabolism (Fig. 8). Structural evidence is at hand for a certain interaction between the lipid granules and the mitochondria, as for instance in liver cells. The intense blackening of lipid granules by osmium tetroxide indicates that these granules contain unsaturated sulfhydryl groups. Saturated fats do not take stain with osmic acid; this can be clearly demonstrated in fat cells where the fat globules are convincingly stained with Sudan III for light microscopy but in the electron microscope show up as unstained vacuoles with a bordering thin membrane.

Pigments. The pigments represent another type of spherical granule which can be encountered in a number of cells. Similar to lipid granules, they stain intensely with osmium tetroxide (Fig. 8). The pigments of the retina are surrounded by a single membrane. Their matrix is homogeneous. The pigments encountered in the cells of the epidermis (often called melanin granules) do not have a limiting membrane but unveil an abundance of small *pigment micelles* each of which has a diameter of about 75A. The pigments of the epidermis are supposedly formed within special cells, the melanocytes, and migrate into the basal cells of the epidermis.

Golgi Apparatus. The Golgi apparatus is located near the nucleus mostly surrounding its one pole like a halo. It consists of a system of paired membranes, small vesicles and granules. The membranes have a smooth surface and enclose clear spaces. The number and length of the membranes vary, presumably because of different functional stages of the Golgi apparatus. There are mostly several pairs of membranes arranged in parallel form with each other and one can occasionally see that the clear space which each pair of membranes encloses is distended to a vacuole of varying size (Fig. 3). The small vesicles are quite numerous and bordered by a smooth membrane. Frequently, the clear centers of the small vesicles become condensed, thus obtaining the appearance of small granules (Fig. 2). The diameter of the small vesicles and the granules ranges between 200A and 1000A. The appearance of the Golgi apparatus as a whole varies greatly from cell to cell and from tissue to tissue. It is best developed in secretory cells where its function presumably is involved in the secretory process. Evidently the secretion products are prefabricated elsewhere in the cell, but the end products appear as small secretory granules within the Golgi zone. Here they enlarge and migrate eventually to the upper part of the cell. In non-secretory cells, the Golgi apparatus presumably plays an important role in the metabolism of the cell, either by offering its membranes as surfaces for enzymatic activity or by being utilized as a system of channels for the intracellular flow of metabolites and fluid.

Small Vesicles. Vesicles of the same order of magnitude as those found within the Golgi zone may be traced elsewhere in the cell. Their origin is unknown but they could possibly be derived from the Golgi apparatus. In some instances, as in non-ciliated cells of the ciliated epithelia of the bronchi and bronchioles (cross reference: ciliated epithelia ultrastructure), in the distal convoluted tubule cells of the kidney, and in

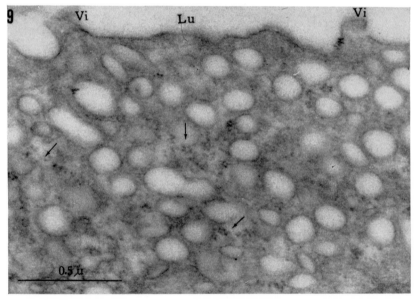

FIG. 9. Surface area of a dark, intercalated cell of the collecting tubule of the mouse kidney. The cytoplasm is pervaded by abundant microvesicles, one in connection with the surface (at 9). Tiny microvilli (Vi) extend into the tubular lumen (Lu). In between the vesicles, which all are bound by a smooth membrane, are abundant granules (arrows) with the size of about 150Å, probably corresponding to granules which in other cells have been demonstrated to contain RNA. Magnification 57,000×

the parietal cells of the gastric mucosa, they appear in great abundance in the luminal portion of the cell. They seem to migrate towards the cell surface and fuse with the surface plasma membrane (Fig. 9). It may be assumed that they participate in a certain secretory process, involving the transport of large amounts of fluid to the cell surface. Similar vesicles are a prominent feature of the capillary wall, where many such structures are found throughout the endothelial cytoplasm as well as in connection with both the surface and the basal plasma membrane (Fig. 10). The theory has been forwarded that they represent the structural evidence of fluid being transported across the capillary wall. In nerve endings and in connection with synapses, similar vesicles have been demonstrated to contain acetylcholine. The presence of synaptic vesicles has suggested that these might be involved in either the formation of the chemical mediator or in its transmission across the synapse.

Ergastoplasm (rough-surfaced endoplasmic reticulum). In the light microscope, areas with basophilic structures have been called ergastoplasm. The electron microscopical analysis of such areas reveals highly complicated systems of paired membranes, each membrane having a thickness of about 40A (Fig. 1). Each pair of membranes surrounds a light space called *cisterna*. It has been demonstrated in nerve cells that the cisternae of the Nissl body communicate with each other. The cytoplasmic aspect of each membrane is studded with numerous small granules with a thickness of 150A (Fig. 2). These granules have been separated from the membranes by cell fractionation and subsequent differential centrifugation. Enzymatic tests prove that they contain ribonucleic acids

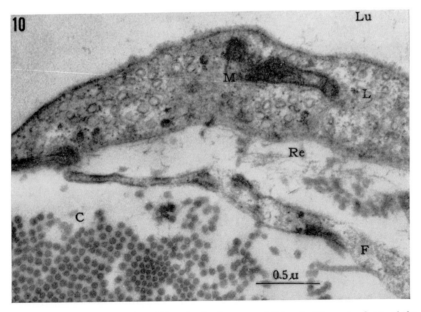

FIG. 10. Part of a lymph capillary in the human epididymis. The cytoplasm of the capillary endothelium (L) contains a large number of microvesicles. One mitochondrion (M) is seen. At the top is the capillary lumen (Lu) and at the bottom part of a fibroblast (F) as well as several cross sectioned collagen fibrils (C). The lymph capillaries lack the usual type of basement membrane. Instead, a network of fine fibrils (Re) probably of reticular nature, establish the immediate base upon which the endothelial cells rest. Magnification 34,500×

and the granules or particles have, therefore, been called RNA-particles. The number of membranes varies from tissue to tissue. In cells engaged in heavy protein synthesis, such as the exocrine cells of the pancreas, the ergastoplasm dominates the cell with its complicated pattern of membranes and cisternae throughout the entire cell except in the Golgi area. Evidently the membranes and cisternae produce the precursors of the zymogen granules which, at a later stage appear within the Golgi apparatus. In nerve cells, the Nissl bodies have the same ultrastructure, participating in the production of proteins needed within the cell itself. Again in other cells the ergastoplasm may be seen as scattered short pairs of membranes with the RNA-particles attached.

The terminology used in connection with the ergastoplasm is somewhat confusing. As mentioned, the term "ergastoplasm" refers to basophilic areas which can be seen in the light microscope. The term "endoplasmic reticulum," introduced by Porter and Kallman (1952), originally referred to a structure presumably vesicular or tubular which was observed in whole cells in tissue cultures. Extended studies demonstrated that the endoplasmic reticulum corresponds to the ergastoplasm. When later structures like infoldings of the plasma membrane, pinocytosis vesicles, and the membranes of the Golgi apparatus were sufficiently analyzed, it was found that some of these structures could be in direct continuity with the ergastoplasm. It was, therefore, suggested that all membranes within the cell, whether smooth or rough surfaced, may represent diverse differentiations of one single membranous system. Therefore, the ergastoplasm with its RNA-dotted membranes is usually referred to as the *rough-surfaced endoplasmic reticulum*, whereas the Golgi membranes, cytoplasmic vesicles and infolded or invaginated portions of the plasma membrane are called *smooth-surfaced endoplasmic reticulum*. For a more detailed dis-

cussion of this problem, consult Haguenau (1958) International Review of Cytology, VII. Another example of a purely smooth-surfaced endoplasmic reticulum is found in striated muscle cells, here called *sarcoplasmic reticulum*. It is an elaborate network of smooth tubules around the myofibrils with expansions of the system specifically localized in relation to the Z-band. It has been suggested that this system might function in the inward spread of the excitation impulse to contract.

Microsomes. When using differential centrifugation the membranes and cisternae of the ergastoplasm break up to form small spheres which can be isolated at a certain centrifugation speed. They then represent the microsome fraction (Fig. 2).

RNA-particles. In most cells, the cytoplasm displays an abundance of small granules or particles with a diameter of about 150A (Fig. 9). They appear single or in clusters of 3–5 and are freely dispersed throughout the cytoplasm. They are identical in size and shape to the particles which are attached to the membranes of the ergastoplasm. It has been clearly demonstrated that either type of granules contains ribonucleoproteins and is, therefore, called either RNA- or RNP-particles.

Glycogen Granules. Particles have been demonstrated in the cytoplasm of the striated muscle and in the heart muscle which have a diameter ranging between 150A and 300A. Thus, they are somewhat larger than the ribonucleoprotein particles with which they can easily be confused. The larger particles are more variable in their size and shape and have less sharply defined margins. Histochemical tests seem to prove that they contain glycogen and it is, therefore, likely that they represent a particulate form of glycogen. One has not been able to demonstrate similar granules in mammalian liver cells. The glycogen-rich areas of the liver cell cytoplasm usually show a diffuse, cotton-wool texture of low density when using solely osmium tetroxide as a tissue stain.

However, in applying an additional stain of heavy metal to the thin sections, as for instance phosphomolybdic acid, the large glycogen particles also become visible in liver cells.

Fibrillar Structures

Fibrillar structures can easily be resolved with the electron microscope. They may be located within the cell cytoplasm as is the case with *myofilaments, tonofilaments,* and the *neurofibrils,* or they are found at the outer surface of the cells or in the interstitial space, here recognized as *collagen, reticular fibers* and *elastin.*

Intracellular. *Striated muscle filaments.* The most evident myofilaments are found in the striated skeleton and heart muscle cell (Fig. 11). Here they occupy the main portion of the cell oriented longitudinally, and they represent the contractile elements of the muscle cell. The myofilaments extend along the whole length of a sarcomere which is the structural, repeated unit of the muscle fiber. The thickness of the individual myofilament varies within different areas of the myofibril, with its smallest diameter related to the area of the I-band and the H-band, and its largest diameter within the Z-band, S-band, and M-band. In a stretched muscle fiber, presumably corresponding to the relaxed position, the mean diameter of the myofilament is about 100A in the H-band, whereas the same value for the M-band is in the neighborhood of 150A. During muscle contraction, the diameter of the individual myofilament increases about three times as compared to its stretched diameter. It has been proposed that each myofilament in turn is composed of three subunits. Each subunit consists of rows of rodlets measuring 20A in length. The subunits are assumed to represent cables of supercoiled α-helices of protein molecules.

The main constituents of the myofilaments are the proteins actin and myosin. As yet, it

has not been convincingly proved what part of the myofilament represents the actin and what represents the myosin. It has been suggested that actin is represented by one set of filaments and myosin by another set. There is also a number of theories about how the contraction occurs from a structural point of view. Further extensive investigations are needed until a definite solution is arrived at regarding the striated muscle.

Smooth muscle filaments. In the smooth muscle cell, the contractile elements are not as easily demonstrated as in the striated one (Fig. 12). This is particularly true in the smooth muscle cells of the blood vessels. Although it is well known that these cells do contract, the cytoplasm is remarkably devoid of any fibrillar structures. However, in the smooth muscle cells of the small bronchi and bronchioles of the lung as well as in those of the intestinal wall, a longitudinal striation can more readily be seen. The diameter of the filaments here average 150A. The length of each filament is more difficult to determine and it seems that it does not extend for a length of more than half a micron. The difference in ultrastructure between the striated and the smooth muscle filaments seems to reflect the difference in their function, since it is well known that the smooth muscle cell has a much slower rate of contraction than the striated one.

Tonofilaments. In the cells of the epidermis an elaborate system of tonofibrils crisscrosses the cytoplasm. The tonofibrils are well distinguished in the light microscope. Their ultrastructure is characterized by an abundance of small tonofilaments, oriented longitudinally to the axis of the tonofibril (Fig. 13). Each tonofilament has a thickness of about 190A and an approximative length of 0.5 micron with seemingly tapered ends. The filaments have a light core and an electron dense wall, the latter with a diameter of about 70A. It has not as yet been possible to determine whether the tonofilaments are spindleshaped or slightly twisted around

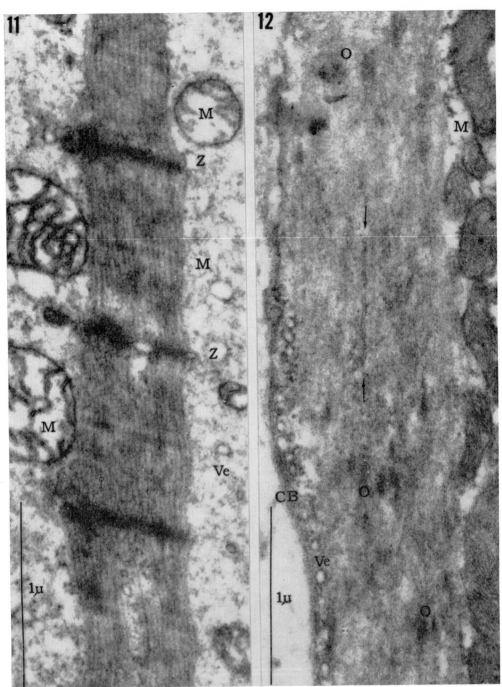

FIG. 11. Myofibril in the specific tissue (impulse conducting system) of the steer heart. The longitudinally arranged myofilaments are seen with their various thickenings related to particularly the Z and M bands. Mitochondria (M) and microvesicles (Ve) are abundant throughout the sarcoplasm. Magnification ×49,000

FIG. 12. Longitudinal section through the contractile region of the sarcoplasm of a smooth muscle cell of the mouse intestine. Fibrillar units may be distinquished (arrows) and a certain longitudinal arrangement is vaguely indicated. In the contractile region is always present a certain number of dense, ovoid structures (O), typical for the smooth muscle sarcoplasm. At the cell boundary (CB) are aggregations of microvesicles (Ve). The mitochondria (M) are clustered in the central portion of the cell. Magnification ×47,000

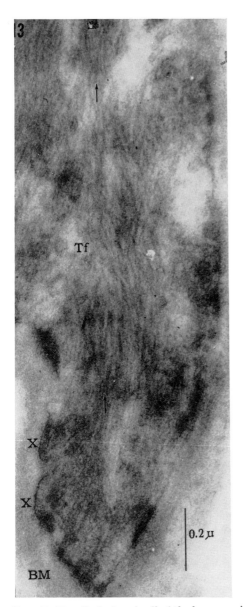

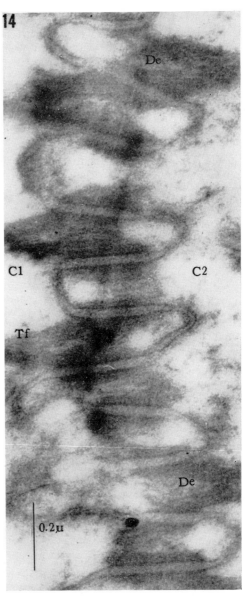

FIG. 13. Detail of a basal cell of the human epidermis. The cytoplasm is run through by abundant tonofilaments (Tf) most of which are sectioned longitudinally. They display a hollow structure (arrows) and originate from dense areas (X) of the plasma membrane which faces the basement membrane (BM). Magnification 83,000×

FIG. 14. Cell boundaries of two adjacent cells (C1 and C2) of the basal part of the human epidermis. The cells are highly interdigitated and the mutual attachment established through desmosomes (De) in association with which the intercellular space is wider than elsewhere. The tonofilaments (Tf) terminate (or originate) at the desmosomes. Magnification 90,000×

each other in the formation of the tonofibrils. The tonofibrils originate from and terminate at the desmosomes which are buttonlike structures associated with the plasma membrane (Fig. 14). Histochemical and biochemical tests prove that the main component of the tonofilaments is keratin, a tough noncontractile, in young tissue quite elastic, structure, which gives the cells of the epidermis a certain elasticity and firmness.

Neurofibrils. In the axoplasm of nerve cells still another fibrillar cytoplasmic structure can be found. The neurofibrils of classical histology represent aggregates of axon filaments large enough to be resolved in the light microscope. Deposition of heavy metals, as with the histological silver and gold technics, favors the detection of the very thin fibrous structures. In the early days of electron microscopy, these structures were mistaken for tubules, hence the first name to be coined was neurotubules. Presently, there seem to be two kinds of fibrils in the axoplasm—the protoneurofibrils and the neurofilaments. The *protoneurofibrils* appear as smooth threads with a thickness of about 60 to 80A. Their length ranges between 0.5 to 1 micron. They have an irregular course and are seen to branch and interconnect. The *neurofilaments* have a thickness of about 150A with indefinite length. They are sometimes of a double-edged appearance. Their surface is smooth and they do not seem to constitute any part of the endoplasmic reticulum. The function of either type of fibrillar structure is unknown.

Extracellular. *Collagen.* The main fine component of the connective tissue is the collagen fibers. The width of the collagen fiber is about one micron and its length is indefinite. Each fiber is in turn built up of numerous *collagen fibrils* which also may be seen single or in groups of two or more fibrils scattered in the interstitial tissue (Fig. 15). Within each group of collagen fibrils the fibrils are usually parallel with each other. The collagen fibril has a thickness which varies between 400 and 2400A depending on the age (Fig. 10); its length is indefinite. The fibril has an axial periodicity of light and dense bands with a length of each period of approximately 640A. In the light and dense segments can be seen several smaller bands of varying density and thickness. The length and number of bands varies from organ to organ and is probably dependent on the age and the function of the fibril. Each collagen fibril is in turn composed of small *protofibrils* or *tropocollagen units* with a diameter of 15A and a length of 2600A. The tropocollagen units are tied up in a staggered fashion to form the collagen fibril. The bands of the collagen fibril represent discontinuities in the staggered arrangement of the protofibrils and stand out in the electron micrograph because heavy metals have a greater affinity for this irregularity. The *formation of the immature collagen* seems to occur at the surface of the fibroblasts, the main cell type of all connective tissues. Small fibrils without periodicity appear at the surface of the fibroblast. These unit fibrils organize out of or polymerize from material present at the cell surface, and from here the fibrils, in many cases already in bundles, are shed into the intercellular space. The fibrils will first appear with an axial periodicity of 210A, but as they increase in size they also change into a 640A periodicity. The subsequent fibril growth apparently occurs by accretion of materials from the general environment of the intercellular spaces and not by fusion of smaller fibrils as believed earlier. Subsequent layers of collagenous material are deposited upon the core, represented by the tropocollagen unit fibril. The origin of the tropocollagen fibril is not settled, but considering the presence of abundant rough-surfaced endoplasmic reticulum in the cytoplasm of the fibroblast which presumably is involved in the protein synthesis, it seems justifiable to suggest the following mechanism as being the most likely regarding the role of the fibroblast in the formation of the collagen fibrils. From the cisternae of the rough-surfaced endoplasmic reticulum of the fibroblast the monomeric form of the tropocollagen unit fibril is discharged to the environment of the cell and is here quickly induced to polymerize by enzymes resident in templates at the cell surface or in the unit fibrils themselves.

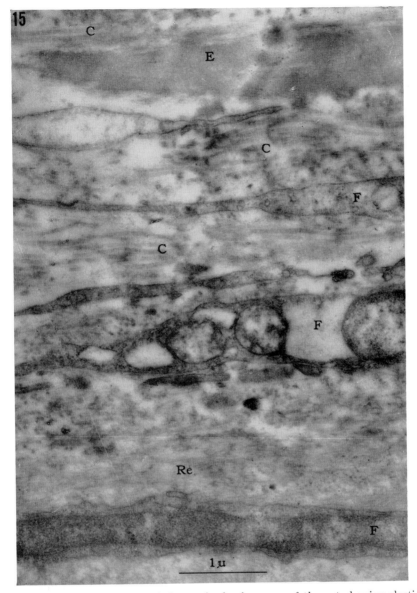

FIG. 15. Connective tissue of the tracheal submucosa of the rat showing elastic fibers (E), collagen fibrils (C), fibroblasts (F) and reticular fibrils (Re). Magnification 24,000×

Reticular fibers. In the light microscope fine fibers are found in loose connective tissue and in the interstitial substance of cartilage which can be electively impregnated with silver and they are, therefore, often called argyrophil fibers (Fig. 15). Their submicroscopic structure is like that of collagenous fibers. They have a thickness of about 200A and have the characteristic cross striations of collagen. In growing tissue it has been demonstrated that the bundles of fibers increase in thickness and finally lose the ability to be impregnated with silver. The reticular fibers found in the interstitial substance of cartilage do not always show the cross striations (Fig. 10), and it may, therefore, be assumed that not all reticular fibers can be transformed into collagenous ones.

Elastin. Elastic fibers are found in loose connective tissue (Fig. 15). They have a thickness of about one micron and seem to have an indefinite length. They are not fibrillar but have a homogeneous appearance in the light microscope. Elastic fibers at most show only a weak positive birefringence, but become strongly birefringent on stretching. This is caused by an orientation of the submicroscopic components in the direction of the fiber axis. These ultrastructural components are difficult to demonstrate in osmium-fixed specimens, but it has been possible to distinguish thin filaments with a thickness of about 70A at the periphery of the elastic fiber. Hence, it seems that the elastic fiber has two main components. The dominating structure is a non-fibrous dense cement substance, presumably an albuminoid which embeds the less apparent elastic filaments.

Crystals

There are only a few examples of where crystals may be found in normal mammalian tissues.

Intracellular. Intracellularly located are the so called crystalloids of the interstitial (Sertoli) cells of the human testis. These crystals are probably of protein nature. The crystals can be seen in the light microscope. They are usually elongated structures with rounded or pointed ends. Each crystalloid body is made up of numerous dense granules with a diameter of about 150A. They are spaced about 190A apart along two axes which are approximately at right angles to each other. This pattern is thought to represent the arrangement of macromolecules in the lattice of a protein crystal. The function of the crystals and the reason for their presence in the Sertoli cells of the testis is unknown. It has been suggested that these cells have an endocrine glandular function and, therefore, the crystals may be involved in the production of the hormone.

Extracellular. Extracellularly located crystals are encountered in the bone tissue where they make up the strong and resistant component of the skeletal system. The crystals have a width of about 35A. They are scattered in the extracellular matrix of the bone tissue but they are also lined up within the collagen fibrils with their long axes oriented parallel to the long axis of the collagen fibril. Selected-area electron-diffraction of these structures has revealed that they are crystals of apatite, more specifically hydroxyapatite $[Ca_{10}(PO_4)_6(OH)_2]$. Similar crystals appear under pathologic conditions in areas undergoing calcification like in aging cartilage, and they also form the main component of concretions precipitated throughout the urinary system (Fig. 16).

Secretion

As already mentioned, most of the large granules encountered in secretory cells are associated with secretory processes and have, therefore, been called *secretory granules*. Although formed within the cell and from the beginning being a part of the cytoplasm, they become discharged and perform their action outside the cell territory. There are two types of secretory cells, namely the *exocrine* and the *endocrine* cells.

Exocrine Secretion. The exocrine secretory granules appear within the Golgi zone, but are evidently preformed in association with the ergastoplasmic sacs (or the cisternae of the rough-surfaced endoplasmic reticulum). The first indication of secretory granules within the Golgi zone is a condensation of the Golgi vacuoles or a swelling of the Golgi vesicles and small granules.

Serous secretion. In secretory cells with a serous production, the individual secretory granules are usually surrounded by a single membrane and there is no indication of a coalescence of granules. The granules mi-

Fig. 16. Hydroxyapatite crystals, located in a concretion, experimentally produced in the tubular lumen of the proximal convolution of the rat kidney by injecting subcutaneously large doses of parathyroid hormone. (From Engfeldt, *et al.*, 1958). Magnification 165,000×

grate toward the luminal part of the cell where, in some instances, it can be seen that the limiting membrane of the granule fuses with the surface plasma membrane and the granule empties its content into the lumen.

Mucous secretion. In secretory cells with a production of mucin, the secretory granules are not bound by a membrane. Frequently, fusion of several mucous granules occurs, and the discharge of mucin does not occur

111

until the whole luminal part of the cell (the goblet) is filled by a multitude of mucous granules which at all times are discharged into the lumen. It is believed that either type of exocrine cell has the ability to regenerate new secretory granules. According to earlier theories, the cell would disintegrate after the secretory cycle is completed.

Endocrine Secretion. The endocrine granules are usually smaller than their exocrine relatives. They are also more electron-dense and are mostly surrounded by a single membrane. Few high resolution studies have so far been performed on endocrine glands, but judging from the data available, the formation of the endocrine granules is similar to what is known about the exocrine. A varying amount of rough-surfaced endoplasmic reticulum (ergastoplasm) as well as an abundance of RNA-particles seem to contribute the necessary prerequisites for the production of the early stages of endocrine granules. In the beta-cells of the endocrine portion of the pancreas, it has been quite convincingly demonstrated that the granules first appear in the Golgi zone. The matter of bringing these products in contact with the capillaries of the gland is still not fully explained but evidence is at hand for a migration of the endocrine granules toward that part of the cell which faces the capillary. In some instances, it has also been possible to demonstrate that the membrane of the granule fuses with the plasma membrane, thus giving the dense granule the opportunity to be discharged into the small extracellular space existing between the plasma membrane and the basement membrane which surrounds the endocrine cells. From here, the content of the granule may quite easily diffuse into the interstitial space and from there into the capillary. Further studies are, however, needed to prove that this occurs in relation to all endocrine organs.

Ground Substance of the Cytoplasm

In light microscopy, the term "ground substance" referred to that part of the cytoplasm which was not organized as mitochondria, Golgi apparatus, specialized cell inclusions like zymogen granules, pigments, or structures such as myofibrils. With the introduction of the ultrastructural era, it was demonstrated that the ground substance does contain particular well-defined structures like cytoplasmic membranes of various kinds, vesicles, RNA-particles, osmiophilic large granules, and various fibrillar structures. These ultrastructures may, of course, still be regarded as being part of the "ground substance" of the cytoplasm. However, it may also be justifiable today to call that which is as yet not defined as discrete structural entities as representing the ground substance awaiting new techniques to be developed before this portion of the cytoplasm can be described. In most electron micrographs, a certain homogeneous background characterized by a certain electron density can always be recorded. This "background" represents the ground substance in our present concept of the cytoplasm. It is conceivable that this background contains a great variety of salts and ions as well as carbohydrates, proteins and fats which available staining techniques and resolving power of the electron microscope fail to bring out. Until these are further developed, let us consider the homogeneous background of our electron micrographs as being the true ground substance. In doing so, we may create the necessary challenge to explore the unknown structural world of the atoms of the cytoplasm.

REFERENCES

General Reviews

SELBY, C. C., "Microscopy. II. Electron microscopy: a review," *Cancer Research*, **13**, 753 (1953).

SJÖSTRAND, F. S., "Electron microscopy of cells and tissues," in *"Physical Techniques in Biological Research,"* **3**, 241 (1956). Eds. G. Oster and A. W. Pollister, Academic Press, Inc., New York.

SJÖSTRAND, F. S., "The ultrastructure of cells as revealed by the electron microscope", *Int. Rev. Cytol.*, **5**, 455 (1956).

OBERLING, C., "The structure of the cytoplasm," *Int. Rev. Cytol.*, **8**, 1 (1959).

MILLER, F., "Orthologie und Pathologie der Zelle im elektronenmikroskopischen Bild," "Vehr. Deutsch. Ges. Pathologie," p. 261. Gustaf Fischer Verlag, Stuttgart, 1959.

SELBY, C. C., "Electron microscopy: techniques and applications in cytology," *in* "Analytical Cytology," p. 273, Ed. R. C. Mellors, Mc-Graw-Hill Book Company, Inc., New York, 1959.

"The cell," Vol. 2: Cell Constituents, Eds. J. Brachet and A. E. Mirsky, Academic Press, Inc., New York and London, 1960.

Basement Membrane

WEISS, P. AND FERRIS, W., "The basement lamella of amphibian skin", *J. Biophys. Biochem. Cytol.*, **2**, 275 (1956) Suppl.

VAN BREEMEN, V. L., REGER, J. F., AND COOPER, W. G., "Observations on the basement membranes in rat kidney," *J. Biophys. Biochem. Cytol.*, **2**, 283 (1956) Suppl.

Centriole

YAMADA, E., "The fine structure of centriole in some animal cells", Proc. 1st. Reg. Conf. in Asia and Oceanic, p. 247, Tokyo, 1956.

BERNHARD, W. AND DE HARVEN, E., "Sur la présence dans certaines cellules de Mammiféres d'un organite de nature probablement centriolaire", *C. r. Acad. Sci. Paris*, **242**, 288 (1956).

DE HARVEN, E. AND BERNHARD, W., "Etude au microscope électronique de l'ultrastructure du centriole chez les vertébrés" *Z. Zellf.*, **45**, 378 (1956).

Cell Surface

FAWCETT, D. W., "Structural specializations of the cell surface," *in* "Frontiers in Cytology," p. 19, Ed. S. L. Palay, Yale University Press, New Haven, 1958.

RHODIN, J. AND DALHAMN, T., "Electron microscopy of the tracheal ciliated mucosa in rat," *Z. Zellf.*, **44**, 345 (1956).

RHODIN, J., "Anatomy of kidney tubules" *Int. Rev. Cytol.*, **7**, 485 (1958).

WEISS, P., "Cell contact," *Int. Rev. Cytol.*, **7**, 391 (1958).

Cilia

FAWCETT, D. W. AND PORTER, K. R., "A study of the fine structure of ciliated epithelia," *J. Morph.*, **94**, 221 (1954).

RHODIN, J. AND DALHAMN, T., "Electron micros-copy of the tracheal ciliated mucosa in rat," *Z. Zellf.*, **44**, 345 (1956).

RHODIN, J., "Ciliated epithelia", *Int. Rev. Cytol.*, **10** (1962).

Collagen

GROSS, J., "The behavior of collagen units as a model in morphogenesis," *J. Biophys. Biochem. Cytol.*, **2**, 261 (1956) Suppl.

Crystals (extracellular)

ROBINSON, R. A. AND WATSON, M. L., "Crystal-collagen relationships in bone as observed in the electron microscope," *Ann. N. Y. Acad. Sci.*, **60**, 596 (1955).

KNESE, K.-H. AND KNOOP, A.-M., "Elektronenoptische Untersuchungen über die periostale Osteogenese," *Z. Zellf.*, **48**, 455 (1958).

GLIMCHER, M. J., "Molecular biology of mineralized tissues with particular reference to bone," *Rev. Modern Physics*, **31**, 359 (1959).

Crystals (intracellular)

FAWCETT, D. W. AND BURGOS, M. H.,"Observations on the cytomorphosis of the germinal and interstitial cells of the human testis," *in* Vol. 2, "Ageing in Transient Tissues, Ciba Foundation Colloquia on Ageing," p. 86, Eds. G. E. W. Wolstenholme and E. C. P. Millar, J. & A. Churchill, Ltd., London, 1956.

Elastin

HALL, D. A., "The fibrous components of connective tissue with special reference to the elastic fiber," *Int. Rev. Cytol.*, **8**, 212 (1959).

Endocrine Secretion

FERREIRA, D., "L'ultrastructure des cellules du pancréas endocrine chez l'embryon et le rat nouveau-né," *J. Ultrastructure Research*, **1**, 14 (1957).

MUNGER, B. L., "A light and electron microscopic study of cellular differentiation in the pancreatic islets of the mouse," *Am. J. Anat.*, **103**, 275 (1958).

LACY, P. E., "Electron microscopic and fluorescent antibody studies on islets of Langerhans," *Exp. Cell Research*, **7**, 296 (1959) Suppl.

EKHOLM, R. AND SJÖSTRAND, F. S., "The ultrastructural organization of the mouse thyroid gland," *J. Ultrastructure Research*, **1**, 178 (1957).

HERMAN, L., "An electron microscope study of the salamander thyroid during normal stimulation," *J. Biophys. Biochem. Cytol.*, **7**, 143 (1960).

Endoplasmic Reticulum

PALADE, G. E., "The endoplasmic reticulum" *J. Biophys. Biochem. Cytol.*, **2**, 85 (1956) Suppl.

HAGUENAU, F., "The ergastoplasm: its history, ultrastructure, and biochemistry," *Int. Rev. Cytol.*, **7**, 425 (1958).

Exocrine Secretion

SJÖSTRAND, F. S. AND HANZON, V., "Membrane structures of cytoplasm and mitochondria in exocrine cells of mouse pancreas as revealed by high resolution electron microscopy," *Exp. Cell Research*, **7**, 393 (1954).

RHODIN, J. AND DALHAMN, T., "Electron microscopy of the tracheal ciliated mucosa in rat," *Z. Zellf.*, **44**, 345 (1956).

PALAY, S. L., "The morphology of secretion," *in* "Frontiers in Cytology," p. 305, Ed. S. L. Palay, Yale University Press, New Haven, 1958.

EKHOLM, R. AND EDLUND, Y., "Ultrastructure of the human exocrine pancreas, *J. Ultrastructure Research*, **2**, 453 (1959).

Glycogen

BERNHARD, W. AND ROUILLER, C., "Close topographical relationship between mitochondria and ergastoplasm of liver cells in a definite phase of cellular activity," *J. Biophys. Biochem. Cytol.*, **2**, 73 (1956), Suppl.

FAWCETT, D. W. AND SELBY, C. C., "Observations on the fine structure of the turtle atrium," *J. Biophys. Biochem. Cytol.*, **4**, 63 (1958).

WATSON, M. L., "Staining of tissue sections for electron microscopy with heavy metals," *J. Biophys. Biochem. Cytol.*, **4**, 475 (1958).

Golgi Apparatus

DALTON, A. J., "A study of the Golgi material of hepatic and intestinal epithelial cells with the electron microscope, *Z. Zellf.*, **36**, 522 (1952).

SJÖSTRAND, F. S. AND HANZON, V., "Ultrastructure of Golgi apparatus of exocrine cells of mouse pancreas," *Exp. Cell Research*, **7**, 415 (1954).

GATENBY, J. BRONTË, "The Golgi apparatus," *R. Micr. Soc.*, **74**, 134 (1955).

HAGUENAU, F. AND BERNHARD, W., "L'appareil de Golgi dans les cellules normales et cancéreuses de vertébrés," *Arch. d'anatomie micr. et morph. exp.*, **44**, 27 (1955).

DALTON, A. J. AND FELIX, M., "A comparative study of the Golgi complex," *J. Biophys. Biochem. Cytol.*, **2**, 79 (1956) Suppl.

Large Granules

RHODIN, J. AND DALHAMN, T., "Electron microscopy of the tracheal ciliated mucosa in rat," *Z. Zellf.*, **44**, 345 (1956).

NILSSON, O., "Ultrastructure of mouse uterine surface epithelium under different estrogenic influences," *J. Ultrastructure Research*, **1**, 375 (1958).

ZELANDER, T., "Ultrastructure of mouse adrenal cortex," *J. Ultrastructure Research*, **2**, (1959) Suppl.

LADMAN, A. J. AND YOUNG, W. C., "An electron microscopic study of the ductuli efferentes and rete testis of the guinea pig," *J. Biophys. Biochem. Cytol.*, **4**, 219 (1958).

Microbodies

RHODIN, J.,"Correlation of ultrastructural organization and function in normal and experimentally changed proximal convoluted tubule cells of the mouse kidney," Thesis, Karolinska Institutet, Stockholm, 1954.

ROUILLER, C. AND BERNHARD, W., "Microbodies and the problem of mitochondrial regeneration in liver cells," *J. Biophys. Biochem. Cytol.*, **2**, 355 (1956) Suppl.

ENGFELDT, B., GARDELL, S., HELLSTRÖM, J., IVEMARK, B., RHODIN, J. AND STRAND, J. "Effect of experimental hyperparathyroidism on renal function and structure," *Acta Endocrinologica*, **29**, 15 (1958).

Microsomes

PALADE, G. E. AND SIEKEVITZ, P., "Pancreatic microsomes," *J. Biophys. Biochem. Cytol.*, **2**, 671 (1956).

SIEKEVITZ, P. AND PALADE, G. E., "A cytochemical study of the pancreas of the guinea pig," *J. Biophys. Biochem. Cytol.*, **4**, 309 (1958).

Mitochondria

PALADE, G. E., "The fine structure of mitochondria," *Anat. Rec.*, **114**, 427 (1952).

SJÖSTRAND, F. S., "Electron microscopy of mitochondria and cytoplasmic double membranes," *Nature*, **171**, 30 (1953).

STEFFEN, K., "Chondriosomen und Mikrosomen (Sphärosomen)," "Encyclopedia of Plant Physiology," p. 574, Ed. W. Ruhland, Springer-Verlag, Berlin, 1955.

SIEKEVITZ, P. AND WATSON, M., "Cytochemical studies of mitochondria," *J. Biophys. Biochem. Cytol.*, **2**, 639 (1956).

PALADE, G. E., "Electron microscopy of mitochondria and other cytoplasmic structures," *in* "Enzymes: Units of Biological Structure and Function," p. 185, Ed. O. H. Gabler, Academic Press, Inc., New York, 1956.

Nerve Cells

PALAY, S. L. AND PALADE, G. E., "The fine structure of neurons," *J. Biophys. Biochem. Cytol.*, **1**, 69 (1955).

FERNANDEZ-MORAN, H. AND BROWN, R., "The submicroscopic organization and function of nerve cells," *Exp. Cell Research*, **5**, (1958) Suppl.

Neurofibrils

ESTABLE, C., ACOSTA-FERREIRA, W., AND SOTELO, J. R., "An electron microscope study of the regenerating nerve fibers," *Z. Zellf.*, **46**, 387 (1957).

SCHMITT, F. O., "Molecular organization of the nerve fiber," *Rev. Modern Physics*, **31**, 455 (1959).

Nucleus

AFZELIUS, B. A., "The ultrastructure of the nuclear membrane of the sea urchin oocyte as studied with the electron microscope," *Exp. Cell Research*, **8**, 147 (1955).

WATSON, M. L., "The nuclear envelope. Its structure and relation to cytoplasmic membranes," *J. Biophys. Biochem. Cytol.*, **1**, 257 (1955).

HAGUENAU, F. AND BERNHARD, W., "Particularités structurales de la membrane nucléaire," *Bulletin du Cancer*, **42**, 537 (1955).

WATSON, M. L., "Further observations on the nuclear envelope of the animal cell," *J. Biophys. Biochem. Cytol.*, **6**, 147 (1959).

Nucleolus

BERNHARD, W., BAUER, A., GROPP, A., HAGUENAU, F., AND OBERLING, C., "L'ultrastructure du nucléole de cellules normales et cancéreuses," *Exp. Cell Research*, **9**, 88 (1955).

Pigments

FALK, S. AND RHODIN, J., "Mechanism of pigment migration," "Proc. Stockholm Conference on electron microscopy," p. 213, 1956, Eds., F. S. Sjöstrand and J. Rhodin, Almquist and Wiksell, Stockholm, 1957.

WELLINGS, S. R. AND SIEGEL, B. V., "Role of Golgi apparatus in the formation of melanin granules in human malignant melanoma," *J. Ultrastructure Research*, **3**, 147 (1959).

WELLINGS, S. R. AND SIEGEL, B. V., "Electron microscopy of human malignant melanoma," *J. Nat. Cancer Inst.*, **24**, 437 (1960).

CHARLES, A. AND INGRAM, J. T., "Electron microscope observations of the melanocyte of the human epidermis," *J. Biophys. Biochem. Cytol.*, **6**, 41 (1959).

Plasma Membrane

ROBERTSON, J. D., "The molecular biology of cell membranes," *in* "Molecular Biology," p. 87, Ed. D. Nachmansohn, Academic Press, Inc., New York and London, 1960.

Reticular Fibers

JACKSON, S. F., "The morphogenesis of avian tendon," *Proc. Royal Soc.*, B, **144**, 556 (1956).

WASSERMANN, F. AND KUBOTA, L., "Observations on fibrillogenesis on the connective tissue of the chick embryo with the aid of silver impregnation," *J. Biophys. Biochem. Cytol.*, **2**, 67 (1956).

PORTER, K. R. AND PAPPAS, G. D., "Collagen formation by fibroblasts of the chick embryo dermis," *J. Biophys. Biochem. Cytol.*, **5**, 153 (1959).

ZELANDER, T., "Ultrastructure of articular cartilage," *Z. Zellf.*, **49**, 720 (1959).

RNA-Particles

PALADE, G. E., "A small particulate component of the cytoplasm," *J. Biophys. Biochem. Cytol.*, **1**, 59 (1955).

PALADE, G. E., "Microsomes and ribonucleoprotein particles," *in* "Microsomal Particles and Protein Synthesis," p. 36, Ed. R. B. Roberts, Pergamon Press, New York, 1958.

Small Vesicles

RHODIN, J. "Anatomy of kidney tubules," *Int. Rev. Cytol.*, **7**, 485 (1958).

HALLY, A. D., "The fine structure of the gastric parietal cell in the mouse," *J. Anat.*, **93**, 217 (1959).

DE ROBERTIS, E., "Submicroscopic morphology of the synapse," *Int. Rev. Cytol.*, **8**, 61 (1959).

FAWCETT, D. W., "The fine structure of capillaries, arterioles and small arteries," *in* "The Microcirculation," p. 1, Eds. S. R. M. Reynolds and B. W. Zweifach, The University of Illinois Press, Urbana, 1959.

VIAL, J. D. AND ORREGO, H., "Electron microscope observations on the fine structure of parietal cells," *J. Biophys. Biochem. Cytol.*, **7**, 367 (1960).

Smooth Muscle

CAESAR, R., EDWARDS, G. A., AND RUSKA, H., "Architecture and nerve supply of mammalian smooth muscle tissue," *J. Biophys. Biochem. Cytol.*, **3**, 867 (1957).

THAEMERT, J. C., "Intercellular bridges as proto-

115

plasmic anastomoses between smooth muscle cells," *J. Biophys. Biochem. Cytol.*, **6**, 67 (1959).

Stereocilia

RHODIN, J., "Ciliated epithelia," *Int. Rev. Cytol.*, **10** (1962).

Striated Muscle

HODGE, A. J., "Fibrous proteins of muscle," *Rev. Modern Physics*, **31**, 409 (1959).
"Structure and function of muscle," Vol. 1, Structure, Ed. G. H. Bourne, Academic Press, Inc., New York, 1960.

Tonofilaments

SELBY, C. C., "An electron microscope study of the epidermis of mammalian skin in thin sections," *J. Biophys. Biochem. Cytol.*, **1**, 429 (1955).
ODLAND, G. F., "The fine structure of the interrelationship of cells in the human epidermis," *J. Biophys. Biochem. Cytol.*, **4**, 529 (1958).
SETÄLÄ, K., MERENMIES, L., STJERNVALL, L., AND NYHOLM, M., "Mechanism of experimental tumorigenesis. IV. Ultrastructure of interfollicular epidermis of normal adult mouse," *J. Nat. Cancer Inst.*, **24**, 329 (1960).

JOHANNES A. G. RHODIN

CILIATED EPITHELIA ULTRASTRUCTURE

Ciliated epithelia are so called because many of the cells which form the epithelial layer are provided with a great number of small motile structures on their surface—the cilia. The ciliated epithelia are found in connection with organs and tissues where a surface has to be kept clean and moist, as in the respiratory tract (nose, trachea, bronchi), or in small ducts where a certain propulsion of the content of the duct is facilitated and aided by the beating of the cilia as in the male reproductive tract (efferent ducts of testis) and in the female reproductive tract (oviduct).

Function

The ciliated epithelium in mammals is characterized by several cell types (Fig. 8) the most prominent of which is the *ciliated cell*. The other cells have been classified as *non-ciliated cells* which comprise *secretory cells* of two types (*serous* and *mucous* or goblet cells), the *brush cells* and the *basal cells*. The functions of the different cells depend on the location of each cell. The *goblet cell* is predominant in all ciliated epithelia and keeps the surface moist by discharging continuously a more or less viscous mucin. The secretion product of the *serous cells* either dilutes the mucin and/or adds enzymes (activators) to the content of the ducts. The *brush cells*, presumably young cells which have migrated from the basal portions of the epithelium, are primarily the precursors of the ciliated cells. They may probably also be transformed into mucous cells as well as serous cells. The appearance of the brush cells of the efferent ducts of the testis indicates that their function here is mainly a secretory one. However, certain structural features speak for the fact that they also have absorptive functions. The *ciliated cells* with their abundant surface extensions, the cilia, participate in keeping the mucus blanket moving. The ciliary beat is rather complicated. It is composed of a rapid forward stroke and a slow backward stroke. The cilium is rigid and erected during the forward stroke, whereas it folds itself beneath the mucus in a limb and yielding movement during the backward stroke. The activity of the cilia is synchronized in local areas and movements of the cilia over larger areas have been compared with the appearance of a rye field when the wind blows across it. The *basal cells* are presumably the precursors of all the cells of the ciliated epithelia. The mitotic activity among these cells is high and they migrate to the upper portions of the epithelial layer in order to replace ciliated or serous cells when they are sloughed off and lost in the moving mucus blanket.

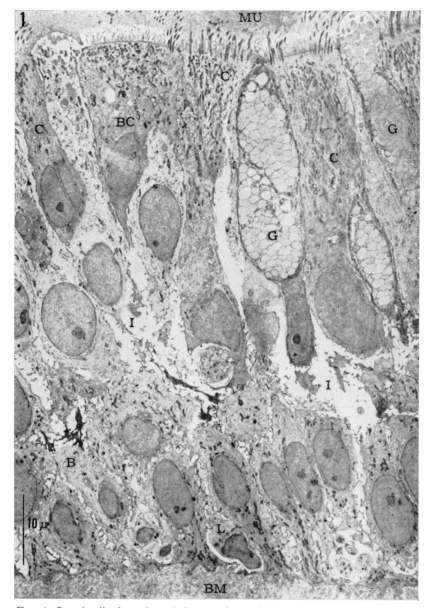

FIG. 1. Longitudinal section of the pseudostratified columnar epithelium of the human trachea composed of ciliated cells (C), mucous cells (G), brush cells (BC), and basal cells (B). At the top is the tracheal lumen with the mucous blanket (MU); at the bottom, the basement membrane (BM) with its abundant reticular and collagenous fibrils. Only the basal cells rest on the basement membrane. Intercellular spaces (I) are evident, and a wandering cell, presumably a lymphocyte (L), is located in the space between the basal cells. Magnification 1,800×

Structure

Goblet cell. The goblet cell cytoplasm is characterized by a high content of ribonucleic acid (RNA) particles, some of which are attached to the membranes of the rough-surfaced endoplasmic reticulum (ergastoplasm). Precursors of the mucin are evidently formed within the cisternae which are

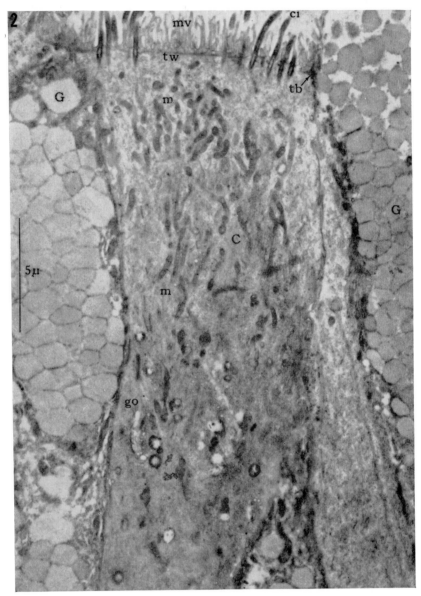

Fig. 2. Detail of Fig. 1 showing two mucous cells (G) and one ciliated cell (C). The mitochondria (m) are abundant in the upper part of the ciliated cell in which the Golgi apparatus (go) is also seen. The cilia (cl) emerge from basal bodies at the top of the cell into the tracheal lumen together with a number of microvilli (mv) beneath which a dense structure, the terminal web (tw), is resolved. The cells are attracted by the terminal bar (tb). The mucous cells (G) are filled with mucin granules which are about to be discharged at the cell surface. Magnification 6,000×

bound by these membranes. The mucous granules appear, however, within the smooth membranes of the Golgi apparatus where a heavy accumulation of various sized mucous granules can be identified previous to the state when the upper part of the mucous cell is transformed into a goblet filled by numerous large mucous granules. A certain fusion of mucous granules occurs intracellularly before they are discharged at the surface of

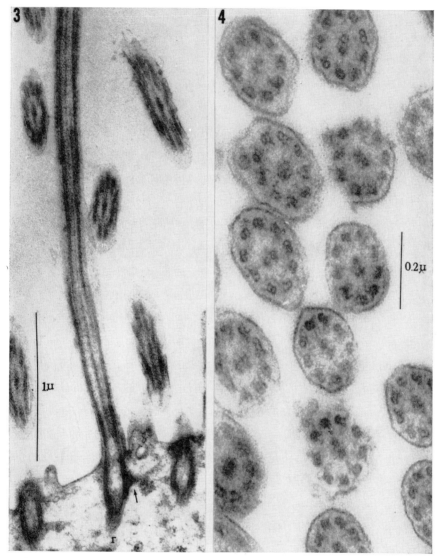

FIG. 3. Each cilium emerges into the lumen from a basal body. Rootlets (r) and a lateral fibrillar projection (arrow) secure the ciliary filaments in the luminal part of the cell cytoplasm. The lateral ciliary filaments are continuous from the ciliary body to the tip of the cilium. The central filaments cannot be demonstrated within the basal body. Magnification 39,000×

FIG. 4. Cross sectioned cilia display a ring of nine paired peripheral filaments and two central single filaments. The plasma membrane which shows up as a single dense line is well preserved in all but two cilia. Magnification 100,000×

the epithelium. The nucleus of the goblet cell is pushed to the base of the cell because of the heavy accumulation of mucous granules. After the discharge of the mucin, the cell resumes its resting columnar shape and a new production cycle of mucin starts again (Figs. 1, 2).

Serous cell. The structure of the serous cells is quite variable, depending on what organ the cells are located in. In the *trachea* only few serous cells have been recognized, but in the fine *bronchi* and in the *bronchioles* they become quite abundant. Their cytoplasm has an abundance of RNA-particles, presumably related to the ability of the cells to secrete enzymes. In addition, a large number of cytoplasmic vesicles indicate that the cells are turning out fluid or substances dissolved and transported within the membrane-bound vesicles. It is believed that these cells play an important role in the mechanism involved in pulmonary edema. In the *oviduct* of some mammals (man not included), the serous cells display a large

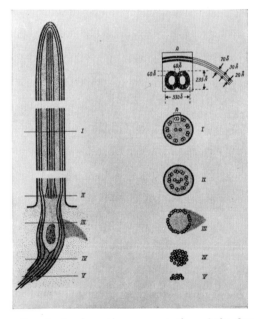

Fig. 5. A schematic representation of the fine structure of the mammalian cilium. (After Rhodin and Dalhamn, 1956).

number of secretion granules. They appear first within the Golgi zone and migrate from here to the cell surface where they are discharged without previous fusion with one another. The granules seem to have some nutritional or enzymatic relation with the ovum when it passes along the oviduct to the uterus. The surface of the serous cells is characterized by a number of microvilli, the size of which is smaller than either the cilia of neighboring cells or the brush border extensions seen on the cells of the intestine or the proximal convolution of the nephron in the kidney. The nucleus is located in the center of the cell and is not dislocated during the secretory cycle, the latter being structurally less obvious than what is noticed in the mucous cells.

Basal cell. The basal cells are always located near the basement membrane upon which most of the cells of the ciliated epithelia rest. The basal cell is round or slightly elongated and does not reach the surface of the epithelium. Its cytoplasm contains small fibrils of unknown function. Eventually, the cell migrates to the upper part of the epithelium where it gains contact with the surface and starts to differentiate into a cell type which is ready to replace any of the two kinds of cells that dominates the epithelium, the ciliated and the mucous cell (Fig. 6).

Brush cell. It is probable that the brush cell represents a basal cell which has recently moved to the surface and started to differentiate into a ciliated cell. This is quite obvious in the *trachea*, where several features of the brush cell are identical with the basal cell. The surface of the brush cell is covered with a large number of brush border-like extensions. In man, a dense plate is found at a distance of about half a micron beneath the surface of the brush cell, presumably the site of differentiation of the ciliary basal bodies. Another typical feature of the brush cell is the clustering of small mitochondria beneath this plate in the brush cell of the

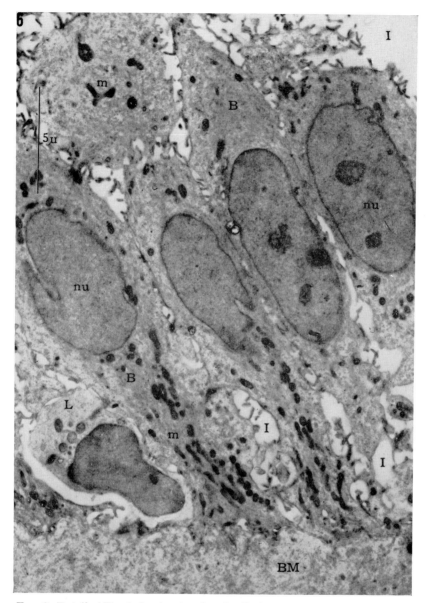

FIG. 6. Detail of Fig. 1 showing four basal cells (B). The nuclei (nu) are large and prominent features of these cells with several darker bodies, the nucleoli, the latter a possible indication of mitotic activity. The mitochondria (m) are mostly aggregated beneath the nucleus. The basal cells rest on the basement membrane (BM). The intercellular spaces (I) are sometimes the site of lymphocytes (L). Magnification 5,600×

human trachea. In the *efferent ducts* of the human testis, the brush cells display an elaborate rough-surfaced endoplasmic reticulum, a multitude of freely dispersed RNA-particles, and a large Golgi zone, indicating that they are obviously secretory cells. The surface structures are predominantly of brush border type, but resemble more those found in the kidney than those of the intestine. Moreover, a highly de-

121

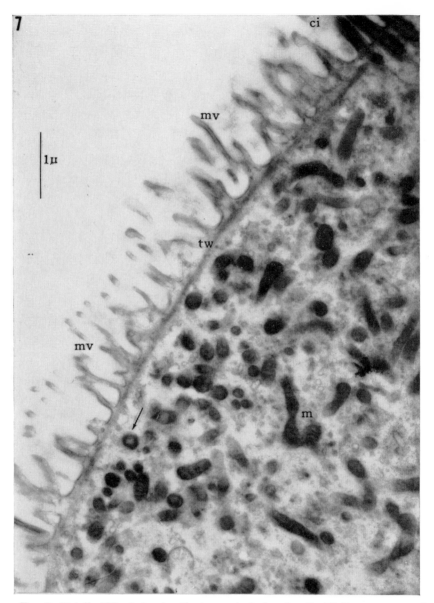

F_{IG}. 7. Detail of Fig. 1 showing the top part of a brush cell with its numerous and slender microvilli (mv). Three cilia (ci) are seen, possibly indicating that the brush cell is being transformed into a ciliated cell. Mitochondria (m) are more abundant than in ordinary ciliated cells, and particularly evident is the large number of quite small mitochondria and small vesicular structures in between. The arrow points to a dense structure with a light center which is reminiscent of a cross sectioned basal body. A developing cilium? The dense line beneath the microvilli, the terminal web (tw), is present only in relation to the microvilli. Magnification 17,500×

veloped system of surface invaginations, reminiscent of tubules, speaks for the fact that structural evidence for micropinocytosis is present. It is, therefore, concluded that the brush cells of the respiratory tract and those of the male reproductive tract are functionally different, although the structure of their surfaces is almost identical (Figs. 2, 7).

Ciliated cell. The ciliated cells have a cytoplasm which contains only a small amount of RNA-particles and endoplasmic reticulum. These cell organelles are probably used only for maintaining the restricted amount of protein that is synthesized for metabolic processes within the cell. The number of cilia per cell is large; in the rat trachea, it amounts to between 250 and 300. The cilium is covered by the plasma membrane and its interior represents an extension of the cytoplasm of the cell. Within this cytoplasm is a number of distinct fibrils oriented longitudinally. They originate from the basal body which is located intracellularly below the level of the cell surface. There are two central single filaments and nine peripheral double ones. They all join in the tip of the cilium. The central ones divide and split within the basal body and wrap around its central core. The peripheral filaments extend below the basal body and terminate at various levels in the upper part of the ciliated cell as ciliary rootlets. Beneath the basal bodies are clusters of mitochondria, the carriers of enzymes in all cells. It is believed that the filaments of the cilium are contractile. The motion center is represented by the basal body, and the energy required for the contraction is derived from the nearby mitochondria. It has been demonstrated that the ciliary beat can occur as long as the contact between the basal body and the cilium proper is maintained. Physical damage, which involves a break between the cilium and the basal body will, therefore, stop the ciliary beat. However, it has also been shown that toxic gases as well as cigarette smoke at a certain concentration stop the

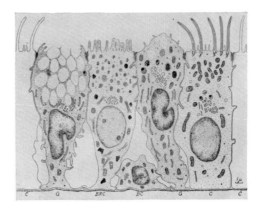

FIG. 8. A schematic representation of the columnar ciliated epithelium of the rat trachea. Contrary to that of man, this epithelium lacks an evident layer of basal cells (BC) although some may be seen in between the bases of the ciliated (C) and the non-ciliated cells. Among the non-ciliated cells are found mucous cells (C) in various states of mucous secretion, and brush cells (BRC). The basement membrane is thinner in rat than in man. (After Rhodin and Dalhamn, 1956).

ciliary activity. Furthermore, infections like influenza damage the ciliated cells so drastically that eventually these cells die and become sloughed off. They are then replaced by basal cells which develop into brush cells and from there into ciliated cells (Figs. 3, 4, 5).

REFERENCES

FAWCETT, D. W., AND PORTER, K. R., "A study of the fine structure of ciliated epithelia," *J. Morph.*, **94**, 221 (1954).

RHODIN, J. AND DALHAMN, T., "Electron microscopy of the tracheal ciliated mucosa in rat," *Z. Zellf.*, **44**, 345 (1956).

RHODIN, J., "Ciliated epithelia," *Int. Rev. Cytol.*, **10** (1962).

JOHANNES A. G. RHODIN

COLLOIDS, LYOPHOBIC

The Colloidal State

The colloidal state is essentially that state in which matter exists with at least one dimension in the size range 10^{-7} to 10^{-4} cm. In this state can be included large molecules such as proteins, enzymes, viruses and high polymers, which have molecular weights in the region of 1,000 to several million and exist in molecular solution, and smokes, mists, gels, etc.. In this size range, many inorganic materials can be prepared as two-phase systems of small particles in liquid media, and are spoken of as colloidal dispersions or sols. The latter groups are usually termed *lyophobic* colloids, and it is with this class of colloidal material that this article is mainly concerned.

The most important properties of a lyophobic colloidal dispersion are:

(a) the size and shape of the particles, and whether the system is dispersed or flocculated,

(b) the chemical structure of the particles,

(c) the nature and structure of the surface,

(d) the mode of nucleation and growth of the particles, and the possible production of monodisperse sols,

(e) the electrical charge on the surface (electrical double layer), and its relation to stability.

Moreover, in phenomena such as nucleation, growth, coagulation and aging of sols the dynamic aspects of the system have to be considered and a knowledge of changes in the system with time is required. The electron microscope may be employed to obtain answers, or some of the answers, to all these questions with the exception of (e). It must be remembered, however, that as specimens are subjected to a high vacuum (*ca.* 10^{-5} mm mercury) in the electron microscope they cannot be investigated in their natural liquid environment. The exposure of the specimen to a beam of high energy electrons also means that suitable precautions must be observed to prevent heating, with subsequent sublimation or decomposition of the specimen; examination of large specimens may be precluded by this factor.

In the case of an optical microscope, when viewing by white light (average wavelength 5600 A) the maximum resolution obtainable is of the order of 2000 A, while with ultraviolet light resolution of the order of 800 A may be obtained; such resolution is totally inadequate for the examination of most colloidal dispersions. However, the wavelength of an electron beam produced at an accelerating potential of 80 kV is 0.043 A and therefore theoretically resolution of the order of one A unit should be possible. Final resolution, however, is limited by the difficulty of correcting the lens aberrations and with earlier microscopes the resolving power was only of the order of 30 to 50 A. With many modern instruments the resolving power is of the order of 5 A and hence it is possible to resolve objects of the order of atomic dimensions.

Experimental Techniques

Preparation of Specimen Supports. The essential criteria for a supporting membrane are that it should be rigid enough to withstand manipulation, remain stable in the electron beam during examination and have a thickness of the order of 100 A. Many types of materials have been suggested as supporting membranes (1) and probably the membranes most commonly used are prepared from "Formvar" or nitrocellulose. The "Formvar" or nitrocellulose membrane is formed on a dish of distilled water and then picked up on the surface of a copper mesh grid (2). These films, however, are not sufficiently stable for high-resolution work; unless they are carefully prepared, they have a tendency to drift under the influence of the electron beam. Greater stability can be achieved by evaporating a thin layer of carbon on to the plastic film, but care must be taken not to increase the support thickness beyond the limits required for high resolution.

One of the most stable supporting membranes can be obtained by evaporating carbon onto carefully cleaned glass slides or freshly cleaved mica. On immersing the slide in water, the carbon film floats on the surface and can be transferred to the grid. If the colloidal dispersions are spread on the glass slide and allowed to dry before applying the carbon, the particles remain embedded in the film on removal and can be used for direct viewing. Although carbon forms a very stable film it is not suitable for the examination of all materials. Electrostatic effects are often encountered which make it difficult to obtain drop adhesion and solutions containing surface-active agents usually disrupt the film; in these cases nitrocellulose-carbon films are the most useful with the liquid applied to the nitrocellulose side.

Silicon monoxide has also been used to obtain a stable supporting membrane, with little structure (2).

Preparation of Colloidal Dispersions. Where colloidal dispersions are produced by the interaction of two ionic reagents, the sol produced usually contains considerable quantities of extraneous electrolyte. This, if left in the sol, tends to crystallize on the supporting membrane and the resultant crystals may be confused with the colloidal particles during examination. Even if actual crystallization does not occur poor backgrounds may result, or flocculation of the sol may occur due to the high concentration of electrolyte reached during evaporation. Removal of any extraneous electrolytes is therefore advisable either by dialysis or electrodialysis; care must be taken, however, not to remove stabilizing potential-determining ions. Small samples may be rapidly dialysed against distilled water in cellophane dialysis sacs; for electrodialysis a number of simple pieces of apparatus have been described which can be readily constructed (3). Electrolyte may also be removed by passage of the sol through a suitable ion-exchange resin provided that precautions are taken to avoid contamination of the sol by particles or complex ions from the resin.

Where sols are too dilute to be used directly, concentration can be achieved by means of electrodecantation (3).

Deposition of Sols on Supporting Membranes. The simplest method of transferring a sol sample to the supporting membrane is by the use of a fine loop of platinum wire. The wire can readily be cleaned by flaming before transference of the specimen. An alternative method, often useful for quantitative measurements, is to spray the sol on to the supporting membrane by means of a nebulizer. Freeze-drying of the sample is often useful and this can be carried out simply by placing the grids on a copper block immersed in a freezing mixture; the aqueous drops then freeze immediately on making contact with the supporting membrane.

Specimen Contrast. In order to obtain an image of the particle in the electron microscope, electrons must be scattered out of the field so that they do not reach the photographic plate. The amount of scatter generally depends upon the atomic number and the density of the specimen, and it is for this reason that materials composed mainly of carbon, hydrogen, nitrogen and oxygen, i.e., of the same composition as a nitrocellulose supporting membrane, are difficult to observe. In the latter case the specimen contrast can usually be increased by staining or by shadowing with a heavy metal vapor such as that of chromium, gold or uranium in a high vacuum.

Owing to the low penetrating power of electrons it is necessary to use very thin specimens if interior details are to be observed (see later). With crystalline specimens considerations other than random scatter have to be taken into account (2).

Resolution of Colloidal Particles. In direct examination of colloidal particles, only the two-dimensional aspects of the particle are seen. In this connection it was realized by von Borries and Kausche (4) that crystalline colloidal particles, which should be bounded by plane faces intersecting in geometrical lines, should be revealed as well

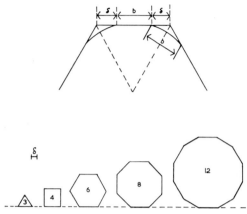

FIG. 1. (top) Diagram illustrating resolution of the shape of a colloidal particle. The shape of the particle can only be recognized if $b \geq \delta$. (bottom) Comparison of the size of particles of different shape required for resolution of that shape. (After Borries and Kausche).

defined shapes in microscopes of infinite resolving power. Such a condition cannot be realized in practice, however, and the effect of finite resolving power has to be considered. von Borries and Kausche (4) supposed that the geometrical boundaries of the object appeared in the image as boundaries of finite width, within which the intensity fell continuously from that of the particle to that of the background. The effective width of the boundary was considered to be twice the resolving power, δ, of the microscope and the physical boundary of the particle at a point midway between the particle and background intensities. As a consequence of the finite resolving power the image boundary at the intersection of two straight lines is rounded, and it was assumed that the curvature was such that the arc of a circle was tangential to the intersecting edges at a distance δ from the point of intersection obtained by geometrical construction (see Fig. 1).

Thus recognition of shape is only possible if the length of the straight portions of the edges, b, is greater or equal to δ. If $b \leq \delta$ the particle would appear circular and in fact many early workers found that small colloidal particles appeared circular, an effect often due to lack of resolving power. On this basis it is clear that the exact shape of a particle having less than six corners should be easier to recognize and therefore triangular particles should be recognizable as such at much smaller dimensions than the hexagonal type. Conversely, octagonal plates must be seven to ten times larger than the triangular particles in order not to appear circular. The sizes of particles, relative to a triangle, required for the resolution of a definite shape are illustrated schematically in Fig. 1.

In order to test the resolution of an electron microscope it is useful to have a suitable test object, and it has been found (5) that silver and silver iodide sols can be prepared which contain particles having sizes approaching the limits of present-day microscopes. Particles having dimensions of the order of 5 A can be clearly resolved from the background (Fig. 2); the fact that these particles could be reproduced on separate photographic plates clearly established their identity as colloidal particles. The limitations in resolving power appear to be mainly governed by chromatic errors (i.e., stabilization of high tension) and lens aberrations. The precise measurement of particle sizes below 10 A becomes difficult due to phase contrast effects at this level of resolution. A suitable test object for high resolution work is also found in the case of metal phthalocyanines; for example, the metal-bearing

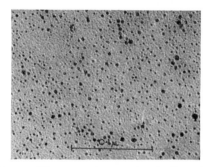

FIG. 2. Electron micrograph of silver iodide sol of small particle size.

planes of platinum phthalocyanine can be resolved in the electron microscope and are found to be 11.97 A apart (6). It is also possible to check resolution by means of Fresnel fringes which are visible when the objective lens is slightly off-focus (7, 8). The use of image intensifiers with the electron microscope may well prove useful in the future in the field of high-resolution work.

Shadow Casting. Normally, only a two-dimensional aspect of the colloidal particle on the grid can be obtained. This is insufficient for many purposes particularly if the 3-dimensional shape of the particle is required. In order to enhance contrast and obtain an approximate idea of the vertical height and shape of the particle, shadowing with a heavy-metal vapor such as that of gold, platinum, chromium or uranium may be employed. The metal is evaporated onto the sample in a high vacuum at a suitable angle; usually a special evaporator unit is needed to meet the strongest requirements of high resolution work (1). From the known angle of shadowing and the length of the shadows, a three-dimensional picture of the particle shape can be built up. These shapes can be checked by constructing models and shadowing with a beam of light. More reliable information can be obtained if the material is shadowed in two directions at right

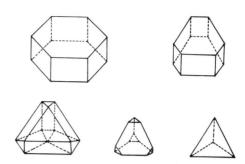

FIG. 4. Diagram of particle models based upon shadowed micrographs of the type illustrated in Fig. 3.

angles, but it is essential that the shadowing be very light; overdeposition of metal completely obliterates the first shadow. In Fig. 3 micrographs of specimens shadowed with uranium at 50° in one direction only and with uranium at 50° in two directions at right angles are shown. From these micrographs particles were found to have shapes such as those shown diagrammatically in Fig. 4.

Replication. One of the most useful techniques for determining the exact shape of particles and also their surface structure is replication; this technique is, moreover, invaluable for the study of specimens which under normal conditions are decomposed by the action of the electron beam. The technique is carried out by depositing samples of the sols either on clean glass slides or freshly cleaved mica and allowing them to dry. A thin film of carbon is then evaporated on to the slide; normally it is advantageous at this stage to shadow very slightly with a heavy metal vapor such as chromium. The carbon film is then removed from the slide using as a liquid substrate a solvent for the embedded particles. When this solvent is a concentrated salt solution it is advisable to follow by washing with more dilute solutions of the salt and then to give a final rinse in distilled water. For the best results from the replication technique it is essential that the films employed should be extremely thin (*ca.* 100–300 A).

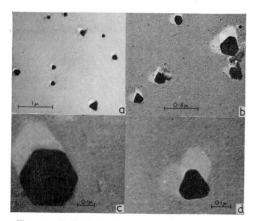

FIG. 3. Colloidal silver iodide particles shadowed with uranium at 50°, a) and c) in one direction, b) and d) in two directions at right angles.

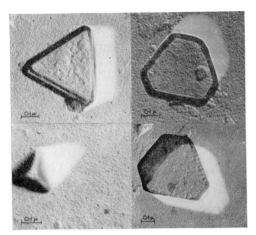

FIG. 5. Carbon replicas of silver iodide particles shadowed with chromium at 50°.

Results obtained by the replica technique with subsequent shadowing are illustrated in Fig. 5.

Distribution Curves. It is possible from electron micrographs of a field containing a large number of particles to determine not only their shapes but also the frequency distribution of diameters, or appropriate dimension. Once these factors are established the surface area of a sample may be obtained, and from a knowledge of the physical density, the weight of the particles. Thus a distribution curve can be made by plotting the frequency of appearance of a certain diameter against that diameter. A typical example is given in Fig. 6. Strictly, a number of photographic plates should be taken of different fields and several thousand particles measured in order to obtain a truly representative curve. In practice, however, counts are usually made on 300 to 400 particles; for reasonable representation it is essential to take several micrographs of different parts of the field.

Such a curve enables information to be obtained on the degree of polydispersity of the system with respect to size and shape and can be of great assistance in following rate processes such as nucleation, particle growth and coagulation. The shape of the size distribution curve depends on the rates of the nucleation and growth processes (see later). In general there is good agreement between the size of particles determined by electron microscopy and those determined by other methods.

Determination of Absolute Particle Number per unit Volume. Two procedures can be employed for this determination. In the first the sol is sprayed on to the grid in the form of fine droplets using a high-pressure nebulizer (9, 10). Under favorable conditions the drops are clearly visible and assuming the diameter of the dried drop to be the same as that in the spray, the drop volume can be estimated. A typical drop formed by spraying a polystyrene latex suspension is shown in Fig. 7. Thence from a count of the number of particles contained in the drop the number of particles per unit volume of the original sol can be calculated.

In the second method it is essential for accurate results that a monodisperse sol should be used. Electron microscopy can be used to determine the diameter, or in the case of non-spherical particles the appropriate dimension, and the volume of a particle

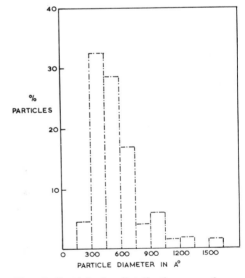

FIG. 6. Particle size distribution curve for a sol of silver iodide.

calculated. Then if the particle density is known the weight per particle can be calculated and if a subsidiary determination is made of the weight concentration of the sol used, the number of particles per unit volume can be calculated.

Both methods have been used extensively, but in some cases care must be exercised in applying these methods since it is not easy to determine drop diameters accurately, and the second method may yield spurious results, either because of particle shrinkage (beam intensity too high), or because the particles do not possess a well-defined geometrical shape.

A comparison has been made (11) between values for particle numbers per unit volume determined by electron microscopy, and those determined by other methods, such as, direct ultramicroscopic counting using a flow method, turbidity measurements and counts using a haemocytometer cell. The results of the comparison which was carried out using polystyrene latex particles are given in Table 1.

In general it was found that the dry-weight method yielded results very close to those determined by other methods, whereas the spray method tended to give rather high results in terms of absolute numbers. A

TABLE 1. A COMPARISON BETWEEN PARTICLE NUMBERS PER ML DETERMINED BY ELECTRON MICROSCOPY AND BY OTHER METHODS

Method	Polystyrene Latex Particles	
	$0.216\,\mu$ Diameter	$1.029\,\mu$ Diameter
Electron Microscopy, spray method	5.60×10^{14}	—
Electron Microscopy, dry weight	1.93×10^{13}	1.76×10^{11}
Particle counter (flow method)	1.90×10^{13}	2.01×10^{11}
Turbidity measurements	2.53×10^{13}	1.26×10^{11}
Haemocytometer	—	3.40×10^{11}

method for the direct application of microdrops of reproducible known volume is clearly desirable.

Processes Involved in Sol Formation and Destruction

A variety of methods exist for the preparation of colloidal dispersions of different types (3) and of these perhaps the most commonly used, and the most studied, is the mixing of two ionic solutions. A typical example is the formation of a sol of silver bromide by mixing silver nitrate and potassium bromide at concentrations sufficiently high to exceed the solubility product; for a stable sol the stabilizing ions Ag^+ or Br^- have to be present in certain proportions. In most cases of low-solubility inorganic materials stable sols can be formed provided that a stabilizing ion is present.

The nuclei originally formed in the solution, which are usually very small crystals, grow to form the larger sol particles which are usually known as primary particles. This phenomenon is known as ageing, and is usually explained as the growth of extremely small particles to form larger ones either by regular addition to the lattice, i.e., smaller particles going into solution so that the larger ones can grow at their expense, or by a process of ordering of the disordered lattice

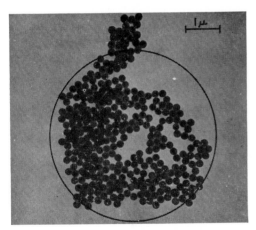

FIG. 7. "Droplet" of polystyrene latex particles obtained by spraying with a Vaponefrin nebulizer.

of the particles originally formed. Sols of primary particles are often stable for long periods of time, but addition of electrolyte beyond a certain concentration, or the addition of strongly adsorbed organic ions, causes the particles to clump together (coagulation); this process may, or may not, be accompanied by recrystallization to form even larger particles, depending on the system. The process of sol formation and destruction of the sol either by coagulation or recrystallization can be represented schematically in the following manner:

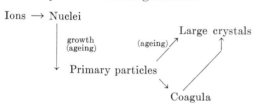

Most of the stages represented in this scheme can be investigated by electron microscopy and will therefore be considered separately.

Nucleation. Nucleation can be defined as the formation of a discrete particle of a new phase in a previously homogeneous solution. Nuclear or amicronic sols contain particles which cannot be resolved as discrete entities in the ultramicroscope. They can be prepared from many materials, e.g., gold, silver, silver iodide etc.. Electron microscopic examination of these sols shows particles down to 10 A or less (see Fig. 2) which can be clearly resolved. The resolution of these particles constitutes one of the highest resolutions so far achieved with the electron microscope. From the point of view of colloid chemistry this illustrates the small size range in which colloidal particles can exist and it is of considerable interest that the regular shapes of many of the particles appear to be maintained down to the limits of resolution. Thermodynamically, the smaller particles would be expected to have a larger solubility than the larger ones and thus would be expected to go into solution as ions

and deposit on the larger particles to increase their size. Charge would be expected to influence this process (12), but in view of the large value of the free energy of most solid-liquid interfaces it is doubtful whether this does in fact play a significant role.

Several theories have been proposed for the mechanism of nuclei formation in dilute solution, of which the impurity, organizer and fluctuation mechanisms appear to have received the most attention. The impurity theory is based on the idea that nuclei are introduced into the system as foreign bodies, e.g., dust particles; it has been found, for example, that in the preparation of colloidal gold different sols are obtained according to the state of the glass vessel used. However, it was concluded by Turkevich, Stevenson and Hillier (13), who prepared gold sols under many different conditions, that impurities were not a variable in their investigation. These authors proposed the organizer mechanism to account for the formation of nuclei in gold sols. Their suggestion was that the nucleating agent, e.g., hydroxylamine, gradually built up a complex between the gold ions, chemically binding a large number of gold ions and reducing agent molecules into large macromolecules. It was suggested that the latter underwent a molecular rearrangement to give metallic gold and oxidation products of the reducing agent. Some support was lent to this hypothesis by the nature of the reducing agents, but there are clearly many conditions under which such a mechanism cannot apply.

The fluctuation theory of nucleation is probably that most widely accepted. It is based on the hypothesis that the formation of a nucleus occurs only when a statistical fluctuation of the ionic (atomic or molecular) concentration brings a sufficiently large number of ions together to form a particle of thermodynamically stable size. This theory has been shown to apply to the formation of colloidal sulfur (14).

Studies of Nucleation by Electron

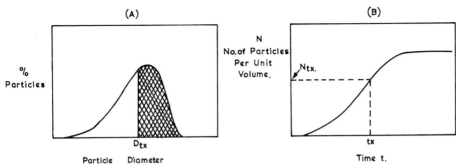

FIG. 8. a) Particle size distribution curve for sol and b) nucleation curve obtained therefrom. (After Turkevich, Stevenson and Hillier).

Microscopy. Two methods can be used to examine nucleation by electron microscopy (13) firstly, quenching the nucleation process at different times and directly examining the samples and secondly examination of the particle size distribution curves of the formed sol. In the first method the reaction can be quenched at suitable time intervals either by addition of a suitable reagent to stop the reaction, or by a large dilution to slow the reaction down by several orders of magnitude. Thus from a direct examination of the samples obtained at different times, particle size distribution curves can be obtained for each sample, and a nucleation curve constructed.

The second method, which is less tedious than the first, was suggested by Turkevich, Stevenson and Hillier (13) and consists of determining the nucleation curve from the particle size distribution curve of the completed sol. The method is based upon the assumption that *the principal cause of spread in particle size of the sol is the spread in time in nuclei formation.* Thus particles formed in the early stages of nucleation commence to grow immediately, while nuclei formed later have smaller sizes corresponding to a shorter growing time. In the final sol therefore the particles first formed have the larger size and the size distribution curve can be considered as a distorted image of the nucleation curve. Thus if a particle size distribution curve of the type shown in Fig. 8a is con-

sidered, particles of diameter D_x may be chosen, which correspond to the diameter attained by these particles at a time t_x on the nucleation curve (Fig. 8b). Thus at a time t_x there are N_{t_x} particles per unit volume, a number which can be expressed as the fraction of the number of particles eventually formed at infinite time, i.e., $N(t)$. The total number of particles formed up to time t_x is represented by the area shaded in Fig. 8a or the number of particles with diameter greater than $D(t_x)$ is given by,

$$N(t) = \int_{D(t_x)}^{\infty} n(D)\, dD .$$

Turkevich, Stevenson and Hillier (13) found that the growth of gold nuclei was given by an equation of the form $t = (a - \log D)/b$, where a was a function of the rate constant and of the time at which an arbitrarily selected reference particle formed; b was proportional to the rate constant. From independent observations of a and b, nucleation curves were constructed from particle size distribution curves.

The Growth Process. The formation of a sol involves two processes, formation of nuclei and growth of nuclei. If the formation of nuclei is slow and growth rapid the sol consists of a small number of large particles; if nuclei formation is rapid and growth slow the result is a large number of small particles. When both processes are slow, a broad distribution of sizes is obtained. In nucleation the number of particles formed as a function of time is studied, whereas in the case of growth the rate of increase in the size of the particle with time is the important factor; strictly, in order to study growth the number of nuclei should be kept constant. One method of maintaining this condition in practice is to add nuclei to a slightly supersaturated solution of the growing species.

The growth process which appears to have been investigated in most detail by electron microscopy is that of colloidal gold. Turkevich, Stevenson and Hillier (13) took advantage of the fact that in a slightly acid solution of chlorauric acid and hydroxylamine hydrochloride, in a very clean closed vessel, colloidal gold was not produced until a sufficient number of nuclei were introduced. Thus when the growth medium was inoculated with nuclei, the chlorauric acid was reduced by the hydroxylamine and the metallic gold was deposited only on the nuclei; hence the nuclei increased in size but not in number. The mean diameter of the resulting particles, D_g, was shown to be given by

$$D_g = D_n \sqrt[3]{\frac{M_n + M_{ce}}{M_n}}$$

where D_n was equal to the mean diameter of the nuclei and M_n and M_{ce} were the respective masses of the metallic gold in the nuclei and ionic gold in the growth medium.

From an examination of the particle size distribution curves obtained from the kinetics of citrate reduction determined chemically, it was found that the growth law was of the form

$$\frac{dD}{dt} = kD$$

where k was a constant dependent on temperature and reagent concentration but not on particle size.

The growth of gold particles in monodisperse gold sols produced by the action of sodium citrate on chlorauric acid has also been studied by Takiyama (15) using electron microscopy. The size of a particle at a time t (minutes) was expressed by the mole number of one particle, x (mole), as calculated from the mean particle diameter D by the relation,

$$x = 4/3\pi(D/2)^3\rho/M$$

where ρ and M are the density and molecular weight of gold, respectively. It was found that the rate of growth was expressed by the equation,

$$\frac{dx}{dt} = kx^{2/3}(x_\infty - x),$$

where x and x_∞ are the mole numbers of the particles at a time t and after completion of growth; k was a rate constant. It was found that the growth process was autocatalytic with respect to the surface of the gold particles.

The Ageing Process. A lyophobic sol is never stable in the thermodynamic sense and is always proceeding in the direction which involves a decrease in the surface free energy of the solid-liquid interface. Thus there is always present a tendency for the total surface area of the sol to decrease, until a pseudo-stable equilibrium is reached; at this stage the sol consists of dispersed primary particles. The process of change from the initial sol, which may consist of a large number of small particles, to the final "stable" sol which may consist of a small number of large particles is termed ageing; the dissolving of smaller particles accompanied by growth of larger ones is sometimes termed Ostwald ripening (Fig. 9). The rate of ageing may be slow or fast, according to the conditions and the material employed. In the case of barium sulfate, for example, the ageing process even at room temperature is rapid and large crystals are formed; it is difficult to prepare a very stable finely dispersed sol. On the other hand, in the case of silver iodide, sols of finely dispersed particles can be prepared which are stable for several years. The

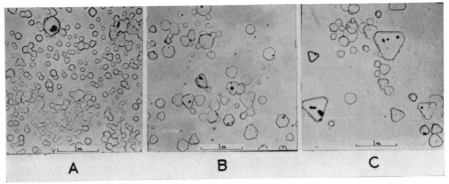

Fig. 9. Sequence of electron micrographs of carbon replicas showing Ostwald ripening of silver iodobromide emulsion crystals in a solution containing gelatin and ammonium bromide at 50°C. a) immediately b) 5 minutes, and c) 20 minutes after mixing. (By courtesy Messrs Ilford Ltd.)

ageing process is very important industrially, principally in the production of photographic emulsions, where the nuclear sols produced in the presence of gelatin are allowed to "Ostwald ripen" before coating onto plates or film base.

The ageing process in polydisperse systems is usually considered to involve the smaller particles going into solution and the larger particles growing at their expense. An alternative explanation is that coagulation of the small particles occurs followed by recrystallization of the coagula to form regular particles. Most evidence would appear to favor the former mechanism but in some cases mosaic crystals have been found (see for example Fig. 17a) which would tend to favor the latter. It is possible that in practice both mechanisms occur with the former usually being the predominant one.

Electron microscopy forms a suitable method for the examination of the ageing process since both the average size of the particles and the number present per unit volume of sol may be evaluated at a given time. Moreover, from the shape of the particles formed during the ageing process, it is possible to tell whether growth of the particles occurs preferentially in certain directions.

A detailed study of the ageing of silver bromide sols has been carried out by Kolthoff and his collaborators (16).

An interesting example of the ageing process is found in the case of vanadium pentoxide sols. The sol particles formed in the initial sol, e. g., in a Biltz sol (17) have been found to be small needles several hundred angstroms long and 140 A thick. On ageing these are transformed into fibrous crystals several microns in length. In detailed studies on the ageing process (18, 19) it was found that the large numbers of small needle-like particles were redistributed to give smaller numbers of large filaments; growth was attributed to recrystallization of the fibrils.

Formation of Monodisperse Sols. Intimately connected with the study of nucleation and growth is the problem of producing monodisperse sols. The latter may be defined as sols in which all the particles contained therein have exactly the same size and shape. The conditions for the preparation of monodisperse sols, which are very important from the viewpoint of colloid chemistry, have been investigated in detail by LaMer and his collaborators (20), and may be illustrated by consideration of Fig. 10. Thus if a slow chemical reaction occurs which continuously generates molecules of a disperse phase, the concentration of these molecules increases steadily, passes the point of satura-

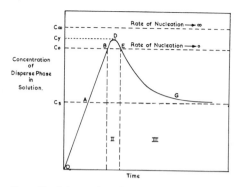

FIG. 10. Schematic diagram illustrating the mode of production of monodisperse sols. (After La Mer).

tion A and exceeds at B the level at which the rate of nucleation becomes appreciable. When the rate of production of molecules is slow, however, the sudden appearance of nuclei relieves the supersaturation so rapidly and effectively that the region of nucleation (II) is restricted in time and no nuclei are formed after the initial outburst. Hence the nuclei produced grow uniformly by a diffusion controlled process (region III) and a sol of monodisperse particles is obtained.

If the initial solutions used are not very dilute, then the rate of production of molecules becomes so rapid that their concentration in solution continually exceeds the saturation concentration (C_0) and continuous creation of nuclei in addition to growth occurs. Thus a polydisperse sol is formed since the size of any particle depends upon the stage at which it was formed.

A number of monodisperse sols have been prepared and investigated by electron microscopy and other methods. The formation and properties of monodisperse sulfur sols were investigated by LaMer and collaborators (20) apparently without detailed examination by electron microscopy. The monodisperse sols most widely investigated by electron microscopy are undoubtedly those of polystyrene latex (21, 22) and sized samples of these particles are now widely used for the magnification calibration of electron microscopes.

Watillon, Grunderbeeck and Hautecer (23) by reducing selenium oxide with hydrazine in the presence of amicronic gold particles produced monodisperse sols of selenium. Examination by electron microscopy showed the particles to be almost perfectly spherical with a deviation from perfect sphericity of about $\pm 2\%$; the spherical shape was confirmed by shadowing experiments (see Fig. 11). Selected area micro-diffraction showed the particles to be essentially amorphous.

Monodisperse barium sulfate sols have been prepared by Takiyama (24) by decomposing the barium-EDTA complex with hydrogen peroxide in the presence of ammonium sulfate. The particles were shown by electron microscopy to be spindle

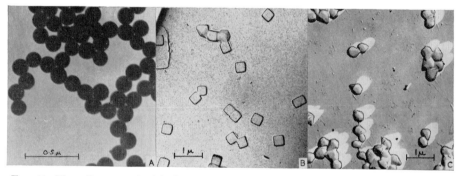

FIG. 11. Monodisperse sols (a) electron micrograph of selenium sol particles (*by courtesy of Dr. A. Watillon*), (b) carbon replica of silver bromide sol particles shadowed with chromium at 60°, (c) carbon replica of silver iodide sol particles shadowed with chromium at 60°.

shaped, and the mole number x per particle was calculated from the equation

$$x = \tfrac{4}{3}\pi(a/2)(b/2)^2\rho/M$$

where a and b were the mean length of the long and short axes, respectively, and ρ and M were the density and molecular weight of barium sulfate. The size of the particles was found to increase with the concentration of the reagents used and the relation between the mole number of the particle and the concentration of the reagents (C) was given by the expression

$$xC^\alpha = K$$

where α and K were constants.

Monodisperse gold sols have also been prepared by Takiyama (15) using the reduction of chlorauric acid by sodium citrate. The sol particles thus prepared were found to be almost spherical, the average diameter being 172 A with a standard deviation of 13 A.

Silver bromide and silver iodide sols have been prepared in a monodisperse form by Ottewill and Woodbridge (25). The silver bromide sols were prepared by slow cooling of a hot solution of silver bromide, which was slightly supersaturated at room temperature, and the silver iodide sols by dilution of the potassium iodide complex with water. The silver bromide particles were found to be cubes and the silver iodide particles rhomboids; typical micrographs of both types of sol particles are given in Fig. 11.

Effect of Additives on Sol Formation.
It is well known that molecules of dyes or surface-active agents often show a preference for adsorption onto particular crystal faces (26) and thus can exert profound influences on crystal shape (27). Support for the idea of preferential adsorption on certain crystal faces has been found in electron microscope studies on the coagulation of sols. For example, in the coagulation of hexagonal plates of silver iodide by dodecylpyridinium ions (28) it was found that the plates were joined by

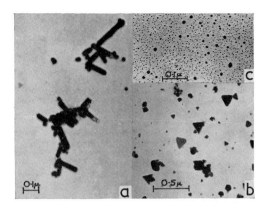

FIG. 12. Electron micrographs illustrating the influence of additives on the formation of silver iodide sol particles, a) sol formed in the presence of 2.2×10^{-4} M mercaptotriazole, b) sol formed in the presence of 4×10^{-6} M dodecylpyridinium iodide, c) sol formed in the presence of 7.74×10^{-4} M dodecylpyridinium iodide.

edge to edge adhesion suggesting a preference for adsorption of the ion on the $01\bar{1}0$, $10\bar{1}0$, $1\bar{1}00$, $0\bar{1}10$, $\bar{1}010$ and $\bar{1}100$ faces.

The influence of different media on the shape of sol particles can conveniently be investigated by electron microscopy. In Fig. 12a are shown particles of silver iodide formed in the presence of 2.2×10^{-4} M mercaptotriazole; comparison with Fig. 12b shows that the crystal form has been altered from predominantly flat plates or tetrahedral particles to rod-like particles. It is advisable when such changes are noticed to carry out micro-diffraction experiments on the particles to determine whether any of the additive has been incorporated into the crystal.

High concentrations of surface-active agents, particularly those above the critical micelle concentration, often have a considerable influence on the sol formation process (28). In the case of silver iodide particles, it appears that a twofold adsorbed layer of surface-active agent ions is formed on the particles at the nucleus stage; the particles formed are finely dispersed with many of diameter less than 25 A (Fig. 12c). Owing to the strongly adsorbed layer the ageing process appears to be retarded and a protected nuclear sol is obtained. Further growth is slow and the sol shows a fairly narrow particle size distribution.

An important additive to the silver halide sols formed for coating photographic plates is gelatin. An electron microscope examination of the growth of silver bromide particles in gelatin has been carried out by Ammann-Brass (29), and the effect of a number of other polymers of high molecular weight by Perry (30). In the latter case the nature of the polymer was found to have a profound effect on the growth process and on the morphology of the crystals obtained.

Studies on Flocculation. The flocculation of sols is usually considered to include both the process of coagulation, i.e., the actual adhesion of the particles, and the subsequent processes of recrystallization etc. Coagulation can often occur during the drying down of specimens for electron microscopic examination and as such is of purely nuisance value. Direct electron microscopic studies, however, do provide a useful method of obtaining information on coagulation processes provided precautions are taken to eliminate artefacts occurring during the drying down process.

Electron microscope studies on the coagulation of silver iodide sols have been carried out by Mirnik, Strohal, Wrischer and Težak (31) and by Horne, Matijević, Ottewill and Horne (28). The former authors studied the formation and coagulation of the sol as a function of time and the latter authors the effect of dodecylpyridinium iodide, at various concentrations, on the sol formation process.

So far electron microscopy does not appear to have been employed to carry out quantitative studies on the kinetics of coagulation, but it does form a useful method of confirming whether effects observed in quantitative measurements by other methods, e.g., spectrophotometry, are really to be attributed to coagulation or to other effects such as recrystallization. Moreover, the form of the

coagula obtained can be determined from micrographs. These are found to vary considerably according to the system and coagulating agent employed, typical examples being edge to edge adhesion of flat plates, irregular clumps, chains and massive "lace-like" aggregates of particles embedded in additive (see Fig. 13).

The Structure of Sol Particles

Micro-diffraction Examination. With an electron beam, as with an x-ray beam, a regular crystal lattice acts as a diffraction grating and gives rise to a diffraction pattern. Thus the electron microscope may be used as a diffraction camera. In earlier machines a different specimen holder was often used for diffraction but in many modern machines the specimen is left in the same position and hence diffraction and microscopy can be carried out consecutively on the same specimen. Moreover, with the electron optical arrangements available it is possible to select a specimen area of diameter down to 2,000 A and to obtain a diffraction pattern from this region alone. It is also possible to modify instruments so that diffraction patterns are produced under the same illuminating conditions as used for microscopy (32). Hence by this means, single colloidal particles can be isolated and diffraction patterns obtained directly from them; in the case of thin plates with a cross-sectional distance greater than 2000 A it is possible to isolate particular regions for examination. Thus with colloidal particles which are single crystals a symmetrical spot pattern is obtained (see Fig. 14). If the inclination of the single-crystal specimen to the electron beam is changed, the diffraction pattern alters according to the amount and direction of the inclination. This effect has been studied in detail by Suito and Uyeda (33) using lamellar gold crystals. For the detailed interpretation and analysis of micro-diffraction patterns the relationship between the reciprocal lattice of the crystal and the Ewald sphere must

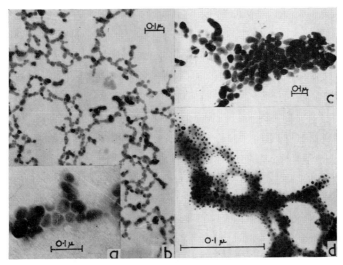

Fɪɢ. 13. Electron micrographs of various types of flocculation, a) side to side adhesion of hexagonal plates, b) formation of chains, c) formation of clumps, d) "lacelike" aggregates of particles embedded in added surface active agent.

be considered, since the section of the former by the latter can be regarded, approximately, as the electron diffraction pattern obtained.

Apart from the direct use of diffraction patterns to obtain the structure of the particles, it is very useful in the colloid chemical field to use the "x-ray" structure of the bulk material, if known, to identify the colloidal particle, or confirm its identity, and to determine the orientation of the particle; moreover, the indices of the crystal faces exposed can be obtained from the disposition of the spots. Diffraction analysis can also be used to give an indication of the imperfections present in the particle. The main limitation to the use of this technique on crystalline colloidal particles is the thickness of the particles since for more than a certain thickness of the particle, which varies according to the nature of the material, too much of the beam is scattered, or absorbed, for a distinct pattern to be obtained.

In Fig. 15b is shown a selected area microdiffraction pattern from a thin colloidal particle of silver iodide (thickness *ca.* 100–200 A) and in Fig. 15a a selected area micrograph

of the portion of the particle from which the diffraction pattern was obtained. The pattern is that expected for a hexagonal crystal of silver iodide of a = 4.59 A and c = 7.49 A resting on the $000\bar{1}$ plane. The clarity of the diffraction pattern demonstrates clearly the almost perfect crystalline nature of colloidal particles of this type.

If instead of a single particle, a field is taken containing a number of small particles then a ring pattern is obtained (see Fig. 14b). Only those planes which satisfy the Bragg equation contribute to the pattern and thus a series of discrete rings are obtained; if only a small number of particles are present the rings are broken up into spots. A typical ring pattern, obtained from a group of silver iodide particles of particle size 300–400 A, is shown in Fig. 16. The angular breadth of the diffraction line depends upon the diameter of the particle D and the wavelength of the incident radiation λ, the quantity λ/D usually being termed the Scherrer breadth. Thus theoretically an estimate of particle size can be obtained from the breadth of the diffraction lines (2, 34). However, other facts

137

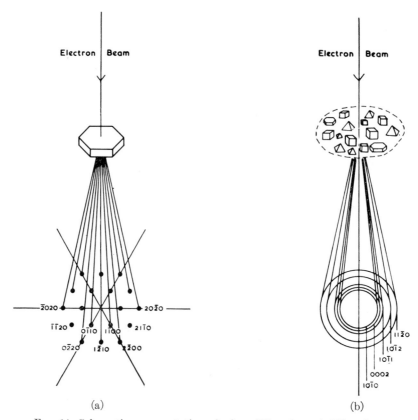

FIG. 14. Schematic representation of micro-diffraction, a) diffraction pattern obtained from a single crystal particle, b) ring pattern obtained from a collection of colloidal particles.

FIG. 15. Micro-diffraction pattern from a colloidal particle of silver iodide, a) selected area of particle, b) micro-diffraction pattern from this selected area.

such as finite aperture of illumination, etc. play a part in line broadening.

Dark Field Image Analysis. A useful complement to micro-diffraction experiments is dark-field image analysis. This method was developed by Mollenstedt and others (35, 36, 37) and has principally been applied to lamellar crystals. The technique consists of isolating a single spot on the diffraction pattern by means of an aperture in the plane of the objective diaphragm, from which the part of the electron beam, focused as the spot, passes through the small aperture; the latter is then moved aside from the normal position on the axis into the position for dark field.

Thus a dark-field image can be obtained which corresponds to the portion of the crystal containing the lattice planes from which diffraction was actually taking place. In this manner each spot of a single crystal diffraction pattern can be studied individually and a set of dark-field images obtained which correspond to the sections of the crystal containing the diffracting lattice planes. Comparison of the dark-field images with the bright-field images reveals that each black line in the latter becomes a bright line in the former, and thus the Miller indices of the lattice planes giving rise to the bright lines in dark field can be identified. An interesting study using this technique has been carried out by Suito and Uyeda (33) on lamellar colloidal gold crystals, in which they were able to identify the crystal planes giving rise to the striped patterns often observed on thin gold crystals (see Fig. 18).

Studies of Internal Structure in Thin Colloidal Particles. Many colloidal particles, when studied by direct electron microscopy, appear completely opaque, and therefore any interior details which might be expected to be visible, such as grain boundaries from mosaic growth, dislocation lines, etc., are completely obscured. Dislocation lines usually appear dark on micrographs, an increase of contrast which is thought to be due to the increased Bragg reflection from the strained region around the dislocation line. Moreover, studies on thin metal foils of aluminum, stainless steel, etc., have shown that such imperfections are readily visible in the electron microscope (38, 39). Very few direct observations have been recorded on the presence of these defects in colloidal particles, although such defects may play an

important role in the stability of colloidal systems. In fact, observation of these defects in colloidal particles does not appear to be an easy problem and may well mean that the particles are very close to perfect crystals. For observations of interior structure it would appear necessary for the thickness of the particles to be of the order of only a few hundred angstrom units.

Thin crystals may often be prepared by the controlled ageing of nuclear sols; this method is particularly successful in the case of silver iodide and some detailed studies on thin hexagonal plates of this material have been carried out by Horne and Ottewill (40, 41). Some crystals were found to exhibit a mosaic appearance, sections of different contrast, which would correspond to different crystal orientations, being clearly visible (Fig. 17a); extinction contours were also clearly visible. In other crystals dark bands were observed (Fig. 17b) which appeared to be due to the presence of dislocations or stacking faults; these were often seen to migrate across the crystal under the influence of the beam.

In the case of thin lamellar particles, such as those of gold, striped or spotted patterns are often observed; a typical example is shown in Fig. 18. These patterns are thought to arise from diffraction effects due to local curvature of the crystal, that is the substrate with which the crystals are in close contact undergoes local curvature in the form of a valley; the crystals follow this curvature and have a common axis of bending along the valley. The thin strips which accompany the central one can be considered to arise from reflections which correspond to the subsidiary maxima which surround the main diffraction spots (33). The crystal planes giving rise to these diffraction effects can be identified by dark-field image analysis. The displacement of the subsidiary maxima from the main spot, which precisely satisfies the Bragg condition, is closely related to the thickness of the crystalline

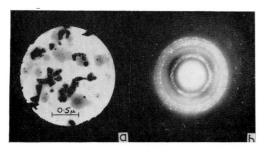

FIG. 16. Micro-diffraction pattern from a group of colloidal silver iodide particles, a) selected area of particles, b) micro-diffraction pattern.

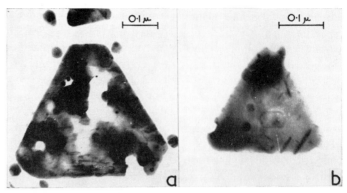

FIG. 17. Electron micrographs of thin colloidal particles of silver iodide showing the presence of imperfections, a) mosaic crystal, b) dislocation lines and hexagonal dislocation loop.

FIG. 18. Patterns formed on lamellar gold crystals due to diffraction effects.

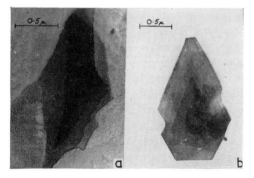

FIG. 19. Electron micrographs of barium tetradecyl sulphate crystals showing surface structure, a) shadowed with chromium at 50°, b) direct micrograph.

particle. This fact has been utilized as a method for the determination of the thickness of such crystals (33). Reasonable agreement was obtained between the thickness of particles obtained by this method and that suggested by shadowing experiments.

Examination of the Surface Structure of Colloidal Particles by Replication. Closely related to the problem of internal structure of particles is the surface structure, since the history of the mode of growth of a particle is often recorded in its surface, in the form of growth spirals, kink sites, twin plane grooves, etc. Such information can usually best be obtained by an examination of very thin replicas of the particles shadowed very lightly with a heavy metal vapor (42). However, in the case of very thin crystals, composed mainly of elements of low atomic weight, it is often possible to detect details of surface structure by direct microscopy or by lightly shadowing the specimen with a heavy metal vapor. Typical examples obtained with a metal detergent crystal, barium tetradecyl sulfate, are shown in Fig. 19. The spiral terraces of the plate-like crystals are clearly visible, the lengths of the shadows indicating the depth of the steps to be of the order of 50 A, i.e. bimolecular, and indicate that growth probably occurs by a screw dislocation mechanism. Similar effects have been observed with single crystals of the paraffin *n*-nonatriacontane and stearic acid (43). In the latter case the crystals were replicated with silicon monoxide and the replicas shadowed with palladium vapor. Dislocation centers were clearly visible, indicating that growth had occurred by a screw dislocation mechanism; the spiral step heights were found to be of the order of 45 A (see Fig. 20).

An interesting example of the use of electron microscopy in elucidating the growth mechanism of crystals occurs in the case of silver bromide. It was suggested by Berriman and Herz (44) that the reason for tabular growth in silver bromide (sodium chloride-type structure) was the occurrence of twinning on the 111 plane; some confirmation was found for this hypothesis in that Laue photographs taken by them exhibited six-fold symmetry. Additional support for the mechanism was obtained by Hamilton and Brady (45) in an electron microscope examination of shadowed carbon replicas of tabular silver bromide crystals. The replicas were examined at an angle of 45° to the incident beam when the convex and concave intersections at the twin planes were visible on the edges of the crystal. Examples of crystal replicas showing the presence of twin planes are given in Fig. 21.

The fact that in the immediate vicinity of a crystal imperfection the lattice has a higher chemical potential than in the more perfect parts means that when the crystal is placed in a solvent preferential attack occurs at this point. Thus, provided the reaction is stopped before extensive solution of the crystal occurs, etch pits are formed at the sites of preferential attack. In the case of colloidal particles this technique appears to have been employed primarily on silver halide crystals in an attempt to detect dislocation sites. For example, Hamilton, Brady and Hamm (46) carried out chemical etching-studies on large grains of silver bromide and silver bromoiodide emulsions. Etching was carried out by immersion of the particles, for a limited time, in a silver halide solvent. The particles were then replicated with carbon, and the replicas

FIG. 20. Silicon monoxide replica of a stearic acid crystal, shadowed with palladium, showing growth from a single dislocation and bimolecular steps. (*By courtesy of Dr. I. M. Dawson*)

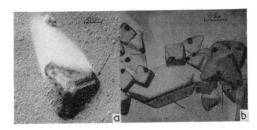

FIG. 21. Carbon replicas of colloidal particles showing evidence of twinning, a) silver iodide, b) silver bromide. Arrows indicate the position of twin planes.

examined after shadowing with platinum-palladium at a 5 to 1 angle. The concentration of chemical etch pits and the geometry of the pits were found to be dependent on the solvent used; potassium bromide gave octahedral pits and sodium sulfite and potassium cyanide dodecahedral pits. A general increase in etching on certain faces was found after intentionally straining the grains, but the effect was not sufficiently strong to establish a one-to-one relationship between etch pits and dislocations. The etching experiments did not provide any conclusive evidence that normal grains of silver bromide were polycrystalline in nature.

A micrograph of a carbon replica of a silver bromide crystal etched with potassium cyanide is shown in Fig. 22.

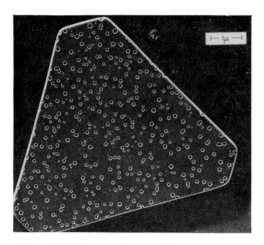

Fig. 22. Carbon replica of a silver bromide particle etched with potassium cyanide. (*By courtesy of Dr. J. F. Hamilton*)

Stability of Colloidal Particles in the Electron Beam. One of the difficulties encountered in electron microscopy is that the amount of energy which is transferred from the beam to electrons in the specimen can often be in excess of the chemical binding energies. Hence, precautions must be taken against possible decomposition of the specimen in the beam. Stability depends on whether, after excitation of electronic energy levels, the substance reverts to its original structure or to a new configuration. Thermal stability is also important, since considerable temperature changes of the specimen can occur; temperatures of the order of 100°C or more can easily be obtained. In many cases decomposition of the specimen in the beam is rapid, making direct examination impossible. For example, both silver chloride and silver bromide rapidly decompose to yield a mass of metallic silver (47, 48); thus replica techniques are normally used for examination of these crystals (49). The interaction of the specimen with the beam, however, may frequently be helpful in studying the decomposition of crystals. It was shown by Sawkill (50) that single crystals of silver azide could be decomposed in the beam of the electron microscope and

that the decomposition could be followed in detail by examining micro-diffraction patterns and electron micrographs taken at various stages. In a similar type of study Goodman (51) has examined the dehydration of single crystals of magnesium hydroxide to magnesium oxide under the influence of the electron beam. Electron microscope observations have also proved useful in studies on the motion of electrons and holes in photographic emulsion grains (52) and in studies on latent image formation (53).

A useful technique for examining dynamic changes in crystals of colloidal dimensions is to employ a cinécamera to record the image obtained on the fluorescent screen of the microscope. The first observations of this type were carried out by von Ardenne (54) using a camera fitted into the microscope, and later by Preuss and Watson (50) using an external cinécamera.

In recent studies on the movement of dislocations in thin metal films (38, 39) and dynamic changes in silver iodide particles (40, 41) ciné recordings were made of the phenomena taking place. In this work the fluorescent viewing screen was tilted at a suitable angle and recordings were made by photographing directly through one of the observation windows at microscope magnifications of 40,000× or 80,000×. A Kodak ciné special camera was used and modified to take a 1 in. f/0.95 Angénieux lens at a working distance of 15–20 cm; a speed of 16 frames per second was generally used.

The studies on silver iodide were made directly on colloidal particles. Two types of effects were noticed under the influence of the beam—mobile changes of contrast within the particles and filament growth from the particles. The first effect was obtained with hexagonal plates of silver iodide. Changes of contrast were observed under the influence of the electron beam which were highly mobile and migrated within the particle boundaries at rates dependent on the beam intensity. The nature of these changes and the speed with which they occurred are illustrated in Fig. 23. Particles are shown which have undergone considerable changes within the period of two frames of ciné film ($\frac{1}{16}$ sec.). The electron-transparent regions moved very rapidly inside the crystal without effecting any change in the external shape, and continued to do so indefinitely under constant beam conditions.

With certain types of silver iodide particles, mainly the tetrahedral variety, fila-

FIG. 24. Filament growth from a single tetrahedral particle of silver iodide.

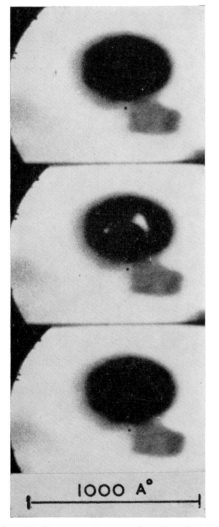

FIG. 23. Sequence from a cine film showing a silver iodide particle undergoing changes of contrast.

ments appeared to be pushed outwards from the interior as the intensity of the electron beam was increased. Fig. 24 illustrates typical filament growth from the interior of a particle. In many cases the filaments appeared to be ribbons with widths as low as 30 A; these remained, however, quite rigid and were able to push holes in the supporting membrane. Some filaments also showed well-defined contrasting bands (see Fig. 24). Filament growth was also observed in some rather coagulated regions which received strong electron irradiation. A sequence from a ciné film of filament growth is given in Fig. 25.

Many other dynamic processes should be amenable to investigation by electron microscopy using this type of technique.

General Morphology of Colloidal Particles. The number of substances which can be prepared in the colloidal state is very

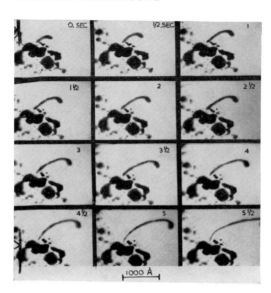

FIG. 25. Sequence from a cine film showing the growth of filaments from irradiated silver iodide particles.

large. Furthermore, the size, shape and structure of particles vary considerably from material to material. No attempt has been made in this article to cover all the work carried out on colloidal particles nor to consider in detail the question of general morphology. This subject has been reviewed elsewhere (56) and it was concluded that the morphological forms in which colloidal particles are formed could be subdivided into amorphous small particles, small regular forms (spheres, cubes, hexagons, octahedra, etc.), fibers and plates. Most of these forms have been described in this article but the main emphasis has been laid upon the description of techniques which enable any colloidal particle to be examined in the electron microscope.

Acknowledgments. It is a pleasure to record my thanks to Mr. R. W. Horne for his continuous enthusiastic collaboration in much of the work described in this article. I should also like to express my thanks to Drs. I. M. Dawson, G. F. Hamilton and A. Watillon for generously supplying the micrographs acknowledged in the text.

REFERENCES

1. COSSLETT, V. E. AND HORNE, R. W., *Vacuum,* **5**, 109 (1955).
2. HALL, C. E., "Introduction to Electron Microscopy," McGraw Hill Book Co., New York, 1953.
3. KRUYT, H. R., "Colloid Science," Vol. I, Elsevier, Amsterdam, 1952.
4. VON BORRIES, B. AND KAUSCHE, G. A., *Kolloid-Z.,* **90**, 132 (1940).
5. OTTEWILL, R. H., AND HORNE, R. W., *Kolloid-Z.,* **149**, 122 (1956).
6. MENTER, J. W., *Proc. Roy. Soc.,* **A236**, 119 (1956).
7. HILLIER, J. AND RAMBERG, E. G., *J. Appl. Phys.,* **18**, 48 (1947).
8. HAINE, M. E. AND MULVEY, T., *J. Sci. Instr.,* **31**, 326 (1954).
9. WILLIAMS, R. C., AND BACKUS, R. C., *J. Am. Chem. Soc.,* **71**, 4052 (1949); *J. Appl. Phys.,* **21**, 11 (1950).
10. GEROULD, C. H., *J. Appl. Phys.,* **21**, 183 (1950).
11. OTTEWILL, R. H. AND WILKINS, D. J., *J. Colloid Sci.,* 15,—(1960); in press.
12. KNAPP, L. F., *Trans. Faraday Soc.,* **17**, 457 (1922).
13. TURKEVICH, J., STEVENSON, P. C., AND HILLIER, J., *Disc. Faraday Soc.,* **11**, 55 (1951).
14. LaMER, V. K. AND KENYON, A. S., *J. Colloid Sci.,* **2**, 257 (1947).
15. TAKIYAMA, K., *Bull. Chem. Soc. Japan,* **31**, 944 (1958).
16. KOLTHOFF, I. M. AND BOWERS, R. C., *J. Am. Chem. Soc.,* **76**, 1503 (1954).
17. BILTZ, W., *Ber.,* **37**, 1095 (1904).
18. TAKIYAMA, K., *Bull. Chem. Soc. Japan,* **31**, 369, 555 (1958).
19. KERKER, M., JONES, G. L., REED, J. B., YANG, N. P., AND SCHOENBERG, M. D., *J. Phys. Chem.,* **58**, 1147 (1954).
20. LaMER, V. K., *Ind. Eng. Chem.,* **44**, 1270 (1952).
21. HARKINS, W. D., *J. Am. Chem. Soc.,* **69**, 1436 (1947).
22. BRADFORD, E. B., VANDERHOFF, J. W., AND ALFREY, T., *J. Colloid Sci.,* **11**, 135 (1956).
23. WATILLON, A., VAN GRUNDERBEECK, F., AND HAUTECLER, M., *Bull. Soc. Chim. Belg.,* **67**, 5 (1958).
24. TAKIYAMA, K., *Bull. Chem. Soc. Japan,* **31**, 950 (1958).
25. OTTEWILL, R. H., AND WOODBRIDGE, R. F., in press.
26. BUCKLEY, H. E., "Crystal Growth," 458, Wiley, New York (1952).

144

27. REHBINDER, P., *Disc. Faraday Soc.*, **18**, 151 (1954).
28. HORNE, R. W., MATIJEVIĆ, E., OTTEWILL, R. H., AND WEYMOUTH, J. W., *Kolloid-Z.*, **161**, 50 (1958).
29. AMMANN-BRASS, H., *Chimia*, **10**, 173 (1956).
30. PERRY, E. J., *J. Colloid Sci.*, **14**, 27 (1959).
31. MIRNIK, M., STROHAL, P., WRISCHER, M., AND TEŽAK, B., *Kolloid-Z.*, **160**, 146 (1958).
32. REICKE, W. D., "Proc. First Regional European Conference on Electron Microscopy," 98, Stockholm, 1956.
33. SUITO, E. AND UYEDA, N., "Proc. International Conference on Electron Microscopy," 223, London, 1954.
34. HEIDENREICH, R. D., *Phys. Rev.*, **62**, 291 (1942).
35. MOLLENSTEDT, G., *Optik*, **10**, 72 (1953).
36. RANG, O., *Z. Phys.*, **136**, 465, 547 (1953).
37. ITO, K. AND ITO, T., *J. Electronmicroscopy* (Japan), **1**, 18 (1953).
38. HIRSCH, P. B., HORNE, R. W., AND WHELAN, M. J. *Phil. Mag.*, **1**, 677 (1956).
39. WHELAN, M. J., HIRSCH, P. B., HORNE, R. W. AND BOLLMANN, W., *Proc. Roy. Soc.*, **A240**, 524 (1957).
40. HORNE, R. W. AND OTTEWILL, R. H., *J. Phot. Sci.*, **6**, 39 (1958).
41. HORNE, R. W. OTTEWILL, R. H., "Fourth International Conference on Electron Microscopy," Berlin, Springer Verlag, *1*, 140 (1960).
42. BRADLEY, D. E., *Brit. J. Appl. Phys.*, **10**, 198 (1959).
43. ANDERSON, N. G. AND DAWSON, I. M., *Proc. Roy. Soc.*, **A218**, 255 (1953).
44. BERRIMAN, R. W. AND HERZ, R. H., *Nature*, **180**, 293 (1957).
45. HAMILTON, J. F., AND BRADY, L. E., *J. Appl. Phys.*, **29**, 994 (1958).
46. HAMILTON, J. F., BRADY, L. E. AND HAMM, F. A., *J. Appl. Phys.*, **29**, 800 (1958).
47. LEVENSON, G. I. P. AND TABOR, J. H., *Sci. and Indust. Phot.*, **23**, 295 (1952).
48. KLEIN, E., *Mitt. Forsch. Agfa*, 10 (1955).
49. HAMM, F. A., AND COMER, J. J., *J. Appl. Phys.*, **24**, 1495 (1953).
50. SAWKILL, J., *Proc. Roy. Soc.*, **A229**, 135 (1955).
51. GOODMAN, J. F., *Proc. Roy. Soc.*, **A247**, 346 (1958).
52. HAMILTON, J. F., HAMM, F. A., AND BRADY, L. E., *J. Appl. Phys.*, **27**, 874 (1956).
53. HOERLIN, H. AND HAMM, F. A., *J. Appl. Phys.*, **24**, 1514 (1953).
54. VON ARDENNE, M., *Z. Phys.*, **120**, 397 (1943); *Kolloid-Z.*, **108**, 195 (1944).
55. PREUSS, L. E. AND WATSON, J. H. L., *J. Appl. Phys.*, **21**, 902 (1950).
56. TURKEVICH, J. AND HILLIER, J., *Anal. Chem.*, **21**, 475 (1949).

R. H. OTTEWILL

CRYSTAL LATTICE RESOLUTION

The ultimate goal of electron microscopy is, of course, the resolution of atoms in any structure, and this possibility has been analyzed theoretically by several of the eminent workers. If atoms or molecules are regularly arranged in a crystal lattice there is a much stronger chance of resolved image formation than in the case of two isolated atoms because there are definite phase relationships between electrons scattered from neighboring noncoherent atoms. The resolving power of the best electron microscopes produced in the world is limited first by diffraction error and spherical error to about 2.8 A, and chromatic error and astigmatism increase this to at least 7 A. At this value it should be possible to observe crystal lattices in crystals with fairly large lattice parameters of the order of 10 A or greater.

Great success prior to 1956 in the investigation of macromolecular crystals of viruses and proteins by the replica technique had been achieved by Wyckoff and associates at the National Institutes of Health (3). The surface of a needle-shaped crystal of the jack bean protein concanavallin, with molecule weight 42,000, among the smallest thus far replicated, reveals a rectangular net of about 62 × 87 A of particles (30–40 A in diameter) which are not in contact. The most likely next step downward in dimensions would be for crystals of organic molecules of intermediate molecular weights, sufficiently thin and properly oriented for direct transmission micrographs.

Menter (1) was the first to produce electron micrographs of the lattice planes in crystals. He was particularly fortunate in his choice of metal phthalocyanins, especially

145

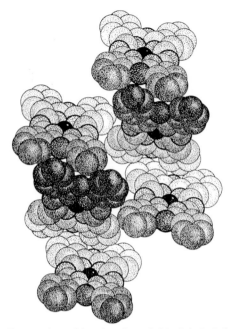

FIG. 1. A packing drawing of the nickel phthalocyanine structure viewed along the b_0-axis. The metallic atom is black, the nitrogen atoms are line-shaded. (*R. W. G. Wyckoff,* "*Crystal Structures*")

the copper and platinum derivations of phthalocyanin, a blue dye with a flat ring structure (Fig. 1) and the metal atom in the center. The crystal structure of platinum phthalocyanin may be considered to comprise fairly widely spaced planes of heavy metal atoms ($d_{201} = 11.94$ A) embedded in a matrix of the light elements nitrogen, carbon and hydrogen. The thin ribbon habit of the crystal is such that when supported on a specimen grid the $20\bar{1}$ planes are almost parallel to the electron beam. The electron micrograph at a magnification of 1,500,000 (Fig. 2) shows the clearly resolved planes spaced 11.94 A apart. Similarly the copper phthalocyanin shows a spacing of 9.8 A. These parallel lines are the image of the projection of the $20\bar{1}$ planes seen edge on. Imperfections are seen sometimes in the form of edge dislocations (Fig. 2) caused by incomplete planes. It has been possible also to resolve the 111 planes of the inorganic crystal sodium faujasite, a silicate with the com-

position 2 $Al_2O_3 \cdot CaO \cdot Na_2O \cdot 10SiO_2 \cdot 20H_2O$, with a spacing of 14.37 A.

The mechanism of image formation depends upon the fact that the thin crystals form a cross grating diffraction spectrum. With a 50-micron objective aperture the spectra contributing to the image from the phthalocyanin crystals are ($20\bar{1}$), ($40\bar{2}$), ($\bar{2}01$) and ($\bar{4}02$). These spectra recombine with the zero order beam in the image plane and form an image of the crystal grating in accordance with the simple Abbe theory of image formation by a lens. Calculations by Menter suggest that it should be possible to resolve planes with spacings considerably smaller than 10 A providing the divergence of the illuminating beam is made sufficiently small.

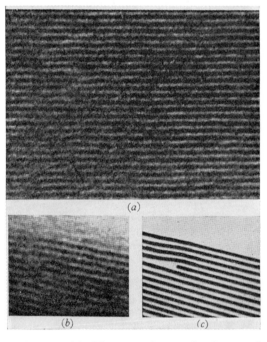

FIGS. 2. (a). Electron micrograph of part of crystal of platinum phthalocyanine showing image of lattice planes 12 A apart. Magnification 1,500,-000×. (b). Part of crystal of platinum phthalocyanine showing edge dislocation. The dislocation line is perpendicular to the plane of the paper. Magnification as before. (c). Sketch copied from (b) showing exact position of extra plane of molecules. (Menter)

If this is accomplished in practice there will be new possibilities for studying crystal structures and detecting imperfections. The images are poor Fourier projections and fail to reveal detail obtained by x-ray analysis; but they do reveal the exact location of imperfections, thus permitting the direct study of the behavior of dislocations in solids under a variety of physical conditions.

Very recently, as reported in the July 4, 1960 *Chem. Eng. News*, it has been demonstrated that electron microscopy can show the actual structure of soap multilayers at the molecular level. Two workers at the Research Institute for Advanced Study in Baltimore, Md., have made micrographs that picture highly regular sequences of light and dark bands. And the spacing of these bands conforms with the length of fatty acid chains that make up the soaps, they find.

This combination of electron microscopy and film techniques is the first observational method to confirm the double-layer spacing of multilayers, Dr. Hans J. Trurnit told the 34th National Colloid Symposium sponsored by the ACS Division of Colloid Chemistry, at Lehigh University. The double spacing (previously derived from optical and x-ray methods) results from a head-to-head, tail-to-tail arrangement when the layers are laid down on the surface.

Dr. Trurnit and his associate, George Schidlovsky, build the multilayer soap films on methacrylic ester slides. Then they expose sample strips of the slides to osmium tetroxide (contrast inducer and fixing agent), imbed them in the polymerizing plastic, and slice them into thin sections (about 500 A.). They could not use free fatty acids because of their solubility in the plastic bed.

Dark bands in the electron micrographs correspond to sheaths of metal ions in the soap layers, when the metal used has a high enough atomic number to give electron scattering. Magnesium ions do not register, but calcium, barium, and other such ions do show up. Also, unsaturated fatty acids show an extra dark band caused by osmium attached to the double bonds.

The RIAS workers have compared separate micrographs of multilayers made from C_{16}, C_{22}, and C_{36} acids salts. Periodicities of the bands show ratios of 16 to 22 to 36. With longer chain barium soaps, the lighter bands increase in width while the dark bands (metal ions) remain constant. The width of the dark bands is greater than the actual thickness (2 to 3 A) of the metal ion double sheath, but resolution of the electron microscope goes down only to 8 to 15 A.

The band image of the micrographs represents actual "multilayer architecture" and not merely interference fringes. For one thing, structures of 40, 80, or 120 double layers of soap molecules (made of saturated fatty acids) show exactly 40, 80, or 120 bands, as the case may be. Moreover, such details as line dislocations in the micrographs are noted as in the case of the metal phthalocyanins.

REFERENCES

1. MENTER, J. W., "Electron Microscopy, Proceedings of Stockholm Conference, Sept. 1956," Academic Press, N. Y., 1957, p. 88.
2. NEIDER, R., *Ibid.*, p. 93.
3. WYCKOFF, R. W. G., *Koninkl. Nederl. Akad. Wetenschappen, Amsterdam, Proc.*, **B59,** 449 (1956).

GEORGE L. CLARK

DISLOCATIONS IN METALS. *See* TRANSMISSION ELECTRON MICROSCOPY OF METALS—DISLOCATIONS AND PRECIPITATION, p. 291.

ELECTRON OPTICS: ELECTRON GUN AND ELECTROMAGNETIC AND ELECTROSTATIC LENSES

The electron optical system of the electron microscope comprises (a) an electron gun in which electrons emitted from the tip of a hot tungsten hairpin-shaped filament are accelerated to produce a narrow conical divergent beam of electron illumination to ir-radiate the object; (b) a condenser lens to concentrate the beam onto the object and incorporate an aperture system to control the angular aperture of the irradiating beam; (c) an objective lens and objective aperture followed by one or two projector lenses to form an image of the object on a fluorescent screen or photographic plate magnified usually between 1,000 and 200,000 times. The condenser lens may be a double one to allow the reduction of the area of illumination to minimize heat dissipation at the object. The objective lens must have the minimum spherical and chromatic aberration and astigmatism consistent with meeting the geometric requirement of allowing adequate space for the object holder and objective aperture, and their manipulation. The projector lenses must be designed to give the widest range of magnification possible without image distortion.

The Electron Gun

The electron gun used in the electron microscope utilizes a tungsten wire hairpin cathode, an apertured grid and an anode. An example of a typical electrode system is shown in Figure 1. The anode is at ground potential and the cathode at the full 50–100 kv accelerating potential. The grid is operated with a negative bias of a few hundred volts with respect to cathode.

To obtain even barely adequate final image intensity at magnifications of 50 to 100,-000 required for high resolution working, the requirements for gun performance are stringent. Since the illumination beam angle is limited to give optimum resolving power, the main gun requirement is to give the maximum possible current density per unit solid angle of emergent beam. Langmuir (1937) has shown that a theoretical limit to the current density per unit solid angle (or "brightness") is imposed by the spread in the emission velocities of the electrons from the cathode. The limiting value of brightness (β) is given by:

$$\beta = \rho_c \phi_0 / \pi k T \qquad (1)$$

where ρ_c is the emission current density, φ_0 the accelerating voltage, k = Boltzman's constant (8.6×10^{-5} e.V./°K) and T the absolute temperature.

It can readily be shown that the current density obtainable in a focused image of the virtual gun source is independent of the magnification of the focusing system where the beam angle is fixed. Haine and Einstein (1952) have shown that the electron microscope gun will give this theoretical brightness, for a wide range of geometrical configurations of the electrodes, provided optimum bias conditions are maintained. A certain choice of geometrical configurations will give a narrower angle of divergence of the beam and hence conserve total current. Thus, increase of the cathode shield diameter and reduction of the height of the cathode behind the shield both reduce beam angle and therefore total current. Under such con-

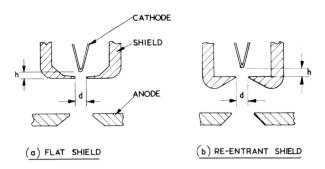

(a) FLAT SHIELD   (b) RE-ENTRANT SHIELD

Fig. 1. The typical geometry of an electron gun.

ditions the optimum bias potential is increased but the brightness and hence the image intensity is unchanged.

Haine, Einstein and Borcherds (1958) have discussed the use of automatic bias, i.e., the generation of bias potential by the potential drop across a resistance connected in series with the high voltage supply. Apart from the simplicity of this arrangement, the negative feedback action of the gun mutual conductance and series resistor gives a high degree of stabilizing action to the beam current. Further restrictions are imposed on the choice of geometrical configuration to ensure that the bias potential is maintained at the optimum value.

To obtain adequate image intensity for very high resolution working (3 to 10 A), the electron gun cathode must be operated at an emission density of 1 to 3 amp/cm². This emission current density requires an operating temperature at which the tungsten cathode life, as limited by evaporation, is only a few tens of hours (Bloomer 1957).

Electron Lenses

The requirements of the electron microscope are met with magnetic or electrostatic lenses which provide a "bell-shaped" magnetic field or electrostatic potential distributions along the axis. The magnetic lens comprises a solenoidal excitation coil wound on an axially symmetric iron circuit with a gap in the core and an axial hole bored to allow the passage of the electrons. Basically the lenses comprise parallel pole pieces spaced S cm apart and an axial hole diameter D cm with an excitation NI ampere-turns applied between the pole pieces (Figure 2). Little or no advantage is gained by changing the shape of the pole pieces from this simple geometry.

The electrostatic lens comprises basically three parallel plate electrodes with axial holes. The outer plates are at ground potential and the central one at the negative potential of the electron gun cathode. The electrodes are usually shaped to minimize the surface electric field strength to avoid flashovers, but the lens theory applied to the

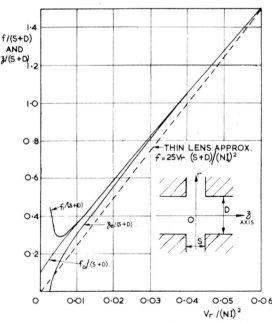

FIG. 2. Curves showing the focal properties of magnetic lenses as functions of the excitation parameter. $V_r/(NI)^2$.

simple shape gives results of adequate accuracy for practical purposes (Archard 1954).

The relations between the geometric factors, applied excitation and the focal properties and aberrations have been calculated and measured by many different workers (e.g., Glaser, 1941, Ramberg, 1942, Lenz 1950, Liebmann and Grad, 1951). The results are now well established and it is more relevant to describe these results than the methods for deriving them. The results are more complete for the magnetic than for the electrostatic lens, but those for the latter are adequate to show its inferiority. All the relevant properties are given in a series of universal curves derived from data calculated by Liebmann and Grad (1951).

The first order focal properties of importance are the focal length (f_0, for objective and f_1, for projector) and focal distance (z_0). These parameters can be expressed in the simple universal curves of Figure 2 in terms of the ratios $f_0/(S + D)$, $f_1/(S + D)$, $z_0/(S + D)$ and the excitation parameter $V_r/$ $(NI)^2$ where eV_r is the relativistically corrected electron energy, and NI the effective ampere-turn excitation of the lens. By effective is meant the ampere-turn excitation drop across the lens gap. The dotted line in the figure represents the thin lens approximation given by

$$f = 25 \, V_r(S + D)/(NI)^2 \qquad (2)$$

It is seen that the projector focal length passes through a minimum. This is of importance in that it determines the maximum magnification which can be obtained with a given stage length.

Of paramount importance is the spherical aberration of the objective lens which sets the ultimate limit of resolving power. The spherical aberration is defined by the constant C_s where $C_s \, \alpha^3$ gives the radial error in position of a ray leaving the object at angle α with the axis, the distance being measured in object space.

The value of C_s/f is given within an error of $\pm 10\%$ for values of the ratio S/D between 0.2 and 2 by the full curve of Figure 3. The

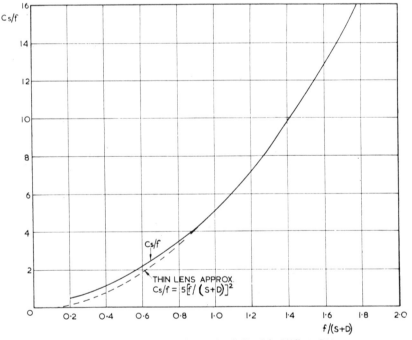

FIG. 3. Variation of the ratio C_s/f with $f/(S + D)^2$.

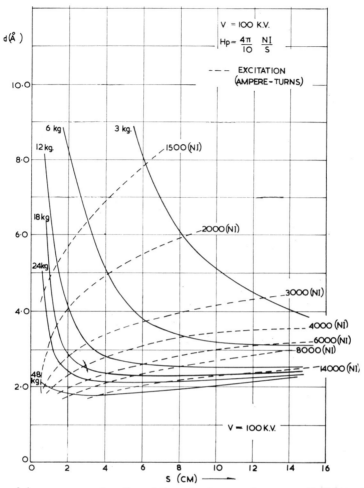

FIG. 4. The resolving power as a function of the pole piece spacing, magnetic field and excitation for 100 KeV electron energies.

dotted curve shows an approximation which becomes accurate for weak lenses and is given by:

$$C_s/f = 5[f/(S + D)]^2 \qquad (3)$$

The resolving power of the microscope is theoretically limited by spherical aberration (requiring a minimum aperture angle) and diffraction (requiring maximum aperture angle) to a minimum value (d) at an optimum aperture angle α, given by:

$$d = 0.43 \ C_s^{1/4}\lambda^{3/4} \qquad (4)$$
$$\alpha = 1.4(\lambda/C_s)^{1/4} \qquad (5)$$

Figure 4 shows the variation of resolving power under optimum aperture conditions as a function of pole piece spacing (S), magnetic field strength (H_p) and excitation (NI) for 100 Kev electron energy. It is seen that for a given field strength a flat optimum occurs around a particular value of spacing.

A further parameter of importance is the chromatic constant (C_c) which gives the variation of focal length with small changes in the high voltage or lens current

$$\delta f = C_c(\delta V/V - 2\delta I/I) \qquad (6)$$

δf must clearly be kept within the depth

151

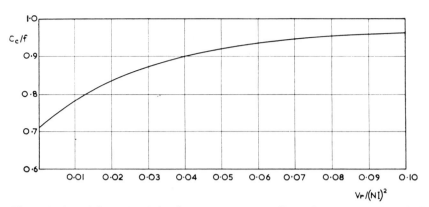

FIG. 5. The variation of the ratio of the chromatic constant (C_c) to the focal length with the excitation parameter $V_r/(NI)^2$.

of focus of the instrument. The value of C_c/f is given by the curve of Figure 5 as a function of the excitation parameter.

To ensure no limitation in resolving power or contrast, the variation in focal length (δf) due to ripple on the electron accelerating voltage or lens current supplies must be kept below one quarter the depth of focus of the instrument:

$$\delta f < 0.7 \; d^2/\lambda$$

This requires a voltage and current stability meeting the requirement:

$$\delta V/V - 2\delta I/I < 0.7 \; d^2/\lambda C_c$$

For a lens near the minimum focal length ($C_c \sim 0.4$ cm) and for a resolving power near the optimum ($\sim$2–4 A), the required stabilities are in the region of 2 or 3 parts in a million (Haine, 1960). The magnetic lens has the peculiar property of rotating the image with respect to the object.

Astigmatism arises in objective lenses as a result of very small departures from axial symmetry of the pole piece bores or faces. Only the elliptical component of asymmetry is of significance. To an adequate approximation the astigmatic distance between the tangential and sagittal foci (z_a) is given by the expression:

$$z_a = 100\delta(2 + 3 \; S/D)V_r/(NI)^2 \qquad (7)$$

where δ is the departure from symmetry.

For the astigmatism not to limit the resolving power, z_a should be small compared with the depth of focus. To achieve the necessary symmetry tolerance, which may be a few millionths of an inch for optimum resolving power, represents an almost impossible mechanical engineering task. Fortunately, it is possible to correct a small degree of residual astigmatism by the inclusion of a weak cylindrical lens of variable power and orientation. The progress of correction has been discussed in detail by Haine and Mulvey (1954).

Design Considerations

The number of stages of magnification included in the microscope is dependent on the maximum magnification and the range of magnification required. A fairly definite optimum of three stages can be deduced, giving two stages following the objective. The various factors affecting the choice of stage length and the focal length of the various lenses include the maximum and range of magnification, the minimum being limited by image distortion. The practical design of a lens for given pole piece geometry must ensure an adequate magnetic circuit, adequate heat dissipation from the excitation coil and a design which can be manufactured within very close symmetry tolerances. The magnetic design is discussed by Mulvey

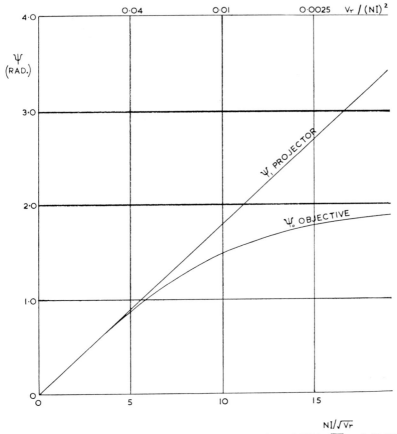

Fig. 6. The image rotation angle in radius plotted as a function of $NI/\sqrt{V_r}$ and $V_r/(NI)^2$ (on top scale).

(1953). Permissible thermal loading of the coil varies from about 800 ampere-turns per square centimeter of cross-sectional area of coil for a lens without water cooling, to 1200 ampere-turns per sq cm for a carefully designed water-cooled coil with no interleaving paper. The values are fairly independent of the wire size used, which may be chosen to give a coil impedance most suitable for the current supplies.

It was at one time thought that the great precision of symmetry required in the objective lens required the pole pieces to be manufactured separately from the main iron shroud and fitted precisely within its bore. That this is not so, and in fact leads to unnecessary complication, has been shown by Haine (1954). Although some manufacturers still utilize separate pole pieces, the tendency is toward the simpler lens made from two pieces of iron.

Electrostatic Lenses

The data for electrostatic lenses cannot be expressed by such simple means as for magnetic lenses. The variation of focal length and spherical aberration with the dimensions for three aperture unipotential lenses of spacing (S), central electrode aperture diameter D and thickness T are given in Figures 7 and 8.

The objective cannot be immersed in the electrostatic field and it will be seen that the spherical aberration is about an order of ten greater than for the magnetic lens.

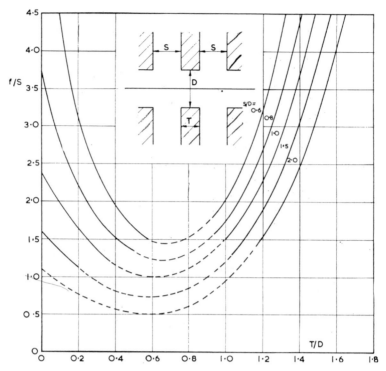

FIG. 7. The focal properties of an electrostatic lens as a function of its geometry.

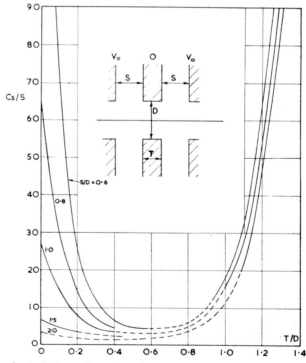

FIG. 8. The spherical aberration of an electrostatic lens as a function of its geometry.

154

REFERENCES

ARCHARD, G. A., "Proc. Internat. Conference on Electron Microscopy," London (1954). Published by the Royal Microscopical Society (1954).

BLOOMER, R. N., Brit. J. Appl. Phys., 8, 83 (1957).

GLASER, W., Z. Physik, 117, 285 (1941).

HAINE, M. E., "Proc. Internat. Conference on Electron Microscopy," London (1954). Published by the Royal Microscopical Society (1954).

HAINE, M. E., "The Electron Microscope" (E. and F. N. Spon Ltd., London).

HAINE, M. E. AND EINSTEIN, P. A., Brit. J. Appl. Phys., 3, 40 (1952).

HAINE, M. E., EINSTEIN, P. A., AND BORCHERDS, P. H., Brit. J. Appl. Phys., 9, 482 (1958).

HAINE, M. E. AND MULVEY, T., J. Sci. Instr., 31, 326 (1954).

LANGMUIR, D. B., Proc. I.R.E., 25, 977 (1937).

LEVY, F., Z. Angew. Phys., 2, 448 (1950).

LIEBMANN, G. AND GRAD, M. E., Proc. Phys. Soc (London), 64B, 956 (1951).

MULVEY, T., Proc. Phys. Soc (London), 66B, 441 (1953).

RAMBERG, E. G., J. Appl. Phys., 13, 582 (1942).

M. E. HAINE

FIBERS (TEXTILES). See GENERAL MICROSCOPY, p. 343.

HISTORY OF ELECTRON OPTICS

The history of electron optics starts more or less with the discovery of cathode rays. The earliest experiment of Plücker in 1859 already showed a rectilinear propagation of these rays. Ten years later, Hittorff discovered that cathode rays can be deflected by a magnetic field, and that an axially symmetrical magnetic field will concentrate such rays. Another ten years elapsed before Crookes demonstrated a better proof of rectilinear propagation. The first attempt to calculate the trajectory of charged particles in fields of forces originated with Riecke in 1881. These were rather incomplete, and the first quantitative theoretical and experimental studies on the deflection of an electron beam had to wait until 1897 when J. J. Thomson determined the ratio of the charge to mass of the elementary particles carrying the elementary quantity of electricity and confirmed, in a manner of speech, the beautiful calculations performed earlier the same year by H. A. Lorentz.

The first intentional use of a solenoid for concentration of cathode rays was done by Wiechert in 1899. He used a relatively long solenoid; a short coil for concentration was not used until 1903 by H. A. Ryan. In the same year, the first electrostatic concentration of an electron beam was performed by Wehnelt. Very extensive calculations of trajectories of charged particles in fields of forces were carried out in 1907 by C. Stoermer. The basic equations of electron optics are implicitly contained in the work of Stoermer, although this had not been recognized for many years.

The haphazard use of electron optical elements and of calculations was followed by a more deliberate one in the middle twenties of this century. De Broglie's thesis in 1924 on the wave nature of the electron became the foundation of physical electron optics. The formal foundation of geometrical electron optics was set down in 1926 by Busch. Busch actually considered a magnetic coil as an optical lens, and derived the lens equation for it, although he failed to use the coil as an imaging element.

The combination of these two discoveries stimulated thinking in two directions. Historically, the first was the development of applied physical electron optics in the form of electron diffraction. The momentous discovery of diffracted electron beams by Davisson and Germer in 1926–27 was soon followed by the similar experiment of G. P. Thomson. On the other hand, geometrical electron optical methods were first applied around 1929, when cathode ray oscillographs were built on the basis of electron optical elements. These attempts were pursued simultaneously by Brüche in Germany and by Zworykin in the United States.

The next step in the development of geometrical electron optics was the study of axially symmetrical fields as lens elements.

These studies started probably around 1929. At least, this is the date of a patent application on electrostatic lenses by Knoll. The first publications on the study of electrostatic and magnetic lens elements date from 1931 when Davisson and Calbick published a note on the focal length of an electrostatic lens and Knoll and Ruska studied the behavior of magnetic lenses. Further studies of electrostatic lenses were published by Brüche and collaborators.

Experimental electron microscopy had its beginning in 1931. The formal beginnings are marked by the patent application of Rüdenberg and the publication of a paper by Knoll and Ruska; however, the subject goes back at least three or four years earlier to discussions in physics colloquia in the Berlin area as seen from a publication by Gabor. Gabor's name should be mentioned here in another respect too. The studies of Knoll and Ruska on magnetic electron lenses were greatly facilitated by the fact that an ironclad magnetic lens had been developed in 1926–27 by Gabor. During 1931–32, the first instruments which merit the name of electron microscopes had been built. The first of these probably is one built by Knoll and Ruska for the observation of emitting objects, which utilized magnetic lenses. A second was the instrument built by Brüche and Johannsen, with electrostatic lenses, to study emission phenomena. Before the end of 1932, Marton had a simple instrument using a magnetic lens to investigate emission phenomena, and later transmission phenomena. During 1933, two instruments were built. One was Knoll and Ruska's revised and improved transmission instrument, using two magnetic stages and having a limiting magnification of 12,000. Marton's second instrument also used magnetic lenses for transmission observation, but it was simpler and its limiting magnification was of the order of 2,000. The first biological observations were carried out with Marton's two-stage instrument in 1934. Marton built in 1934 an improved two-stage instrument, incorporating a specimen chamber with two-way motion of the specimen and an air lock, as well as a photographic chamber for internal photography of the electron micrographs. This photographic chamber was also provided with an air lock.

The first electron micrographs of biological objects in 1934 were made on material impregnated with osmium salts because of the then prevalent notion that the electron beam would destroy any biological material. Within a year, it was recognized that this impregnation was not absolutely necessary and that by reducing the total exposure time and beam intensity one can achieve biological pictures without destroying the material. This was possible because of the introduction of the internal photography described above.

During 1934, Ruska had also demonstrated that the electron microscope had a resolution somewhat greater than that of the light microscope. These observations, combined with the theoretical prediction that the electron microscope is able to reach a resolving power exceeding that of the light microscope by a factor of several hundred, led to increasing efforts toward an improvement of the resolving power of the electron microscope.

From the beginning, it was understood that a good part of the mechanism of the image formation is due to scattering of the electrons within the transmission-type objects. Both Ruska and Marton referred to a scattering mechanism in their 1934 papers. In 1936, Marton made the first quantitative attempt to explain the image formation on the assumption of multiple scattering by the object. The same approach was used a couple of years later by von Ardenne. Very soon, however, it became obvious that the average specimen of electron microscopy is much too thin for multiple scattering. Consequently, Marton and Schiff in 1941 studied image formation assuming single scattering. In the postwar years, single scattering calculations were further improved by von Borries, Lenz and others.

In the meantime, efforts were under way

to improve the performance of the electron microscopes. These were twofold—one was building new microscopes of which a few merit brief mention: The instrument by Scott and McMillen (1936) for the emission-type observation of biological subjects. This was the first compound emission microscope in America. Second, the instrument of Martin, Whelpton, and Barnum in England (1937) which sparked the British work in this field; and the third, the new instrument of Ruska and von Borries (1938). This last instrument paved the way to the first commercial model, completed in 1939. There were also advances in applications. In 1937, Marton had taken the first bacteriological pictures. These were followed in 1938–39 by improved bacteriological pictures by Ruska and collaborators. The first virus pictures were obtained by Helmut Ruska, brother of Ernst Ruska, in 1940.

In 1938–39, some papers also appeared by von Ardenne analyzing some of the defects of the microscope. The most important single item probably was an analysis of the alignment defects on the basis of which von Ardenne built a very complicated and highly successful instrument establishing a temporary world record of 30 A for resolving power. Coincident with that development was development also of the first electrostatic microscope by Mahl and Boersch, as well as the development of the first Canadian microscope by Burton, Prebus and Hillier. This was followed by the development of the first American commercial model—the RCA Type A was completed by Marton in 1940, followed by RCA Type B in 1941 by Zworykin, Hillier, and Vance. These two last-named instruments were the first ones to use highly regulated electronic power supplies. The German work relied on the stability of storage batteries to achieve the required constancy of the magnetic lenses.

Japanese work on electron microscopy started in 1939 partly by Higashi and Tani, also by Tadano.

All the above-described instruments used two-stage magnification. Around 1941, Hillier attempted to use a compound projection lens. Three-stage magnification was introduced in 1942–43 by Marton. This idea was taken up, probably independently, late in 1944 by Ruska and von Borries in a patent application, and in 1944–46 by Le Poole. Le Poole also introduced selected area diffraction as an adjunct to electron microscopy, using a three-stage arrangement.

The postwar years have seen the rapid development of commercially available models in different countries. An important contribution to the present-day development was recognition of the role of lens astigmatism by Hillier and Ramberg in 1946. Recognition of this defect led, in the ensuing years, to the development of different types of electrostatic or magnetic stigmators and produced the present high resolving power of modern instruments. The existence of the high resolution transmission type microscope stimulated the development of several related instruments. First of these was the so-called scanning microscope proposed by von Ardenne in 1938, followed by further improvements by Zworykin, Hillier, and Snyder in 1942. In 1939, the electron shadow microscope was proposed by Boersch. In the same year, 1939, von Ardenne proposed the X-ray shadow microscope. The practical development of this instrument had to wait until the 1950's when Cosslett and Nixon built the first working instrument. Another related instrument is the microprobe analyzer of Castaing first described in 1951. Ion microscopes are another group of derived instruments. The first attempt was made with lithium ions in 1947 by Boersch. In 1949, Magnan and Chanson published the first description of a proton microscope.

The 1932 attempts of Knoll and Ruska, as well as Brüche and Johannsen, in emission microscopy has been mentioned earlier. The resolving power of these emission microscopes was quite poor, and no progress was made until Recknagel in 1941 developed a theory of immersion objectives. In 1942,

Mecklenburg and Mahl produced much better emission micrographs with thermionic electrons.

Secondary electrons for producing emission microscopy had been first used in the middle thirties. A crude image had been shown in 1933 by Zworykin, and a year or two later Knoll had shown better results. The best results to date are those of Möllenstedt in 1953, who replaced the primary electrons with ions for the excitation of secondary electrons.

Photo emission as a source of emission microscopy had been first used by Brüche and by Pohl in 1933 and 1934. The method has been further developed in the hands of Grivet and Septier in 1956.

The most spectacular emission microscope is not a true microscope in the optical sense. Field emission microscopy started with a two-dimensional model of Johnson and Shockley in 1936. Very soon thereafter, in 1935–37, Mueller developed the point emission microscope. This was followed in 1951 by the invention of a field ion microscope with a best achieved resolving power of about 2.7 A.

A method derived from dark field microscopy is the so-called schlieren observation of electrostatic and magnetic fields and other perturbations of the optical medium. One of the first observations of this kind was published by Boersch in 1937, when he demonstrated the dark field image of a vapor stream. In 1943–44, von Ardenne deliberately produced schlieren conditions. Due to the war, this paper was not known in the United States, and it was independently discovered by Marton in 1946–47 who with Simpson and Lachenbruch applied this method for quantitative evaluation of magnetic fields.

As this review is limited to the electron microscopical aspects of electron optics, a very brief enumeration of other developments of electron optics may be sufficient. The oscilloscope tube development was started in 1894 by A. Hess and in 1897 by F. Braun. These early tubes used gaseous discharge with cold cathodes. The hot cathode in the cathode ray tube was introduced by Wehnelt in 1903. The first proposals for the use of cathode ray tubes as image transmitting elements were made in 1906–07 by Dieckmann and Glage, as well as by Rosing. Storage of the image now used in television pickup tubes was first announced in 1908 by Campbell-Swinton. Modern development is linked to the names of Zworykin between 1925–33, Round in 1926, Farnsworth in 1927, and Henroteau in 1929.

Mass spectrographs are another interesting chapter of electron optics. They were first conceived by J. J. Thomson in 1897; 180° magnetic deflection was first used by Classen in 1908. Ten years later, Dempster used magnetic focusing; and in 1919, Aston invented velocity focusing. Modern mass spectroscopy (developed in 1932–34) is linked to the names of Herzog and Mattauch who developed the electron optics of mass spectroscopy devices, as well as Bainbridge, Barber, and Stephens.

The development of electron optical theory is linked to three names essentially: Stoermer we mentioned earlier, but the formal theory of axially symmetrical devices was not developed until the years 1933–36. Foremost are the names of Glaser and Scherzer: the first used an essentially Fermat-Hamiltonian approach, whereas the latter preferred the trajectory method. The first linking of geometrical electron optical theory to wave mechanics was done by Glaser in 1943.

We now present a short description of the development of physical electron optics. Electron diffraction instrumentation for the observation of crystallographic structures has been greatly improved by the addition of a magnetic lens to the diffraction instrumentation by Lebedeff, in 1931. Modern diffractographs took advantage of the high resolving power of combined electron optical and diffraction elements as manifested by the instrument developed by Cowley and Rees in 1952.

Boersch has contributed greatly to the understanding of the physical optics of electron microscopical phenomena. First he had shown, in 1936, the correlation between diffraction diagram and the electron optical image. Recognition of this fact was essentially responsible for the development of all modern combined electron microscopical and diffraction instrumentation. In 1941, he showed the correlation between image properties of crystalline objects and Bragg reflection. Then, in 1943, he discovered the existence of Fresnel diffraction in electron microscopical images. This discovery led in 1946 to the observation of phase contrasts by Hillier and Ramberg and to the method called "microscopy by reconstructed wavefronts" invented by Gabor in 1948.

Electron interferometry started with a proposal by Marton in 1952. Following this proposal, Marton, Simpson, and Suddeth built a three-crystal, wide beam interferometer in 1953. About the same time, accidental interferences had been observed in electron microscope images by Rang. The use of Fresnel biprisms for electron interferometry was introduced in 1954 by Möllenstedt and Düker.

L. Marton

IMAGE FORMATION MECHANISM

Two criteria are commonly used for judging an image formed by an optical system: one is resolution, and the second is contrast. Some of the factors governing both are common, and for this reason the ensuing discussion will consider both. The essential mechanism, responsible for both qualities, is scattering of electrons in the broadest physical sense. It is customary, however, to designate the coherent effects of scattering from an aggregate of atoms by the term "diffraction," reserving thus the expression "scattering" to

the manifestations of localized electron-specimen interaction at the atomic or quasi-atomic level. These two effects constitute the major contributions to resolution and contrast in the image. Two minor contributions are called "refraction" and "absorption." Refraction is that process in which the major change brought about by the scattering is limited to a change in the phase of the wave function, while in absorption there is a large change in the amplitude of the wave function due to the scattering.

In this discussion of image formation, we will consider only those effects which arise from the interaction of the electrons with the object and those modifications of these effects which are produced by the properties and defects of the optical system. However, the general effect of the optical properties of the system on image formation will not be treated.

Diffraction is due to the wave nature of the electron which produces deviations from the simple geometrical model of energy propagation. These deviations are manifested by the appearance of dark and bright bands, the Fresnel diffraction fringes. The least resolved distance of an optical instrument (most commonly called resolving power) can be taken to be the distance at which the first diffraction maximum from a point-like object coincides with the zeroth diffraction maximum of the next object. Using this so-called Rayleigh criterion in the Abbè relation, we obtain

$$\delta = \frac{0.61\lambda}{n \sin \alpha} \tag{1}$$

where δ is the least resolved distance, λ is the wave length of the electron ($\lambda = h/p$, where h is the Planck constant and p is the momentum of the electron), and α is the aperture angle of the optical system. n is the refractive index of the electron optical medium which for many applications can be assumed to be unity. The numerical constant 0.61 changes if another criterion is substituted for the Rayleigh criterion in the definition of the least resolved distance. Equation (1) can be derived either from the theory of Fraunhofer diffraction or from the quantum mechanical uncertainty relation. Both relations give qualitatively the same results within a small numerical factor.

Contrast is also governed to some extent by the diffraction phenomena at the edge of an object. Using the theory of diffraction, the fringe distribution at the edges of an opaque or semi-opaque object can be calculated; and such calculations have been found to be in reasonably close agreement with experiment, provided that in the case of semi-opaque objects a refractive index of the material, corresponding to an internal potential of 10–15 ev, is assumed. The experiments show that fringes appear in out-of-focus images and that the fringe spacing depends upon the degree of defocusing of the image. The apparent contrast at the edge of an image is optimum in the slightly defocused image. For perfect focusing, the contrast is found to be lower than for the out-of-focus condition.

The intensity distribution in Fresnel diffraction fringes can be interpreted as interference phenomena. Accidentally occurring interference fringes can be observed also in selected specimen areas illustrating again the role played by interference phenomena in the contrast in the image plane.

In the case of crystalline specimens, diffraction from the lattice planes can produce an important modification of the intensity distribution in the image plane. Electrons which are scattered from a crystal lattice will show diffraction maxima according to Bragg's equation

$$2 d \sin \Theta = n\lambda \qquad (2)$$

where d is the distance between the lattice planes, Θ is the angle between the direction of the incident beam and the diffracting planes, and n is an integer.

If an electron beam is directed so that it makes an angle Θ (satisfied by equation (2)) with a lattice plane of the crystal, essentially specular reflection may occur from this lattice plane. If the optical system of the electron microscope has a wide enough aperture to collect both the primary beam and the reflected (diffracted) beam, and the objective is properly focused so that the two beams are brought to the same focus, the intensity distribution in the image of the crystal will appear to be what may be called "normal." If the objective aperture, however, is small with respect to the Bragg angle, such that the reflected beam will be intercepted (most of the intensity being in the reflected beam), the directly transmitted part of the image will appear unusually dark. A further manifestation for this phenomenon is when a wide aperture system is slightly defocused and both the dark and bright images appear side by side. This variation in intensity, due to Bragg reflection, contributes also to appearances of the so-called extinction contours. These extinction contours appear in slightly bent crystals where, accidentally, part of the crystal happens to be at the proper angle to show Bragg reflection. Under action of the electron beam, thin crystals may warp, showing a displacement of the extinction contours while under observation.

Related also to Bragg reflection is the observation of crystal defects, such as dislocations, stacking faults, etc. Due to the existence of these crystal defects, certain lattice planes show different orientations from the surrounding lattice planes and produce in this manner a marked contrast in the final image.

While the above considerations are restricted to Fresnel diffraction and to crystalline diffraction, Gabor has demonstrated that diffraction phenomena may be important in noncrystalline specimens too. He proposed the use of a coherent electron beam for forming a diffraction image, called hologram, of the specimen. In principle, such a diffraction image should contain all information about the specimen except the phase. Through the use of proper optical equipment, the image can be reconstructed from such a hologram in a process called "microscopy by reconstructed wave fronts." Although practical difficulties until now made it impossible to reach high resolutions by this method, its existence amply shows the importance of diffraction in the image forming process.

At extremely high resolution, crystal lattices and other periodic structures can be observed provided that the aperture of the system allows the zero order spectrum to pass together with at least one of the first-order diffraction spectra. This is in agreement with the Abbé theory of image formation in light optics. Moiré patterns are due to the combination of a doubly diffracted beam, originating on overlapping crystals, with the incident beam.

The intensity at any point of the image is governed by the number of electrons which have been scattered within the solid angle formed by the aperture of the objective lens. This number can be written as

$$I = I_0 e^{-N\sigma x} \tag{3}$$

where I_0 is the number of electrons in the primary beam before interacting with the specimen, x is the thickness of the specimen, N is the number of scattering atoms per unit volume, and σ is the scattering cross section. The scattering cross section is essentially made up of two components

$$\sigma = \sigma_e + \sigma_i \tag{4}$$

where σ_e is the elastic scattering cross section, i.e., the scattering cross section for all electrons which have not suffered any change of energy in the scattering act; σ_i is the inelastic scattering cross section i.e., the cross section for those electrons which suffered an energy loss in the scattering act.

There have been a number of attempts to calculate these cross sections. As an example, we follow the treatment of Lenz as given in a recent paper. This calculated cross section

for the elastically scattered electrons is given by

$$\frac{d\sigma_e}{d\Omega} = \frac{4}{a_H^2 q^4} (Z - f)^2 \tag{5}$$

where

$$d\Omega = \sin \vartheta d\vartheta d\varphi \tag{5'}$$

$$a_H = h^2 (4\pi^2 m_0 \epsilon^2)^{-1} \tag{5''}$$

$$q = \frac{4\pi}{\lambda} \sin \frac{\vartheta}{2} \tag{5'''}$$

Z is the atomic number of the element constituting the specimen, f is the so-called form factor, ϑ and φ are the angles defining the solid angle, m_0 is the rest mass of the electron, ϵ is its charge, and h again Planck's constant.

For the description of the inelastic process, Lenz adds an inelastic scattering function, S, to the right side of equation (5) and obtains

$$\frac{d\sigma}{d\Omega} = \frac{4}{a_H^2 q^4} (Z - f)^2 + S \tag{6}$$

in this equation, (5''') is modified so that

$$q \approx \frac{2\pi}{\lambda} \sqrt{\vartheta^2 + \left(\frac{\Delta E}{2E}\right)^2} \tag{6'}$$

and the inelastic scattering function is

$$S = Z - \frac{f^2}{Z} \quad \text{for} \quad \vartheta \ll 1 \tag{6''}$$

provided Wentzel's approximations are correct. In equation (6'), E represents the energy of the incident electron and ΔE the energy lost in the scattering act. In earlier calculations for this last quantity, half of the average ionization energy was assumed. In some cases, it may be more justified to substitute, instead of the ionization energy, the measured characteristic energy losses in the specimen.

Attention should be called to the fact that calculations of cross sections at best are approximations. Accurate wave functions are generally unavailable and, in their absence, all calculations have to be taken with a grain of salt. In addition, the reader should be warned that experimental data on this subject are equally unreliable at present. In fact, some papers on scattering cross section of atoms to electrons do not report cross sections at all, but relative numbers of electrons scattered into small angles.

Indications of how to enhance the contrasts may be obtained by studying the above equations. The simplest way is by increasing the atomic number of selected areas of the object. In a specimen of homogeneous constitution, where the object has only variations in thickness, this may not be always easy to do and shadowing techniques can be of great help, preferably if shadowing is done with material of high atomic number. An alternate method is staining. Staining in the electron optical sense is the introduction of higher atomic number elements in the material of the specimen. Reduction of the primary energy of the electron also enhances contrast in special cases, because the scattering cross section increases with decreasing energy. In similar cases the reduction of the objective aperture enhances contrast because of the higher proportion of large-angle scattered electrons from the electron optically denser portions of the specimen.

Another mechanism for producing intensity modulation in the image is called phase contrast. A variation of the refractive index within the specimen will produce phase changes. By causing various parts of the beam to interfere, one can introduce intensity changes caused by the phase changes. The intensity at any point of the image plane is related to a phase change in a corresponding element of the object. These phase shifts have been calculated, and they are given by

$$\gamma = \beta^4 - n_\beta^2 \tag{7}$$

where

$$\beta = \sqrt[4]{\frac{\pi C_s}{2\,\lambda}} \tag{7'}$$

Here C_s is the spherical aberration constant of the lens.

The last mechanism affecting the intensity distribution in the image plane is absorption; both true absorption and what may be called "partial" absorption will be discussed. True absorption refers to an electron which is stuck in the substance of a specimen and cannot get out. Scattering considerations alone show that this is a highly unlikely event. At the conventional energies, at which electron microscopes operate, and the usual specimen thicknesses, the mean free path of an electron exceeds the specimen thickness by a very large amount. The probability of direct absorption is therefore practically nil. We may consider very briefly the number of electrons which may be deflected at 90° angle so that they take off within the specimen plane. Again the above expressions for the distribution of both elastically and inelastically scattered electrons as a function of angle show that this is a very unlikely event, and will not contribute substantially to the contrast in the image.

However, so-called "partial" absorption must be considered. This may be a misnomer because we are considering here the energy losses suffered by electrons passing through a specimen and interacting in an inelastic manner. Any electron which leaves the specimen with an energy different from the primary energy will contribute to an enlargement of the radius of the circle of least confusion. This radius is usually defined by

$$r = \alpha C_c \frac{\Delta E}{E} \tag{8}$$

where C_c is the chromatic aberration constant of the lens, and the other quantities are as defined above. Assuming that the primary beam has an energy distribution with a certain half width, an additional intensity distribution due to energy losses can be linearly superimposed.

For contrast considerations, we have to distinguish between two special cases. One is that the energy losses are all the so-called characteristic energy losses and are very well defined. In this case, we will have an object represented in the image plane by two circles of least confusion, one corresponding to the primary energy and the one to the primary energy minus the characteristic energy loss. This will result, in principle, in a doubling of the images, but as the difference in primary energy and primary energy minus characteristic energy are relatively small (of the order of 10–15 electron volts), the resulting doubling will be of the order of a few angstroms and will be hardly noticeable.

Furthermore, the effect will depend upon the relative cross sections for the elastic and inelastic event. If these two are widely different, then one of these circles of confusion will be predominant and the other will be disappearing in the background. The situation is changed if we consider not the characteristic event but a continuous energy distribution of inelastically scattered electrons. Such inelastically scattered electrons exist and have been measured extending over an energy range of several hundred electron volts below the primary energy. Although the cross section is relatively low, the wide energy distribution will contribute to a washing out of both the resolution and the contrast in the final image.

It is interesting to see in detail what the effect may be in approximately spherical objects. For very thin and small objects, a loss of contrast induced through the chromatic aberration of the inelastically scattered electrons is negligible. If the aperture of the illuminating beam is very small (α ill. $< 10^{-3}$ rad), the loss of contrast may be 15 % as defined by the scattering process alone (phase contrast is favored by a very small illuminating aperture). For objects of medium thickness (i.e., objects whose thickness corresponds approximately to the mean-free path of the electrons in the object) and for large objective apertures, a good part of the in-

elastically scattered electrons will be concentrated in the image and therefore the loss of contrast may be quite marked.

REFERENCES

BOERSCH, H., *Naturwiss.*, **28**, 709, 711 (1940); *Phys. Zs.*, **44**, 202 (1943); *Ann. Phys.*, **26**, 631 (1936); **27**, 75 (1936); *Zs. Phys.*, **118**, 706 (1942).

GABOR, D., *Proc. Roy. Soc.*, **A197**, 454 (1949); **B64**, 449 (1951); Nat. Bur. Stand. Circular **527**, 237 (1951).

GLASER, W., "Grundlagen der Elektronenoptik," Springer, Wien (1952); "Elektronen und Lonenoptik" in "Handbuch der Physik," Vol. XXXIII, Springer, Berlin (1956).

MENTER, J. W., *Phil. Mag. Supplement*, **7**, 27, p. 299 (1958).

MARTON, L., *Physica* **9**, 959 (1936); MARTON, L. AND SCHIFF, L. I., *J. Appl. Phys.*, **12**, 759 (1941).

BOERSCH, H., *Zs. Naturforsch.*, **2a**, 615 (1947).

MOTT, N. F. AND MASSEY, H. S. W., "The theory of atomic collisions," 2nd ed., Oxford (1949).

VON BORRIES, B., "Die Übermikroskopie," Edition Cantor (1949); *Zs. Naturforsch.*, **4a**, 51 (1951).

MASSEY, H. S. W. AND BURHOP, E. H. S., "Electronic and ionic impact phenomena, Oxford 1952).

LENZ, F., *Zs. Naturforsch.*, **9a**, 185 (1954); WYRWICH, H. AND LENZ, F., *Zs. Naturforsch.*, **13a**, 515 (1958).

UYEDA, R., *J. Phys. Soc. Japan*, **10**, 256 (1955).

HAINE, M. E. AND AGAR, A. W., *Brit. J. Appl. Phys.*, **10**, 341 (1959).

BOERSCH, H., *Mh. Chemie*, **78**, 163 (1947).

SCHERZER, O., *J. Appl. Phys.*, **20**, 20 (1949).

LOCQUIN, M., "Proc. Int. Conf. El. Micr.," London 1954.

LEISEGANG, S., "Elektronenmikroskope" in "Handbuch der Physik" **33**, Springer, Berlin, 1956.

MARTON, L., LEDER, L. B., MENDLOWITZ, H., "Adv. in Electronics and Electron Physics," **7**, 183 (1955).

MARTON, L., *et al.*, *Compt. Rend. Toulouse*, p. 175, 1955.

L. MARTON

KIDNEY ULTRASTRUCTURE

The mammalian kidney is a highly vascularized organ and the contact between its capillary bed and its functional units, the nephrons, is extensive. Each *nephron* consists of the *glomerulus*, a small spherical body in which the urine is formed by filtration from the blood capillaries; and the attached elongated *tubule*, which conducts the urine towards the renal pelvis by a simultaneous reabsorption of fluid and substances. The reabsorbed units are returned to the blood stream by a matter of diffusion into abundant capillaries which wind around the tubule. By this mechanism the body is prevented from a loss of large amounts of fluid and important substances.

While the glomerulus offers a fairly simple structural background for the filtration process, the tubule is more complicated from a structural point of view. The explanation for this is to be found in the manner in which reabsorption occurs. The tubule is divided into several structurally different segments and each segment seems to be responsible for the reabsorption of only certain substances.

The segmentation of the nephron can easily be revealed in the light microscope. The first portion of the tubule following the glomerulus is called *proximal convolution*. The next part is the *loop of Henle*, consisting of the straight descending loop, the thin segment, and the thick (straight) ascending limb. The latter connects with the *distal convolution* in the neighborhood of the glomerulus, followed by the short *cortical collecting duct*. This in turn leads into the *collecting tubule* and conducts the urine all the way to the renal pelvis.

In low magnification electron micrographs, the various segments of the nephron are easily compared and identified with those seen in the light microscope. But it is easier to note in what respect they differ structurally. The complexity of structures seen in high magnification electron micrographs more than well stresses the physiological differences recorded in the function of different parts of the nephron.

Glomerulus. The glomerulus is essentially a richly branched and interconnected · capillary network which is indented at the beginning of the tubular duct, the capsule of Bowman (Fig. 1). An afferent arteriole leads the blood into the capillaries and an efferent arteriole drains the vascular bed, directing most of the blood towards the capillary network which winds around the tubule. The wall of the *afferent arteriole* contains a number of highly granulated cells, the so called juxtaglomerular apparatus. These cells have been suggested to play a certain role in the production of the hormone renin which seems to have a constringent effect upon the wall of the arterioles. The fine structure of the granules in the juxtaglomerular cells is reminiscent of that which characterizes the granules of the endocrine glands elsewhere in the body. When the afferent arteriole has entered the capsule of Bowman, it divides into several main branches, each of which in turn gives rise to a number of interconnected smaller capillaries. The blood leaves the capillary bed of the glomerulus through the *efferent arteriole* which is formed by a confluence of several main capillary branches. No granulated cells can be detected in the wall of the afferent arteriole.

The capsule of Bowman is lined by squamous epithelial cells which are continuous with the columnar epithelial cells of the proximal convolution. The squamous cells form the parietal layer of Bowman's capsule, whereas the cells which cover the capillaries and actually represent the indented portion of Bowman's capsule form the visceral layer of Bowman's capsule. The space between the parietal and visceral layers is called the space of Bowman's capsule. This space is continuous with the lumen of the tubule and it is into this space the urine is filtered. The entire Bowman's capsule is surrounded by a basement membrane which, at the vascular pole (where the arterioles enter and leave the capsule) is continuous with the basement membranes of the arterioles and at the urinary pole (beginning of the tubule) is continuous with the basement membrane of the tubule.

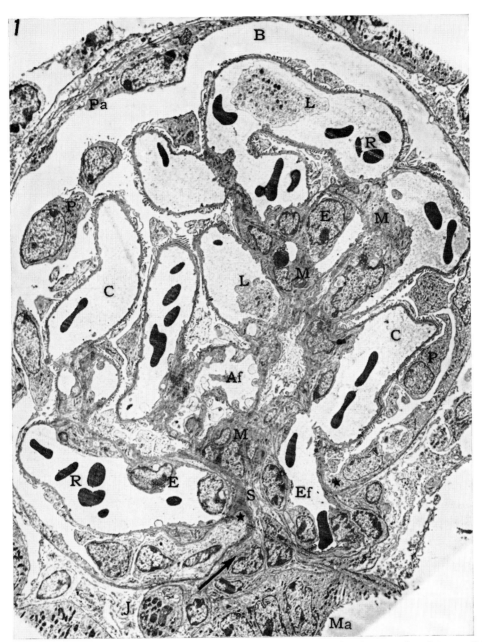

Fig. 1. Renal corpuscle of the mouse kidney. The afferent arteriole has been sectioned tangentially (arrow) and appears cross sectioned (Af) in the center of the stalk (S). A granulated juxtaglomerular cell is seen (J) close to the vascular pole, and a portion of the macula densa (Ma) is wedged between the afferent and efferent (Ef) arterioles. The arterioles pierce through the basement membrane of the Bowman's capsule (*) where a fusion of the basement membranes occurs. The glomerulus consists of richly branched capillaries (C) with lymphocytes (L) and erythrocytes (R) in their lumina. The parietal layer of Bowman's capsule (Pa) consists of simple squamous cells whereas the visceral layer is formed by the podocytes (P) with numerous and elongated thin processes, the pedicles, which interdigitate and attach at the surface of the capillaries. Between the parietal and visceral layers is the space of Bowman's capsule (B) which is continuous with the tubule (not shown). The arterioles and capillaries are lined by endothelial cells (E) which rest on a continuous basement membrane. With the glomerular stalk are carried in cells of mesenchymal origin (M), with the ability to lay down connective elements like collagen, elastin and basement membrane-like material. These cells have been called mesangium and are on all sides surrounded by capillary basement membranes. Magnification ×1,800.

The capillaries of the glomerulus are not freely suspended within the space of Bowman's capsule, but are attached to each other by the so called *mesangium* (Fig. 1). This is formed by a number of cells which lie in the center of the capillary bed and attach to the sides of the main capillaries which face the center of the capillary stem. The cytoplasm of the mesangial cells is quite electron dense and contains a fair number of fibrillar structures, possibly indicating that the cells are of mesodermal (connective tissue) origin.

The cells of the visceral layer of Bowman's capsule are squamous but quite different from the squamous cells of the parietal layer. The cytoplasm of the cell is pulled out into long and coarse extensions, the *podocytes*, each of which sends out numerous small processes, the *pedicels*, which surround the capillary and attach to its basement membrane, frequently interdigitating with each other (Fig. 2). The interdigitation occurs with pedicels of neighboring podocytes, be they podocytes of the same cell body or those of a neighboring cell. It is frequently seen that the pedicels not only interdigitate with each other but also penetrate underneath other pedicels. The foot processes (pedicels) leave a small, slit-formed space free in between each other, the width of this space ranging between 70 and 100A. These spaces have been called *slit-pores*. The pedicels and the slit-pores are believed by some to constitute the structures which are responsible for the filtration mechanism of the glomerular filtering membrane. By a certain swelling or shrinkage of the pedicels, the width of the slit-pores could be regulated, thus, either hindering or letting through various amounts of fluid or substances (particles) of various sizes.

The *basement membrane* of the capillaries has the usual ultrastructural appearance found in mammalian tissues (Fig. 2). It is quite homogeneous and only occasionally can there be detected fibrillar units as components. It is believed that the mucopoly-saccharides which represent the main content of the basement membrane may have a definite influence upon the filtration of the urine.

The innermost layer of the capillary wall is made up of the *endothelial cells*. These cells are extremely flat and the cytoplasm displays a number of pores regularly distributed (Fig. 2). The width of each pore ranges between 200 and 900A. Except for the area where the nucleus is located, the cytoplasm has an average thickness of about 800A.

In considering the complexity of the glomerular filtering membrane, it is believed that the size of the substances filtered is determined not only by one of the components of this membrane, but rather by a combined effort of all three together. This would explain why pathologic damages to one or several components of the filtering membrane may sometimes result in a similar functional impairment of the filtration process.

Proximal Convolution. The first part of the tubule is called the proximal convolution because it is highly coiled and intertwined with neighboring tubules as long as the tubules are located within the cortex of the kidney and are in the vicinity of the glomerulus. The cells of the proximal convolution are of a cuboidal or slightly columnar type. Their cytoplasm is quite dense in the electron micrographs because of a large number of mitochondria and also because of the fact that abundant RNA-particles are densely packed within the cells. In a cross section of the tubule, two to three nuclei are seen as compared to three to five nuclei in a cross section of a distal convolution. In the light microscope, it is virtually impossible to see the cell borders. They can be seen in the electron micrograph, but they are difficult to trace throughout because of the high degree of interdigitation that exists between adjacent cells.

In well preserved tissue the lumen is usually closed (Fig. 3). The reasons for this may be that a certain collapse of the tubule or

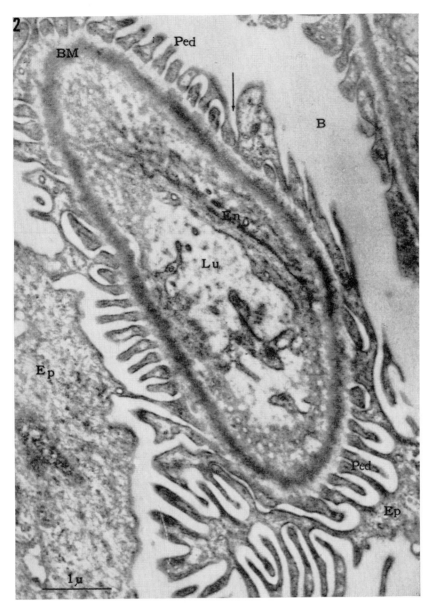

FIG. 2. Tangential section of a glomerular capillary. The epithelial cells or podocytes (Ep) send out numerous processes, the pedicles, (Ped) which leave a slit-pore (arrow) between them, continuous with the space of Bowman's capsule (B). The pedicles attach at the capillary basement membrane (BM). The capillary endothelium is thin (En) and perforated by abundant pores. In the lumen of the capillary (Lu) small particles in the blood plasma have taken up stain with osmium tetroxide. Magnification 19,000×.

swelling of the cells is caused by the fixative and the subsequent dehydration of the tissue preceding the embedding. It could also represent the natural appearance of this particular tubular section. The cells of the proximal convolution are supplied with numerous *brush border extensions* which are elongated profiles densely packed and oc-

167

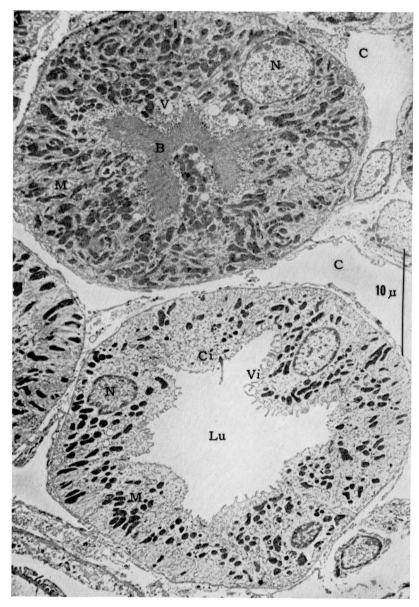

FIG. 3. Cross section of a mouse kidney proximal convolution (top) and a distal convolution (bottom) with surrounding capillaries (C). In both tubules the nuclei (N) and mitochondria (M) are evident. The lumen is usually closed in the proximal convolution but open (Lu) in the distal. Numerous brush border extensions (B) line the cells in the proximal convolution but only few microvilli (Vi) in the distal convolution. Vacuoles (V) containing autofluorescent material are prominent. Occasionally, a cilium (Ci) is encountered in the distal convolution. Magnification 2,900×.

cupying the space that normally would be called the lumen of the tubule. Evidence is at hand showing that about 85 per cent of the urine reabsorption takes place in the proxi-mal convolution and the abundance of brush border extensions seems to facilitate this activity of the cells by largely increasing their absorptive surfaces. Therefore, the way the urine seems to be passed along the proximal convolution is probably more like the slow filtration through a finely porous sieve than like the rapid drainage of a sink with a wide open plumbing system. The "pores" of this particular sieve are then represented by the narrow slits between the millions of brush border extensions. It can be recorded in high resolution micrographs that the plasma membrane which covers the extensions has a thickness of about 50A. However closely packed, the extensions do not get in closer contact than 100A apart. The intervening space is occupied by a substance with less density than the plasma membrane. It has been suggested that this substance represents an additional layer of possibly lipid molecules with a depth of 50A, identical with the intervening layers between adjacent cell borders. When the urine passes along the proximal convolution, it expands slightly the two lipid layers of adjacent brush border extensions, thus creating the narrow slits mentioned above. By this mechanism is established a much closer contact between the urine and the surface membrane of the brush border extensions than would be the case with a wide open lumen.

Some substances, as for instance proteins, which cannot be absorbed through the surface membrane, are taken up by the *tubular invaginations*. These structures are located between the bases of the brush border extensions and represent minute tubules which are in open connection with the tubular lumen (Fig. 8). The tubular invaginations are expanded to vacuolar profiles when fluid and substances are taken in. A certain condensation of the vacuolar content is noted concomitantly with a breaking-off of the connection between the expanded tubular invagination and the lumen of the nephron. The condensed vacuole can then be found anywhere in the cell and as the condensation of its contents proceeds, the vacuole is transformed into what has been called a large granule in electron microscopy. This whole

mechanism of taking in fluid-dissolved substances has been called *micropinocytosis* or *membrane flow*.

The mechanism by which substances other than protein are taken up by the cells of the proximal convolution is structurally not clear. It involves substances and ions such as glucose, sodium, potassium, phosphate, sulfate, amino acids, urea, and creatinine to mention some of them. The reabsorption of water is a passive process, but most of the substances listed involve an active process which requires energy. The enzymes required for these active processes are supplied by the multitude of *mitochondria* present in the cells of the proximal convolution (Fig. 4). The ultrastructure of the mitochondria has been thoroughly investigated (cross reference: cell ultrastructure) and it is believed that the efficiency of the mitochondrial work is increased by the number of mitochondria and the presence of structurally intact internal membranes. Organelles have been recorded in these cells which presumably constitute mitochondrial precursors. They have been called *microbodies*, and represent small spherical bodies without internal membranes and with a single membranous capsule as compared with the double-contoured mitochondrial outer membrane.

Structures have been found in the basal portion of the cells of the proximal convolution which probably facilitate the flow of reabsorbed fluid and substances through the cell body. They represent *infoldings of the basal plasma membrane* which extend to a varying degree into the cell (Fig. 4). The mitochondria have a close relationship with these infoldings and it is tempting to assume that this facilitates a certain interaction between the enzymes carried by the mitochondria and the infolded plasma membrane (Fig. 8). Once the reabsorbed fluid and substances have obtained contact with the basal plasma membrane, they may penetrate it by means of an enzymatic activation (Fig. 9). And when the extracellular space is

169

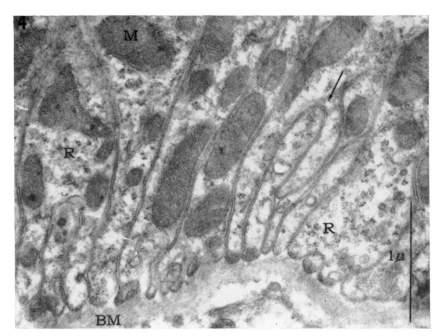

FIG. 4. Basal part of a proximal convoluted tubule cell of the mouse kidney. The plasma membrane which faces the basement membrane (BM) is highly infolded, but at the point where it turns (arrow) another portion of the cytoplasm is always interposed. The basal cell cytoplasm is thus divided into coarse lamellae which contain mitochondria (M) and abundant RNA particles (R). Magnification 32,000×.

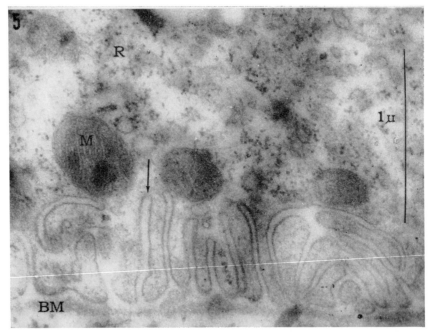

FIG. 5. Basal part of a collecting tubule cell of the mouse kidney. As in the proximal convolution, the basal plasma membrane is infolded, but as a rule, the turning point (arrow) can be seen without any interposed cytoplasmic lamella. The cytoplasmic lamellae are here thinner than in the proximal convolution and not broad enough to house mitochondria (M). Some RNA-granules (R) are located in the lamellae. The basement membrane (BM) is quite thin. Magnification ×46,000.

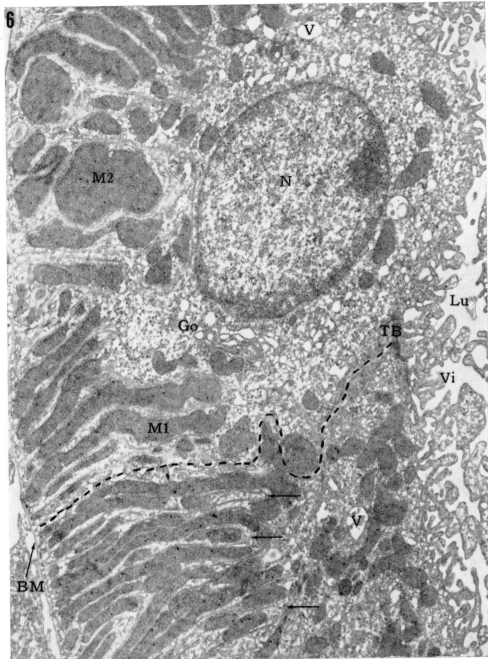

Fig. 6. Two cells of the thick, ascending limb of Henle's loop resting on the basement membrane (BM) and joined by a terminal bar (TB). The cell boundary is indicated by the dotted line. The nucleus (N) is located in the apical part of the cell with the Golgi zone (Go) close to it. Extending into the tubular lumen (Lu) are numerous microvilli (Vi). The cytoplasm is finely granulated because of the presence of abundant RNA particles. The autofluorescent vacuoles (V) are less numerous than in the proximal convolution. The mitochondria (M1) are long and densely packed. Sometimes, their shape is more like an ice cream bar than that of a sausage, which can be seen when they are sectioned at an angle (M2). The basal cell membrane is deeply infolded and the turning points clearly seen at the arrows show that cytoplasmic lamellae, also containing mitochondria, are always interposed in an interdigitating fashion. Magnification 11,000×.

171

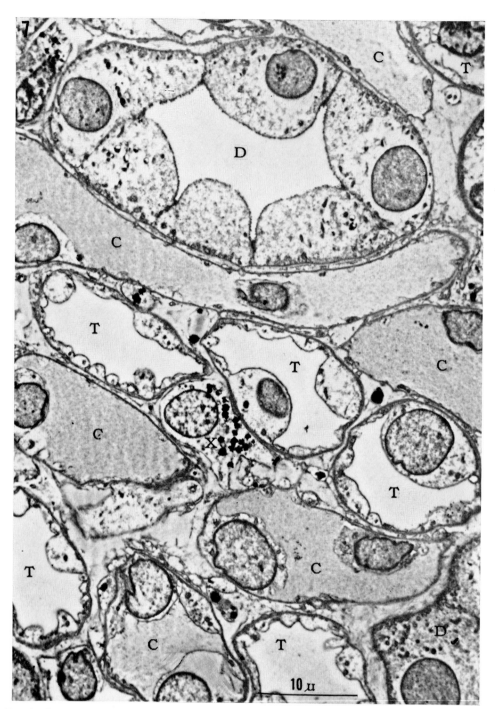

FIG. 7. Survey of the papilla of the rat kidney showing mostly cross sectioned collecting tubules (D), thin segments of Henle's loop (T) and capillaries (C). The cells of the collecting tubule are cuboidal with few mitochondria, easily recognized cell boundaries, and tiny microvilli on the surface. The cells of the thin segment are fairly squamous in sections showing scalloped appearance due to the frequently inter-digitating, narrow cell extensions. The endothelium of the capillaries is extremely thin. In the electron micrograph, there seems to be no chance of mistaking a thin segment for a capillary because of the difference in thickness of the lining cells, but also because of the obvious staining of the blood plasma in the capillaries. The interstitial cell (X) is unidentified. Magnification 2,700×.

reached, the access to the surrounding capillaries is easily achieved.

The *Golgi zone* of these cells is quite restricted and it is believed that it is mainly involved in secretory processes, particularly in the synthesis of protein used either by the cell itself or for extracellular purposes. This hypothesis is supported by the fact that rough-surfaced endoplasmic reticulum is absent in these cells, but the cytoplasm is filled by numerous RNA-particles which presumably are the structural evidence of cytoplasmic proteins.

The Loop of Henle. When the nephron leaves its convoluted portion in the cortex of the kidney, it assumes a straight course down into the medulla and papilla. The first part of this portion is called the *straight descending loop of Henle*. Once down in the papilla, it bends back again and the turning part is called the *thin segment of Henle's loop*.

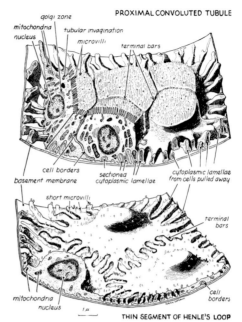

FIG. 9. Three-dimensional reconstruction of cells of the proximal convolution and thin segment of the mouse kidney. The reconstruction is not based on serial sections. (After Rhodin, 1958).

From there on, it approaches again the cortex and the neighborhood of the glomerulus. This portion is called the *ascending (thick) limb of Henle's loop*. It should be stressed that in most nephrons, the thin segment comprises a considerable part of the descending loop, the hairpin turn itself, and for some distance, the ascending loop.

Straight Descending Loop. The cells of the straight descending loop of Henle have a light cytoplasm due to a certain scarcity in mitochondria and RNA-particles. The surface of the cells shows scattered brush border extensions, but these are shorter and coarser than those found in the proximal convoluted portion of the nephron (Fig. 10). The lumen of the tubule is frequently open, presumably because of the relatively few brush border extensions. Tubular invaginations of the surface plasma membrane are few and the basal infoldings of the plasma membrane, so numerous in the proximal convoluted part, are shallow and few, often completely absent.

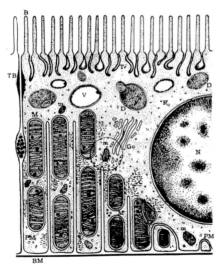

FIG. 8. Schematic representation of the basic structures of the proximal tubule cells of the mouse kidney: nucleus (N), mitochondria (M), microbodies (m), Golgi apparatus (Go), autofluorescent vacuoles (V), large dense granules (D), ribonucleoprotein particles (R), brush border extensions (B), tubular invaginations (Ti), plasma membrane (PM) with infoldings, terminal bars (TB), and basement membrane (BM). (After Rhodin, 1954).

173

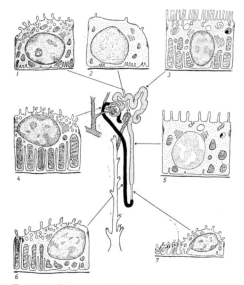

FIG. 10. Diagram showing the essential features of the cells lining different parts of a typical cortical nephron in mammalian kidney as seen with the electron microscope.

1) Collecting tubule (arched or proximal part): dark intercalated cell; 2) Collecting tubule (arched or proximal part): light cell; 3) Proximal convoluted tubule: proximal part; 4) Distal convoluted tubule: intercalated part (Schaltstück); 5) Proximal convoluted tubule: terminal portion; 6) Distal convoluted tubule: thick (ascending) limb; 7) Thin segment of Henle's loop. (After Rhodin, 1958)

These phenomena seem to indicate that less resorptive activity is performed by the straight descending loop as compared with the convoluted proximal part of the nephron when judging from a structural point of view.

Thin Segment. The epithelium of the thin segment of Henle's loop is of a squamous type with extremely flattened cytoplasm (Fig. 7). The cell surface shows only scattered short microvilli and tubular invaginations are not recorded. The mitochondria are scarce and exceedingly small. The cytoplasm is light due to a small number of RNA-particles. Basal infoldings are present only beneath the nucleus where the cytoplasm is of greater thickness than elsewhere. The attenuated part of the cell shows some quite characteristic features of this portion of the nephron. It displays a large number of cyto-

plasmic extensions which rest on the basement membrane. These extensions resume the shape of the arms of a starfish and they interdigitate frequently with similar extensions of neighboring cells (Fig. 9). This pattern is reminiscent of the way the epithelial cells of the glomerular capillaries are arranged. However, in the case of the thin segment, the interdigitated cell processes always show a terminal bar close to the surface which presumably secures the firm attachment of individual cell processes to one another. It can, therefore, be assumed that there do not exist any "slit-pores" between the cells of the thin segment as was indicated to be the circumstances regarding the glomerular capillary epithelial cells.

In the papilla and deeper portions of the medulla, the descending and ascending parts of the thin segment are closely opposed to each other as well as to the capillaries (vasa recta) and the collecting ducts. It has been suggested that the close juxtaposition would facilitate the mutual exchange of fluid, substances and energy because of the close resemblance of this system to the basic principle of a counter current system with streams moving in opposite directions. The ultrastructure of the thin segment seems to support this hypothesis. The thin walls of its loop are evidently ideal to serve this exchange of fluid and substances.

Ascending (Thick) Limb. The ascending limb of Henle's loop is slightly wider than the other portions of the nephron and has, therefore, been called the thick limb. The cells have a cuboidal shape and a free open lumen is always to be found. The extreme multitude of mitochondria makes this section of the nephron stand out more clearly than the others, both in light and electron microscopy. Not only are the mitochondria numerous, but they also have a coarse and elongated shape as compared to the spherical form of the other parts of the nephron (Fig. 6). The mitochondria are densely packed and arranged with their long axes perpendicular to the basement membrane of the tubule. They extend from the basement membrane to a level of about one micron from the cell surface. The mitochondrial fine structure is of the same appearance as elsewhere in the nephron with the exception that the inner membranes (or plates) are more frequently seen arranged parallel with the long axis of the mitochondrion.

The free surface of the cells displays a number of small and scattered microvilli. The luminal portion of the cells, more or less devoid of mitochondria, is pervaded by abundant microvesicles bounded by a smooth single membrane. Some of the vesicles are connected with the surface plasma membrane. The Golgi apparatus of the cells occupies a restricted area around the upper part of the nucleus. Its fine structure is identical with the one recorded in the proximal convolution. The basal plasma membrane is deeply infolded between the elongated mitochondria leaving but a narrow strip of cytoplasm in between. The RNA-particles are numerous and scattered among the small vesicles in the apical cytoplasm.

It is obvious that the work performed by the thick limb requires a big supply of enzymes judging from the great number of mitochondria present in the cells. Sodium is taken up by these cells by an active process which also leads to a simultaneous retention of water. Furthermore, formation of ammonia and the acidification of the urine seem to take place in this portion of the nephron. It may be reasonable to assume that the numerous microvesicles are structural evidence for one or both of these processes. Similar microvesicles are a prominent feature of the parietal cells of the gastric mucosa. These cells supposedly are responsible for the production of the hydrochloric acid of the stomach.

Distal Convolution. The thick ascending limb of Henle's loop is gradually transformed into a convoluted position, the distal convolution, when the nephron again reaches the cortex of the kidney. The distal convolution is less coiled than the proximal one. The cells become small and a wide lumen opens up (Fig. 3). The surface of the cells usually has longer microvilli than is the case in the thick limb, but the length varies from cell to cell. The mitochondria decrease noticeably in number and size, as does the number of RNA-particles, features which all contribute to a light appearance of the cell cytoplasm. A few shallow and narrow infoldings of the basal plasma membrane can be recorded, but they are too narrow to admit any mitochondria to be enclosed in the small cytoplasmic strands they give rise to (Fig. 5). A fair number of small vesicles is still to be found in the luminal part of most of the cells, but cells can be recorded which are completely devoid of these structures.

When the distal convolution approaches the neighborhood of the vascular pole of the glomerulus, it becomes attached to the angle between the afferent and efferent arterioles. This part of the distal convolution has been called the *macula densa* because it can be seen that the cells of the distal convolution here assume a more columnar shape than elsewhere, thus causing the nuclei to stand out very clearly in close juxtaposition (Fig. 1). Apart from their extreme columnar shape, the cells of the macula densa do not show any peculiarities as far as their fine structure is concerned which would discriminate them from other cells of the distal convolution.

Cortical Collecting Duct. This part of the nephron immediately follows the distal convolution and serves only as a short connection between this part and the collecting tubule. It is characterized by two cell types, the first identical with the one occurring in the distal convolution, the second, with the appearance of the cells found in the collecting tubule. As the cortical collecting duct is gradually transformed into the collecting tubule, the cell type reminiscent of that of the distal tubule disappears. Because these cells seem to be interposed between the main cell type, they have been called *intercalated* *cells.* The intercalated cell has a large number of spherical mitochondria which are clustered mostly above the nucleus, thus giving the cell a dark appearance which has lead some investigators to call it a *dark cell* (Fig. 10). This seems justifiable when considering that the main cell type has few mitochondria and a light cytoplasm. This cell is therefore called a *light cell*. There are other structurally important differences between the two cell types. The luminal surface of the dark cell usually has quite abundant microvilli, whereas the light cell has few or none. The vesicles of the luminal part of the dark cell cytoplasm and the RNA-granules are numerous as against a scarcity of these structures in the light cell. The similarity between the dark intercalated cells of the cortical collecting duct and the cells of the distal convolution strongly suggests that the former actually represents a certain variety of cells of the distal convolution which are distributed along the cortical collecting duct.

Collecting Tubule. The collecting tubule begins in the outer cortex and runs in a straight course toward the medulla, each nephron being connected to a collecting tubule by the cortical collecting duct. The convergence of successive orders of collecting tubules in progressively deeper layers gives rise to vessels of increasing caliber until finally the papillary ducts are reached. These ducts discharge their contents into the renal pelvis.

It is believed that very few processes related to the composition of the urine occur in the collecting tubule. The final concentration of the urine seems, however, to be established here, possibly mediated by a certain reabsorption of sodium chloride. It has also been suggested that the permeability of the cells of the collecting tubules may be influenced by the action of the antidiuretic hormone (ADH) of the pituitary.

Structurally, the cells of the collecting tubule are rather poor (Fig. 7). The cells are of a cuboidal type with a very light cyto-plasm containing a small amount of RNA-particles and a few small and widely scattered spherical mitochondria. Large granules of the lipid type occur frequently, together with a small Golgi complex. The luminal surface displays a varying number of very short microvilli and the basal plasma membrane shows remnants of extremely shallow infoldings. The cell borders are straight and the cells are held together by distinct terminal bars close to the surface. The nuclei are fairly large, occupying a good portion of the cell body.

REFERENCES

SJÖSTRAND, F. S. AND RHODIN, J., "The ultra-structure of the proximal convoluted tubules of the mouse kidney as revealed by high resolution electron microscopy," *Exper. Cell Research*, **4**, 426 (1953).

HALL, B. V., "Studies of the normal glomerular structure by electron microscopy," *Proc. Annual Conf. Nephrotic Syndrome*, 5th Conf., p. 1, 1953.

RHODIN, J., "Correlation of ultrastructural organization and function in normal and experimentally changed proximal convoluted tubule cells of the mouse kidney," Thesis, Stockholm 1954, Karolinska Institutet.

PEASE, D. C., "Fine structures of the kidney seen by electron microscopy," *J. Histochem. Cytochem.*, **3**, 295 (1955).

HALL, B. V., "Further studies of the normal structure of the renal glomerulus," *Proc. Annual Conf. Nephrotic Syndrome*, 6th Conf., 1955.

RHODIN, J., "Electron microscopy of the glomerular capillary wall," *Exper. Cell Research*, **8**, 572 (1955).

PEASE, D. C., "Electron microscopy of the vascular bed of the kidney cortex," *Anat. Rec.*, **121**, 701 (1955).

PEASE, D. C., "Electron microscopy of the tubular cells of the kidney cortex," *Anat. Rec.*, **121**, 723 (1955).

RUSKA, H., MOORE, D. H., AND WEINSTOCK, J., "The base of the proximal convoluted tubule cells of rat kidney," *J. Biophys. Biochem. Cytol.*, **3**, 249 (1957).

RHODIN, J., "Anatomy of kidney tubules," *Int. Rev. Cytol.*, **7**, 485 (1958).

RHODIN, J., "Ergebnisse der elektronenmikroskopische Erforschung von Struktur und Funktion der Zelle," *Verhandl. deutsch., Gesellsch. Path. 41st. Tagung*, **18**, 274 (1958).

Rhodin, J., "Electron microscopy of the kidney," *Am. J. Med.*, **24**, 661 (1958).

Johannes A. G. Rhodin

LEAF SURFACES

The electron microscope and its associated techniques have now reached a stage in development where they can be used by biologists as tools of research, not simply as instruments for making interesting new morphological discoveries or for confirming information gained from other sources. Our investigations, using the new techniques, have demonstrated the existence of a fine structure on the surfaces of many plants. Although some such structure beyond the resolution of the light microscope had been inferred, because plant surfaces vary widely in their ability to repel water droplets, its morphology, diversity, and the problems of its development had never been suspected.

Prior to this work several attempts had been made to examine the surfaces of animal and plant cuticle with the electron microscope. Holdgate, Menter and Seal (1954) used reflection electron microscopy to study insect cuticle. This technique, although successful in demonstrating changes in the insect cuticle, suffered from the disadvantages associated with reflection electron microscopy; the difficulty of interpretation is due to distortion and a restricted magnification only a little above that of the light microscope.

Most of the work on plant cuticle has used some form of replica technique. The pioneer work by Mueller, Carr and Loomis (1954) and Schieferstein and Loomis (1956) used liquid polyvinyl alcohol as the first stage of a two-stage replica method. However, it was necessary in their technique to wet the surface of the leaf with wetting agents to make the liquid plastic adhere. The liquids used to wet the surface ought to affect both the behavior and fine structure of those surfaces, and their results appear to confirm this.

A technique which does not involve wetting the leaf's surface has therefore been devised. It is basically the single-stage carbon method of Bradley (1954) in which the specimen is coated with a film of carbon, and everything but the carbon is subsequently dissolved away. The technique is as follows with leaf specimens (Juniper and Bradley, 1958). The leaf to be examined is fixed to a glass slide with cellulose adhesive tape, and the slide is then placed in the evaporating chamber along with a porcelain/oil marker to gauge the thickness of carbon deposited. The chamber, which in the work described was an Edwards Coating Unit Model 12 EA, is then evacuated. While pumping is in progress very little gas would appear to be given off by the leaf and a level of vacuum (10^{-3} mm Hg) sufficient to allow the evaporation of carbon is easily obtained. Carbon is evaporated by passing a heavy alternating current through the points of two carbon rods lightly pressed together. The points of the rods are 15 cm above the specimen to be coated. A film of carbon 15–20 mμ thick is deposited on the leaf surface and the leaf is then removed from the vacuum.

In spite of the level of vacuum reached in the chamber, the leaf does not suffer any superficial distortion due to the escape of gas provided that the pumping time is kept short. The pumping time for most leaves is about 9 minutes, but succulent leaves may take up to 11 minutes. The subsequent stages of the technique are described with reference to Fig. 1. The carbon film is backed successively with thin layers of "Formvar" and "Bedacryl" 122x, allowing each in turn to dry completely (Fig. 1b). "Formvar" and "Bedacryl" 122x are quick-setting liquid plastics, flexible when dry and extremely soluble in certain solvents. Then the combined film of carbon and plastic (Fig. 1b) is backed with cellulose adhesive tape and the leaf is peeled away from this composite film (Fig. 1c). The film is then immersed in acetone (Fig. 1d). This removes the "Bedacryl" from between the cellulose tape and the "Formvar," but does not affect the latter, which is insoluble in acetone, and keeps the carbon film flat and intact in the solvent. Specimen grids are inserted into the space made by the removal of the "Bedacryl" (Fig. 1d). Athene, New 200, 3.05 mm grids have been used in this work. The "Formvar"

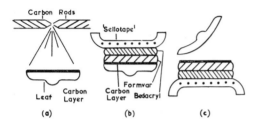

(a)   (b)   (c)

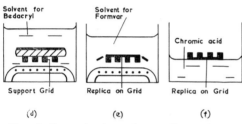

(d)   (e)   (f)

FIG. 1. Stages in the carbon replica technique.

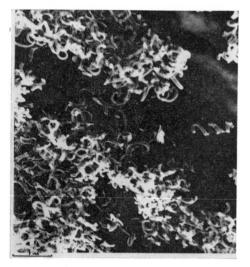

FIG. 2. Adaxial leaf surface of Chrysanthemum segetum.

and the carbon film is then lifted on the grid from the acetone bath and dried. The "Formvar" is finally washed away in a chloroform bath (Fig. 1e). A final stage (Fig. 1f), which is rarely necessary, is to clean the film in a bath of chromic acid. This is only necessary where field material is examined and dirt picked up from the leaf might contaminate the microscope. Finally the replica is shadowed with gold/palladium through the grid bars at a fairly high angle, i.e., 1:1 or 2:1.

Although originally intended as a high-resolution shadow-casting technique, the method of Bradley (1959) for the simultaneous evaporation of carbon and platinum has been used to make self-shadowed carbon replicas. The carbon/platinum film is deposited from 45° or 33° and the later stages of the technique are as described above. Very successful results with this adapted technique have been achieved. The compound replicas are tougher, the shadows more clearly defined and the tedium of two stages of making a replica and shadowing are avoided. The fact that one can, apparently at the same time, shadow and form a complete replica of a specimen would appear to be a contradiction. The explanation is that evaporating carbon, but not platinum, does not travel in a straight line. The carbon replica is in a sense a negative of the original leaf surface and the design of the electron microscope reverses original densities in the image. The practice has therefore been adopted of using an extra negative stage in printing from the original electron microscope plates. This is contrary to certain conventions in electron microscopy, but it results in dark shadows and light protrusions from the plant surfaces—a result which is aesthetically more satisfying and easier to interpret.

The contact angle of a drop of liquid on a surface is a measure of the wettability of that surface. The contact angle for water of a smooth surface of wax is about 100°. Many plant surfaces have contact angles for water above 140° and some micro-roughness was inferred to be responsible for these high contact angles. Two examples of the micro-roughness revealed by this technique are shown in Figs. 2 and 4. Projections above the level of the cuticle of many different forms have been discovered. They vary in height from 0.25 μ to 4 μ and are assumed to be mainly of wax. We believe that it is this fine structure which is responsible for the bloom in many species, for contact angles above 100°, and (most important to the agronomist) for the lack of adhesion of water droplets. All species which are found to have this fine 'wax blanket' structure on their surfaces have initial contact angles for those surfaces above 140°.

A number of problems connected with the retention of liquids on plant surfaces and thought to be associated with properties of the cuticle have been investigated with this technique. Fogg (1947) showed that different parts of the same plant differed in their abilities to shed water droplets. The electron microscope shows that the fine structure of the surface of a plant may vary with its position on a plant. Figures 3 and 4 show, respectively, the abaxial and adaxial surfaces of the same leaf of a pea plant.

Differences were thought to occur in the fine structure on the surfaces of plants with variations in the light intensity (Dorschner and Buchholtz, 1956). Figures 4 and 5 show the adaxial surfaces of pea leaves grown at 5000 and 1500 ft-candles, respectively; as the light intensity falling on the leaf is progressively reduced, the wax projections developed on those surfaces are smaller, less dense and more angular in appearance. This agrees with the observation that the surfaces of plants grown under reduced light conditions are more delicate and more susceptible to mechanical damage.

Differences in susceptibility to mechanical damage are apparent between different species of plants grown at the same light intensity. The leaf surface of *Oxalis corniculata*

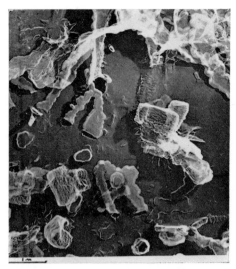

Fig. 3. Abaxial leaf surface of Pisum sativum var. 'Alaska'.

Fig. 4. Adaxial leaf surface of Pisum sativum var. 'Alaska'.

is practically impervious to mechanical damage and the leaves usually remain unwettable until senescence; *Hyacinthus orientalis*, on the other hand, is readily damaged by ordinary aerial weathering, and the leaves are wettable soon after they have emerged. Very little is known about the comparative chemistry of leaf waxes which must contribute to hardness.

179

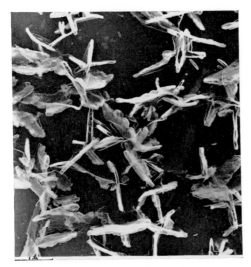

Fig. 5. Adaxial leaf surface of Pisum satium var. 'Alaska'. Grown at 1500 ft. candles light intensity.

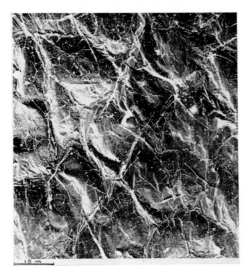

Fig. 6. Adaxial leaf surface of Pisum sativum var. 'Alaska'. Immediately after transfer from darkness to light.

Treating the soil in which peas are germinating with 2,2-dichlorpropionic acid ("Dalapon") affects the susceptibility of the pea plants subsequently sprayed with certain herbicides (Dewey, Gregory and Pfeiffer, 1956). It was thought that the "Dalapon" interfered with the wax formation of the cuticle and so enhanced the retention and penetration of the herbicides. The electron microscope shows that there is a progressive reduction in the complexity, size, and density of the wax projections on the pea leaf surfaces with increasing concentration of "Dalapon" in the soil. Increases in the concentration of "Dalapon" in the soil beyond 0.32 lb per acre finally result in a smooth cuticle with no wax projections visible at all (Juniper, 1959).

The initial development of the fine structure of a leaf is shown by the electron microscope to take place before the earliest stage at which replicas can be made. The stages of the development of the fine structure of a pea leaf surface have therefore been followed by growing the pea plant to an advanced stage in darkness (during which time no projections are developed) and then transferring it to light. Replicas are then taken of corresponding leaves at 24 hour intervals. The projections from the surface develop very rapidly. Figure 6 is of a pea leaf surface immediately after transfer. The appearance of Fig. 4 is achieved after about five days.

New techniques and the electron microscope have revealed the existence of a fine structure on the surfaces of many plants which had never previously been suspected. Our investigations have confirmed some of the observations made by other workers using different techniques in the same field. It has revealed morphological differences resulting from environmental changes which were not previously suspected because the techniques for detecting such changes in the fine structure were not sufficiently refined. The results are interesting both to the developmental morphologist and to the agronomist because the view that everything external to the epidermal cells is static and immutable can, with present evidence, no longer be held.

REFERENCES

Bradley, D. E., "Evaporated carbon films for use in electron microscopy," Brit. J. Appl. Phys., 5, 65 (1954).

Bradley, D. E., "High-resolution shadow-casting

technique for the electron microscope using the simultaneous evaporation of platinum and carbon," *Brit. J. Appl. Phys.*, **10**, 198 (1959).

DEWEY, O. R., GREGORY, P., AND PFEIFFER, R. K., "Factors affecting the susceptibility of peas to selective dinitroherbicides," *Brit. Weed Control Conf. Proc.*, **1**, 313 (1956).

DORSCHNER, K. P. AND BUCHHOLTZ, K. P., "Effect of wetting ability of herbicides on alfalfa stands," *Agron. J.*, **48**, 59 (1956).

FOGG, G. E., "Quantitative studies on the wetting of leaves by water," *Proc. Roy. Soc.*, **B134**, 503 (1948).

HOLDGATE, M. W., MENTER, J. W., AND SEAL, M., "A study of an insect's surface by reflection electron microscopy and diffraction," *Proc. Int. Conf. Electron Microscopy*, **129**, 555 (1954).

JUNIPER, B. E. AND BRADLEY, D. E., "The carbon replica technique in the study of the ultrastructure of leaf surfaces," *J. Ultrastructure Res.*, **2**, 16 (1958).

JUNIPER, B. E., "The effect of the pre-emergent treatment of peas with trichloracetic acid on the sub-microscopic structure of the leaf surface," *New Phyt.*, **58**, 1 (1959).

MUELLER, L. E., CARR, P. H., AND LOOMIS, W. E., "The submicroscopic structure of plant surfaces," *Am. J. Bot.*, **41**, 593 (1954).

SCHIEFERSTEIN, R. H. AND LOOMIS, W. E., "Wax deposits on leaf surfaces," *Plant Physiol.*, **31**, 240 (1956).

B. E. JUNIPER

METALS BY TRANSMISSION*

Although replica techniques have been used with great success for the examination of metals, these methods have their limitations. With the development, therefore, of instruments having high resolving power and fitted with a double condenser lens that enables high beam intensities to be obtained on the specimen, a new approach was made to the problem of preparing metals in a form suitable for examination by transmission in the electron microscope. During the past few years a number of suitable techniques for preparing metal foils with a thickness of 100–2000 Å have been devised. These tech-

* Abridged from paper in *Jour. Inst. Metals*, **87**, 385 (1959), by permission

niques, which will be reviewed in this paper, can be classified into three principal groups:

   (*a*) Deposition.

   (*b*) Deformation.

   (*c*) Dissolution.

The deposition methods involve the production of metal foils by condensation of the metal vapor *in vacuo*, the precipitation or electrodeposition of thin crystals from aqueous solution, and the casting of foils from the liquid state. These techniques are of limited use only, since the results obtained from foils prepared in this way are seldom typical of bulk material.

The deformation methods used to prepare thin foils comprise beating and machining in diamond-bladed microtomes. The former is very limited in its application, but the latter shows interesting possibilities, particularly for the examination of multiphase alloys.

The dissolution techniques are perhaps the most generally applicable to the preparation of foils of pure metals and alloys. The methods adopted have involved simple chemical etching, ionic bombardment, and electropolishing. The latter is the most successful and has been widely used, since it is thought that the structures obtained from foils prepared in this way are typical of those to be expected in bulk material.

Deposition Methods

Vacuum Evaporation. It has been known for some time that thin films of metal, transparent to electrons, can be produced by evaporating a metal *in vacuo* and condensing the vapor onto a substrate. The evaporated film may then be stripped from the substrate, or the substrate dissolved away. If the vapor is deposited onto a crystalline substrate at high temperatures, the metal film exhibits "epitaxy," an effect discussed by Pashley (1). In this way it is possible to grow single-crystal films of certain metals.

The structure of evaporated films is not on the whole typical of bulk material, and these films are useful only in affording information about the properties of thin films as such, although they may give indications of changes which might occur in bulk materials.

Evaporated films of iron, subsequently nitrided, austenitized, and quenched to martensite, have been examined by Pitsch (2) by transmission electron microscopy. The martensitic product and the mechanism proposed for its formation differ markedly from those in bulk material. This is due to the absence of a constraining lattice on either side of the thin film.

Takahashi and his co-workers (3–6) have prepared evaporated foils of aluminium–copper alloy by simultaneous evaporation of the two metals. These have been examined by transmission electron microscopy and electron diffraction in the as-deposited condition and after heating in the microscope. Again, the structure of these evaporated alloys differs from that of the bulk alloy.

Deposition from Solution. Large thin single-crystal flakes of gold have been prepared by Suito and Uyeda (7) by reduction of a dilute auric chloride solution. The thin crystals (100–200 Å thick and several microns across) showed trigonal and hexagonal habit and grew parallel to (111). The value of such thin crystals in giving information about bulk properties is limited.

Electrodeposition. Two methods have been used to produce thin electrodeposits for examination in the electron microscope. The first, developed by Weisenberger (8), consists in using thin carbon supporting films as conducting electrodes onto which the metal is electrodeposited. This method can be used to investigate the nucleation of electrodeposits, but beyond this the technique is severely limited.

The second method, first used by Weil and Read (9), consists in electroplating nickel onto copper or zinc and stripping the thin electroplate from the cathode. This technique was applied by Reimer (10) to the study of the epitaxial growth of electrode-

posits. Apart from the investigation of the structure of electrodeposits, this technique has little application.

Thinning Molten Drops by Surface Tension. Takahashi and Kazato (11) have developed a technique for the preparation of thin metal foils from molten material. Foils are made by dipping an elliptical loop (major axis = 1 cm., minor axis = 0.3 cm.) of wire into molten metal and withdrawing it at the rate of 2 cm./sec. This must be done in an inert atmosphere, when dealing with metals that oxidize readily in air, but otherwise the technique should be applicable to most metals and alloys. Alloys of tin and lead, aluminium and silver, and aluminium with tin or copper have been investigated by Takahashi and his co-workers (6, 11, 12). It was found that the microstructure of the thin parts of the foil was not typical of bulk material, but that the structure of the thicker portions resembled the microstructure of the bulk alloy. This shows that the transition from thin foil to bulk behavior occurs in the thickness range of a few thousand Ångstroms. However, other properties and other alloys may show a different lower limit of thickness for truly bulk behavior, and it is dangerous, therefore, to extend results obtained from such foils to bulk material.

Deformation Methods

Thickness Reduction by Mechanical Work. Some very ductile materials such as gold, silver, and platinum can be beaten into foil ∼1000 Å thick. Such foils are so heavily distorted as a result of the deformation that they are virtually useless for providing data on the properties of the metal. Beaten gold foils were examined in the electron microscope by Hirsch, Kelly, and Menter (13), but the examination yielded only limited information.

Thin Sections Cut from Bulk Material with an Ultramicrotome. An ultramicrotome utilizing thermal expansion for advancing the specimen and the magnetostriction of a nickel rod for withdrawal during the return stroke, was developed by Haanstra (14) for cutting thin biological specimens 50–100 Å thick could be cut from a specially shaped specimen by a diamond knife, but the resulting structure was heavily deformed.

Reimer (15) used a diamond knife and an ultramicrotome developed by H. Fernadez-Moran to cut thin metal foils of Al, Ni, Cu, Au, Fe, Pd, Pt, and Ag, but in this case, too, the foils were very heavily deformed. In spite of the severe deformation introduced, thin sections can be readily prepared in this way, and, in the case of alloys containing dispersed phases, the results are not likely to be very different from those found by examining electropolished foils. This technique holds great promise as a rapid method of obtaining foils.

Dissolution Methods

Chemical Etching. To produce a thin foil that is representative of bulk material, it is necessary to remove metal from a large section without destroying or modifying the structure of the material. One method of doing this is by chemical etching of a sheet of material 1 μ or more thick. Hirsch, Kelly, and Menter (13) examined gold by etching the beaten foil in a dilute solution of potassium cyanide. The foils produced were very uneven in thickness, but the heavily cold-worked structure of the foil before etching was preserved. Dislocation movements and arrangements in aluminium were studied by Hirsch, Horne, and Whelan (16), on thin foils, made from sheet 0.5 μ thick by etching in dilute hydrofluoric acid. The foils showed large uniform areas which were transparent to electrons, and there was no evidence of substructure due to etching.

This technique produces good results, but its application is limited to pure metals or single-phase alloys since it is difficult to prevent preferential attack of one of the phases

in multiphase alloys. Even with pure metals a difficulty is the formation of an etching substructure (17), but this can be avoided by proper choice of etching reagents and conditions.

Ion Bombardment. A method of thinning metals from the bulk state by bombarding a thin disc (1–2 μ thick) of the material with a beam of ions has been developed by Castaing (18, 19). In using ions to remove metal atoms from a specimen, the energy of the ions must be adjusted to give random atom removal. Too high an energy of the ions will result in heating and possible damage to the structure, while too low an energy will give an etching effect. Therefore, critical adjustment of the accelerating potential (3000 V in the case of aluminium) is necessary. Attempts to extend this technique to stainless steel (21) and α-brass (18) have been unsuccessful.

A difficulty in ionic thinning is the very low speed of metal removal—10 μ in 24 hr. Thus, although with great care the method is capable of producing clean, uniform foils from bulk material, the technique is complicated, tedious, and difficult to control in the final stages.

Electropolishing. Heidenreich (20), using an electropolishing technique, produced the first thin metal foils from bulk material in a form suitable for transmission electron microscopy. His technique consisted in electropolishing discs of aluminium and aluminium–copper alloy, 3 mm. in dia., cut from rolled sheet 125 μ thick. The electropolishing produced holes at the center of the specimen and the areas near these holes were thin enough to be transparent to electrons. The foils were often dirty and thin areas were not obtained from every specimen, but when success was achieved the results were very encouraging. Many workers have since used electropolishing techniques of different types to prepare thin foils of a wide variety of metals. These techniques are based mainly on experiment, with very little theoretical understanding of the conditions necessary to produce a uniform thin foil.

The main difficulty in producing a thin foil is that of attaining random removal of metal from the surface of the specimen. In order to achieve this during electropolishing, the current density at all points on the specimen must be the same. Since it is difficult to measure the thickness of the metal in the region 200–2000 Å, the criterion that the specimen is thin enough is usually the appearance of one or more holes. Thin regions occur near the edges of the holes, but as soon as a hole is formed the current-density distribution is disturbed, with the result that the edges of the holes become rounded and the thin regions lost.

When a sheet-metal specimen is placed vertically as the anode in an electropolishing solution, with a flat vertical cathode, it is found that the current density is maximum at the edges of the specimen and at the "waterline" of the solution. In addition, electropolishing solutions can be divided into two classes:

(i) Solutions forming a viscous layer which flows down under gravity.

(ii) Solutions which evolve bubbles of gas at the anode.

Solutions of the first type will give enhanced attack at the top of the specimen, since the viscous layer is flowing away from that region and is increasing in thickness as it flows down the specimen. Solutions of the second type will form a blanket of gas bubbles which is thin at the bottom of the specimen and thick at the top; as a result metal is removed more quickly from the bottom of the specimen. A horizontal anode eliminates the effect of gravity on the viscous layer and on the bubbles, but now the conditions are different on the two sides of the specimen. Hence, in this case it will be difficult to attain the correct polishing conditions on both sides of the specimen, especially if the current-density range for polishing is small for the electrolyte.

To eliminate the effect of preferential polishing at the edges of the specimen, these may be coated with a non-conducting lacquer. The result of this is preferential polishing at the edge of the lacquer coating, leaving the center of the specimen thicker than the outside.

To overcome this difficulty, Bollmann (21, 22) used pointed cathodes mounted close to the center of a metal disc ($\sim$2 cm. in dia. and 25–200 μ thick). The specimen was electropolished until a hole appeared in the center, when the electrodes were moved $\sim$1–2 cm. away and polishing was continued. Perforation then occurred at the edge of the lacquer coating and continued toward the central hole. The specimen was then removed and washed, and foils were cut from the regions near the junction of the two holes.

To avoid removing the specimen from the solution to adjust the position of the cathodes, a modification of the electrode assembly has been designed in which there are two sets of cathodes, a set of pointed cathodes close to the specimen and a set of flat cathodes far away from the specimen. Either set may be connected to the negative of the power supply, so that the same sequence of events can be followed merely by switching from one set to the other.

The Bollmann technique is limited to polishing solutions with a low throwing power and may produce wedge-shaped foils, but otherwise the method is simple and versatile.

The preferential polishing of a vertical specimen due to the formation of a heavy viscous layer has been utilized in the "window" technique developed by Nicholson, Thomas, and Nutting (23) for use with aluminium alloys, and later by Tomlinson (24) for making thin foils of Mg, Ni, Al, Cu, Fe, and Co. This consists of lacquering the edges of a thin sheet (25–200 μ thick) and mounting it vertically with a vertical cathode in an electropolishing solution. Perforation occurs at the top edge of the lacquer coating and advances downward. When perforation has extended about half-way down, the specimen is removed and washed, and foils are cut from the edge of the hole. Tomlinson states that the foils are more uniform in thickness over larger regions if the current is switched on and off rapidly near the end of the polishing. No explanation of the mechanism of this phenomenon has been given.

Better foils are obtained if the specimen is removed as soon as perforation begins at the top, and the perforated edge coated with lacquer. The specimen is then inverted, replaced, and polished until perforation occurs at the other end of the specimen. This can be repeated until there is a narrow band at the center of the specimen from which the foils are cut.

The advantages of both the "window" and the Bollmann methods have been incorporated in a low-temperature polishing technique for copper alloys, developed by Swann and Nutting (25). The "window" technique is used first, the specimen being inverted after each successive perforation, until a band about half the width of the original specimen is left. The Bollmann technique is then used to thin the center of this band until perforation occurs. The final polishing is done with the "window" technique.

In producing thin foils of copper alloys, there are two main difficulties. First, the solution used polishes very rapidly at room temperature and this gives little control over the final stages of thinning; secondly, the anodic layer is so reactive that even immediate washing after removal of the specimen from the solution is not enough to prevent etching and oxidizing of the specimen. To slow down the rate of attack and give the required degree of control over polishing, the temperature of the bath was kept below $-20°C$. Just before the specimen was removed, sufficient liquid nitrogen was poured onto the top of the solution to form a layer, through which the specimen was withdrawn, without switching off the current. Washing

was carried out immediately in methyl alcohol kept below $-20°C$ to prevent attack by the anodic layer before it was completely removed.

Another technique employing the viscous polishing layer has been developed by Brandon and Nutting (26) for use with iron. A sheet of material 50–100 μ thick was electropolished down to ~20 μ in the usual way. If perforation occurred during this polishing, its progress was stopped by coating with lacquer. When the thickness of the specimen had been sufficiently reduced, one surface was painted with non-conducting lacquer to give a "figure-of-eight" outline. The specimen was further electropolished and perforation occurred at the top of the specimen and under the "arms" of the "eight," leaving the portion between the "arms" suitable for thin foils.

To avoid the preferential rounding off of the edges of holes, Mirand and Saulnier (27) have backed the specimen with a piece of the same material; thus, when a hole appears, attack continues on the backing metal. The polishing was continued until fragments dropped from the specimen into the electrolyte, where they were collected for examination. This technique works well for titanium alloys, but the difficulty in extending it to other metals lies in finding an appropriate polishing solution. Most electropolishing solutions will etch the metal, unless a current is applied, and therefore etch the fragments as soon as they fall from the specimen. Electrolyte may also seep between the specimen and the backing piece, thus etching the back of the specimen. However, when suitable conditions have been established the technique of Mirand and Saulnier provides a rapid and easy method of preparing thin foils.

The production of exact geometrical shapes and the preservation of certain profiles during electropolishing have been investigated by Michel (28). This work gives an indication of the methods to be adopted if uniform thinning is to be attained. By plotting the equipotentials, Fisher (29) has found the appropriate shape of the anode, placed at a given distance from a pointed cathode, necessary to give uniform current density over the anode surface. The anode must be pear-shaped at its periphery, with a flat central portion. Such a configuration could be achieved by placing suitable washers on either side of a flat sheet. The specimen perforates almost simultaneously at a number of points in the flat area. Polishing must be stopped as soon as the first holes appear in order to maintain a uniform current-density distribution and to stop rounding of the edges. This technique, which seems the most promising of those reviewed above, has so far been applied to stainless steel, iron, gold, and iron–cobalt. It can obviously be extended to other metals and alloys.

Electrolytic Jet Machining. The techniques for obtaining thin foils from bulk material described above are limited to materials that can be obtained in the form of thin sheets $<200\ \mu$ thick. The other criticism which can be made of these methods is that thermal and mechanical treatments carried out on sheets $\sim100\ \mu$ thick may give results which are not typical of bulk material. To overcome this difficulty and to extend the existing thin-foil techniques to hard materials such as alloy steels, which cannot conveniently be made into sheets of the required thickness, a technique of removing metal uniformly and rapidly from a specimen ~1 mm. thick has been developed by Kelly and Nutting (30). This consists in machining the specimen electrolytically with a jet of acid. A glass jet ~1 mm. in dia., connected to a copper-tube cathode, is moved horizontally backward and forward at constant velocity 30 times a minute, while the specimen, mounted perpendicular to the jet at a distance of 1–2 mm., is moved vertically up and down once every 6 min., also at constant velocity. The cams imparting these motions have a 1-in. throw, so that a square area on

the specimen of 1-in. side is covered by the jet. The accuracy of the machining is better than 2 % of the metal removed. Using a hydrochloric acid electrolyte at 2 amp. and 50 V on a steel specimen, the rate of metal removal is $\sim250\ \mu$/amp./hr. Since it is possible to eliminate the effects of mechanical cutting and grinding by electromachining, without destroying or modifying the structure of the interior of a metal, thin foils can be prepared from as large a specimen as required. In this way foils of 1 % carbon steel and 20 % nickel, 0.8 % carbon steel were produced from material 0.75 mm. thick, electromachined to 75 μ and then electropolished by the Bollmann technique.

REFERENCES

1. Pashley, D. W., *Advances in Physics*, **5**, 173 (1956).
2. Pitsch, W., *Phil., Mag.*, **4**, 577 (1959); see also *J. Inst. Metals*, **87**, 444 (1958–59).
3. Trillat, J. J. and Takahashi, N., *Compt. rend.*, **235**, 1306 (1952).
4. Takahashi, N. and Trillat, J. J., *ibid.*, **237**, 1246 (1953).
5. Takahashi, N. and Mihama, K., *Acta Met.*, **5**, 159 (1957).
6. Takahashi, N. and Ashinuma, K., *J. Inst. Metals*, **87**, 19 (1958–59).
7. Suito, E. and Uyeda, N., "Proceedings of the Third International Conference on Electron Microscopy," p. 223 (London, 1954).
8. Weisenberger, E., *Z. wiss. Mikroskop.*, **62**, 163 (1955).
9. Weil, R. and Read, H. J., *J. Appl. Physics*, **21**, 1068 (1950).
10. Reimer, L., *Z. Metallkunde*, **47**, 631 (1956).
11. Takahashi, N. and Kazato, K., *Compt. rend.*, **243**, 1408 (1956).
12. Takahashi, N. and Ashinuma, K., *ibid.*, **246**, 3430 (1958).
13. Hirsch, P. B., Kelly, A. and Menter, J. W., "Proceedings of the Third International Conference on Electron Microscopy," p. 231 (London, 1954).
14. Haanstra, H. B., *Philips Tech. Rev.*, **17**, 178 (1955).
15. Reimer, L., *T. Metallkunde*, **50**, 37 (1959).
16. Hirsch, P. B., Horne, R. W. and Whelan, M. J., *Phil. Mag.*, **1**, 677 (1956).
17. Phillips, R. and Welsh, N. C., *ibid.*, **3**, 801 (1958).

18. CASTAING, R., "Proceedings of the Third International Conference on Electron Microscopy," p. 379 (London, 1954).
19. CASTAING, R., *Rev. Mét.*, **52**, 669 (1955).
20. HEIDENREICH, R. D., *J. Appl. Physics*, **20**, 993 (1949).
21. BOLLMANN, W., "Electron Microscopy: Proceedings of the Stockholm Conference, 1956", p. 316. **1957**, (Almqvist and Wiksell), Stockholm.
22. BOLLMANN, W., *Phys. Rev.*, **103**, 1588 (1956).
23. NICHOLSON, R. B., THOMAS, G. AND NUTTING, J., *Brit. J. Appl. Physics*, **9**, 25 (1958).
24. TOMLINSON, H. M., *Phil. Mag.*, **3**, 867 (1958).
25. SWANN, P. R. AND NUTTING, J., private communication.
26. BRANDON, D. G. AND NUTTING, J., *Brit. J. Appl. Physics*, **10**, 255 (1959).
27. MIRAND, P. AND SAULNIER, A., *Compt. rend.*, **246**, 1688 (1958).
28. MICHEL, P., *Sheet Metal Ind.*, **26**, 2175 (1949).
29. FISHER, R. M., private communication.
30. KELLY, P. M. AND NUTTING, J., *J. Iron Steel Inst.*, **192**, 246 (1959).
31. NICHOLSON, R. B., PH.D. Thesis, Cambridge University.
32. SILCOX, J. AND HIRSCH, P. B., *Phil. Mag.*, **4**, 72 (1959).
33. IRVING, B. A., Institute of Physics Exeter Conference, 1959.
34. KERRIDGE, J. F., JOHNSON, A. A. AND MATTHEWS, H. I., *Nature*, **184**, 356 (1959).
35. SAULNIER, A. AND MIRAND, P., *Compt. rend.*, **247**, 2351 (1958).
36. WILSDORF, H. G. F., CINQUINA, L. AND VAKKER, C. J. *Proc. Int. Conf. Electron Micr.* (in press) (1958).

P. M. KELLY

J. NUTTING

MICROTOMY. *See* **GENERAL MICROSCOPY, p. 343.**

MINERALS

The sizes, shapes and surface features of minerals and mineral particles provide essential and sometimes otherwise unobtainable information about such important subjects as atomic structure, the nature of origin and growth, and the reaction of minerals to physical and chemical forces imposed either by nature or man. Textural relationships of minerals with other materials of their own or a different kind are often keys to the nature of bonding forces and to the probable behavior of the aggregate—be it rock, soil, ceramic body, paint film, or drilling mud—under the various conditions to which it is subjected.

Considered on the basis of the size range of mineral particles and their surface features, one-third of the mineral kingdom was "invisible" prior to the advent of electron microscopy. The light microscope, penetrating to the tenths-of-a-micron region, leaves unseen all objects measured in tens and hundreds of Angstrom units; and although some of these objects are reproduced in larger mineral particles, many have no counterpart in the world of the light microscope or unaided eye. Such, for example, are the detailed features of tubular crystals of halloysite clay, seen in replica in Figure 1, and of chrysotile asbestos, shown in ultra-thin section in Figure 2. Until 1948 when the tubular form of halloysite crystals was first revealed by the electron microscope and the structure explained (1), it was not known that cylindrical crystals with curved planes of atoms existed as stable structures in the mineral kingdom. In this and many other cases the electron microscope removed the barriers standing in the way of direct observation of one of the most fertile parts of the mineral kingdom, that lying beyond the realm of the light microscope and bordered on the other side by the land of measurement of the atoms themselves. In mineralogy, therefore, as in other fields, the electron microscope has two functions: to serve as a supplement to the eye and the light microscope by providing further data on features visible at lower magnification; and to reveal to the eye the details of objects indigenous to the 10 to 10,000 Å region.

The ability of the microscope to perform these functions has depended on the development of technique. Early mineralogical applications such as studies of mineral dusts, clays, and pigments involved the morphol-

FIG. 1. Halloysite clay, Wendover, Utah. Platinum-carbon replica of a fracture surface showing tubular and lath-shaped crystals. The scale in all illustrations is one micron except where otherwise indicated. (All micrographs not otherwise credited were taken by Joseph J. Comer, electron microscopist, College of Mineral Industries, The Pennsylvania State University.) ×84,300.

ogy of fine particles that could be, or already were, dispersed for direct observation. Thus, as soon as the instrument became available it began to fill the long standing needs of the mineralogist concerned with the shape, size, concentration, interaction, behavior, production, separation, and use of particles measured in microns. The effect in areas of research such as silicosis and clay mineralogy was immediate and dramatic; and although new techniques have greatly extended the area of applicability of electron microscopy, many present day problems can be solved by the simple technique of directly viewing particles that are dispersed upon a suitable substrate.

Two techniques provide additional infor-

mation to the scientist interested in the nature of particles in dispersed systems: shadow casting and freeze drying. The former soon became standard procedure in electron microscope laboratories because it produced additional contrast and provided a means of measuring particle thickness. The freeze-dry technique is invaluable when the morphology and interaction of particles in suspension is important. In Figure 3 the convolutions of the Wyoming bentonite flakes suspended in water were "captured" when the embedding water droplet was suddenly frozen. Had the particles been allowed to settle and the water removed by evaporation the resulting shape of the films would bear no relationship to that which, to a large extent, controls the behavior of clay-water bodies. In this illustration note the effect of

FIG. 2. Chrysotile asbestos, Transvaal. Ultrathin section showing circular cross sections of tubular crystals. The scale is 0.1 micron. ×94,000. (*Courtesy Robert V. Rice, Electron Microscope Laboratory, Mellon Institute*)

shadow-casting in giving depth to the field and revealing the size, shape and texture of the smaller particles that make up the twisted flakes.

The development of replica methods extended the applicability of the electron microscope to particles of any size and to the study of surfaces, thus removing many of the limitations of the instrument for mineralogical and petrographic work. As a result, electron microscopy began to play a more significant role in studies of crystal growth and solution, chemical reactivity and physical wear, high temperature reactions, texture of natural and artificial mineral aggregates, and applications of minerals in many industrial uses. Early replica work, particularly using plastic films, was restricted to relatively smooth, impermeable and non-porous surfaces. Later a very important forward step was the successful application of the platinum-carbon replica technique to clays (2, 3) and other porous substances, thereby extending the method to all mineral materials, including rocks and soils. Thus, Figure 1 is a platinum-carbon replica of a fractured surface of the halloysite clay. The technique is especially suitable for minerals of this type where sensitivity to hydration state may result in severe morphological changes if preparation procedures become too involved and time consuming. Thus, replicas of fractured surfaces may indicate a very different particle size distribution than that revealed when particles have been dispersed and allowed to settle on a substrate.

Thin sectioning for the electron microscope is a technique that, until recently, has been of limited use to mineralogists because of the hardness and brittleness of the materials involved. However, improvements in diamond knives have permitted an important "breakthrough" in this area (4) and it is to be expected that sectioning of minerals and mineral aggregates will provide important new data in the future. Figure 2 demonstrates how effectively application of this

Fig. 3. Wyoming bentonite, Upton, Wyoming. Freeze-dry preparation of montmorillonite clay from aqueous suspension. ×20,200.

technique to a bundle of chrysotile asbestos fibers supports previous data as to the tubular morphology and the packing arrangement of the individual crystals as seen in cross section (5).

Fine-grained Minerals

Mineral particles that belong in the size range appropriate to effective electron microscope study of morphological features fall into two categories. In one are those that are simply small scale representatives of minerals which also occur in the form of coarser

189

crystals and fragments easily studied at lower magnification. Many of the particles in mineral dusts, paints and pigments, fine-grained rocks, ceramic bodies and other synthetic aggregates fall in this group. Thus, Figure 4 pictures quartz crystals that have grown in parallel to near-parallel orientation in a minute fissure in chert, a high-silica rock. Although, for minerals of this group, the morphological characteristics and behavior of the finest particles can frequently be predicted from larger specimens of the same material, the electron microscope still provides vital information as to size limitations and distribution of the fine particles; as to surface features, textural relationships, nucleation and growth phenomena; and as to chemical and physical stability under various conditions.

The second group, smaller in number, consists of the "dwarfs" of the mineral kingdom

which, because of restrictions imposed by their crystal chemistry, rarely attain sufficient size to be studied effectively with the light microscope. It was at this group that the electron microscope was first "aimed" because it was here that the resolution of the instrument was most needed to provide basic information of the type long known for coarse-grained minerals. The clay minerals were among the first investigated (6, 7, 8, 9) and have been more thoroughly subjected to electron microscopic study than any other mineral family (see, for example, 10, 11, 12, 13, 14). Not only do these minerals fall in just the right size range but, because of the large number of commercial applications of clay and clay products, detailed high magnification study has been industrially as well as scientifically important. The morphological complexity of the minerals is revealed by a comparison of Figures 1 and 5, replicas of two

FIG. 4. Quartz crystals in chert, Caddo Gap, Arkansas. Particles on most fracture surfaces in this rock do not show the crystal forms exhibited here. ×12,100.

members of the kaolin group, halloysite and kaolinite, respectively, which have the same chemical composition but crystallize as tubes or laths in the former case (15), and hexagonal plates in the latter. A similar situation exists in the serpentine minerals where tubes of chrysotile (Figure 2) contrast sharply with laths and flakes of antigorite (16, 17, 18, 19). Such striking morphological differences within single mineral groups reflect differences in environment and growth conditions, and obviously must be taken into account in any application which depends on the physical attributes of the materials.

Figure 3, referred to previously, provides further evidence of the large morphological variation among clay minerals. Of all the clays, those of the so-called montmorillonite group demonstrate the greatest morphological variation with change of hydration state (20, 21, 22). Precise measurement shows that individual sheets approach unit cell thickness of 10 to 30 Å yet have a real extent of the order of hundreds of square microns. Such characteristics are basic to the applicability of bentonite in oil-well drilling-mud and as filler in many industrial materials, as well as in many areas of colloid chemistry, agronomy and mineralogy where ion exchange and surface behavior of such materials are of interest.

Synthetic minerals occur in both groups discussed above but deserve particular mention because of the important role played by the electron microscope in their study. In the field of geochemistry, particularly, where much emphasis is placed on high temperature, high pressure phase equilibrium studies, conditions are frequently not conducive to the formation of large crystals and the products may be visible only at high magnification. Such is the case for synthetic chrysotile (Figure 6) produced from Mg-Si gels under hydrothermal conditions at a temperature of 450°C and a pressure of 40,000 psi (23). The tubular character of the fibers is apparent, as is also the "cone-in-cone"

FIG. 5. Kaolinite-coated paper. The characteristic platy form and hexagonal outline and cleavage of the clay particles are apparent in this platinum-carbon replica of a sheet of high-gloss paper. ×15,000.

growth feature only rarely observed in natural material.

Minerals are now being synthesized under a wide variety of conditions, many for use in numerous industrial applications, and the electron microscope has an important role in the research involved with the development, production and control of the product. Figure 7 shows an aggregate of crystals of a synthetic zeolite, the mineral group so important in water softening.

Whether the minerals be synthetic or nat-

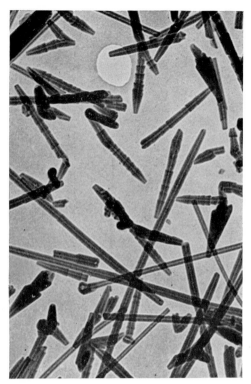

FIG. 6. Synthetic chrysotile asbestos. The tubular crystals have internal diameters of 50-100Å but vary widely in outer diameter. The "cone-in-cone" habit is common only in synthetic material. ×62,000.

ural the electron microscope has been invaluable in studying their applicability to and usefulness in many industrial applications. The replica showing the kaolinite flakes in Figure 5, for example, was made of a sheet of paper such as that you are now reading, the role of the clay particles being to provide the high gloss necessary for good reproduction of illustrations. To obtain maximum reflectivity the perfection and orientation of individual crystals is of utmost importance, and platinum-carbon replicas such as that shown have provided vital information to the paper coating trade (24). Similarly, fundamental work has been done on subjects such as TiO_2, iron oxide and other mineral pigments in paint and enamel (25, 26, 27, 28), crystals in glass (29, 30), diamond powders (31), and

calcium-silicate hydrates in cement (32, 33, 34), just to mention a few.

Along "biomineralogical" lines much research has been conducted on such subjects as mineral dust (35, 36) and its concentration in lung tissue (37, 38); and the structure and chemical resistance of apatite tooth enamel (39, 40). Diatoms with their intricate structures have long been a favorite subject of microscopists (41, 42), and high magnification studies of their structures and mode of occurrence in diatomaceous earth are of academic and industrial importance. Studies of coal surfaces have revealed structures, such as those shown in Figure 8, which are presumably of botanical origin.

Surface Features of Minerals and Mineral Aggregates

The development of replica techniques opened the way to the study of mineral structures which either were not well represented or could not be observed on or in mineral fragments. Study of fracture surfaces of crystals or fragments of single minerals provides evidence about such features as cleavage, fracture patterns, and inclusions (43, 44, 45, 46); whereas in compounds, aggregate textures, morphology and relative hardness of mineral components, and the amount and role of cementing material can be evaluated. External surfaces yield data on features produced during growth or by subsequent physical or chemical action under conditions imposed by nature or man. This area of study penetrates many branches of science and thousands of electron micrographs of mineral materials appear throughout the scientific literature of the mineralogist, chemist, physicist, soil scientist, ceramist and engineer. Surface changes on catalysts (47), the abrasion of diamond (48), oxidation of sulfides (49), dislocations in crystals (50, 51), grain growth at high temperatures (52), nucleation of ice crystals (53), epitaxial relationships (54), gliding, twinning, scratches: all these and many more

FIG. 7. Synthetic zeolite A. The crystals are bounded by cube and dodecahedron faces and show good penetration twins. ×16,500. (*Courtesy of D. W. Breck, Linde Company*)

FIG. 8. Subbituminous coal, Gilette, Wyoming. The platinum-carbon replica was obtained from a collodion replica stripped from the fractured coal surface. The identity of the various objects is unknown. ×11,000. (*Courtesy of R. R. Dutcher, Coal Petrography Laboratory, College of Mineral Industries, The Pennsylvania State University*)

193

FIG. 9. Synthetic sylvite (KCl). The beautifully revealed cubic cleavage contrasts strikingly with curved surfaces. ×10,300.

FIG. 10. Quartz fracture surface. Collodion-carbon replica, Pd-shadowed. Evidence of crystallographic control of the fracture pattern is prominent in the fine as well as the coarse fracture lines. ×5,700. (*Courtesy of A. van Valkenburg and Elisabeth Mitchell, Constitution and Microstructure Section, Mineral Products Division, National Bureau of Standards*)

subjects have received much attention from electron microscopists. Figures 9–14, illustrating some typical surface features, can only suggest the nature and extent of this large and rapidly expanding area of mineralogical study.

Figures 9 and 10 contrast the cubic cleavage of sylvite (KCl) with the more irregular but apparently crystallographically-controlled fracture parallel to the X-cut of a quartz crystal. Figure 11 shows 50 Å growth steps observed at very high magnification on a crystal of the zeolite pictured in Figure 7. In studies such as this the electron microscope has played an important role in helping to delineate the type of growth step pictured here from that produced in spiral growth.

Etching techniques have long been important in the investigation of structure, crystal growth and chemical stability (55) and the electron microscope has greatly extended the applicability and utility of this

FIG. 11. Synthetic zeolite A. Platinum-carbon replica showing 50A growth steps on a cube face. ×59,000. (*Courtesy of D. W. Breck, Linde Company*)

method of investigation (56, 57). The vastly different results produced by etching synthetic NaCl with ethyl alcohol as compared to water are illustrated in Figure 12 (58). An entirely different type of surface reaction is shown in Figure 13 which pictures crystals of mullite which have formed from a kaolinite clay surface (see Figure 5) held at a temperature of 1130°C for 20 hours. The arrangement of the mullite needles results from the pseudo-hexagonal symmetry of the clay mineral. Similar application of electron microscopy to the study of minerals in various ceramic materials has been extensive (see 59 for references).

The type of result that may be obtained from a study of fine-grained aggregates is illustrated in Figures 1, 4 and 14. Whereas the first two show textural and crystallographic features of particles in monomineral-

lic specimens, the pyrite in Figure 14 occurs in a fine-grained shale containing many mineral varieties. The area pictured here is part of a pyrite nodule made up of an assemblage of pyritohedrons in parallel orientation. Other examples of electron microscopy in petrographic studies involve studies of such subjects as slate (60), ore textures (61, 62), meteorites (63), and glacial till (64) as well as cherts and fine-grained limestones.

Despite the extensive research done with the electron microscope in the study of minerals and rocks (for general articles see 65, 66, 67, 68, 69), the potential of the instrument is far from realized. One reason has been the tendency to regard the areas covered by electron and light microscopy as separate rather than overlapping fields. With the increased application of the replica technique supplemented by devices designed to

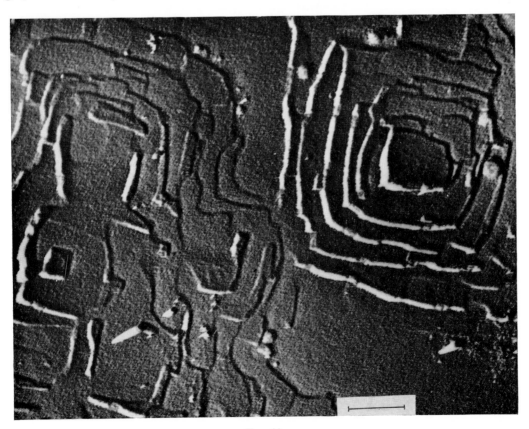

FIG. 12a

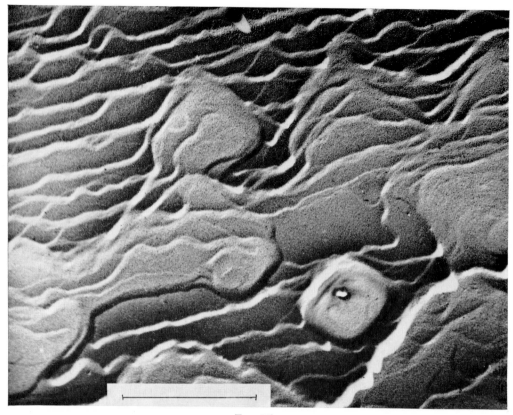

FIG. 12b

FIG. 12. Synthetic halite (NaCl). A, Chromium-shadowed formvar replica of a crystal face etched with water. ×15,300. B, the same after etching with ethyl alcohol. ×36,500. (*Courtesy of A. Oberlin, Laboratoire de Minéralogie, Faculté des Sciences, Paris*)

FIG. 13. Mullite crytals grown from a kaolinite surface at 1320°C. The hexagonal arrangement results from the structure of the parent material. ×14,000.

196

facilitate study of a selected area of the subject with both light and electrons, the boundaries between the two disciplines are disappearing and a more integrated picture is being obtained of the entire mineral kingdom. With the further development of ultrathin sectioning of hard and brittle substances it is probable that no morphological feature of minerals and mineral compounds will long remain "invisible."

FIG. 14. Pyrite nodule, Chattanooga shale. Fracture took place around rather than through individual crystals revealing their pyritohedral habit. ×16,700.

FIG. 15. Step fracture of calcite crystal in Solenhofen limestone. ×28,000. (*Courtesy of H. P. Studer, Shell Development Company*)

REFERENCES

1. BATES, T. F., HILDEBRAND, F. A. AND SWINEFORD, A., "Morphology and structure of endellite and halloysite," *Geol. Soc. Am. Bull.*, **59**, 1310 (1948); *Am. Mineral.*, **35**, 463–485 (1950).
2. COMER, J. J. AND TURLEY, J. W., "Replica studies of bulk clays," *J. Appl. Phys.*, **26**, 346–350 (1955).
3. BATES, T. F. AND COMER, J. J., "Electron microscopy of clay surfaces," *Natl. Acad. Sci.-Natl. Res. Council Publ.* **395**, 1–25 (1955).
4. PFEFFERKORN, G., THEMANN, H., AND URBAN, H., "Anwendungen der mikrotomschnitttechnik auf elektronenmikroskopische mineraluntersuchungen," Proc. Stockholm Conf. on Electron Microscopy, 333–334 (1956).
5. MASER, M., RICE, R. V., AND KLUG, H. P., "Chrysotile morphology," *Am. Mineral.* **45**, 680–688 (1960).
6. EITEL, W. H., MULLER, H. O. AND RADCZEWSKI, O. E., "Examination of clay minerals with the ultramicroscope," *Ber. Deut. Keram. Ges.*, **20**, 165–180 (1938).
7. ARDENNE, M. VON, ENDELL, K., AND HOFFMANN, E., "Examination of the finest fractions of bentonite and cement with the universal microscope," *Ber. Deut. Keram. Ges.*, **21**, 209–227 (1940).
8. HUMBERT, R. P. AND SHAW, B. T., "Studies of clay particles with the electron microscope," *Soil Sci.*, **52**, 481–487 (1941).
9. ENDELL, K., "Significance of the electron microscope for identifying the microstructure of clays," *Tonind. Ztg.*, **65**, 69–72 (1941).
10. PINSKER, Z. G., "Electrographic and electronomicroscopic study of clay minerals," *Trudy Biogeokhim. Lab., Akad. Nauk SSSR*, **10**, 116–141 (1954).
11. BATES, T. F., "Electron microscopy as a method of identifying clays," Proc. 1st Natl. Conf. on Clays and Clay Minerals,

Calif. Dept. *Nat. Res., Div. Mines Bull.* **169**, 130–150 (1955).

12. TAGGART, M. S., MULLIGAN, W. O., AND STUDER, H. P., "Electron micrographic studies of clays," *Natl. Acad. Sci.—Natl. Res. Council Publ.* **395**, 31–64 (1955).

13. NEUWIRTH, E., "The determination of clay minerals with the electron microscope," *Tschermaks mineralog. u. petrog. mitt.*, **5**, 347–361 (1956).

14. SUITO, EIJI, "Electron microscopy of clay minerals," *Nendokagaku no Shimpo*, **1**, 166–180 (1959).

15. BATES, T. F. AND COMER, J. J., "Further observations on the morphology of chrysotile and halloysite," "Clays and Clay Minerals," 237–248, Pergamon Press, New York, 1959.

16. BATES, T. F., SAND, L. B., AND MINK, J. F., "Tubular crystals of chrysotile asbestos," *Science*, **111**, 512–513 (1950).

17. NOLL, W. AND KIRCHER, H., "Zur morphologie des chrysotilasbest," *Naturwiss.*, **37**, 540–1 (1950).

18. ZUSSMAN, J., BRINDLEY, G. W., AND COMER, J. J., "Electron diffraction studies of serpentine minerals," *Am. Mineral.*, **42**, 133–153 (1957).

19. KALOUSEK, G. L. AND MUTTART, L. E., "Studies on the chrysotile and antigorite components of serpentine," *Am. Mineral.*, **42**, 1–22 (1957).

20. CORBET, H. C. AND WOLFFES, J., "The use of a freeze-drying technique in the investigation of sodium-montmorillonite by electron microscopy," "Proc. Stockholm Conf. on Electron Microscopy," 334–335 (1956).

21. MERING, J., OBERLIN, A., AND VILLIERE, J., "Etude par electrodeposition de la morphologie des montmorillonites. Effet des cation calcium," *Bull. Soc. franc. mineral. et crist.*, **79**, 515–522 (1956).

22. HOFMANN, U., FAHN, R., AND WEISS, A., "Thixotropie bei kaolinit und innerkristalline quellung bei montmorillonit. Wirkung der austauschfahigen kationen der flussigkeit und der elektrolyte einer wassrigen losung," *Kolloid-Z.*, **151**, 97–115 (1957).

23. ROY, D. M. AND ROY, R., "An experimental study of the formation and properties of synthetic serpentines and related layer silicate minerals," *Am. Mineral.*, **39**, 957–975 (1954).

24. COMER, J. J., STETSON, H. W., AND LYONS, S. C., "A new replica technique for making electron micrographs of surfaces of paper sheets," *Tech. Assn. Pulp Paper Ind.*, **38**, 620 (1955).

25. SCHMIEDER, F., "Electron microscopic investigation of the relation between covering quality and grain size of pigments," *Kolloid-Z.*, **95**, 29–33 (1941).

26. HONDA, T. AND MUKAI, F., "Electron microscopic observation of pigment (hematite) particles in a porcelain glaze," *Rept. Osaka Pref. Ind. Research Inst.*, **3**, 56–57 (1950).

27. COOPER, A. C., "The electron microscope examination of pigment powders and their dispersions in oil media," 1st Int. Cong. Electron Micros. Paris, 1950, Proc. 461–463, Paris Ed. Rev. Optique.

28. SMITH, N. D. P., "The electron microscope in the study of paints," *Trans. Inst. Metal Finishing*, Advance Copy, No. 12, 10 pp. (1955).

29. BATES, T. F. AND BLACK, M. V., "Electron microscope investigation of opal glass," *Glass Ind.*, **29**, 487 (1948).

30. FADEEVA, V. S. AND YAKOVLEVA, M. E., "Investigation of opaque zirconium glazes with the electron microscope," *Doklady Akad. Nauk SSSR*, **81**, 667–669 (1951).

31. MELDAU, R. AND HARSEWINKEL, "Electron microscopy investigations of diamond powders; Electron-optical study of types I and II diamonds," *Industrial Diam. Rev.*, **11**, 7–8 (1951).

32. RADCZEWSKI, O. E., MULLER, H. O., AND EITEL, W., "The hydration of tricalcium aluminate," *Naturwiss.*, **27**, 837–838 (1939).

33. SLIEPCEVICH, C. M., GILDART, L., AND KATZ, D. M., "Crystals from Portland cement hydration; an electron microscope study," *Ind. Eng. Chem.*, **35**, 1178–1187 (1943).

34. SHEKHTER, A. B., SER-SERBINA, N. N., AND REBINDER, P. A., "Investigation with the electron microscope of the effect of a surface admixture on the crystallization of hydrated minerals of cement clinker," *Doklady Akad. Nauk., SSSR*, **89**, 129–132 (1953).

35. CARTWRIGHT, J. AND SKIDMORE, J. W., "The measurement of size and concentration of airborne dusts with the electron microscope," Ministry Fuel and Power (G. Brit.) Safety in Mines Research Estab. Research Rept. No. 79, 31 p., 1953.

36. TALBOT, J. H., "Identification of minerals present in mine dusts by electron diffraction and electron microscopy," Proc. Stockholm Conf. on Electron Microscopy, 353–355, 1956.

37. PFEFFERKORN, G., "Vergleichende untersuchungen uber den mineralinhalt von

silikoselungen," *Arch. Hyg. u. Bakteriol.,* **135**, 14–22 (1951).

38. RIMSKY, A., OBERLIN, A., AND CECCALDI, P. F., "Le diagnostic cristallographique des silicoses pulmonaires," *Bull. Soc. Franc. Mineral. et Crist.,* **78**, 418–424 (1955).

39. SCOTT, D. B. AND WYCKOFF, R. W. G., "Studies of tooth surface structure by optical and electron microscopy," *J. Am. Dent. Assn.,* **39**, 275–282 (1949).

40. GRAY, J. A., SCHWEIZER, H. C., ROSEVEAR, F. B., AND BROGE, R. W., "Electron microscopic observations of the differences in the effects of stannous fluoride and sodium fluoride on dental enamel," *J. Dental Res.,* **37**, 638–648 (1958).

41. KRAUSE, F., "Electron-optical pictures of diatoms with the magnetic electron microscope," *Zeits. f. Physik,* **102**, 417–422 (1936).

42. MAHL, H., "Photographs of diatoms with the supermicroscope," *Naturwiss.,* **27**, 417 (1939).

43. ZAPFFE, C. A. AND WORDEN, C. O., "Fractography as a technique in crystal chemistry," *Acta Cryst.,* **2**, 377–382 (1949).

44. PFEFFERKORN, G. AND WESTERMAN, H., "Electron microscope study of the deformation of calcite," *Neues Jahrb. Mineral., Monatsh,* **1951**, 97–103 (1952).

45. SEAL, M. A., "Reflection electron microscope study of diamond cleavage surfaces," Proc. Stockholm Conf. on Electron Microscopy, 341–343, 1956.

46. WOLFF, G. A. AND BRODER, J. D., "Microcleavage, bonding character and surface structure in materials with tetrahedral coordination," *Acta. Cryst.,* **12**, 313–323 (1959).

47. SHEKHTER, A. B. AND TRETYAKOV, I. I., "Electron-microscopic study of the surface changes of massive catalysts at work," *Bull. Acad. Sci. USSR Div. Chem. Sci.,* 397–402 (1953).

48. SEAL, M., "The abrasion of diamond," *Proc. Royal Soc. A,* **248**, 379–393 (1958).

49. WATANABE, M., "Submicroscopic topography of oxidized surface of stibnite and etch surface of sphalerite," *J. Phys. Japan,* **12**, 874–882 (1957).

50. INDENBOM, V. L., "Dislocations in crystals," *Soviet Physics. Crystallography,* **3**, 112–132 (1957).

51. HASHIMOTO, H. AND UYEDA, R., "Detection of dislocation by the moire patterns in electron micrographs," *Acta Cryst.* **10**, 143 (1957).

52. STUIJTS, A. L. AND HAANSTRA, H. B., "Grain growth in a ceramic material, studied by means of electron microscopy," *Trabajos reuion Intern. Reactividad Solidos,* 30 Madrid, **1**, 671–701, 1956.

53. MARUYAMA, H., "Electron microscopy study of the ice crystal nuclei," *Papers Meterolo. and Geophys. (Tokyo),* **7**, 251–266 (1956).

54. HOCART, R. AND OBERLIN, A., "Epitaxie des microcristaux d'or sur le graphite. Etude au microscope electronique et par diffraction electronique," *Compt. Rend. Acad. Sci.,* **239**, 1228–1230 (1954).

55. HONESS, A. P., "The nature, origin, and interpretation of the etch figures on crystals," 164 pp. Wiley and Sons, New York, 1927.

56. PFEFFERKORN, G., "Electronmicroscopic investigation of calcite and its true crystal structure," *Optik* **7**, Sonderheft 2, 208–216 (1950).

57. STANLEY, R. C., "Etch pits on calcite cleavage faces," *Nature,* **183**, 1548 (1959).

58. HOCART, R., ROULT, G., AND OBERLIN, A., "Decroissements par strates d'une face (001) de chlorure de sodium naturel et artificiel. Observations au microscope electronique," *Compt. Rend. Acad. Sci.* **240**, 2245–2247 (1955).

59. COMER, J. J., "The electron microscope in the study of minerals and ceramics," *Am. Soc. Testing Materials, Spec. Tech. Publ.* **257**, 94–120 (1959).

60. BATES, T. F., "Investigation of the micaceous minerals in slate," *Am. Mineral.,* **32**, 625–636 (1947).

61. SYROMYATNIKOV, F. V. AND FILIMONOV, A. F., "Study of ore structure with the help of the electron microscope," *Izvest. Akad. Nauk. SSSR., Ser. Geol.,* **5**, 135–140 (1953).

62. OHMACHI, H. AND HAGAMARA, T., "On the studies of structure and texture of the manganiferous iron ore by electron microscopy," *Kagaku (Tokyo),* **25**, 637–638 (1955).

63. ORSINI, P. G. AND MAGGI, N., "Electron microscopy of an iron meteorite," *Gazz. Chim. Ital.,* **88**, 482–486 (1958).

64. DROSTE, J. B., WHITE, G. W., AND VATTER, A. E., "Electron microscopy of the till matrix," *J. Sediment. Petrol.,* **28**, 345–350 (1958).

65. O'DANIEL, H., "Mineralogical research with the electron microscope," 1939–1946, *Mineralogy,* **1**–6 (1948).

66. BATES, T. F., "The electron microscope applied to geological research," *New York Acad. Sci. Trans. Ser. II,* **11**, 100–108 (1949).

67. OBERLIN, A., "Application of the electron

microscope in the study of crystallized media," *Bull. Soc. Franc. Mineral. et Crist.* **77**, 833–839 (1954).

68. DWORNIK, E. AND ROSS, M., "Application of electron microscope to mineralogic studies," *Am. Mineral.* **40**, 261–274 (1955).

69. FAHN, R., "Applications of the electron microscope for the investigation of rocks and minerals," *Tonind. Ztg. u. Keram. Rundschau*, **80**, 171–180 (1956).

THOMAS F. BATES

PAINT SURFACE REPLICA TECHNIQUES

Since it is impractical to view paint surfaces directly because of difficulties in electron transmission it was necessary to develop indirect methods. These procedures classified as replicating methods are based upon a reproduction of the surface. The reproduction may be in the form of a negative or positive replica. In the negative replica the heights and hollows are reversed with respect to the original surface. The positive replica requires an intermediate replica from which the final replica is made and the heights and hollows are in the same relative order as on the original surface. As a rule both methods employ metal shadow casting to enhance the contrast of the replica and to emphasize the dimension normal to the surface.

Both negative and positive replication techniques may be employed in the study of paint surfaces. However, the replica technique employed is governed strictly by the nature of the surface; that is, the solvent system used in replication should not attack the paint surface and introduce artifacts. A detailed description of various replica techniques which may be used in the examination of paint surfaces will be presented as well as examples illustrating paint films in various stages of degradation. No attempt will be made to discuss the mechanism of paint film formation since this paper will be confined strictly to techniques.

Replicating Systems

The organic nature of most paint surfaces presents a problem in replication since the solvents used may attack the organic phase and cause some uncertainty in the replication process. However, this problem may be circumvented by using water-soluble intermediate plastic replicas or by carefully selecting replicating media the solvent systems of which are known not to be miscible with the paint surface under study.

Perhaps the simplest method of replicating paint films is by making unbacked negative replicas; this method will be discussed first.

Negative Replica (Unbacked). In the unbacked negative replication technique the surface is reproduced in such a manner that the replica represents a surface in which the heights and depressions are reversed with respect to the original surface. This method employs only one replicating medium. A schematic representation of the steps used in the preparation of an unbacked negative replica of a paint surface is given in Figure 1.

A plastic solution from a dropper is flowed over a small portion of the paint surface and the excess solution drained off by drying the film at room temperature on the paint panel in a vertical position. Some typical plastic solutions are given below:

(1) 1–2 % parlodion or collodion in amyl acetate.

(2) Freshly prepared 1 % solution of Formvar in ethylene dichloride or dioxane.

(3) 1–2 % ethyl cellulose in ethylene dichloride.

One should remember that the chemical nature of the sample should be such that it is not attacked by the replicating solution. To remove the replica from the paint surface, moisture from the breath is condensed onto the surface and then removed with Scotch tape; first, however, several specimen screens about $\frac{1}{4}''$ apart are placed on the replica. If there is some tendency for the replica to wrinkle on the screen after stripping, this difficulty may be eliminated by immersing the screen in dilute solution of an adhesive before placing the screen on the replica.

The tape is carefully pulled away and the plastic replica of the surface removed with it. To remove film-coated screen from the Scotch tape, a dissecting needle which has been sharpened to a fine point is used to cut the film around the edge of screen. Fine-tipped tweezers are then used to remove the screen from the tape. Sticking of the screen to the tape may be eliminated by placing a small circular disk of paper ($\frac{1}{8}''$ diameter) between the tape and screen. The replica is then shadowcast by coating the surface with a suitable metal, but more about the shadow-casting process later.

Negative Replica (Backed). An alternate procedure for preparing a negative replica of a paint surface is to back the negative replica with a heavy coating of plastic, as shown schematically in Figure 2. This procedure is used in cases where stripping an unsupported film is difficult, as in rough paint surfaces, and the resultant replica would be distorted or torn by stresses applied in stripping. Plastic #1 is applied to the surface with a dropper and allowed to drain vertically. When dry, plastic #2, in a heavy concentration which is not miscible with plastic #1, is applied similarly and dried. Some typical plastic combinations which have been applied successfully to the study of selected paint surfaces are given below.

(A) 1–2 % solution of "Formvar" in ethylene dichloride followed with 2–3 % solution of "Parlodion" in amyl acetate.

(B) 1–2 % solution of "Parlodion" in amyl acetate followed with 4–5 % of polyvinyl alcohol in water.

The double film is then stripped and brought in contact with an appropriate solvent to remove the backing film. In the case of (A) amyl acetate would be used to remove the "Parlodion" while in (B) warm water

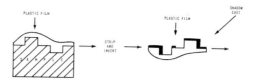

FIG. 1. Negative replica technique (unbacked).

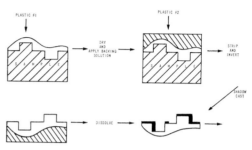

FIG. 2. Negative replica technique (backed).

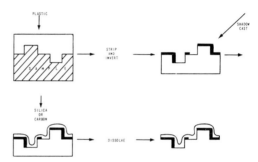

FIG. 3. Intermediate shadowed negative replica.

would be used to solubilize the polyvinyl alcohol. In both cases, plastic #1 should be uppermost and once solution is complete the replica is mounted on grids (200 mesh stainless steel wire disks) brought from below and shadowcast with an appropriate metal.

Intermediate Shadowed Negative Replica. Another variation of the negative replica technique requires the use of an intermediate as shown in Figure 3. In this case, a thick plastic is applied to the paint surface, dry stripped with Scotch tape, inverted and shadowed obliquely with a suitable metal and then coated at normal incidence with 200 Å of silica or 100 Å of carbon in the vacuum evaporator. The plastic replica is removed by washing in a suitable solvent. The silica or carbon replicas are picked up on specimen screens and studied as usual. The use of carbon and silica will be covered in greater detail in the section on positive techniques. Preshadowed replicas afford the obvious advantage of providing better detail by eliminating the interference of the replica structure itself.

Shadow Casting

Shadowing of paint replicas with metal is needed in order to increase the contrast since the replica alone scatters electrons more or less uniformly over the entire area and contrast in electron microscopy is dependent mainly on the difference in electron scattering among area increments of the specimen. After shadowing, areas in which the deposited metal is the densest are the most opaque to the electron beam.

This process of shadowcasting requires the use of a vacuum evaporator which consists essentially of a bell jar evacuated by a diffusion pump backed with a forepump. The mechanics of evaporation can be best illustrated with the aid of Figure 4. Here, the replica preparation at B is placed below and to one side of the tungsten filament C, which can be charged with a given weight of metal and heated electrically to the temperature required for vaporization of the metal.

If a sufficiently good vacuum exists in the bell jar at the time of evaporation (10^{-4} mm. of Hg) the metal atoms will travel in straight lines in all directions from the filament and some of them will be deposited on the sample. If a metal is used that does not ingrate after deposit, its thickness will be greatest on those aspects of the preparation that face the oncoming atoms, and there will be regions of the substrate lying behind high detail that will be so shielded as to receive no metal. These clear regions will appear as if they were shadows when viewed under the electron microscope. The varying opacity that results from the varying thickness of the metal creates the impression that one is seeing the preparation in three dimensions illuminated by light having the direction of the oncoming shadowing atoms.

Although in principle the process of vacuum evaporation is simple there are certain conditions which must be fulfilled if satisfactory preparations of paint films are to result. A suitable shadowing material must be used and the evaporation must take place under vacuum. It would be expected that sharp shadows could not be obtained unless the mean free atomic path in the vacuum evaporator bell jar exceeds the distance from the heater to the sample, that is, unless the evaporated atoms can follow a collision-free path. Experience has shown that the vacuum should be considerably better than this minimum. Seemingly, this good vacuum is needed partly for adequate degassing of the surface of the preparation before evaporation and partly to take care of some of the gas evolved during evaporation.

The best material to use for shadowing will depend both on the type of preparation and the kind of observation to be made. A shadowing material must not have any perceptible structure of its own and must not migrate over the face of the paint replica after deposition. In addition, it must absorb or scatter so strongly that the needed thickness does not appreciably distort the shape or detail of the sample.

Chromium was the first metal to be successfully used for metal shadowcasting and it continues to be used for much work. However, when the thickness of the chromium

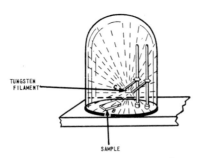

TUNGSTEN FILAMENT

SAMPLE

Fig. 4. High vacuum evaporation.

layer (40Å) is objectionable, either platinum or palladium (4–8Å) may be substituted. The metal is deposited at an angle of from $\tan^{-1}$ 1:1 or 1:3 depending on the inherent roughness of the surface. The lower angle is preferable for fine detail (high gloss paint surfaces) whereas the higher angle is used for coarse structures (weathered paint surfaces).

Positive Replica Technique

A schematic representation of the steps used in the preparation of the positive replica is given in Figure 5. In this technique (3) an intermediate thick replica is required from which a thinner second replica can be stripped. Careful control of the solution concentration of the intermediate replicating medium is highly critical since too low a concentration results in stripping difficulties while too high a concentration results in excessive shrinkage of the medium at the contact surface of the sample resulting in the development of wrinkles.

For paint surfaces a 5% aqueous solution of methylcellulose (Methocel, Dow Chemical Co.) or polyvinyl alcohol (DuPont) in distilled water is employed as the intermediate replicas. The solution is applied uniformly with the aid of a dropper maintaining the paint surface in a horizontal position. When dry, the film is detached slightly with a sharp razor and then carefully pulled off with tweezers. The stripped film is then attached with Scotch tape to a microscope slide and placed in the vacuum evaporator for coating with carbon or silica at normal incidence.

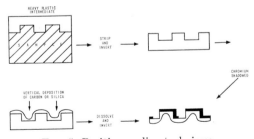

FIG. 5. Positive replica technique.

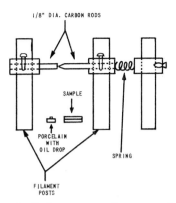

FIG. 6. Carbon evaporation apparatus.

Carbon Evaporation Procedure

The method of carbon evaporation consists of passing 60-cycle alternating current of approximately 20 to 50 amperes through ⅛″ diameter graphite rods (National Carbon, pure spectrographic grade) in a vertical position above the specimen with one rod tapered to a fine point. The carbon rods are held in close contact by a spring as shown in Figure 6 so they do not separate during the evaporation process. Intense local heating occurs at the regions of contact.

A satisfactory carbon thickness is maintained by visually observing the color (light brown) developed on a piece of white porcelain containing a small drop of oil (Apiezon B) (1, 2). The condensed carbon is clearly visible on the porcelain but not on the oil drop which shows up in sharp contrast.

When the evaporation is completed the carbon plastic-coated slide is removed, cut into 0.3 cm squares with a sharp razor and placed on the surface of a Petri dish containing distilled water until the methycellulose is completely dissolved. From two to three hours are required for complete solution of the methylcellulose, with frequent replacement of distilled water. Specimen screens are placed on top of the floating carbon sections and removed with forceps. When dry, the carbon-coated screens are placed in the evaporator and shadowcast with a suitable metal.

203

Silica Evaporation Procedure

In the process of silica evaporation (4, 5) the intermediate replica of the paint film is placed about 7 cm below a conical tungsten (0.5 mm) wire basket containing about a 1 mgm chip of quartz. The evaporator is evacuated to about 10^{-4} mm of Hg and a current of 20 to 30 amps passed through the basket for 20 to 30 seconds. If some difficulty is experienced in evaporating the (quartz) silica, a colloidal suspension of colloidal silica (Ludox) may be substituted and micropipetted on a comparable tungsten filament, dried and evaporated. Another alternative is to use SiO which evaporates more readily than quartz and does not attack the tungsten.

As in the carbon technique, the plastic-silica combination is immersed in water to solubilize the plastic. Once solution is complete the silica replica is picked up on specimen screens, shadowcast and examined as normally. Sometimes if the silica films are extremely thin, special lighting conditions may have to be employed to enhance the visibility.

Photographic Procedure

An RCA-type EMU electron microscope equipped with self-biased electron gun and binocular viewer was employed. A platinum objective aperture with an opening of 50 microns was used to increase the contrast in the final image. Negatives were taken at an electronic magnification of 1500 X and enlarged optically to 8000 X. Kodak Medium Plates were used and developed in Kodak Versatol Developer. Electron micrographs of the paint surfaces prepared by the negative replica technique were processed to the positive print stage, while micrographs prepared by the positive replica technique were processed to the negative print stage. This was done to make heights and depressions more readily appreciated.

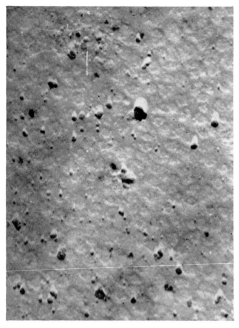

(a) Cellular pattern (X 8000) (b) Pigment flocculation near air interface (X 8000)

FIG. 7. Negative replicas of paint surfaces; a. Unbacked technique; b. Backed technique.

(a) Enamel (× 8000)

(b) Flat paint (× 8000)

FIG. 8. Positive replicas of two different paint surfaces.

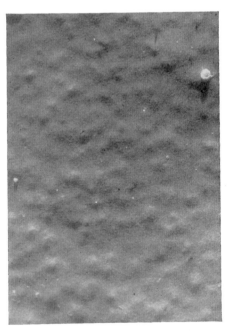

(a) Before weathering (× 8000)

(b) After weathering (× 8000)

FIG. 9. Positive replicas of paint surfaces.

ELECTRON MICROSCOPY

Applications

A typical example of the utilization of the unbacked negative replica technique for the examination of a paint surface is illustrated in Figure 7a. The surface in this case is basically smooth, illustrating a typical cellular pattern. Loose material attached to the replica during stripping can be observed in the background. The micrograph of the paint surface illustrated in Figure 7b was prepared by the backed negative replica technique. The roughness in this case appears to be caused primarily by pigment flocculates near the air interface.

The positive replica technique using a water-soluble intermediate with either carbon or silica as the final replica offers more versatility than the simple negative technique and for this reason is used quite extensively in the study of paint surfaces.

Typical examples of the utilization of this technique for the examination of paint surfaces are illustrated in Figures 8a, 8b, 9a and 9b. Figure 8a shows an enamel with a smooth glossy surface while Figure 8b shows a flat paint with a roughened surface. Figure 9a demonstrates an automative enamel before weathering, while Figure 9b illustrates the enamel after outdoor exposure to test the resistance of the coating to weathering.

Acknowlegments. The author is indebted to Mr. A. E. Jacobson for helpful discussions and to the National Lead Company for supporting this program.

REFERENCES

1. BRADLEY, D. E., *J. Appl. Phys.*, **5**, 65–6 (1954).
2. BRADLEY, D. E., *J. Appl. Phys.*, **27**, 1399–1412 (1956).
3. LASKO, W. R., *Anal. Chem.*, **29**, 784–786 (1957).
4. TWISS, S. B., TEAGUE, D. M., AND WEEKS, W. L., *Off. Dig.*, **28**, 93 (1956).
5. BOBALEK, E. G., LEBRAS, L. R., POWELL, A. S., AND VON FISCHER, W., *Ind. Eng. Chem.*, **46**, 572 (1954).

W. R. LASKO

PATHOLOGY: KIDNEY

The method for renal biopsy was introduced by Iversen *et al.* (1951) and further developed by Kark and Muerhcke (1954). It affords an excellent opportunity to collect material for electron microscopy from living patients with different stages of kidney disease. As a consequence of this the electron microscope is used in many institutes all over the world where human renal pathology is studied, and several reports have been published concerning this subject.*

A large number of electron microscopic investigations of experimentally produced renal lesions in animals have also been performed. It must be emphasized, however, that experimental lesions are not always identical to human diseases. Our investigation on the normal anatomy of the human kidney has also convinced us that there are important morphological differences between the kidney of man and that of animals. Thus the diameter of the basement membrane of the glomerular capillaries has been calculated at 800–1200 ÅU in different animals and at about 3500 ÅU in adult man (Bergstrand and Bucht, 1958). The "physiological" variations due to differences in function of the tubular epithelial cells seem to be much greater in man than in animals which are inbred and kept under uniform environmental conditions (Bergstrand and Ericsson, 1959). Thus observations on animal kidneys should be carefully and critically evaluated when used in discussions of human pathology.

The word "pathological" must also be used with great care. The electron microscope reveals cell organelles such as vacuoles, membranes and mitochondria which are probably continually changing their structure, parallel

* When not stated otherwise, all works dealing with human pathology and referred to in this paper have been performed on material obtained with this method.

to changes of function, also in the healthy subject. It is very difficult and many times impossible to ascertain which are physiological variations and pathological phenomena. The latter word is used in this paper to describe morphological changes which differ with reasonable certainty, quantitatively or qualitatively, from what is seen in healthy subjects.

Glomerulonephritis

Experimental. Electron microscopic studies of glomerular changes in nephrotoxic serum nephritis in rats and mice have been published by a number of authors (Simer, 1954; Piel et al., 1955; Reid, 1956; Miller and Bohle, 1957; Sakaguchi et al., 1957; Vernier et al., 1958b; Miller et al., 1958; and Bohle et al., 1959). The earliest lesions observed one hour after the serum injection was a diffuse thickening of the basement membrane and a slight swelling of the capillary endothelial and epithelial cells. According to Bohle et al., an increased swelling and vacuolization of the epithelial cells takes place during the first 24 hours, accompanied by a gradual and slow decrease of the diameters of the basement membrane to normal values. Between 24 and 72 hours the epithelial-cell changes subside and instead a marked swelling of the endothelial cells takes place. These cells increase in size to such an extent that the capillary lumina may be completely obliterated. The latter changes have been observed by all authors and are commonly regarded as typical for experimental glomerulonephritis.

Similar changes have been observed in rabbits (Feldman, 1959) and in rats (Sitte, 1959) after single intravenous injections of bovine serum.

It is possible that the initial swelling of the basement membrane is produced by the reaction between antigen and antibody which, according to many authors, takes place in this site. This cannot be proved, however (Bohle et al., Feldman), since the techniques used for demonstration of the localization of antibodies does not permit an absolutely certain separation of the pedicels and the thin covering of endothelium from the basement membrane. Thus the reaction may take place in any of these structures. Considering the chemical nature of the basement membrane, as far as it is known, and the experimental evidence referred to above, the basement membrane is the most probable localization, however.

Renal lesions in the acute generalized Schwartzman reaction were studied in rabbits by Bohle et al. (1958) and in rats by Pappas et al. (1958). The animals were treated twice with 24 hours interlude with an intravenous injection of lipopolysaccharides from Escherichia coli. Light microscopy showed abundant thrombi in the glomerular capillary lumina eight hours after the last injection. Electron microscopy demonstrated vacuolization of the endothelial cell cytoplasm and fibrils with a periodicity of 371.5 ÅU, probably representing fibrin in the thrombi.

Experimental glomerular lesions have also been produced by Bencosme et al. (1959) in rats treated with uranyl nitrate. They observed a fusion of the foot processes and a vacuolation of the epithelial cell cytoplasm with an accumulation of dark bodies corresponding to hyaline droplets observed in the light microscope. A foreign substance was precipitated between the capillary basement membranes and large cells inside them, which the authors regard as intercapillary cells. In the newly formed masses collagen fibers were formed and the authors therefore consider that the intercapillary cells are not of endothelial origin.

Human Glomerulonephritis and Lupus Erythematosus. A case of subacute hemorrhagic glomerulonephritis was described by Bergstrand and Bucht (1956). A number of large vacuoles were found in the endothelial cell cytoplasm. In the capillary lumina there were numerous rounded bodies bordered by a single membrane and containing small cell organelles, mostly vacuoles. The authors concluded that these bodies were parts of the cell cytoplasm ejected from the endothelial cell which was damaged by the inflammation. Later investigations have shown that this may also be observed in healthy humans and animals, but in the authors' opinion the process was markedly increased in the case of glomerulonephritis. There were no definite changes in the basement membrane or in the epithelial cells.

Farquhar et al. (1957a) have described two cases of acute, two of subacute and three of chronic glomerulonephritis. They observed in the acute stage of the disease a proliferation and swelling of the endothelial cells and later of the epithelial cells in the glomeruli. The epithelial foot process organization appeared normal in contrast to the observations in nephrosis (see below). The basement membranes were thickened and large masses of a basement membrane-like material was accumulated probably inside endothelial cells. They concluded that this material was produced by the endothelial cells. In the later stages of the disease the capillaries were destroyed and replaced by masses of the basement membrane-like substance. Collagen fibrils were not observed.

Similar alterations were seen by the same authors in three cases of Lupus Erythematosus. The thickening of the basement membrane was more pronounced than in glomerulonephritis. Nodular accumulations of a basement membrane-like substance were also observed in the endothelial cells. Collagen fibrils were not found. These observations were confirmed by Putois (1959).

In a subsequent paper by Vernier et al. (1958a) 11 cases of glomerulonephritis and four cases of Lupus Erythematosus in children were described. Proliferative changes in the endothelium dominated in the acute cases whereas the thickening of the basement membrane and accumulations of a newly formed material were most striking in the subacute and chronic cases. The large masses of this material seen in two cases of Lupus Erythematosus correspond to the wire loops observed with the light microscope.

Cases of subacute and chronic glomerulonephritis with similar observations have also been reported by Spiro (1958, 1959).

Judging from these reports glomerulonephritis is primarily a disease of the vascular endothelium in the glomeruli with a swelling and vacuolization of the cytoplasm of these cells followed by a precipitation of a foreign material in the basement membrane and probably also in the endothelial cell cytoplasm. The basement membrane is thickened and subsequently the epithelial cells are also destroyed along with the whole glomerulus, as is well known from light microscopic studies. From the following sections it will be seen that similar changes also occur in other renal diseases.

Morphological Changes Associated with the Nephrotic Syndrome

Experimental Nephrosis. The glomerular lesions in aminonucleoside nephrosis in rats have been studied by Feldman and Fisher (1959), Harkin and Recant (1959), and Vernier et al. (1958, 1959). Daily subcutaneous injections of small amounts of this substance evoked proteinuria in seven days. Simultaneously a swelling and vacuolization of the capillary epithelial cells were observed. The foot process structure was dissolved and the outer surface of the basement membrane covered by a nearly continuous layer of epithelial cell cytoplasm. After prolonged treatment there was also a diffuse thickening of the basement membrane and a precipitation of a foreign material on the endothelial side of the membrane (Vernier et al.). There were no changes of the endothelial cells. In the tubular epithelium a swelling of the mitochondria and a number of large vacuoles in the cytoplasm were observed.

Similar changes were produced in rats with rabbit anti-kidney serum (Ehrich and Piel, 1953) and in rabbits by intravenous injection of saccharated iron oxide (Ellis, 1959).

A nephrotic syndrome has occasionally developed in children during treatment with trimethadione "Tridione". Electron microscopic investigation of biopsy material has shown glomerular lesions very similar to those observed in aminonucleoside nephrosis (Gribetz et al., 1959).

Lipide Nephrosis and Familial Nephrosis. A great number of reports on electron microscopic studies of renal changes in patients with lipide nephrosis or familial nephrosis has been published recently (Vernier et al., 1956, 1958, 1959; Farquhar et al., 1957a, b, c; Piel and Williams, 1957; Folli et al., 1957, 1958, 1959; Dalgaard, 1958a; Spiro, 1958, 1959a, b; Fiaschi et al., 1959; Putois, 1959). The glomerular changes were very similar to those observed in experimental nephrosis. They were first localized to the capillary epithelial cells. The organization of the foot processes was destroyed. The various epithelial cell processes on the outside of the capillary wall were fused so that the wall was covered by a practically continuous layer of epithelial cells. These cells also showed an increased number of large vacuoles and canaliculi belonging to the endoplasmic reticulum. These findings were observed in all cases regardless of the clinical phase of the disease. In more severe cases of long duration irregular thickenings were noted in the basement membranes alternating with empty-appearing spaces. The endothelial cells were also swollen but contrary to what was observed in glomerulonephritis, this occurred only in late stages of the disease.

In the epithelial cells of the proximal convoluted tubules there was a focal loss of the brush border. Many large vacuoles were observed in the apical part of the cells. The mitochondria were fragmented or swollen with loss of the inner structure as observed during increased protein resorption (see be-

low). The basal folds of the cell membranes had almost disappeared. Similar changes, but less prominent, were also present in the loops of Henle and the distal convoluted tubules.

Most authors consider the swelling of the epithelial cells with loss of foot process organization to be the first observable lesion in these diseases. Experimental observations indicate that there is a causal relation between proteinuria and epithelial cell changes. Several authors have discussed the possibility that the primary lesion (swelling) is in the basement membrane with an increased permeability and leakage of proteins. The presence of proteins in considerable amounts in the filtrate would give rise to the changes of the epithelial cells. (Vernier et al., 1958a, b; Movat and McGregor, 1959a, b; Sitte, 1959.)

It has been shown by several authors that the epithelial cell changes may be reversible. They disappear in cases which respond favorably to hormone treatment simultaneously with the proteinuria. (Piel and Williams, 1957; Dalgaard, 1958a, b; Folli, 1958; Putois, 1959; McDonald et al., 1959; Vernier et al., 1958a, 1959b.)

Membranous Glomerulonephritis. In cases with a long standing nephrotic syndrome and light microscope changes described as chronic membranous glomerulonephritis there is a more marked thickening of the glomerular capillary basement membranes (Pollak et al., 1958; Fiaschi et al., 1959). There is also a swelling and proliferation of the endothelial cells comparable to what is seen in acute glomerulonephritis. In some cases ("mixed type") the epithelial cells may also be destroyed or increased in number as in proliferative glomerulonephritis.

Experimentally Produced Renal Amyloidosis. Miller and Bohle (1956) have produced amyloidosis in mice with sodium-caseinate and ACTH. They were able to demonstrate a diffuse thickening and nodular protrusions of the glomerular capillary basement membranes. The nodules bulged into

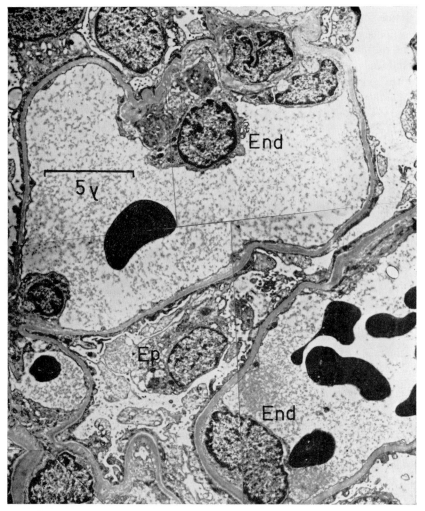

Fig. 1. "Pure" Nephrosis. Very little changes in the endothelial cells (End). The epithelial cell is swollen with several vacuoles and partial destruction of the foot processes.

the epithelial cells, i.e., toward the cavity of Bowman's capsule. Within the protrusions a fine spongy or felt-like structure with interwoven filaments was observed. The thickness of the filaments was calculated as 30–40 ÅU. There were no pores in the altered basement membranes. Earlier observations with the light microscope indicated that amyloid is deposited between the basement membrane and the endothelium. The authors therefore concluded that the changes in the basement membranes were probably not due to amyloid but to an increased leakage of protein through the capillary walls.

Human Amyloidosis. A case of renal amyloidosis secondary to chronic osteomyelitis was reported by Geer *et al.* (1958). The glomerular capillary basement membranes were uniformly thickened with a diameter of approximately 0.5 micron. Large masses of material with the same structureless appearance as the basement membrane but with less density were observed in the basement membranes in the "basilar" portions of the capillaries. They corresponded to the amyloid masses which were observed in the light microscope. The endothelial cells were vacuolated and the number of perforations of the cytoplasm (pores) was decreased. There was also a proliferation of the endothelial cells. The epithelial cells showed no damage other than a focal loss of organization of foot processes similar to what has been observed in lipide nephrosis.

There were small nodular thickenings of the basement membranes in the epithelial cells from the proximal and distal tubules. Similar material as described above was observed in the interstitial tissue, but it could not be demonstrated with certainty that this was amyloid. The brush border of the proximal tubular epithelium was flattened with a decreased number of cytoplasmic processes and the basal infoldings of the cell membranes were also diminished in number. In the cytoplasm of the tubular epithelium were droplets of fat and large opaque granules.

Further observations on renal amyloidosis in man have been published by Spiro (1959a). This author has treated his sections with PTA (phosphotungstic acid) for 24 hours after the routine preparation. In these sections dense and thickened areas were found in the glomerular capillary basement membranes alternating with apparently empty spaces with a diameter of several hundred ÅU. The author considered the latter to be large "pores" in the basement membranes and responsible for the abundant proteinuria in his patients. We have not been able to confirm these observations in our laboratory; we do not think that it is possible to exclude that they are artifacts due to the prolonged treatment with PTA. Spiro also observed destruction of the epithelial cells and fine filaments in the amyloid masses, similar to those described by Miller and Bohle. In severe cases larger fibrils with a striation similar to that of collagen were observed.

Bergstrand and Bucht (1959a) have stud-

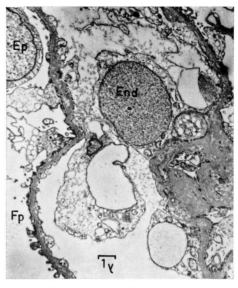

Fig. 2. Nephrotic Syndrome. "Mixed type" Nephrosis. Severe swelling and vacuolization of the endothelial cell (End). Slight focal thickening of the capillary basement membranes. Also marked swelling of the epithelial cell (Ep) with partial loss of foot process structure (Fp).

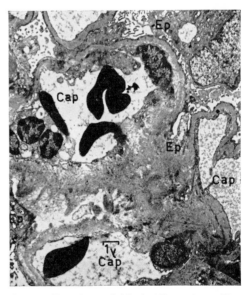

Fig. 3. Renal amyloidosis. Several capillary lumina (Cap) with a thin covering of endothelium. The amyloid masses are localized to the capillary basement membranes and to the space between them where remnants of destructed epithelial cells (Ep) are seen.

211

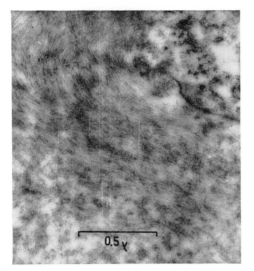

FIG. 4. Renal amyloidosis. Detail of amyloid precipitate inside an endothelial cell. A system of parallel fibrils are seen in the amyloid.

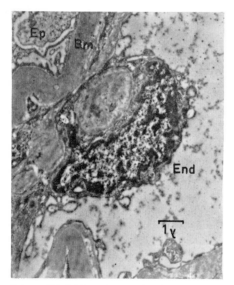

FIG. 5. Diabetic glomerulosclerosis. Diffuse thickening of the capillary basement membrane (Bm) and focal accumulation of foreign material between the basement membrane and the endothelial cell (End).

ied seven patients with renal amyloidosis. Clinical examination showed massive proteinuria, decreased glomerular filtration and a low filtration fraction. Electron microscopy of renal biopsies showed changes similar to those described by Geer *et al.* In early cases

there was swelling and vacuolization of the endothelial cells. The basement membrane was thickened and folded but without visible structure. In more severe or prolonged cases a foreign substance accumulated between the endothelial cells and the basement membranes. The epithelial cells were also altered and finally completely desquamated and replaced by amyloid masses. Similar observations have been described by Movat (1959), Putois (1959) and Meriel *et al.* (1960). In severe cases very fine filaments were seen in the newly formed substance in the basement membranes and above all in the desquamated epithelial cells.

Diabetic Glomerulosclerosis. The glomerular lesions in diabetic glomerulosclerosis have been described by Irvine *et al.* (1956); Bergstrand and Bucht (1957, 1959); Dalgaard (1958b); Cossel *et al.* (1959); Farquhar *et al.* (1959); and Hartman (1959). The histologic alterations as viewed with the electron microscope were very similar to those of renal amyloidosis. The foreign "hyaline" substance was accumulated between the endothelial cells and the glomerular capillary basement membranes which were uniformly thickened. These changes correspond to the "diffuse" type of glomerulosclerosis as observed by light microscopy. The hyaline masses also bulged into the vacuolated endothelial cell cytoplasm. The endothelial cells were partly destroyed by the large masses which obliterated the capillary lumina. These changes correspond to the "nodular" lesions, observed through the light microscope. In the hyaline material close to the endothelial cell membrane very fine filaments could be demonstrated. There was little damage to the epithelial cells in early stages of the disease, and these changes, which included a loss of foot process organization, were regarded by the authors as secondary to the lesions in the basement membrane.

Conclusions. The diseases which are associated with the nephrotic syndrome are by many authors regarded as metabolic disor-

212

ders of the connective tissue ground sub-stance and related structures. In the diseases described here, the first and most important changes are considered to be located in the capillary basement membranes. According to Gersh and Catchpole (1949) the latter are condensations of the ground substance.

The changes of the basement membranes probably include a precipitation of a foreign protein-containing substance, such as amy-loid, and perhaps also a metabolic change, such as a depolymerization, of the muco-polysaccharides pre-existing in the basement membrane. It may be presumed that a change in permeability is evoked simultane-ously with the thickening of the basement membrane which may explain the apparently controversial observations of a decrease in filtration fraction and proteinuria in the same patient (Bergstrand and Bucht, 1959b; Sitte, 1959).

Important differences exist, however, between the diseases associated with a ne-phrotic syndrome. In lipide nephrosis and fa-milial nephrosis the epithelial cells are se-verely changed whereas little or no damage is seen in the endothelium. In renal amyloi-dosis both kinds of cells are damaged and in glomerulosis the lesions are mainly located in the endothelial cells. Furthermore, in the cases of lipide and familial nephrosis, the glomerular filtration seems to have been nor-mal. In amyloidosis and glomerulosis a de-crease in filtration fraction was observed in most cases.

It is interesting to note that in glomerulo-nephritis the main changes are also located in the capillary basement membranes and the endothelial cells. No definite conclusions concerning eventual relationships between the latter disease and those described above should be drawn from this fact at the pres-ent moment, however.

Shock Kidney

Electron microscopic investigations of the renal changes in acute anuria (post-opera-tive shock) have been published by Dalgaard

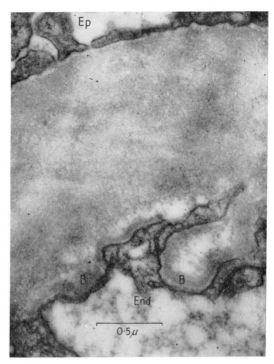

FIG. 6. Diabetic glomerulosclerosis. Capillary basement membrane without apparent structure but about three times thicker than normal and with a thin band (B) of foreign material close to the endothelial cell membrane (End).

(1958a; 1959) and Putois (1959). There were no glomerular lesions but severe damage to the epithelial cells in the proximal and distal convoluted tubules. The brush border was partially or completely destroyed and in the cytoplasm large vacuoles, severely damaged mitochondria and "macrobodies" were ob-served. The basal infoldings of the cell mem-branes were decreased in height or com-pletely absent. In many cells these changes had developed into complete necrosis with destruction of most cell organelles. No re-generation phenomena were observed.

Experimental Tubular Changes

Engfelt et al. (1957) have studied the in-fluence of parathyroid hormone on the kid-neys in rats. Electron microscopy, which has been reported in more detail by Rhodin (1958), showed an accumulation of very dense bodies in the basal parts of the epithelial cells of the proximal convoluted tubules when very small amounts of the hormone were given. When larger doses were used, extremely dense small granules were found in the basement membranes of the tubular epithelium. The authors presumed that these granules were precipitations of calcium salts. In the apical parts of the epithelial cells of the proximal convoluted tubules large bodies were formed, which had a very low density and were PAS-positive. They increased in size and occasionally filled the larger part of the cells. In the basal parts of the cells the number of mitochondria was decreased, probably because several of them had developed into the above-mentioned electron-dense bodies. The tubular lumina were filled by the same PAS-positive substance as is seen in the tubular epithelium. The formation of concrements probably started by the precipitation of calcium salts in this substance. Electron microscopy of the concrements showed a structure quite similar to that of apatite crystals. Similar observations have been made by this author in biopsy specimens from patients with hyperparathyroidism and renal calcifications.

Rhodin (1954) first studied the effect of intraperitoneal injections of egg white on the proximal tubular epithelium in mice. There were no changes in the appearance of the brush border. In the apical parts of the cells there was increased vacuolization. Large opaque bodies were found in the cytoplasm corresponding to the hyaline droplets seen by light microscopy. Inside these bodies were remnants of double membranes. The author concluded that these bodies developed from the mitochondria during resorption of protein as previously described by Oliver (1948) and others.

These observations were confirmed by Miller and Sitte (1955) and by Gansler and Rouiller (1956). According to Miller (1959), the association between the hyaline droplets and the mitochondria is only secondary. The

droplets are formed in the apical parts of the cells, where there are no mitochondria, probably from the vacuoles or from enzyme-producing granules (cytosomes). An occasional fusion between a mitochondrion and a droplet may take place if they are located close to each other. A primary accumulation of protein inside the mitochondria is not probable.

Policard et al. (1957) produced lesions in the epithelial cells of the proximal convoluted tubules in rats by injecting a colloidal solution of 5 per cent sodium silicate in the peritoneum. The brush border was partly destroyed and in cells with more severe damage the apical parts of the cells were cut off and ejected into the tubular lumen. The basal infoldings of the cell membrane disappeared. The mitochondria were large and pale with vacuoles or a severely changed inner structure.

Rouiller and Modtjabai (1958) perfused a sodium-free 5 per cent solution of glucose through the peritoneal cavity of rabbits. The cells of the proximal convoluted tubules showed a marked increase in size and were very pale in the light microscope, as is observed in human subjects which have been treated with large intravenous infusions of, for instance, dextran. Electron microscopy showed an extremely low contrast in the cytoplasm of some cells of the proximal convoluted tubules and very large and numerous vacuoles inside or between the cells. The apical part of the cells were partly destroyed and ejected into the tubular lumen. The mitochondria were few and small. According to the authors, these changes were due to an increased content of water in the tubular cells. In some mitochondria were accumulations of small dark granules, which were regarded by authors as evoked by the resorption of glucose. Similar changes were induced in mice by Yolac (1959) with sucrose.

The tubular lesions in potassium-depleted rats were studied by Tauxe et al. (1957), and Muehrcke and Bonting (1958). There were no changes in the proximal tubules. In the collecting ducts the mitochondria were enlarged or destroyed. Ten days after potassium had been administered the mitochondria had regained a normal appearance. An increased number of macrobodies and lipoid droplets was observed in the tubular epithelium of animals with cholin deficiency (Ashworth, 1959a, b).

The effect on the tubular epithelium of heavy metals has been studied by several authors. Dempsey and Wislocki (1955) studied the site of accumulation of silver in the tissues by giving a solution of silver nitrate in the drinking water to mice, rats and guinea pigs for 6 to 12 months. The silver was mainly located in the basement membranes of the glomerular capillaries and the tubular epithelium. In the epithelial cells of the proximal tubules silver could be demonstrated inside mitochondria which had retained their original structure and were easily identifiable. The metal appeared as very dense and small particles with a size of about 20–30 ÅU or as larger aggregates with a diameter of one or several microns. Similar observations on rats have been made by van Breemen *et al.* (1956) and by Olcott and Richter (1958).

Richter (1957) gave repeated injections of hemoglobin intraperitoneally to rats. Hemosiderin could be demonstrated in the proximal tubular epithelium. Electron microscopy revealed large opaque bodies in the cells containing numerous very dense particles with a mean diameter of 55 ÅU. Similar particles could be demonstrated in the cytoplasm without apparent connections to any cell organelles. The author named the large bodies "siderosomes" and considered them to be derivatives of mitochondria. The small particles corresponded in size to the iron miscelles of purified ferritin, and the author concluded that ferritin is probably a component of hemosiderin. Similar iron-containing bodies have been described under the name of cytosomes in other organs and in macrophages (Lindner, 1958; Miller, 1959).

Electron microscopic investigations of the excretion of radioactive mercury compounds through the kidneys of rats have been made by Bergstrand *et al.* (1959). Mercury was demonstrated in the proximal tubular cells as accumulations of very small and dark particles inside large bodies similar to the "siderosomes" described by Richter. The presence of mercury in the cytoplasm could not be demonstrated by the electron microscope. After homogenization of the kidneys and centrifugation at high speed, a very high activity could be demonstrated in the microsome fraction which contained only the smallest cell organelles, such as RNA-granules, but no traces of mitochondria or "siderosomes." Thus it is very probable that mercury was also present in the cytoplasm as was demonstrated with iron by Richter. The amounts of mercury were low and there was no destruction of the tubular cells.

Bencosme *et al.* (1959) have studied the effect of uranyl nitrate on the kidneys of rats with the electron microscope. Extensive damage to the epithelial cells was observed in the proximal tubules. The intercellular spaces were widened, forming large cisternes probably containing resorbed tubular fluid. No deposits of the metal were observed in the epithelial cells. The author concludes that the passage of fluid through the tubular walls takes place mainly through the intercellular spaces.

Conclusions on the Morphological Basis of Glomerular Filtration

Electron microscopy of normal glomeruli from man and animals has failed to reveal the structures in the capillary walls which are necessary for the filtration process. Several attempts have been made to elucidate the problem through a comparison of clinical data from patients with impaired renal function to the corresponding morphological changes of the capillary wall as revealed by the electron microscope.

Hall (1957) has concluded from studies on

normal kidneys that the slit-pores between the foot processes are the filtration pores postulated by Pappenheimer (1955). It could therefore be expected that in cases where the foot process organization was impaired, filtration should also be low. As pointed out by Farquhar *et al.* (1957a, c), Vernier *et al.* (1958a) and Rhodin (1959), this is not the case in familial nephrosis or lipide nephrosis. On the contrary, a decreased renal function was observed in cases with subacute glomerulonephritis where the foot processes were intact.

The problem has been discussed by Bergstrand (1959) on the basis of investigations in amyloidosis and diabetic glomerulosis. According to this author, changes in filtration rate cannot with certainty be correlated to changes of the capillary wall. A severe reduction in filtration fraction, on the other hand, is most probably a sign of an increased resistance to filtration through the capillary walls. This was observed in most of his cases and he concluded from the electron microscopical observations that the most probable cause of the decrease in filtration fraction was a thickening of the basement membrane, perhaps associated with a change of its ultrastructure, which could not be demonstrated with certainty with the present techniques. Bergstrand presumes that the filtration pores in the normal capillary wall are localized in the basement membrane. The same opinion has been expressed by Sitte (1959).

Other attempts to solve the problem have been made by studying the passage of very small particles through the glomerular capillary wall. Farquhar and Palade used ferritin molecules, Latta and Maunsbach thorotrast, and Vernier silver-labeled protein molecules. These studies were performed both in normal and nephrotic animals. The authors observed a very rapid passage of particles with a diameter less than 75 ÅU, whereas larger particles, above all thorotrast, were retained in the bloodstream. No changes of structure could

be observed in the basement membrane when particles were passing through. No definite conclusions could thus be drawn about the morphological basis of glomerular ultrafiltration.

REFERENCES

1. Ashworth, C. T., "Ultrastructural Aspects of Renal Patho-Physiology," *Tex. Rep. Biol. Med.*, **17**, 60–72 (1959a).
2. Ashworth, C. T. and Grollman, A., "Electron Microscopy in Experimental Hypertension," *A.M.A. Arch. Path.*, **68**, 148–153 (1959b).
3. Bencosme, S. A., Stone, R. S., Latta, H., and Madden, S. C. "Acute Reactions with Collagen Production in Renal Glomeruli of Rats as Studied Electron Microscopically," *y. Ultrastr. Res.*, **3**: 171–185 (1959).
4. Bergstrand, A., "The Morphological Basis for the Filtration Process in the Glomeruli," *Acta Chir. Suppl.* **245**, 336–342 (1959).
5. Bergstrand, A. and Bucht, H., "Electron Microscope Investigation on Biopsy Material frum Patients with Renal Diseases: A Case of Subacute Glomerulonephritis," *Proc. Stockholm Conference on Electron Microscopy*, 256–258, 1956.
6. Bergstrand, A. and Bucht, H., "Electron Microscopic Investigations on the Glomerular Lesions in Diabetes Mellitus (Diabetic Glomerulosclerosis)," *Lab. Invest.*, **6**, 293–300 (1957).
7. Bergstrand, A. and Bucht, H., "Anatomy of the Glomerulus as Observed in Biopsy Material from Young and Healthy Human Subjects," *Z. Zellforsch.*, **48**, 51–73 (1958).
8. Bergstrand, A. and Bucht, H., "Electron Microscopic Observations on Renal Amyloidosis," (1959a) (to be published).
9. Bergstrand, A. and Bucht, H., "The Glomerular Lesions of Diabetes Mellitus and Their Electron-Microscope Appearances," *J. Path. Bact.*, **77**, 231–242 (1959b).
10. Bergstrand, A., Friberg, L., Mendel, L., and Odeblad, E., "Localization of Subcutaneously Administered Radioactive Mercury in the Rat Kidney," (Abstract) *y. Ultrastruct. Res.*, **3**: 238, 1959.
11. Bergstrand, A. and Ericsson, J., "Electron Microscopic Investigation on the Anatomy of the Kidney Tubules in Young and Healthy Human Subjects," (1959) (To be published).
12. Bohle, A., Sitte, H., and Miller, F., "Elek-

tronenmikroskopische Untersuchungen am Glomerulum des Kaninchens beim generalisierten Schwartzmann - Phänomen," *Verh. deut. Ges. Path.*, **41**, 326–332 (1958).

13. BOHLE, A., MILLER, F., SITTE, H., AND YOLAC, A., "Frühveränderungen bei der Masugi-Nephritis der Ratte. Immunopathologie. I. Int. Symposium," Basel, Seeligsberg, 1958 70–81 (1959).

14. V. BREEMEN, V. L., REGER, J. F., AND COOPER, W. C., "Observations on the Basement Membranes in Rat Kidney," *J. Biophys. Biochem. Cytol.*, **2**, suppl. 283–286 (1956).

15. COSSEL, L., LISEWSKI, G., AND MOHNIKE, G., "Elektronenmikroskopische und klinische Untersuchungen bei diabetischer Glomerulosklerose," *Klin. Wschr.*, **37**, 1005–1018 (1959).

16. DALGAARD, C. Z., "Electron Microscopic Investigation of Material from Renal Biopsy in Two Patients with so-called Genuine Lipoid Nephrosis," *Ugeskr. Laeg.*, **120**, 1358–1363 (1958a).

17. DALGAARD, C. Z., "Electron Microscopic Investigations on Renal Biopsies from Patients with Renal Diseases. Verh. IV Int. Kongress Elektronenmikroskopie," Berlin, (1958b) In print.

18. DALGAARD, C. Z. AND PEDERSEN, K. J., "Renal Tubular Degeneration. Electron Microscopy in Ischaemic Anuria," *Lancet* **11**, 484–488 (1959).

19. DEMPSEY, E. W. AND WISLOCKI, G. E., "Use of Silver Nitrate as a Vital Stain, and its Distribution in Several Mammalian Tissues as Studied with the Electron Microscope," *J. Biophys. Biochem. Cytol.*, **1**, 111–118 (1955).

20. EHRICH, W. AND PIEL, C. F., "Morphologic Differentiation of Nephritis in the Rat and the Therapeutic Effects of Anticoagulants and Proteolytic Enzymes," Proc. 5th Ann. Conference Nephrotic Syndrome, p. 117, Nat. Nephrosis Foundation Inc., New York (1953).

21. ELLIS, J. T., "Glomerular Lesions in Rabbits with Experimentally Produced Proteinuria as Disclosed by Electron Microscopy," (Abstract.) *Am. J. Path.*, **34**, 559–560 (1959)

22. ENGFELT, B., GARDELL, S., HELLSTRÖM, J., IVEMARK, B., RHODIN, J., AND STRANDH, J., "Effect of Experimental Hyperparathyroidism on Renal Function and Structure," *Acta Endocrinol.*, **29**, 15–26 (1958).

23. FARQUHAR, M. G., VERNIER, R. L., AND GOOD, R. A., "An Electron Microscope Study of the Glomerulus in Nephrosis, Glomerulonephritis, and Lupus Erythematosus," *J. Exper. Med.*, **106**, 649-660 (1957a).

24. FARQUHAR, M. G., VERNIER, R. L., AND GOOD, R. A., "Studies on Familial Nephrosis II: Glomerular Changes Observed with the Electron Microscope," *Am. J. Path.*, **33**, 791–805 (1957b).

25. FARQUHAR, M. G., VERNIER, R. L., AND GOOD, R. A., "Application of Electron Microscopy in Pathology: Study of Renal Biopsy Tissues," *Schweiz. Med. Wschr.*, **87**, 501–510 (1957c).

26. FARQUHAR, M. G., HOPPER JR., J., AND MOON, H. D., "Diabetic Glomerulosclerosis: Electron and Light Microscopic Studies," *Am. J. Path.*, **35**, 721–754 (1959).

26a. FARQUHAR, M. G., AND PALADE, G. E., "Segregation of Ferritin in Glomerular Protein Absorption Droplets," *J. Biophys. Biochem. Cytol.*, **7**: 297–304 (1960).

27. FELDMAN, J. D., "Electron Microscopy of Serum Sickness Nephritis," *J. Exptl. Med.*, **108**, 957–962 (1959).

28. FELDMAN, J. D. AND FISHER, E. R., "R nal Lesions in Aminonucleoside Nephrosis as Revealed by Electron Microscopy," *Lab. Invest.*, **8**, 371–385 (1959).

29. FIASCHI, E., AMDRES, G., GIOCOMELLI, F., AND NACCARATO, R., "Renal Histopathology in the Para-Nephritic Nephrotic Syndrome," *Sc. Med. Ital.*, **7**, 639–742 (1959).

30. FOLLI, G., POLLAK, V. E., REID, R. T. W., PIRANI, C. L., AND KARK, R. M., Electron Microscopic Studies of Renal Biopsies Taken from Nephrotic Patients before and after Diuresis. (Abstract.) *J. Lab. Clin. Med.* **50**, 813 (1957).

31. FOLLI, G., POLLAK, V. E., REID, R. T. W., PIRANI, C. L., AND KARK, R. M., "Electron Microscopic Studies of Reversible Glomerular Lesions in the Adult Nephrotic Syndrome," *Ann. Int. Med.*, **49**, 775–795 (1958).

32. FOLLI, G., "Studi di microscopia elettronica nelle nefrosi," *Atti. Soc. Lombarda Sci. Med. Biol.*, **13**, 200–207 (1958).

33. FOLLI, G. AND ONIDA, L., "Biopsy and Electron Microscopy of the Kidney," *Sc. Med. Ital.*, **8**, 19–58 (1959).

34. GANSLER, H. AND ROUILLER, C., "Modifications physiologiques et pathologiques du chondriome," *Schweiz. Z. Path. Bact.*, **19**, 217–243 (1956).

35. GEER, J. C., STRONG, J. P., MCGILL JR., H. C., AND MUSLOW, I., "Electron Microscopic Observations on the Localization of Amyloid in the Kidney in Secondary Amyloidosis," *Lab. Invest.*, **7**, 554–565 (1958).

36. GERSH, I., AND CATCHPOLE, H. R., "Organization of Ground Substance and Basement Membrane and Its Significance in Tissue Injury, Disease and Growth," *Am. J. Anat.*, **85**, 457–507 (1949).

37. GRIBETZ, A., MANTNER, W., AND KOHN, J. L., "Trimethadione (Tridione) Nephrosis: Renal Biopsy and Electron Microscopic Studies," (Abstract.) *A.M.A. J. Dis. Child.*, **98**, 76, (1959)

38. HARKIN, J. C. AND RECANT, L., "Earliest Lesion in Aminonucleoside Nephrosis; an Electronmicroscopic Study,"(Abstract.) *Am. J. Path.*, **34**, 559 (1959)

39. HARTMAN, J. F., "Elektronenmikroskopie der menschlichen Niere bei Diabetes Mellitus im Vergleich mit Nephritis und Nephrose," *Zentrbl. Allgemeine Pathologic und Pathologische Anatomie*, **98**, 313 (1958) Abstr.

40. HALL, V., "The Protoplasmic Basis of Glomerular Ultrafiltration," *Am. Heart J.*, **54**, 1–9 (1957).

41. IRVINE, E., RINEHART, J. F., MORTIMORE, G. E., AND HOPPER JR., J., "The Ultrastructure of the Renal Glomerulus in Intercapillary Glomerulosclerosis," *Am. J. Path.*, **32**, 647–648 (1956) Abstract.

42. IVERSEN, P., AND BRUN, C., "Aspiration Biopsy of the Kidney," *Am. J. Med.*, **11**, 324–330 (1951).

43. KARK, R. M. AND MUEHRCKE, R. C., "Biopsy of Kidney in Prone Position," *Lancet*, **1**, 1047–1049 (1954).

43a. LATTA, H., AND MAUNSBACH, A., *Rep. I Int. Congress Nephrol.* Evian 1–4 Sept. (1960). In print.

44. LINDNER, E., "Der elektronenmikroskopischen nachweis von Eisen im Gewebe, *Ergebn. Allgemeine Pathologic und Pathologische Anatomie*, 46–91 (1958).

45. McDONALD, M. K., LAMBIE, A. T., AND ROBSON, J. S., "Resolution of Glomerular Lesions in the Nephrotic Syndrome treated with Cortisone: Electron Microscopic Studies in an Adult Case."

45a. MERIEL, P. MOREAU, G., SUE, Y. M., AND PUTOIS, Y. Rep. I Int. Congr. of Nephrol. Evian, 1960.

46. MILLER, F., "Orthologie und Pathologie der Zelle im elektronenmikroskopischen Bild," *Verh. deut. Ges. Path.*, **42**, 261–332 (1959).

47. MILLER, F. AND SITTE, H., "Elektronenmikroskopische Untersuchungen an Mäusenieren nach intraperitonealen Eiweissgaben," *Verh. deut. Ges. Path.*, **39**, 183–190 (1955).

48. MILLER, F. AND BOHLE, A., "Comparative Investigation by Means of the Light and Electron Microscope of the Glomerular Capillary Basement Membrane in Experimental Renal Amyloidosis of the Mouse, *Klin. Wschr.*, **34**, 1204–1210 (1956a).

49. MILLER, F. AND BOHLE, A., "Electron Microscopy of the Glomerular Basement Membrane in Experimental Amyloidosis in the Mouse," *Proc. Stockholm Conference Electron Microscopy*, 254–256 (1956b).

50. MILLER, F. AND BOHLE, A., "Elektronenmikroskopische Untersuchungen am Glomerulum bei der Masugi-Nephritis der Ratte," *Virchows Arch.*, **330**, 483–497 (1957).

51. MILLER, F., SITTE, H., AND BOHLE, A., "Elektronenmikroskopische Befunde am Glomerulum bei der Masugi-Nephritis der Ratte," *Ver. deut. Ges. Path.*, **41**, 333–335 (1958).

52. MOVAT, H. Z., "The Fine Structure of the Glomerulus in Amyloidosis," (Abstract.) *Am. J. Path.*, **35**, 708 (1959).

53. MOVAT, H. Z. AND McGREGOR, D. D., "Fine Structure of the Glomerulus in Membranous Glomerulonephritis (Lipide Nephrosis) in Adults," *Am. J. Clin. Path.*, **32**, 109–127 (1959a).

54. MOVAT, H. Z. AND McGREGOR, D. D., "Fine Structure of the Glomerulus in Membranous Glomerulonephritis (Lipoide Nephrosis)," (Abstract.) *Am. J. Path.*, **35**, 670, (1959b)

55. MUEHRCKE, R. C. AND BONTING, S. L., "Electronmicroscopic and Ultrabiochemical Studies of the Potassium-depleted Kidney," *Clin. Res.*, **6**, 413–414 (1958).

56. OLCOTT, C. T. AND RICHTER, G. W., "Experimental Argyrosis. VI. Electronmicroscopic Study of Ingested Silver in the Kidney of the Rat," *Lab. Invest.*, **7**, 103–109 (1958).

57. OLIVER, J., "Structure of the Metabolic Process in the Nephron," *J. Mt. Sinai Hosp.*, **15**, 175–222 (1948).

58. PAPPAS, G. E., ROSS, M. H., AND LEWIS, T., "Studies on the Generalized Schwartzmann Reaction. VIII. The Appearance by Electron Microscopy of Intravascular Fibrinoid in the Glomerular Capillaries during the Reaction," *J. Exptl. Med.*, **107**, 333–340 (1958).

59. PAPPENHEIMER, J. R., "Über die Permeabilität der Glomerulummembranen in der Niere," *Klin. Wchschr.*, **33**, 362–365 (1955).

60. PIEL, C. F., DONG, L., MODERN, F. W. S., GOODMAN, J. R., AND MOORE, R., "The Glomerulus in Experimental Renal Disease in Rats as Observed by Light and Electron Microscopy," *J. Exper. Med.*, **102**, 573–580 (1955).

61. PIEL, C. F. AND WILLIAMS, G. F., "Long Continued Adrenal Hormone Therapy in Childhood Nephrosis," *J. Am. Med. Women's Assoc.*, **12**, 273–279 (1957).

62. POLICARD, A., COLLET, A., AND PREGERMAIN, S., "Sur quelques points de la cytopathologie des néphrites toxiques," *Presse Med.*, **65**, 1685–1688 (1957).

63. POLLAK, V. E., PIRANI, C. L., MUEHRCKE, R. C., AND KARK, R. M., "Asymptomatic Persistent Proteinuria: Studies by Renal Biopsy," *Guy's Hosp. Rep.*, **107**, 353–372 (1958).

64. PUTOIS, J., "Structure et ultrastructure rénale. Aspects normaux et pathologiques," *Librairie Arnette, Paris*, 1959.

65. REGER, J. F., NEUSTEIN, H. B., AND HUTT, M., "Observations on the Fine Structure of Nephron Units in Various Diseases," (Abstract.) *Anat. Rec.*, **130**, 460 (1958)

66. REID, R. T. W., "Electron Microscopy of Glomeruli in Nephrotoxic Serum Nephritis," *Australian J. Exp. Biol. Med. Sci.*, **34**, 143–150 (1956).

67. RHODIN, J., "Correlation of Ultrastructural Organization and Function in Normal and Experimentally Changed Proximal Convoluted Tubule Cells of the Mouse Kidney," Thesis, Stockholm, 1954.

68. RHODIN, J., "Ergebnisse der elektronenmikroskopischen Erforschung von Struktur und Funktion der Zelle," *Verh. deut. Ges. Path.*, **41**, 274–284 (1958).

69. RHODIN, J., "Microscopie électronique du rein," *Bruxelles-Med.*, **39**, 409–426 (1959).

70. RICHTER, G. W., "A Study of Hemosiderosis with the Aid of Electron Microscopy," *J. Exptl. Med.*, **106**, 203–218 (1957).

71. ROUILLER, G. AND MODTJABAI, A., "La néphrose expérimentale du lapin. Comparaison entre la microscopie optique et électronique. I. Les modifications des cellules à bordure striée," *Ann. Anat. Path.*, **3**, 223–250 (1958).

72. SAKAGUCHI, H., SUZUKI, Y., AND YAMAGUCHI, T., "Electron Microscopic Study of Masugi Nephritis," *Acta Path. Japan*, **7**, 53–66 (1957).

73. SIMER, P. H., "Electron Microscopic Studies of the Glomerulus in Nephrotic Mice of the NH Strain," *Anat. Rec.*, **118**, 409 (1954).

74. SITTE, H., "Changes in the Glomeruli of Rat Kidneys after Administration of Foreign Proteins and a Hypothetical Explanation of the Glomerular Filtration," *Verh. deut. Ges. Path.*, **42**, 225–32 (1959).

75. SPIRO, D., "Electron Microscopic Studies on Human Renal Biopsies. The Structural Basis of Proteinuria. Verh. IV.," Int. Kongress Elektronenmikroskopie, Berlin, 1958. In print.

76. SPIRO, D., "The Structural Basis of Proteinuria," *Am. J. Path.*, **35**, 47–74 (1959a).

77. SPIRO, D., "Further Studies on the Ultra Structure of the Kidney in the Nephrotic Syndrome," (Abstract.) *Am. J. Path.*, **35**, 716 (1959b).

78. TAUXE, W. N., WAKIM, K. G., AND BAGGENSTOSS, A. H., "Renal lesions in experimental deficiency of potassium," *Amer. J. Clin. Path.*, **28**, 221–232 (1957).

79. VERNIER, R. L., FARQUHAR, M. G., BRUNSON, J. G., AND GOOD, R. A., "Studies on Familial Nephrosis," (Abstract.) *J. Clin. Invest.*, **35**, 741 (1956)

79a. VERNIER, R. L., *Rept. I Int. Congress Nephrol.* Evian 1–4 Sept. (1960). In print.

80. VERNIER, R. L., FARQUHAR, M. G., BRUNSON, J. G., AND GOOD, R. A., "Chronic Renal Disease in Children," *A.M.A. J. Dis Children*, **96**, 306–343 (1958a).

81. VERNIER, R., PAPERMASTER, B., ARHELGER, R., AND MECKLENBURG, P., "Electron Microscopy of Experimental Renal Disease," *A.M.A. J. Dis. Child.* **96**, 597–598 (1958b).

82. VERNIER, R. L., PAPERMASTER, B. W., AND GOOD, R. A., "Light and Electron Microscopic Pathology of Experimental Aminonucleoside Nephrosis: Relations to Nephrosis in Man," *Fed. Proc.*, **17**, 463 (1958c) Abstract.

83. VERNIER, R. L. AND GOOD, R. A., "Renal Biopsy in Children," *Pediatrics*, **22**, 1033–1034 (1958d).

84. VERNIER, R. L., PAPERMASTER, B. W., AND GOOD, R. A., "Aminonucleoside Nephrosis I. Electron Microscopic Study of the Renal Lesions in Rats," *J. Exptl. Med.*, **109**, 115–126 (1959a).

85. VERNIER, R. L., WORTHEN, H. G., AND GOOD, R. A., "Electron Microscope in Medical Research," *Journ.-Lancet*, **79**, 423–27 (1959).

86. YOLAC, A. B., "Electron Microscopic Studies Concerning the Morphology of the Epithelium of the Proximal Convoluted Tubules of Mouse Kidneys after Injection of Sucrose Solution," *Verh. deut. Ges. Path.*, **42**, 235–40 (1959).

ANDERS BERGSTRAND

PLASTICS. *See* GENERAL MICROSCOPY, p. 390.

PULP AND PAPER. *See* GENERAL MICROS-
COPY, p. 394.

REFLECTION I

In the early days of electron microscopy prior to the development of replica methods, most specimens were so thick as to be electron-opaque and only their silhouettes could be examined. To enable direct surface studies to be made, Ruska (1) in 1933 attempted to image electrons scattered from a metal surface. The specimen was irradiated with an electron beam which was at 90° to the axis of the imaging system, but the resolution was limited in this first experiment to about 20 to 30 microns by the chromatic aberration of the lens and the very large bandwidth of the energy spectrum of the scattered electrons. Further work by Ruska and Müller, (2) using glancing angles of incidence, and viewing at 90°, yielded a resolution of 5,000 Å. Von Borries (3) in 1940 suggested the use of glancing angles of both illumination and viewing, thus reducing the energy loss in the scattered beam and giving a resolution of about 250 Å. Such low angles (the total deviation of the beam being about 8°) make for extremely difficult interpretation of the

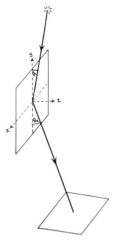

FIG. 1. Schematic diagram of reflection electron microscope.

image and moreover only the smoothest surfaces can be examined. It was for these reasons that with the advent of replica methods, interest in reflection electron microscopy diminished.

There was a revival of interest in the years 1951 to 1953 when it was realized that in certain circumstances the reflection method of Von Borries could have distinct advantages over the now well established replica method and this revival took place almost simultaneously in several schools. Kushnir, Biberman and Levkin (4), Cosslett and Jones (5), and Fert and Saporte (6) worked with microscopes designed and built for reflection work while Menter (7), and Haine and Hirst (8) made adaptations for the Metropolitan Vickers microscope.

The characteristics of the image in this type of work are very different from those pertaining to other forms of microscopy and can be considered under the following headings:

Viewpoint. The highly oblique viewpoint is a most unusual one; Von Borries stated that the image has the appearance of a road illuminated by the headlights of an approaching car. The most important feature of this oblique viewpoint is the marked foreshortening effect in the image. Distances along the line of sight (direction y, Fig. 1) are foreshortened with a viewing angle of for example 5° by a factor of 12:1. Thus a circle in the plane of the specimen appears as an ellipse of this eccentricity; this led Emerton (9) to suggest that the scale on reflection electron micrographs should be indicated by ellipses, the diameter of which could be quoted. It also follows that linear features on the specimen appear to be oriented more nearly perpendicular to the line of sight (direction x). A line at an angle of 45° to the line of sight appears in a micrograph (foreshortened 12:1) to be at an angle of 85°.

This viewpoint does nevertheless have certain advantages. The form of the surface in the direction perpendicular to the plane of the specimen (direction z) is often brought out with a clarity which is not possible by other microscopical methods and the reflection image is very sensitive to changes in this direction.

Contrast. This is high and arises largely from the difference between the intensity from illuminated areas and from areas "in shadow" behind raised features. In addition, there is a tone range within the illuminated areas due to the local variation in angle between the surface and the axis of the imaging system. The contrast is thus extremely easy for the eye to interpret and this accounts for the very pleasing appearance of reflection micrographs.

Resolution. Electrons are scattered in all directions, evenly illuminating the objective aperture the size of which therefore governs directly the confusion in the image due to aberrations. Of these, chromatic aberration is the overriding effect due to the large energy spread in the scattered beam.

The radius of the disc of confusion is given by

$$d = \alpha C_c \delta v / v \qquad (1)$$

where α is the semi-angular aperture of the accepted beam

C_c is the chromatic aberration constant of the objective lens

δv is the half width of the energy spread of accepted electrons

v is the accelerating voltage

d can be reduced by reducing C_c, although this appears to be limited by the present design of lenses to approximately the focal length, or by reducing the objective aperture. There is a limitation to the latter course due to the increasing effect of diffraction, but this is in fact never a problem because a reduction in α decreases the intensity of the image. In practice the lowest value of α is chosen which gives an image just sufficiently bright to be focused and recorded at the necessary magnification.

Fig. 2. Cleavage fracture on mica. (After Menter). ● $_1$ + ● $_2$ = 14° Magnification 5,100 ×.

Typical values are as follows:

$$\alpha \quad = 1.5 \times 10^{-3}$$

$$C_c \quad = 1.0 \text{ cm}$$

$$\delta v / v = 0.0015$$

This gives a resolution of about 200 Å, and this cannot be appreciably improved on.

Equation (1) gives the resolution on the axis of the system. Abaxial points generally have an inferior resolution because of the field chromatic aberrations. Page (10) has shown the importance of these and has given a practicable method for their correction in a triple lens electron microscope.

Depth of field. This is given by

$$D = 2d/\alpha \quad (=2C_c \delta v / v) \qquad (2)$$

The typical values above give a depth of field of about 30 microns and this ensures that any part of the specimen is entirely in

221

Fig. 3. Scratch on brass surface (after Page). $\bullet_1 + \bullet_2 = 26°$. Magnification 1,200×.

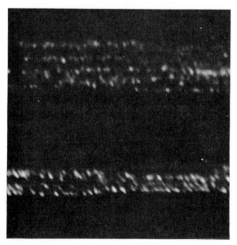

Fig. 4. Etched germanium surface. (After Halliday and Newman). $\bullet_1$ and $\bullet_2$ adjusted to select electrons diffracted from (400) planes. Magnification 66,000×.

focus in a direction perpendicular to its plane.

The advantages and disadvantages of the Von Borries reflection method may be summarized as follows.

Advantages

(1) Direct observation of the specimen
(2) Large depth of field
(3) Contrast easily interpreted
(4) Information available in the dimension perpendicular to the specimen plane.

Disadvantages

(1) Extremely foreshortened image
(2) Unsuitability for rough surfaces
(3) Resolution limited to 200 Å
(4) Damage to some specimens by high intensity electron beam

In spite of the disadvantages, the reflection method has been of value in the fields of metallurgy and crystallography, in the examination of fibers both natural and synthetic and in the study of wear.

More recent work has enabled some of the above disadvantages to be overcome. Bradley (11) has suggested the use of solid metal replicas for those specimens which suffer beam damage. Halliday and Newman (12) have photographed etched germanium surfaces at high resolution by imaging diffracted electrons which have a lower energy spread than scattered electrons. The greatest advance has, however, been in a return to much larger angles of beam deviation though not to the extreme value of 90° used by Ruska. Fert, Marty and Saporte (13), Page (14) and Ito, Ito, Aotsu and Miyamae (15) have all used angles of deviation in the region of 25 to 30°. The considerably reduced foreshortening obtained at the higher angles of viewing gives to the image a strikingly three-dimensional appearance which can be highly informative. It would seem though that no further significant advance in the reflection technique will be made until lens designers can find a practical method for the correction of axial chromatic aberration. If such a correction became feasible we might have an instrument capable of direct and rapid observation of surfaces at a resolution comparable to that attained at present by replica methods.

REFERENCES

1. Ruska, E. Z., *Phys.*, **83**, 492 (1933).
2. Ruska, E. and Müller, H. O., *Z. Phys.*, **116**, 366 (1940).
3. von Borries, B., *Z. Phys.*, **116**, 370 (1940).
4. Kushnir, Yu. M., Biberman, L. M., and Levkin, N. P., *Bull. Acad. Sci., URSS Fer. Phys.*, **15**, 306 (1951).
5. Cosslett, V. E. and Jones, D., *J. Sci. Instrum.*, **32**, 86 (1955).
6. Fert, C. and Saporte, R., *C. R. Acad. Sci., Paris*, **235**, 1490 (1952).
7. Menter, J. W., *J. Inst. Metals*, **81**, 163 (1952).
8. Haine, M. E. and Hirst, W., *Brit. J. Appl. Phys.*, **4**, 239 (1953).
9. Emerton, H. W., *Research (London)*, **7**, S56 (1954).
10. Page, D. H., *Brit. J. Appl. Phys.*, **9**, 268 (1958).
11. Bradley, D. E., *Brit. J. Appl. Phys.*, **6**, 191 (1955).
12. Halliday, J. S. and Newman, R. C., "Fourth International Conference on Electron Microscopy," Berlin, September 1958.
13. Fert, C., Marty, B., and Saporte, R., *C. R. Acad. Sci., Paris*, **240**, 1975 (1955).
14. Page, D. H., *Brit. J. Appl. Phys.*, **9**, 60 (1958).
15. Ito, K., Ito, T., Aotsu, T., and Miyamae, T., *J. Electron Microscopy*, **5**, (1957).

D. H. Page

REFLECTION II

In electron microscopy, as in light microscopy, it is possible to examine both translucent and opaque objects—the former with transmitted and the latter with reflected illumination. Most of the electron microscopes built have been of the transmission type since higher resolutions are attainable with this arrangement. Only the thinnest films are translucent to electrons and so it has been common practice to use replica methods when information about the surface structure of solid specimens was wanted. However, considerable progress has been made with techniques for the direct examination of the surfaces of solid objects. Those used at present include scanning, emission, and reflection electron microscopy. Each gives a different type of information and this article will deal with one of them only—reflection electron microscopy.

In the reflection electron microscope the electron gun is tilted with respect to the axis of the objective and projector lenses. The specimen is also tilted with respect to this axis but at a smaller angle to it. The arrangement is shown in Figure 1. The beam of electrons from the electron gun strikes the specimen at an angle θ_1 and the electrons are there scattered in all directions. Those scattered at angle θ_2 to the surface in the direction of the objective aperture pass through it and subsequently through objective and

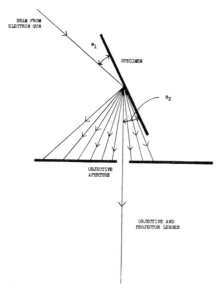

BEAM FROM
ELECTRON GUN

θ_1

SPECIMEN

θ_2

OBJECTIVE
APERTURE

OBJECTIVE AND
PROJECTOR LENSES

FIG. 1. Schematic diagram of a reflection electron microscope.

projector lenses to form an image of the surface.

Factors governing the choice of θ_1 and θ_2. The first reflection electron microscope built by Ruska in 1933 had $\theta_1 + \theta_2 = 90°$. The image was faint and the resolution only about 5000 Å. Von Borries (1940) had better results using glancing angles of illumination and viewing (θ_1 and θ_2 about 4° each). The potentialities of the technique were not at that time fully explored, but after the war a number of workers developed the method further. These included Kushnir, Biberman, and Levkin (1951), Menter (1952), Fert and Saporte (1952), Haine and Hirst (1953), Cosslett and Jones (1955). In all this work the von Borries arrangement of glancing angles of incidence and viewing was used— values of θ_1 of about 1° and θ_2 about 8° were common. Images of moderately good resolution and intensity were obtained, but since the surfaces were viewed obliquely they appeared foreshortened. In such images the magnifications are different in different directions and it is usual to call the maximum magnification (in the direction perpendicular to the plane of incidence) $m_\perp$ and the mini-

mum magnification (in the foreshortened direction parallel to the plane of incidence) $m_\parallel$. Then $m_\parallel = m_\perp \sin \theta_2$ and with an angle θ_2 of about 8° the foreshortening factor $(m_\perp / m_\parallel)$ is about 7; hence there is a considerable distortion of the image. This makes it difficult to interpret the pictures—nevertheless, much work has been done with this type of arrangement with useful results.

The electrons scattered at the specimen change velocity by different amounts, which can be quite large. Consequently, chromatic aberration in the objective lens becomes the factor limiting the resolution of the reflection electron microscope. The best resolution so far obtained is about 300 Å and this is probably somewhere near the limit attainable unless some means of reducing the chromatic aberration (e.g., a velocity filter or achromatic lens) can be developed. The figure of 300 Å represents the resolution in the direction of maximum magnification. The resolution in the foreshortened direction is worse by the foreshortening factor since a circle of confusion at the image corresponds to an ellipse at the specimen.

It would obviously be desirable to reduce the foreshortening and several methods of doing this have been tried. The simplest is to view the final image through a cylindrical glass lens arranged to magnify it in the foreshortened direction. An alternative is to use a cylindrical electron lens (Fert, 1956) to correct the distortion before the image is formed on the fluorescent screen of the electron microscope. This approach is not very fruitful since the resolutions differ in different directions in the image. The most promising method is to use larger values of θ_2. The main reason for the common use of small values of θ_2 is that the intensity of the image falls off very rapidly as the total angle of deviation is increased. It is difficult to see to focus the image if θ_2 is too big. However, by using a sufficiently powerful electron gun Fert and his colleagues at Toulouse have obtained good images with $\theta_1 = 2°$ and $\theta_2 = $

23° or 38° (see Figure 2). The distortion was then by a factor of 2.6 or 1.6 only and the pictures were comparatively easy to interpret. One difficulty encountered was the rapid contamination of the specimen surface by the intense electron beam. Fert overcame this by using ionic bombardment of the surface to remove the contamination continuously or, if desired, to etch the surface. The resolution in the direction of maximum magnification was again about 300 Å and was affected very little by the value of θ_2. The resolution in the direction of minimum magnification was worse by a factor of $1/\sin \theta_2$ because of the foreshortening. Hence as θ_2 was increased the resolution in this direction improved markedly. The high quality of the images was at first thought to be rather surprising since it had generally been supposed that the energy losses of the scattered electrons would increase as the deviation of the electron beam increased, thereby introducing a serious loss in resolution because of the increased chromatic aberration. When the spectrum of energy losses was measured (Fert, Pradal, Saporte, and Simon 1958) it was found that this supposition was incorrect, for the proportion of electrons with high energy losses actually decreased as the scattering angle was increased.

It has thus been shown that for best results the largest practicable value of $\theta_1 + \theta_2$ should be used. Page (1958a) has taken good pictures with $\theta_1 + \theta_2 = 26.5°$ using a modified commercial instrument and without ionic bombardment of the specimen. Unfortunately the commercial instruments available at present do not allow very large angles of tilt of the electron gun.

The choice of angle θ_1 is important. Since the surface of the specimen is illuminated obliquely any asperity on it will cast a shadow. If θ_1 is small this shadow will be long compared with the height of the asperity. Vertical features may thus be given very high contrast: suppose for instance that

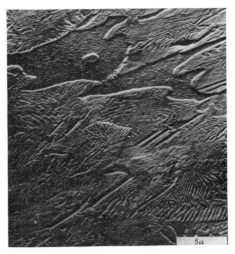

FIG. 2. Pearlitic steel specimen after ionic etching: montage of three reflection electron micrographs. $\theta_1 = 2°$, $\theta_2 = 23°$. (*Photograph reproduced by courtesy of Professor C. Fert.*)

$\theta_1 = 1°$; then a step 100 A high would cast a shadow 5700 Å long and at a magnification $m_\perp$ of 2000 $\times$ would have a length in the image of 0.16 mm if $\theta_2 = 7°$ or 0.50 mm if $\theta_2 = 25°$. This shadowing effect is one of the most valuable features of reflection electron microscopy, and in order to obtain good contrast it is normal to use an angle θ_1 of about 1° or if the surface is very smooth a smaller angle which may be as low as 0.1°. Also it is necessary to use a small value of θ_1 to obtain good resolution. Fert, Marty, and Saporte (1955) have shown that θ_1 must be less than 3 or 4° if the resolution is not to suffer. They attribute this to the fact that if θ_1 is small the electrons will not penetrate far into the specimen and there will be less chance of an electron scattered there in the direction of the objective suffering a second collision before leaving the specimen (particularly if θ_2 is large). Thus the angles θ_1 and θ_2 should be chosen as follows: θ_1 should be made small ($\sim 1°$) and its exact value chosen to give the desired contrast for the particular specimen being examined, and θ_2 should be made as large as is practicable.

FIG. 3. Reflection electron micrograph of the surface of a polished sapphire ball (diameter 1.27 cm). Though curved, the surface is well focused. $\theta_1 + \theta_2 = 11°$, $\theta_1 \sim 1$ to $2°$ (varying across field). $m_\perp = 2500\times$, $m_\parallel + 400 \times$.

Applications

There are two main types of specimen for which reflection electron microscopy is a particularly suitable method of surface examination. First, there are very smooth surfaces such as polished metals, glass, cleavage surfaces of some crystals, etc. Figure 3 shows a micrograph of the surface of a polished sapphire ball and is representative of the results which can be obtained from this type of surface. If the angles θ_1 and θ_2 are known, then the heights of asperities can be calculated from the shadow lengths using simple geometry. The method can give useful quantitative information but there are a number of possible sources of error to be kept in mind. There may be transmission of the electron beam through the edges of asperities; the local surface on which the shadow falls may be at an angle to the plane of the specimen surface as a whole; the incident electron beam may not be strictly parallel and may therefore give penumbra; electron-induced contamination can build up on the edges of scratches, etc. and give misleading results. However, comparison of results obtained by this and other methods (see e.g., Bailey and Seal 1956) has shown that for surface roughnesses of 100 Å or more the method gives accurate results provided that reasonable care is taken in the operation of

the instrument and interpretation of results. Features down to about 30 Å in height can be resolved by the shadows they cast, but for such small features the quantitative results are less reliable.

The second type of application depends on another effect. This is the high depth of field inherent in the electron microscope because of the very small angular aperture of the objective lens. The depth of field of a microscope objective is $\pm \delta/\tan \alpha$ where δ is the resolution and α the semianglar aperture of the objective. For an optical microscope at high magnification δ would be about 2500 Å and α about $\frac{1}{2}$ radian giving a depth of field of $\pm \frac{1}{2}$ μ. A reflection electron microscope would have δ about 300 Å and α about 3.10^{-3} radian giving a depth of field of ± 10 μ. Thus the depth of field of a reflection electron microscope is considerably greater than that of an optical microscope at similar magnification. Consequently, focused pictures of highly curved objects such as balls, wires, fibers, etc., and of features such as scratches or grooves can be obtained. Examples are shown in Figures 3 and 4: the polished sapphire surface shown in Figure 3 had a radius of curvature of 0.63 cm; Figure 4 shows one groove of a gramophone recording.

Although it is possible to examine gross features of this kind there is a restriction: they must either be single isolated features on an otherwise smooth surface or have extent in one direction only. It is not possible to examine rough surfaces of large extent since the shadows cast by asperities would obscure neighboring detail: in such cases the mountain tops only are illuminated and the valleys left in shadow. With a feature such as a scratch the illumination should be parallel to the scratch since otherwise the edge would probably cast too long a shadow. Figure 5 shows a surface (of lathe-turned brass) which is about as rough as can usefully be examined by this technique.

In reflection electron microscopy one examines the specimen directly and there is therefore the possibility of performing experiments on the surface while observing it. This has not received the attention it deserves, but Cosslett and Jones (1955) have built a reflection electron microscope with a hot-stage and have been able to observe the changes brought about by heating silver and other materials.

Most work in reflection electron microscopy has been done with metal specimens but it is possible to examine other materials. It is necessary for the specimen surface to be electrically conducting since otherwise it becomes charged and repels the electron beam. If an electrical non-conductor is to be examined, it is usual to render its surface conducting by evaporating a layer of metal (usually a few hundred angstroms thickness of silver) onto it. There are also some difficulties in examining organic materials since these are readily decomposed by the electron beam: the use of very low beam intensities is often necessary in order to obtain pictures of these materials. These difficulties can be overcome by using the replica technique of Bradley (1955)—a rigid metal replica of the surface to be examined is prepared and forms a robust specimen for the reflection electron microscope. There appears to be no loss in resolution, but the advantage of direct examination of the surface is of course lost.

A few references to typical applications of reflection electron microscopy follow. Metals with different surface preparations have been studied by Halliday (1955, 1957); diamond surfaces of different types by Seal and Menter (1953) and Seal (1956, 1958a and b); the epicuticular surfaces of insects by Holdgate and Seal (1956); natural and synthetic fibers and the effect of abrasion on them by Chapman and Menter (1954); lubricant layers of graphite and other lamellar solids by Deacon and Goodman (1958); cleavage faces of zinc crystals by Moore (1955); surface damage on mica by Bailey and Courtney-Pratt (1955) and on rocksalt by King and Tabor (1954); paper and pulp

Fig. 4. Reflection electron micrograph of a single groove of a gramophone record. There is a sine wave modulation of which rather more than one cycle is visible. $\bullet_1 = 2°$, $\bullet_2 = 9°$. $m_\perp = 570 \times$, $m_\parallel = 90 \times$

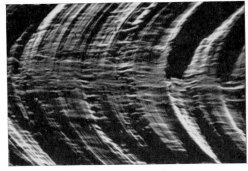

Fig. 5. Reflection electron micrograph of part of a lathe-turned brass surface. The circular grooves left by the cutting tool appear foreshortened as portions of ellipses. $\bullet_1 = 2°$, $\bullet_2 = 9°$. $m_\perp = 1000 \times$, $m_\parallel = 160 \times$.

fibers by Amboss, Emerton, and Watts (1954); the fretting corrosion of mild steel by Halliday and Hirst (1956).

Since the main part of this article was written, further papers on the subject have appeared. Halliday and Newman (1958, 1960) have published the results of an investigation of reflection electron microscopy using diffracted electrons. In these experiments crystalline specimens were used and the angles of tilt of the electron gun and specimen adjusted so that a diffracted beam passed through the objective aperture. This beam was used to form an image, analogous to the "dark field" image often used with transmission specimens. It was stated that the resolution should be higher than usual since the energy spread of electrons diffracted at a Bragg angle would be smaller than that of inelastically scattered electrons. A resolution of 80 A was obtained experimentally.

Kushnir and Der-Schwarz (1958) discussed various problems in reflection electron microscopy and described some experimental results. They dealt with the spatial intensity distribution and velocity spectrum of electrons scattered at a massive object, the correction of chromatic aberration and geometrical distortion, and the effects of objective aperture displacement.

Further use has been made of the possibility of carrying out experiments on a specimen whilst observing it in a reflection electron microscope. Halliday and Rose (1959) described the direct observation of wear processes in this way. There was also an earlier paper by Takahashi, Takeyama, Ito, Ito, Mihama, and Watanabe (1956) describing a hot stage for reflection electron microscopy and some results obtained from this.

Equations

A number of equations relevant to the interpretation of reflection electron micrographs and the use of the instrument follow. The magnifications in directions parallel to and perpendicular to the plane of incidence are related by

$$m_{\parallel} = m_{\perp} \sin \theta_2 , \qquad (1)$$

and the resolutions in these directions by a similar equation

$$\delta_{\parallel} = \delta_{\perp}/\sin \theta_2 . \qquad (2)$$

Angular relationships in the image are distorted because of the foreshortening. A line in the specimen at azimuth φ (measured to a line in the specimen in the plane of incidence) will be imaged as a line at azimuth φ' where

$$\tan \varphi' = \tan \varphi/\sin \theta_2 . \qquad (3)$$

The magnification along a line in the image at azimuth φ' is

$$m_{\varphi'} = \frac{m_{\perp} \sin \theta_2 \sec \varphi'}{\sqrt{1 + \tan^2 \varphi' \sin^2 \theta_2}}, \qquad (4)$$

and a circle in the specimen will be imaged as an ellipse. The height of an asperity h is related to the length of the shadow it casts L (measured in the image) by

$$h = \frac{L \sin \theta_1}{m_{\perp} \sin (\theta_1 + \theta_2)}. \qquad (5)$$

If the validity of this equation is not to be affected by penumbra, a restriction must be imposed on the angular spread of the incident electron beam

$$2\Delta\theta_1 \leq \frac{\delta_{\perp} \sin^2 \theta_1}{h \sin \theta_2}. \qquad (6)$$

Thus good collimation becomes important for small θ_1. Other factors affecting the validity of equation 5 have been listed on page 225. The depth of field is approximately

$$\pm \delta_{\perp}/\alpha, \qquad (7)$$

where α is the semi-angular aperture of the objective lens. The chromatic aberration of the objective lens limits the resolution to

$$\delta_{\perp} = \alpha C \frac{\Delta V}{V}, \qquad (8)$$

where C is the chromatic aberration coefficient of the objective lens, ΔV the half-width of voltage spread of the scattered electrons, and V the accelerating voltage. With present instruments, other aberrations are negligible compared with chromatic aberration and, therefore, α should be made as small as possible. There will be an optimum value of α when diffraction becomes important, but this is of no practical significance since it corresponds to an image which is too faint to be focused or recorded.

In a three lens electron microscope the chromatic field aberrations can be kept to a minimum by correct choice of the intermediate lens current and by exciting lenses in opposition to minimize the over-all rotation of the image. The relevant formulas and tolerances in the correction settings are given in a paper by Page (1958b). The tolerances in the alignment of the objective aperture (which must be accurately centered) are also given in this paper.

REFERENCES

AMBOSS, K., EMERTON, H. W., AND WATTS, J., "Proc. International Conference on Electron Microscopy," London, 1954, p. 560 (London, Royal Microscopical Society, 1956).

BAILEY, A. I. AND COURTNEY-PRATT, J. S., *Proc. Roy. Soc. A*, **227**, 500 (1955).

BAILEY, A. I. AND SEAL, M., *Industrial Diamond Review*, **16**, 145 (1956).

VON BORRIES, B., *Zeits. f. Phys.*, **116**, 370 (1940).

BRADLEY, D. E., *Brit. J. Appl. Phys.*, **6**, 191 (1955).

CHAPMAN, J. A. AND MENTER, J. W., *Proc. Roy. Soc. A*, **226**, 400 (1954).

COSSLETT, V. E. AND JONES, D., *J. Sci. Instr.*, **32**, 86 (1955).

DEACON, R. F. AND GOODMAN, J. F., *Proc. Roy. Soc. A*, **243**, 464 (1958).

FERT, C., "Electron Microscopy," Proc. Stockholm Conference, 1956, p. 8 (Stockholm, Almquist and Wiksell, 1957).

FERT, C., MARTY, B., AND SAPORTE, R., "Les Techniques Récentes en Microscopie Electronique et Corpusculaire," p. 91, colloque du C.N.R.S., Toulouse, 1955.

FERT, C., PRADAL, F., SAPORTE,, R., AND SIMON R., "Proc. International Conference on Electron Microscopy," Berlin, 1958, p. 197, (Berlin, Springer-Verlag, 1960).

FERT, C. AND SAPORTE, R., *C. R. Acad. Sci., Paris*, **235**, 1490 (1952).

HAINE, M. E. AND HIRST, W., *Brit. J. Appl. Phys.*, **4**, 239 (1953).

HALLIDAY, J. S., *Proc. Inst. Mech. Eng.*, **169**, 777 (1955).

HALLIDAY, J. S., "Proc. Conference on Lubrication and Wear," 1957 (London, Institution of Mechanical Engineers).

HALLIDAY, J. S. AND HIRST, W., *Proc. Roy. Soc. A*, **236**: 411 (1956).

HALLIDAY, J. S. AND NEWMAN, R. C., "Proc. International Conference on Electron Microscopy," Berlin, 1958, p. 195, (Berlin, Springer-Verlag, 1960).

HALLIDAY, J. S. AND NEWMAN, R. C., *Brit. J. Appl. Phys.*, **11**, 158 (1960).

HALLIDAY, J. S. AND ROSE, D. A. S., *Brit. J. Appl. Phys.*, **11**, 24 (1960).

HOLDGATE, M. W. AND SEAL, M., *J. Expt. Biology*, **33**, 82 (1956).

KING, R. F. AND TABOR, D., *Proc. Roy. Soc. A*, **223**, 225 (1954).

KUSHNIR, U. M., BIBERMAN, L. M., AND LEVKIN, N. P., *Izvest. Akad. Nauk. S.S.S.R. (Fiz.)*, **15**, 306 (1951).

KUSHNIR, U. M. AND DER-SCHWARZ, G. W., "Proc. International Conference on Electron Microscopy," Berlin, 1958, p. 222 (Berlin, Springer-Verlag, 1960).

MENTER, J. W., *J. Inst. Metals*, **81**, 163 (1952).

MOORE, A. J. W., *Acta Metall.*, **3**, 163 (1955).

PAGE, D. H., *Brit. J. Appl. Phys.*, **9**, 60 (1958a).

PAGE, D. H., *Brit. J. Appl. Phys.*, **9**, 268 (1958b).

RUSKA, E., *Zeits. f. Phys.*, **83**, 492 (1933).

SEAL, M., "Electron Microscopy," Proc. Stockholm Conference, 1956, p. 341, (Stockholm, Almquist and Wiksell, 1957).

SEAL, M., *Proc. Roy. Soc. A*, **248**, 379 (1958a).

SEAL, M., *Nature*, **182**, 1264 (1958b).

SEAL, M. AND MENTER, J. W., *Phil. Mag.*, **44**, 1408 (1953).

TAKAHASHI, N., TAKEYAMA, T., ITO, K., ITO, T., MIHAMA, K., AND WATANABE, M., *J. Electronmicroscopy*, **4**: 16 (1956).

MICHAEL SEAL

REPLICA AND SHADOWING TECHNIQUES

Nowadays there are very few types of specimen which cannot be examined in the electron microscope. Internal structure can be studied by means of thin sections, and surface topography by replication or shadowing. It is with the latter that this article is concerned. Many replica and shadowing methods described in the literature are complicated, hence only the principles of the basic techniques will be described here.

Many specimens which are small enough to be examined directly in the electron microscope are opaque to electrons, so that the image produced consists of silhouette. Large specimens cannot be examined directly except by means of reflection electron microscopy. Thus it can be seen that a study of the surfaces of most objects demands special techniques if examination is to be in the electron microscope. These techniques consist of the preparation of replicas. A good replica must faithfully reproduce even the smallest details of the specimen surface topography, down to the limit of resolution of the electron microscope, and yet it must be very thin so that the electrons may pass through it without excessive scattering.

Replicas can be made from a number of different materials each of which requires its own particular specimen preparation techniques. Plastics, certain metal-oxide films, and vacuum-evaporated materials have been used and the physical characteristics required of all three are basically the same. The replica material must be transparent to electrons so that the final replica can be thick enough to mount on an electron microscope specimen support grid without breaking. While the electron transparency of plastics and some oxide films is high, many evaporated materials are dense to electrons. It is thus clear that while almost any plastic is suitable for the preparation of a replica, relatively few evaporated materials can be used.

Plastic Replicas

The methods used in the preparation of plastic replicas for the electron microscope are essentially very simple (1). A thin plastic replica, between 200 and 800 Å in thickness, can be formed by applying a solution of the plastic onto the surface of the specimen. After removal from the specimen, it is mounted on an electron microscope support grid for examination in the instrument. This type of replica is used almost exclusively in the examination of the surfaces of specimens of large bulk.

Many of the plastic replica techniques described in the literature consist of complex variations in handling procedures for the removal of the replica from the specimen surface and its subsequent mounting on a support grid. Different plastics are also used. To illustrate the preparation of a plastic replica a typical routine procedure is briefly described here.

First, the specimen surface must be suitably prepared. For example, in the case of a piece of metal the preparation will be more or less identical with standard metallographic procedures required for optical microscopy. The metal is then dipped into a solution of "Formvar" (polyvinyl formal) in dioxane. It is next held vertically in a dry atmosphere with the bottom touching a filter paper, which absorbs the surplus solvent, and the specimen is allowed to dry. The "Formvar" film can be removed from the metal specimen in two ways. If it is a reasonably thick film the following procedure can be safely adopted. A specimen support grid (a $\frac{1}{8}$-in. diameter copper disc perforated 200 mesh/in.) is fixed to a length of cellulose adhesive tape by its edges only, the center area of the grid being separated from the tape by a small disc of very thin paper. The grid and tape are now pressed against the surface of the "Formvar" film, care being taken to ensure that the surrounding tape is firmly pressed into position. Next, the tape is pulled away from the metal, the "Formvar" film being removed at the same time. The film should now cover the area of the support grid in addition to the surrounding adhesive tape. Because the grid is only adhering to the tape at its edges, it can be removed without difficulty from the adhesive tape with the plastic film still mounted on it. If the film is thin, it must be removed from the metal by floating onto water. It can then be picked up on a grid for examination in the electron microscope.

The mechanism of image formation encountered in plastic replicas is of interest, the contrast being produced by variations in thickness across the film. Ideally, the back surface of the plastic replica should be flat, but in practice much of the surface structure of the specimen is visible on this back surface (2). The contrast mechanism is thus not as simple as it first appears. Because of the thickness of the plastic film required and this mechanism of image formation, the resolving power obtainable with plastic replicas is not high and is in the region 50–100 Å. A "Formvar" replica of pearlite structure in steel is shown in Figure 1.

Oxide Replicas

Replicas made from thin oxide films (3) are almost entirely confined to aluminum and aluminum alloy specimens. The following method is widely used.

An aluminum specimen is anodized in a suitable bath (e.g., Na_2HPO_4—48 gm, H_2SO_4 (conc.)—2 ml water—400 ml at 30 volts for 4 mins with a platinum cathode) so that a thin oxide film a few tens of angström units in thickness is produced on the surface. This oxide film accurately conforms to the surface topography of the original specimen and it can be separated from the specimen by immersing the whole in mercuric chloride solution. Mercury forms at the interface between the aluminum metal and the oxide, thus releasing the oxide film into the solution. The film is then washed in water to remove mercuric chloride and mounted on an electron microscope support grid. While the method is very simple, careful control of anodizing conditions is required. Aluminum oxide films have a high electron transparency, are non-crystalline, thermally stable, and hence are eminently suitable for the preparation of replicas. It is unfortunate, however, that they possess a self-structure of 100–200 Å (4) and can only be used in a limited number of cases. Their applications have been widened by means of the so-called aluminum-pressing replica technique (5) in which a piece of aluminum is compressed against a prepared metal surface under very high pressure. The soft aluminum takes up the structure of the metal to a reasonable degree of accuracy. An aluminum oxide replica can then be prepared from the aluminum pressing.

The mechanism of image formation in aluminum oxide replicas is quite different from that in plastic replicas. The thickness of the oxide film, measured at right angles

FIG. 1. "Formvar" replica of pearlite structure in carbon steel. ×4500. (After Agar and Revell)

to the surface structure, is uniform so that contrast is produced by differences in thickness, in the direction of the electron beam, due to the local changes in slope of the replica. Once again it can be seen that this type of replica is almost entirely confined to metal specimens. Figure 2 shows an aluminum oxide replica of a typical anodizing structure and an etchpit in aluminum.

Vacuum-Deposited Replicas

A number of evaporated materials can be employed to make electron microscope replicas. Two of the most suitable are silicon monoxide (6) and carbon (7). The manipulative techniques are basically similar for both materials and depend upon the type of specimen to be examined. The vacuum evaporation techniques are, however, quite different. In the case of silicon monoxide the material is evaporated from a molybdenum foil boat.

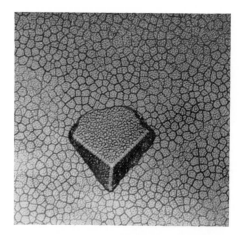

Fig. 2. Aluminum oxide replica of aluminum showing structure produced by the anodization process. ×20,000. (After Welsh)

In the case of carbon the material is evaporated by passing a high electric current through two pointed carbon rods lightly sprung together *in vacuo*. Resistance heating at the points causes the carbon to evaporate. Carbon can also be deposited by a "gas discharge" method (8), but this is not in general use.

Replica techniques employing evaporated materials can be divided into two main groups: single-stage methods and multistage methods. The former are most suitable for particulate specimens and the latter for specimens such as metal surfaces. The two basic procedures using evaporated carbon are shown in Figure 3. In a typical single-stage technique (9) (Figure 3) a particulate suspension is dried onto a glass microscope slide, which is then placed in a vacuum chamber and coated with the replicating material. The replica film, with the particles still embedded in it, is floated onto a water surface. It is next transferred to the surface of a bath containing a solvent for the particles. When the particles have dissolved, the remaining replica film can be washed, by floating on water, and mounted on an electron microscope support grid. This replica is then ready for examination in the electron microscope. If it is made from silicon monoxide or carbon it will follow the surface to a very high degree of accuracy. Figure 4a shows photographic halide crystals replicated in this way.

In two-stage methods (10), the specimen is coated with a layer of plastic (generally "Formvar") from a solution in a suitable solvent, and then backed with a further thick layer of another plastic, for example, "Bedacryl." The double plastic film is dry-stripped by means of adhesive tape, and then placed in a vacuum unit. The structure surface of the "Formvar" is coated with silicon monoxide or carbon, and after removal from the plant, the tape is placed in a solvent for the backing plastic; after this has been dissolved, the "Formvar"/carbon or "Formvar"/silicon monoxide film is separated from the tape and mounted on grids. Finally, the "Formvar" is washed away, leaving a replica film on the grid ready for examination.

There are a number of variants to these techniques, for example, thick layers of evaporated metals can be used instead of "Formvar" in the first stage of a two-stage process. Sometimes it may be more advisable to use a thermoplastic such as polystyrene for the first stage (11). Of course, a piece of metal can be coated with carbon and the carbon separated by dissolving the metal (12). This constitutes a single-stage process for a metal specimen but has the disadvantage that the surface structure is destroyed.

Extraction Replicas

A replica technique specially designed for use with metallurgical specimens has been developed by Smith and Nutting (13) and is known as the carbon extraction replica technique. The aim is to replicate the surface of the matrix and to extract any precipitates. Thus the arrangement and size distribution of the precipitates can be found and their constitution determined by means of electron diffraction.

To prepare such a replica the metal surface

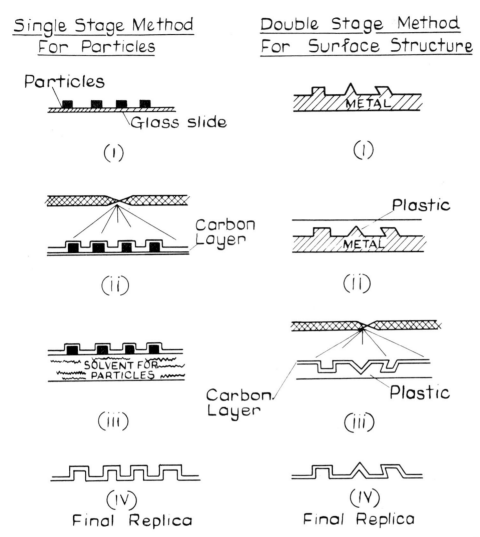

Single Stage Method
For Particles

Double Stage Method
For Surface Structure

FIG. 3. Diagrammatic representation of two basic carbon replica methods. (By courtesy of the *Journal of Applied Physics*)

is ground, polished and etched, so as to leave the precipitates protruding above the matrix. The surface is then coated with a thin film of carbon and subsequently more of the matrix is dissolved by continued etching through the carbon film. This has the effect of releasing many secondary phase inclusions, and when the carbon replica is removed from the metal surface, either by electro-polishing or floating onto water, the secondary-phase inclusions remain attached

to it. The film can now be mounted on an electron microscope grid.

The precipitates are sometimes too thick to permit identification by electron diffraction. However, Booker has identified such crystals by rolling the replica up and inserting it into an X-ray diffraction camera. Figure 5 shows a typical extraction replica; this contains two secondary phases, fine needles (Mo_2C) and larger particles (Cr_7C_3).

233

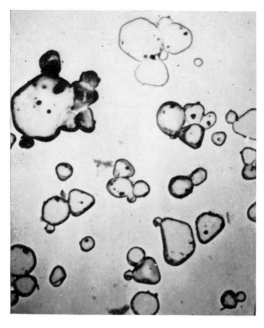
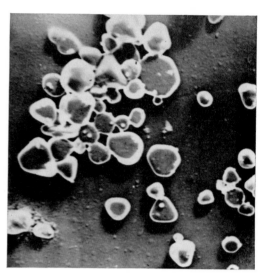

A.   B.

FIG. 4. (a) Unshadowed carbon replica of Ilford H.P.3. photographic emulsion particles. ×9,000 (b) The same, shadowed.

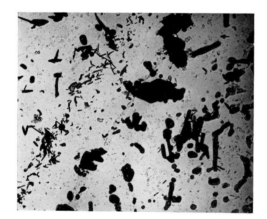

FIG. 5. Carbon extraction replica of chromium molybdenum steel; the needles are molybdenum carbide and the larger particles chromium carbide. ×16,000. (After Nutting)

Selected Area Techniques

Various methods have been devised for the study of selected areas of surfaces or selected particles by means of replicas (14–19). These areas or particles are first studied in the light microscope and the region of interest replicated while still in position and transferred to a marked specimen support grid, usually by means of a device attached to the objective lens of the light microscope. This enables electron and light micrographs of the same portion of a specimen to be compared.

Applications of Replicas

The field in which replicas have been most widely used is metallography. For routine work "Formvar" replicas have been employed; more recently carbon replicas have been used both as simple replicas or extraction replicas. Similar techniques are employed in the examination of bulk specimens such as clays and other minerals.

The single-stage methods mentioned for use with particulate specimens have been widely employed in chemistry and biology. Studies of photographic grains and the development process and of wear particles give

234

two examples. In biological applications the carbon replica has been used widely in the study of algae, pollen grains, leaf surfaces, viruses, large molecules and bacillus spores. There is no universally correct method for producing replicas, since every type of specimen may require variations of one or two basic techniques to be developed for it.

Shadowing

The technique of shadowcasting (20) was devised for two purposes. First to increase the contrast of a specimen if necessary, and second, to produce a three-dimensional effect in the resulting electron micrograph. These objectives were accomplished by depositing a thin layer of electron-dense material by vacuum evaporation at an angle onto the specimen. It can be seen from Figure 6 that the "shadow" cast by a protrusion on the surface is transparent, while the surrounding area is relatively dense to electrons. Shadows appear bright in the electron microscope but dark on the negative of the electron micrograph. Therefore, if the negative of the electron micrograph is viewed, the specimen surface will appear as if it is illuminated obliquely with white light. For this reason shadowed electron micrographs are printed as negatives. It can be seen from the electron micrograph, Figure 4b, that both an improvement of contrast and a three-dimensional effect is obtained by the shadowcasting technique.

Materials suitable for preparing replicas are not suitable for shadowcasting. A shadcasting material must be dense to electrons, i.e., it must have a high mean atomic number, so that only a thin layer, about 20 Å thick, need be deposited on the specimen. If the layer is thick, the material will pile up on the side of the protrusion nearest the source, thus distorting the shape of the protrusion. This is illustrated in Figure 7 where spherical particles have been heavily shadowed with a material of low electron density (carbon).

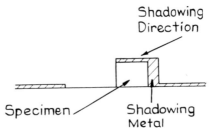

FIG. 6. Diagrammatic representation of the topographical distribution of a layer of shadowing material.

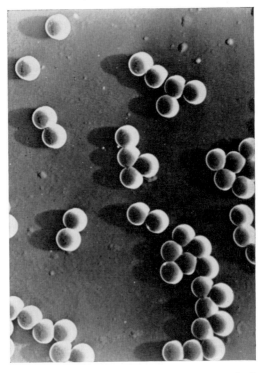

FIG. 7. Self-shadowed carbon replica of spherical polystyrene latex particles (diameter 2,600 Å) showing distortion caused by the piling up of the evaporated carbon on one side. (By courtesy of the *British Journal of Applied Physics*)

Many materials have been used for shadowcasting, for example, chromium, an alloy of gold and palladium, platinum, uranium, and tungsten oxide. These can all be evaporated *in vacuo*, either from V-shaped tungsten filaments, molybdenum foil boats, or tungsten wire baskets. The technique is

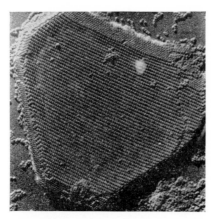

FIG. 8. Pre-shadowed carbon replica of a crystal of the Southern Bean Mosaic Virus protein. ×26,600. (After Wyckoff and Labaw, by courtesy of *Nature*)

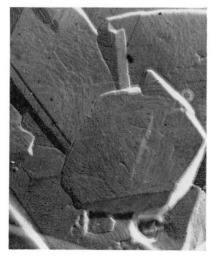

FIG. 9. Platinum/carbon replica of the surface of a crystal of sodium faujasite showing very fine steps about 10 Å in height. ×50,000.

simple and is carried out by the following procedure. A V-shaped tungsten filament is connected across a suitable transformer and a short length of wire of shadowing metal is wound on to it. The specimen is placed at least 10 cm from this source and the apparatus pumped out. When a suitably low pressure (better than 10^{-4} mm Hg) has been reached, the tungsten wire is heated, melt-

ing the shadowing material which forms a globule in the V of the filament. At the appropriate temperature this globule of metal will vaporize and be deposited onto the specimen which has been tilted with respect to the source at the required angle. The amount of material needed is calculated so that, for a mean atomic number of 50, no more than 20 Å of material is deposited on the specimen.

Unfortunately, these shadowing materials generally form minute crystallites on the specimen, which are visible in the electron microscope at high magnification and therefore limit the resolution obtainable. The size of the crystallites depends on the nature of the material used, and the resolution of the resulting electron micrograph will be limited accordingly. Thus, if gold is used, crystallites or granules more than 100 Å across form, giving a resolution of perhaps twice this value. One of the best materials available is platinum and, if this is used, the crystallites are usually between 20 Å and 30 Å in diameter and a greatly improved resolution is obtained. Obviously it is necessary that the shadowing material should have the finest possible structure. Those most widely recommended materials in this respect are platinum and uranium but they are difficult to evaporate. Gold-palladium alloy, while having a limited resolving power, can be evaporated much more easily and is most often used for routine work when a resolution of not better than 50 Å is required. Figure 8 shows a particularly striking example of shadowcasting; it is a palladium-shadowed carbon replica of a plant virus protein crystal (21). The molecules are 230 Å in diameter.

A technique has recently been developed for producing dense deposits which are non-crystalline and do not granulate in the electron microscope (22). This technique involves evaporating a mixture of platinum metal and carbon in a manner similar to that described for carbon. The resulting deposit enables a high resolving power to be obtained; the shadows cast are extremely sharp.

A mixture of platinum and carbon in the form of rods is evaporated by the passage of a high current through the points of the rods which are sprung together in a vacuum. These points are situated a short distance from a 2-mm aperture which is aligned with the specimen to be shadowed. The aperture reduces inherent background structure to a very small size.

The electron micrographs obtained appear to have a resolving power better than that obtained using platinum metal. Very fine step structures can be seen in Figure 9, which is a platinum/carbon replica of a crystal of the mineral sodium faujasite.

Many other devices, such as nozzle systems (23), have been employed in attempts to improve the results obtainable by conventional shadowcasting materials.

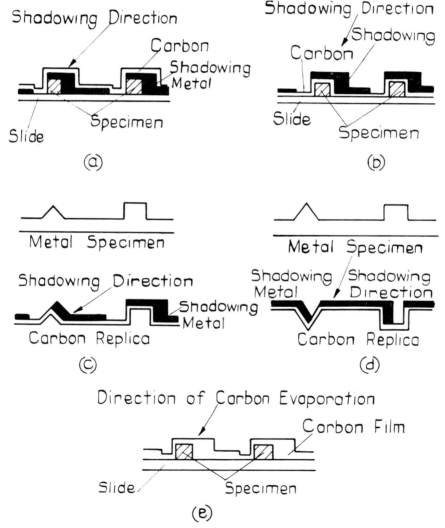

FIG. 10. Diagrammatic representation of the various ways of shadowing a replica. (By courtesy of the *Journal of Applied Physics*)

Replicas and Shadowing

When shadowing replicas, various factors must be taken into consideration. In the case of plastic replicas it must be borne in mind that the top surface of the replica does not accurately follow the surface topography of the specimen beneath. If a plastic replica is to be shadowed the material must, therefore, be deposited on the surface which has been in contact with the specimen. It will then produce a "negative picture" of the specimen surface, i.e., projections on the specimen will appear as hollows on the replica. This can be appreciated from Figure 10, which shows the different ways in which a carbon replica can be shadowed.

When carbon, silicon monoxide and other evaporated replicas are to be used, shadowing can be carried out in two ways. The specimen itself can be shadowed prior to the deposition of the replicating material, in which case it is known as a "pre-shadowed replica" (Figure 10a). Otherwise the replica can be shadowed on the outer surface after it has been mounted on the electron microscope grid (Figure 10b). In fact there is little to be gained from one or the other of these procedures, although a pre-shadowed replica is obviously better laboratory practice, and if a specimen is likely to be distorted during a replica process, it is essential.

Choice of Materials

The choice of a replicating or shadowing material will of course depend on the nature of the specimen to be examined. There are, however, a number of general points to be considered. The first and most obvious is the required resolving power of the ultimate electron micrograph. If a high resolution image is required then a carbon or silicon monoxide replica and Pt/C shadowing is desirable. Both shadowing and replication can be carried out in one single evaporation by using "self-shadowed" platinum/carbon replicas. Where a pre-shadowed replica is to be made, and two evaporations are required, a high-resolution replica can be obtained from platinum or uranium shadowed silicon monoxide or carbon. If a fairly easily prepared replica of limited resolution is required then "Formvar" replicas from a metal surface are suitable and can be made quickly.

An important factor is the strength of the replicating material. If the material tends to break or move in the electron beam it will be difficult to obtain good electron micrographs. Many workers have found that carbon is the strongest replicating material. It has a further practical advantage in that it is very easily visible by transmitted light whereas silicon monoxide is difficult to see. This factor is of great importance in the handling and mounting of replicas. A useful advantage of carbon is that it can be treated by very strong acids, such as hydrofluoric acid, without any effect on the film.

If stereoscopic electron micrographs are to be obtained, it is essential that a shadowed carbon or silicon monoxide replica be employed. The contrast-forming mechanism of a "Formvar" replica is such that it is not possible to obtain satisfactory stereoscopic pairs.

There is no doubt that replicas and shadowing play a very important part in electron microscopy. Where they are not of prime importance in the study of a particular type of specimen, they can often be usefully employed in conjunction with such methods as ultra-microtomy.

Acknowledgments. The author would like to thank Dr. T. E. Allibone, F.R.S., Director of the Research Laboratory, for permission to publish this article.

REFERENCES

1. SCHAEFER, V. J. AND HARKER, D., *J. Appl. Phys.*, **13**, 427 (1942).
2. AGAR, A. W. AND REVELL, R. S. M., *Brit. J. Appl. Phys.*, **7**, 17 (1956).
3. KELLER, F. AND GEISLER, A. H., *Trans. Am. Inst. Min. Met. Eng.*, **156**, 82 (1944).
4. WELSH, N. C., *J. Inst. Metals*, **85**, 129 (1956).
5. HUNGER, J. AND SEELIGER, R., *Metallforschung*, **2**, 65 (1947).

6. Hassard, G. and Scott, N. W., *J. Opt. Soc. Am.*, **179**, 39 (1949).
7. Bradley, D. E., *Brit. J. Appl. Phys.*, **5**, 65 (1954).
8. König, H. and Helwig, G., *W. Phys.*, **129**, 491 (1951).
9. Bradley, D. E., *Brit. J. Appl. Phys.*, **5**, 96 (1954).
10. Bradley, D. E., *J. Inst. Metals*, **83**, 35 (1954).
11. Heidenreich, R. D. and Peck, V. G., *J. Appl. Phys.*, **14**, 23 (1943).
12. Pfeiffer, I., *Naturwiss.*, **42**, 508 (1955).
13. Smith, B. A. and Nutting, J., *Brit. J. Appl. Phys.*, **7**, 214 (1956).
14. Hyam, E. D. and Nutting, J., *Brit. J. Appl. Phys.*, **3**, 173 (1952).
15. Nankivell, J. A., *Brit. J. Appl. Phys.*, **4**, 141 (1953).
16. Booker, G. R., *Brit. J. Appl. Phys.*, **5**, 349 (1954).
17. Bradley, D. E., *Brit. J. Appl. Phys.*, **6**, 430 (1955).
18. Halldal, P., Markali, J., and Naess, T., *Mikroskopie*, **9**, 197 (1954).
19. Bradley, D. E., *Mikroskopie*, **12**, 257 (1957).
20. Williams, R. C. and Wyckoff, R. W. G., *J. Appl. Phys.*, **17**, 23 (1946).
21. Labaw, L. W. and Wyckoff, R. W. G., *Nature*, **176**, 455 (1955).
22. Bradley, D. E., *Brit. J. Appl. Phys.*, **10**, 198 (1959).
23. Hibi, T. and Yada, K., "Proc. 3rd International Conf. Electron Microscopy," London, 1954.

D. E. Bradley

REPLICAS, REMOVAL FROM SURFACES

The carbon replica technique of examining surfaces with the electron microscope is widely used on ceramic and metallic solids. The technique consists of first shadowing the surface to be examined with a noble metal such as platinum or palladium at an angle of 10° to 30° to the surface. The shadow is then backed by evaporating a carbon film at 90° to the surface to complete the replica. To be usable this replica must then be removed from the surface by etching away the sample from beneath the carbon and shadowing material. It is this step which is the most difficult since the fragile carbon film with its attached shadow must be floated off the sample by some etchant and the floating replica picked up on a grid. In the case of ceramic materials, strong etchants of low pH, such as aqua regia or HF-HNO$_3$ mixtures, are frequently required to effect a separation within a reasonable period of time. The electron microscope grids, usually of copper, stainless steel or titanium, are attacked by the low pH solutions when they are placed in contact with the replica; this often results in severe tearing of the carbon film. Diluting of the solution in order to raise the pH frequently causes sufficient turbulence to damage the replica. The technique described herein has been found successful in circumventing these obstacles. It consists essentially of (1) placing the specimen in a wedge-shaped specimen holder which serves to maintain the specimen at the proper angle with respect to the surface of the etchant, thus permitting progressive solution of the substrate and causing the replica to float on the surface of the liquid as it is released; and (2) subsequently diluting the etchant solution without appreciably disturbing the floating replica.

This technique was developed during an investigation of fused ceramic coatings on tungsten wires in which it was necessary to examine the interface between the ceramic coating and the tungsten. Because of the chemical stability of the ceramic material and the tungsten, it was necessary to use etchants containing 4% nitric acid and 8–12% hydrofluoric acid by volume to separate the replica from the sample. As was previously noted, these solutions attacked the grids and caused severe tearing of the replicas. This necessitated diluting the etchant after the separation was accomplished.

Because of the corrosive nature of the releasing etchant, the samples were first mounted in a block of a thermoplastic material and then polished by ordinary ceramographic techniques to produce a flat

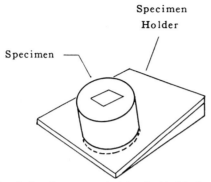

FIG. 1. Specimen mounted in plastic block and placed in wedge-shaped specimen holder.

polished cross section of the coating and tungsten wire. Upon completion of the polishing, the samples were etched in a 10 % nitric + 3 % hydrofluoric acid solution for approximately five minutes. This etch was sufficient to reveal the crystallographic detail in the interfacial region. This surface was then replicated by the process previously described.

The plastic block containing the sample was then mounted in a "Lucite" wedge, as shown in Fig. 1. The wedge containing the sample and block was placed in the polyethylene Buchner funnel, as shown in Fig. 2. With the hosecock closed, etchant was added until the surface of the liquid had crossed the lower edge of the mounting block and was nearly in contact with the lower edge of the shadowed specimen. Distilled water was then added from the buret until the edge of the etchant surface was properly positioned at the bottom edge of the sample. Prior to this step the edges of the sample had been scored so as to break the carbon film and permit the etchant to attack the sample material.

The progress of the etchant was followed by means of a 15 × microscope which could be swung over the sample on a pivot arm. As the etching progressed, water was added from the buret to raise the level of the liquid and hence help pull the replica from the sample and float it upon the etchant surface.

When the separation was completed the replica floated freely upon the surface of the etchant. The etchant level was then raised by means of the buret until it was completely free of the mounting block. It was then necessary to dilute the etchant to approximately twenty times its volume to raise the pH to a level where the replicas could be picked up on the metal grids. The hosecock shown in Fig. 2 was opened and the stopcock of the buret opened. The flow into and out of the funnel was adjusted so that the liquid level remained essentially constant. The distilled water from the buret was introduced below the surface of the etchant via a polyethylene tube. This step greatly reduced the turbulence of the surface and hence reduced

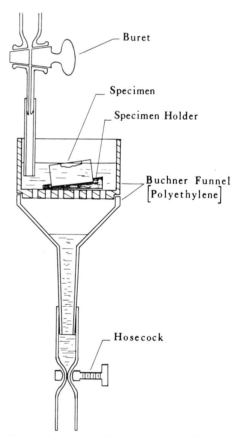

FIG. 2. Apparatus for separating replica from specimen in solutions of low pH.

the tearing of the replicas during the dilution. When the pH of the solution in the top of the funnel was approximately 5, the replica was placed on a grid.

The diluting process could be accelerated by removing the plastic block containing the sample from the etchant after the replica was released. The danger of the resulting turbulence tearing the replica usually precluded the use of this time-saving step.

This technique should be applicable to the removal of carbon replicas from any solid material which can be etched from beneath the replica by acidic solutions, particularly those containing hydrofluoric acid.

V. J. Tennery, C. G. Bergeron,
and R. Borasky

RESINOGRAPHY. *See* p. 525.

SCANNING

In the scanning electron microscope, an electron optical system is used to produce a fine electron spot which, in turn, is caused to move over each point of the specimen. The electron current leaving the specimen is collected and amplified, and the resulting signal is used to modulate a recording device moving in synchronism with the electron spot but with a greater amplitude. If the specimen possesses some property which causes the electron current leaving it to vary from point to point, then a record will be built up which will represent in some way the variation of that property over the area of the specimen which is scanned. The resolving power of such a microscope is determined by the size of the electron spot.

A microscope intended for the study of secondary emission phenomena and based upon the above principles was first proposed by Knoll (1) in 1935. The first practical scanning microscope was described by von Ardenne (2, 3) in 1938, the main purpose of this instrument being the examination of thick specimens in the transmission mode*. This instrument, which used electrostatic lenses and electromagnetic scanning, possessed no amplifying device; instead, the electron beam, after passing through the specimen, was allowed to fall on a film moving in synchronism with the beam but with a greater velocity. The magnification was given in this case by the velocity ratio of the beam and the moving film. This early instrument possessed several practical disadvantages among which were very low efficiency, necessitating recording times of 30 minutes or more, and no direct means of observing and focusing the picture before recording.

von Ardenne suggested that living biological specimens might be examined in air by first passing the beam through a thin Lenard window, and further that the surfaces of opaque specimens could be examined by collection and amplification of the secondary electrons to modulate a cathode-ray tube display.

A scanning microscope designed specifically for the direct examination of the surfaces of metallurgical specimens was described by Zworykin *et al.* (4, 5) in 1942; it used electrostatic lenses and electromagnetic scanning of the beam. The specimen was placed with its surface in a plane perpendicular to the axis of the objective lens, and secondary electrons emitted from the surface were accelerated back through this lens to be detected by a fluorescent screen followed by a photomultiplier. After further amplification, the signal was applied

---

* In the scanning instrument the electron beam does not permit any focusing after its interaction with the specimen; hence, energy losses occurring in a thick specimen observed in transmission are less serious than in the case of the conventional transmission instrument. In practice, however, the scanning method is only advantageous for one particular type of specimen typified by highly scattering particles lying on or near the surface of a substrate of much lower scattering power (see reference 6).

to a facsimile recorder scanning in synchronism with the electron beam. Contrast in the image was produced partly as a result of variations in the composition of the surface and partly because of the surface topography. The energy of the electron beam incident on the specimen was made low, only 800 volts, in order to achieve a high secondary-emission coefficient. Focusing of this instrument was achieved by observation of the video signal with an oscilloscope; the high-frequency content of the signal was used as a criterion for adjustment.

A disadvantage of this instrument was that no means was provided for observing the field prior to recording. The use of a low-energy beam reduced the intensity of the spot, thus necessitating rather long recording times of about 10 minutes. Also, at low primary energies, contamination of the specimen surface with organic vapors, always present in a demountable vacuum system, was likely to affect significantly the secondary-emission coefficient.

A scanning electron microscope, similar to the above instrument but incorporating several new features, was proposed by Oatley and McMullan in 1948 and constructed by McMullan at the Engineering Department, University of Cambridge. This instrument used high-energy electrons (10–40 kV) to reduce the effects of surface contamination, oblique scanning of the specimen, direct amplification of the emitted electrons with an electron multiplier suitable for use in a demountable vacuum system, and direct observation of the field on a long persistence cathode-ray tube display prior to recording the picture. While oblique scanning resulted in a foreshortening and reduction of resolving power in the vertical direction of the image, it allowed a much simpler and more efficient collection arrangement. The features incorporated in this instrument removed most of the disadvantages of earlier instruments. In particular, the reduction of recording times to 5 minutes (or less) together with direct viewing of the picture realized the possibility of an instrument suitable for practical laboratory application.

The techniques and applications described in the following sections relate largely to this instrument (6) and developments therefrom (7, 8, 9).

Formation of the Electron Spot. The function of the electron optical system is to focus a fine electron spot of high intensity onto the specimen. Two principal factors limit the performance in this respect—aberrations of the lenses, and limited brightness output from the electron gun. Expressions are derived below which indicate how these factors affect the performance.

The electron spot which is a reduced image of the virtual cross-over in the electron gun is formed by a two-stage lens system (Figure 1). By varying the strength of the first lens, the demagnifying power of the system, and thus the size of the spot, may be controlled over a wide range without affecting significantly the position of the spot. Because the effective aperture at which the first lens works is very minute, the aberrations of this lens do not contribute significantly to the limitation of the performance.

The spot is focused on the specimen by means of the final or objective lens. The specimen, which may be as large as 1 cm in diameter, is placed as close to this lens as possible since the focal length and consequently the spherical aberration is reduced thereby. If ferrous specimens are to be examined, the working space must also be field-free. The requirements of a magnetic scanning objective are best satisfied by an asymmetrical pole-piece design (10); typical values of focal length and spherical aberration coefficient for this type of lens with a working distance of 0.5 cm are 1 cm and 3 cm, respectively. Astigmatism of the objective caused by pole-piece ellipticity may also be a significant limitation.

Spherical aberration and astigmatism of the objective and, at the smaller spot sizes,

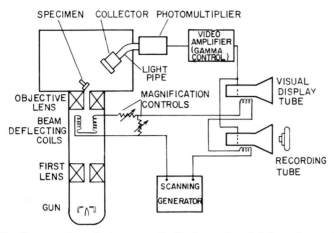

SPECIMEN   COLLECTOR   PHOTOMULTIPLIER

VIDEO
AMPLIFIER
(GAMMA
CONTROL)

LIGHT
PIPE

VISUAL
DISPLAY
TUBE

OBJECTIVE
LENS

MAGNIFICATION
CONTROLS

BEAM
DEFLECTING
COILS

FIRST
LENS

RECORDING
TUBE

GUN

SCANNING
GENERATOR

Fɪɢ. 1. Schematic diagram of an electromagnetically focused and deflected scanning microscope.

diffraction at the objective aperture will each cause a point object to be imaged in disks of confusion, the diameters of which are given by the following expressions.

Spherical aberration

$$d_s = \tfrac{1}{2} C_s \alpha^3 \tag{1}$$

Astigmatism $\quad d_a = Z_a \alpha \tag{2}$

Diffraction $\quad d_f = 1.22 \, \lambda/\alpha \tag{3}$

where C_s is the coefficient of spherical aberration, Z_a is the axial astigmatism, λ is the electron wavelength and α is the semi-angular aperture which the objective subtends at the specimen.

In order to estimate the combined effect of spherical aberration and diffraction in the conventional transmission microscope, the disks of confusion may be assumed to contain a Gaussian distribution of intensity and their diameters may be added in quadrature (11). This procedure will be applied in the present case to estimate the total effective diameter of the electron spot, i.e.

$$d^2 = d_0{}^2 + d_s{}^2 + d_a{}^2 + d_f{}^2$$

or

$$d^2 = d_0{}^2 + \frac{C_s{}^2}{4} \alpha^6 + Z_a{}^2 \alpha^2 + \frac{(1.22\lambda)^2}{\alpha^2} \tag{4}$$

where d_0 is the Gaussian spot diameter.

The maximum current density, j_a, in the Gaussian spot, i.e., in the absence of aberrations, may be determined from Langmuir's formula (12) which in the form applicable to the electron microscope is

$$j_a = j \, \frac{eV}{kT} \, \alpha^2 \text{ amp/cm}^2 \tag{5}$$

where e is the electronic charge, V is the accelerating voltage, T and j are, respectively, the temperature and emission density of the gun filament and k is Boltzmann's constant. [Haine and Einstein (13) have verified that the current density predicted by this equation is achieved by the type of gun used in the electron microscope when operated at moderate values of emission density (≤ 2 amp/cm²). For higher values of emission the current density falls below the predicted value because of space charge effects.]

Langmuir's theory predicts that away from the center of the spot the current density will fall off according to a Gaussian distribution, hence, the diameter of the spot is often defined as being the width of the Gaussian distribution curve at half-height (13). A definition for the effective diameter which appears to be more satisfactory for cathode-ray tubes and for the scanning microscope is that diameter which includes 80 % of the total current (14, 15).

Using this definition, the total current, i, in the spot will be

$$i = 0.62 \frac{\pi d_0{}^2}{4} \cdot j_a \text{ amp}$$

where the numerical factor 0.62 adjusts for the Gaussian distribution of intensity and applies only to this particular definition of d_0 given above.

$$i = 0.62 \frac{\pi d_0{}^2}{4} \cdot j \frac{eV}{kT} \alpha^2$$

$$i = 5.65 \times 10^3 \frac{Vj}{T} d_0{}^2 \alpha^2$$

In terms of electron wavelength

$$i = 8.48 \times 10^{-11} \frac{j}{T\lambda^2} d_0{}^2 \alpha^2 \qquad (6)$$

Equation 6 may be transposed for d_0 and combined with equation 4 to give:

$$d^2 = \left[1.177 i\lambda^2 \frac{T}{j} \times 10^{10} + (1.22\lambda)^2 \right] \frac{1}{\alpha^2}$$
$$+ \frac{C_s{}^2}{4} \alpha^6 + Z_a{}^2 \alpha^2 \qquad (7)$$

Thus, for a fixed value of spot current, the contribution of the first term in $1/\alpha^2$ is to reduce the diameter of the spot with increase of α while the contribution of the remaining terms is to increase the diameter with increase of α. For any given current, there will be an optimum aperture setting and a corresponding optimum setting of d_0 (determined by equation 6) at which the total spot diameter will be a minimum. This minimum may be derived from equation 7 as it stands, but the resulting expressions are less cumbersome if two cases are considered, (a) for an objective corrected for astigmatism and (b) for an uncorrected objective. In the latter case, astigmatism will in general predominate and the spherical aberration term may be neglected. However, since correction for astigmatism is relatively easily accomplished, spherical aberration imposes the more fundamental limitation. Therefore,

considering the case for the corrected lens, equation 7 becomes

$$d^2 = \left[1.177 i\lambda^2 \frac{T}{j} \times 10^{10} + (1.22\lambda)^2 \right] \frac{1}{\alpha^2} + \frac{C_s{}^2}{4} \alpha^6$$

and d is a minimum when $\alpha = \alpha_{opt}$ given by

$$\alpha_{opt} = 1.09 \left(\frac{\lambda}{C_s} \right)^{1/4} \left(7.92 \times 10^9 i \frac{T}{j} + 1 \right)^{1/8} \qquad (8)$$

$$d_{min} = 1.29 C_s{}^{1/4} \lambda^{3/4} \left(7.92 \times 10^9 i \frac{T}{j} + 1 \right)^{3/8} \qquad (9)$$

It may be shown from the foregoing equations that the Gaussian spot diameter, d_0, must be set to approximately $\sqrt{3/2} \, d_{min}$ for the optimum conditions.

Expressions equivalent to 8 and 9 may be derived for the case of an uncorrected objective in which astigmatism is predominant.

Equation 9 shows clearly the limitations imposed by spherical aberration, diffraction, and by the electron gun. If only very small spot currents are required, the first term in the brackets may become insignificant, in which case the optical aberrations become the ultimate limitation. For the usual values of filament temperature and emission existing in the electron microscope, this occurs at spot currents of approximately 10^{-13} amp. Currents somewhat greater than this are required in the scanning microscope.

Limitations Imposed by Fluctuations in the Electron Beam Current. Because of the particulate nature of an electron beam, the illumination of an object in the electron microscope is a random process. A mean number of electrons n, falling on an element of the object, has associated with it a fluctuation of r.m.s. magnitude $\sqrt{n}$. The basic signal-to-noise ratio is then $n/\sqrt{n} = \sqrt{n}$. If the secondary emission ratio at the specimen is not less than unity and no further noise is introduced during interaction with the specimen, a change Δn in the number of electrons emitted from the surface as the beam is scanned from one element to the next will be detectable as a change ΔB in the brightness of the picture only if the basic signal-to-noise ratio exceeds $B/\Delta B$ by a factor of about 5 [Rose (16)]. $\Delta B/B = C$ is then the threshold contrast.

It may be shown (9, 17) that during interaction of the beam with the specimen, the signal-to-noise ratio may be reduced by roughly a factor of 4. Further, possibly only one-third of the emitted electrons are effectively collected, thus

$$\sqrt{\frac{n}{3}} \geq \frac{20}{C}$$

or

$$n \geq \frac{1200}{C^2} \quad (10)$$

Therefore, to detect a contrast change of 5% between adjacent picture elements requires a minimum of 4.8×10^5 electrons per element.

If the specimen is scanned in a square raster containing N lines, i.e., N^2 elements, in a total time T_s seconds, then each element is covered in a time T_s/N^2 seconds and the required spot current will be

$$i = ne\frac{N^2}{T_s} \text{ amp}$$
$$i = 1200\frac{N^2}{C^2T_s}\, e_{\text{amp}} \quad (11)$$

(For a 300-line picture, a threshold contrast of 5% and a scanning time of 5 minutes, $i = 2.31 \times 10^{-11}$ amp). Substitution of this expression for i in equation 9 gives for the minimum spot diameter

$$d_{\min} = 1.29 C_s^{1/4}\lambda^{3/4}\left(1.52 \times 10^{-6}\frac{N^2}{C^2T_s}\frac{T}{j}+1\right)^{3/8} \quad (12)$$

This basic equation includes all the factors which affect the resolving power of the scanning microscope. In Figure 2, the spot diameter is plotted for three different values of N as a function of the recording time for the following typical parameters: $C_s = 3$

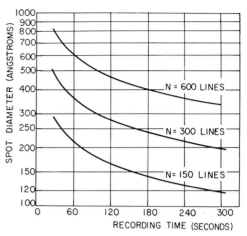

Fɪɢ. 2. Electron spot diameter, $d_{\min}$, as a function of recording time, T_s, according to equation 12.

cm, $\lambda = 10^{-9}$ cm, $(V = 15\ kV)$, $c = 5\%$, $T = 2800°K$, $j = 3.5$ amp/cm² [effective emission density at a filament life of 8–10 hours (13, 18)]. It will be seen that a resolving power close to 100 A is theoretically obtainable if the field is reduced to 150 lines.

Poor focusing will occur at the top and bottom of the picture if the number of lines or elements scanned in the vertical direction of the picture is too great. The more oblique the angle of observation the fewer the number of lines or elements which can be resolved. At an angle of 45° this will be about 300 lines. The number of elements scanned in the horizontal direction may be much greater, although this will entail either longer recording times or lower resolving power according to equation 12.

The Beam Scanning System. The deflecting system may be electromagnetic or electrostatic. The latter allows a somewhat simpler physical construction and associated circuitry but, at high beam-voltages, the deflecting potentials may become inconveniently large, the deflection sensitivity being proportional to the beam-voltage, and raster distortion may be introduced. These disadvantages may be overcome by intro-

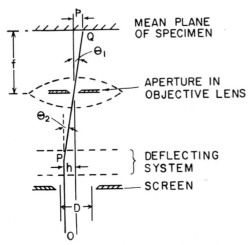

MEAN PLANE
OF SPECIMEN

APERTURE IN
OBJECTIVE LENS

DEFLECTING
SYSTEM

SCREEN

FIG. 3. Geometry of beam scanning system.

ducing the deflecting system into the lower pole-piece of the scanning objective lens (26). While the electromagnetic system is slightly more complex, the change of magnification of the instrument with change of beam-voltage is considerably less than in the case of the electrostatic system because in the electromagnetic system the deflection sensitivity is inversely proportional to the root of the beam voltage.

One of the simplest electromagnetic systems utilizes the square counterwound yoke type of configuration (19) which may be conveniently fabricated from ferrite rods of rectangular cross section (7).

The geometry of the scanning system is shown in Figure 3. The deflecting system is placed immediately before the objective since there is not sufficient space between objective and specimen. With this arrangement, the portion of the beam which is used to form the spot changes during the scan; since the magnification is reduced and the scanning amplitude thus increased, the spot is formed by rays further from the axis of the beam. It should be noted that at the higher magnifications the amplitudes involved are so small that the use of slightly off-axis rays has no significant effect on resolving power.

The portion of the beam represented by ray OP is very nearly parallel to the axis of the beam since h is small; therefore, the deflection angle θ_2 is approximately equal to $\theta_1 = p/f$, where 2p is the amplitude of scan on the specimen and f is the focal length of the objective. The magnification of the instrument will change with focal length; allowance must be made for this when traversing an obliquely scanned specimen in the vertical direction. The deflection system is placed as close to the lens as possible because this will, at a given minimum magnification, reduce h; the deflecting system may be made smaller and the efficiency increased.

The lowest operating magnification in the scanning instrument is about ×200. If the picture on the display is 12 cm square, the amplitude of the raster on the specimen, 2p, will be 0.6 mm and θ_1 and h would have the typical values of 0.03 radian and 3 mm, respectively.

When operating at high values of spot current, the beam diameter, D, may be reduced sufficiently to cause the beam to be completely swept off the objective aperture at low magnifications. This will result in vignetting of the picture. A balanced double-deflection system in which the axis of the beam is arranged to always pass through the objective aperture prevents vignetting under these conditions (7).

The magnification of the scanning instrument is altered simply by altering the scanning amplitude on the specimen while maintaining that of the display constant. As shown in Figure 1, this is accomplished in the electromagnetic system by a simple combination of shunt and series resistors, the scanning generator providing a constant-current output.

Formation of the Image. The image observed in the scanning electron microscope is foreshortened in the vertical direction according to the angle, θ, which the incident beam makes with the mean plane of the surface. The effect is exactly as if the surface were viewed at this angle; accordingly, the interpretation of the geometry of the image is not difficult, particularly if stereomicrographs are taken. Angles between 20° and 45° are commonly employed, giving foreshortening ratios of between 3:1 and 1.4:1, respectively. The position of the collector does not affect the geometry of the image.

Contrast in the image depends upon several factors, chief among which are the energies of the primary and secondary electrons, the observation angle of the specimen and the arrangement for collection of the emitted electrons.

According to their energies, electrons which are emitted from the surface of the specimen may be classified into two groups. There are the true secondary electrons which have a mean energy of about 6 eV and a maximum of about 40 eV, and there are the electrons mostly with energies of between one-half and three-quarters of the primary beam energy which may be termed "reflected" electrons.

The collector may be made to respond to either or both of these groups, the resulting image being characteristic of the group detected. Collection of the secondary component has been found to give the most informative image and is the normal mode of operation in the scanning microscope. Contrasts in this case result mainly from changes in the local angle of incidence. If only the reflected component is collected, contrast is to a certain extent dependent also upon the surface composition. For example, there is an appreciable difference between brass and aluminum in the magnitude of the reflected component (17).

If only the secondary component is collected, then the signal strength, s, at the output of photomultiplier may be represented quite closely by

$$s = K \operatorname{cosec} \theta \quad \text{for} \quad 20° \leq \theta \leq 40°$$

where K is a constant

thus

$$\delta s = -K \operatorname{cosec} \theta \cot \theta \delta \theta$$

$$\delta s/s = -\cot \theta \delta \theta \tag{13}$$

Taking the threshold contrast as 5%, i.e., $\delta s/s = 0.05$, equation shows that a change in angle of 1.3° at $\theta = 25°$ should be detectable. This of course applies only to small changes in the angle between relatively large flat areas. For rough surfaces the contrast mechanism is somewhat different.

Consider a large asperity BCD, on the surface of the specimen (Figure 4). The region ABC is partially screened from the collector with the result that the electron current entering the collector from this region will be reduced. However, a proportion of the secondary electrons will still be collected since, if emitted at a favorable angle, these electrons may follow curved paths to reach the collector, the input of the collector being normally biased a few hundred volts positive. Thus detail may be seen in the image from such regions if the secondary component is collected, whereas in the case of the reflected component, no detail may be seen because these electrons, having high energy, can follow only straight-line paths to the collector.

At the tip of the asperity, C, there will be a region thin enough to allow complete penetration of the primary beam and a large number of secondaries will be released on the side of the asperity nearest the collector. This will give rise to a region of high intensity in the image. At beam voltages of 10–20 kV, the mean depth of penetration into a metal is of the order of 1–2 μ and the bright bands along thin edges in the scanning

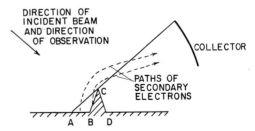

Fig. 4. Image formation at a large asperity.

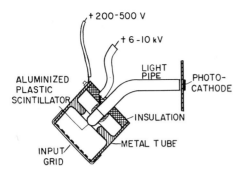

Fig. 5. Electron collector using a plastic scintillator.

image are of the same order. Under these conditions surface detail on the incident side of a thin edge can have little effect on the magnitude of the collected current and in fact no detail can be seen in such regions of high intensity. The beam accelerating voltage in the scanning microscope is made relatively low in order to reduce the penetration and, therefore, the regions of high intensity. On parts of the surface remote from thin edges, the secondaries released by deeply penetrating primaries cannot reach and escape from the surface. Wells (8, 17) has shown theoretically that the diameter of the region from which the secondaries escape does not exceed the diameter of the incident beam by much more than 100 A. Under these conditions, penetration effects are only likely to be important when resolution of detail of the order of 100 A, or less, is attempted. Resolutions of about 300 A have so far been obtained with the scanning microscope.

The Collector and Amplifying System. The current leaving the specimen is of the order of 10^{-11}; a simple electrode collector followed by an amplifier would introduce too much noise at this low level, consequently, some form of electron multiplication is necessary. In McMullan's scanning instrument, a direct electron multiplier was used which, while giving very satisfactory results, necessitated a somewhat com-

plicated floating head-amplifier and introduced various other complications.

A collection system devised by Everhart (9, 17) avoids many of the difficulties of the earlier systems. The secondaries are accelerated towards a copper mesh grid covering the end of a short metal tube (Figure 5). The tube and grid are at a potential of a few hundred volts positive with respect to the specimen. After passing through the grid, the electrons are further accelerated through a potential of several kilovolts to strike an aluminized plastic scintillator. Each electron produces a large number of photons which are registered by a photomultiplier via the light pipe. In this system, each collected electron produces several electrons from the photo-cathode of the multiplier, hence, the conversion is noise-free. The scintillator has a much shorter time constant than a fluorescent screen at low intensities and is adequate to deal with the highest video-frequencies used. This arrangement also has the additional advantage of allowing direct coupling throughout the system, thus avoiding the necessity for any form of beam modulation.

A band width of about 160 kc/s is used in the video amplifier. This passes satisfactorily the highest video-frequencies which occur when viewing the picture directly. A gamma-control stage (20) for controlling contrast and correcting nonlinearity in the display tube has been found to be a useful feature.

The Time Bases, Display and Recording Systems. The time bases provide a wide range of sweep speeds for direct observation of the picture and for recording. During direct observation, the picture is displayed at the rate of about one frame per second with a maximum of about 400 lines per frame. By using a long persistence screen on the display tube, three or four successive frames are integrated, thus improving the signal-to-noise ratio considerably.

For recording, a range of sweep speeds

from 15 sec to 6 min has been found convenient; the shorter recording times are used for low magnification work when high spot-currents may be employed.

When it is desired to examine a particular portion of a chosen field at a better signal-to-noise ratio but at the same magnification, facilities are provided for reducing the size of the picture and the area scanned in the same ratio and for shifting the raster to explore different regions of the original field. This feature is also useful for critical focusing.

Because of the D. C. shift and low recording speeds involved, the time bases are direct coupled throughout.

The resolution of the long persistence screen is not high, and it has been found to be more satisfactory to record the picture using a second tube possessing a short persistence high-resolution screen. This tube is conveniently photographed using an oscilloscope-type camera and 35-mm film. An additional advantage of the two-tube display is that during recording the picture may be monitored on the direct display tube.

Applications of the Scanning Microscope (21). The examination of the surfaces of small specimens and the interpretation of micrographs are rapid and simple in the scanning microscope as compared with the more usual replica method used with the transmission microscope, although these facilities are gained at the expense of a somewhat inferior resolution. No preparative techniques are involved for metal specimens but non-conducting specimens have to be metalized by means of the vacuum evaporation of a 100–500 A thick layer of gold-palladium. A method of examining non-conducting specimens in the scanning microscope, without metalizing, has been demonstrated (27) in which the beam accelerating voltage is reduced to the order of 0.5 − 2kV. In this voltage range the secondary emission ratio stabilizes at unity and the surface of the specimen remains at ground potential. The

FIG. 6. Worn facet on one knuckle of a woven phosphor-bronze wire mesh (Fourdrinier wire) used in the paper-making industry. (×200 horizontal, ◓ = 45°).

reduction of resolving power at lower accelerating voltages is partially offset by the higher secondary emission ratio.

The scanning method may also be applied in the case of very rough surfaces containing re-entrant features, surfaces of a loose particulate nature and for specimens of intricate shape; in all these cases the replica method may be difficult or impossible to apply. The scanning instrument may be operated at magnifications as low as ×200 an in this range may be advantageous as compared with the light microscope because of the great depth of field obtainable.

Some of these advantages are illustrated in Figure 6, which shows a worn facet of a Fourdrinier wire mesh upon which newsprint is formed. Scale-like corrosion products can also be seen in this micrograph.

Being a direct method of examination, the scanning instrument is particularly suited to

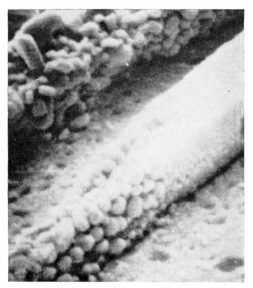

FIG. 7. Needle of silver azide undergoing thermal decomposition. (×10,000 horizontal, ◗ = 25°).

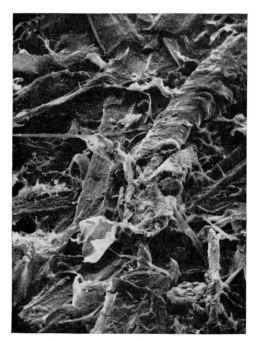

FIG. 8. Surface structure of newsprint. (×600 horizontal, ◗ = 45°).

the performance of dynamic experiments such as studies at elevated temperatures. One example is shown in Figure 7. In this

study (22), needles of silver azide were grown on a silver disk which could be heated in the microscope. The micrograph shows that thermal decomposition is proceeding from the end of the needle making better contact with the disk, leaving behind a pebble-like structure.

The conventional electron microscope may also be adapted for the direct examination of surfaces of specimens by the well-known reflection method. A comparison of this method with the scanning technique shows that the obtainable resolution is about the same but that the latter possesses certain advantages. First, while the angle of observation used in the reflection method is usually about 10° with a maximum of 25° using a refined technique and in special circumstances (23, 24), in the scanning method an angle of about 45° is used, hence foreshortening and obscurity in the image is much reduced. Second, contrast formation in the scanning instrument is not primarily a process of shadow formation. Unlike the reflection method, therefore, in which the angle of illumination is only a few degrees, no dense foreground shadows are formed to obscure parts of the surface. Third, the beam intensity in the scanning instrument is extremely low and quite delicate specimens of fibers and other material may be examined without damage. The silver azide specimen, for example, would be decomposed instantly under the high beam intensity of the conventional instrument. Figure 8, showing the surface of newsprint paper, is an example of a very rough and, at the same time, delicate type of specimen.

Quantitative information concerning the micro-geometry of a surface may be obtained by taking stereomicrographs and by taking micrographs at two different observation angles. The specimen stage of the scanning instrument is, therefore, provided with tilt and rotation as well as the usual traverse motions.

Another special application of the scanning instrument concerns the observation of variations of potential across the surface of a specimen (17). This may be done by suitably arranging the conditions at the input aperture of the collector. A study of reverse-biased p-n junctions has been carried out using this facility (17).

Other applications have included a study of the forming processes in point-contact rectifiers (7) and the direct examination of the small bores of spinnerets (8).

The optical system of the scanning microscope is basically similar to that of the x-ray projection and x-ray scanning microscopes. It is possible, therefore, that an instrument combining all three facilities could be constructed using special adapters to convert from one mode of operation to another.

A versatile scanning instrument (25) which has facilities for x-ray projection microscopy and which may also be used for conventional transmission microscopy has been designed and constructed in the Engineering Department, University of Cambridge.

REFERENCES

1. KNOLL, M., *Z. Techn. Phys.*, **16**, 767 (1935).
2. VON ARDENNE, M., *Z. Phys.*, **109**, 553 (1938).
3. VON ARDENNE, M., *Z. Techn. Phys.*, **19**, 407 (1938).
4. ZWORYKIN, V. K., HILLIER, J., AND SNYDER, R. L., *Bull. Am. Soc. Test. Mater.* **117**, 15 (1942).
5. ZWORYKIN, V. K. *et al.*, "Electronic Optics and the Electron Microscope" (Wiley, 1945).
6. MCMULLAN, D., *Proc. Inst. Elec. Engrs.*, Pt. II, **100**, 245 (1953).
7. SMITH, K. C. A. Ph.D. Dissertation, Cambridge, 1956.
8. WELLS, O. C. Ph.D. Dissertation, Cambridge, 1957.
9. EVERHART, T. E. Ph.D. Dissertation, Cambridge, 1958.
10. LIEBMAN, G., *Proc. Phys. Soc.*, B, **68**, 682 (1955).
11. COSSLETT, V. E., "Practical Electron Microscopy" (Butterworths, London, 1951).
12. LANGMUIR, D. B., *Proc. Inst. Radio Engrs.* **25**, 977 (1937).
13. HAINE, M. E. AND EINSTEIN, P. A., *Brit. J. Appl. Phys.*, **3**, 40 (1952).
14. JACOB, L., *Phil. Mag.*, **28**, 81 (1939).
15. MOSS, H. *Brit. Inst. Radio Engrs.*, Pt. I, **5**, 10 (1945).
16. ROSE, A., "Advances in Electronics," **1** (Academic Press, N. Y., 1948).
17. EVERHART, T. E., WELLS, O. C., AND OATLEY, C. W., (to be published).
18. BLOOMER, R. N., *Brit. J. Appl Phys.*, **8**, 83 (1957).
19. WORONCOW, A., *J. Inst. Elect. Engrs.*, Pt. III A, **93**, p. 1564 (1946).
20. LAX, L. AND WEIGHTON, D., *Proc. Inst. Elect. Engrs.*, Pt. III A, **99**, 804, (1952).
21. SMITH, K. C. A. AND OATLEY, C. W., *Brit. J. Appl. Phys.*, **6**, 391 (1955).
22. MCAUSLAN, J. H. L. AND SMITH, K. C. A., "Proc. Stockholm Conf. on Electron Microscopy" (Academic Press, New York, 1956).
23. FERT, C., "Conf. on Recent Progress in Corpuscular Microscopic Techniques," Toulouse, 1955.
24. PAGE, D. H., *Brit. J. Appl. Phys.*, **9**, 60 (1958).
25. SMITH, K. C. A., (to be published).
26. BERNARD, A., BRYSON-HAINES, D., MULVEY, T., *J. Sci. Instruments*, **10**, 438 (1959).
27. THORNLEY, R. F. M., European Regional Conference on Electron Microscopy, Delft, 1960.

K. C. A. SMITH

SELECTED DIFFRACTION

Selected diffraction electron microscopy is that type of microscopy in which one or more of the diffracted beams from the object ("Bragg reflections") is selected by means of a suitable aperture system and used to form the image. All the transmitted rays and the remaining diffracted rays are stopped out and prevented from contributing to the formation of the image. In this way it is possible to observe alone that part of the image responsible for a particular part of the diffraction pattern. It may be regarded as the converse of selected area electron diffraction in which a small part of the object is selected and the diffraction pattern of that part alone obtained.

Two methods of achieving selected diffraction images are shown in Figure 1. The first method may be achieved with any electron microscope having an externally adjustable

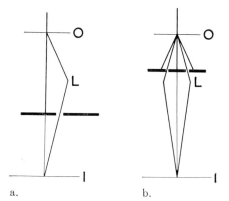

a.   b.

FIG. 1. Methods of achieving selected diffraction images: (a) using normal circular aperture off-centre, (b) using annular aperture.

objective aperture diaphragm, simply by positioning the aperture off-center so that it accepts the desired diffracted beams. This method is generally used when the specimen consists of a few isolated single crystals, giving rise to a diffraction pattern consisting of a number of isolated spots. The second method is generally used with an object containing a large number of minute crystals the diffraction pattern of which consists of concentric rings. An annular aperture concentric with the optical axis of the microscope is adjusted along the optical axis in the space between the object and the back focal plane of the objective lens to accept the desired cone of electrons corresponding to a particular ring of the diffraction pattern.

Resolution and Optimum Operating Conditions. For simplicity consider the object to be a disc-shaped crystal of diameter a, illuminated by a coherent electron beam normal to the plane of the crystal. Assume the crystal to be so orientated that it gives rise to a Bragg reflection. This will be of angular aperture $2\lambda/a$, where λ is the wavelength. If the lenses are perfectly corrected so that the resolution is limited only by diffraction then the resolution d is given by the well-known formula

$$d = 0.6\lambda/\text{N.A.}$$

In the electron microscope where apertures are small the semi-angular aperture is very nearly equal to the numerical aperture so that

$$d = 0.6\lambda/\lambda/a = 0.6a,$$

i.e., three-fifths of the crystal diameter.

Decreasing the coherence of the illumination until the distance l in the object over which the illumination is coherent becomes smaller than the crystal diameter makes the angular aperture of the diffracted beam $2\lambda/l$, and the resolution $d = 0.6l$.

The radius of the circle of confusion in the Gaussian plane due to spherical aberration alone is

$$r = \frac{3C_s\lambda^3}{(d_{hkl})^2 l}$$

where C_s is the spherical aberration constant and d_{hkl} the interplanar spacing of the crystal planes responsible for the Bragg reflection (1). Owing to the marked spherical aberration of electron lenses the Gaussian plane is not the plane of best focus for selected diffraction images. In the plane of best focus the radius of the circle of confusion due to spherical aberration is given approximately by

$$r = C_s(\lambda/l)^3,$$

for small Bragg angles.

The combined effects of diffraction and spherical aberration result in a resolution

$$d = \sqrt{(0.6l)^2 + \{C_s(\lambda/l)^3\}^2}.$$

Best resolution is obtained when d is a minimum, i.e., when

$$l = \sqrt[4]{2.9C_s\lambda^3}.$$

A typical value of C_s would be 10^8A and for λ, 5×10^{-2}A, giving an optimum value for l of 14A. In most microscopes this value of l is approached at critical illumination. In practice best resolution is usually attained very close to critical illumination, where the image deteriorates. This is probably due to the presence of astigmatism in the objective.

As the illuminating aperture is decreased from the near-critical condition the resolution slowly deteriorates. The optimum resolution approaches that of bright-field operation.

Secondary Effects. A small proportion of the inelastically scattered electrons will always be accepted by the aperture. These produce faint images of parts of the object which scatter electrons strongly. The diffraction images are usually much brighter and can therefore usually be recognized. Often the images of individual crystals have a faint comet-like tail. This is believed to be caused by electrons which have undergone both elastic and then inelastic scattering.

Applications

Location and Sizes of Crystallites. The method is useful for locating the positions of crystallites in polycrystalline films or finely divided solids. Very often individual crystallites which cannot be distinguished in bright-field micrographs owing to lack of contrast are easily visible in the selected diffraction image, enabling their positions to be located and their sizes to be measured. Some good examples of this are given in Reference 1.

Deformation of Single Crystals. O. Rang and H. Schluge (2) have used the method to study the deformation of single crystals in the form of very thin plates or foils. Many dark bands are often to be seen in the bright-field images of such crystals. These occur where parts of the crystal are orientated at a Bragg angle to the incident electron beam. Electrons incident on these parts are diffracted strongly out of the primary beam to form a Bragg reflection which in the bright-field case is stopped out by the objective aperture diaphragm. Adjusting the diaphragm to accept the Bragg reflection and stop out the transmitted electrons makes the crystal appear dark with bright bands on it. To determine the deformation of the crystal the electron diffraction pattern is first recorded and indexed. The aperture is then adjusted to accept the diffracted electron beams corresponding to each spot of the diffraction pattern in turn and the corresponding selected diffraction images are recorded. By this means the Bragg angles corresponding to each of the bands are determined and hence the orientation of different parts of the crystal can be plotted. It is sometimes useful to be able to tilt the stage through known angles and to follow the movement of the bands as the stage is tilted.

Distribution of Crystalline Constituents. The aperture system shown in Figure 1(b) has been used by J. H. Talbot to determine the distribution of certain crystalline constituents, first identified by electron diffraction, in samples of mine dust. These samples contained numerous minute crystals the diffraction patterns of which consisted of concentric rings. By varying the position of the aperture diaphragm along the optical axis, different rings of the diffraction pattern could be selected and the corresponding selected diffraction images formed.

When using this type of aperture it must

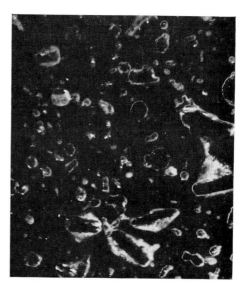

Fig. 2. Sample of mine dust showing the distribution of calcium sulfate. Selected diffraction image using 60° arc of the $d = 2.85$A ring.

be remembered that some crystals may contribute more than one spot to a particular ring of the diffraction pattern and if the aperture is a complete annulus, more than one image of each crystal may be formed. Because of aberrations, the images will not necessarily coincide. For this reason it is usually better to use a 60° or 90° arc of an annulus. Often the particles of a particular constituent possess some peculiar feature which enables them to be identified in the bright-field micrograph once the connection between the feature and the particular constituent has been established by selected diffraction microscopy.

REFERENCES

1. HALL, C. E., "Dark-field electron microscopy. I. Studies of crystalline substances in dark-field." *J. Applied Physics*, **19**, 198 (Feb., 1948).
2. RANG, O. AND SCHLUGE, H., "Dunkelfeld-Mikroskopie mit definierten gitter-reflexen." *Optik*, **9**, Heft 10, p. 463 (1952).
3. RANG, O. AND SCHLEICH, F., "Elektronenmikroskopische Dunkelfeld-Abbildung als Mittel zur Identifizierung kleiner Kristalle." *Z. Phys.*, **136**, 547 (1954).
4. TALBOT, J. H., "Identification of minerals present in mine dusts by electron diffraction and electron microscopy." Proc. Stockholm Conference on Electron Microscopy," p. 353, 1956.
5. TALBOT, J. H., "A method of determining the distribution of crystalline substances in electron microscope specimens." Paper presented at the Annual Conference of the South African Institute of Physics, July 1957 (to be published).
6. SCOTT, ROBERT G., "Structure of spherulites as revealed by selected area electron diffraction and electron microscopy." *J. Applied Physics*, **28**, 1089 (Oct. 1957).

J. H. TALBOT

SNOW CRYSTAL NUCLEI

Snow Crystals and Ice Crystals. In the field of physical meteorology, the electron microscope is used for the studies of nuclei of snow crystals, fog and clouds, of the surface nature and the growth of snow crystals, and of atmospheric aerosols. Snow crystals are solid precipitations which are observed on the earth's surface. They are born at a high altitude and grow into various forms while falling through the atmosphere. The factors (13) that influence snow crystal types are mainly air temperature and the humidity at which the crystal grows. The initial stage of a snow crystal can be seen in the cirrus cloud. This small crystal is called an ice crystal. In the process of formation of a snow crystal in the free atmosphere, the ice crystal is first formed. An ice crystal may be formed by the spontaneous transformation of a supercooled water droplet under the threshold temperature for nucleation, by the direct condensation of water vapor on a solid nucleus or as the result of natural and artificial seeding. After nucleation, ice crystals grow in an atmosphere of water vapor supersaturated with respect to ice.

Method of Making Specimens. *Snow crystal nuclei.* The difficulty of this experiment lies in making certain that the image obtained in the electron micrographs is the nucleus of snow. For this purpose, great care must be taken in locating the center of a snow crystal in the field of the mesh. Also, since there are many aerosols in the free atmosphere, it is desirable to choose a spot where the natural dust is at a minimum.

This writer undertook research in Hokkaido and in Upper Michigan where the aerosols were at a minimum in the midwinter. The specimens of snow-crystal nuclei for the electron microscope were prepared in an igloo, i.e., a snow cavern made for this purpose. The temperature in the igloo was between −5 and −15°C, and snow crystals could be handled without any fear of melting. A long and slender wooden piece resembling a match stick was made and broken into two pieces. The whisks of the broken end were convenient for picking up a snow-crystal without melting it because of the thermal insulation of the stick.

When the central part of a snow crystal is examined under an ordinary microscope, it is usually seen as a tiny ice crystal of a stellar crystal with an hexagonal or small stellar pattern having a diameter of about 30 μ, in the case of a hexagonal plate type. These central patterns are called the central portion of the snow crystal in this article. Since the mean diameter of the central portion was 20 μ or 30 μ, this central portion could be arranged in a void of the mesh. In the case of snowfalls not accompanied by strong wind, snow crystals fell into the igloo through a window opened in the ceiling of the snow cavern. They were received on a clean glass plate. Then a snow crystal was picked up and put on a mesh which was covered with collodion film. It was important to observe the mode of sublimation of snow crystals to see whether the supposed nucleus could be expected to remain on the collodion film without displacement. Successive stages of sublimation of specimen crystals were taken through a microscope with a magnification factor of about 60. A snow crystal begins to evaporate by sublimation from the tips of the crystal, and the thicker central portion of the crystal remains to the last stage without marked displacement, as shown in Fig. 1. It takes about 10 minutes for a small crystal to vanish by sublimation. The snow crystal, thus arranged on the collodion film, was kept in a desiccator in the igloo. In this condition the snow sublimated, leaving the nucleus on the collodion film. It was concluded that the nucleus remains safely on the collodion film of the mesh. The central portion which vanished in the last stage of the optical micrograph could be observed through an electron microscope, and the center nucleus pattern could be taken in an electron micrograph.

The nuclei (9, 16, 21) of cloud and fog are prepared in a similar method. They are collected on a collodion film of the mesh by the use of an impactor (5). Millipore (2, 10) filters also are used to identify atmospheric particles of micron size.

Replicas of Snow Crystals. Replicas of snow crystals for electron microscopy are made by using 0.2–0.01 per cent solution of Formvar (18) dissolved in ethylene dichloride. Snow crystals are received on a piece of black velvet, then a suitable crystal is picked up and put on a mesh. The snow crystal is kept in a cold chamber at $-20°C$ and is gradually evaporated by sublimation from the crystal surface. At the midpoint of the evaporation, the crystal surface is coated with 0.1 per cent "Formvar" solution. The replica film is not peeled off from the mesh, but it is used *in situ*. The shadowing is done in a vacuum vessel by evaporating chromium to the top surface of the replica with a suitable angle.

Fig. 2 shows a center nucleus and etched surface (12, 14) of a natural snow crystal. The shape of the snow crystal is an hexagonal plate with dendritic branches. The nucleus is 3.5 μ in the largest extension. The rounded pattern around the nucleus is the image of the center of the crystal. The diameter of this rounded pattern is 8 μ. Numerous

FIG. 1. Sublimation of a snow crystal on a mesh.

255

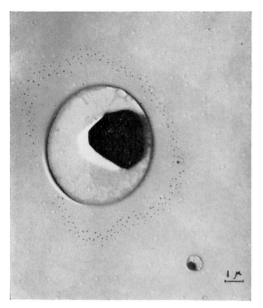

FIG. 2. A center nucleus and the etched surface of a snow crystal.

minute crystals of cubic nature are observed outside the rounded pattern.

Replicas of Ice Crystals. Silver iodide particles become active as nuclei of ice crystals. The particles are produced in the laboratory by evaporating silver iodide on an electric hot wire. The particles are then introduced into an undercooled cloud at a temperature below $-4°C$ (17, 20). Small ice crystals are formed soon after the seeding. The meshes of the specimen are covered with collodion film and are arranged on a clean glass slide. Just before the replicas are made, each mesh is covered with a droplet of "Formvar" solution. The meshes are exposed to the falling

crystals to collect samples (6, 11), or the ice crystals are collected on a mesh by the use of an impactor. Then the specimens are kept in the cold box for several hours while the solvent and the crystals evaporate. The solution for preparation used is about 0.01 per cent "Formvar" in ethylene dichloride.

In general, a solid particle can be seen at the center of the crystal replica by the use of an electron microscope. The result of the particle examined by the electron diffraction method shows the Debye-Scherrer rings due to AgI and Ag[4]. Silver is produced by decomposition of silver iodide as the result of electron bombardment.

Center Nucleus and Condensation Nuclei of a Snow Crystal. It was found that a relatively large, solid nucleus (4, 7, 8, 15) always exists at the central portion of the crystal, with innumerable minute nuclei observed in the remainder of the crystal. The former is called "center nucleus" and the latter are called "condensation nuclei" in this article. The material of the center nuclei was estimated from the shape by comparing it with the electron micrographs of known substances or by observing specimen changes (3, 21) due to electron bombardment in the electron microscope. Better estimation was obtained from electron diffraction patterns.

Fig. 3a shows a dendritic snow crystal. After sublimation, a solid particle remained at the position where the crystal center vanished by sublimation, as shown in Fig. 3b. Many small particles were found around

FIG. 3. Dendritic snow crystal and the nucleus.

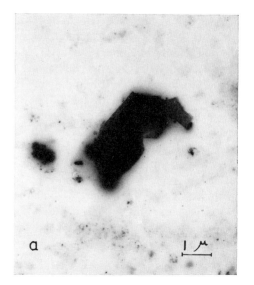

FIG. 4. A nucleus and the electron-diffraction pattern.

the center nucleus. The particles had been in the branch of the snow crystal. The particle of 4 μ diameter in Fig. 3c is the nucleus of this snow crystal. The nucleus consists of two kinds of materials which are divided into two parts, upper and lower, as shown in Fig. 3c. The shape and electron diffraction pattern of the lower part of the nucleus is similar to an attapulgite, and the upper part is similar to kaolinite. They are a kind of clay mineral which is of wide distribution. Fig. 4a shows the center nucleus of a dendritic snow crystal. The nucleus is a thin hexagonal crystal. The shape is similar to kaolinite, whose largest extent of the nucleus is 4 μ. Many minute substances are seen around the nucleus; some of them are found to be soluble in water. The electron diffraction pattern of the nucleus in Fig. 4b shows an hexagonal cross grating which is expected to be obtained when the direction of the incident beam is normal to the base plane of kaolinite, a clay mineral.

The size of the condensation nuclei lies between 0.01 and 0.5 μ, and it seems that there are two kinds of this nuclei. Fig. 5 shows this point clearly. A frequency curve the size of condensation nuclei has been made

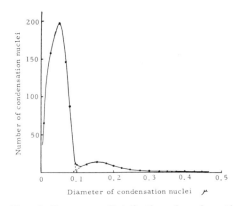

FIG. 5. Frequency distribution of condensation nuclei.

from 1200 data obtained from four electron micrographs. One sees clearly two kinds of condensation nuclei, the most frequent diameter of the smaller kind being 0.05 μ, as compared with 0.15 μ for the larger kind. The concentration of condensation nuclei is larger in thick-rimmed crystals than in thin crystals, and also influences the concentration of air pollution in the atmosphere in which the snow crystal grows and through which it passes.

The Center Nucleus Substance. A snow crystal is formed on a nucleus by sublimation

257

of water vapor in the undercooled cloud. The nucleus is an aerosol in the atmosphere. Aerosols consist of many kinds of materials from various sources: from the ground, from the ocean, from air pollution as a result of human activities and from outer space (micro-meteorites) (1, 19).

The nuclei of snow crystals can be classified as soil particles, hygroscopic particles, combustion products, micro-organisms and unknown materials. The last classification shows that some nuclei were not identifiable in this research. Table 1 shows the comparison of snow crystal nuclei observed in Hokkaido, Honshu and Upper Michigan. Some differences are found, depending on the meteorological conditions or the locations where the specimens have been collected, in the percentage of nuclei substance among Hokkaido, Honshu and Upper Michigan. The data concerning snow-crystal nuclei in Honshu agree well with that of Upper Michigan. Soil particle nuclei occupied 57 per cent in Hokkaido, 87 per cent in Upper Michigan. There is a smaller percentage of hygroscopic nuclei in Upper Michigan than in Hokkaido. All hygroscopic nuclei in Upper Michigan

were potassium chloride, but in Hokkaido most were sea salt particles; the remainder were potassium chloride. This is because Upper Michigan is located far from the ocean, Honshu is a large island, but Hokkaido is a relatively small island. The percentage of combustion products or carbon particles is smaller for Upper Michigan than for Hokkaido. Micro-organisms, that is bacteria, are not found in Upper Michigan. In Hokkaido five per cent of the center nucleus was unobservable; in Upper Michigan one per cent was unobservable. These facts show that the nuclei in the form of snow crystals are mainly soil particles.

Acknowledgments. The investigation in Upper Michigan was conducted as a part of Ice Nucleation Research under a grant from the National Science Foundation at the University of Chicago. The writer is much indebted to Drs. H. R. Byers, R. R. Braham, Jr. and U. Nakaya, to Miss B. J. Tufts and to The Snow Ice and Permafrost Research Establishment, U. S. Army Corps of Engineers.

TABLE 1. THE COMPARISON OF SNOW CRYSTAL NUCLEI WERE OBSERVED AT HOKKAIDO AND HONSHU, JAPAN AND UPPER MICHIGAN, U. S. A.

Probable material	Hokkaido, Japan 1948–1956		Honshu, Japan Isono[4]		Upper Michigan, U.S.A. 1959	
	Number	%	Number	%	Number	%
Soil particle	176	57	46	88	235	87
Hygroscopic particle	57	19	0	0	2	1
Combustion product	26	8	2	4	6	2
Micro-organism	3	1	0	0	0	0
Unknown material	30	10	4	8	25	9
Not observed	15	5	0	0	3	1
Total	307	100	52	100	271	100

REFERENCES

1. BOWEN, E. G., "The influence of meteoritic dust on rain," *Austral. J. Phys.*, **6**, 490–497 (1953).
2. BYERS, H. R., SIEVERS, J. R., AND TUFTS, B. J., "Distribution in the atmosphere of certain particles capable of serving as condensation. Artificial stimulation of rain." H. Weickman (ed.), Pergamon Press, New York, pp. 47–72, 1955.
3. BURTON, E. F., SENNETT, R. S., AND ELLIS, S. G., "Specimen changes due to electron bombardment in the electron microscope," *Nature*, **160**, 565 (1947).
4. ISONO, K., "Microphysical processes in precipitation mechanism," *Japanese Journal of Geophysics*, 1-57 (1959).
5. JUNGE, C., "Die Rolle der aerosole und der gasformigen beimengungen der luft in spurenstoffhanshalt der troposhare." *Tellus*, **5**, 1–26 (1953).
6. KOENIG, L. R., "The chemical identification of silver iodide ice nuclei." Technical Note, No. 19. Dept. of Meteor., Univ. of Chicago, 1959.
7. KUMAI, M., "Electron-microscope study of snow-crystal nuclei." *J. Meteor.*, **8**, 151–156 (1951).

8. KUMAI, M., "Electron-microscope study of snow-crystal nucli II." *Geofisica pura e applicata-Milano*, **36**, 169–181 (1957).

9. KUROIWA, D., "Electron-microscope study of atmospheric nuclei." T. Hori (ed.) "Studies on fog," Sapporo, pp. 349–382 (1953).

10. LODGE, J. P., "Analysis of micron-sized particles." *Anal. Chem.*, **26**, 1829–1831 (1954).

11. MARUYAMA, H., "Electron-microscope study of the ice crystal nuclei." *Meterology and Geophysics, Tokyo*, **7**, 251–266 (1956).

12. MUGURUMA, J. AND HIGUCHI, K., "On the etch pits of snow crystals," *J. Meteor. Soci. of Japan. Ser. II.* **37**, 71–75 (1959).

13. NAKAYA, U., "The formation of ice crystals." Compendium of Meterology, American Metero. Soc., pp. 207–220 (1951).

14. NAKAYA, U., "Surface nature of ice crystals," in "Artificial Stimulation of rain," H. Weickman (ed.) Pergamon Press, New York, pp. 386–389, 1955.

15. NAKAYA, U. AND KUMAI, M., "Electron-microscope study of center nuclei of snow crystals III. *J. Meteor. Soci. Japan*, 75th anniversary volume, pp. 49–51, 1957.

16. OGIWARA, S. AND OKITA, T., "Electron-microscope study of cloud and fog nuclei," *Tellus*, **4**, pp. 233–240 (1952).

17. SCHAEFER, V. J., "The formation of ice crystals in the laboratory and the atmosphere," *Chem. Rev.* **44**, 291–320 (1949).

18. SCHAEFER, V. J., AND HARKER, D., "Surface replicas for use in the electron microscope," *J. Applied Phys.* **13**, 427–433 (1942).

19. SCHAEFER, V. J., "The question of meteoritic dust in the atmosphere," in "Artificial stimulation of rain," H. Weickman (ed.) Pergamon Press, New York, pp. 18–23, 1955.

20. VONNEGUT, B., "Nucleation of ice formation by AgI particles." Final Rep. No. RG 140, Gen. Elec. Res. Labs., pp. 26–34, 1948.

21. YAMAMOTO, G. AND OHTAKE, T., "Electron microscope study of cloud and fog nuclei," *Science Report. Tohoku Univ. Ser. 5 Geophys.*, **5**, 141–159, 1953.

MOTOI KUMAI

SPECIAL METHODS

One of the aims of electron microscopy is to observe the arrangement of constituent atoms and molecules of materials. Recent improvement in the electron microscope has made it possible to observe the lattice image of crystals of which spacing is less than 10 A. Müller, using the field emission type electron microscope, has succeeded in observing directly the arrangement of atoms such as W, Re, etc. Besides the problem of high resolution, various special methods for electron microscopic observation have been tried to develop the fields of its application. In this chapter some of these special methods, which have been studied mainly in Japan, are introduced and their constructions, performances and experimental results are briefly described. They are as follows:

(1) Reflection method
(2) Specimen cooling method
(3) Specimen heating method
(4) Gas reaction method

Reflection Method

In observing solid surfaces by the transmission electron microscope, we usually use the replica film which is reprinted from the surface structure of the solid. Then, a method for direct observation of solid surfaces is naturally desired, just as for an optical microscope for metallurgy. There are two methods in the deflecting mechanism of the electron beam in a reflection microscope: (1) makes the electron beam strike the specimen by mechanically inclining the electron gun and condenser lens at any desired angle; the other (2, 3) makes the electron beam strike the specimen by using two pairs of deflecting coils without inclination of the illuminating system. This article describes the latter.

Construction of Reflection Electron Microscope. Fig. 1 shows the principle of the reflection device for JEM-5Y universal electron microscope and Fig. 2 the specimen chamber equipped with this device. For changing the incident angle β, two pairs of deflecting coils are inserted between the condenser lens and the specimen chamber as shown in Fig. 1. The electrons emitted from the electron gun are deflected from the optical axis by the upper pair and again to the specimen by the lower pair. It is possible to

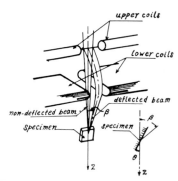

FIG. 1. Principle of reflection method.

FIG. 2. JEM-5Y Electron microscope equipped with reflection device.

change the angle β to any angle between 0° and 30°. The reflection specimen may be tilted to any angle between 0° and 30° from the lens axis, about an axis perpendicular to the plane of incidence, and may be rotated in its own surface plane, i.e., azimuthal plane. It is helpful to change the azimuthal angle for the reflection method, because many observations from several directions are needed to give a perfect interpretation of the image obtained. The specimen-shifting mechanism for the two horizontal directions

is the same as that for general use of the transmission type.

In the reflection electron microscope, the electrons striking the specimen surface at a small angle are scattered to the angle θ and then the scattered electrons are imaged. When the angle θ becomes larger, the intensity of the image is much lower; when the angle θ is smaller, the distortion of the image is more marked. The relation between the angle θ and the distortion of the image is shown in Fig. 3. In the present device, as an angle θ larger than 20° is used, distortion of the image can be considerably reduced. Because of its large chromatic aberration, however, the resolution of reflection is less than that of transmission.

On the other hand this method has two features. The change of the specimen at high temperature can be directly observed by using a specimen-heating device at the same time. It is also possible to obtain the electron diffraction pattern and microscopic image from almost the same area of the specimen. In the reflection method, however, it is difficult to obtain the diffraction pattern of the

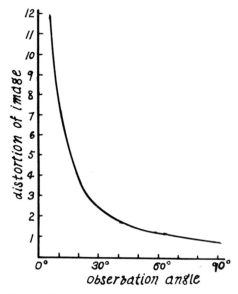

FIG. 3. Relation between image distortion and observation angle.

selected area corresponding completely to the reflection image except in some special cases, because in electron diffraction the incident angle of the electron beam to the specimen is less than 1°.

Considerations on Resolution. In general the resolution of the electron microscope is determined mainly by spherical and chromatic aberrations, astigmatism and diffraction. In the reflection electron microscope, chromatic aberration is comparatively great because of the larger amount of inelastic scattering suffered by an electron beam. Therefore, it is considered that chromatic aberration is mainly responsible for limiting the resolution obtainable in the reflection microscope.

Here, the order of magnitude of the resolution is estimated which is expected in a direction perpendicular to the plane of incidence of the electron beam. Neglecting all aberrations except chromatic, we may write:

$$\delta_\perp = \alpha \cdot f \cdot \frac{\Delta V}{V} \qquad (1)$$

where $\delta_\perp$ is the radius of the disc of confusion in a plane perpendicular to the plane of incidence due to chromatic aberration, α the semi-angular aperture, f the focal length of the objective, V the accelerating voltage and ΔV the average energy loss of electrons scattered from the specimen. The variations in the high tension supply voltage and excitation current in the objective lens being much smaller compared with energy losses due to scattering at the specimen, their effects are neglected in equation (1). According to Kushnir et al., ΔV is $100V$ when the accelerating voltage is 80 kV. Thus, $\Delta V/V = \frac{1}{800}$. Putting $\alpha \cong 3 \times 10^{-3}$ rad. and $f \cong 5$ mm, we can find:

$$\delta_\perp \cong 190 \text{ A}$$

The resolution in a direction in the plane of incidence will be worse by a factor $1/\sin \theta$, i.e., for $\theta = 6°$, $\delta_\parallel \cong 2000$ A and for $\theta = 30°$, $\delta_\parallel \cong 400$ A.

To achieve higher resolution, it is necessary for the objective aperture to be smaller. For example, to obtain a resolution better than 100 A, it is estimated that the objective aperture about 10 μ would be required. But by using such a small aperture, it is doubtful whether the intensity of the image would be adequate for precise focusing at high magnification.

Menter has obtained the resolution better than 400 A using a 30 μ aperture in electron microscope with a focal length somewhat longer than that in the above calculation.

Application of Reflection Device. Fig. 4 is a reflection image of pearlite structure. (a) is taken at $\theta = 8°$ and (b) at $\theta = 30°$. It is found that the distortion of the image is reduced by increasing the observation angle. Fig. 5 shows the reflection image of martensite structure and Fig. 6 the reflection image of pearlite structure of drawn high carbon steel. They were taken at 30°.

Studies by a reflection method have not so far given any further information to that obtained by the replica method, but in future

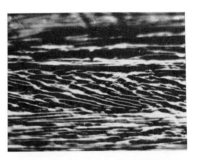

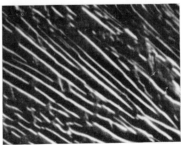

Fig. 4. Reflection image of pearlite (above) $\theta = 8°$, (below) $\theta = 30°$.

FIG. 5. Reflection image of martensite $\theta = 30°$.

FIG. 6. Reflection image of pearlite of drawn high carbon steel $\theta = 30°$.

its applications may be developed by attainment to its higher resolution and by using a specimen heating or gas reaction method.

Specimen Cooling Method

In electron microscope the specimen must be irradiated by electron beams in the vacuum. Therefore, in the ordinary method

it is impossible to study the substance of high vapor pressure, that of low melting point or organic substances easily damaged by electron irradiation. Cooling of the specimen to a large extent can prevent these effects and develop the field of its application. This is the best advantage in specimen cooling methods.

Construction and Performance of Specimen-Cooling Device. The specimen cooling device previously reported (5) had many unsatisfactory points in its construction and was not suitable for obtaining high resolution. A new specimen cooling device has since been constructed (Figure 7) (6) for JEM-5Y electron microscope. A is the pouring port of refrigerant, B the refrigerant reservoir with capacity of about 30 cc and E the draught port. The refrigerant reservoir B, the pouring port A and the draught port E are connected to each other by sylphon bellows C and D. The draught port E makes it easy to pour the refrigerant into the reservoir. The specimen holder F is attached to the center of the round porcelain H, which is set up to the specimen shifter I. The temperature is measured by copper-constantan thermocouple J fixed on the specimen holder F. The heater K is used to control the temperature of the specimen.

To set up this device with JEM-5Y, the refrigerant reservoir is kept at the position shown by the dotted line, by rotating the pinion N with the lever M. Then the whole

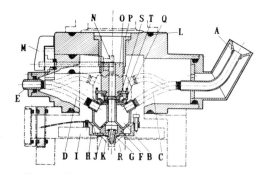

FIG. 7. Construction of new type specimen cooling device.

Fig. 8. Cu-Phthalocyanine taken at $-50°C$, spacing $12.5°A$.

device is inserted into the round port located at the head of the specimen chamber. When the specimen is to be exchanged, the reservoir is elevated in the same way. Then the specimen cartridge G is moved in and out independently through another chamber for pre-evacuation. The specimen cartridge can be inserted deep in the field of the objective lens R. In order to cool the specimen, the refrigerant reservoir is lowered to contact the specimen holder F. At the lowest position the reservoir is pushed down to the specimen holder by the release of spring S and the elongation of sylphon bellows C and D.

The specimen-shifting mechanism is just the same as that for general use of electron microscope and can control the specimen position as fine as 0.1μ. When the reservoir was filled with liquid oxygen, the temperature of the specimen holder reached to $-160°C$. This temperature could be obtained within 15–20 min, using about 150 cc of liquid oxygen.

The resolution obtained by using this device is measured by copper phthalocyanine. Fig. 8 shows the lattice image of spacing 12.5 A of this specimen taken at $-50°C$.

(7). The performance of this device has proved very satisfactory.

Contamination of Specimen. One of the principal difficulties of the specimen-cooling device is the contamination of specimen due to materials condensing from residual vapors. In the conventional vacuum of 5×10^{-4} to 1×10^{-5} mm Hg, condensed materials increased remarkably below $-80°C$ to $-100°C$ and covered the specimen surface within a few minutes. Fig. 9 shows an electron micrograph and diffraction pattern of ice condensed on collodion film at $-80°C$ from residual vapor pressure of 1×10^{-4} mm Hg. This proves that the larger part of the residual vapors is usually water vapor.

Contamination of another nature has been observed in electron microscopic experi-

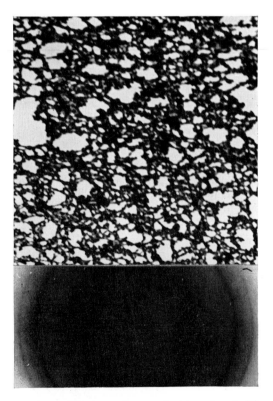

Fig. 9. Electron micrograph (above) and diffraction pattern (below) of ice condensed on collodion film.

263

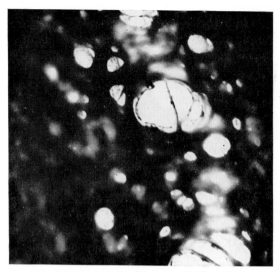

FIG. 10. Contamination on collodion film produced by electron irradiation.

ments. Fig. 10 shows contamination on collodion films produced by electron irradiation for several minutes at liquid nitrogen temperature in conventional vacuum of the order of 1×10^{-4} mm Hg. This micrograph was taken after the films were rewarmed to 200°C. It is considered that this contamination is caused by electron irradiation, because the amount of deposit depends on dosage of electron irradiation. It is very likely that this contamination is a product of hydrocarbon vapor decomposed by electrons, which is observed in ordinary electron microscope.

In order to reduce contaminations, we must improve the working vacuum as far as possible. First, the inside walls of all parts of the apparatus are thoroughly cleaned, warmed and baked up to 70° to 150°C in the dryer, before assembly. Photographic plates were pre-evacuated in another vacuum system. When the vacuum was broken, well-dried air was introduced into the apparatus. Then, using a 4-inch oil diffusion pump backed by a phosphorus pentoxide trap and a 150 l/min oil rotary pump, the vacuum of the order of 1 to 2×10^{-5} mm Hg could be obtained after half an hour. The refrigerant was poured into the reservoir without inserting the specimen. At this stage the vacuum of the specimen chamber became about 1 to 2×10^{-6} mm Hg. Finally, after being bombarded by the electron beam for several minutes, the specimen was put into the apparatus.

This procedure efficiently reduced contaminations. Fig. 11 shows a pair of electron micrographs of a collodion film of about 400 A thick; (a) taken before cooling and (b) at liquid nitrogen temperature after a continual observation of 45 min. There is no appreciable change in the contrast between the film itself and its holes. This proved that contaminations were completely eliminated.

Application of Specimen Cooling Device. *Study of Mercury* (5): This study concerned the following points: (a) The char-

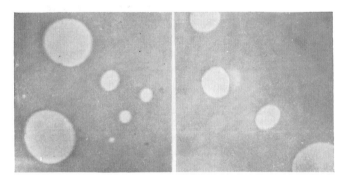

FIG. 11. Collodion film about 400°A thick. (left) at room temperature before cooling. (right) after 45 minute continual observation at liquid nitrogen temperature.

acteristic crystal growth "whiskers" suggested by Sears (8), and (b) the temperature rise of the specimen caused by electron irradiation, which it was hoped could be checked by observing the liquid-solid phase transition. Fig. 12 (a) shows hair-like crystals formed by condensing mercury vapor at about −100°C. (b) was taken two minutes after (a). The crystal indicated by the arrow completed its growth within a fraction of a second. Fig. 13 (a) shows a droplet of liquid mercury. This droplet was formed at −39° to −38°C by heating the solid state crystal. This droplet of liquid mercury was poligonized through crystallization at about −100°C as shown in (b).

Study of Natural Cellulose Fiber (9). The atomic structures of an organic substance like cellulose fiber are so liable to be damaged by irradiation of electron beams that the diffraction patterns can be observed for only a very short time. We can avoid this difficulty by using a method of cooling the specimen. Fig. 14 reproduces two pairs of electron micrographs and diffraction patterns of Valonia microfibril taken by Boersch-le Poole's method; (a) and (b) were taken without cooling and (c) and (d) by cooling the specimen to −40°C. This specimen is composed of two sheets of microfibril having fiber axes along the directions indicated by the arrows. In the electron diffraction patterns of Valonia microfibril cooled to −100°C taken by Hilliers method, a very large number of reflections having fairly good resolution up to as high as tenth layer line has been observed. By analyzing these patterns, the new structure different from that proposed by Meyer and Misch (10) for cellulose I has been obtained.

Specimen-Heating Method

The specimen heating method makes it possible to observe continuously the change of a specimen at high temperature, by attaching a heating furnace of a specimen to ordinary electron microscope. This method is divided into two parts: (1) in which a heating device with a small electric furnace is used for both reflection and transmission (11, 12) and (2) in which the temperature

FIG. 12. Hair-like crystals of mercury. (above) Hair-like crystalso frmed by condensing mercury vapor at about −100°C. (below) Two minutes after picture above.

FIG. 13. Mercury droplet. (above) Liquid state. (below) Solid state, crystallized at about −100°C.

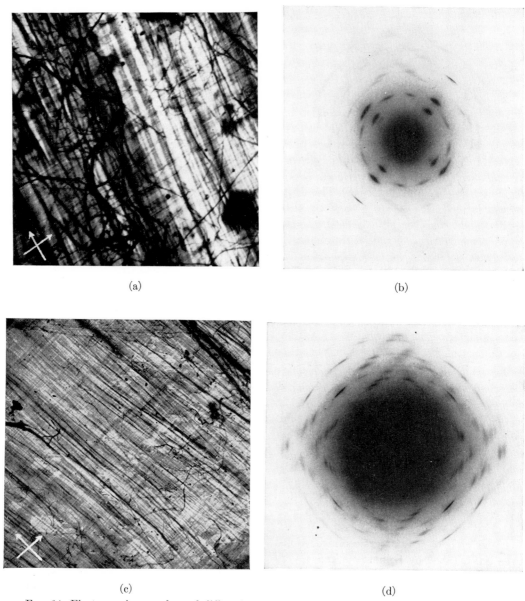

(a)

(b)

(c)

(d)

Fɪɢ. 14. Electron micrographs and diffraction patterns of Valonia microfibril: (a) and (b) without cooling; (c) and (d) cooled to −40°C.

of metallic thin wires as the specimen can be elevated by passing the electric current directly through them (13). In the latter case, only 0.6 to 6 watts is sufficient to raise the temperature of the specimen from 700°C to 3,000°C and some gas, when necessary for the chemical reaction with the specimen, can be introduced. Here, only the former in which we have experience, is described.

Construction and Performance of Specimen-Heating Device. Fig. 15 shows the construction of the transmission type of the new specimen heating device (12) for JEM-5Y electron microscope and Fig. 16

the outside view of it. A is a connecting ring for setting this device on to the specimen shifting mechanism of ordinary type electron microscope. B shows a ring-shaped insulator of porcelain. C, D and E are the outside walls of the furnace, which are made of porcelain. F is a heater of Mo-wire. G is an inside wall of the furnace, made of Mo-sheet. The specimen cartridge, composed of Mo and Porcelain I, can be put into and taken out of the furnace, which is heated beforehand, through another chamber for pre-evacuation. L is used as a guide plate, when the cartridge is inserted in the furnace. The temperature of the specimen is measured by Pt - Pt,Rh thermocouple mounted to G. To avoid charging due to electron irradiation, the outer surface of the porcelain is covered with evaporated carbon. The pole piece of the objective lens is so well protector O that it cannot be damaged by heating.

Reflection type of the specimen heating device is also made according to the same design with the only exception that it is equipped with a mechanism by which the glancing angle of the specimen is arbitrarily changeable.

A battery is employed as power source and the specimen temperature reached up to 1,000°C at about 14 V, 8 amp. The drift of the specimen due to thermal expansion from room temperature to 1,000°C was about 0.2 mm. This drift can be easily controlled, as the specimen-shifting mechanism is the same as that of ordinary electron microscope. The difference between the temperature of the specimen and that indicated by a meter was about 50°C at about 600°C, from the test of melting point of Al film.

The resolution obtained with this device in operation was determined by measuring the distances of two evaporated particles of Pt-Pd. Fig. 17 shows two serial micrographs taken with the specimen heated at 300°C. The resolving power is better than 30 Å.

This proved that such a high resolution is also obtainable at high temperature.

Application of Specimen-Heating Device. One example of its application is shown. Evaporated thin films of Al-Cu (50–50) alloy have been used as the specimen

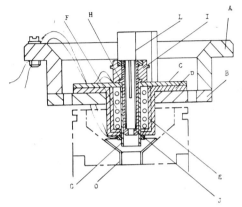

Fig. 15. Construction of new specimen heating device, transmission type.

Fig. 16. Out-side view of specimen heating device.

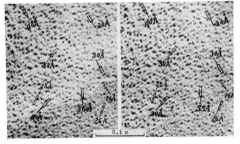

Fig. 17. Evaporated particles of Pt-Pd, heated at 300°C.

(14). The transformation $CuAl_2 \rightarrow CuAl \rightarrow Cu_9Al_4 \rightarrow Cu_3Al$ has been confirmed by selected area diffraction. Fig. 18 shows some of these processes:

(a) corresponds to $\kappa + \theta$ phases in the phase diagram of this alloy. The microscopic image is structureless and the diffraction pattern shows the structure of a face-centered cubic lattice corresponding to κ-phase. The diffuse ring superposed on (200) ring of κ-phase suggests the existence of θ-phase.

(b) shows η-phase (CuAl) which was taken at 400°C, 100 min after (a). It is observed that the single crystal of η-phase

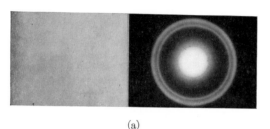

(a)

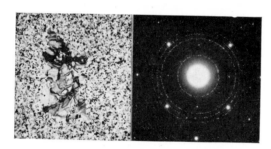

(b)

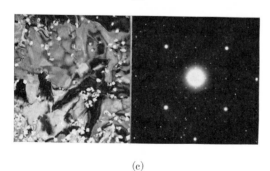

(c)

FIG. 18. Transformation of Al-Cu alloy due to heating in vacuum. (a) Room temperature $k + \theta$-phases; (b) 400°C η-phase; (c) 450° C γ-phase.

about 1 μ came out of the micro-grain of θ-phase. The diffraction pattern shows the structure of CsCl type.

(c) shows γ-phase (Cu_9Al_4) which was taken at 450°C, 120 min after (a). In the image, conspicuous change was not observed except that the single crystal plate has grown further. The orientations of γ-phase relative to η-phase are as follows:

(i) $(114)_\gamma // (110)_\eta,$ $[\bar{1}10]_\gamma // [\bar{1}10]_\eta$

(ii) $(110)_\gamma // (110)_\eta,$ $[\bar{1}10]_\gamma // [\bar{1}10]_\eta$

The diagram here shows the latter orientation.

Gas Reaction Method

Gas reaction method makes it possible to observe continuously the process of chemical reaction of a specimen. The construction of this device is almost the same as that of specimen heating device except the mechanism of gas inlet.

Construction. Fig. 19 shows the construction of the specimen chamber to which the old type gas reaction device (15) is attached. The diaphragm (1) faced to the lower side of the condenser lens is of clearance of about 0.1 mmϕ and its position can be adjusted outside the vacuum by two pairs of rods (2) which are placed perpendicular to one another. The diaphragm (3) is of clearance of about 0.2 mmϕ and set tightly into the clearance of the pole piece of the objective lens. The diaphragms (1) and (3) are used for preventing diffusion of gas from the specimen chamber. Reaction gas in the

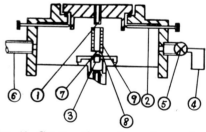

FIG. 19. Construction of specimen chamber equipped with old type gas reaction device.

reservoir (4) is introduced through the leak valve (5) into the specimen chamber and evacuated through outlet (6) on the occasion of reaction with a specimen. The gas pressure in the specimen chamber is able to be controlled from about 10^{-4} to 1 mm Hg and is measured by a manometer and McLeod gauge. A specimen can be heated up to 1,000°C from the room temperature by the heating device, which is the same as the old type; (9) is the heating coil and (8) is the thermocouple for measuring the specimen temperature.

When the electron beam passes through the atmosphere of gas, it is scattered by the gas molecules. Here it is significant to introduce the concept of mass thickness into the discussion on the interaction of electrons with the gas molecules. When the present device is filled with 1 mm Hg of air, the mass thickness is 3×10^{-6} g/cm^2 and when with 1 mm Hg of hydrogen, it is 2×10^{-7} g/cm^2. (In the present device the path length that electron passes through in the gas atmosphere is 2 cm.) Since the mass thickness of copper film with thickness of 300 A is 2.7×10^{-6} g/cm^2, that of gas molecules in the present device is as small as one tenth that of the copper film of 300 A. Accordingly, the gas pressure can theoretically be raised. When the gas pressure in the device is raised more than 1 mm Hg, however, high tension discharge occurs at the electron gun. To prevent leakage from the specimen chamber, the diaphragm must be doubled and evacuated separately.

Taking the above into consideration, a new type of gas reaction device (16) has been constructed (Fig. 20). Since its performance has been tested, only its construction is mentioned here: (1) is inlet of gas, (2) gas reaction chamber and (3) a specimen. The gas diffused through diaphragm (4) is evacuated through the evacuation chamber (5) and (6), and gas diffused through diaphragm (7) is evacuated by the evacuation system of the electron microscope. The specimen shifting mechanism of this device is the same as that for general use of electron microscope.

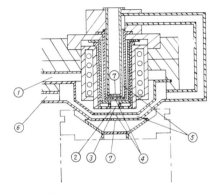

Fig. 20. Construction of new type gas reaction device.

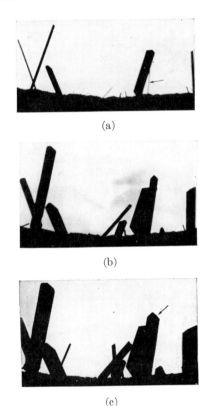

(a)

(b)

(c)

Fig. 21. Crystal growth of copper sulfide in an atmosphere of 10^{-2} mm Hg. (top) at 300°C; (center) at 350°C. 5 min. after above; (bottom) at 400°C, 15 min. after center.

Application of Gas Reaction Device.

One example of its applications of the old type device is shown (17). Copper mesh is used as a specimen and hydrogen sulfide as reaction gas. Though hydrogen sulfide is a very corrosive gas, the furnace and the surfaces of the pole piece were not remarkably corroded in the gas atmosphere of 10^{-3} to 10^{-1} mm Hg at temperatures up to 500°C. At 1 mm Hg, however, the conduction wires of copper and the sylphon bellows which give allowance for the specimen shifting, were covered by corrosion layers after a few hours' operation at about 500°C.

Fig. 21 shows some stages of the crystal growth of copper sulfide in an atmosphere of 10^{-2} mm Hg; (a) was taken at 300°C, (b) at 350°C, 5 min after (a) and (c) at 400°C, 15 min after (b). In (a), a needle crystal below 0.1 μ in breadth, marked by an arrow, has grown to a finite length within a part of one second. Then, the axial growth became so slow that it could hardly be observed on the screen, whereas a growth perpendicular to the axial direction began. In (c), the crystal, marked by an arrow, has grown to 1 μ in breadth.

REFERENCES

1. BORRIES, B. VON, JANZEN, S., *VDI-Zeitschrift.*, **85**, 207 (1941).
2. ITO, K., ITO, T., AND WATANABE, M., *J. Electron Microscopy, Jap.*, **2**, 10 (1954).
3. ITO, K., ITO, T., AOTSU, T., AND MIYAMAE, T., *J. Electron Microscopy, Jap.*, **5**, 3 (1957).
4. MENTER, J. W., *J. Inst. Met.*, **81**, 163 (1952).
5. HONJO, G., KITAMURA, N., SHIMAOKA, K., AND MIHAMA, K., *J. Phys. Soc. Jap.*, **11**, 527 (1956).
6. WATANABE, M., OKAZAKI, I., HONJO, G., AND MIHAMA, K., "Proc. 4th Int. Conf. Elect. Micros.," Berlin (1958).
7. WATANABE, M., OKAZAKI, I., AND HONJO, G., (unpublished).
8. SEARS, G. W., *Acta Metal.*, **1**, 457 (1953); **3**, 361 (1955).
9. HONJO, G. AND WATANABE, M., *Nature*, **181**, 326 (1958).
10. MEYER, K. H. AND MISCH, L., *Helv. Chem. Acta*, **20**, 232 (1937).
11. ITO, K., ITO, T., AND WATANABE, M., "Proc.
3rd Int. Conf. Elect. Micros., London," 658 (1954).
12. OKAZAKI, I., WATANABE, M., AND MIHAMA, K., "Proc. 4th Int. Conf. Elect. Micros.," Berlin (1958).
13. HASHIMOTO, H., TANAKA, K., AND YODA, E., *J. Electron Microscopy, Jap.*, **6**, 8 (1958).
14. TAKAHASHI, N. AND MIHAMA, K., *Acta Met.*, **5**, 159 (1957).
15. ITO, T. AND HIZIYA, K., *J. Electron Microscopy, Jap.*, **6**, 4 (1958).
16. ASHINUMA, K. AND WATANABE, M., (unpublished).
17. HIZIYA, K., HASHIMOTO, H., WATANABE, M., AND MIHAMA, K., "Proc. 4th Int. Conf. Elect. Micros.," Berlin (1958).

MASARU WATANABE
KAZUO ITO

SPECIMEN PREPARATION—SPECIAL TECHNIQUES AT LOS ALAMOS

A Modified Aluminum Pressing Replica Technique

Modifications of an aluminum pressing replica technique for metallic and other suitable surfaces, first introduced in Germany by Hunger and Seeliger, afford greater yield and wider applicability, which make the method considerably more effective. The necessary pressure within the die is produced by hydrostatic force, transmitted through a medium of hot liquid plastic in place of "cold-pressing" as before. In this way, sensitive surfaces can be replicated nondestructively. The method also permits simultaneous replication of both surfaces of any given specimen and/or similar multiple treatment of several samples in one operation. No additional apparatus is required for application, since the necessary routine equipment, such as metallurgical presses and dies found in most laboratories, may be used without alterations.

The modifications as described therefore extend application of this method to surface studies in powder metallurgy, metal-ceramics and related industries.

The technique entails the use of a standard laboratory metallurgical specimen press to produce the necessary pressure to form aluminum foil replicas. The pressure is transmitted through a liquid medium of molten plastic.

The loading of the mold is accomplished by the following successive steps:

1. Insert the bottom male die
2. Place a "Lucite" disc on the die
3. Several layers of cut-to-fit filter papers
4. One lead (Pb) foil
5. One thick aluminum (Al) foil
6. One thin aluminum (Al) foil
7. Specimen
8. Filter papers
9. "Lucite" disc
10. Insert upper male die

For multiple sample replication, the above steps 2 through 8 may be repeated up to full mold capacity.

For two-sided replication of a specimen the loading is repeated in reverse on the opposite side of the specimen.

Molding is accomplished by heating the thermoplastic to its melting point, with no pressure applied until this temperature is reached. Pressure is then applied evenly and continuously to maximum, and cooling commenced at once. The pressure is not released until the mold has cooled to room temperature.

The separating filter "circles" prevent contact of the plastic with the specimen and foils. There is, however, circumferential flow along the die edges, hence the finished molding must be separated mechanically.

The aluminum foils are then stripped carefully from the specimen to prevent the formation of strain lines in the foil itself.

Immediately after removal, the aluminum foils are anodized. The foil side bearing the replica and oxide film is then scribed in squares and stripped as usual by chemical means.

The mold components were chosen for the following reasons:

1. Solid discs of thermoplastic instead of molding powders are used in order to form a stable support for the foils and specimens and to alleviate the uneven melting conditions inherent in loosely packed porous powders.

2. The lead (Pb) foil is added only as mechanical backing for the multiple aluminum (Al) foils.

This technique as described permits high-speed, high-production rate of specimen replication.

Fractured surfaces which prevent stripping of routinely applied primary plastic coatings can also be successfully treated in this way.

Recent work has shown this method to be effective in preparing "cool" replicas of plutonium and its alloys by washing the Al foil replica several times in 10% HNO_3 before anodizing.

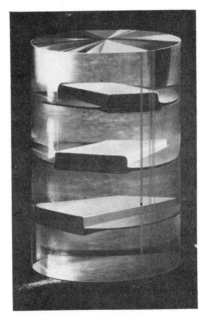

FIG. 1. Modified Al pressing. Composite molding. (Los Alamos Scientific Laboratory) GMX-1 GT-SITE

FIG. 2. Modified Al pressing. Fractured, unpoled BaTiO$_3$. 7,000×. (Los Alamos Scientific Laboratory) GMX-1 GT-SITE

Examples: Fig. 1: A Composite Molding
Fig. 2: Fractured Surface of unpoled BaTiO$_3$, 14,000×

J. H. BENDER AND E. H. KALMUS

Preparation of Aerosols

Fall-out particles from dust clouds, commonly called aerosols, may be prepared for observation with the electron microscope. Specimens are collected by means of various types of precipitators on membrane filters made from cellulose esters. During the process of dissolving this material in acetone, particles adhering to the filter surface are transferred to "Formvar"-coated specimen screens. Losses are negligible, residual filter background is eliminated and particles are clearly visualized for measuring.

Procedure:

1. Prepare "Formvar-" or carbon-coated specimen screens.

2. Cut membrane filters into small squares to fit the screens.

3. Place three supporting bridges made from coarse and fine brass mesh into a large Petri dish.

4. Load filter-screen combinations into marked compartments on bridge surfaces.

5. Fill Petri dish with acetone up to bridge level. Principle of "liquid film" action for dissolution of the filter material.

6. Make three solvent changes, washing 30 minutes each.

7. Cover dish during and in between steps.

8. After discarding last solvent change, transfer screens onto filter paper for drying over night under vacuum.

Examples: Figure 3. Bridge; Figure 4. UO$_2$ aerosol after transfer.

E. H. KALMUS

Dispersion of Aerosols

Ultrasonic dispersion techniques for carbon black and graphite particles, with the equipment available (100 KC to 1000 KC output), left much to be desired in effectively breaking up large agglomerates.

A simple method of producing artificially airborne particles was devised, for better over-all particle distribution; it involved using a large cardboard box and spraying the inside with "Krylon" to prevent contamination by cellulose fibers, sealing the

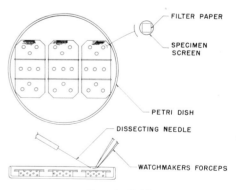

FIG. 3. Bridge.

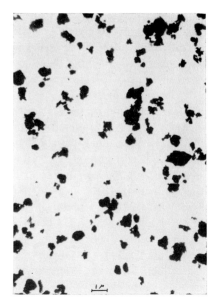

FIG. 4. UO₂ aerosol after transfer.

box, and cutting a small opening in the bottom to admit a microscope slide with "Formvar"-coated specimen screens.

Procedure for sample preparation:

A small amount of the sample is placed in an atomizer, the hand bulb removed and the atomizer attached to a compressed air line. The nozzle of the atomizer is inserted into the box opening and a short blast of air applied.

Immediately after, the coated screens are placed on the floor of the "cloud chamber" and the door is sealed. Settling times from 20 minutes up to several hours, according to particle size range desired, proved to be sufficient.

With this technique, although the agglomerates are not completely broken up, particles appear in preferential chain-type agglomeration with a good percentage of single layers evident; statistical counting, individual particle shape determinations as well as electronmicrography are thus facilitated.

Example: Figure 5 carbon black particles 74,000×.

J. H. BENDER AND J. D. STEELY

Sorting and Fractography of Particles

Particles in the size range of 400 to 325 mesh (37–44 mμ), of interest to powder metallurgists, are sometimes coated with a dissimilar material to enhance or change the basic physical properties and/or form alloys in the sintering process.

Since statistical counting of coated *vs.* uncoated particles and determination of the coating thickness were not feasible by standard E.M. techniques, the following method was developed:

Statistical counting may be accomplished optically by color difference at $\sim$1000 × on as-received powders using reflected, polarized, full-wave compensated light. Standard samples of the coating and base material are used for reference. Coating thickness may be determined in the following way:

1. Mix proportional amounts of particles and epoxy resin.

2. Cast this mixture in a "pencil-shaped" mold.

3. Cut thin sections from the cured casting with a biological microtome.

4. Direct stripping plastic replicas can then be taken from the *cut* end of the casting.

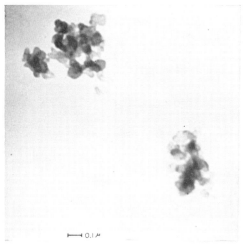

FIG. 5. Carbon black particles. 40,000×. (Los Alamos Scientific Laboratory GMX-1 GT-SITE)

5. Examination of the replicas will show some percentage of particles fractured in a manner that will permit thickness measurement of the coating material.

6. The thin sections are used for optical microscopy to correlate E. M. findings.

J. H. BENDER AND E. H. KALMUS

Uncurling Carbon Replicas

The carbon replica technique introduced by Bradley is by now well established among electronmicroscopists and modifications are probably as numerous as there are microscopists using it.

A fact familiar to most workers is that silica and carbon replicas with or without backing have a strong tendency to curl up; straightening out these replicas more often than not becomes extremely difficult and time-consuming, if not impossible.

During the course of our experiments we noted that carbon replicas are especially prone to curl if primary plastic coatings are used. It was found, however, that such rolled-up squares will unfold immediately and straighten out by transferring them onto the surface of distilled water.

Replicas made in this manner contain few, if any, holes and/or breaks.

W. B. ESTILL* AND E. H. KALMUS

STAINING, ELECTRON

Electron staining is a technique for enhancing contrast in the electron images of biological specimens. The most widely used electron stains are aqueous and/or solvent-soluble compounds containing heavy metal compounds. Examples of the most commonly used electron stains are phosphotungstic acid, osmium tetraoxide, and uranyl acetate. Some of these compounds, e.g., osmium tetraoxide, are also used as fixatives.

The theoretical basis for the use of heavy metal compounds as electron stains is as fol-

* Sandia Corporation, Albuquerque, N. M.

lows. Biological materials for all practical purposes consist of the elements hydrogen, carbon, nitrogen and oxygen. These are low atomic number elements, and therefore have low electron density or electron scattering power. Thus, the difference in electron density of a specimen and its plastic supporting film is very slight. Consequently contrast between the electron image of the specimen and the supporting film is low. However, when one treats the biological specimen with a solution of a compound containing a heavy metal element, the heavy metal, or ion containing the heavy metal is (1) absorbed on the surface, (2) absorbed into or (3) chemically combined with specific reactive groups of the specimen. In either event elements of high electron density (or electron scattering power) become part of the specimen, thus enhancing the contrast between the electron image of the biological specimen and its supporting film.

Electron staining reactions may be correlated with data obtained by other analytical methods. In the case of collagen an elegant correlation is obtained by comparing electron staining reactions with hydrothermal stability (shrinkage temperature) data (1). Phosphotungstic acid treatment stains the collagen, but has no effect on the hydrothermal stability. From this it may be postulated that the anionic complexes containing tungsten may combine with certain reactive groups (e.g. $-NH_3^+$ groups of the basic amino acid side chains) but do not introduce cross-links to increase the hydrothermal stability of the collagen. Osmium tetraoxide and uranyl acetate increase the hydrothermal stability of collagen. Thus it is postulated that the collagen reacts with the heavy metal containing ions and in the process cross-links are introduced to increase the hydrothermal stability of the collagen.

Lead nitrate has a lyotropic effect upon the collagen. The fibrils are markedly swollen. Hydrothermal stability is decreased substantially yet the fibrils appear to be stained. However, close inspection of the micrographs of lead nitrate-treated collagen reveals that there are numerous small particles adsorbed on the surface and deposited in the microcrevices of the fibrils. This type of enhancement of contrast may be termed pseudo-electron staining. There is no chemical combination of collagen with metal in pseudo-staining.

Figures 1 and 2 compare unstained (i.e., non-treated) and electron stained (phosphotungstic acid treated) collagen fibrils, respectively. Note the greater contrast and enhancement of ultrafine structure in the electron stained material.

Figures 3 and 4 compare "negative" electron-stained collagen with electron-stained collagen, respectively. In both instances the stain is a chromium complex. The enhanced contrast of the "negative" electron stain is

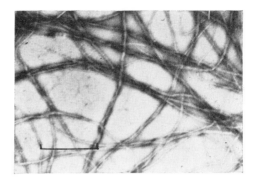

FIG. 3. Cowhide collagen fibrils. 15,400✕. Treated with chrome alum (3% $KCr(SO_4)_2 \cdot 12H_2O$ + 10% $NaCl$) liquor—pH 2.8. Note that the chromium is concentrated along the edges of the fibrils.

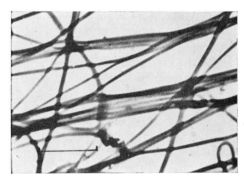

FIG. 4. Cowhide collagen fibrils. 15,400✕. Same preparation as in Figure 3 only after neutralization with sodium bicarbonate to pH 4.5. Note that the chromium is now incorporated in the fibrils.

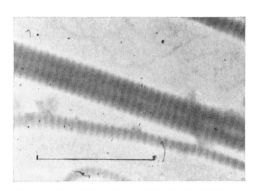

FIG. 1. Cowhide collagen fibrils. 31,500✕.

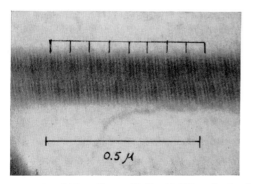

FIG. 2. Cowhide collagen fibrils. 82,600✕. Stained with 0.1% phosphotungstic acid ($H_3PW_{12}O_{40} \cdot 24H_2O$).

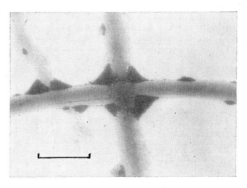

FIG. 5. Cowhide collagen fibrils. 15,400✕. Treated with lead nitrate ($Pb(NO_3)_2$). The lead particles are distributed evenly on the surface of the fibrils delineating fine periodic structure both parallel and perpendicular to the fibril axis.

275

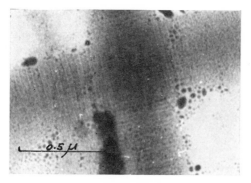

FIG. 6. Cowhide collagen fibrils. 52,500×. Same as Figure 5.

due to the fact that the electron-dense chromium complex deposited on the plastic film supporting the collagen fibrils, especially along the edges of the fibrils, acts as a dark background for the light fibrils.

Figures 5 and 6 show collagen treated with lead nitrate. These are examples of pseudo-electron staining as explained in the text above.

REFERENCES

1. Borasky, R., J. Am. Leath. Chem. Assoc., **52**, 596–610 (1957).
2. Hall, C. E., J. Biochem. Biophys. Cytol. **1**, 1 (1955).
3. Mudd, S., and Anderson, T. F., J. Expt. Med., **76**, 103–108 (1942).
4. Porter, K. R., and Kallman, F., Exp. Cell. Res., **4**, 127 (1953).
5. Symposium on Electron Staining, J. Roy. Micro. Soc., Series III, **78**, Parts 1 and 2 (1959).
6. Watson, M. L., J. Biochem. Biophys. Cytol., **3**, 1017 (1957).

R. Borasky

TISSUES (CONNECTIVE), BONES AND TEETH

Apart from cancer, most of the non-infectious maladies from which the human race suffers are related to changes in the structure or function of the connective or hard tissues. The primary aim of the work which has so far been done on this group of tissues has been to establish a clear picture of their normal appearance to compare with similar preparations of pathological specimens. These tissues, which form the framework of the body, consist mostly of a matrix of long chain polymeric compounds with which their formative cellular elements are associated. In bones and teeth the matrix is made rigid by the deposition of calcium salts. Strictly speaking, the connective and hard tissues are mesodermal in origin, and consist of fibrous proteins embedded in a polysaccharide-containing medium. Two ectodermal structures will also be considered in this chapter: tonofibrils, which have as their main function the holding of the epidermis together; and dental enamel, which fits naturally into the group of hard tissues.

Collagen and polysaccharide-containing ground substance are universal in the animal kingdom. Leech connective tissue and developing human connective tissue have fibroblasts and collagen which look identical; while in teeth one has to get as far away from the human as a sea urchin to find calcium salts which are not predominantly hydroxyapatite. On the other hand, there are minor differences in many closely related species. Thus, some details in the development and calcification of the epiphyseal cartilage of the rat and rabbit, both rodents, show different appearances.

In any study of tissue structure the greatest amount of information is obtained when the electron microscopic appearance is considered in conjunction with findings from other methods. It has not superseded other established techniques, the most important of which is still the light microscope. Sometimes it is sufficient for the electron microscope to fill in details after the greater part of the work has been done using light microscope techniques, involving staining, as in the detailed investigation of the growth of epiphyseal cartilage. At other times, the most important part of the investigation is done using the electron microscope, as in the sorting out of the mechanism of dental caries.

However, in all cases mistakes can be avoided when orthodox light microscopy is used as a control. The most obvious example of this has been the work on elastica, in which many workers who had not used adequate controls reported observations on the non-elastic components of the tissues. Other methods which have been used are X-ray and electron diffraction, to identify components and indicate orientation; injection methods, to trace blood vessels; microradiography and direct experiments.

The use of light microscopy to prevent mistakes is an example of one of the most important aspects of this type of investigation—the recognition of artefacts. Some are comparatively obvious: for example, the fact that both embedding media and many tissue components are polymers of similar density. The divergence of opinion on whether collagen fibrils were solid rods or hollow tubes has been enlightening. Those supporting the first theory left their embedding medium in; those in favor of the hollow tube theory had removed it. Viewing stereoscopically, which has been found a useful method for detecting a number of artifacts, supports the observations that at least those collagen fibrils which are of large diameter are hollow.

In this account, emphasis will be placed on the electron microscopic appearances of the extra-cellular matrices, since a survey of the literature suggests that the present state of knowledge of the cellular components is still very uncertain. One of the few conclusions about these cells for which there is a substantial mass of evidence from a number of lines of approach, including the use of labeled precursors (e.g. I. Karpishka, C. P. Leblond and J. Carneiro, *Arch. oral Biol.* **1,** 23, 1959), is that the systems of approximately parallel membranes in the cytoplasm, such as that seen in the cytoplasm of the chondrocyte shown in Fig. 1, are closely concerned with protein formation.

First, individual components will be discussed, and then the architecture of the main

tissues concerned. In the available space a comprehensive list of references is not feasible, so many of those quoted in detail will be important ones likely to be missed in a casual survey of the literature. Except for Figures 5 and 10, photographs are of a white object on a black background.

Components

Tonofibrils. The surface of the skin is covered with a layer of keratin. Immediately under this are the prickle cells, which, when viewed with a high-power light microscope, appear to be connected by fibrils. When reasonably thick sections are viewed in the electron microscope, so that the slightly wavy fibrils remain in the plane of the section and are not cut away, it is seen that these tonofibrils do, in fact, pass from one cell to another through intercellular bridges. When viewed stereoscopically, the thickness of the section shown in Fig. 2 is seen to be about equivalent to the depth of three inter-

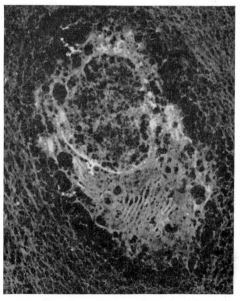

FIG. 1. Section of chondrocyte from primitive cartilage of rabbit. The system of parallel membranes is believed to be the site of production of the matrix. Formalin fixed. Embedding medium removed. ×6000.

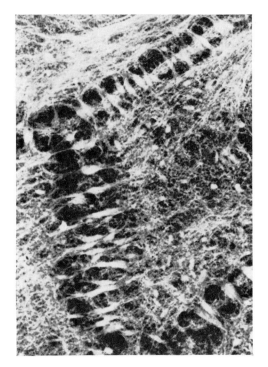

FIG. 2. Section of human epidermis, showing portion of prickle cell. Tonofibrils pass through the intercellular bridges from one cell to another. Formalin fixed. Embedding medium removed. ×10,000.

cellular bridges. What is normally regarded as inadequate fixation has been found useful, since with other cytoplasmic components degraded and removed, individual fibrils can easily be traced through a series of cells. When entering a cell near the nucleus the fibrils are seen to turn through almost a right angle as soon as they are clear of the cell wall. There has been no suggestion that these fibrils are associated with ground substance, but there is a limited amount of evidence suggesting that they might be keratinous.

Ground Substance. Ground substance is ubiquitous, and may be regarded as the glue that holds all the extra-cellular tissues together. Its characteristic components are polysaccharides. The texture of the ground substance varies from thin tough sheets, as

in reticulin (Fig. 3), to a three-dimensional gel, as in articular cartilage. Fig. 4 is a section of cartilage, necessarily dried out, where the spaces are caused by loss of fluid from the gel. Collagen is never found without ground substance, though the proportion of the two may vary considerably, both between different types of tissue and within any one type. Their association is fundamentally that of a mixture and not a chemical compound. The ground substance adheres to the outside of the collagen fibrils with particular tenacity at the bands. In tissue such as the epiphyseal growth cartilage, where the banded structure of the collagen is not very apparent, the 640A spacing is most clearly demonstrated by the ground substance stretching between fibrils (see Fig. 16).

Collagen. While the ground substance holds it together, collagen fibers provide the mechanical strength for the framework of the

FIG. 3. Fragment of reticulin from human liver. Uranium shadowed. ×5000. Specimen prepared by Dr. H. Kramer.

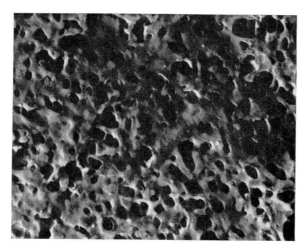

Fig. 4. Section of articular cartilage from rabbit. The thickness of this section is less than the diameter of the thicker collagen fibrils. Two or three are shadowed on their inner surfaces. Embedding medium removed. Uranium shadowed. ×10,000.

body. In the preceding paragraph it was implied that the ground substance is composed of a group of related polysaccharides. Similarly, it is most probable that collagen is made up of a group of related proteins, with the 2.86A spacing of X-ray diffraction patterns and a periodicity of the order of 640A along the fibrils as the common factors. Solubility, shape of fiber and mode of formation can vary. The evidence at present available suggests that, like ground substance, collagen is polymerized in the cytoplasm of cells. It is then precipitated in a fibrillar form either at the surface of the cell, or away from the cell in a medium of ground substance.

So far two types of collagen have been distinguished in the human. The form which can be more easily brought into solution occurs as very fine fibrils, is most abundant in the infant, and is the predominant form of collagen in tissues such as primitive anlage cartilage and growth cartilage. The second form is the more commonly illustrated one, less soluble, with a tubular appearance of its fibrils and more prominant 640A spacings. It is the major component of mature tendon. Most tissues such as articular cartilage and

osteoid matrix contain a mixture of the two. When specimens of the two types are separated in a relatively pure form, by making use of the solubility differences, minor differences are noticed in the wide-angle X-ray diffraction pattern.

One type of cell which produces collagen directly is the fibroblast. Various workers have studied it with the electron microscope, using thin sectioning techniques. Fig. 5, taken by Dr. J. A. Chapman and Dr. R. Peach of Manchester University, is a photograph of regenerating tendon at 6 weeks. This type of specimen is invaluable for showing cytoplasmic detail, but is not so well suited for demonstrating the surrounding matrix. Thus, Chapman and Peach do not think that there are collagen fibrils within the cytoplasm, while Fitton-Jackson and others think there may be. Fig. 6 is from a thick section of fibrocartilage containing a cell in which the cytoplasm has disintegrated as a result of delayed fixation. This treatment does not affect collagen. Here there is no sign of collagen fibrils crossing the cell wall. At one point this wall is expanded into a very fine net-like structure. This observation is common to fibroblasts from a number

279

of different sites. The collagen fibrils formed by a single fibroblast appear to be tubular and of more or less uniform diameter.

Collagen fibrils laid down away from cells tend to have a different appearance. Often they are very fine, as in the collagen from epiphyseal growth cartilage (Fig. 16), and separated from the cells by an even finer mesh of ground substance. A much larger range of fiber diameters is also frequent. In Fig. 14, from a specimen of normal adult articular cartilage, a collagen fiber of very large diameter is seen in the plane of the section.

Elastin. Many papers have been written on the electron microscopy of elastin, and much confusing and contradictory information offered. There is now, however, a measure of agreement. R. W. Cox (Thesis, Oxford 1957) has carefully compared the appearance in the electron microscope with alternate sections stained and prepared for light microscope examination. He has also isolated it chemically. When wet it has rubber-like elasticity; when dry it is brittle. Elastin is found in those tissues where a quick recovery from applied stresses is necessary, and there is some evidence to suggest that it is polymerized *in situ*, rather than being precipitated in a manner analogous to collagen. Its form and size can be very irregular, and in the electron microscope the safest method of identification is to examine the texture in

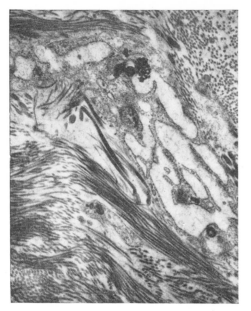

FIG. 5. Fibroblast from 6 week regenerating tendon. Fixed with osmium tetroxide and stained with P.T.A. Embedded in araldite. ×10,000. Photograph by J. A. Chapman and R. Peach, Manchester University.

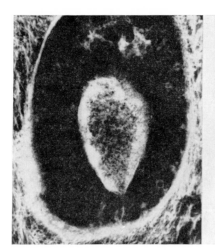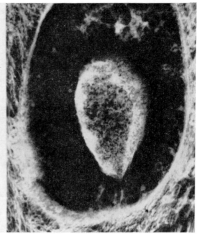

FIG. 6. Fibroblast from dog intervertebral disc. Delayed fixation with formalin. The cytoplasm is degraded, thus showing that no collagen fibrils have penetrated to cell wall. Part of this wall is expanded as compared with the rest. Embedding medium removed. Stereoscopic photograph.

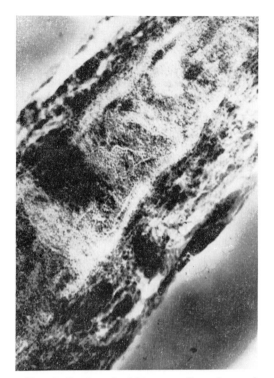

FIG. 7. Section of rabbit aorta. Smooth muscle cells and elastic tissue alternating. Note the increased density of the elastic tissue at its surface. Osmium tetroxide fixation. Embedding medium removed. No shadowing. ×10,000.

hydroxyapatite. As far as the characteristics of the individual crystallites are concerned, a great deal of work has produced remarkably few unequivocal results. This is partly because some of the difficulties inherent in the method of examination could not be appreciated until the appearance of such phenomena as dislocations, twin boundaries and total reflection were commonly recognized. The crystallites in bone and dentine are very small compared with those in enamel. They are rod-shaped, with diameters of approximately 40–50A, and it is now generally agreed that their average length is of the order of 600A (T. W. Speckman and W. P. Norris, *Science*, **126,** 753, 1957). The X-ray diffraction results of D. Carlstrom and A. Engstrom are in agreement with these dimensions. Experimentally, enamel crystallites are easier to observe. Even with

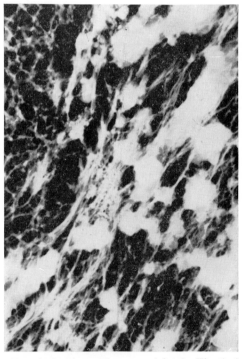

FIG. 8. Section of human epiglottis. Elastin in cartilage matrix. The shadowing metal on the cut surface gives a false impression of density. Osmium tetroxide fixation. Embedding medium removed. Uranium shadowed. ×10,000.

sections viewed stereoscopically. In sites such as developing arteries, elastin can be found well away from fibroblasts or any similar cells. For instance, in Fig. 7 elastin is seen on either side of a smooth muscle cell, with no different components in the immediate vicinity. D. C. Pease is of the opinion that ground substance is necessary for the formation of elastin, and this view is supported by the fact that in areas such as that shown in Fig. 8, taken from a section of elastic cartilage, the elastin is confined to one type of surrounding matrix. Fig. 9 is from the loose connective tissue of skin, and here it can be seen that the elastin has tended to engulf some of the surrounding collagen fibrils—a very common occurrence.

Calcium Phosphates. The mineral which imparts rigidity to the hard tissues is

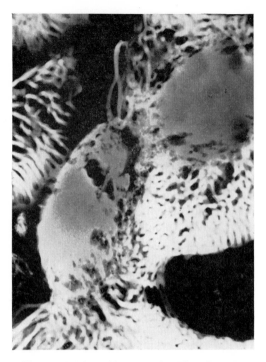

FIG. 9. Section of human skin. The edges of the elastic tissue have embedded some of the neighbouring collagen fibrils. Large spaces are due to the high fluid content of the tissue, Osmium tetroxide fixation. Embedding medium removed. No shadowing. ×10,000.

the low magnification of Fig. 21 they are clearly distinguishable. But they are composite crystallites, so that in addition to the apparent detail produced by the physical phenomena already mentioned, there are the real sub-boundaries of a column of bricks. This is demonstrated in photographs such as Fig. 10, taken by R. W. Fearnhead at the London Hospital, in which total reflection of many of the sub-units can be seen in one photograph but not in the other. The angular difference of these two photographs was 3°. The width of crystallites is of the order of 500A (they are usually thinner) and total lengths are upwards of 2000A.

In cartilage and bone the crystallites are first laid down in a haphazard manner bearing no relationship to the direction of the collagen fibrils. This has been observed both directly (R. A. Robinson and D. A. Cameron, *J. Biophys. Biochem. Cytol. Suppl.* **2**(4), 253, 1956) and indirectly, using other techniques (G. Wallgren, *Acta Paediatrica,* Suppl. 113). In Oxford, a combination of electron microscopy and electron diffraction has shown that in newly calcified dentine the orientation of the hydroxyapatite crystal-

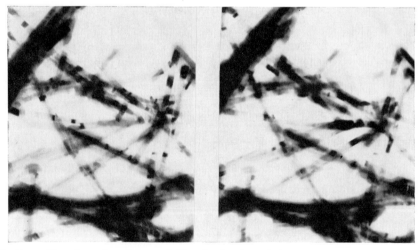

FIG. 10. Crystallites from dental enamel. Total reflection of electrons occurs in different regions in the two photographs, taken at an angle of 3°. ×50,000. Photographed by R. W. Fearnhead at the London Hospital.

lites is also unrelated to the orientation of the neighboring collagen fibrils. The alignment observed in mature tissues is apparently a secondary rearrangement caused by physical stresses.

Tissues

Reticulin. This is the tissue that holds the various parts of the body in place. Spread underneath the epidermis is a basement membrane. Various structures and organs, and sometimes even individual cells, are surrounded by similar membranes. The thickness varies according to the mechanical strength required at any given site. The thinnest membranes found in such organs as the kidney, spleen and liver are of the order of 100A, while at the other end of the scale they may be several thousand Angstrom units thick. Several workers consider that there are distinct forms of reticulin. E. L. Benedetti and R. Tiribelli have described two in the glomeruli of kidneys (*Arch. Ital. Anat. Istol.*, **27**, 1954) and A. Bairati and B. Pernis (*Boll. Soc. Ital. Biol. Sper.* **34**(6), 250, 1958) suggest that there is a different form for each tissue with which the reticulin is associated.

In sections, reticulin membranes are seen to be sometimes single and sometimes multiple, with the material of an apparently more or less uniform texture. When fragmented material is treated with alkali, the reticulin is observed to be very resistant chemically, as compared with most other tissue components. Consequently it can be isolated, and individual membranes viewed using transmitted electrons. When this is done, the finer fragments (e.g., those from liver, kidney, spleen, adrenal and lung) which are sufficiently thin to allow electron penetration are seen to contain an almost random two-dimensional network of collagen fibrils (H. Kramer and K. Little "Nature and Structure of Collagen", p. 33, 1953). The proportion of collagen to the polysaccharide-containing ground substance varies

Fig. 11. Fragment of reticulin from human liver. The positions of some of the collagen bands suggest a non-fibrillar structure. Metal shadowed. ×5000.

from one site to another. A fragment of reticulin isolated from liver is shown in Fig. 11.

Capillary walls consist of a reticulin membrane, with cells arranged at intervals on its surface, and occasionally on the inner surface. Capillaries may be distinguished from veins or arteries by the fact that cells are not a necessary component part of the wall (that is, after it has been manufactured). There is as yet no definite evidence whether or not capillary walls contain collagen. In Fig. 12 is seen a portion of a capillary wall, the lumen being clearly demonstrated by the presence of the barium sulfate particles used as an injection medium. This injection method is particularly useful when the capillary is passing through loose tissue. The one shown in Fig. 12 is taken from a specimen of the metaphysis of a growing bone. Its wall can be seen to consist of more than one layer. D. C. Pease (*J. Histchem.*

Fig. 12. Capillary wall in metaphysis of rabbit tibia. Blood has been replaced by the fine particles of a barium sulphate injection medium. Formalin fixed. ×3000.

Cytochem., **3**(4), 295, 1955) has studied the glomerular capillaries in kidneys. He found that a fenestrated endothelial sheath was cemented onto the basement membrane of the capillary walls, and in many places found a layer of the cementing material on either side of the membrane. In the sections he examined he found no evidence for a fibrillar structure in the basement membrane.

Loose Connective Tissue. It is this tissue which is mainly responsible for allowing bodily structures to move relative to one another without friction. It contains nerves and blood vessels; too great a mobility, which might damage these, is prevented by a loose interweaving of bundles of collagen fibrils. These bundles are the collagen fibers observed by histologists using the light microscope. The fibroblasts producing these fibers are commonly observed to form bundles of fibrils of uniform diameter. This is seen in Fig. 9. In the foetus and infant the fibroblasts of the loose connective tissue produce fibrils of smaller diameter than those found in mature tissue. The tissue contains much fluid, so that there are many spaces in the dried sections used in the electron microscope. In areas where there are greater stresses, notably the subcutaneous tissues, elastin is also found. Such elastic tissue appears to be laid down after the collagen bundles, and the edges of these are often embedded in the adjoining elastin (Fig. 9). The elastic "fibers" are of variable size, shape and arrangement.

In the *Ehlers-Danlos* syndrome, in which the skin, and sometimes other tissues, has unnatural mobility, it has been reported (L. H. Jansen, *Arch. Belg. derm. syph.* **10**(3), 251, 1954) that collagen formation is defective, with the fibers less entangled than usual. Unless sufficient elastic tissue is present to compensate for this, the tissues have a very low tensile strength.

Tendon and Ligament. Tendons are a specialized form of compact connective tissue, designed to take a high tensile load. Bundles of collagen fibrils are tightly interwoven, with their orientation predominantly parallel to the long axis of the tendon. Unlike the loose connective tissues, it can be seen that a single collagen bundle contains fibrils of different diameters. It has been observed that the greater the forces to which a tendon is habitually subjected, the larger and more robust are the individual fibrils. Thus larger fibrils with more marked 640A banding are found in kangaroo tail tendon than in human Achilles tendon. The latter, in turn, are larger than those in some of the smaller tendons. These visual observations are in accord with the results of solubility experiments on tendons of experimental animals. Solubility tends to vary from one tendon to another. Considerable variation is also observed in the proportion of polysaccharide present in the tendon or ligament. In identically prepared untreated sections, individual fibrils will be clearly distinguishable in human Achilles tendon, and almost obscured by ground substance in the ligamentum nuchae. It was in tendon specimens that the tubular structure of at least some collagen fibrils was first established (J. J. Kennedy, *Science*, **121**: 673, 1955). The methods of preparation developed by R. W. G. Wyckoff are particularly well suited for the examination of this type of tissue.

Ligaments subjected to lateral stresses are usually found to contain elastin. Thus, while the human ligamentum nuchae has been observed to contain predominantly collagen and ground substance, specimens of the ligamentum nuchae from goats, sheep and similar animals with the head held in a forward direction are frequently seen to contain more elastin than collagen. In these elastic ligaments, the appearance of the elastin is more genuinely fiber-like than in any other site, excepting the vocal cords. It is also noticeable that, whereas in most tendons collagen fibrils lie practically parallel within their bundles, in elastic ligaments the collagen fibrils between the elastic fibers present a wavy appearance—no doubt to allow for a greater extension.

Fibrocartilage. Tissues such as the meniscus of the knee and the intervertebral discs are compact connective tissues, with tightly interwoven bundles of collagen produced by fibroblasts. In each bundle, the individual fibrils are approximately parallel, but there is not the same over-all linear orientation as is found in tendons. The directions of orientation are related to the forces to which the tissue is subjected. When these are variable, as in the meniscus, the average orientation is very low, whereas in the disc it tends to be parallel to the circumference. Such observations are best made using X-ray diffraction (W. G. Horton, Thesis, London, 1956). When specimens of more limited size are examined in the electron microscope the finer details of structure are more apparent. In the bundles there is often seen a distinct tendency for fibrils to be arranged in sheets (Fig. 13), while bundles of fibrils with different orientation can be glued together by ground substance almost as efficiently as the individual sheets within the bundles. In sites subjected to deformation, the collagenous matrix is usually reinforced by elastic tissue (Fig. 8). The proportion in adult epiglottis is often high.

Primitive Cartilage. Cartilage proper—the tissue produced by chondrocytes—is of three main types. Articular cartilage and growth cartilage both develop from a primitive cartilage which has cells of the type shown in Fig. 1. Frequently these are in groups of two or four, with adjacent faces flattened against one another. They do not have the prominent cell walls of the fibroblasts, but have ones which are finer than the nuclear membrane. Most cells or groups of cells are in a capsule appearing, when dried, as a very fine network. The matrix between cells, or groups of cells, in their capsules appears as a dried gel containing only very fine fibers. There is no indication that any collagen fibrils are formed at the cell wall, but the appearances are consistent with them having been precipitated *in situ*.

Articular Cartilage. Bones develop from a model, or anlage, of primitive cartilage. In

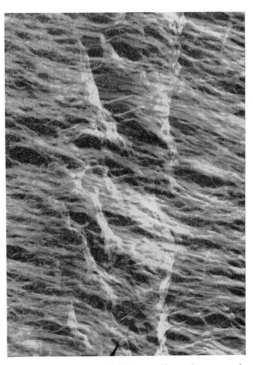

Fig. 13. Section of fibrocartilage from meniscus of the knee. Embedding medium removed. Metal shadowed. ×10,000.

its early stages it is not subjected to many stresses. When these do arise—in a joint which is beginning to be used—and when these applied stresses are in variable directions, articular cartilage makes its appearance. This is characterized by less prominent cell capsules and the precipitation of fibers of larger diameter in the intercellular matrix, such as those shown in Fig. 4 and 14. The greater the load the joint has to bear, the higher the proportion of fibrils of large diameter. The cartilage is made up of cells and matrix, but it contains no vessels. The nourishment for the cells is probably provided by natural movement causing an intermittent pumping action which circulates synovial fluid through the tissue (J. Trueta). All the observed facts are in accord with this hypothesis (for example, articular cartilage wiped dry and then compressed yields synovial fluid), and it also provides a rational explanation of the appearances of the cartilage in osteoarthritis.

Osteoarthritis occurs whenever the various forces acting across a joint become unbal-

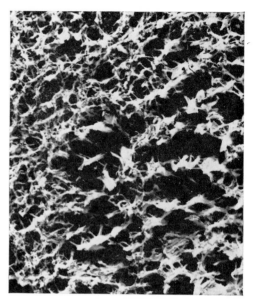

FIG. 15. Section of adult human articular cartilage from a case of osteoarthritis. The section has been cut parallel to the surface of the bone. Embedding medium removed. Metal shadowed. ×10,000.

anced as a result of injury, unnatural activity, or disease; J. Trueta and his collaborators have produced it in experimental animals in an analogous manner, by upsetting local forces acting on the joint. On the microscopic scale the first manifestation is the onset of degradation of the ground substance (an observation which is confirmed by chemical analysis) and a lining up of collagen fibrils normal to the surface of the bone. Fig. 15 shows the appearance of a section cut parallel to the surface of the bone from a fairly early case where the surface of the cartilage was still almost intact. The amount and direction of orientation is best demonstrated by a combination of X-ray diffraction and electron microscope observations (K. Little, L. H. Pimm and J. Trueta, *J. Bone and Joint Surg.*, **40B**: 123, 1958). In the experimental animals removal of the undesirable forces and tensions was followed by recovery of the cartilage, as judged by both macroscopic and microscopic appearances.

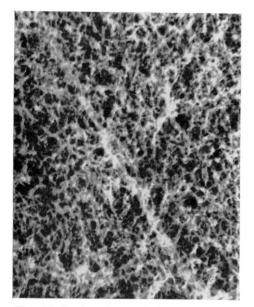

FIG. 14. Section of normal adult human articular cartilage. Embedding medium removed. Metal shadowed. ×10,000.

286

Growth Cartilage. In regions where forces are predominantly unidirectional the third type of cartilage is found. This growth cartilage is mainly found at the growing ends of long bones. Instead of the cells being in groups of two or four, as in the primitive cartilage, a whole column of cells is seen as a single unit. The cells in the column are flattened. with evidence of frequent division, and the direction of the columns is along the lines of force. Between the columns of cells is collagen, oriented in the same direction (Fig. 16).

At the metaphyseal end of the cartilage the cells in the columns expand, to form the hypertrophic cells, which are of the order of 40 μ across. At the same time that expansion occurs there is normally a change in the matrix between the cells. This shows up in the electron microscope as a change of texture, the matrix assuming a more compact appearance. It is this altered matrix which can

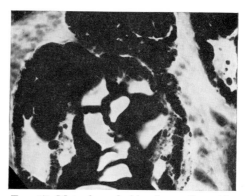

FIG. 17. Metaphyseal side of growth cartilage in rabbit. A vessel containing red cells has invaded the last hypertrophic cell space. The vessel wall is not yet complete. The first osteoblasts can be seen between the vessel walls and calcified cartilage. Formalin fixed. Embedding medium removed. ×2000.

calcify, when the necessary vessels, calcium, phosphate and vitamins are present. The cells, thus removed from their source of nourishment, die and are replaced by the encroaching vessel, as shown in Fig. 17. Here red cells are within the capsule of a hypertrophic cell, with calcified cartilage on either side. It may be seen that the capillary wall is incomplete—a very common observation. (J. Trueta and K. Little, *J. Bone and Joint Surg* 42B: 367, 1960).

Bone. At different stages of its development bone contains primitive cartilage, articular cartilage, growth cartilage and calcified cartilage; but the greater part of the bone matrix, for most of the life of a man or animal, is the osteoid matrix. The osteoid is laid down by cells which differ in form from fibroblasts or chondrocytes. In Fig. 17 are seen the first osteoblasts, which appear to be on or near the capillary walls, and are sending out processes toward the calcified cartilage. Previously existing calcified tissue appears to be necessary for the complete development of osteoblasts. When mature, these lay down a collagenous matrix. As with fibroblasts, the collagen of bone matrix appears to originate at the cell wall of the osteoblast. The cell processes remain, and lie

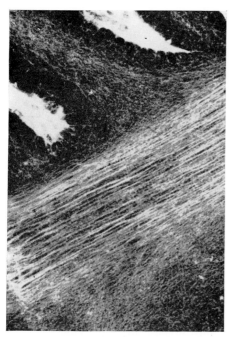

FIG. 16. Section from epiphyseal growth cartilage of rabbit. The collagen fibrils are parallel to the columns of cells. Formalin fixed. Embedding medium removed. ×4000.

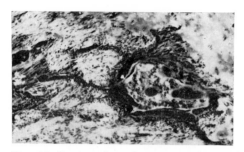

FIG. 18. Section through osteocyte in poorly calcified trabeculum. Processes from the cell can be seen to pass through canaliculi in the as yet uncalcified matrix. Formalin fixed. Embedding medium removed.

in channels in the matrix—the canaliculi. Observation of sections of areas of active bone formation seem to show that the osteoblasts bury themselves within the matrix they manufacture, whereupon they are referred to as osteocytes. The osteocyte in Fig. 18 has several canaliculi cut in the plane of the section, and processes from the cell can be seen to lie in these. Normally by this stage the matrix would be completely calcified, but the cell chosen for illustration was from an experimental animal with deficient calcification, so that only about a quarter of the matrix in the photograph was calcified. The matrix contains collagen fibrils of assorted diameters.

R. A. Robinson and D. A. Cameron (*J. Biophys. Biochem. Cytol. Suppl.* **2**(4), 253, 1956) have pointed out that age in itself is not responsible for the character of different types of fibril. They found the fibrils from osteoblasts to have 2–5 times the diameter of those seen in growth cartilage, and to possess obvious periodic structure, both types of collagen having been laid down at about the same time.

In the normal formation of bone, the stages appear to be the laying down of collagen and ground substance, followed by the deposition of apatite crystallites in the gelatinous ground substance. R. Frank (Thesis, Strasbourg, 1957) has examined a case of *post-traumatic osteoporosis*. X-ray diffraction

showed no change in the mineral composition, while in the electron microscope the changes were consistent with the disappearance of first the crystallites and ground substance, leaving collagen fibrils prominent, followed by the gradual breakdown of these fibrils. The changes occurred in a patchy and irregular manner.

Dentine. As compared with bone, a great deal of time and effort has been expended on the electron microscope examination of dentine, but the conclusions are by no means unequivocal. Many photographs of carious dentine with bacteria within the tubules have been published, particularly by R. W. G. Wyckoff, D. B. Scott and R. Frank; and M. U. Nylen and D. B. Scott have produced a compilation of photographs of early developing dentine (U. S. Public Health Service Publication No. 613). The odontoblasts differ from chondrocytes and osteoblasts, but have some of the characteristics of each. They are found on the border of the developing dentine, and produce matrix, but unlike the osteoblast they never become completely surrounded by it. They have a single large process which passes through the dentinal tubule, and a number of workers have reported small branches from these, which are analogous to the canaliculi in bones. Like chondrocytes, they do not produce bundles of fibers on their surfaces, but the collagen is mainly found between the tubules in a manner which has originally only a small degree of ordering.

Fig. 19 shows the arrangement of collagen fibrils round a tubule near the pulp. Vessels penetrate to the odontoblast layer, and calcification of the matrix takes place at the point farthest from cells and vessels. This may be compared with calcified cartilage in which calcification is at the end away from the vessels which supply the cartilage with its nourishment. M. U. Nylen and D. B. Scott report a change in the appearance of the ground substance of the matrix which precedes calcification. It has been known for

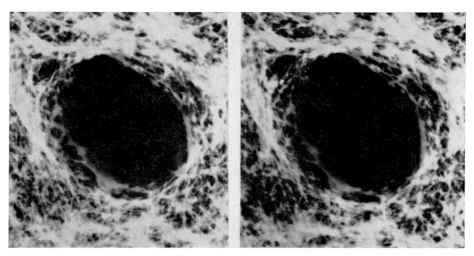

FIG. 19. Section of dentine near pulp. The tubule contents have been removed and the section decalcified, showing the arrangement of collagen fibrils around the tubule. Embedding medium removed. Stereoscopic photograph. ×10,000.

some time (M. Deakins, *J. Dent. Res.*, **27**, 429, 1942) that there is a water loss in the matrix immediately before calcification. A changed appearance of the calcified matrix, in response to pressure or caries is often observed, and Von Th. Spreter (*Schweiz. Med. Woch.*, **88**, 635, 1958) has shown that 12–13 % dentine by weight is a liquor containing adequate amounts of protein, amino acids, sugars and minerals for further polymerization or precipitation. As a reaction to caries, crystallites of the same size as those in enamel have been observed randomly precipitated within the dentine matrix.

Near the pulp, the tubules are observed to be completely filled by the odontoblast processes. Towards the enamel, between the matrix proper and the odontoblast process, a 'peritubular zone' has frequently been reported. Its nature is as yet unresolved. A good factual description has been given by R. Frank (*Arch. Oral Biol.*, **1**, 29, 1959).

Dental Enamel. Tooth enamel has a matrix and crystallites which are completely unlike any of the other calcified tissues, doubtless because it is the only calcified ectodermal structure. The matrix consists of two main compounds, which from chemical analysis and X-ray diffraction studies can probably be regarded as members of the keratin group. Some reports indicate that a small proportion of polysaccharide may be present. The prismatic appearance of enamel in sections prepared for the light microscope is due to the arrangement of these two compounds. Since the composition of neither is certainly known, they will be referred to here by the names of the workers who first provided an adequate description of each— the less soluble and denser as Pincus' protein, and the less dense and more unstable as Stack's protein. Fig. 20 shows the arrangement in a section of developing enamel shortly before the calcification commences. Both proteins form an oriented network, and during calcification apatite crystallites are laid down in pockets of these networks. Calcification in Stack's protein occurs shortly before calcification of Pincus' protein at the same level in the enamel. When fully calcified, enamel has a very much higher proportion of apatite to matrix than is found in any other tissue. There are considerable difficulties in cutting thin sections (diamond knives chip easily) and most published photographs of mature enamel are of replicas. When

289

lightly etched with acid the Stack's protein dissolves, so that the prismatic structure is enhanced.

The chalky enamel of *enamel caries* (which is known to be the first stage of all carious lesions) can be sectioned more easily, and it is seen that at this stage Stack's protein has gone, and the crystallites in it are being washed away, while Pincus' protein and the crystallites embedded in it remain (K. Little, *J. Roy. Micr. Soc.*, **78**, Dec., 1958). Bacteria are not seen in this earliest stage of caries (Fig. 21). This problem of enamel caries pro-

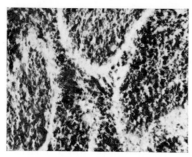

FIG. 20. Section of developing human dental enamel, before calcification. Stack's protein, liable to be degraded in dental caries, is the less dense of the two organic components of the matrix. Formalin fixation. Embedding medium removed. Uranium shadowed. ×5000.

vides a good example of how, while the initial observations must be made using electron microscopy, since the important details are too small to resolve with the light microscope, work with the light microscope can then be interpreted by making use of this information, as has been done by A. I. Darling (*Brit. Dent. J.*, **105**, 119, 1958).

Once it was shown that the initial stage of caries was almost certainly the loss of Stack's protein; further advances are possible using histological methods. For example, if teeth are treated with ethylene diamine, a protein solvent in which apatite is completely insoluble, sections viewed under polarized light show the translucent appearance typical of the earliest zone of enamel caries. (A. I. Darling and K. V. Mortimer, IADR British Section, 1959). Again, by normal histological methods it can be demonstrated that an important action of fluorine is to modify the formation of enamel matrix (A. I. Darling and A. W. Brooks, IADR British Section, 1959). In normal enamel treated with a formic acid solution, sections viewed in the electron microscope show chalky enamel apparently identical with that formed in natural caries. When fluorized teeth are similarly treated, electron microscope exam-

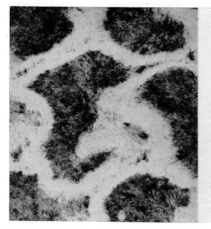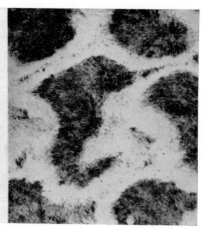

FIG. 21. Section of chalky enamel. Stack's protein has mostly gone, leaving the crystallites which had been embedded in it free to be washed out during processing. The prism walls are intact, with the crystallites still held in place by the organic matrix. Embedding medium removed. Stereoscopic photograph. ×3000.

ination shows that in large areas of the sections both components of the matrix remain intact. This suggests that fluorine protects teeth from decay by drastically reducing the solubility of the organic matrix.

K. LITTLE

TRANSMISSION ELECTRON MICROSCOPY OF METALS—DISLOCATIONS AND PRECIPITATION

All high resolution electron microscopy is made by transmission, but the phrase "transmission electron microscopy" is used here in a restricted sense, whereby the electrons having transmitted a specimen form an image which furnishes information about the interior of the material and not merely about the surface, as in the replica method. Electrons passing through matter can be absorbed or scattered inelastically or elastically. In the latter case the scattering may be incoherent or coherent; coherent scattering is known as "diffraction". Absorption and incoherent scattering give "radiograms" indicating variations in thickness and density, but the interesting information justifying a separate article on "transmission electron microscopy" is obtained from diffraction effects. This means that the specimens to be studied have to be crystalline. For practical reasons most of the specimens studied until now have been metallic but minerals are in principle not excluded. A further advantage of transmission electron microscopy is that in addition to microscopy, selected area diffraction can be applied, which furnishes information about the crystal structure and the orientation of the specimen.

Certain transmission effects have been observed since the beginning of electron microscopy, but transmission electron microscopy in its proper sense started in 1949 with Heidenreich's paper "Electron Microscope and Diffraction Study of Metal Crystal Textures by Means of Thin Sections" (1). In this paper lies the origin of practically all the future developments in the field of transmission electron microscopy—the theoretical explanation of the observed effects, the preparation technique and the applications to metal physics, like deformation, recrystallization and precipitation. In Europe the work was continued by Castaing (2) on the precipitation of $CuAl_2$ in $Al + 4\%$ Cu. Other transmission microscopy was done in Japan by Suito and Uyeda (3), Hashimoto (4), Takahashi et al. (5).

Until 1956 essentially the effects due to perfect crystals and two-phase systems (precipitates) were studied, for example, extinction contours (dark bands arising from Bragg diffraction). A new possibility appeared when it was shown by Hirsch, Horne and Whelan (6) for aluminum, and independently by Bollmann (7) for stainless steel, that dislocations could be observed directly inside the metal by transmission electron microscopy. The theory of dislocations had been extensively developed before. (The books of Cottrell (8) and Read (9) appeared in 1953). Transmission microscopy furnished direct verification of these theories. In particular the cinefilms of the group Hirsch, Whelan et al. showing the movement of dislocations in aluminum (6) and in stainless steel (10) helped to make the dislocation theory appreciated by metallurgists. So transmission electron microscopy today is an important tool for research in metal physics.

It is of interest that the first pictures of dislocations by transmission microscopy were published by Heidenreich in his basic article (1) and that he even mentioned that: "... a study of the fine details of the contours in sections plastically deformed under controlled conditions may yield important information concerning dislocations". But the theory of dislocations at that time was not sufficiently developed to give a full interpretation of the pictures.

291

The next section will describe the different preparation techniques for obtaining thin specimens. After that, a short introduction to dislocations is given and an enumeration of different metallurgical applications. In this article no work on moiré patterns (the interference patterns of different superposed crystal layers) will be discussed. We shall refer as far as possible to review papers.

The papers of a symposium on thin film techniques are published in the August 1959 issue of the *Journal of the Institute of Metals* (11). A review of Japanese work on electron metallography including transmission work is given in the booklet "The World through Electron Microscopes (Metals)" (12).

Note added in proof: Since this article was sent in, many new papers have appeared, most of which are collected in the Proceedings of the Delft Conference 1960 (72).

Preparation Techniques

To be traversed by 100 keV-electrons a crystalline specimen has to be thinner than about 5000 A, and to get information about the interior, the surface has to be as smooth and clean as possible. When these conditions are fulfilled, the information in the pictures depends only on the internal state of the specimen and its orientation. Specimens can be prepared in two main ways:

A. they can be built up directly as a thin foil or

B. they can be cut out of a block and thinned.

Class A covers specimens produced by vapor condensation in vacuum, e.g., on cold or hot rocksalt or by electrolytic deposition. A method, where a metal ring is dipped into liquid metal to produce a metal skin, analogous to a soap skin, has been developed by Takahashi *et al.* (13). The evaporation technique has been perfected to a high degree by D. W. Pashley *et al.* (14).

While the specimens of class A are used mostly to study the behavior of the thin films themselves, specimens produced by a method of class B are considered as representative of the bulk material. Most of the thinning techniques are based on the electropolishing method introduced by Heidenreich (1). Heidenreich electropolished a mechanically thinned disk in a special holder, protecting the edges, branched as anode against a pointed cathode, first from one side to take away the mechanically damaged surface layer and then from the other side until the first tiny hole broke through. In the surroundings of these holes, the specimens were thin enough to be penetrated by the electrons. Castaing (2) added to the electropolishing an ion bombardment treatment with the ion gun built directly into the electron microscope, and was able to control this treatment to obtain the optimum conditions. This technique is especially useful for studying precipitation, e.g., $CuAl_2$ in Al, where the aluminum is preferentially dissolved by electropolishing, while the precipitates are thinned by the ion bombardment. While Hirsch and his co-workers (6) studied beaten Al foils annealed and chemically etched in hydrofluoric acid, Bollmann (7) continued on the line traced by Heidenreich. The modifications to Heidenreich's arrangement were that

(a) the electrolytic attack was symmetrical from both sides of a specimen,

(b) instead of stopping the attack when the first small holes appeared, two large holes were produced and the attack was stopped when these holes joined.

The symmetrical attack has the advantage that the specimen is a symmetry plane of the potential distribution, thus the current is not especially concentrated at the edges of a hole and does not round them off, so that the edges remain sharp. The point (b) has the advantage that the right moment to stop the treatment can be foreseen. The best specimens are found normally at the point where the two holes join, and may be cut out after cleaning in water and methyl alcohol. It is even possible to continue the attack after this and obtain other fairly good specimens. Surveys of electrolytic polishing methods, with detailed information concerning the polishing solutions and conditions for various metals and alloys, are given by Tomlinson (15), and Kelly and Nutting (16). Other variations, such as the "Window Method," the "Figure of Eight Method," and the "Uniform Field Method" are also described in reference 16.

Another technique was introduced by Mirand and Saulnier (17), who treated specimens, first mechanically thinned down to 0.04 mm, in a commercial electropolishing apparatus for metallographic purposes (Disa-Electropol). The specimens were attacked alternately from both sides over a diameter of about 5 mm and then polished down until nothing remained of the original area, except for a few small flakes of metal swimming in the solution; this was subsequently decanted and the flakes were rinsed several times and then fished out with a specimen grid. A certain danger of this method may be that a flake, having remained a short time in the polishing solution without current can become etched, but this will depend on the metals and solutions.

There are a lot of possible electropolishing techniques but normally it takes some time to master any one of them. It is not important which way one originally goes, but it is very important to see from a result in which sense the conditions have to be corrected. For electropolishing it is essential to know that polishing, i.e., the non-specific uniform attack, is only achieved at high current density in a relatively small range. At low current density the attack is metallographic which means that grain boundaries etc. are specifically attacked. On the other hand when the specimen shows a crust on the surface or a spotty attack, the current density or the temperature of the bath is too high.

As the electropolished specimens are used to study the internal situation of the bulk material, especially the distribution of dislocations, the question arises how far this situation has been affected by the preparation. Our impression is that the effect on the distribution of dislocations is small, though minor local changes, as for example straightening of dislocations or a weak relaxation of piled up groups (Fig. 19) may take place. It should be said that the dislocations usually are pinned at the surface of the foil and that dislocation networks are very stable. Another case arises when dislocations start to move after a certain irradiation or after heating or stressing. Here the situation changes and the velocities of movements of dislocations, as filmed by the group Hirsch, Whelan et al. (6, 10) are expected to be quite different in thin foils from those in the bulk material.

A preparation technique for semiconductors, such as germanium and silicon by chemical etching has been developed by Irving (18). For different crystal faces different etchants have been used (e.g. 1% sodium hypochlorite solution for the (111)-face of germanium). Also bismuth telluride has been chemically etched by Geach and Phillips (19).

A completely different way of obtaining thin metal specimens is microtome cutting with a diamond knife, introduced by Fernandez-Moran (20). Metals have been cut in this way by Haanstra (21), Tsuchikura and Ichige (22) and Reimer (23, 24). This method can be useful for obtaining information on different phases but the metal is strongly distorted by the cutting process.

Dislocations

Definition. In a perfect ideal crystal all the atoms are arranged in a periodic lattice structure. After a plastic deformation of the crystal this periodicity is disturbed. For reasons of energy content, the disturbances of the lattice are concentrated locally in lines while the great part of the lattice is periodic as before, except that it is elastically

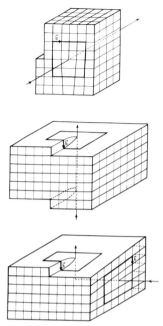

FIG. 1. Schematic representations of dislocations. (top) in edge-orientation (center) in screw orientation (bottom) changing from edge to screw orientation.

strained. Such localized line defects of the plastically deformed lattice are called "dislocations". Schematic representations of dislocations are shown in Fig. 1. The material in the core of the dislocation line, where the crystal order is destroyed, is called "bad" material; the crystalline material around the core even if elastically strained is called "good" material. From the geometry of crystal lattices it follows that dislocation lines cannot end inside the material. They have to be closed loops or must end at the surface of the crystal or at grain boundaries in polycrystalline material.

In transmission electron microscopy of crystals the contrast is essentially given by diffraction effects which are described by Bragg's law

$$2d \sin \theta = n\lambda$$

where d is the spacing of lattice planes, θ the diffraction angle, λ the wavelength of the electrons, and n the order of diffraction

(integer). Dislocation lines become visible because the lattice is strained around the line core which means that d varies locally and thus the Bragg condition and consequently the distribution of the electron intensity between the direct and the diffracted beam varies. As the diffracted beam does not contribute to the image, because it is eliminated by the aperture diaphragm, the intensity of the image is given by the intensity of the direct beam only. A survey of the theory of the contrast due to dislocations and stacking faults etc. is given by Whelan (26).

Fig. 2 shows pictures of dislocations as they can be seen by transmission electron microscopy. As dislocations cannot end inside the material, the ends of the lines lie on the top or the bottom of the foil.

A quantitative characteristic of a dislocation line is the so-called "Burgers vector" which is defined in the following way:

First the dislocation line is given an arbitrary direction. Then, around the line a circuit is marked in the *sense of a right-hand screw* far enough from the core of the dislocation to be always in "good" material. The circuit has to be traced in such a way that it would be closed in a perfect crystal

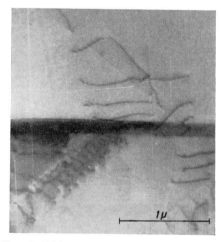

FIG. 2. Dislocations lines in stainless steel, crossing the foil top to bottom and traversing a twin boundary.

(as many steps to the right as to the left, etc.). The vector pointing from the end to the beginning of the circuit is the "Burgers vector" $\vec{b}$. Examples are shown in Fig. 1. The sign of the Burgers vector has only a meaning in connection with the direction of the dislocation line. Changing the one also changes the other (right-hand screw!).

Frank has given another definition of the Burgers vector, where a closed Burgers circuit in a dislocated crystal is imaged onto an ideal crystal where the closure failure there is the Burgers vector. The result is essentially the same but the procedure is academically more correct.

The Burgers vector in magnitude and

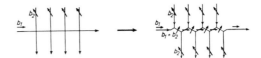

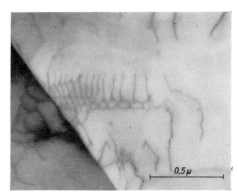

FIG. 4. Interaction of dislocations forming a network during cold-working. (Whelan,[29] Courtesy Royal Society)

direction is constant along a dislocation line, even when the line changes its direction (Fig. 1c). That part of a dislocation line perpendicular to its Burgers vector is said to be in an "edge" orientation, that parallel to its Burgers vector in a "screw" orientation. A dislocation line can be curved and follow all intermediate stages between edge and screw orientations.

Dislocations can interact and form nodes. The law here is that the sum of the Burgers vectors of all dislocations entering the node is equal to the sum of the Burgers vectors of those emerging from the node (analogous to Kirchoff's law). Complicated network can be formed, of which examples are given in Figs. 3, 4 and 5. A detailed analysis of dislocation interactions in stainless steel has been given by Whelan (29).

Movement. Essentially two kinds of movement of dislocations have to be distinguished—"glide" and "climb"; these are schematically shown in Fig. 6 and 7. Glide is a movement parallel to the Burgers vector, while climb is perpendicular to it. Glide does not need material transport, as it is the movement of a configuration analogous to a

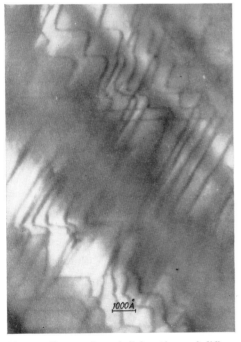

FIG. 3. Interaction of dislocations of different orientations but the same Burgers vector in stainless steel during cold-working. (Whelan [29] Courtesy Royal Society)

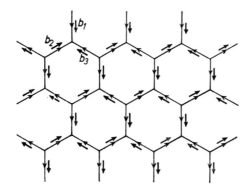

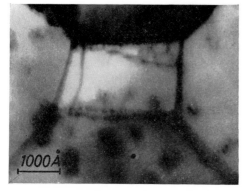

FIG. 5. Hexagonal network forming a twist boundary between two (111)-planes during polygonization in aluminium. (*Hirsch, Horne and Whelan,*[6] *Courtesy Philosophical Magazine*)

wave, while climb does. Glide is produced by a shear stress, while climb needs hydrostatic pressure or tension. Glide is essentially responsible for cold working, while climb contributes to high temperature creep because diffusion is only possible at high temperatures.

The glide of dislocations is shown in the films of the group Hirsch, Whelan *et al.* (6, 10) on aluminum and stainless steel (Fig. 8). The specimen is locally heated by the electron beam inside the electron microscope. The thermal stresses produced by this heating perhaps in connection with the surface contamination through oil vapor act so as to move the dislocations. This movement can be slow because of pinning of the dislocations at the oxide layer on the surface or it

can be so quick that only the slip traces left by the moving dislocations mark their path. Wilsdorf (30) and also Berghezan and Foudreux (31) have studied the movement of dislocations due to externally applied stresses.

A moving dislocation cuts the volume into two domains, one of which is displaced (dislocated!) with respect to the other. Which one is displaced and how much can be recognized in the following way.

$$(\vec{v} \times \vec{l}) = \vec{m}$$

where v is the velocity vector of the dislocation, $\vec{l}$ a vector in the direction of the

GLIDE

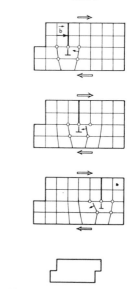

FIG. 6. Glide movement of a dislocation in edge orientation (*Courtesy Schweizer Archiv*)

CLIMB

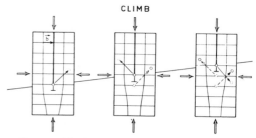

FIG. 7. Climb movement of a dislocation in edge orientation (*Courtesy Schweizer Archiv*)

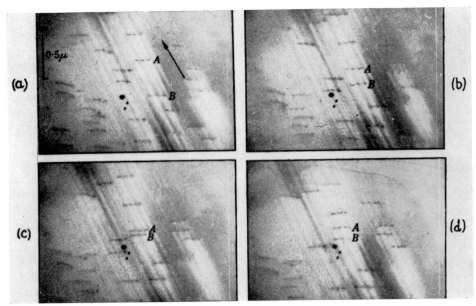

FIG. 8. Sequence of the film on stainless steel showing the glide movement of dislocations. The black dots in the center are marks on the fluorescent screen of the microscope. The object has been displaced during observation. (*Whelan, Hirsch, Horne and Bollman*[10] *Courtesy Royal Society*)

line in the defined line direction, $\overrightarrow{m}$ is a vector which points to one of the two domains. This indicated domain is displaced with respect to the other by the Burgers vector $\vec{b}$ when the dislocation passes. This rule can be verified for the cases in Fig. 1. Thus glide steps on the surface of a material are produced by the sum of the displacements due to the individual dislocations; these have been studied at the edges of thin films by Hirsch *et al.* (32) (Fig. 9).

Forces Between Dislocations. The energy of a dislocation, i.e., the work that has to be done to produce a unit length of a dislocation line is proportional to $\vec{b}^2$ ($\vec{b}$ = Burgers vector). This shows that a dislocation always tends to attain the smallest possible Burgers vector. The energy E of a dislocation with a Burgers vector $(2\,\vec{b}_0)$ would be twice the energy of two separate and sufficient far apart dislocations with Burgers vector $\vec{b}_0$ each: $(2\,\vec{b}_0)^2 = 2(\,\vec{b}_0{}^2 + \vec{b}_0{}^2)$. Two parallel dislocation lines, the Burgers vectors of which include an angle smaller than

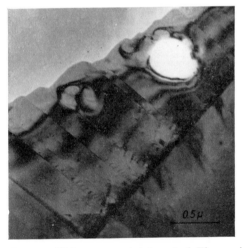

FIG. 9. Glide steps on stainless steel. The specimen was etched only from one side. (*Hirsch, Partridge and Segall*,[32] *Courtesy Philosophical Magazine*)

90° repel each other. If this angle is larger than 90° they attract each other. (The 90°-case corresponds to the theorem of Pythagoras!) A detailed analysis of the stress field between dislocations shows that the forces

297

can be noncentral ones. Such problems are discussed in the previously mentioned books on dislocation theory, (8, 9, 25) and the repulsion and attraction of dislocations are

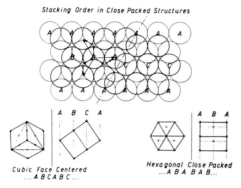

FIG. 10. Stacking order in close packed structures.

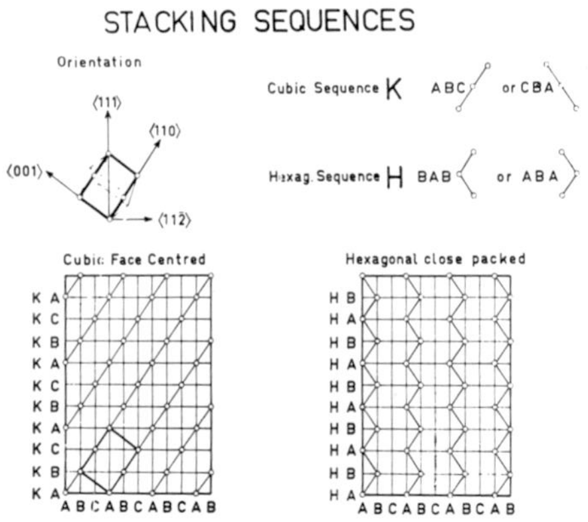

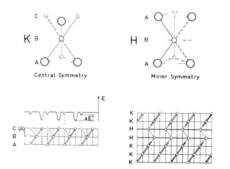

FIG. 11. Stacking sequence in the face-centered cubic and hexagonal close-packed structures.

FIG. 12. Symmetry of nearest neighbour atoms in relation to the stacking energy.

directly observable in the films (6, 10) (Fig. 8).

Stacking Faults and Partial Dislocations

As is well known, a cubic face-centered lattice can be understood as a close-packed structure of spheres. On a basic layer in position A a second layer can be placed in two different ways, in position B or C (Fig. 10). If the position B is chosen for the second layer there remain C and A for the third one and so on. A stacking sequence ...ABCABC... builds up a face-centered cubic lattice, a stacking sequence...ABAB... a hexagonal close-packed lattice.

The fact that a given material crystallizes in a certain structure, e.g. face centered cubic, shows that once the first two layers A and B are ready, the work to build up the third layer must be lower for position C than for position A, because if there would be no difference the stacking sequence would be random (Fig. 11). Looking at all connections to nearest neighbors of an atom in the second B layer one sees that these connections (directions of binding forces) are of central symmetry in the f.c.c. structure (ABC sequence) and of mirror symmetry in the hexagonal c.p. structure (ABA sequence), Fig. 12. Thus in a f.c.c. lattice the ABC (CBA, BCA, etc.) sequence with central symmetry marked by K has a lower energy (needs less work to be built up) than the ABA (CAC, BCB, etc.) sequence marked by H.

Different kinds of faults can occur in the stacking sequence; here we consider only the f.c.c. case. A single H inserted into all K means a growth fault (twin boundary; Figs. 13a and b). Two consecutive H mean a so-called "deformation stacking fault" (Figs. 14a and b).

Thus to a first approximation a deformation stacking fault has twice the energy of a twin boundary (Fig. 12).

The Burgers vector of a (total) dislocation line normally is the shortest connection between two atoms in the lattice surrounded by atoms in the same symmetry. In a f.c.c. lattice it is of the type $(a/2)$ (110) (connection between the corner to the centre of the face in the unit cell). At the same time it is the connection between two spheres in a close packed plane (Fig. 15). When a dislocation moves between a layer A and a

layer B, the atoms in the layer B have to jump from the starting position to the neighboring position the Burgers vector $\vec{b}$ away. This jump can be achieved in two steps $B_1 \rightarrow C$ and $C \rightarrow B_2$. C in this case is not a lattice site but the site occupied when a stacking fault is at this place. Such a splitting of a total dislocation into two "partial dislocations" or "partials" is described by the equation in Fig. 15 for the Burgers vectors. A partial dislocation is not a dislocation line in the usual sense but the boundary of a stacking fault.

As the Burgers vectors of the two partial dislocations include an angle smaller than 90° they repel each other. By separating, the two partial dislocations have to do work to produce a stacking fault in between them. When the stacking fault energy is high, the stacking fault ribbon between the two partials becomes narrow and vice versa. The splitting of dislocations into stacking fault

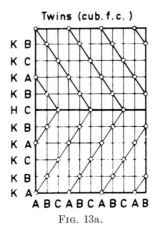

Twins (cub. f.c.)

FIG. 13a.

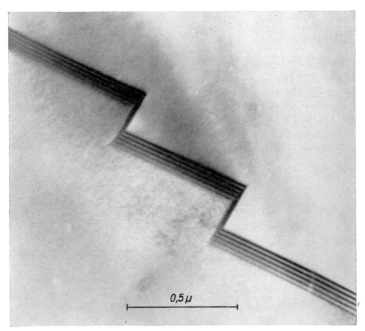

0,5 μ

FIG. 13b.

FIG. 13. Twin boundary in stainless steel. (*Whelan, Hirsch, Horne and Bollman*[10] *Courtesy Royal Society*)

Stacking Fault (cub. f.c.)

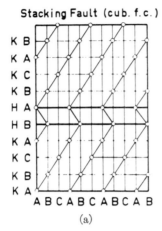

(a)

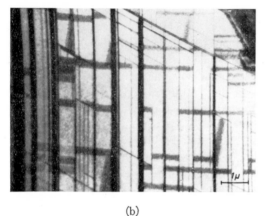

(b)

FIG. 14. (a) Schematic representation of a stacking fault. (b) System of stacking faults in cobalt on all 4 (111)-planes. These stacking faults stabilize the observed region in the cubic phase at room temperature although it normally would be hexagonal.

ribbons can be seen in the film on dislocations in stainless steel (10) (Fig. 16).

Dislocations glide especially easily on certain planes (the so-called glide planes) which in the case of the cubic face centered lattice are (111)-planes (close-packed planes perpendicular to the space diagonal of the unit cell). If a dislocation ribbon is narrow, it can easily change from one glide system to the other, when the Burgers vector is parallel to both glide planes. This movement is called cross-slip (Fig. 17). It has been observed in aluminum, which is a metal

with high stacking fault energy and thus with narrow dislocation ribbons. If the dislocation ribbon is wide, the Burgers vector is composed of the two vectors of the partial dislocations, both lying in the glide plane. To change the glide plane, the ribbon has to be contracted and to dissociate again into two new partial dislocations lying in the new glide plane. In a metal with low stacking fault energy like stainless steel, this is only possible at a serious obstacle as for example a twin boundary (Fig. 18) but another dislocation on the same slip plane is not sufficient to introduce cross slip so that series of dislocation originating from the same source become piled up against each other (Fig. 19) and thus form piled up groups.

Contrast Due to Stacking Faults

A theory explaining the observed fringes from stacking faults has been given by Whelan and Hirsch (33, 34) on the basis of the kinematical and dynamical theory of electron diffraction. These authors showed

SPLITTING OF A DISLOCATION LINE INTO PARTIAL DISLOCATIONS

$$\vec{b}_1 = \vec{b}_2 + \vec{b}_3$$
$$\frac{a}{2}[10\bar{1}] = \frac{a}{6}[11\bar{2}] + \frac{a}{6}[2\bar{1}\bar{1}]$$

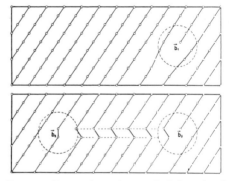

FIG. 15. Separation of a total dislocation into partials.

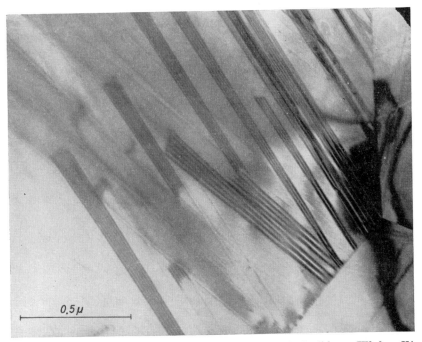

FIG. 16. Splitting of dislocations in stainless steel into stacking fault ribbons (*Whelan, Hirsch, Horne and Bollman*[10], *Courtesy Royal Society*)

that the fringes are shifted by half a period, when two stacking faults are present, and disappear completely when three or a multiple of three stacking faults follow each other (Fig. 20).

Condensed Vacancies

A theory of Kuhlmann-Wilsdorf (35) concerns the condensation of vacancies, when a metal is quenched from a high temperature. These features have been observed by Hirsch *et al.* (36). In aluminum the vacancies condense in a close packed plane as small disks, which collapse. Such a collapsed disk would form a stacking fault surrounded by a so-called sessile partial dislocation with a Burgers vector of the type (a/3) (111). As the stacking fault energy of aluminum is high, the disk does not collapse perpendicular to the plane but inclined, adding a glissile partial dislocation (a/3) (111) + (a/6) (11$\bar{2}$) = (a/2) (110) thus forming a dislocation ring (Fig. 21). As the Burgers vector

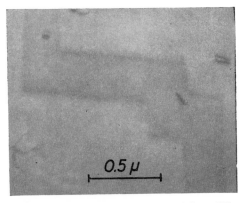

FIG. 17. Cross slip trace in aluminium (Silcox (in 27) *Courtesy Institute of Metals*)

sticks out of the plane this dislocation ring can only glide on a cylinder parallel to the Burgers vector. Under shear stress, the dislocation ring expands over the cylinder, one part gliding downward, the other upward.

In a metal with low stacking fault energy, like gold, the disks of condensed vacancies collapse really to a stacking fault, but to

301

lower the energy even more this extends over all 4 (111)-planes, thus forming small tetrahedra of stacking faults (Silcox and Hirsch (37)), (Fig. 22).

In other cases the interactions between vacancies and dislocations produce helical dislocations as observed by Thomas and Whelan (38) (Fig. 23).

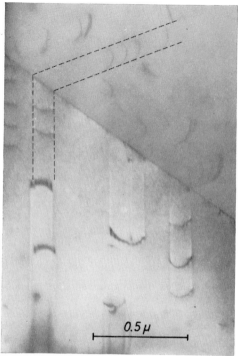

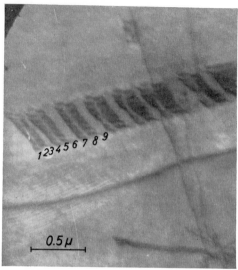

FIG. 20. Superposed stacking faults. (*Whelan and Hirsch,*[34] *Courtesy Philosophical Magazine*)

FIG. 18. Dislocation lines traversing a twin boundary (*Whelan, Hirsch, Horne and Bollmann,*[10] *Courtesy Royal Society*)

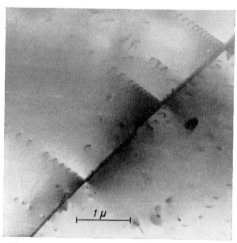

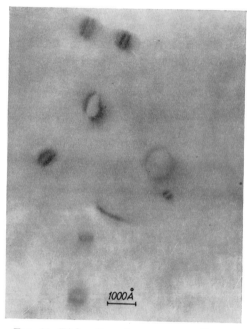

FIG. 19. Groups of dislocations piled up against a twin boundary (*Whelan, Hirsch, Horne and Bollmann,*[10] *Courtesy Royal Society*)

FIG. 21. Dislocation loops surrounding collapsed disks of condensed vacancies in quenched aluminum. (*Hirsch, Silcox, Smallman and Westmacott,*[36] *Courtesy Philosophical Magazine*)

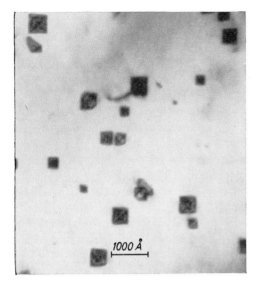

FIG. 22. Tetrahedra of stacking faults in quenched gold. (*Silcox and Hirsch*,[37] *Courtesy Philosophical Magazine*)

Some Metallurgical Topics Studied by Transmission Electron Microscopy

Transmission electron microscopy is now used to a large extent to get a deeper insight into metallurgical effects. Here only a short and incomplete list can be given of work achieved in this field. This kind of research is in full development.

Work hardening finds its explanation in the networks of dislocations which hinder the movement of further dislocations. As the movement of dislocations means plastic deformation, a hindrance of this movement means increased resistance against plastic deformation, i.e., hardening. Metals with high stacking fault energy like aluminum work-harden less than those with low stacking fault energy like stainless steel, because of the possibility of cross slip. Herein belongs a lot of work on dislocation reactions (6, 10, 29). Thomas and Hale (39) investigated the relation between surface structure and underlying dislocations due to deformation.

Quench hardening is explained by the formation of dislocation loops (35, 36) or

stacking fault tetrahedra by condensed vacancies (37). The interaction of dislocations and vacancy clusters has been discussed by Wilsdorf and Kuhlmann-Wilsdorf (40).

Fatigue has been studied by Segall and Partridge (41). In aluminum dislocation loops of condensed vacancies and complicated shapes of dislocation lines were observed which indicate the importance of vacancies in this process (Fig. 24). In stainless steel (41) very narrow slip bands and extrusions and intrusions were seen.

Observations on *recovery* and *recrystallization* have been made by Fujita and Nishijama (42), and Berghezan and Foudreux (43) on aluminum by Saulnier and Develay on titanium (44), by Bollmann (45) on nickel (Fig. 25) and by Bailey (46) on silver. These studies have given an insight into the polygonization and the formation of new crystal grains in heavily rolled material as well as into recrystallization by the move-

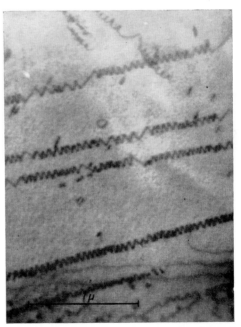

FIG. 23. Helical dislocations produced by the condensation of vacancies on dislocation lines. (*Thomas and Whelan*,[38] *Courtesy Philosophical Magazine*)

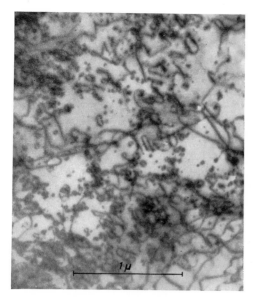

FIG. 24. Dislocation arrangements in fatigued aluminum: loops of condensed vacancies and irregular dislocation shapes resulting from climb. (*Segall and Partridge,*[41] *Courtesy Philosophical Magazine*)

FIG. 25. Crystal grain containing twins growing in incompletely polygonized surroundings in nickel. (*Bollman,*[45] *Courtesy Institute of Metals*)

ment of old grain boundaries at low deformation.

A study on the formation of *precipitates* in Al-Ag alloy has been made by Funkano and Ogawa (47). A review on precipitation phenomena has been given by Nicholson, Thomas and Nutting (48), (Fig. 26) who took a ciné film showing the formation and dissolution of precipitates.

Eutectic structures have been studied in SnPb by Takahashi and Ashinuma (49) and on pearlite by Nishiyama *et al.* (50).

Studies of Silcox and Hirsch (mentioned in (27)) on *radiation damage* in copper show the production of condensed vacancy loops and the growth of these loops with higher neutron doses (Fig. 27). Wilsdorf (51) has shown similar effects in neutron irradiated nickel.

Anti-phase domains in a CuAu-alloy and in AuCuZn-alloy have been studied by Ogawa *et al.* (52, 53) and in CuAu by Glossup and Pashley (54). CuAu II shows a super-lattice, with layers of copper and of gold atoms stacked on each other in the (001) direction while the sequence changes every five elementary cells in the (100) direction, so that phase boundaries are regularly spaced every 20 A. The formation of these domains was directly observed whilst the specimen was heated (Fig. 28). This work is reviewed by Pashley and Presland (55).

Observations on *martensitic transformations* in thin films of iron alloys have been published by Nijama and Shimizu (56) and

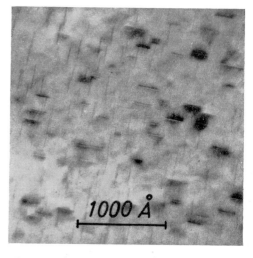

FIG. 26. Guinier-Preston zones in Al-4%-Cu.

by Pitsch (57). Pitsch suggested a transformation mechanism for thin foils and gave evidence for the mechanism in bulk material by a combination of transmission microscopy and diffraction.

Thin metal films and their properties have been studied for the case of condensed layers by Takahashi and Mihama (58) for an Al-Cu alloy. The recrystallization was followed, while the object was heated on a hot stage inside the microscope. Twins in condensed layers of silver, gold, copper and nickel (59) as well as electrodeposited nickel (60) have been investigated by Ogawa *et al.* Reimer made similar observations on electrodeposited metals (61) and condensed silver (62). Studies on the formation of condensed layers (63) and the mechanical properties such as crack propagation within films are reviewed by Bassett and Pashley (64). Beaten gold (65) and precipitated gold flakes have been studied by Brüche *et al.* (66). Brame and Evans (67) studied the deformation of thin films on solid substrates.

Studies on *different alloys* are summarized by Saulnier and Mirand (68). Observations on *semi-conductor material* as germanium,

FIG. 28. CuAu II in the stage of formation. (*Pashley and Presland,*[55] *Courtesy Institute of Metals*)

silicon (69, 70) and bismuth telluride (19) have been made by Geach, Phillips and Irving.

Surface together with the underlying structure have been investigated for the case of deformation by Thomas and Hale (39) and for studying an etching structure of aluminum by Phillips and Welsh (71). This kind of research is possible by electropolishing only one side of the specimen, while the other is protected by a varnish.

These few examples may show that transmission electron microscopy is a powerful means for the study of defects and precipitates in crystalline solids, the knowledge of these defects being of great importance for the understanding of the physical behavior of crystallized matter.

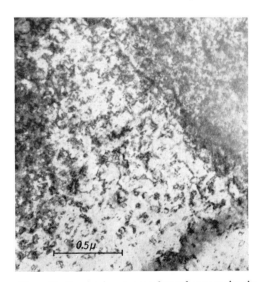

FIG. 27. Loops due to condensed vacancies in neutron irradiated copper. (*Silcox (in 27) Courtesy Institute of Metals*)

REFERENCES

1. HEIDENREICH, R. D., *J. Appl. Phys.*, **20**, 993 (1949).
2. CASTAING, R., "Proceedings the Third International Conference on Electron Microscopy" (London 1954) p. 379.
3. SUITO, E. AND UYEDA, N., Proc. of the Japan Academy, **29**, 324–330 (1953).
4. HASHIMOTO, H., *J. Phys. Soc. Japan*, **9**, 150–161–(1954).

5. TAKAHASHI, N., TAKEYAMA, T., ITO, K., ITO, T., MIHAMA, K., AND WATANABE, M., *J. Electronmicroscopy*, **4**, 16–23 (1956).

6. HIRSCH, P. B., HORNE, R. W., AND WHELAN, M. J., *Phil. Mag.*, **1**, 677 (1956).

7. BOLLMANN, W., *Phys. Rev.*, **103**, 1588–1589 (1956); "Proc. Stockholm Conference on Electron Microscopy," 1956, p. 316–317, Stockholm (1957).

8. COTTRELL, A. H., "Dislocations and Plastic Flow in Crystals," (Oxford, 1953).

9. READ, W. T., JR., "Dislocations in Crystals," New York (1953).

10. WHELAN, H. J., HIRSCH, P. B., HORNE, R. W., AND BOLLMANN, W., *Proc. Roy. Soc.* **A240**, 524–538 (1957).

11. *J. Inst. Metals*, **87**, 385–458 (Aug., 1959).

12. "The World through Electron Microscopes," Japan Electron Optics Laboratory Co. Ltd., (Tokyo, 1959).

13. TAKAHASHI, N., ASHINUMA, K., AND WATANABE, M., *J. Electronmicroscopy*, **5**, 22–27 (1957).

14. PASHLEY, D. W., *Phil. Mag.*, **4**, 316 (1959).

15. TOMLINSON, H. M., *Phil. Mag.*, **3**, 867–871 (1958).

16. KELLEY, P. H. AND NUTTING, J., *J. Inst. Met.*, **4**, 385–391 (1959).

17. MIRAND, P. AND SAULNIER, A., *Compt. rend.* **246**, 1688 (1958).

18. IRVING, B. A., *Brit. J. Physics* (in press).

19. GEACH, G. A. AND PHILLIPS, R., 4. Int. Kongress f. Elektronenmikroskopie (1958) Berlin 1960, p. 571–574.

20. FERNANDEZ-MORAN, H., *J. Biophys. Biochem. Cytol.* **2** (suppl.), 29 (1956).

21. HAANSTRA, H. B., *Philips Techn. Review*, **17**, 178–183 (1955).

22. TSUCHIKURA, H. AND ICHIGE, K., *Nature*, **181**, 694 (1958).

23. REIMER, L., *Z. Metallkunde*, **50**, 37 (1959).

24. REIMER, L., *Naturwiss.*, **46**, 68 (1959).

25. FRIEDEL, J., "Les Dislocations," Paris, 1956.

26. HIRSCH, P. B., *Metallurgical Reviews*.

27. HIRSCH, P. B., *J. Inst. Metals*, **87** (12), 406–418 (1959).

28. WHELAN, M. J., *J. Inst. Metals*, **87** (12) 392–405 (1959).

29. WHELAN, M. J., *Proc. Roy. Soc.*, **A249**, 114–137 (1959).

30. WILSDORF, H., 4. Int. Kongress f. Elektronenmikroskopie (1958) Berlin 1960, p. 559–562.

31. BERGHEZAN, A. AND FOUDREUX, A., *Compt. rend.*, **248**, 1333–1335 (1959).

32. HIRSCH, P. B., PARTRIDGE, P. G., AND SEGALL, R. L., *Phil. Mag.*, **4**, 721 (1959).

33. WHELAN, M. J. AND HIRSCH, P. B., *Phil. Mag.*, **2**, 1121, (1957).

34. WHELAN, M. J. AND HIRSCH, P. B., *Phil. Mag.*, **2**, 1303 (1957).

35. KUHLMANN-WILSDORF, D., *Phil. Mag.*, **3**, 125–139 (1958).

36. HIRSCH, P. B., SILCOX, J., SMALLMAN, R. E., AND WESTMACOTT, K. H., *Phil. Mag.*, **3**, 897 (1958).

37. SILCOX, J. AND HIRSCH, P. B., *Phil. Mag.*, **4**, 72 (1959).

38. THOMAS, G. AND WHELAN, M. J., *Phil. Mag.*, **4**, 511 (1959).

39. THOMAS, K. AND HALE, K. F., *Phil. Mag.*, **4**, 531 (1959).

40. WILSDORF, H. G. F. AND KUHLMANN-WILSDORF, D., *Phys. Rev. Letters*, **3**, 170–172 (1959).

41. SEGALL, R. L. AND PARTRIDGE, P. G., *Phil. Mag.*, **4**, 912–919 (1959).

42. FUJITA, H. AND NISHIYAMA, Z., *Metal Physics (Japan)* **3**, 108 (1957) (in Japanese) (to be published in English).

43. BERGHEZAN, A. AND FOUDREUX, A., *Compt. rend.*, **247**, 1194–1196 (1958).

44. SAULNIER A., AND DEVELAY R., "Symposium de métallurgie spéciale Saclay" (1957).

45. BOLLMANN, W., *J. Inst. Metals*, **87**, (12) 439–443 (1959).

46. BAILEY, J., Thesis, Cambridge University, 1959.

47. FUNKANO, Y. AND OGAWA, S., *Acta Cryst.*, **9**, 917 (1956).

48. NICHOLSON, R. B., THOMAS, G., AND NUTTING, J., *J. Inst. Metals*, **87**, (12), 429–438 (1958).

49. TAKAHASHI, N., AND ASHINUMA, K., *J. Inst. Metals*, **87**, 19–23 (1958–59).

50. NISHIYAMA, Z., KORE'EDA, A., AND SHIMIZU, K., *J. Electronmicroscopy*, **7**, 41–47 (1959).

51. WILSDORF, H. G. F., *Phys. Rev. Letters*, **3**, 172–173 (1959).

52. OGAWA, S., WATANABE, D., WATANABE, H., AND KOMODA, T., *J. Phys. Soc. Japan*, **14**, 936–941 (1959).

53. OGAWA, S., WATANABE, D., WATANABE, H., AND KOMODA, T., *Acta crystal.*, **11**, 872–875 (1958).

54. GLOSSOP, A. B. AND HASHLEY, D. W., *Proc. Royal Soc.* **A250**, 132–146 (1959).

55. PASHLEY, D. W. AND PRESLAND, A. E. B., *J. Inst. Metals*, **87** (12), 419–428 (1959).

56. NISHIYAMA, Z. AND SHIMIZU, K., *Acta Met.*, **7**, 432 (1959).

57. PITSCH, W., *J. Inst. Metals*, **87** (12), 444–448 (1959).

58. TAKAHASHI, N. AND MIHAMA, K., *Acta Met.* **5**, 159 (1957).

59. OGAWA, S., WATANABE, D., AND FUJITA, E., *J. Phys. Soc. Japan*, **10**, 429 (1955).

60. OGAWA, S., MIZUNO, J., WATANABE, D., AND FUJITA, E., *J. Phys. Soc. Japan*, **12**, 999 (1957).

61. REIMER, L., *Z. Metallkunde*, **47**, 631 (1956).

62. REIMER, L., *Optik*, **16**, 30 (1959).

63. PASHLEY, D. W., *Phil. Mag.*, **4**, 324 (1959).

64. BASSETT, G. A. AND PASHLEY, D. W., *J. Inst. Metals*, **87** (12) 449–458 (1959).

65. BRÜCHE, E. AND SCHULZE, K. J., *Z. Physik*, **153**, 571–591 (1959).

66. BRÜCHE, E. AND DEMNY, J., *Z. Naturforschung*, **14a**, 351–354 (1959).

67. BRAME, D. R. AND EVANS, T., *Phil. Mag.*, **3**, 971–986 (1958).

68. SAULNIER, A. AND MIRAND, P., *Revue de l'Aluminium*, **266**, 687–697 (1959).

69. GEACH, G. A., IRVING, B. A., AND PHILLIPS, R., *Research*, **10**, Oct., 1957.

70. PHILLIPS, R., *J. Inst. Metals* (July 1958) p. 72 (Bull. Vol. 4).

71. PHILLIPS, R. AND WELSH, N. C., *Phil. Mag.*, **3**, 801 (1958).

72. The Proceedings of the European Regional Conference on Electron Microscopy Delft 1960 (Delft 1961).

W. BOLLMANN

UNSOLVED PROBLEMS

The following comments are germane only to applications of the electron microscope and related microscopy in non-biological areas. In general, it appears that the electron microscope has been used in the biological sciences more as a research tool than as an analytical service instrument.

Quantitative Particle Size Distribution Data. This is in principle a very important application and yet there are essentially no accurate studies of this kind in the available literature. Size and shape assays of paint pigments, magnetic powders, semiconductor powders, etc., are of fundamental importance particularly where the peak of the size distribution curve is of the order of several hundred angstroms. The color or tone of duplicating media is often related to the Mie theory for particle scattering which in turn uses the sixth power of the particle (sphere) radius. Also the surface area and surface to volume ratio are important to properties of semiconductors such as photo- and dark conductivity.

Ultrathin Sections. Multilayer coatings such as magnetic tapes and photosensitive copy papers exhibit properties which are dependent on the distribution and orientation of particulate solids within a binder. Thin sections normal and parallel to the plane of the coating are needed, but to date little progress has been made in preparing sections suitably thin for electron microscopy. Unlike the biological tissue sections, the difference in hardness of the two or more components in the sample militate against the preparation of sections of the order of 500 angstroms thick. However more effort is needed in this area.

Somewhat related to this problem is the inability of x-ray microscopy to provide useful information in such studies of coated samples. Overlapping of particles makes interpretation difficult, or smallness of size with respect to the resolving power of the instrument makes interpretation impossible. For the most part the significant applications of the x-ray microscope have been confined to metallic and biological materials.

Replicas. Again, it is very difficult to prepare surface replicas of certain coatings such as magnetic tape and photosensitive papers. The inertness and insolubility of the binder impairs isolation of the replica by dissolution. Hydrophyllic stripping layers have not proved to be successful. In many cases, despite the inertness of the binder, the effects of heat and pressure, solvents, or the radiation and vacuum attendant to evaporation techniques make the isolation of good quality replicas difficult, or they may vitiate the results. Nondestructive studies are often obviated by the inadequacy of the stripping layers.

A few remarks are in order in regard to the responsibility of industrial management to the microscopist. First, where feasible the management should establish two distinctly different groups: a service group and an entirely separate exploratory research group. The two groups carry out radically different functions which need no further defining. It is unwise to mix the two.

Second, it is imperative that the personnel in these groups be different. Specifically, those people in the service group should be adept at preparing specimens, maintaining and operating the instrument, cognizant of the limitations of their techniques, and certainly conversant with a broad spectrum of people with whom they have to deal. In short, they should be internal consultants. On the other hand, those in the basic research group, having their own instruments, should be primarily chemists, physicists, biologists, metallurgists, etc. They should be left alone to "get lost" in their particular long-range programs. Communication between the two groups should be encouraged in the interest of mutual assistance.

As to the cost of duplicating equipment it may be said—and not facetiously—that only money is needed to purchase the instruments. Intelligent, productive people cannot be so easily obtained, whatever the available funds may be. In short, equipment is a comparatively inexpensive investment.

FRANKLIN A. HAMM

WEAR AND LUBRICATION

Wear may be defined as the displacement or removal of material from a surface; it has many forms, its nature and magnitude being dependent on a variety of factors. The more significant of these are speed, load, surface condition, metallurgical structure, the presence of abrasive matter and corrosive environment. The wear process can be classified generally into two main types—mechanical and chemical. Mechanical wear involves processes which may be associated with friction, abrasion, fatigue and vibration, whereas chemical wear is caused by an at-

tack of the surface by reactive compounds or corrosive media and the subsequent rubbing or breaking away of the reaction products. The various wear processes may occur singly, simultaneously or in sequence. Progress in wear prevention can be made only after a real understanding of the basic mechanisms has been achieved. Toward this end microscopes and ancillary equipment are probably the most useful and widely used tools available to research workers and investigators (1).

The topography, chemical and physical nature of surfaces can influence the wear behavior of many materials, thus the starting point of any investigation should be a study of the surfaces involved. Many techniques are available to examine the topography of surfaces but optical methods allow the specimen to be investigated without destroying it or subjecting it to strain or wear. Stylus methods provide an immediate numerical characterization of a surface, but may be subject to the uncertainty of the extent of damage done to soft materials by the stylus itself. The profile microscope (Tolansky (2)), like stylus methods, gives a single line profile and it may be necessary to observe many different recordings in order to form a comprehensive conception of the surface. Observing an enlarged image of the surface from above by normal microscopic examination is useful, but permits no conclusion regarding roughness. The interference microscope on the other hand can be used to reveal and evaluate minute surface irregularities. In the image these appear as deviations in the bands or fringes which represent contour lines connecting all points of the same level (Fig. 1). The difference in level between different fringes corresponds to half a wavelength of the light used. The magnification is irrelevant and the geometric shape of the test piece plays only a subordinate role.

In wear studies, suitable selection of the method of specimen illumination can extend the versatility and range of the modern

(a) Normal illumination.

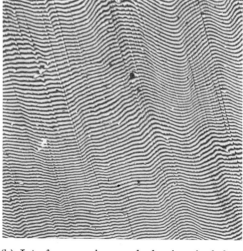

(b) Interference micrograph showing rippled nature of the surface.

FIG. 1. Surface of a worn gear tooth. (After Scott[1]) 50×

microscope. A particular surface feature may be emphasized by a specific form of illumination. Some surface irregularities may be revealed more easily by dark field or oblique illumination, the irregularities which diffract the light appearing light on a dark background. Phase-contrast microscopes may be used to advantage to examine wear damage and surface deformation as phase contrast is very sensitive to changes in surface levels and can reveal minute slip lines and fine surface irregularities hardly visible or quite invisible under normal illumination (Fig. 2). The use of polarized light can supplement information obtained with phase-contrast and interference techniques.

In order to examine microscopically selected surface areas of large, unwieldy specimens or parts of machines without dismantling the machine or seriously interrupting its use, replica techniques may be used to advantage (1). Replicas may be rendered more highly reflecting by coating *in vacuo* with a metal such as aluminum.

To study both surface and sub-surface changes brought about by rubbing, sliding, rolling or corrosive action it is usual to cut a cross-section for microscopic examination; if the specimen is sectioned at an acute angle to the plane of the surface, a further magnification factor is obtained of dimensions perpendicular to the original surface. Taper-sectioning (Moore (3)), carried out by grinding at a predetermined small angle to the plane of the surface following suitable plating and mounting of the specimen, is useful in studying changes of surface profile and sub-surface metallographic changes (1, 4, 5).

To those engaged in a detailed study of wear and the changes caused by rubbing contact, knowledge of the physical properties of individual crystals, aggregates and surface films, etc., is essential, and micro-hardness testing technique (Taylor (6)) may be used in conjunction with microscopic and metallographic examination. It is often important to determine the extent of work hardening on a surface, the depth and hardness of surface films, as well as to elucidate metallographic changes produced by the wear process (Fig. 3).

The success of microscopic and metallographic investigations of surface and sub-surface changes depends largely on the

309

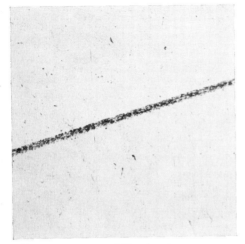

(a) Normal illumination.　　　　(b) Phase-contrast showing nature of the surface

FIG. 2. Stylus trace on an anodized aluminium surface. (After Scott[1]) 100×

FIG. 3. Taper section of a worn surface showing the surface contour, sub-surface metallographic changes and indentations of a micro-hardness survey with V.P.N. superimposed. Etched Nital. (After Scott[1])

$$H = 140\times, \quad V = 1400\times$$

careful use of metallurgical techniques of sectioning, polishing and etching. It is essential that the methods used do not change, obliterate, or destroy in any way the evidence being sought. Besides the conventional methods, spark erosion machining (Nosov and Bykov (7)) offers many advantages for harder materials and specific applications while electropolishing (Jacquet (8)) is useful. Electroplating is used to protect the edges of specimens and surface films from damage during preparation for microscopic and metallographic examination, and specimens which have a non-conducting surface may be successfully plated if a thin film of metal is first deposited in a high vacuum. For ease of manipulation specimens may be mounted in a suitable plastic.

Although much information can be derived from the use of optical microscopy, as the initiation of surface damage may be expected to occur on a sub-microscopic scale a more detailed surface examination is sometimes required and the electron microscope can be used to follow paths of exploration to higher degrees of resolution (9). Examination may be made directly by reflection (Halliday (10)) or by preparing surface replicas which are examined in transmission. The first method is limited to the use of specimens sufficiently small to be accommodated in the microscope, while the latter method although occasionally subject to artefacts has the advantage that the replica may be taken from worn surfaces *in situ* (Figs. 4 and 5). The transmission electron microscope has successfully been used for studying the initiation of wear and fretting corrosion (4, 9).

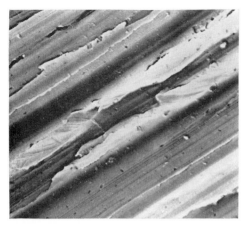

FIG. 4. Electron micrograph of a positive carbon replica of a finely ground steel surface (1212 micro-inches C. L. A.) 5000×

FIG. 5. Direct reflection electron micrograph showing a scratch on a mechanically polished surface finished with finest abrasive paper. 2500×

Debris from worn surfaces and abrasive particles which have been separated from the lubricant by centrifuging (9) may be conveniently examined in the electron microscopes by standard methods (Fig. 6). Such examination may reveal the size, shape and possibly the abrasive nature of the debris while micro-diffraction may be used for identification. Both optical and electron microscopy can be used together with metallographic methods to elucidate changes effected by deformation and strain. Elegant extraction replica techniques (11, 12) are

available which in conjunction with electron diffraction can be used to determine precipitation segregation while the recent microprobe analysis technique (13) can be applied to elucidate solution segregation especially on a micro-scale.

In prevention of wear, the principal task of a lubricant which may be liquid, solid or gaseous is to enable one solid surface to move over another with low friction and with a minimum of damage. This object can be achieved if the lubricant film is thick enough to keep the surfaces apart and hydrodynamic conditions prevail. However for these conditions to be realized loads must generally be low and sliding speeds high. If such ideal conditions cannot be maintained other forms of lubrication such as boundary or mixed film may exist. Where this is so the surfaces come into contact and damage in the form of wear occurs (14, 15).

Useful information concerning the behavior of lubricating oils can be obtained by microscopic investigation of the insoluble carbon with which they become contaminated in practice (Matthews *et al.* (16)). Electron microscopy can also be used to study the additives which are incorporated in modern lubricating oils to impart or reinforce some desirable property. The elec-

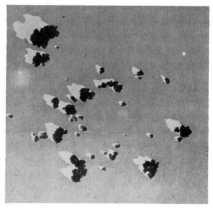

FIG. 6. Electron micrograph of debris from fretting corrosion damage of a steel surface. Shadowed at 450° with gold-palladium. 10,000× (After Scott and Scott[9])

311

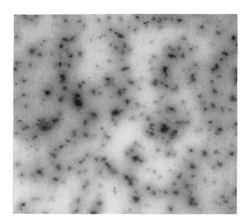

FIG. 7. Electron micrograph of particles in a used (10,000 miles) heavy duty detergent crankcase oil. 6000×

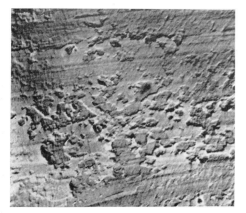

FIG. 8. Reversed print of an electron micrograph of a shadowed "Formvar" replica of a worn steel surface lubricated with a mineral oil containing an E. P. additive. 13,500×

tron microscope has been successfully used to study the solubility and dispersivity of detergent additives (17, 18) and also, by employing special specimen techniques, to compare contaminants in used plain and detergent oils (19) (Fig. 7).

The so-called extreme pressure (E.P.) additives are principally lead or other heavy metal soaps and organic compounds of sulfur, phosphorus and chlorine used in various combinations to prevent destructive metal-to-metal contact between relatively moving surfaces. E.P. additives react

chemically with the metal of the surface to form a surface film which has a lower shear strength than the metal itself, and acts as a boundary lubricant. The electron microscope has provided experimental evidence of this (4) (Fig. 8).

Conventional lubricating greases contain soap fibers or other particles as thickening agents. As the structure of the thickening agents largely determines the physical characteristics of the bulk grease it is often important to examine them microscopically. The optical microscope using polarized light and the phenomenon of birefringence has been used to show the orientation of fibers in grease due to shear (20) as fibers are crystals in the true sense of the word. Knowing how they orientate helps to elucidate grease structure.

As the finer fibers of lubricating greases are beyond the resolving power of optical microscopy the electron microscope is the only tool at present available for studying the changes which soap fibers undergo when a grease is subjected to mechanical work, heating, etc. (21). The successful application of electron microscopy to the study of grease structure depends upon a satisfactory method of specimen preparation which can give reproducible results free from artefacts. The oil phase must be removed and the method of removal must not disturb the fiber arrangement. Solvent techniques (20, 22), bulk freezing and slicing (23) and vacuum evaporation (21) have been successfully applied to achieve this (Fig. 9).

Solid lubricants are used where other lubricants are unsuitable due to temperature limitations or inaccessibility. The mechanism of lubrication is similar for all lubricants, a thin film supporting the surfaces is sheared during relative movement. Solid lubricants usually have a layer lattice structure and present planes on which shear may easily occur but which are resistant to compression at right angles to the plane. Their success depends on the size and shape

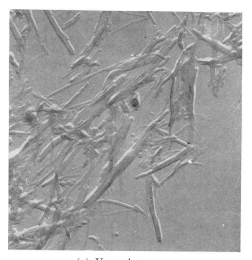

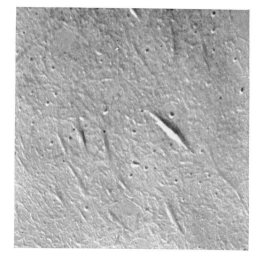

(a) Unused grease. (b) Fine fibres in a mechanically worked grease.

FIG. 9. Electron micrographs of fibers in lime-base greases. Oil phase removed by vacuum evaporation 20,000×

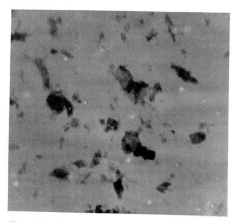

FIG. 10. Transmission electron micrograph showing size and layer nature of graphite solid lubricant. 7500×

of the dry powders and the method of bonding on to the surface. Control of all these factors can be assisted by microscopic and electron microscopic examination (Fig. 10).

REFERENCES

1. SCOTT, D., (Instn mech. Engrs) "Proc. Conference on Lubrication and Wear" Paper **57**, 670–673, 1957 (London).
2. TOLANSKY, S., *Nature*, **169**, 445 (1952).
3. MOORE, A. J. W., *Proc. Roy. Soc.* **195**, 231 (1948).
4. MILNE, A. A., SCOTT, D., AND MACDONALD D., (Instn mech. Engrs) "Proc. Conference on Lubrication and Wear" Paper **97**, 735–741 (London) (1957).
5. WELSH, N. C., *ibid.*, **77**, 701–706 (1957).
6. TAYLOR, E. W., *J. Inst. Met.*, **74**, Part 10, 493 (1948).
7. NOSOV, A. V. AND BYKOV, D. V., "Working of Metals by Electro-sparking" (translation from Russian, H. M. Stationery Office, London), 1956.
8. JACQUET, P. A., *Inst. Met. Metall. Rev.*, **1**, Part 2, 157 (1956).
9. SCOTT, D. AND SCOTT, H. M., (Instn mech. Engrs) "Proc. Conference on Lubrication and Wear" Paper **14**, 609–612 (1957) (London).
10. HALLIDAY, J. S., (Instn mech. Engrs) "Proc. Conference on Lubrication and Wear Paper **40**, 647–651 (1957) (London).
11. FISHER, R. M., "A.S.T.M. Symposium on Techniques for Electron Microscopy," 49 (1953).
12. SMITH, E. AND NUTTING, J., *Brit. J. Appl. Phys.*, **7**, 214 (1956).
13. MELFORD, D. A. AND DUNCUMB, P., Metallurgia, **57**, No. 341, 159–161 (1958).
14. BOWDEN, F. P. AND TABOR, D., "The Friction and Lubrication of Solids," Clarendon Press, Oxford, 1950.
15. MING FENG, I., *Lubric. Engg.*, **10**, 34 (1954).
16. MATTHEWS, J. B., *et al.*, *J. Inst. Petrol.*, **39**, 429 (1953).

17. BROUGHTEN, J. L., *et al.*, *Sci. Lubric.*, **4**, No. 12, 23 (1952).
18. McBRIAN, R., A.S.M.E., Paper 52-A40 (1952).
19. BARWELL, F. T., GRUNBERG, L., AND SCOTT, D., (Instn mech. Engrs, London) "Proc. Auto Div." No. 5, p. 153 (1955).
20. BROWN, J. A., HUDSON, C. N. AND LORING, L. D., Inst. Spokesm. nat. Lubric. Gr. Inst. Vol. XV, No. 11, p. 8, 1952.
21. MILNE, A. A., SCOTT, D. AND SCOTT, H. M., (Instn. mech. Engrs) (London) "Proc. Conference on Lubrication and Wear," Paper **45**, 450–453 (1957).
22. RENSHAW, T. A., *Ind. Eng. Chem.*, **47**, (4), 834 (1955).
23. VOLD, M. J. AND VOLD, R. D., *J. Inst. Petrol.*, **38**, No. 339, 155 (1952).

D. SCOTT

WILSKA LOW-VOLTAGE MICROSCOPE

The first successful experiments with early electron microscopes showed that almost all the objects that were known from light microscopy appeared more or less like silhouettes. Even bacteria were too thick to be seen through. With higher accelerating voltage the electrons gained more penetrating power. At about 200 kV the bacteria became fairly translucent but because of the difficulties of shielding and regulating voltages of this range, the usual laboratory electron microscopes have an anode potential between 50–100 kV only.

Such a potential gives a good penetrability for objects of a thickness from a few hundred to a few thousand Angstrom units. The resolving power of these instruments may be as high as 10 A when measured using objects with heavy atoms. Most biological objects consist of atoms of relatively light weight, and of these practically no image is formed even if their size is several times this optimum resolution limit. The use of heavy-atom stains or relief shadowing *in vacuo* increases the contrasts to some degree; yet most of the structures in the 10–50 A region have remained unseen.

The need of more contrast became clear about ten years ago. Electrons of 50 kV gave no hope of revealing structures that one wanted to see. For this reason experiments were begun with slower electron speeds, down to 25, 10, and even 5 kV. On the fluorescent screen it was easy to see how the contrasts were dramatically improved. Holes that were hardly observable on the transparent collodion membrane at 50 kV were surrounded by a pitch-black area caused by the same membrane at 5 and also at 10 kV. The images were too unstable to be photographed with sharpness, however. Low-voltage electron beams are considerably influenced by disturbances of magnetic stray fields as well as impurities on the walls of the column and at the edges of aperture holes. These impurities become charged by the electrons and affect the beam in an irregular manner. Similar charges on the photographic emulsion itself may affect a low-voltage image much more than a high-voltage one.

For these reasons it was necessary to build an entirely new instrument to meet the extra demands of low-voltage work. The present electron microscope is the fifth in the series of trial models of "home-made" low-voltage electron microscopes. All its predecessors and the main parts of this instrument have been built in Finland.

The construction of the present electron microscope in the United States is now practically completed, too. The instrument is probably the smallest of its kind, the column measuring only 13 inches from the cathode to the fluorescent screen. It has four electromagnetic lenses: condenser, objective, intermediate lens, and projector. Within the objective lens circuit there is an electromagnetic stigmator consisting of eight minute coils. The alignment is purely electromagnetic. Both tungsten and oxide-coated platinum cathodes can be used. To protect against damage by positive ion bombardment, there is an ion trap between the anode and the cathode. To prevent negative charges from accumulating on the photographic emulsion during the exposure, there is a tiny generator of positive ions in the image chamber.

The change of specimen is both simple and rapid. The specimen cap is inserted into the hole on a rod-like support. Before entering the high vacuum the specimen passes through a fore-vacuum zone. The little amount of air in the specimen cap escapes into the fore vacuum, and the high vacuum remains practically intact. For this reason there is no waiting when changing the specimens.

The microscope can be operated in any position between vertical and horizontal. Tilting does not disturb the image on the screen. Visual observation of the image can be made more accurate by using a magnifying lens or an auxiliary light microscope, the latter of which can be put in place in 2–3 seconds. The use of a special fine-grain viewing screen in the electron microscope makes optical magnification of 50–100 times practical. At low voltages there is very little of the "splashing" of scattered and secondary electrons that would seriously limit the possibilities of similar high optical magnification at 50–100 kV. For the same reason a high photographic enlargement of low voltage electronic images is made possible. The 35 mm film used is non-perforated, and about 160 pictures can be made without reloading the camera.

Although ultimate refinements of the instrument are still being made, numerous kinds of specimens have been examined with it, using 18 kV as an accelerating potential. The main difference between images obtained with this voltage and the usual 50–100 kV is the strength of contrasts. Many structures that are too thin or too weak when viewed with the usual voltages are much better visualized with this lower voltage. On the other hand, many specimens that are ideal for 50 to 100 kV are quite too thick for our instrument, a circumstance applying to supporting membranes as well. Fortunately, it is easy to make membranes that cast very little shadow even at 18 kV. It is somewhat more difficult to make sections thin enough with the present ultramicrotomes.

At the present, the resolving power of the microscope is about 25 A which is quite good considering the greater wavelength associated with the lower velocity of the electrons used.

To quote Dr. Frank N. Low: "Many biologically significant macromolecules such as those of hemoglobin and pepsin possess a size well within the resolving power of current electron microscopes, but have never been visualized because of contrast problems. A low voltage electron microscope is able to produce images of such macromolecules without the previous use of heavy-metal shadowing or any structural alteration of the specimen such as staining. This should open up a vast field of research in the visualization of organic substances at the macromolecular level of structural organization."

As encouraging as results have been so far, the real era of low-voltage electron microscopy will first come when its superiority in contrasts can be combined with a resolving power of only a few Angstrom units. This will enable observation of the elementary shapes of most of the biological structures, e.g., polypeptide chains. There is no hope of doing this without first correcting at least a part of the tremendous spherical aberration inherent in all existing electron lenses.

ALVAR P. WILSKA

ELECTRON MIRROR MICROSCOPY

In electron mirror microscopy the electrons do not penetrate the specimen as they do in conventional electron transmission microscopy nor do they originate from the specimen as they do in the different categories of electron emission microscopy. In electron mirror microscopy the electrons are not reflected by the material of the specimen, as in conventional electron reflection microscopy, but are reflected without any scattering at the equipotentials in front of the specimen.

The characteristic feature of an electron mirror microscope is an electron optical mirror playing a dual role. The mirror serves as an electron optical element and simultaneously constitutes the specimen. In general, the mirror-specimen remains untouched by the image-forming electrons because the specimen, being an electron optical mirror, is

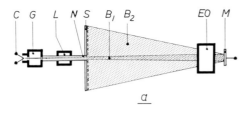

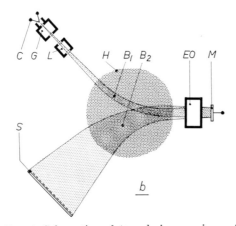

FIG. 1. Schematics of two design versions of electron mirror microscopes.

biased slightly negative with respect to the source of the electrons, that is with respect to the cathode. The electrons approaching the mirror-specimen are slowed down to zero axial velocity shortly before reaching it and then reverse their direction of motion. Any irregularity on the mirror-specimen capable of deflecting the approaching and receding electrons will modify the spatial density distribution of the returning electron beam. This returning electron beam, therefore, carries back information about the distribution of the irregularities it encountered during the time it was close to the mirror-specimen. Electron mirror microscopy utilizes the fact that such information can be presented on a phosphorescent screen as a magnified, visually observable image of the distribution of the electron-deflecting irregularities on the mirror-specimen.

The specific design characteristics distinguishing an electron mirror microscope from other types of electron microscopes stem from the introduction of an electron optical mirror and its dual function. The reversal of the electron beam on the equipotentials in front of the mirror specimen poses the problem of either magnetically separating the incoming, illuminating electron beam from the outgoing image-carrying beam or tolerating the inconveniences of a simpler straight design in which the axes of both beams remain identical.

Figure 1 shows simplified schematics of these two possible design versions of electron mirror microscopes. The one version (1a) uses the straight design (1) in which the two beams are not separated. The incoming illuminating electron beam B_1 originating from a cathode C in an electron gun G and collimated by an electron lens L is shot through a small neck N located in a hole in the center of the viewing screen S. After traversing the electron optical system EO the electron beam is reflected on the equipotentials in front of the specimen M which is generally biased a few tenths of a volt negative with respect to the cathode C and acts therefore as an electron optical mirror. Every electron-deflecting irregularity on the mirror-specimen whether caused by the topographical relief structure or by differences in contact potentials, in surface charges, in electrical conductivities or in magnetization, influences the low velocity electron beam. The electrons returning through the electron optics EO, which may consist of electric or magnetic lenses, project a magnified pictorial representation, a kind of shadow-schlieren image, of the irregularities on the specimen M onto the viewing screen S.

The other design version (2) of an electron mirror microscope is shown in Figure 1b. Here the incoming illuminating electron beam B_1 is separated for part of its path from the returning image-carrying beam B_2 by a magnetic field H normal to the plane of drawing. (Separation of the two beams by simply deviating from normal "incidence" of the electron beam on the mirror-specimen would not be feasible because the mirror-specimen necessarily constitutes a part of the electron optical system, in the vicinity of which axial symmetry must be retained in order to avoid intolerable aberrations.) The auxiliary magnetic field H and the resulting knee-shaped design necessarily complicate the design and construction but result in two basic advantages. First, it leaves the viewing screen unobstructed and, second, it permits the introduction of separated lenses to act on the electron beam before entering and after leaving the auxiliary magnetic field H. This is advantageous because these separated lenses can be optimized independently for their different tasks. The one lens can be designed for optimal performance of the incoming, illuminating beam whereas the other lens can be operated for optimal image formation and magnification.

In the case of the less complicated straight design, the entire electron optics acts on both the incoming electron beam as well as on the returning, image-carrying beam so that the electron optics cannot be of optimal design for either purpose but must be a compromise.

The capabilities of electron mirror microscopy are numerous and varied. In general, every electron-deflecting field caused by an irregularity on the mirror-specimen can be depicted because it is the electron deflection which forms the image contrast. Electron mirror microscopy permits, therefore, visual observation of the distribution of such purely electrical properties as contact potentials (1), surface charges, space charges (2) and electrical conductivities (1, 3). It also proved to be a feasible method for the visual observation of magnetic patterns (4), particularly of magnetic domain patterns. Electron mirror microscopy is also capable of depicting the surface relief structure (2, 5) on a specimen because this structure is retained in the structure of the equipotentials immediately in front of the mirror-specimen.

Figure 2 illustrates this latter possibility. It shows an electron mirror micrograph of a cleaved surface of a LiF single crystal (5) onto which a thin Pt film had been evap-

FIG. 2. Electron mirror micrograph of a cleaved surface of a LiF single crystal.

orated to make the surface conductive. Depiction of the topography of a specimen is certainly not a unique feature of electron mirror microscopy and, in many cases, other microscopic methods are available which are either more convenient, such as optical microscopy, or have considerably higher resolving power, such as conventional electron transmission or reflection microscopy. In special cases, however, electron mirror microscopy might be utilized quite advantageously for the observation of the surface relief structure on a specimen because the image-forming electrons do not penetrate, nor even impinge on the specimen and thus no specimen heating problems exist. Furthermore, no recourse to replica techniques is necessary; the resolving power, although not approaching that of electron transmission microscopy, is somewhat better than that of light microscopy, and, perhaps most important, the elevation differences or step heights necessary to form sufficient image contrast are extremely small.

The step height of a single barium stearate monolayer (24.4 A) can, for instance, be observed with such pronounced contrast that

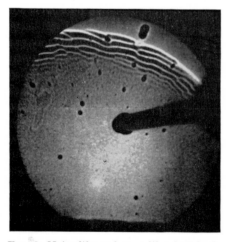

Fig. 3. Noise-like and wave-like electric charge movements on amorphous selenium film. Single frame of a motion picture taken from the screen of the electron mirror microscope. Magnification approx. 23×

considerably smaller step heights should certainly be observable. A genuine and somewhat unique feature of electron mirror microscopy is, however, its capability of depicting purely electrical and magnetic patterns. Besides depicting contact potential distributions or surface charge distributions, it can, for example, also depict the electrical conductivity distribution of layers of very low conductivity above conductive substrates. This can be achieved by letting a few electrons from the tail end of the Maxwellian distribution impinge on the mirror-specimen, using the majority of the electrons, however, for image-forming purposes. It is a particularly valuable property of electron mirror microscopy that it can, in such cases, depict without any time delay electrical charge movements which occur on such layers if their conductivity is extremely low.

Figure 3 shows as an example a single frame of a 16-mm motion picture taken directly from the screen of an electron mirror microscope. (The dark shadow extending from the center of the picture to the right is caused by the electron gun protruding from the center of the viewing screen.) The specimen was an amorphous selenium film deposited on a germanium film substrate. The observations which can be made if one applies a small positive bias potential to the substrate film of such a specimen demonstrate quite well that electron mirror microscopy has some unique capabilities not to be found in any other type of microscopy.

One of the many phenomena which can be observed on such an amorphous selenium film is briefly described here as an example. The small positive bias potential on the substrate of the mirror specimen lets some electrons impinge on the selenium, thus creating a voltage drop across the thickness of the selenium film. This voltage drop in turn causes a slightly negative surface potential equilibrium so that most of the electrons are still reflected by the equipotentials in front of the selenium film. A genuine electron mirror type image prevails, therefore, despite positive applied bias potentials. This is the case around the electrical center because a voltage drop occurs across the thickness of the selenium film caused by a small percentage of the electrons impinging there. It is also the case outside this area because there the normal component of the velocity of the electron is not sufficient to cause electron impingement on the mirror-specimen. The inner area, increasing in diameter with increasing positive bias potential, is filled with random, noiselike fluctuations which are more pronounced in the center of that area than near the border (see Fig. 3).

A single frame from the motion picture cannot, of course, adequately portray the movements observable on the screen. For example, one has to imagine the granular structure close to the center area in constant random, noise-like fluctuations. At a certain positive applied bias potential a pronounced wave-like motion begins which originates most often in parts of the white-rimmed border (see upper part of Fig. 3), and moves in a general direction toward the center of the area. Long before reaching this center, the intensity of the waves diminishes and they disappear in random fluctuations. The velocity of the wave-like motion described could be changed from practically zero to a few centimeters per second on the screen, corresponding, at an average magnification of about $50\times$, to velocities from zero to about one millimeter per second on the specimen. At present, neither the random fluctuations nor the waves moving toward the electrical center are fully understood. There is no doubt, however, that these phenomena are of electrical origin. That means electron mirror microscopy reveals here for direct visual observation the movements of electrical charges.

Electron mirror microscopy is also capable of depicting the conductivity distribution in thin films of semiconductors deposited on insulating substrates. Such "conductivity pictures" of thin films are obtained by passing an electric current across the specimen, thus creating in the direction of the current flow, on the specimen and in front of it, a potential pattern related to the conductivity pattern. A high potential gradient in the direction of the current flow will correspond to a low conductivity and a low potential gradient to a high conductivity. Where the gradient of the potential changes, i.e., where the area conductivity changes, areas of convex or concave curvature of the equipotentials on the specimen and in front of it will be transformed by the particular kind of image formation of electron mirror microscopy into dark or bright areas on the viewing screen. Areas of lower conductivity will therefore appear as areas with dark borders on the one side and bright border areas on the opposite side. Because of this configuration of dark and bright areas, conductivity pictures appear as elevated areas, corresponding to areas of higher conductivity, illuminated by a light source from the side where the negative voltage is applied. By taking two consecutive electron mirror micrographs distinguished solely by the amount of current passing through the specimen, it is even possible in certain cases to obtain pairs of stereomicrographs which are three-dimensional pictorial representations of the electrical conductivity distribution in thin films (3). With electrical current applied, potential gradient distributions across p-n junctions (6) or low angle grain boundaries or dislocation lines in semiconductors can also be observed by electron mirror miscropy. Figure 4 shows as an example an electron mirror stereomicrograph pair of the electrical potential gradient across a low angle grain boundary in germanium.

Finally, there is the broad field of magnetism which may profit considerably from the potentialities inherent in electron mirror miscropy. Whenever the task arises to observe visually the distribution of magnetic field intensity above a surface, electron mirror

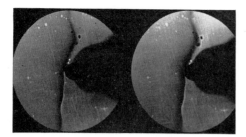

FIG. 4. Electron mirror stereomicrograph pair of the electrical potential gradient across a low angle grain boundary in germanium.

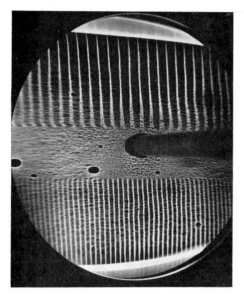

FIG. 5. Magnetic pattern recorded on magnetic tape as revealed by electron mirror microscopy. The double track pattern was recorded with an audio frequency of 1000 cps, the upper track at a tape speed of 7½ in./sec and the lower one at a speed of 3¾ in./sec.

microscopy can, in general, be used for this purpose. One can, for instance, observe the magnetic pattern recorded on magnetic computer tapes or the magnetic pattern recorded by conventional audio frequency recording (7). Figure 5 shows as an example a magnetic pattern recorded on magnetic tape as revealed by electron mirror microscopy. The double track pattern was recorded on a ¼-inch wide tape with an audio frequency of 1000 cps, the upper trace at a

tape speed of 7½ inches/sec, the lower one at a speed of 3¾ inches/sec.

For the observation of magnetic domain patterns electron mirror microscopy is particularly well suited. Electron mirror microscopy reveals magnetic domain patterns in materials with a uniaxial direction of easy magnetization (4) as well as in materials with several directions of easy magnetization, exhibiting basically flux closure domain configurations (8). Figure 6 shows as an example of the first type of material an electron mirror micrograph of a magnetic domain pattern on barium ferrite at a magnification of about 1500×.

Electron mirror microscopy is inherently suited for the instantaneous depiction of domain patterns in motion. A few micrographs cannot, of course, adequately portray the quite impressive view of domains in motion as viewed directly on the microscope screen. Motion pictures taken from the screen portray the appearance of domain patterns in motion quite well but are still slightly inferior to direct viewing, particularly in cases where domain walls at very low applied magnetic fields are to be observed. Direct

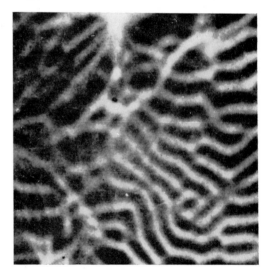

FIG. 6. Electron mirror micrograph of magnetic domain pattern on barium ferrite. Magnification approx. 1500×

visual observation of the magnetic stray fields on grain boundaries in magnetic materials is also made possible by electron mirror microscopy (9). This possibility might be of significance for the still controversial subject of grain size effects on the magnetic properties of such important magnetic materials as silicon-iron and in studies concerned with the basic physics of magnetism in such narrow regions of distorted order.

The wide field of thin magnetic films which is becoming more and more important might also profit from the capabilities of electron mirror microscopy. For instance, magnetic domain patterns and their movements with applied magnetic fields can be observed in films of the "Permalloy" type by electron mirror microscopy. Another application in the area of thin magnetic films is the depiction of magnetic patterns recorded on ferromagnetic thin films such as MnBi films. For example, Figure 7 shows an electron mirror micrograph of a sine wave south pole trace in north pole surroundings recorded on MnBi film with an electron beam (10) by utilizing the method of Curie point writing (11).

Image and contrast forming in electron mirror microscopy is not of the Gaussian dioptrics type, but is based on a point-to-direction correlation rather than on a point-to-point correlation. Optically speaking, electron mirror microscopy resembles the shadow-schlieren method (12) in which the specimen is also used as a mirror and wherein inhomogeneities in the equipotentials in front of the mirror represent the electron optical "schlieren." Formation of the image contrast therefore requires the deflection of the electron pencils by the object points which are to be depicted against their background. Contrast formation is thus based on a kind of deflection modulation of the electron paths by that component of the electric field which is parallel to the mirror-specimen. The force causing the deflection is proportional to and in the direction of the electric field. This force is independent of electron

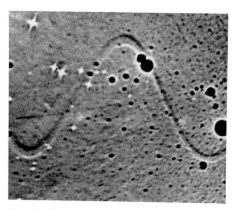

FIG. 7. South pole trace recorded onto MnBi film by writing with an electron beam as revealed by electron mirror microscopy. Magnification approx. 60×

velocity and thus independent of the direction of the velocity. The force exerted by the electric field providing the deflection retains, therefore, the same direction for the electrons when they approach the mirror-specimen as when they recede from it. In the electrical case, and also, of course, in the case of the depiction of a surface relief structure, the resulting contrast-forming deflection is therefore the sum of both deflections.

If one desires, however, to use the inhomogeneities of a magnetic field in front of a specimen as electron optical schlieren to obtain a pictorial representation of the distribution of magnetic fields on a specimen, the case is quite different. The force on an electron caused by a magnetic field (Lorentz force) is more complex and velocity-dependent. There is in the magnetic case, therefore, a deflection canceling trend, because for the electron's velocity component normal to the plane of the mirror the direction of the force on the electrons approaching the mirror-specimen is opposite to the direction of the force exerted on the receding electrons. Yet there remains the possibility of utilizing the radial component of electron velocity, small as this may be, for image and contrast formation in the magnetic case. This radial velocity does not reverse its sign, and thus the

Lorentz force, which stems from the radial component of the electron's velocity, has the same direction at a given object area for approaching as well as receding electrons. This radial component will be very small most of the time, but immediately in front of the mirror-specimen it will generally become predominant, making possible its utilization for image and contrast forming in the magnetic case.

Image contrast formation in the magnetic case is therefore more complex than in the other cases; yet this difference provides the criteria which permit the discrimination of magnetic patterns from those of other origin, a possibility which is of great value for the practical applications of this novel research tool. In the magnetic case of electron mirror microscopy image contrast-forming deflection is caused by that component of the Lorentz force which stems from the radial component of electron velocity and that component of the magnetic field which is normal to the plane of the mirror-specimen. The sensitivity of electron mirror microscopy for magnetic fields is zero at the electrical center of the mirror-specimen. (The electrical center is defined as the location on the specimen plane where the radial velocity of the electrons becomes zero or, in practical terms, where the electrons first impinge if the negative bias of the specimen is decreased.) With increasing distance from this electrical center, the magnetic sensitivity increases.

To obtain high magnetic sensitivity, a shift of the electrical center to the border of the viewing area or even outside is therefore advantageous. To utilize this advantage one must, of course, decrease the negative bias of the specimen to permit sufficiently deep electron penetration into the magnetic fields under observation. Shifting of a pattern into the electrical center, therefore, is one possible criterion for distinguishing magnetic patterns from others. If the pattern under consideration is magnetic in origin, it must disappear in the center, while patterns of other origin will remain the same or may in many cases become even more contrasty and detailed.

A second criterion for distinguishing magnetic patterns from those of electrical or relief origin is most convenient experimentally. It requires the shifting of the pattern in question through the electrical center to the opposite side of the viewing screen, an operation which must result, if the pattern is magnetic, in a reversal of the brightness of the border lines, i.e., dark border lines must become bright and the bright must become dark.

Radial extensions of magnetic pattern elements are depicted as more contrasty than those which extend azimuthally. This is in itself a third criterion if the pattern contains preferred directions azimuthally as well as radially. If this is not the case, it can still be used as a third criterion by rotating a pattern in such a way as to let the pattern configuration extend preferentially in the radial direction first and then in the azimuthal direction. In the first position the pattern, if it is magnetic, will be much more contrasty than in the second position. If one lets electrons impinge on the electrical center of the specimen, the image content is lost within the area of impinging electrons. The electrons reflected there, either elastically or as secondary emission, are scattered, thus having lost their predetermined definite direction. This fact then makes the proper kind of image formation of electron mirror microscopy impossible, as it is based on a point-to-direction correlation rather than a point-to-point correlation.

The shape of the spot representing the area where the electrons impinge will generally be circular in the nonmagnetic cases of electron mirror microscopy. If in the magnetic case, however, magnetic field components are present which are parallel to the plane of the mirror-specimen, the shape will be deformed and the spot representing the impinging electrons will become displaced.

One can, therefore, use as a fourth criterion for the presence of magnetic fields in front of the specimen the displacements and shape deformations of the area corresponding to the area of impinging electrons. In practice, this check can be executed most conveniently by lateral movements of the specimen. In the presence of magnetic field components parallel to the plane of the specimen the spot representing the impinging electrons will move not only against the reference coordinate system of the specimen (as it does in the nonmagnetic case) but also with respect to the coordinate system of the viewing screen. Simultaneously, the shape of the spot representing the area of impinging electrons will be deformed, depending upon the shape of the magnetic field.

Because of the peculiar kind of image formation, care must be taken in the interpretation of electron mirror micrographs. The potential relief in front of the mirror is the actual image-forming medium. Optically speaking, it represents a medium of changing refractive index with inhomogeneities in front of an irregular electron-reflecting surface. This irregular reflecting surface in connection with the inhomogeneous refracting medium forms the image. The image is in fact the electron density distribution of the caustic of these two inhomogeneities in the plane of the screen. The amount of the small negative bias of the mirror against the cathode determines how far the electrons penetrate into the potential relief in front of the mirror specimen and which potential surface will become the reflecting one. This potential relief rapidly loses its detail and its refracting influence on the electron beam with increasing distance from the mirror. The closer the electrons are permitted to penetrate toward the mirror-specimen the more detailed the image formed by the potential relief will be. One is, of course, inclined to bias the mirror to obtain the most detailed image, i.e., in such a way that the focal points of those focusing irregularities which represent the fine

details fall into the plane of the screen. Hence, "focusing" is accomplished by applying proper bias to the mirror rather than by adjusting the voltages of the electron lenses. The lenses mainly provide the desired magnification and are not used as focusing elements in the meaning of the Gaussian dioptrics. This requires, of course, that the electrical as well as geometrical roughness of the specimen be rather small and uniform within the viewing area. This is a disadvantage in this kind of electron microscopy. The rather high field strength in front of the specimen is another disadvantage.

There exists another mechanism for image contrast formation. Differences in surface potential across the specimen can result in an area-dependent variation in the intensity of the reflected beam. More electrons from the velocity spectrum of the electron beam will impinge on an area which is more positive than its surroundings. This "intensity modulation" type of image contrast formation is in most cases, however, masked to a considerable extent by the normal "deflection modulation" which is also always present and is in general more sensitive.

Electron mirror microscopy has a different goal from optical microscopy or conventional electron microscopy. Maximal resolving power, a major goal in conventional categories of microscopy, is not the major objective in electron mirror microscopy; rather, it makes accessible to direct visual observation the distribution of those physical properties which are not normally depicted by other microscopic methods. Instead of revealing the distribution of absorption, reflection or mass density scattering with high resolution, electron mirror microscopy strives for the observation of electrical and magnetic patterns even if the resolving power is more limited. Nevertheless, the resolution of the few presently existing rather crude laboratory models of electron mirror microscopes is about 1000 A, which is slightly better than the resolution of conventional optical microscopes. One can reasonably expect that the resolution will be improved to about 100 A. The factor finally limiting the resolving power is the rather long de Broglie wavelength of the rather slow electrons at the location where the information is picked up in the form of the image-forming deflections.

Theoretically (13), the smallest resolvable distance δ should be

$$\delta[\overset{\circ}{A}] = \frac{3.3 \cdot 10^3}{\sqrt[3]{E \left[\dfrac{\text{volts}}{\text{cm}} \right]}}$$

in which E stands for the electrical field strength on the surface of the mirror-specimen. Such a reasonable field strength as 40,000 volts/cm at the viewed area of the specimen leads to the above mentioned figure for the obtainable resolving power.

Electron mirror microscopy has a number of advantageous properties and it also has some inherent disadvantages. The requirement of a very smooth and uniform specimen surface and the fact that there will always be inherently a comparatively high field strength in front of the specimen have already been mentioned. The peculiar kind of image formation can sometimes result in a rather complicated correlation between the object and the object's electron mirror microscopical image, a correlation which at first sight appears in some cases as not easily interpretable. Fortunately, however, there is an additional parameter available, namely, the bias potential on the mirror-specimen. By varying this bias potential and observing the corresponding changes in the electron mirror microscopical images a correct interpretation of the images becomes comparatively easy after some experience has been gained in this respect.

Electron mirror microscopy may appear at first thought as a unique research tool for the broad field of surface physics which is becoming increasingly important. In many respects, of course, it can be utilized for that purpose; in many cases, however, its applica-

bility is severely restricted by the vacuum obtainable in present day electron mirror microscopes. The design of a normal electron mirror microscope neither permits outbaking nor sealing off; the obtainable vacuum will therefore not be considerably better than 10^{-6} mm Hg. This in turn does not permit a clean surface in the meaning of present-day surface physics. Difficult as it may be, it should not be impossible, however, to design simplified electron mirror microscopes for special applications in which the extremely high vacua required in modern surface physics could be maintained.

Despite its shortcomings electron mirror microscopy promises to become a valuable research tool extending microscopic observations into areas which are not easily accessible by other means. What makes it even more interesting and versatile is the fact that rather often one can observe with an electron mirror microscope not only static electric and magnetic patterns but actually observe some dynamic behavior, such as strangely moving and changing electric charge patterns or magnetic domains set in motion by mechanical strain or applied magnetic fields or magnetic stray fields growing out of grain boundaries. Although the basic features of electron mirror optics have been known for many years (14), its utilization for a new type of electron microscopy is rather recent. But even with only a few electron mirror microscopes now in operation, the flow of information from them is considerable and often exceeds the observers' capabilities to digest it.

REFERENCES

1. MAYER, LUDWIG, *J. Appl. Phys.*, **26**, 1228 (1955).
2. BARTZ, G., WEISSENBERG, G., AND WISKOTT, D., "Proc. Third Interntl. Conf. Electr. Microscopy," London, 1954, p. 345; LUDWIG MAYER, *J. Appl. Phys.*, **24**, 105 (1953). See also ref. 14.
3. MAYER, LUDWIG, *J. Appl. Phys.*, **28**, 259 (1957).
4. MAYER, LUDWIG, *J. Appl. Phys.*, **28**, 975 (1957); G. V. SPIVAK, *et al.*, *Dokl. Akad. Nauk SSSR*, **105**, 965 (1955).

5. BARTZ, G., WEISSENBERG, G., AND WISKOTT, D., "Radex Rundschau," Heft ⅘, p. 163 (1956).
6. BARTZ, G., AND WEISSENBERG, G., *Naturwiss.*, **44**, 229 (1957).
7. MAYER, LUDWIG, *J. Appl. Phys.*, **29**, 658 (1958).
8. MAYER, LUDWIG, *J. Appl. Phys. Suppl.*, **30**, 252S (1959).
9. MAYER, LUDWIG, *J. Appl. Phys.*, **30**, 1101 (1959).
10. MAYER, LUDWIG, *J. Appl. Phys.*, **29**, 1454 (1958).
11. MAYER, LUDWIG, *J. Appl. Phys.*, **29**, 1003 (1958).
12. "Encyclopedia of Physics" (Springer Verlag, Berlin, 1956), Vol. **34**, pp. 565 and 585; H. HANNES, *Optik*, **13**, 34 (1956).
13. WISKOTT, DETMAR, *Optik*, **13**, 463 (1956); **13**, 481 (1956).
14. HENNEBERG, W., *Z. tech. Phys.*, **16**, 621 (1935); A. RECKNAGEL, *Z. Physik.*, **104**, 381 (1937); G. HOTTENROTH, *Z. Physik.*, **103**, 460 (1936); R. ORTHUBER, *Z. angew. Phys.*, **1**, 79 (1948).

LUDWIG MAYER

FIELD EMISSION MICROSCOPY

The basic purpose of microscopy is to produce a detailed enlarged image of the specimen. The final objective must be to reveal the arrangement of the individual atoms as the finest building stones of matter. Of all presently known microscopic devices the field emission microscope has come nearest to that goal. In the form of the field electron microscope it is able to show the presence and behavior of monoatomic layers on specimen surfaces, and in the form of the recent field ion microscope it has made visible the individual atoms that constitute the surface of a solid.

The field electron microscope was invented by Müller (1) in 1936. He had observed that at high temperatures surface migration on a clean metal point tends to produce a perfectly rounded nearly hemispherical tip which is smooth almost down to the lattice steps of atomic dimensions. Such a tip is placed as a cathode opposite a fluorescent screen on anode potential. If the applied voltage is high enough to produce a field of about 40 million volts per centimeter at the cathode, electrons are emitted which travel on essentially radial trajectories toward the screen. There they display an electron image of the emitter tip at a magnification approxi-

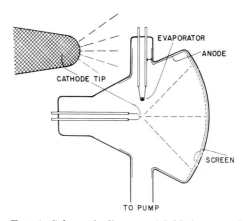

FIG. 1. Schematic diagram of field electron microscope, and of highly enlarged electron emitting tip section at upper left.

mately equal to the ratio of tip-screen distance and tip radius. Typical data are 2000 A for the tip radius, 10 cm for the tip screen distance, a voltage of 4000 volts, the image current in the microampere range, and the magnification 500,000×. The observation is done visually or by photography of the screen. The image brightness is sufficient for taking motion pictures.

Theory of Field Emission

The mechanism of field emission is understood by using the concepts of quantum mechanics. Electrons inside a metal are moving in a potential trough, from which they can escape by adding thermal energy (thermionic emission), by energy transfer from photons (photoelectric effect) or by penetrating the potential barrier at the surface (tunnel effect) when the external field is so high that the barrier width is narrowed down to be comparable with the electron wavelength inside the metal. According to the Fowler-Nordheim theory of field emission the current density J (amps/cm²) as a function of field strength F (volts/cm) and work function ϕ (e-volts) at the surface can be described by

$$J = 1.55 \times 10^{-6} \frac{F^2}{\phi} e^{-(6.85 \times 10^7 \phi^{3/2})/F}. \quad (1)$$

If in a more elaborate theory the electronic image force is taken into account, the exponent will be reduced by a factor slightly smaller than unity dependent upon $\sqrt{F}/\phi$. This reduces the field strength necessary for a given current density by some 10 to 20 %. As field emission is essentially independent of temperature, the behavior of the emitter surface can be observed in a wide temperature range from liquid helium temperature to white heat, which is quite valuable for the study of adsorption.

The resolution of the field emission microscope is limited by the random lateral velocity component of the emitted electrons, and also by diffraction of the electron waves. At a tip radius of 1000 A the theoretical resolution is 20 A, and at 3000 A radius, 40 A. This is in agreement with practical experience. At small protrusions at the tip surface the resolution may be better due to local field distortions. The image details or the contrast are the result of local variations in current density, which according to Eq. (1) is determined by the local field F and the work function ϕ. The interpretation of the image is usually based on the assumption of a homogeneous field strength over the depicted tip area, falling off toward the shank of the emitter, and by ascribing the finer image details to variation in work function. Sometimes, however, it is evident that small crystallites or asperities appear in the image because of the local field enhancement.

Field Emission Patterns from Clean Surfaces

There is hardly another experiment that shows as clearly as field electron microscopy the difficulty of obtaining and investigating really clean metal surfaces. The number of gas molecules striking a square centimeter of surface in a conventional high vacuum of 10^{-6} mm amounts to 4×10^{14} per sec, and as the sticking probability on a clean metal surface is near unity, it takes only a few seconds to build up a monolayer of adsorption at that pressure. Therefore, studies of clean surfaces or of adsorption films under reproducible conditions require ultra high vacuum techniques. In field electron microscopy the criterion for a clean surface is that the emission pattern should be independent of the annealing temperature except for small changes in the relative size of the dark areas.

Only a few crystallographic planes of low Miller index appear on a clean surface as dark regions, indicating a higher work function than the rest of the surface. Probe measurements of the current density in various regions revealed large differences in work function. On tungsten ϕ_{111} was found to be 4.31 e-volt, and ϕ_{011} as high as 5.99 e-volts.

Observations of field electron microscope patterns of other metals strongly suggest the general occurrence of such previously not expected large work function differences between different crystal planes. On body-centered cubic crystals, such as W, Mo, Ta, αFe, the highest work functions are on 011, followed by 112 and 100 planes. Face-centered cubic crystals, such as Ir, Pt, Ni, have the highest work function in 111 and 100 planes, and on hexagonal Re crystals the highest work function is on the 0001 plane, followed by $10\bar{1}0$.

Field electron microscopy of clean metal surfaces also provides information on the rate of surface migration as a function of temperature, so that activation energies for various surface sites can be derived from Arrhenius plots. Changes in tip geometry due to surface migration have been observed at temperatures as low as one quarter of the absolute melting temperature.

Adsorption Studies

Adsorption plays a basic role in many surface phenomena, such as gas-solid reactions, catalysis and corrosion. Both general types of adsorption, physical adsorption and chemisorption can be studied with the methods of field electron microscopy, which provide the following special features: The specificity of various crystal planes is immediately recognized. Low degrees of coverage down to a small fraction of a monoatomic layer are detected, and the particular stability of monolayers or multilayers is readily observed. The same surface can be studied in an extremely wide temperature range, from liquid helium temperature to above 2000°K.

Most of the adsorption studies have been made with tungsten tips. The alkali and earth alkali metals develop dipole layers which lower the work function considerably, thereby increasing the current density at a given field strength. Surface migration of these adsorption films can be measured as a function of tip temperature, crystallographic direction, degree of coverage, and applied field. The conventional technique is to condense the adsorbate on one side of the tip from an evaporation source, and then to observe the spreading of the film under various conditions. Physically adsorbed single and sometimes multilayer films of the rare gases, easily observed at low temperatures, also lower the work function.

The common gases all decrease the electron emission by forming dipole layers with the negative end directed away from the sur-

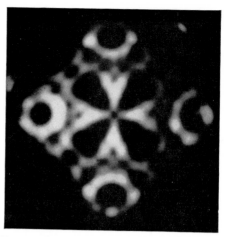

FIG. 2. Field electron microscope pattern of an iron tip in 001 orientation with an adsorption film of CO on it.

face. Oxygen has the greatest effect, a monolayer of which may reduce the emission at a fixed field strength by more than six orders of magnitude. Since the inception of field emission microscopy oxygen on tungsten has been the subject of a considerable number of investigations, as the adsorption of oxygen and the initial stages of oxidation are of such great importance. If the microscope is immersed in a bath of liquid helium, (2) oxygen can be condensed on one side of the tip only, just as the deposits of electropositive metals at room temperature, and the same type of surface migration experiments can be made by heating the tip gently. A very thin film of oxygen shows mobility only above 450°K, while a film thicker than a monolayer can migrate already at 40°K. Heating of an oxygen covered tungsten tip to 700 or 1000°K produces small oxide crystals, which spread out again at higher temperature. In the range from 1000 to 2000°K the field emission pattern of oxygen on tungsten goes through several quite distinct stages, while desorption is taking place. Concurrent with the desorption is a deformation of the tungsten surface. Rearrangement of tungsten atoms takes place because of the crystallographic specificity of the free surface energy of the oxygen covered substrate. Beginning at 1500°K the 111 plane is built up to assume a locally smaller radius of curvature. A greatly enhanced electron emission is the result of the local field increment rather than a lowering of work function. Only by heating above 2100°K in high vacuum can all the oxygen be desorbed from a tungsten surface.

The interpretation of the crystallographic specificity of adsorption patterns has often been attempted on the basis of matching the atomic size of the adsorbate with the spacings on the various substrate lattice sites, and also with the number of bonds to next nearest neighbors that can be made (3). While this procedure is often successful, it is also found that chemical differences, e.g., the electron structure of the metal plays a role. For instance, tungsten and molybdenum differ only by .6 % in their lattice constants. Their clean state field emission patterns are identical. Nevertheless their adsorption patterns with oxygen or other adsorbates differ considerably, even when compared at relative equal temperatures matched to their melting points. To make such observations unambiguous, special field emission microscopes have been used

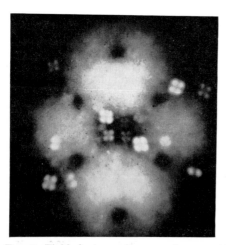

Fig. 3. Field electron microscope images of individual phthalocyanine molecules adsorped on a tungsten tip in 011 orientation.

with the two different tips mounted in one vacuum vessel, so that both metals are exposed to the same adsorbate gas under identical conditions of pressure, time, temperature and possible contaminations.

The chemisorption of hydrogen is crystallographically less specific than of oxygen, probably because of the small size of the adsorbate. Surface migration is possible at temperatures as low as 20°K. The dipole moment of a monolayer at room temperature is such as to make the work function of tungsten rise by approximately .5 e-volt. At liquid nitrogen temperature the formation of a second layer with lower work function can be seen. Similar observations can be made with nitrogen or carbon monoxide on tungsten.

Some adsorbates form very specific and characteristic adsorption layers of low electron emission and with quite sharp borders when the substrate temperature is raised to allow a rearrangement of the substrate atoms, or maybe the formation of epitaxed compounds. Most characteristic are the 334 planes caused by carbon on tungsten above 1000°K, and the 256 planes developed when a nitrogen film is present above 800°K. Very specific patterns are also obtained with zirconium, or the oxides of copper, strontium, beryllium, aluminum, and uranium evaporated onto tungsten.

It appears quite possible that in spite of the limited resolution of the field electron microscope large atoms may become visible individually as blurred scattering disks (1). The granulation of very thin barium films was explained as being due to individual atoms. It is definitely established that some flat organic molecules can be seen individually, although their patterns do not necessarily represent the actual shape of the molecule. The image formation mechanism is not yet fully understood. The fourfold symmetric patterns of the 10 by 10 angstroms large phthalocyanine molecule, for instance, appear only on tungsten, molybdenum and vanadium tips, while the same molecules show up as doublets on tantalum, rhenium or platinum emitters.

Very little work has been done so far with adsorption on metals other than tungsten. Exploratory investigations were made with tips of Re, Ta, Mo, Nb, Ir, Pt, Zr, Ti, Ni, Fe, V, Cu and Ag. Some chemical reactions were studied such as the reduction of oxygen films by hydrogen, the oxidation of carbon films, the formation of tungsten and molybdenum carbides and silicides and the ammonia synthesis on platinum. Recently the soft metals became available as emitter tips by using whiskers grown *in situ*; however, so far only patterns of clean surfaces of Fe, Cu, Au, Ag, Al, Ge and Hg have been studied by this method.

Another promising new technique for either the preparation of perfectly clean surfaces without the application of heat or for obtaining new data on the binding energy of adsorbates is desorption by a reversed field. Field desorption (1) of a barium film from tungsten requires about 100 million volts per centimeter at room temperature, the exact value depending upon the degree of coverage and the crystal plane, while the removal of an oxygen film needs as much as 400 Mv/cm.

A basic difficulty of field electron microscopy is that only the ratio of $\phi^{3/2}/F$ can be derived from measurements of current density, which makes the interpretation not unambiguous. Rate determinations for finding activation energies may be influenced by the electric field present during the observation, although the field effect is usually small and may sometimes be eliminated by observing with microsecond pulses (4) rather than with d.c.

The Field Ion Microscope

A most promising new research tool is the field ion microscope (1, 5, 6), which is a modification of the field emission microscope in that it uses positive ions rather than electrons to depict the emitter tip. The microscope tube is operated with the tip at a positive potential, and it is filled with a few microns of gas, preferably helium. At a field of about 450 MV/cm, e.g., more than 10 times higher than needed for field electron emission from a negative tip, helium atoms coming near the tip surface will be ionized by tunneling out an electron. The helium ions thus formed travel to the screen on the same radial trajectories as the electrons in the field electron microscope, producing there an ion image of the tip. With the field properly adjusted ionization will only occur where the local field is slightly enhanced due to the protrusion of the metal atoms of the surface. Because of the attraction of the helium atoms that are polarized in the highly inhomogeneous field, the approaching atoms travel so fast that only a few are ionized. Most of them touch the tip surface, accommodate to its low temperature and rebound only very slowly by performing a hopping motion up to a few angstroms above the surface, until they become ionized in the locally enhanced field above a protrusion. Then they take off to the screen. The great improvement in resolution, compared to the field electron microscope, is possible because of the small random tangential velocity component (equivalent to kT_{tip}) and because of the short de Broglie wavelength associated with the relatively heavy ion. For the first time in the history of microscopy the individual atoms as they constitute the lattice of metals have become visible. The theoretical resolution is about 1.5 A, and experimentally the individual atoms on the 111 plane of silicon, with a triangular spacing of 2.3 A have been resolved visually. Adjacent tungsten or platinum atoms, 2.74 and 2.77 A apart, have been photographed. The image intensity is low, corresponding to an ion current of 10^{-9} amp on a 4-inch image screen, so that a typical exposure time is one minute.

Field ion microscopy is applicable only to

the more refractory metals. At a sufficiently high field atoms of all metals will be "field-evaporated" in the form of positive ions, even at a temperature close to absolute zero. In order to observe a steady surface the evaporation field of the tip material must be above the field necessary for the ionization of the image producing gas.

Helium, requiring 450 MV/cm for ionization and giving the best images, can be used for tips of C, W, Re, Ta, Mo, Nb, Ir, Pt, Rh, and with restrictions also for tips of Zr, Pd, Ni, Fe, Co, Si, and of alloys of these metals. Gases with lower ionization potentials require less field strength, and fairly good images have been obtained with neon, hydrogen, nitrogen, oxygen, and argon, although the resolution is inferior and difficulties are encountered with adsorption and possibly field induced chemical reactions of these gases.

The unique feature of operating the field ion microscope with helium is that, once the tip surface has been cleaned from all contaminations by field evaporating a few surface layers of the metal, not one contamination atom can reach the tip surface as long as the high field is maintained. All gases have a lower ionization potential than helium, so that all contamination molecules will be ion-

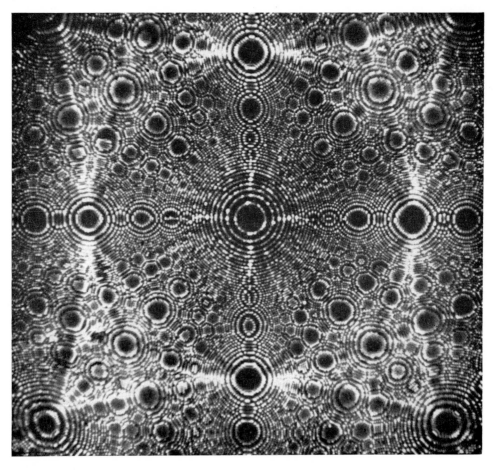

FIG. 4. Ion microscope picture of a platinum crystal with nearly perfect lattice, with 001 in the center, and the four 111 planes in the four corners. Many of the about 1000 high index net planes are resolved in individual atoms.

ized way above the surface, and carried away by the field. This makes it possible to design a field ion microscope with very modest vacuum requirements, providing, for instance, greased joints for easy tip specimen replacement. In spite of the resulting poor vacuum conditions (10^{-6} mm residual pressure), a specimen surface stays atomically clean for any desired length of time, that is without even the adsorption of only one contaminating atom. The best results are obtained when the microscope is cooled with liquid hydrogen or liquid helium, although quite useful images can be made with liquid nitrogen cooling.

The most promising application of the field ion microscope is the direct observation of individual imperfections in metal crystals. The regular arrangement of the atoms in the faultless crystal can more accurately be determined by the classical x-ray diffraction methods. The field ion microscope, however, shows directly the individual imperfections such as single vacancies, interstitials and dislocations, the structure of lattice steps and of grain boundaries. Although only the surface is shown in the image, controlled field evaporation can be used to remove one surface layer of the specimen after another, so that with this "sectioning technique" the interior of the tip crystal becomes accessible. The high field exerts a large electrostatic stress $F^2/8\pi$ at the surface, which amounts to approximately 1000 kg/mm² when helium ions are used. Nevertheless, all the metals mentioned above can stand this stress in spite of their much lower bulk strength. By pulsing the field the fluctuating stress can be used for fatigue experiments *in situ*. As no heating is necessary for removing surface contaminations by field evaporation, it is possible to study metal structures that are subject to changes at elevated temperatures, such as cold work effects, quenched-in

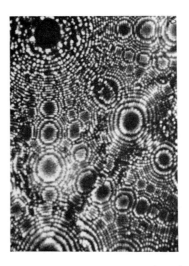

Fig. 5. Ion image of a section of a platinum crystal with many defects. Each fine bright dot represents an individual atom.

defects, precipitation in alloys, or damage by irradiation with high energy particles. The impact of one individual α particle can be seen directly, and the disarrangement of the metal atoms in the displacement spike can be investigated in detail. It can be assumed that in the future the field ion microscope will increasingly contribute to our knowledge of the atomic structure of solids.

REFERENCES

1. GOOD, R. H., JR., AND MÜLLER, E. W., "Encyclopedia of Physics" (2nd ed.), Springer Verlag, Vol. **21**, p. 176–231 (1956).
2. GOMER, R. "Advances in Catalysis," Academic Press, Vol. 7, p. 93–134 (1955).
3. BECKER, J. A., "Solid State Physics," Academic Press, Vol. 7, p. 379–424 (1958).
4. DYKE, W. P. AND DOLAN, W. W., "Advances in Electronics," Academic Press, Vol. 8, p. 90–185 (1956).
5. MÜLLER, E. W., "Fourth International Congress on Electron Microscopy," Berlin, 1958, Springer Verlag, p. 820–835 (1960).
6. MÜLLER, E. W., "Advances in Electronics," Academic Press, Vol. **13**, p. 83–179 (1960).

ERWIN W. MÜLLER

FLUORESCENCE MICROSCOPY*

The examination of fluorescing preparations differs fundamentally from the general method of microscopy in which the light transmitted or reflected by the preparation is observed.

In fluorescence microscopy the preparation becomes self-luminous while the radiation exciting the luminosity does not contribute to the image formation but is eliminated by barrier filters. The fluorescing part of the preparation appears bright, usually colored, against a dark background. For excitation, light is used of shorter wavelength than that emitted by the preparation. Thus blue and green fluorescence can only be excited by ultraviolet (UV), while yellow and red fluorescence may also be excited by intense blue-violet (BV).

Since only a small part of the incident radiant energy is converted into fluorescent light, it is necessary in fluorescence microscopy to employ the most intense sources of light available. These however, besides the excitation radiations of short wavelength, also emit light of greater wavelength which would completely flood the relatively weak fluorescences.

Therefore two kinds of filters are a part of every fluorescence microscope: (1) excitation filters, which transmit in the illuminating beam only the excitation radiation of the total radiation emitted by the light source; (2) barrier filters, which bar the further passage of excitation radiation in the imaging beam.

Just as the inherent color of a substance is due to its transmission or reflection of the nonabsorbed light falling upon it, so likewise a primary fluorescence, where it occurs, is mainly a function of the chemical constitution. On this basis, guided by the presence or absence of fluorescence of definite quality,

conclusions can be drawn concerning basic chemical composition (fluorescence analysis). Besides the inherent color, affinity for certain stains may be characteristic. The use of stains in histology is a familiar application of topochemical staining technique. Similarly the method can also be extended to fluorescence and the affinity of so-called fluorchromes for specific substances. Fluorchromes do not necessarily have a pronounced color—in fact some of them are practically colorless. But they brightly fluoresce in a characteristic color when exposed to appropriate exciting radiation. Among others, the following are suitable:

basic fluorchromes
berberine sulfate, auramine, euchrysin, acridine orange, coriphosphin, rivanol, trypaflavin
neutral fluorchromes (lipophil)
rhodamine B
acid fluorchromes
fluorescein, thiazine red, sulforhodamine, primuline

Various tissues or cellular constituents show a specific affinity for the fluorchromes. A peculiar phenomenon, occurring more frequently with fluorchromes than with ordinary stains, is the so-called metachromasia. By this is meant that different parts of a specimen "stain" differently with the same fluorchrome, both quantitatively and qualitatively, dependent on their chemical constitution.

But the application is not restricted to histology. Fluorchromes are specially suitable above all in physiology for tracing the transportation and distribution of metabolites (absorption, imbibition, secretion, excretion, transportation) and their storage. In general these examinations are carried out in reflected light, since usually the organs cannot be transilluminated.

Organs and organelles plainly show fluores-

* From a Carl Zeiss brochure, by permission.

cence after treatment with greatly diluted fluorchrome solutions in contrast to staining with vital stains, which are effective only at relatively high concentrations. Hence it is possible to fluorchrome any organ in full function without damaging it.

In addition to basic research, fluorescence microscopy is being employed more and more for routine clinical diagnostic purposes in the following:

hematology

    for leucocyte counts, for differentiating leucocytes, and for counting thrombocytes;

bacteriology

    for streak cultures, differentiation of acid-resistant bacilli (t.b. and leprosy) from nonacid-resistant bacilli, for the demonstration of spirochaetes;

parasitology

    for the demonstration of trypanosomes and other flagellates, plasmodia, and other sporozoa.

By means of fluorchroming it is also possible to demonstrate the elementary bodies of the so-called large virus types. For this purpose even small outfits are suitable, equipped solely for fluo-violet (BV) excitation, since all these fluorchromed objects have their fluorescence in the long-wave region.

For characterizing the fluorescent substances one uses the spectral distribution of the fluorescent phenomena. This is done by means of a pupillary spectroscope attached to the tube of the microscope, using the UV filter combination as excitation filter. Since the spectroscope furnishes an average color value of the observed field of view, an iris diaphragm is mounted in the eyepiece of the pupillary spectroscope for eliminating all structures which do not fluoresce in the same color. Above all, the pupillary spectroscope in connection with the various excitation filter combinations permits adapting the choice of barrier filters to the spectral emission of the fluorescing substance and thus to utilize fully the filter intermediate tube.

Naturally the fluorescence outfit is also adapted to the observation and evaluation of virtually structureless fluorescent material, i.e., for observing the fluorescence of liquids and (cell) suspensions. For this purpose one places on the microscope stage a small shallow cell which after filling is closed with a cover glass. Preferably an objective of low magnification is used. The fluorescence spectrum can be observed through the pupillary spectroscope. The great advantage of this micro method of observing the fluorescent spectrum is the possibility of carrying out the examination of very small samples. (See also *Fluorescence, Fluorophotometry* in the "Encyclopedia of Spectroscopy."

REFERENCES

RICHARDS, O. W.: (Latest advances with extended bibliography) *Medical Physics*, Vol. III, p. 375. Year Book Publ. Inc., Chicago, Ill., 1960.

LEHMANN, H., "Lumineszenzanalyse mittels der UV-Filterlampe." *Verh. Dtsch. Physik. Ges.* **13**, 1101–1104 (1911).

REICHERT, K., "Das Fluoreszenzmikroskop," *Phys. Z.*, **12**, 1010–1011 (1911).

LEHMANN, H., "Das Luminiszenz-Mikroskop, seine Grundalgen und seine Anwendungen," *Z. wiss. Mikroskopie*, **30**, 417–470 (1913).

DHÉRÉ, CH., "Nachweis der biologisch wichtigen Körper durch Fluoreszenz und Fluoreszenzspektren in: Abderhalden, "Handbuch der biologischen Arbeitsmethoden," Abt. II, Teil 3, Hälfte 1, 3097–3306. Verlag Urban and Schwarzenberg, Berlin-Vienne, 1934.

HAITINGER, M., "Die Methoden der Fluoreszenzmikroskopie," *Ibid.*, 3307–3337.

HAITINGER, M., "Fluoreszensmikroskopie. Ihre Anwendung in der Histologie und Chemie," Akademische Verlagsgesellschaft, Leipzig, 1938.

DE MENT, J. "Fluorescent Chemicals and their Application," New York, 1942.

MEYER, H. AND SEITZ, E. O., "Ultraviolette Strahlen. Ihre Erzeugung, Messung und Anwendung in Medizin, Biologie und Technik," Verlag Walter de Gruyter and Co., Berlin, 1942.

FONDA, G. R. AND SEITZ, F., "Preparation and characteristics of solid luminescent materials," John Wiley and Sons, New York, 1948.

DANCKWARDT, P. W. AND EISENBRAND, J., "Lumineszenz-Analyse im filtrierten ultravioletten Licht." 5. Edition Akademische Verlagsgesellschaft Geest and Portig. K. F. Leipzig, 1949.

BANDOW, F., "Lumineszenz, Ergebnisse und Anwendung in Physik, Chemie und Biologie," Wiss. Verlagsgesellschaft, Stuttgart, 1950.

FÖRSTER, TH., "Fluoreszenz organischer Verbindungen," Göttingen, 1951.

PRINGSHEIM, P. AND VOGEL, M., "Luminescence of liquids and solids and its practical applications," Interscience Publishers, Inc. New York, N. Y., 1942.

G. L. CLARK

FLYING SPOT MICROSCOPY

In 1912, Tschachotin (1, 2) devised an ultraviolet microbeam for the purpose of irradiating selected areas of living protoplasm. This ultraviolet microbeam was brought to focus by the use of refracting lenses and was rather crudely positioned on the specimen. In 1954, Uretz, Bloom and Zirkle (3) reported a much improved method for ultraviolet microbeam irradiation of living protoplasm. In 1956 Montgomery, Roberts and Bonner (4) announced the development of the ultraviolet flying-spot television microscope and a new tool for the study of ultraviolet irradiation effects came into being.

In brief outline, the ultraviolet flying spot television microscope utilizes as a light source an ultraviolet-emitting flying-spot scanner tube. A 250-line raster may be traced upon the face of this tube at variable sweep speeds from one sweep every 10 seconds to one sweep every 1/20th of a second. For intermittent irradiation studies, the raster may be switched on and off for any integral number of frames following any predetermined number of sweeps. The image of the raster of the ultraviolet emitting cathode-ray scanner tube is minified by reflecting it in reverse through the optical components of a suitable microscope. The unabsorbed energy transmitted by the specimen is allowed to strike the photocathode surface of an ultraviolet sensitive photo-

multiplier tube. The resulting current generated in the photomultiplier tube is suitably amplified and used to modulate a monitor tube locked in synchrony with the ultraviolet flying-spot scanner tube. In this way, a black and white ultraviolet absorption image of the living specimen is traced out on the monitor tube. Since the spectral characteristics of the ultraviolet emitting cathode-ray scanner tube are centered at 2600 A, the black and white image of the specimen on the monitor tube represents, in the main, a nucleoprotein absorption image of the living protoplasm. By appropriate photographic techniques these images may be recorded by time-lapse motion picture photography. A block diagram of this system may be seen in Figure 1.

Modifications of this basic equipment have provided a technique for spot irradiation of a specimen and this has been reported by Montgomery and Bonner (5). In brief this system functions by feeding the horizontal and vertical sweeps to variable delay, pulse-width generators. The pulses thus generated are compared in a coincidence circuit and at the time when both occur, and output from the coincidence circuit modulates the scanner tube grid, causing an intensified spot to appear on the scanner tube. This spot may be moved about on the raster

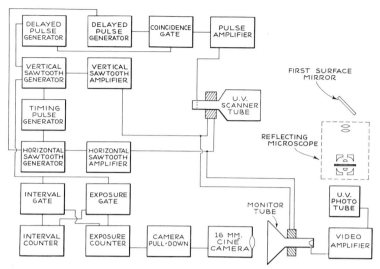

FIG. 1. Variable sweep-speed UV flying-spot TV microscope.

by means of the delay circuit and by varying the pulse widths, the spot size may be varied down to one picture element. Figure 3 shows the operation of these circuits. The drawings in this Figure lettered A and B show the individual effect of the pulses and their combined effect is shown on the face of the scanner tube.

A recent modification of the equipment now allows simultaneous viewing of the specimen in visible and ultraviolet light. A visible light tube has been mounted on the equipment at 90° to the ultraviolet tube. A first-surface mirror and beam-splitter arrangement allow the two outputs to be combined optically.

To view a specimen simultaneously in both wavelengths of light, opposite halves of each raster are masked off and the remaining output is brought into optical registration. The first half of the horizontal scan, in the focal plane, is then ultraviolet and the second half is visible light, and the two scan the same area of the specimen. The monitor tube then displays the two images in a side-by-side presentation. This arrangement is shown in Figure 4.

With only the ultraviolet tube available, positioning the intensified spot required that the background intensity be brought up to a level which would allow viewing of the entire field. This would require increasing the video gain to a level that would cause overloading of the video amplifier in the intensified area

FIG. 2. Arrangement of equipment.

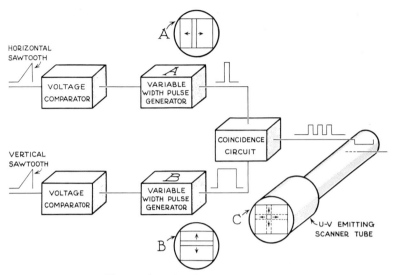

FIG. 3. Spot-irradiation technique.

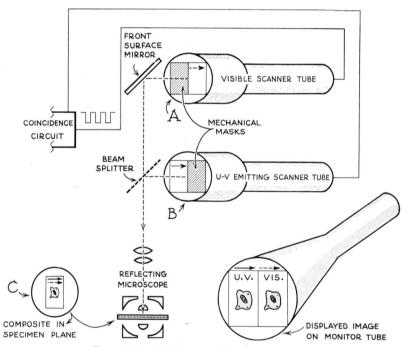

FIG. 4. Double scanner tube arrangement.

and a subsequent loss of information. There was also the possibility that the background radiation would cause biological damage to the cells in the field which were to be used as controls.

These difficulties were overcome by apply-

to the visible light tube a pulse of opposite polarity to that applied to the ultraviolet tube. The two rasters were brought into optical registration. This allowed the ultraviolet background to be at zero level and the background to be filled in with visible light

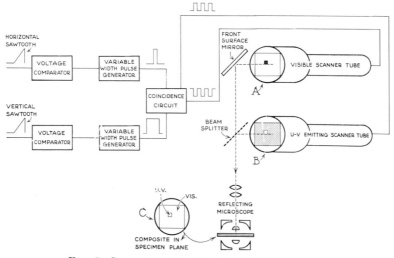

FIG. 5. Composite ultraviolet visible light system.

of the same intensity as the spot. The video system could then be adjusted to the proper level to view the entire field and the danger of ultraviolet damage to the control area was removed. This arrangement is shown in Figure 5.

By reversing the pulse polarities, the converse situation may be achieved. The background is in ultraviolet and a portion of the cell is protected and simultaneously viewed in visible light.

Time-lapse motion pictures demonstrating the application of the above briefly described techniques to living cell systems have been taken to demonstrate the following experiments:

(1) Continuous, or intermittent, intense differential ultraviolet irradiation of the nucleolus of a living cell with simultaneously obtained ultraviolet absorption images of the remainder of the cell (Figure 6).

(2) Continuous, or intermittent, intense ultraviolet irradiation of the nucleolus of a living cell with a simultaneously obtained visible light image of the remainder of the cell.

(3) Continuous, or intermittent, intense differential ultraviolet irradiation of the nucleus of a living cell with a simultaneously

obtained ultraviolet absorption image of the remainder of the cell.

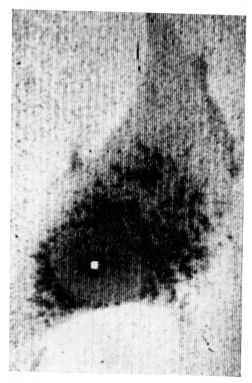

FIG. 6. Ultraviolet absorption image of a living HeLa cell. The brightened spot centered in the nucleolus represents a one micron square microbeam of ultraviolet irradiation.

(4) Continuous, or intermittent, intense ultraviolet irradiation of the nucleus of a living cell with a simultaneously obtained visible light image of the remainder of the cell.

(5) Continuous, or intermittent, intense ultraviolet irradiation of the cytoplasm of a living cell during which time the nucleus of the cell is entirely excluded from ultraviolet irradiation.

(6) Continuous, intermittent, intense ultraviolet irradiation of the entire living cell with a simultaneously obtained ultraviolet absorption image or a visible light image of the cell.

(7) Simultaneous presentation of the same image side-by-side on the same monitor, as seen when illuminated by visible light-dark field and ultraviolet dark field.

(8) Simultaneous side-by-side presentation of the same specimen as seen when illuminated by ultraviolet light and visible light.

REFERENCES

1. TSCHACHOTIN, S.: "Die Mikroskopische Strahlenstichmethode, eine Z elloperationsmethode," *Biol. Zentralbl.* **32,** 623–630, (1912).
2. TSCHACHOTIN, S., in "Handbuch der biologischen Arbeitsmethoden" edited by E. Abderhalden, Berlin, Urban & Schwarzenberg, 1938, p. 877.
3. URETZ, R. B., BLOOM, W., AND ZIRKLER, R. E.: "Irradiation of Parts of Individual Cells. II," *Science,* **120,** 197–199 (1954).
4. MONTGOMERY, P. O'B., ROBERTS, F., AND BONNER, W.: "The Flying Spot Monochromatic Ultraviolet Television Microscope," *Nature,* **117,** 1172 (1956).
5. MONTGOMERY, P. O'B. AND BONNER, W.: "A New Technique for Ultraviolet Microbeam Irradiation of Living Cells," *Arch. Path.,* **66,** 418–421 (1958).

P. O'B. MONTGOMERY, WM. A. BONNER, AND L. L. HUNDLEY

FORENSIC MICROSCOPY

Forensic microscopy can be defined as the use of microscopic techniques for the examination, study, and evaluation of minute specimens or minute structures related in some way to a legal investigation. This legal application of microscopy is not solely the province of criminal investigations, but may also involve civil litigations. The field of forensic microscopy, as well as the spectrum of specimens examined, is almost too vast to be encompassed by a book, much less by an article. However, with a few exceptions, the methods used by the criminalistician do not differ from standard procedures used by other laboratory investigators. Therefore, as in other areas of microscopy, standard reference works are used as they apply to specific problems.

An enumeration of some of the microscopic techniques used and the specimens examined will give an insight into the problems arising from efforts to solve crimes. Petrographic and crystallographic procedures are used in identifying narcotics, pharmaceuticals, and other toxic compounds in connection with illicit drug traffic and poisonings. By determining physical constants with nondestructive microscopic methods, the maximum information can be extracted from small samples, while often preserving them for confirmatory tests and subsequent court presentation. Inorganic compounds and mixtures must also be studied by petrography; these specimens lying chiefly in the fields of building material, paint, safe insulation, and soil. A microscopic study after initial sorting from extraneous debris is often a prelude to spectrographic or x-ray diffraction analysis.

In some forensic examinations the microscope plays an ancillary role; in others it plays a major part in the examination. It is significant that through the microscope the possible source of a specimen of hair on a murder weapon can be determined, bloodstains found on the clothing of a suspect can be typed, seeds transported from a crime scene can be identified, dust contaminating the clothing of a burglary suspect can be evaluated, and many more possible clues to the perpetrator can be studied. The important contribution of microscopy to the medicolegal determination of the cause of death through the histological study of various tissues removed at autopsy is well established.

Since most of the microscopic methods employed in the forensic field are either standard methods, or adaptations of standard methods, they need not be discussed in detail here. One examination procedure not commonly found in analytical laboratories, yet frequently used in criminalistics, is comparative micrography. By the use of the comparison microscope, tools are related to marks left at the scene of a crime, bullets and cartridges to firearms. The first of these applications is called tool-mark comparison, and the second is referred to as firearms identification. Like many other areas of laboratory endeavor, these fields are part art, part skill, and part science.

Basically, the identification of a tool as responsible for an evidence or a crime scene mark is possible only because each tool has many randomly situated, microscopic imperfections that are not duplicated, even by machine production, on any other tool or working surface. These minute imperfections are then transferred to any materials softer than the working edge, leaving on the surface what is equivalent to a fingerprint of the tool that was used. The final comparison

or identification of the tool is made by comparing test marks made in a suitable manner on lead, wax, or other similar material with the original mark, or an accurate reproduction, from the crime scene. In making this comparison, such variables as the hardness of the material, speed of the operation, and the angle of the work surface to the test piece must be controlled and altered systematically until the right combination produces what is termed, a "match".

Each tool-mark will possess certain definite characteristics which will identify the type of work operation performed by the tool, that is to say, the mark may be the result of straight compression or it may be the result of some sliding or cutting action by the tool. The gross dimensions and general appearance of the tool mark will suggest the type of tool that is involved and these would be called class characteristics. Distributed throughout the tool mark will be fine striations of a more or less microscopic nature which will represent the individual characteristics of the tool-mark which will be the basis upon which an identification is ultimately made.

The requirements of a "match" are met when the gross dimensions and appearance and the fine striations or individual characteristics are sufficiently alike to permit an experienced technician to render an opinion that the same tool made both test and evidence marks. Although the identification is based upon fundamental principles of probability, the work in the field of comparative micrography has not progressed to the point of feeding sufficient individual identity data into a formula and producing, automatically, a determination of positive identification. The merits of the decision must be weighed against the skill and experience of the technician in each and every identification.

An example of tool mark identification is shown in Figure 1, where a comparison is made between a drill bit mark in lead, as the standard, and a silicone rubber reproduction

Fig. 1. A comparison photomicrograph of a silicone rubber reproduction of an evidence tool mark (left) and test tool mark (right).

Fig. 2. Comparison microscope using metallurgical microscopes, comparison eyepiece and paired Ultrapaks.

of a similar drill bit mark made in soft sheet metal. While the nature of the mark is dictated by the tool used, the over-all identification procedure is fairly standard throughout comparative micrography and the universal instrument employed for this work is the comparison microscope, made up either as a single unit or constructed by spanning two metallurgical microscopes with a comparison bridge. It is necessary that all optics employed be carefully matched as to magnification and field and in some instances, it is desirable to employ matched vertical illuminators such as represented by the Ultrapaks shown in Figure 2. For the most part, low magnification of the order of 10 to 20 diameters will be employed for this work. For special problems, it is useful to have paired optics capable of producing comparative examinations as high as 200 to 300 diameter magnification.

Although the techniques employed in firearms identification are similar to, and probably an offshoot of comparative micrography, nevertheless, this technique is usually given separate identity. Firearms identification—or what is popularly, though erroneously, called "ballistics"—entails more than the simple matching of bullets or cartridge cases. For the sake of simplicity, let us say that a weapon will be examined, proved in working order, and will be fired into some collecting medium, such as water, cotton batting or waste, oiled sawdust, or anything soft enough to stop the projectile without mutilating the surface. On the surface of the fired bullet there will be parallel or slightly diverging lines, inclined slightly from the vertical axis of the bullet. The more prominent visible grooves are the impressions of the rifling of the barrel. These are the result of a manufacturing operation which puts a very slow-pitched series of grooves in the interior of the barrel as shown in Figure 3; the purpose of these is to cause the bullet to rotate and produce gyroscopic stability in flight. The raised portions in the barrel are referred to as "lands" and the depressed areas as "grooves". These, of course, produce their negative counterpart on the fire projectile so that a depressed area or groove on the bullet corresponds to the land of the barrel. The number of lands and grooves and their inclination, as well as other dimensional characteristics depend upon the manufacturer's notions as to what will produce the most accurate and highest velocity projectile when the gun is in use. Figure 4 shows fired projectiles from two popular American handguns.

The identification procedure regarding bullets involves first determining that all class characteristics are in conformity. These consist of the caliber of the weapon, the number of lands and grooves and direction of twists, the relative speed of twist, and the width of the lands and grooves. Any major deviation observable in class characteristics immediately suggests nonidentity. The second step in the identification or comparison of the bullets is to place two tests from the same weapon under the objectives of the comparison microscope and to study their surface characteristics in order to determine what sort of a "match picture" is presented by tests fired from this particular weapon. One of the test projectiles is then removed and in its place, the evidence or "fatal" projectile is substituted. A study is then made of the surface of both bullets as viewed through the comparison microscope, and by suitable manipulations of their position the technician attempts to match or line up the individual characteristics until a pattern closely duplicating the comparison of the two test bullets is achieved as shown in Figure 5.

The basis upon which an identification is made is not amenable to formula computation. Although both bullets might have been fired in the same weapon, not all fine striations on one projectile will be found reproduced on the second projectile. The fine striations observed will consist of those made

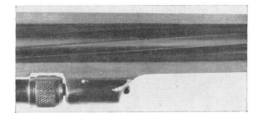

FIG. 3. Cross section of .38 cal. Smith and Wesson barrel showing land running at a slight angle to the barrel axis.

FIG. 4. Fired projectiles from .38 Special Colt (left) and .38 Special Smith and Wesson (right) revolvers. Land impression appears in the center of each bullet.

Fig. 5. Comparison photomicrograph of two projectiles fired from the same weapon.

by fixed structures in the interior of the barrel and those produced by transient material such as rust, unburned powder, accumulated carbon and metallic deposits, and so forth. Consequently, it is necessary for the examiner to study thoroughly the pattern presented by two tests to differentiate between striations produced by significant, stable and permanent imperfections and those of a transient nature. Because of the complexity presented by this changing pattern, it is not possible to establish any percentage criteria of matching lines by which an identification can be assured. Only through the experience of having studied the comparison of numerous projectiles can a technician arrive at a properly qualified opinion as to the identity of the source of two projectiles. After a "match" has been determined, it is possible to take photographs through the comparison microscope. As a rule, this final procedure is not employed since the presentation of photographs in court is not often helpful to the jury in making a decision in the case.

Of equal importance in the field of firearms identification are the fired cartridge cases ejected at the scene from either hand-operated or semi-automatic or automatic weapons. When a cartridge is ignited in a weapon, the high pressures developed force the rear face or head or the cartridge case against a vertical surface, called the breech-face. At the time of this action, any imperfections, striations, pits, and so forth on the surface of the breech-face are recorded as negative impressions on the primer of the cartridge case. These breech block markings, in conjunction with the firing pin impression, represent valuable areas for identity study. Their usefulness and significance is on a par with rifling impression on the fired projectile. In addition to these two areas, an automatic weapon imparts additional identification features in the form of extractor and ejector marks resulting from the cyclic operation of the weapon. All these features, separately or together, can afford sufficient individual characteristics to substantiate an identification of two cartridge cases as having a common origin. In a broad sense, the same philosophy and procedure is followed as would be followed in an identification of a fired projectile. Figures 6 and 7 show examples of identification through breech block markings and ejector markings.

The results of firearms identification and comparative micrography examinations are expressed in court as opinions. As indicated, it is not possible to subject the observations made to the rigorous procedures of mathematics. Therefore, the opinion rendered is based upon the experience and qualifications of the individual expressing it. Only through a proper background and intimate familiarity with procedures and literature in the field can this information or opinion be accepted as well-founded in court.

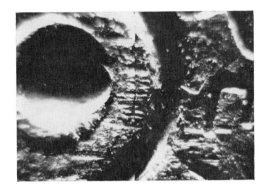

FIG. 6. Comparison photomicrographs of breech block markings on two cartridge cases fired in the same weapon.

FIG. 7. Comparison photomicrograph of ejector marks on two cartridge cases fired in the same weapon.

REFERENCES

Journal of Criminal Law, Criminology and Police Science," Northwestern School of Law (Chicago), Williams & Wilkins Company, Baltimore, Md.

Journal of Forensic Sciences, American Academy of Forensic Sciences, Callaghan & Company, Chicago.

Analytical Chemistry, American Chemical Society, Washington, D. C.

The Microchemical Journal, Interscience Publishers, Inc., New York.

Mikrochimica Acta, Springer-Verlag, Vienna.

Kriminalistik, Hamburg, West Germany

HATCHER, J. S., JURY, F. J., AND WELLER, J. "Firearms Investigation, Identification and Evidence," Stackpole Company, Harrisburg, Pa.

DAVIS, JOHN E., "An Introduction to Tool Marks, Firearms and the Striagraph," C. C Thomas, Springfield, Ill.

O'HARA, C. E., AND OSTERBURG, J. W., "An Introduction to Criminalistics," Macmillan Company, New York.

KIRK, PAUL L. "Crime Investigation," Interscience Publishers, Inc., New York

GONZALES, T. A., VANCE, M., HELPERN, M., AND UMBERGER, C. J., "Legal Medicine, Pathology and Toxicology," Appleton-Century-Crofts, Inc., New York.

JOSEPH D. NICOL

GENERAL MICROSCOPY

FIBERS (TEXTILE)

Microscopic methods are used in fiber technology for: (1) Fiber identification, (2) detection of damage, (3) structural investigation, (4) fiber measurement.

On the whole, normal light microscopic methods are in most general use; electron optical methods are important only for *fine* structural examination. With the bright-field microscope, fibers are examined longitudinally or in cross section usually after staining.

The *projection microscope* is much used for fiber research. The special instruments used for this purpose are known as lanameters or

Table 1. Birefringence Values of
Principal Fibers

	n_γ	n_α	n_γ-n_α	Δ in $m\mu$
Wool	1.556	1.546	0.010	10
Wool, chlorinated	1.556	1.548	0.008	8
Silk	1.591	1.538	0.053	53
Casein wool	1.534	1.538	0.004	4
Ardil	1.545	1.545	0.000	0
Cotton	1.578	1.532	0.046	46
Cotton, bleached	1.578	1.532	0.046	46
Cotton, mercerised	1.554	1.524	0.030	30
Linen	1.595	1.522	0.073	70
Linen, bleached	1.594	1.530	0.064	60
Jute	1.577	1.536	0.041	40
Viscose rayon	1.547	1.521	0.026	26
Copper rayon	1.548	1.527	0.021	20
Acetate rayon	1.478	1.473	0.005	5
Nylon	1.580	1.519	0.061	58–60
Perlon	1.582	1.525	0.057	57
Orlon	1.500〉1.515〉	1.500〉1.518〉	−0.003	4
Acrilan	1.520	1.524	−0.004	4
X 51	1.516	1.520	−0.004	4
Dynel	1.530	1.525	0.005	5
Dacron 〉 Terylene 〉	1.745	1.630	0.115	115
Kuralon	1.535	1.526	0.009	9
Arnel	1.472	1.471	0.001	1
Creslan	1.517	1.521	−0.004	3
Verel	1.538	1.539	−0.001	1
Zefran	1.512	1.519	−0.007	7

fibroscopes. In projection they give a constant magnification of about 700×. Measuring tables are supplied with this instrument, which permit rapid determination of fiber thickness.

The *phase contrast* and *interference* microscopes are used for structural investigation. This method can be recommended mainly for longitudinal and cross sections. Especially with the interference methods it is possible to observe and measure even minute refractive index differences in the fibers.

Birefringence measurements of fibers are very important both for fiber identification and for structural investigation. These measurements can be made with a polarizing microscope with the aid of a capillary rotator. Very accurate measurements can also be made with the immersion method.

The average birefringence values for a number of fibers are listed in Table 1.

Fibers are rather seldom subjected to a fluorescent microscopic examination. The fluorescence inherent in most fibers differs only slightly and is moreover fairly weak. The method can be successfully employed, however, in examining cotton for mercerization. These fluorescent colors may be important in conjunction with other data. In some cases the use of fluorochromes has provided important data. In the case of wool, for instance, the nature of damage can be demonstrated very well by staining with a mixture of Rhodanine 6 GD and Coriphosphine.

Data so far obtained do show that fluorescence investigation is definitely useful for fiber microtechnology.

Both electron and x-ray microscopy are widely used for fiber research. They are of great importance especially for more fundamental structural investigation. Investigations are made with replicas, thin sections and breakdown products. In surface examination, good results have already been obtained with the electron scanning microscope. It appears that this method, together with x-ray microanalysis and ion etching is going to be very important in fiber research.

Techniques of Fiber Microscopy

The technical part of fiber microscopy can be divided into: preparation methods, staining methods, mounting methods and microscopic techniques. Most of the preparation techniques can be used for examining all types of fibers, but this is not the case with staining methods. Subdivision according to the nature of the fibers is necessary.

Preparation Techniques. *Making Cross-sections.* Three methods are employed for making cross-sections.

(1) Plate Method. A bunch of fibers is pushed through a 0.5-mm hole in a 0.5-mm thick copper plate. The opening must be well filled so that the fibers are tightly packed. The fibers are severed on both sides with a

sharp razor blade. The cut surface is now examined under a microscope without further preparation.

(2) Hardy Microtome. Relatively thin sections can be made with this simple instrument. It consists of two rectangular plates held together by lateral ridges. In the middle of one plate there is a very narrow slot. From the middle of the other plate a thin metal lip protrudes which fits exactly into this slot. If the two plates are fitted together a very small part of the slot remains open. By means of a micrometer screw a second metal lip can be pressed into this open part from underneath.

In order to make a section, the slot is filled with a bunch of fibers. Next, the second plate is affixed. The fibers are severed with a razor blade above and below the plate. The micrometer screw is fitted in such a way that the lip is immediately under the slot. By means of this, the bunch of fibers can now be pressed several microns out of the slot. After the protruding fibers have been coated with cellulose lacquer, the cut is made with a sharp razor blade pressed as close to the plate as possible.

Sections of 10μ can easily be made, and with sufficient experience sections of 3μ are not unusual.

(3) Freezing Microtome. If a bunch of fibers is imbedded in celloidine or gelatin, it it possible to make a $1–3\mu$ section with a sledge freeze-microtome. On the whole the sections are more regular than with the previous methods and hence more suitable for examination with phase contrast and interference microscopes.

Making Longitudinal Sections. If a bunch of fibers laid exactly parallel is mounted in gelatin, thin longitudinal sections can be made therefrom with a sledge freeze-microtome. It is essential for the knife to be movable while the specimen holder is stationary. It must, however, be possible to set the holder three ways relative to the knife.

If a freezing microtome is not available, it is quite possible to make good longitudinal sections with Stove's method, as follows:

A cellulose acetate film is applied to a slide. This film is moistened with xylene. On top of this a bunch of fibers is laid exactly parallel. It is advisable to apply some tension by affixing a 2-gram weight at each end of the bunch. When the xylene has evaporated, a drop of ethyl lactate is added, while next a solution having the following composition is applied in abundance:

Cellulose acetate film	5 gr
Tricresyl phosphate	3 ml
Ethyl lactate	10 ml
Amyl acetate	75 ml

The whole must then dry for 36 hours at room temperature and can next be mounted in paraffin with a melting point of 50°C. It is better to use a mixture of paraffin and beeswax, the hardness then being adapted to that of the fibers.

Surface Examination. The surface structures of fibers can be examined by the following methods: (1) replica, (2) semi-embedding, (3) interference microscopy, and (4) electron scanning method.

(1) In the replica method, cellulose acetate (12 g) is usually used, dissolved in ethyl lactate (10 ml) and amyl acetate (78 ml). A film of this solution is made on a slide by the smear method customary for microbiology. The fibers are placed carefully on this film. After about 30 min. they can be pulled off the film. The replica can be examined forthwith under a microscope. Instead of cellulose acetate solution a normal cellulose lacquer can be successfully used.

(2) In semi-embedding, the fiber is carefully pressed into a swollen film with about the same refractive index as the fiber. In the microscopic image the influence of the lower half of the fiber is thus eliminated.

Protein glycerin can be effectively used for protein fibers. For wool and keratin fibers ROX 1 (Chroma) is particularly suitable. For cellulose fibers ROX 2 (Chroma) or cellulose lacquer may be used.

For synthetic fibers, cellulose lacquer can be used. In these cases it is advisable, after the lacquer has dried, to apply a thin shadow coating to the upper surface of the fibers. This coating is especially necessary if the fibers are matted.

(3) The normal interference methods can usually be employed for surface examination of fibers.

(4) A very good method for fibers is the electron scanning method. On the whole the images are much better than those obtained with the reflection electron microscope (q.v.) The foreshortening of the image is not a serious drawback. This method can be particularly important for examining keratin fibers and paper suspensions.

Staining Methods and Chemical Reactions. Of the numerous staining methods and chemical reactions used in textile and paper microscopy, only the most important will be mentioned. A complete list of all the customary reactions can be found in the references.

Cuoxam (copper oxide ammonia) reagent for cellulose. Ammonia is added to an aqueous solution of copper sulfate. The precipitate is washed and dried and put in as little concentrated ammonia as possible.

Herzberg's Solution (zinc chloroiodide) (A) 20 g dry zinc chloride in 10 g water; (B) 2.1 g KI and 0.1 g iodine in 5 cc water. Solutions A and B are mixed together. Allow precipitate to settle, decant and keep in the dark, a crystal of iodine being added.

Iodo-potassium iodide (KI_3). 0.6 g KI and 1 g iodine dissolved in 100 cc water.

Phloroglucine-acid. An approx. 5% solution of phloroglucinol in absolute alcohol. Always used with concentrated HCl. Reagent for lignified cell walls.

Millon's reagent. 1 part mercury is dissolved, with application of heat, in 2 parts HNO_3 (conc.). Next 2 parts of water are added. Reagent for proteins.

Ruthenium Red. 0.1 g ammoniacal oxychloride of ruthenium is dissolved in water (10 cc). After staining, the fibers are mounted in glycerol. General reagent for best fibers.

Victoria Blue B. Reagent for distinguishing raw and bleached cotton. 3% Victoria Blue in 10 cc water. The fibers are boiled in this solution. Wash in cold water until no more stain comes off.

Colotex B. Stain made by Union Chemical Company, New York; similar to Neocarmine W. The fibers are stained for 3–5 minutes in the solution, washed in water and then washed again in water containing several drops of ammonia, washed once again in distilled water and then dried.

Shirlastain A (I.C.I.). The fibers are eluated for 1 minute at room temperature, stained in the solution, washed in distilled water and examined under the microscope.

Iodo-sulfuric acid. 3 g KI is dissolved in 60 cc water, while 1 g iodine is added. 10 parts of water are added. The sulfuric acid solution is prepared by adding together 3 parts glycerin, 1 part water and 1 part concentrated sulfuric acid. After the fibers are stained in the iodine solution they are mounted in the sulfuric acid.

Allwörden's reaction. Reagent for damage to wool (see Fig. 1b). The wool fibers are treated with saturated chlorine or bromine solution. Depending upon the thickness of the fiber, the temperature, and the acid or lye damage, a number of small blisters occur on the fiber. The time needed for bringing about the blisters indicates the state of damage. In the case of wool damaged by acid the blisters occur earlier than normal, while in the case of lye-damage the reaction takes longer than normal. The normal reaction times at 17° C are:

for fine wool	20–25 μ diam.	30 sec
for wool	25–30 μ "	70–80 sec
for coarse wool	>30 μ "	120 sec

The reaction time must always be compared with a control to eliminate influences of temperature, reagent and fiber diameter.

K.M.V. reagent. (Fig. 1.) 20 g KOH is dissolved in 50 cc liquid ammonia; after about 1 hour the liquid is decanted and stored in a stoppered flask. The reagent keeps for 6 to 8 weeks.

Pieces of wool not longer than 3 mm are treated with the reagent. The moment the reagent begins to act a stopwatch is pressed. The reaction time is the time elapsing before the first blisters appear on the fiber. This depends upon:

(a) the thickness of the fibers (thinner fibers have a short reaction time).

(b) temperature (higher temperature—shorter reaction time).

(c) state of damage (acid-damage shortens reaction time; lye-damage lengthens it).

(d) age of reagent (the reaction time is increased through loss of NH_3).

(e) chroming of wool (chromed wool reacts more slowly than unchromed).

Factors (a), (b) and (d) can be eliminated by using a control of the same thickness.

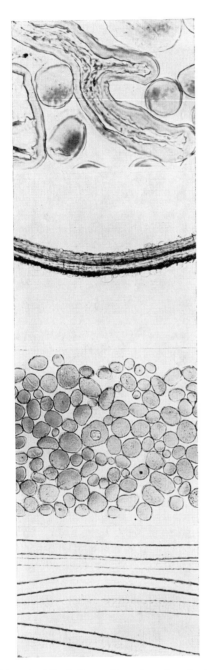

FIG. 1a. Wool fibers (from top down): ASTM 40, cross section, 450×. ASTM 56, longitudinal, 110×. ASTM 56, cross section, 110×. ASTM 58, longitudinal, 110×.

FIG. 1b. Wool fibers (from top down): ASTM 56, KMV reaction, 110×. Allwörden reaction, 450×. Damaged by heat, 110×. Re-used wool, 225×.

The following reaction times at 18°C can be taken as normal for several thicknesses of wool:

Dutch wool (37μ)	12 min
New Zealand (24μ)	8 min
Cape wool (20μ)	8 min

The first indication of blistering is at the ends of the pieces.

Cumulative damage may result in a normal reaction time.

Methylene Blue Test. 0.002–0.003% methylene blue in distilled water. Pieces of wool about 5 mm long in methylene blue are microscopically examined after the dye has acted for about 10 minutes. This reaction is used mainly to distinguish damage by heat from damage by alkali.

Methyl Orange Test. The normal indicator solution is used. In the case of wool this test is used for:

(a) detection of damage by light
(b) retention of chemicals distinguishable by color and formation of crystals of the acid form of methyl orange, which is far less water-soluble than the sodium salt itself.

Congo Red Test. The Congo Red test is based on:

(1) The varying diffusion at room temperature of stains in the cuticula and in the secondary cellulose layer of cotton fiber after this has been made accessible to the stain to a greater or less extent by swelling in caustic soda solution, with the result that the cellulose layer is stained a deeper shade.

(2) The behavior of cotton fiber when swollen with caustic soda solution, especially as regards the constricting effect of the cuticula.

(3) Spiral splitting of the cuticula. The specimen of cotton for examination is:

(a) soaked for 3 min in a sodium hydroxide solution of a certain strength; this may contain a wetting agent if desired.
(b) washed with water.
(c) placed for 10 min in a concentrated solution of Congo Red.
(d) rinsed.
(e) placed in an 18% caustic soda solution.

This test is used for detecting various forms of damage to cotton. Although on the whole it allows of explicit conclusions, it should be stated that the result is entirely qualitative.

Cotton Blue-Lactophenol. The fibers are heated for 1 min in lactophenol, then stained for 5–10 min with a warm aqueous solution of cotton blue. After rinsing with warm lactophenol they are microscopically examined. This test is used mainly for damage by molds.

Mounting Methods. It is of major importance for the fibers to be mounted in a medium whose refractive index does not vary too much from that of the fibers. The following media are very satisfactory:

(1) Glycerin-gelatin: 7 g gelatin is soaked for 2 hr in 42 cc distilled water; 50 g glycerin and 0.5 g phenol crystals are added; it is heated on a water bath for 10–15 min, while stirring, and is filtered through a glass filter. (n = 1.474.)

(2) Canada balsam.

(3) Broadfoot and Schwarz. Constituent parts: isobutyl methacrylate (Du Pont), Aroclor 1242 (Monsanto), Xylene.

IBM (cc)	Aroclor (cc)	Xylene (cc)	Refractive index
10	—	30	1.495–1.506
18	3	27	1.500–1.505
18	6	24	1.505–1.510
18	9	21	1.510–1.520
18	12	18	1.520–1.525

(4) Aquamount (Gurr)

(5) Glycerin 85%

Special Micro-techniques. The following techniques are important in fiber research:

Micro-elongation tests. The fibers are fixed tight at one end, and run over a pulley at the other, on which a weight may be suspended. To ensure that the same piece is examined throughout the test, the method may be varied by having a pulley and a weight at each end.

Micro-torsion tests. Here again the fibers are fixed tight at one end. The other end is fixed in rotating metal jaws. Great care must be taken to ensure that the bearing and centering of the rotating part are very accurate to avoid the fiber disappearing from view during the test.

Capillary rotator. For exact birefringence measurement of fibers the fiber is placed in a glass capillary. The capillary is filled with a liquid whose refractive index is the same as that of glass, and it can be rotated in the same liquid. It is possible with a simple disc to rotate the capillary with the fiber through an angle of 90°. The double refraction of the fiber is now measured, while the rotator is turned 90± to measure the fiber thickness.

Special measuring methods. Special methods that may be mentioned are the micrometer plates for determining denier and fullness and the measurements for determining lumen percentage.

Various methods have been suggested in the course of the years but few have become widely used (e.g., the "Universalokular nach A. Herzog" marketed by VEB Optik, Jena). In this ocular, a reticulated micrometer makes it possible to determine the titre of viscose fibers direct from the cross section. Calibration of the micrometer also makes it suitable for all other fiber sections.

The fullness of fibers of irregular section can be calculated by determining the true surface with a planimeter and calculating the area of a circle described from the section. The fullness V, as a percentage, is then $V = (400 \, F/\pi B^2) = 127.32 \, (F/B^2)$, in which F is the fiber-section and B the greatest dimension of the section. If a projection microscope is not available the true area can easily be determined with a reticulated micrometer.

The lumen percentage can be determined most easily using a fixed magnification projection microscope. The fibers are compared with a number of round "ideal" sections, in which both lumen and sections are circular.

Preparation Methods for Electron Microscopic Examination. *Duglosz' semi-embedding method for making replicas.* As fibers are usually bigger than 10μ in diameter, it is difficult to make replicas that have retained their original form after the necessary manipulation. With the semi-embedding method, fibers are dropped on to a photographic plate, the gelatine layer of which has been swollen. After the gelatine layer has dried, a microscope slide covered with a marco-resin film with catalyst and accelerator is placed on the gelatin layer. When the plastic has hardened, the photographic plate is pressed off. The slide with the resin and the fibers fixed in it are now used to make a replica by the silver-carbon method.

Page's replica method for extensive surfaces. Fibers out of a suspension are put to dry on a clean slide. A film of methyl methacrylate swollen at the surface in plasticizer is pressed on the slide. After hardening, the film is removed together with the fibers. With the aid of a film of polyvinyl alcohol, allowed to form from a 10% solution, the fibers are pulled from the methacrylate. Lastly, a positive replica is formed, again with 10% polyvinyl alcohol.

Other replica methods. (1) Impressions in polyisobutyl methacrylate which softens at the surface at 100°C. (2) Semi-embedding in polystyrene. The upper surface is then used for making a replica. (3) Bradley's two-stage replica technique is also widely used for fibers.

Fiber embedding for ultra-microtomy. Cutting ultra-thin sections of fibers necessitates embedding them in a synthetic resin. This raises the following problems:

(1) The embedding medium must infiltrate properly into the fiber and must not change its structure.

(2) During hardening the plastic must not loosen from the fiber.

(3) It must be possible to orient the fiber properly in the synthetic resin.

Embedding media that are used are 50/50 mixtures of butyl and methyl methacrylate or epoxy resins. The latter are more suitable because they do not loosen from the fibers so readily. The fact that the epoxy resins have a rather distinct structure under the electron microscope is a drawback however.

Electron staining reactions. Various staining reactions are recommended for electron microscopic examination of fibers. Good results are obtained with osmium tetroxide, ferrialum and $ZnCl_2$. For cellulose fibers, 20% $AgNO_3$ for several hours also gives good results.

Hess successfully used KI_3 (Iodine 5%, KI 10%, pH 5). He got very good results with thallium ethylate in benzene. All these methods can be used successfully for cellulose fibers and polyvinyl alcohol.

Fiber Microscopy and Morphology

Fibers can be classified as: (1) protein fibers, (2) cellulose fibers, (3) synthetic fibers.

Protein Fibers. The most important protein fibers are the keratin fibers. As regards textile techniques wool is the chief one of these. In addition to wool, are hairs that are used for "effect" or for other special purposes, e.g., mohair, cashmere and goat hair, from the Angora goat, the Cashmere goat and the common goat, respectively, camel hair, llama, alpaca and Vicuna, allied to the camel. There are many kinds of fur-producing animals, for instance: the rabbit, muskrat, skunk, mink, wolf, ocelot, seal, tiger cat, lamb. Brush fibers come from the horse, cow, pig, marten, skunk and squirrel.

It is important to be able to identify all these fibers microscopically. No good systematic method for this exists as yet. An important contribution has been made by Wildman who systematically classified the scales, according to the shape of the margin, as follows:

1. (a) *Smooth:* Margins which are on the whole smooth with little or no indentation.

    (b) *Crenate:* This means "notched" and is restricted here to margins which have fairly shallow indentation and in which the majority of the "teeth" taper to a relatively sharp point.

    (c) *Rippled:* Margins having indentation, the majority of which are deeper than those of the crenate type and in which most of the "peaks" are rounded instead of ending in sharp points.

    (d) *Scalloped:* Scalloped margins are relatively rare among the textile fibers.

2. The distance apart of the external margins of the scale comparison is at a standard magnification.

    (a) *Close:* Successive scale margins along the fiber which are very close together l:h (length:height) = >10.

    (b) *Distant:* Scale margins which are far apart in the direction of the long axis of the fiber l:h = 3:10.

    (c) *Near:* Successive scale margins which are spaced at distances intermediate between the above extremes l:h < 3.

3. *Type of Over-all Pattern.* All the following patterns may be qualified by the terms defined above to indicate the form of the scale margins and their spacing intermediate patterns can be described by combining the names of the basic patterns.

    (a) *Mosaic:* The term is self-explanatory but is qualified as follows:
    Regular mosaic: The units of which are very approximately the same size.
    Irregular mosaic: The units of which are obviously not of the same size.

    (b) *Waved:* Some form of wave occurs commonly in scale pattern and the term is applied to any pattern which appears to be wavy; where the waves follow a continuous course around the fiber their uninterrupted character is inferred from the term waved without further qualification.
    Interrupted wave. A pattern which has a general wave form but which is clearly interrupted falls into this category.
    Simple regular wave: This type has waves which are continuous and are of approximately the same wavelength and amplitude.
    Streaked wave: The waves are interrupted at regular intervals by longitudinally running bands of steeply inclined scale margins.
    Shallow, deep and medium waves: These adjectives indicate the relative depth of the majority of the waves in the pattern irrespective of the distance apart of the scale margins.

(c) *Chevron:* This pattern consists of waves, usually regular, but some times irregular, with either the crests or the bottoms of the troughs or both, relatively narrow and V-shaped. There are two varieties of chevron pattern, namely.

Single chevron: in which only one of the crests or troughs is narrow and V-shaped.

Double chevron: in which both the crests and the bottoms of troughs of the waves are narrow and V-shaped.

(d) *Pectinate* (comblike): The term is self explanatory, but two basic varieties are recognized.

Coarse pectinate describes the pattern in which the "teeth" of the comb are relatively large and set wide apart. *Lanceolate* is the pattern in which the teeth of the comb are long, narrow and rather more pointed than in the coarse pectinate type.

(e) *Petal patterns:* The general appearance of these resembles a series of overlapping flower petals due to the imbricate or overlapping appearance of the scales. There are several varieties of petal patterns and they are really modified wave forms, sometimes interrupted, regular waves and sometimes interrupted irregular waves. It must be clearly understood that a pattern does not qualify as a petal pattern unless its appearance strongly suggests a series of overlapping or imbricate elements.

Irregular petal: This is a form of interrupted irregular wave.

Diamond petal: The wave crests overlap the troughs of the succeeding series of waves toward the tip end of the fiber.

With the aid of this scale system it is certainly possible to identify the types of hair, especially if intermediate forms are concerned and the differences between root end, shaft and tip of the hair are examined separately. The medulla of fibers can be used for identification in only a few cases. We can distinguish:

1. Continuous thin medulla—diameter $< \frac{1}{2}$ the fiber diameter.
2. Continuous full medulla—diameter $> \frac{1}{2}$ the fiber diameter.
3. Continuous, regularly pectinate. Cell partitions divide the medulla into regular chambers
   (a) chambers in one row
   (b) chambers in several rows.
4. Continuous spiral.
5. Interrupted at regular intervals, predominant type.
6. Interrupted at irregular intervals, predominant type.
7. Sporadic types.
8. Irregular shapes.

Many of these types occur with one kind of fiber. Only 2, 3 and 4 have any systematic significance.

Structure of Wool and Other Animal Hair (Figs. 1a and 1b).

In general animal hair consists of the following parts:

The medulla, the innermost part of the hair, recognizable by less elongated cells not highly pigmented. After cornification, fairly large air cavities occur in the medulla, which may help to bring about the color of the hair (interference colors). As a rule the medulla is fairly easy to see in wool preparations.

The cortex, a zone consisting of spindle-shaped cells. Each of these cells is enveloped in membrane about 500 A thick. The contents consist of fibrils (tonofibrils). These tonofibrils are well oriented along the fiber axis. In between the fibrils there is an evaporated protein substance, the cement. The tonofibrils consist of keratin. The cortex outer layer is formed by a less oriented fibrillary mass: the *cortex mantle.* This cortex mantle forms a screen in the fiber against the penetration of dyes and chemicals.

The scale layer, a layer of flat overlapping elements. The scales also have a fibrillary structure. They consist of macro-fibrils which can be seen in isolated scales with a phase microscope and micro-fibrils observable only with an electron microscope. In between these fibrils is the scale cement.

This heterogeneous structure of the scales has led some authors to classify them as endocuticula and exocuticula. But this distinction has no significance in practice.

The scales play an important part in the occurrence of crimp. Outside a curve the scales are thicker than inside and there is also more matter there.

Chemicals and dyes can penetrate better into the scales inside the curve than into those on the outside.

The epicuticula, a membrane about 100 A thick completely enveloping the wool hair on the outside. It is very resistant to attack by acids and bases. Its composition, however, does not differ fundamentally from normal keratin.

Some authors state that the epicuticula is the cortex cell membrane. Kassenbeck showed in ultra-thin sections with an electron microscope (1) that the scale edges which are visible under the normal microscope are ridges on the actual scales which envelop the fiber like a cuff; (2) that the epicuticula was membrane enveloping the scale.

Methods of Examining the Various Fiber Elements

The epicuticula. The structure of the epicuticula can be examined with Von Allwörden's reaction. The defatted wool is placed in saturated bromine solution and is examined through a microscope until the first blisters occur. Water is then sucked through, the blisters usually increasing in size. The blisters may be stained with 0.1 % methylene blue. The time elapsing before the first blisters occur and the shape and size of these blisters are important and may be used as important characteristics to detect damage.

The scale cells can best be examined with the semi-embedding methods discussed under *Surface Examination* (p. 345) or by making a replica. If the hair is pigmented it must first be bleached in hydrogen peroxide.

The cortex cells. The course of the cortex layer can most suitably be examined with normal glycerin preparations. The individual cortex cells can be examined by disintegrating the hair in caustic potash or by the trypsin-sulfuric acid method.

The caustic potash treatment is effected in 5 % KOH for 2–3 hours at 50°C. The drawback is that the cells swell greatly. Shape and size are rather uncertain.

The better way is first to dissolve the cement substance by the trypsin treatment and then to make a preparation in sulfuric acid.

Trypsin solution: 0.75 g trypsin and 0.3 g sodium bicarbonate are dissolved in 100 cc distilled water. (The sodium bicarbonate must be very pure). The solution is fully active for only one hour. The hair is defatted properly in petroleum ether or benzene, dried, washed and cut in 0.5–1 mm pieces. Per 30–50 mg hair, 10 cc trypsin solution is used. The suspension is left standing for 3 hours in a closed Erlenmeyer flask at 40°C ± 3°C.
Sulfuric acid: 85 parts analytically pure sulfuric acid, s.g. 1.84 and 15 parts distilled water are mixed.

The *cortex mantle* can best be prepared by treating the wool fibers with 1.6 % peracetic acid followed by extraction with 0.1 N ammonium hydroxide. The insoluble portion is 7–10 % of the fibers. A cross-section shows that besides the cortex mantle the cell membrane of the cortex cells can also be seen, while in phase contrast part of the scales is also found to be present.

The medullary sheath. The size and course of the medullary canal can best be studied from a longitudinal preparation. To study the size and shape properly, the air in it must be expelled.

The most effective way to do this by laying short pieces in KOH or turpentine. A 17 % KOH solution at room temperature is mostly used. If the 17 % KOH solution is just brought to the boil, this if necessary being repeated, scale layer and cortex disintegrate. The cement substance between the medullary cells also disintegrates.

Bilateral structure of wool. The Japanese, Horio and Kondo, found that if frizzy hair was stained with Janus green or Ponceau R the hairs showed a bilateral structure, one lengthwise half showing greater affinity for Ponceau R and the other a greater affinity for Janus green. They concluded that it had a bilateral structure. Mercer has called the two halves the para-cortex and the ortho-cortex.

The difference between the two parts of the fiber is very easy to see if the wool hair is first stained with methylene blue and if this is followed by Allwörden's reaction. The inside curve of frizzy hair is then much more strongly affected than the outer.

Examination of cross-sections shows that on the whole the ortho-cortex consists of larger cells.

The difference between para and ortho-cortex is found to some extent with all keratin fibers. Although mohair was originally described as 100 % ortho fiber, close examination has shown that a part of this is also para cortex, although the percentage is low.

The dividing line between the para and ortho parts is usually very irregular. In some cases there may be two ortho parts with the para cortex between, while fibers have also been observed with a central "ortho" strand enveloped in para cortex.

Fluorescent microscope examination shows that besides the differences between the cortex parts there are also fairly strong differences between the scales of the outer and inner curves of wool fiber. In the case of dyed fibers, the scales on the ortho are found to allow dye to penetrate better than those on the para side.

Microbiological and Biological Attack on Wool

Microbiological Attack. As wool and other animal hair contains a specific protein (keratin) which is limited in quantity as compared with cellulose, microorganisms capable of attacking this complex substance are not found as commonly as cellulose decomposing organisms. Nevertheless, the keratin-attacking organisms are sufficiently represented to necessitate adequate precautions in handling and storing woolen products.

Wool can be easily attacked by bacteria and by molds. The most severe is caused by several strains of Penicillia and/or Aspergillus, which cause colored spots. These spots, which are serious because they are difficult to remove and may moreover cause trouble in dyeing, are a fairly superficial attack usually caused through microorganisms growing on fiber such as wax, soap, oil, fat or nitrogenous waste products.

Molds of the genera Alternaria, Stemphylium, Oöspora and Penicillia cause the spots on wool but to a certain extent attack the wool as well. Other strains causing such effects are Aspergillus, Fusarine, Trichoderma and Cephalothecium.

The aerobic bacilli include several which may attack wool. One of the best known is Bacillus mesentericus. Furthermore, there is Bacillus subtilis. A very strong attack is caused by Actinomycetes which quickly brings about a loss of mechanical characteristics of the wool. There are strong indications that this damage is caused only if the fiber has already been damaged mechanically or chemically.

Proteolytic bacteria and molds rapidly attack wool fiber under favorable conditions, loosen the scales, dissolve the intercortical cement, and disintegration into the spindle-shaped cortex cells occurs. These effects can be seen directly with microscopic examination. This form should be distinguished from normal mechanical damage because hyphae and sometimes spore carriers are usually present.

Especially after staining with 0.1 % methylene blue, the hyphae are easy to see, while mold attack can be rendered very clearly visible with a phase contrast microscope.

Even a fairly slight attack causes a loss in double refractivity and therefore a polarization microscope can also be used.

Bacterial attack can be observed very well and very quickly with a phase contrast microscope. Staining methods also make the bacteria clearly demonstrable, e.g., with methylene blue or fuchsine (2–3 min.) or with carbol fuchsine or carbol gentian violet (20–30 sec.).

Finally, it should be stated that attack by molds and bacteria can occur only if there is sufficient moisture, whilst soluble nitrogenous material is likewise essential.

Biological Attack. Biological attack is largely accounted for by moths and the larvae of the carpet beetle (*Anthrenus verbasci L.*). Here again, it may be mentioned that neither moths nor carpet beetles can attack wool unless fats and salts are present.

Attack by insects can be detected microscopically immediately, owing to the typical morphology of the damage. Moreover, threads of the moth larva's web are often present and beetles often leave hairs behind. Diagnosis therefore causes no difficulty.

Morphology of Fibers

Silk (Fig. 2a). Raw silk consists of two filaments of fibroin stuck together with sericin. The filaments are triangular. Longitudinally, the fiber is very irregular. It shows constrictions, creasing, folding and thickenings. Both the shape and dimensions of the triangular fibroin filaments are important. If the cross section is slightly rounded the fibers take dye less readily than the larger purely triangular ones.

Degummed silk is a smooth, almost structureless fiber. A barely visible longitudinal striation can be observed. Zinc chloroiodide sometimes stains silk light yellow. In *Millon's reagent* the fibers turn red. Provided it is not weighted, silk dissolves in Cuoxam.

Tussah silk (Fig. 2a). The filaments are flat and wide, show pronounced longitudinal striation and cross-wise imprints of fiber intersections due to the fibers hardening. After maceration in cold chromic acid the "fibrils" can easily be isolated. The diameter of the fibrils is $0.3–1.5\mu$. Furthermore, there is coarser striation caused by air canals. The cross section is somewhat cuneiform. In zinc chloroiodide the fiber remains colorless. In Millon's reagent it turns red. In Cuoxam it dissolves.

Cellulose Fibers. Cellulose fibers may be classified as bast, leaf, and seed.

Bast fibers. This category comprises flax, jute, hemp and ramie. The fibers are found in the fibro-vascular region of the phloem. The fiber bundles are bound together with cellular tissue and waxy substances. The fibers are usually known as "soft" fibers.

Leaf fibers. These are obtained from the leaves of monocotyledonous plants. The fibers occur in bundles, i.e., accumulations of individual cells overlapping at the ends and thus forming continuous filaments. These cells are also held together by waxy substances. Unlike the bast fibers they are called "hard." The complete bundles are used for textile purposes. Most plants producing leaf fibers are related. The main fibers belonging to this group are sisal and manilla.

Plant hair. The seed hairs of various plants can be used for textile manufacture. The main kinds used industrially are cotton, coconut and kapok.

Microscopic identification of the various cellulose fibers is not particularly difficult. Characteristics such as "fiber bundles," shape of lumen, whether the lumen is air-filled and the shape of the cross section are adequate.

For microscopic examination generally only the ordinary light microscopic methods are used. The electron microscope is used only for fundamental investigation of the cell wall.

Cotton (Fig. 2b). The microscopy of cotton is very important both as regards mor-

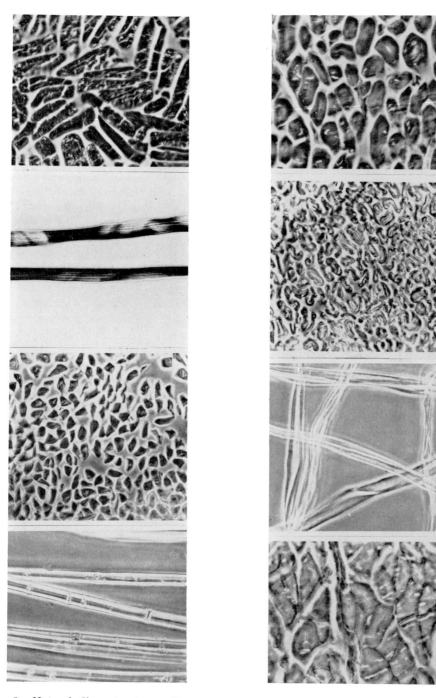

FIG. 2a. Natural fiber structures (from top down): Tussah silk, phase contrast, cross section, 450×. Tussah silk, phase contrast, longitudinal, 110×. Silk, phase contrast, cross section, 225×. Flax bleached, phase contrast, longitudinal, 225×.

FIG. 2b. Natural fiber structures (from top down): Linen, phase contrast, cross section, 450×. Cotton, phase contrast, cross section, 225×. Cotton, phase contrast, longitudinal, 225×. Hemp, phase contrast, cross section, 450×.

phology and examination with special methods such as micro-chemical reactions and examination in polarized light. The normal bright field methods can be applied very suitably. Phase contrast microscopy with special mounting methods is very important for examining micro structures and for tracing mercerizing. Dark field microscopy can also be used for examining surface structures, and the same applies to incident light microscopy.

The fiber is a single cell and looks like an irregularly twisted, collapsed tube with a central canal or lumen. No lumen can be seen at the top of the unbroken fibers. In its undamaged state the basal part of the fiber shows a membrane (part of the fiber that was underneath the seedcoat). The twists often change from Z to S spirals. There are three cross-sectional shapes—round, elliptic and linear.

Dead cotton fibers are often U-shaped in cross section, no lumen being visible.

The cross section varies very greatly from fiber to fiber. In this cross section the primary wall, the secondary wall, and the lumen can be distinguished.

The outside of the fiber is covered with a cuticula consisting of wax and pectin. The primary wall consists of fibrils oriented at random. The secondary wall consists of various layers deposited within each other, which are easiest to see in swollen material. The secondary wall also consists of fibrils oriented spirally.

The usual swelling medium is copper oxide ammonia. This swells the fiber irregularly. At certain intervals there are zones which do not swell. Often a spiral structure is also left, probably originating from protoplasm residues. In iodo-sulfuric acid the fibers swell and turn blue; protoplasm residues turn yellow. Ruthenium red, together with copper oxide ammonia, has the result that the cuticula, the wall of the lumen and the protoplasm residues turn red.

Zinc chloroiodide stains the fiber reddish violet. Mercerized cotton and bleached cotton color with this reagent more strongly than raw cotton. With copper oxide ammonia mercerized cotton forms no globules.

The fibrils lie next to one another in each layer of the secondary wall and are oriented spirally relatively to the long axis. The direction of the spiral is often reversed and coincides with a reversal in the external twisting. The dimensions of the fibrils have been determined with an electron microscope.

Damage to Cotton Fibers. *Mechanical Damage.* The forms of mechanical damage that may occur are irregular cross fracture, bruises and places where the fiber has been unevenly torn off.

Chemical Damage. This results in gradual decomposition of the cuticula, shown by an emphasizing of the spirals. In the case of chemical attack by acids, the spirals can be seen all over the fiber. Photo-chemical decomposition is usually more highly localized.

Biological Attack. Morphologically this closely resembles chemical damage. As a rule, however, the hyphae of the fungi or bacteria colonies are demonstrable.

Flax (Fig. 2a). Flax consists of cylindrical cells which are usually smooth except at the location of the usually X-shaped internode. The cross section is round to polygonal; the cell wall is thick. There is a narrow, well-defined lumen. At the end of the cell the lumen is lacking. The lumen has an independent existence. In Cuoxam it forms a small tube that remains even after the fiber is completely dissolved. Zinc chloroiodide colors unbleached flax pale violet, while bleached flax colors dark violet. In Neocarmine W flax turns blue.

Hemp (Fig. 2b). Hemp is often difficult to distinguish from flax. The differences are: (1) hemp cells are blunt-ended, forking laterally; (2) in iodine-sulfuric acid hemp shows cross striation and a blue-green color (flax: blue); (3) hemp fibers are not as transparent as flax fibers; (4) the cross section is different; (5) the parenchyma tissue often attached to the fiber contains calcium oxalate crystals.

With iodo-sulfuric acid a blue-green color

occurs. With zinc chloroiodide a blue or violet color occurs. With ammoniacal fuchsine a pale red color occurs. In Cuoxam the fiber does not dissolve as quickly as flax, while the primary wall remains.

Jute (Fig. 3a). Jute consists of fiber bundles overlapping at the ends, thus creating a continuous filament. The fibers are held together with gum, wax and lignin. The surface of the fiber is smooth with few internodes. The lumen is bigger than in flax. The cross section is polygonal.

In Cuoxam the fiber does not dissolve, but swells. In zinc chloroiodide a pronounced yellow coloration occurs. With phloroglucino-hydrochloric acid the fiber turns red.

Ramie (Fig. 3b). A flat, ribbon-like fiber. The elementary fiber is 8–10 cm long. The surface is characterized by small cross striation and folds. The cell wall is thin, the lumen flat. In Cuoxam the fiber dissolves completely. With zinc chloroiodide it turns blue-violet.

Sisal. Stiff fibers, roughly cylindrical in shape, with a characteristic widening in the middle. Ends blunt and thick. Cross section polygonal. Lumen usually fairly big. The fibers often contain air bubbles. Iodo-sulfuric acid gives a yellow color. Defatted fibers afterwards bleached in sodium hypochlorite and rinsed in 90%-alcohol give a red color in NH_3 vapor.

Manila (Fig. 3b). Cylindrical fibers with pointed ends. Cross section irregular to polygonal. Lumen round. Cell walls thin. In the fiber bundles there are often stigmata, i.e., thick, silicon-containing plates. They can be easily detected by macerating fibers in *chromic acid*. With iodo-sulfuric acid a golden yellow to green color occurs.

Kapok (Fig. 3a). *Air-filled*, thin-walled, long, smooth cells. The lumen is large. The cross section is round to elliptical. With zinc chloroiodide a yellow color occurs; with phloroglucino-HCl pink.

Regenerated Natural Fibers. Besides protein fibers this category contains the cellulose fibers.

The protein fibers are made from casein, zein, groundnut or soyabean protein. All these fibers show very slight double refractivity and have irregular structures. Undissolved or prematurely coagulated protein particles can be distinguished in the fibers. Usually they have an irregular skin: air pockets, spherulitic structures and crystals are often found.

More important than the protein fibers are the cellulose fibers.

Most kinds of regenerated cellulose have a skin, which is formed directly in the coagulation bath, and a medulla. In cross section the fibers are irregularly sinuate. They show clear longitudinal striation.

The structure, skin, medulla, are particularly easy to see with the polarizing microscope as the skin has a higher specific double refractivity than the pith. Irregular double refractivity is also to be seen in the cross section.

The refractive index differences occurring in the cross sections are readily demonstrable with an interference microscope. The skin is then particularly easy to see. Phase contrast microscopic examination of cross and longitudinal sections is also useful for structural examination. With the electron microscope it was possible, in addition to the skin, to detect a very thin membrane, the cuticula (Kassenbeck). In the medulla, fibrillar structures are found. The elementary fibrils are 70–90 A in diameter. These elementary fibrils form packs of various sizes.

Electron microscopic examination shows the skin usually to have a spongy structure.

With thallium and iodine reactions Hess showed that viscose fibers had crosswise striation in the fibrils. In addition to a "small" period of approx. 150 A, this striation showed a large period of 550–670 A.

In many cases, both light and electron microscopic examination shows the skin to consist of several layers.

Casein and Milk Wool. The fiber section is round with several scallops. There is slight longitudinal striation.

357

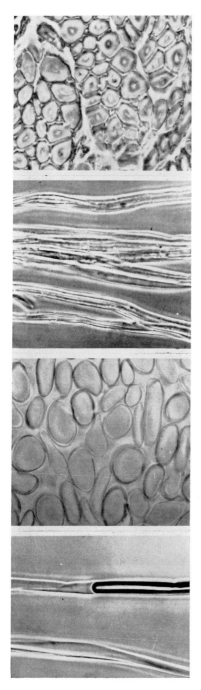

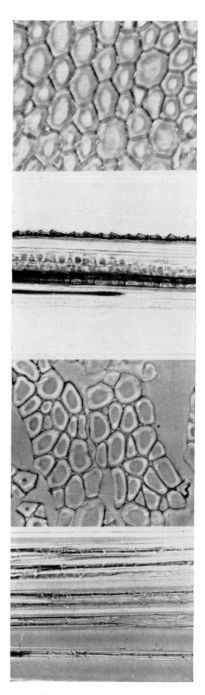

Fig. 3a. Natural Fiber Structure (from top down): Jute, phase contrast, cross section, 450×. Jute, phase contrast, longitudinal, 225×. Kapok, phase contrast, cross section, 450×. Kapok, phase contrast, longitudinal, 225×.

Fig. 3b. Natural fiber structures (from top down): Manila, phase contrast, cross section, 450×. Manila, phase contrast, longitudinal, 225×. Ramie, phase contrast, cross section, 450×. Ramie, phase contrast, longitudinal, 110×.

Reactions: In zinc chloroiodide the fiber turns yellow. In Millon's reagent a red color occurs. In Cuoxam it is insoluble, but turns blue.

Viscose Rayon (Fig. 4b). The best medium for examining viscose rayon and copper rayon is glycerin, mineral oil (n = 1.46) or monobromonaphthol (n = 1.66). Striation is pronounced in longitudinal specimens. This varies considerably. The cross section shows many irregular scallops. A "skin" is clearly visible on the cross section.

In Cuoxam viscose and copper rayon are soluble. In zinc chloroiodide the fiber colors blue to red-violet but eventually turns black. With Neocarmine W viscose rayon turns red-violet and copper rayon blue.

Acetate Rayon (Fig. 4a). The surface of the fiber is smooth. The cross section shows some round lobes visible as longitudinal ridges in longitudinal specimens. In polarized light the fibers are weakly double refractive. In cross section some parts are dark and others light between crossed Nicol prisms. This can be explained by the orientation of the elementary micelles.

Acetate rayon is soluble in acetone. If Vinyon, which is also soluble, is present it is better to use acetic acid, which leaves Vinyon unaffected. With zinc chloroiodide a pronounced yellow coloration occurs (nylon also turns yellow!). In Cuoxam the fiber is insoluble. Acetate rayon is also soluble in saturated phenol solution (as is nylon).

Synthetic Fibers. Microscopic examination of synthetic fibers employs practically all microscopic methods. Birefringence measurements are important for detecting differences in specific birefringence. These differences have been partly correlated with physical-mechanical characteristics.

In addition to this birefringence determination it is very important to judge the homogeneity of the fiber with the phase contrast and interference microscopes. The finer structures, however, can be rendered visible only with an electron microscope.

Usually it is necessary to study the fibers by means of longitudinal or cross sections. It is advisable to assess the importance of all divergencies and inhomogeneities by means of microtorsion, microtension and microwear tests.

In synthetic fibers the following divergencies and inhomogeneities in structural details may occur:

(1) Places with a lower specific birefringence than the rest of the fiber. In both torsion and tensile tests these places prove to be weak. Their effect on fiber characteristics is least if many such places occur in close proximity. In all specimens necks form at these places.

(2) Divergencies in birefringence caused by the skin. A skin of irregular thickness is found in many cases with this group of fibers. Especially if the skin has a higher double refractivity than the medulla, an interruption in it may greatly affect the strength.

(3) *Irregular birefringence divergencies.* Small places which are either more birefringent or less double refractive than the rest of the fiber may greatly affect its characteristics. These divergencies often occur together with great or small divergencies in cross sectional shape.

(4) *Stress concentrations.* Where there are many inclusions in the fiber, for instance in the case of some large matting particles, stress figures occur. At such places fibrillar splitting of the fiber may occur.

(5) *Spherulites.* Spherulitic structures are found fairly commonly in these fibers. When small they nearly always cause fibrillar splitting. Large specimens or a number of small ones in proximity cause cross breakage. If there is a skin they cause less harm.

(6) *Isotropic particles.* On the whole the same applies to these as to spherulites. Fibrillation usually follows the occurrence of these inhomogeneities. Their effect is greatest in skinless fibers. If no stress concentration exists around these particles they are of little importance.

359

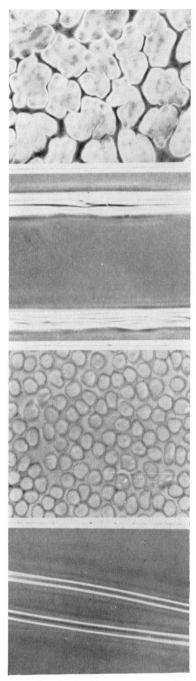 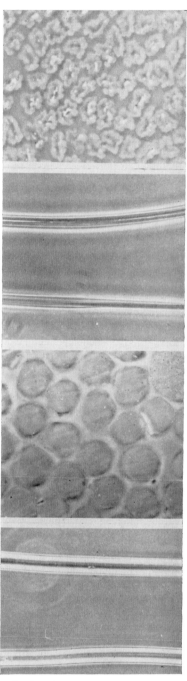

FIG. 4a. Synthetic fiber structures (from top down): Acetate rayon, phase contrast, cross section, 450×. Acetate rayon, phase contrast, longitudinal, 225×. Cuprammonium rayon, phase contrast, longitudinal, 450×. Cuprammonium rayon, phase contrast, longitudinal, 225×.

FIG. 4b. Synthetic fiber structures (from top down): Viscose rayon, phase contrast, cross section, 450×. Viscose rayon, phase contrast, longitudinal, 225×. Nylon, phase contrast, cross section, 450×. Nylon, phase contrast, longitudinal, 225×.

(7) *Air pockets*. Both elongated, spindle-shaped and unelongated air pockets occur. Usually they are characterized by a wide light refractivity zone and a pronounced stress figure. Fibrillar splitting in torsion and tensile tests is usually the result. With originally negatively birefringent fibers, such as Orlon, a positive form of birefringence may occur through strong fibrillar splitting if there is a skin.

(8) *Fibrillar fiber structure*. Most synthetic fibers have a fibrillar structure. In most cases this can be seen only with an electron microscope from replicas or thin cross sections. In Orlon and polyvinylalcohol the fibrillar structure is to be clearly seen with a light microscope. With Terylene and Dacron it is visible with a light microscope, but is clear only under an electron microscope. The fibrillar structure of nylon can be seen only with an electron microscope.

(9) *Surface structure*. This refers in the first place to variations in cross section. In addition, however, small structures such as the fairly common spiral grooves are important. Frosted fibers may have an irregular surface through the protrusion of frosting crystals. These can best be detected by shadowing the fiber slightly and examining it with a normal reflector microscope.

(10) *Lacunose effect*. Elongation of synthetic fibers until necks are formed may cause more or less spindle-shaped opaque spots in the fibers. These spots consist of a large number of small cracks in close proximity. Except in the case of cold drawing, the effect is also found normally in some fibers.

Nylon (Fig. 4b). Homogeneous, optically "empty" fiber. In polarized light, variations in double refractivity $\Delta = 56$–62. There is sometimes a skin. The cross section is round. In zinc chloroiodide nylon turns yellow and later orange to brown. In saturated phenol solution it is soluble. In 50 % formic acid nylon is insoluble at 80°C, Perlon is soluble.

Orlon (*Polyacrylic*) (Fig. 5a). The cross section is dumb-bell shaped to irregular. This causes striation in longitudinal specimens. In polarized light a positively birefringent skin and a negatively double refracting pith can be distinguished. Double refractivity varies from $\Delta = +3$ to $\Delta = -10$.

In various types the "pith" contains dark particles which are spindle-shaped to round. These may be double refractive, but also isotropic. Air pockets are also found. In saturated phenol solution the fiber is hardly visible. Upon heating, visibility increases. In dimethylformamide the fiber dissolves when heated.

Acrilan (*Polyacrylic*). The cross section is mostly kidney-shaped. Usually there is a pronounced skin. The pith often contains isotropic particles and air pockets. The fiber is weakly negative birefringent $\Delta =$ approx. 4.

X 51 (*Polyacrylic*). The surface is fairly smooth. The continuous filament is optically clear, the staple fiber is less transparent. The cross section is round with a very pronounced, fairly thick skin. The birefringence is fairly low: $\Delta =$ approx. 4.

Dynel (*Polyacrylic*) (Fig. 5a). Fairly smooth fiber with a ribbon-shaped cross section. Under a polarizing microscope birefringence varies from $\Delta =$ approx. $+6$ to $\Delta =$ approx. -6.

Polyvinylalcohol 11 ("*Kuralon*") (Fig. 5a,b). Fiber with the most pronounced skin and pith. The pith contains many spindle-shaped to round bodies which are partly double refractive, partly amorphous. In some cases there are air pockets.

The cross section is dumb-bell shaped to irregular. The fiber is weakly birefringent and both positive and negative birefringence is found.

Dacron, *Terylene* (*Polyester*)	Fiber with a fibrillar structure which can only be seen in longitudinal sections. Otherwise homogeneous. Birefringence 115. Cross section: Round

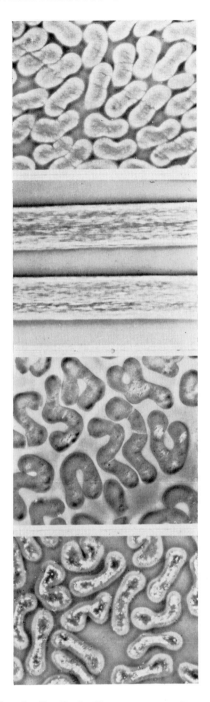

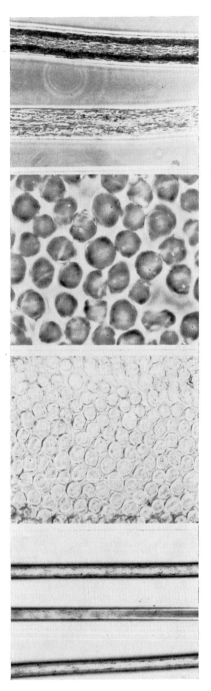

FIG. 5a. Synthetic fiber structures (from top down): Orlon, phase contrast, cross section, 450×. Orlon, phase contrast, longitudinal, 450×. Dynel, phase contrast, cross section, 450×. Kuralon, phase contrast, cross section, 450×.

FIG. 5b. Synthetic fiber structures (from top down): Kuralon, phase contrast, longitudinal, 225×. Perlon, phase contrast, cross section, 450×. Dacron, phase contrast, cross section, 225×. Dacron, phase contrast, longitudinal, 225×.

Creslan.   Cross section: Round, bean or dogbone; negative birefringent, Δ approx. 4.

Verel.   Cross section: Dogbone; birefringence low negative, approx. 1.

Zefran.   Cross section: Round; birefringence low negative, approx. 1.

REFERENCES

MATTHEWS, MOMERSBERGER, "Textile Fibers," Wiley, New York, 1954.

LUNIAK, "Die Unterscheidung der Textilfasern," Zürich, 1954.

HERZOG, "Handbuch der Mikroskopischen Technik für Fasertechnologen," Berlin, 1951.

HERZOG, "Mikrophotographischer Atlas der Technisch-wichtigen Pflanzenfaser," Berlin, 1955.

STOVES, J. L., "Fiber Microscopy," London, 1957.

WILDMAN, "The Microscopy of Animal Textile Fibers," WIRA, 1954; "Proceedings Internat. Wool Textile Res. Conf." (Austr. 1955, Vol. F).

WOLFF, TOBLER, F.v.G., "Mikroskopische Untersuchung Pflanzlicher Faserstoffe," Leipzig, 1951.

TURNER, "The structure of Textile Fibres," Manchester, 1953.

"Proceedings Electron Microscopy Conference," Stockholm, 1956.

"Proceedings Electron Microscopy Conference," Berlin, 1958 (at printers).

Annales Scient. Textile Belges, Nos. 1–4, 1955.

J. ISINGS

INDUSTRIAL RESEARCH

Both light and electron microscopy are being used extensively for research in many technical operations which are far removed from the long-established applications in the biological sciences. Almost every industry, in some phase of its operation, has need for these tools and associated techniques. Actually, microscopy has been used in industry for a long time. The light microscope has contributed to the solution of problems in control, development, and research ever since the technological revolution. Recently the electron microscope also has become established as a supplement to the light microscope. Electron microscopy is covered elsewhere in this Encyclopedia. However, it must be emphasized that both techniques are employed in industrial research in a complementary fashion, and are strongly interdependent.

Although application of microscopy is likely to vary with the particular industry, it is possible to provide basic information about the instruments and techniques in use, which should be of common interest to all. The microscopist has at his disposal a very powerful tool which can be adapted to meet his special needs through the use and development of appropriate techniques. It is essential, however, that he not only be familiar with the instrumentation, but also have an adequate knowledge of the disciplines appropriate to his specific problems. The purpose of this article is to discuss briefly the more important aspects of the microscope as a tool, together with related techniques, and to provide references which deal comprehensively with these subjects.

The most obvious function of microscopy is to reveal directly the fine-scale structure of a subject by means of combinations of lenses which resolve and magnify structure. Each of the various types of microscope shares this function. Some are capable of revealing exceedingly fine structure, whereas others can obtain higher contrast in the image, make certain measurements, or accept special specimens.

The foremost problem in microscopy is the obtaining of contrast to reveal significant structure at high magnification. Much progress has been made in this area through new techniques of specimen preparation as well as by advances in optical design of the microscope.

The maximum useful magnification of lenses has not been greatly extended in recent times, but modern microscope construction has made it easier to realize the full potential of the instruments. No longer is it necessary for the microscopist to be pre-occupied with optics; nevertheless, there are certain rules which must be observed in order to realize the best instrumental performance.

Resolving Limit, Useful Magnification, and Contrast

Detailed accounts of the factors governing resolution, and, in turn, useful magnification have been given in many publications (1, 2). The resolving limit of a microscope may be defined as the ability to register two objects whose centers are separated by the least distance, d, at which the objects may be detected as distinctly separate. The minimum object diameter is usually not less than twice the least detectable distance of separation, the latter varying directly with the wavelength of light, λ, and inversely with the refractive index, n, of the medium in which the object is immersed and with sin α, where α is one-half the angular aperture of the objective lens. Thus,

$$d = \frac{\lambda}{2n \sin \alpha}.$$

The resolution of a microscope is controlled simultaneously by the numerical aperture (N.A. $= n \sin \alpha$) of the objective and condenser lenses. In fact, the numerical aperture of a system may be expressed as the average of these two numerical apertures:

$$\text{N.A. (system)} = \frac{\text{N.A.}_{\text{obj}} + \text{N.A.}_{\text{cond}}}{2}.$$

For highest resolution, oil immersion lenses are available today with numerical apertures up to 1.4, and a corresponding resolving limit of the order of 0.2 micron. Since no lens, objective, or condenser can exceed a numerical aperture of 1.0 in air, it is essential to use high index immersion oil on the condenser as well as on the objective to realize the ultimate in resolution and magnification from a light microscope.

The useful magnification of a microscope may be roughly calculated by multiplying the numerical aperture of the system by 1000. This rule is based upon the relationship between the resolving limits of the eye and the microscope system. The resolving limit of the human eye is 0.2–0.3 mm at the normal viewing distance of 25 cm. Therefore to render visible the structure resolved by a lens of 1.4 numerical aperture, a minimum magnification of 1000× is required. If a photomicrograph is going to be viewed at distances greater than 25 cm, then a magnification exceeding that indicated by this rule is warranted.

Until now we have been dealing with lateral resolution, ignoring vertical resolution, or as it is usually termed, "depth of field." As lateral resolution increases, depth of field decreases. Therefore, to perform an observation of structure in depth, usually some compromise is necessary. Obviously, it is not always of greatest advantage in a study to exploit upper resolving limits of a system.

The rendition of contrast also is of prime consideration. Although a subject may contain structure on a resolvable scale, this structure may not be visible microscopically. This lack of visibility is frequently due to the inherent optical properties of the specimen, namely, that the structure possesses the same light-transmitting or reflecting qualities as the surrounding or background medium. Contrast can be improved, both by optical methods and by specimen preparation.

A microscope "sees" structure because of the optical characteristics inherent in a given specimen preparation which interact with the incident illumination and modify it. Consequently, contrast may be improved by better optical monitoring of these alterations or by enhancing the degree of light alteration by the sample through suitable preparative methods. The most commonly encountered optical factor controlling contrast is the numerical aperture of a system. As with depth of field, there is a loss of contrast accompanying an increase in the numerical aperture. Frequently there must be a compromise toward lower numerical aperture, this time to achieve desired contrast. Optical aids to increase contrast have been developed and have proved of special interest to the biologist whose living preparations are best studied in that condition. Nevertheless, the industrial microscopist also has a persistent need for these special tools, which include phase contrast, interference, and polarizing microscopes, and filters.

Phase, Interference, and Polarizing Microscopes. The phase microscope takes advantage of the optical-path differences within the specimen which result in the existence of phase differences among the light waves transmitted by the various portions of the specimen. Further phase changes are introduced in the light passing through the optical system and add to the phase differences created by the specimen and thereby render the object visible (3). Briefly, the diffracted rays are altered by a phase-retardation coating at the back focal plane of the objective, the intensity of the undeviated light is reduced by a filter in the form of a ring at the back focal plane of the objective. The deviated beam interferes with the diffracted rays at the focal plane of the eyepiece to form an image, the contrast of which is derived from these exploited phase differences. Special phase microscopes, both of transmitted- and vertical-illumination types, or components for conversion of existing microscopes, are available commercially from several manufacturers. The resolving limits of phase objectives are not as high as comparable objectives for conventional bright-field work, but the increase in contrast may overshadow the lack in resolving power.

The interference microscope, as the name implies, produces contrast in the image by optical interference. Contrast is apparent because of differences in color (when white light is used) rather than in differences in light intensities observed in the field, as in phase microscopy. Interference microscopy is very new and has been used principally by the biologist, but should find application in industry, especially in the study of transparent films comprised of structures having small differences in refractive index or thickness.

Polarized-light microscopes are useful in increasing contrast and in making optical measurements on crystalline and paracrystalline subjects. Differences in orientation of crystalline and fibrous materials are especially well revealed. A polarizing microscope is unique in that specimens are studied while illuminated with polarized light. A polarizer, transmitting light vibrating in one plane, is usually placed between the condensing lens and the source of illumination, and an analyzer, also of polarizing material, is located in the tube between the eyepiece and objective. Generally the polarizer and analyzer are used in the crossed position so that their respective planes of vibration are perpendicular. In this position, the field of view is completely dark, and the sample is visible only by virtue of any effect it might have on the original plane of vibration of the light with which it is illuminated. Figure 1 shows an image produced by anisotropic crystals under polarized light. Optical properties of substances have been measured for many years by means of polarized light. Mineralogists, chemical microscopists, and crystallographers use qualitative and quantitative optical data such as refractive index, birefringence, optic sign, extinction, etc., as an adjunct to other information in the identification of crystalline materials. Although these methods are highly useful in industrial studies, no attempt will be made to present any detailed information in this area. Excellent coverages of these techniques appear in the literature (4, 5). Polarized-light microscopy is equally applicable to either transmitted or vertical illumination. In metallographic and ceramic research, the

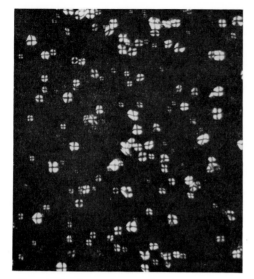

Fig. 1. A photomicrograph of starch grains under polarized light. The black cross exhibited by each starch grain indicates that it has anisotropic crystals radiating from the center. Such a structure is called a spherulite.

latter is employed to enhance contrast and to compare orientation among the grains of polished and etched specimens. It has been found especially useful in locating corrosion and other reaction products.

Dark-Field Illumination. Dark-field illumination is effective in obtaining contrast and for observing the colors of structures. Incident dark-field has been used very successfully in the detection of small quantities of materials lying on the surface of a substrate, particularly when sparsely distributed. The dark-field condenser is constructed to prevent any light from entering the objective but that which is scattered by the specimen. The specimen is illuminated by a hollow cone of light of too large an angle to permit the direct beam to enter the objective. The dark-field image is characterized by a dark background with more or less bright structures revealed in the subject. There is an intermediate case of hollow conical illumination in which a portion of the undeviated beam is allowed to enter the objective, in order to enhance contrast. This

is discussed in further detail later in this article.

Improvement of Contrast by Specimen Preparation. As mentioned previously, contrast can be improved by specimen-preparation methods. Staining, etching, metal shadowing, selecting appropriate mounting media, and replicating are some of the sample manipulations used to increase the contrast of the preparation.

Staining (6) has been used in biological preparation for years, and it is feasible to extend staining techniques to industrial samples, even metallurgical preparations. Some techniques are already developed, but frequently it is required that a technique be devised to satisfy a specific need. In view of the numerous stains now available and also the known reactions which yield colored reaction products, usually it is not difficult to select or develop a suitable staining procedure. Stains are employed to dye selectively certain structures of interest. They may be merely selective in the sense that they reveal structure without being recognizably indicative of chemical composition, or on the other hand, they may be strictly specific for a chemically reactive ion or group. In the latter case it is obvious that much is to be gained in relating the distribution of the chemical substance which reacts with the stain to the over-all structure of the specimen.

Thin sections sliced with a microtome (6) are quite appropriate for staining. Even in the unstained condition, microtome-produced thin sections are inherently more contrasty subjects with less confused structure than is the larger sample from which they were cut and thus permit the observation of the internal morphology of the sample. The biologist has pioneered in the field of microtomy, but again this is an effective technique for the industrial worker who need not be limited to employing the techniques of the biological micromotist. Because, in nonbiological problems, it is not generally required that the morphology of a living specimen be preserved, it is permissible to be less inhibited as to embedding techniques, in particular, the solvents, temperatures, and embedding media employed.

Metal-shadow casting (7) is a technique by which a thin film of metal is vacuum evaporated onto the surface of a sample or a replica of that surface. This method creates a subject on which differences in surface morphology are evident due to an increase in reflectivity or absorption of the surface and/or a shadow effect. Metallization of specimen surfaces by vacuum evaporation has been used extensively in electron microscopy; however, there are many applications of the technique in light microscopy, particularly in conjunction with surface replicas. Details of replication, metallizing, and shadowing by vacuum evaporation are given in the section on specimen preparation.

This discussion of resolving limits, useful magnification, and contrast is by no means complete; nevertheless, it is believed that the factors most significant to industrial microscopy were mentioned. Further detailed information may be found in the references cited or in other sections of this publication.

Alignment, and Related Methods of Illumination

Microscopes and methods of illumination (1, 2) used with them cannot very well be divorced in any discussion of the principles involved. Consequently, they will be treated together; however, emphasis will be placed first on microscope function and construction. Later, attention will be shifted to methods of illumination, and finally the selection of microscopes for nonbiological application will be considered.

Although there are many types of microscopes, they are closely related in function, and possess comparable components. Therefore, an understanding of the basic construction and operation of one microscope may be applied in some degree to others. However,

the best possible instrumental performance cannot be realized unless certain precautions are taken regarding adjustment, alignment of components, and the choice of optics and illumination.

Fundamentally, a microscope consists of an objective, eyepiece, and condenser, and, as such, is called a compound microscope. These components are held and manipulated on a stand which is usually equipped with a stage to hold the specimen. The condenser directs light to the specimen, the objective receives the light changed by the specimen and produces the initial magnification of the image. The eyepiece, through which the specimen is viewed, magnifies the image created by the objective. The total magnification of the viewed image is a product of the magnifications of the objective and eyepiece. There are many variations in types of objectives, condensers, and eyepieces. For example, in vertical illumination a single lens may serve at the same time the purposes of condenser and objective. Again, since many types of illumination are required, condensers are individually designed to achieve specific results.

Objectives are the most expensive components of a microscope and from this standpoint, as well as from that of their role in image formation, deserve the concentrated attention of the microscopist as to their selection. Objectives are classified with respect to optical correction. Some are chromatically corrected to bring two wavelengths of light into focus at the same plane, and also corrected spherically for one wavelength. Objectives having this degree of correction are called achromatic objectives and are only about one-third as expensive as apochromatic objectives which are chromatically corrected for three wavelengths and spherically for two. Unless the microscopist is well grounded in the use of the microscope, images inferior to those obtained from achromats are likely to be realized from apochromats. Achromats have smaller numerical apertures than corresponding apochromats, but greater depth of field, less curvature of field, and a better rendition of contrast. These factors make achromats easier to use. There are other objectives which are of intermediate correction, i.e., they are not as well corrected as apochromats but better so than ahcromats. These are called fluorite objectives. Generally lower magnifications do not require the employment of apochromats; however, the latter must be used at the highest magnification in order to attain the ultimate resolution. Consequently, it is often advisable to acquire a set of objectives by which the lower magnifications are achieved with achromats, intermediate magnifications wtihout oil immersion, by fluorites, and the ultimate resolution at the highest magnification by an oil-immersion apochromat.

Objectives are classed also as to magnification, working distance, focal length, and numerical aperture. All of these are interrelated. Generally, the longer the focal length, the smaller is the magnification and the numerical aperture, but the greater the working distance. The exception is a special type of long-working distance objective of high N.A., which has a front lens of unusually large diameter. Even in this case, the depth of field is low. Some objectives are especially designed for the observation of particular samples. Some are optically corrected for use on a sample covered by a coverglass of a specified thickness; others are not corrected in this sense, and are to be used on uncovered specimens. Some are constructed so as to be strain-free and suitable for polarized-light studies, and yet others are made to perform observations by phase contrast, dark field, etc. It is of utmost importance that the potential worker in microscopy be cognizant of the demands to be placed upon the objectives, so that a judicious selection may be made. Excellent publications are available, which provide detailed information on microscope optics

(8). Newly computed lens formulas have made it possible for several manufacturers to place high-quality flat-field objectives on the market. These are not mentioned in the above-cited publications, but one should look into their description by the manufacturer. They yield images which are in focus over the entire field of view, making it possible to obtain photomicrographs of large areas with objectives of high numerical aperture.

Eyepieces (oculars) are designed by the makers to be used with their microscopes and objectives. An eyepiece of one manufacturer should not be combined in a system with the objective of another unless suitable corrections in tube lengths are possible. The following chart illustrates the magnitude of discrepancies which exist among microscope tube lengths and ocular focal plane positions supplied by various manufacturers.

Make	Mechanical Tube Length, mm	Location of Lower Focal Plane of Ocular Below Upper Rim of Tube
Leitz	170	18
Zeiss	160	13
Bausch and Lomb	160	12
Reichert	160	15

Several types of oculars are available, but it does not fall within the scope of this article to describe them in detail. However, it should be pointed out that specific objectives may require matching oculars. For example, to compensate for the chromatic undercorrection of apochromatic objectives, certain eyepieces are overcorrected. Logically these are called compensating oculars; they should always be used with apochromats. Other oculars which are intermediately corrected are recommended by several manufacturers to be used with their objectives. Examples are Hyperplane and Periplan eyepieces. Oculars may be provided with net reticules, scales, etc., to facilitate making measurements under the microscope. Care should be exercised in combining oculars and objectives to avoid exceeding useful magnifications based upon the previously discussed criterion of numerical aperture. This is especially true when measurements of images are made. The halo around an over-magnified image may cause the structure to appear much larger than it is in reality.

Condensers direct light to the specimen and, along with the objective, determine the numerical aperture of the microscope systems. Therefore, their numerical aperture must be adjustable to that of the objective. The condenser lens system should also be corrected chromatically, spherically, and be free of coma. Coma results when different regions of a lens have different magnifications, creating spurious tailed images. A condenser which has been corrected for all three is referred to as an achromatic-aplanatic condenser. Ordinarily the effective numerical aperture of a condenser is subject to alteration by means of an adjustable iris-aperture diaphragm placed in an appropriate position to define the angle of the cone of light illuminating the specimen. This is important to reduce glare as well as to achieve resolution.

Alignment and Illumination. The use of the condenser is so closely allied to methods of illumination and microscope alignment that at this point it becomes desirable to consider all three. In fact, condensers are designated according to methods of illumination. There are both bright-field and dark-field condensers, phase contrast, and light-polarizing condensers. Certain requirements for alignment and illumination have been expressed by several authors (1, 2, 9). One of the best step-by-step charts available is one published by Shillaber (1). Briefly, the centration of light source and optical components is accomplished, a field-limiting aperture is imaged by the condenser onto the sample plane and adjusted to coincide with the field of view, and the aperture

(condenser) diaphragm is used to control glare. In general, these steps are suited to bright-field alignment in both transmitted and vertical illumination.

When a sample is illuminated, the light modified by the sample creates the image. If excessive amounts of undeviated light pass through a specimen, inherently low in contrast, and enter the objective, the deviated beam is unable to compete favorably and, therefore, the image is comparatively weak. If the ratio of the intensities of the undeviated to the deviated beams is reduced, the image can be made relatively stronger. The latter condition may be achieved by illuminating the sample with a hollow cone of light, whose inner angle is too great for undeviated light to enter the objective lens; only the light widely scattered by the sample is seen in the image. This is dark-field illumination. Although highest possible numerical apertures are employed in dark field, the image is not as informative in some respects as others observed under conditions of lower resolution. This is because much of the deviated light from the specimen is also prevented from entering the objective.

Dark-field condensers suited to both transmitted and incident illumination are available. It is possible to employ varying degrees of hollow conical illumination approaching dark field, and permitting some of the undeviated beam to enter the objective. More often for expediency in obtaining contrast, the undeviated beam is reduced by adjusting the bright-field condenser diaphragm to illuminate the specimen with a narrower solid cone of light. Resolution suffers in the latter method, and not in the former. Several manufacturers make phase-contrast condensers which illuminate the sample with a hollow cone suitable for semidark field, and which may be used effectively in producing image contrast in conjunction with ordinary objectives. Besides dark-field and bright-field effects, there are special condensers for optical staining, that is, they create different colors in the image to promote visibility and rendition of contrast photographically.

It was stated that all components of the illuminating and microscope system should be centered to obtain good alignment; however, this is not always true. Sometimes it is advisable to illuminate the specimen obliquely. Several condensers are provided with centerable aperture diaphragms, which when decentered, direct light at an angle onto the specimen. The effect of optical shadowing is thus achieved.

Equipping a Microscopy Laboratory. The requirements for equipping an industrial microscopy laboratory are different for each situation. Nevertheless, the authors hope that the following comments, taken from their experience, will be helpful. The versatile universal research microscope is very well suited to industrial application. Interchangeability of parts, freedom of alignment, choice of optics and illuminations impart the flexibility required to examine the wide variety of samples found in most non-biological laboratories. Of course, if one type of sample must be dealt with continuously, it may be advantageous to acquire a more specialized instrument. For example, a metallograph is definitely needed in a metallurgical laboratory. This is a microscope of inverted design which will accept relatively large polished metal specimens. Metallographic examination falls within the capabilities of the universal microscope, but the latter is not so convenient to use routinely for this purpose.

One objection to the universal-type instrument is that, although various arrangements of optics are available, it can be used only for one operation at a time. This is not serious when there is only one microscopist, and when more become involved, the problem can be solved by acquisition of another stand of the same make. At this time, all the optical components need not be duplicated; only those necessary for special problems could be added as indicated.

The universal microscope is designed for photomicrography as well as for viewing. This is essential since the microscopist's recorded data are in the form of written observations and photomicrographs. The Leitz Ortholux is a typical microscope of this type. It may be attached to the Aristophot II photographic camera. This camera is equipped with a reflex housing which facilitates the composition and focusing of the image prior to taking the picture, and includes the conventional shutter, bellows, and camera back. The microscope body consists of an inclined binocular tube for viewing and a single vertical ocular tube for photomicrography. The stage, nose pieces, illuminators, tubes and condenser rack are attached to the stand by dovetail devices which make it simple to change setups. The new Ortholux UAM stand has two illuminating systems, one for incident illumination and the other for transmitted illumination, which may be used individually or in combination. Either illumination may be arranged for dark- or bright-field, phase-contrast, fluorescence, polarized-light, etc., studies.

In addition to the one illustrated, Reichert, Zeiss, and American Optical, among others, provide instruments which are somewhat similar.

Approach to the Problem and Applications

Assuming a reasonable knowledge of available techniques and the operation and limitations of the equipment, increased proficiency in the field of microscopy can only be gained through research experience. In fact, it is difficult to learn otherwise of the diverse applications within a particular area of investigation. Many phenomena, although manifest on a larger scale, actually take place on a microscopic scale, and therefore, are most profitably studied microscopically. The background, interest, and ingenuity of the investigator influence greatly the course of the research. For example, a chemist using a microscope may be motivated to set up a wet analytical laboratory centered about a microscope under which he observes reactions between minute quantities of sample and reagents. In contrast, a metallurgist may make microhardness tests on his particular specimen with the aid of a microscope. Whatever the specific purpose, one of the most important abilities developed by experience is that of devising techniques which will yield more significant data from the samples to be studied. Frequently, the development of techniques involves only the adaptation of existing ones to specific needs, but sometimes leads to a drastic departure from conventional methods. Appropriate techniques are often the products of crossing disciplines, instrumentation, or sample manipulation. It may be found that there is a need to resort to one or all of these expedients during the course of a research project.

This article is based on experience which can be classed as applied industrial research, part developmental and part trouble shooting. There is little difference in the general approach to either type problem.

Sample selection is an important prerequisite to the experimental work. Because of the limitations in the size of the microscopical sample, utmost attention must be devoted to the problem of taking a representative sample. Sampling should be accomplished with critical awareness of the prior history of the sample, the sequence of events occurring throughout the entire process from which the sample is extracted, and the nature of the chemical and physical environments in all stages of the sample history. In general, it is safer to take large samples first, and then later, as decided by more critical examination, to reduce the sample size. This necessitates that observations of gross structure be made first at unit or low magnification and subsequent study carried out at higher magnification. Initially,

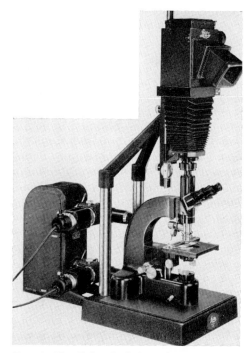

FIG. 2. The Leitz Ortholux microscope shown in combination with the Aristophot photomicrographic camera.

for example, the binocular stereomicroscope is indispensable.

The decision in the choice of samples is usually followed by sample preparation and the selection of types of illumination. Therefore, the remainder of this section will be confined to comments upon combination of disciplines and sample preparation. The employment of a microscope to study structure does not exclude the application simultaneously, or at another time, of other disciplines such as wet chemistry, photometry, absorption and emission spectroscopy, to name but a few. There should be no restrictions which prevent the microscopist from bringing any suitable tools to bear upon the problem. For example, microscopy is an excellent tool to select and isolate specimens suitable for identification by X-ray diffraction and other microanalytical methods, and it should be possible to use these freely, where indicated.

371

Combination of Disciplines. *Chemical Microscopy.* Chemistry and microscopy have been used in combination for many years (10). Chamot and Mason in their "Handbook of Chemical Microscopy" have presented one of the most authoritative works in this field. It is felt, therefore, that no lengthy discussion of their techniques belongs here. These authors have emphasized the identification of inorganic ions in small specimens by means of microscopical recognition of characteristic crystalline forms in reaction products. They recommend using a polarizing chemical microscope to facilitate identification. These methods are covered in some detail in pages 13 to 72 of this Encyclopedia.

Wet Chemistry and Microscopy. Another combination with microscopy is straight wet chemistry on a reduced scale to provide direct microscopic observation of the course of the reaction. In this area, the specimen contained in small vessels, pipettes, etc., is handled with a micromanipulator while under observation. Strikingly quantitative methods have been developed; even titrimetry is possible.

Spot-Test Reactions and Microscopy. Although the use of spot-test reactions (12, 13) in conjunction with microscopy is not generally recognized, it has been found to be quite informative in the authors' laboratory. Spot tests yield colored reaction products which indicate the presence of ions or groups, and are most applicable in inorganic microscopical analysis, but also have been found useful for organics. If these reactions are chosen judiciously, distributions as well as species of ions or organic groups frequently may be shown. Some biological stains fall into this category, but very few of these have proved applicable to industrial specimens. More often greater success has resulted from adapting spot tests which had not been used previously in connection with microscopy. The criteria for selecting a spot test have been that it must have the desired selectivity within the bounds of the system, it must

produce a very intense color which is, in low concentration, visible microscopically, and it should preferably form a product which does not migrate seriously from the site of reaction. Adsorption complexes and precipitates, for example, are the most generally suitable reaction products in this sense. Although many of these reactions have been successfully employed here, only one typical example will be cited. The following detailed description of adaptation of a spot test to a metallographic specimen serves to illustrate the nature of the specific difficulties as well as advantages.

A steel to which lead had been added to improve machinability was being examined to locate the lead. The samples were polished and etched with picral. The most predominant structures were elongated manganese-sulfide inclusions in both the leaded specimen and the control specimen containing no lead, but the leaded specimen exhibited small structures, not evident in the control specimen, at the ends of the manganese-sulfide inclusions. Consequently, it was immediately suspected that the observed structures were lead-bearing. A search made for a suitable spot-test reaction resulted in the choice of the reagent diphenylthiocarbazone (dithizone). Reacted with lead, it yields a water-insoluble red inner complex (11).

First the dithizone was applied in chloroform solution to the sample after the lead had been reacted superficially with potassium chromate solution to produce a film of lead chromate; however, the lead dithizonate was soluble in the chloroform. Further literature search (12) provided a satisfactory means of preserving the reaction product at the site of the reaction. Dithizone is itself water insoluble; however, it was learned that dithizone would transfer from a chloroform solution to a water solution of potassium cyanide. The chloroform and water are immiscible, and the dithizone is only sparingly soluble in the aqueous potassium cyanide solution. The reaction product is insoluble in the aqueous solution. If the solutions are placed together in a container, the chloroform solution sinks to the bottom of the dish, and acts as a reservoir to replenish the aqueous KCN with reagent as it is depleted from solution in the latter. When the surface of the polished and etched specimen was exposed to the aqueous solution no migration of the reaction product occurred. The presence of lead chromate was later shown to be unessential in providing sufficient quantity of lead-salt reactant; in fact, it was observed to have migrated disturbingly. Therefore, the potassium chromate reaction was omitted. Instead it was found that the picric acid and alcohol etchant had created a surface film of nonmigrating reaction product which was present in quantities quite adequate to yield microscopically visible lead dithizonate (13).

Figure 3 shows a photomicrograph of a leaded steel specimen treated in this manner. The structures at the ends of the manganese-sulfide inclusions were stained red indicating that they are indeed lead-bearing. No other structures reacted to yield this stain. Due to the random nature of the plane of metallographic sectioning, it is possible for some of these structures to appear dissociated from the manganese sulfide.

Examples of other spot-test reactions used to show chemical distributions by microscopy are rubeanic acid for copper, 5(p-dimethylaminobenzylidene) rhodanine for silver, and manganous sulfate and silver nitrate for hydroxyl ion. The last example is one in which the hydroxyl ion triggers a redox reaction between manganous and silver ion, producing precipitates of black manganese dioxide, and black finely divided metallic silver. No insoluble reaction product forms between the reagent and the ion for which the test is performed. This ion merely influences the components of the reagent to react with one another. This illustrates the point that indirect as well as direct reactions which result in insoluble products should be

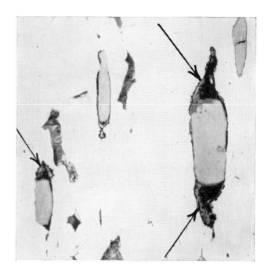

FIG. 3. A polished and etched leaded steel specimen stained with dithizone to show the distribution of lead. The arrows indicate the location of the lead bearing structures which stained red.

investigated when attempting to develop a microscopical spot-test technique.

New spot-test reagents are rapidly being discovered; however, most of them are used in the conventional manner. It is hoped that increased selectivity by means of more appropriate reagents for microscopy will make it feasible to devise relatively simple systematic methods of analysis. Ultimately, it may be possible to place these tests on a quantitative basis through microspectrophotometry.

Physical Methods. Microspectrophotometry is an example of the combination of physical methods (14). Some absorption spectra may be obtained by this means from microscopical specimens for purposes of identification and analysis. Biologists have been able to gain insight into the chemistry of components of single cells with this tool. Spectra in the ultraviolet, visible, and the near infrared have been studied. This science is in the beginning stages of development, and, therefore, suffers from rapidly changing instrumentation, but holds great future promise. (See the "Encyclopedia of Spectroscopy".)

In general, microspectrophotometry is accomplished in two ways. One is by illuminating the specimen with white light, and subsequently analyzing the light transmitted by the subject. The other is by illuminating the specimen with monochromatic light and monitoring the sample transmittance as the wavelength is varied. Jelley's microspectrograph (15) is an example of the first method. He uses a transparent replica of a grating to break down into its component wavelengths the light transmitted by the specimen, and records the spectra photographically. The second method requires a monochromatic light source, special optics if the range is to be extended into the ultraviolet and infrared, and suitable sensing devices for the wavelengths encountered. As usual, as the refinements are made, the complexity of instrumentation becomes formidable. Some of the Perkin-Elmer spectrophotometers are suited to alteration for microspectrophotometry through a commercially available microscope accessory. Beckman also has provision for a similar modification of its equipment. It is anticipated that specialized equipment of this type soon will be developed and made available.

Microspectrophotometry is especially useful for the identification of organic compounds or, more particularly, the chemical groups found in these compounds. Spectra in the infrared are more definitive; nevertheless, significant comparisons can be made by means of ultraviolet and visible spectra among certain specimens giving information as to the course of chemical reactions.

Physical properties of small quantities of materials can be determined microscopically. Melting point, sublimation temperature, hardness, solubility, deformation behavior, and tensile strength are some of these.

For example, the tensile strengths of single textile fibers have been measured with the aid of a microscope and a modified microtensiometer. The torsion wire tensiometer, conventionally used for surface tension measurements, was modified by the addition of a lever arm. The extension of an attached fiber could be observed directly in the microscope. This apparatus was found quite suitable for exerting force of the proper magnitude and with the desired control to make tensile tests on individual wood pulp and cotton fibers. The fibers were attached to the tensiometer under a stereobinocular microscope (16).

Melting points, sublimation temperatures, and fusion data in general can be accumulated with a heating or cooling stage. W. C. McCrone (17) in his book "Fusion Methods in Chemical Microscopy" has presented many of the possibilities in this area. He covers observations of temperature-dependent phenomena of crystalline compounds individually and in mixtures. Mixed fusion of the unknown with a standard reference compound has been emphasized. These methods are suited to organic chemical analysis.

Fluorescence microscopy (19) involves physicochemical phenomena from which chemical inferences are drawn. Aside from inherent fluorescence to be found in certain specimens, fluorescence can be created by suitable dyes which selectively attach to specific compositions within a structure. These dyes are called fluorochromes, and are used by biologists, for example, in immunological chemistry, to locate structures in organs which are most active in antibody production. The fluorochromes are designed to form true chemical bonds (not adsorption complexes) with the antigenic protein substances which are collected by certain organs. It is proposed that by this fluorochrome technique, selected nonbiological substances could be traced through a chemical and physical process. One of the outstanding advantages of this method is the high sensitivity. Dyestuffs in concentration as low as 10^{-18} g can be detected.

Microscopes for fluorescence observation are supplied with ultraviolet illumination to excite fluorescence in the specimen. Normal optics may be used in most applications; however, sometimes it is desirable to utilize the shorter wavelengths which are absorbed by glass. Then it is necessary to substitute quartz or reflecting optic components plus first-surface aluminum mirrors in the illuminating system. Even the microscope slide should be made of quartz. Most often an adequate illuminating system for fluorescence studies can be set up by employing a mercury arc lamp with an appropriate filter as a source, together with a dark-field condenser. Only the fluorescent light from the specimen and small amounts of scattered radiation are thereby permitted to enter the objective. If bright-field illumination were used, the undeviated beam entering the objective would be highly objectionable from the standpoint of harm to the eye as well as of exciting fluorescence in the cement of the objective lens.

Not always is it necessary to excite with ultraviolet light. In some cases, visible light which is shorter than that of the anticipated fluorescence may provide the excitation.

Combining Light and Electron Microscopy. Light and electron microscopy can and should be used in combination. Ordinarily it is inadvisable to proceed directly to electron microscopy without first having done light microscopy. This statement is consistent with the recommendation that a microscopical study should be initiated at lower magnifications than that of which the electron microscope is capable. It finds further justification in the narrowly limited nature of electron-microscope specimens. Obviously, the sampling problem in electron microscopy is more acute, in view of the required smaller specimen size. Furthermore, a suitable specimen preparation for electron microscopy is likely to exhibit structure in an unrecognizable form unless the transition in the rendition of structural detail is related first by light microscopy. Very often much of the true structure can be distinguished

from artifact by the establishment of this relationship. Interpretation is thereby facilitated when structure is ultimately seen at the same and higher magnifications from the perspective of the image produced by electrons rather than by light.

Further discussion of the crossing of disciplines could lead to an inappropriately lengthy section. These examples have been cited here, not only because of their individual value, but also because they serve to exemplify an effective approach in microscopical research.

Specimen Preparation. It must be emphasized that specimen preparation is one of the most important aspects of microscopical research, and therefore, deserves considerable attention. Fine structure on one scale or another is present in almost any object. When the order of magnitude of some detail or inhomogeneity of that structure falls within the resolving range of the microscope, such material is amenable to study by the techniques outlined above. However, without some prior treatment, the object does not usually exhibit the detail required for exhaustive examination. The treatment given a sample to create a specimen appropriate for microscopy is construed here as specimen preparation.

Ordinarily specimen preparative methods are performed to confine observation and to reveal structure in the chemical and physical sense, both specific with regard to certain constituents, and nonspecific. In order to delineate sufficient detail for interpretation of the morphology, it is often possible to use nonspecific preparations. These most frequently include treatments which modify the optical properties of the sample. However, they may not entail changing the sample, but rather defining certain features of the sample for microscopical viewing. An example of the latter is surface replication of an untreated sample, and of the former, the reduction of optically confusing surface roughness by polishing. These general methods are often followed by specific ones unique to the problem under investigation.

Once a representative sample has been decided upon, it is advisable, even before preliminary preparation, to obtain from it as much information as is possible. This should be done to decide upon a preparative procedure, as well as to ascertain the appearance of the unaltered structure, and thereby assist in the recognition of spurious phenomena (artifacts) which may be created by the specimen preparation.

The data collected from a specimen preparation are limited by many factors, some of which can be anticipated and others which are not easily predicted. One of the foremost problems is learning to distinguish true structure, especially that which is significant, from the above-mentioned artifact introduced by the sample treatment. Obviously, an accurate prediction of the type of artifact likely to be encountered in a specimen would be quite helpful. This is possible to a certain degree in almost any situation, but never entirely so. Recognition of artifact is of prime importance, both during specimen preparation and in the interpretation of data. It is hoped that some assistance will be provided by mentioning some of the inherent artifact hazards incidental to the preparative methods discussed in this section. Nevertheless, major emphasis is devoted to the proper choice of technique from the perspective of sample character.

Logically, specimen preparations may be classed in two categories according to whether the material is transparent or opaque. The importance of this classification is brought out by the existence of the two major types of microscopes, which have been designed for the express purpose of examining opaque or transparent specimens. There are other qualities of samples which determine specimen preparation, some of which are size, hardness, roughness, solubility, elasticity, fluidity, and crystallinity. However, none of these has the marked effect on the decision concerning specimen preparation as has the transparency.

There is no hard-and-fast rule which must be observed stating that all opaque samples are best studied by reflected light, or conversely that transparent samples must be studied by transmitted illumination. In many instances, it is advantageous to make specimens of opaque materials to be studied by transmitted illumination (e.g., opaque particles to be studied in profile) and vice versa; nevertheless, in general, the examination will be carried out using the conventional combinations. It may be added that not all specimens are strictly opaque or transparent, and they may be viewed profitably in either or both illuminations. All of these various situations will be discussed here.

Specimen Preparation for Reflected Light. Metallographic, some mineralogical, and ceramic specimens fall into this category. Several available publications describe in detail the conventional techniques in this area (19, 20) Briefly, the sample is mounted in a plastic material which aids in holding it during subsequent grinding, polishing, etching, and viewing. The mounting medium may be thermoplastic and, therefore, can be formed in molds under pressure and temperature, or thermosetting, as for example, the epoxy resins, which can be polymerized at low temperatures and under no pressure to produce a suitably hard mount of soft materials. These mounting materials should be examined critically to look for materials which may be mistaken for constituents of the sample. For example, some thermosetting formulations contain highly reflective particulate structures. The effects of the mounting temperatures and pressures upon the sample also deserve consideration. They may induce changes which render the specimen useless.

Sectioning of materials after mounting can be done with a cutoff wheel. The grinding and polishing can be carried out with abrasive papers, and the metallographic polishing performed on wheels covered with cloth bearing different grades of abrasives. In cutting, grinding, and polishing, flow or cold work is usually produced, but may be essentially eliminated in most specimens by repeated etching and repolishing with the finer grades of abrasives. The pulling out of structures is another common difficulty in grinding and polishing. When this takes place, the holes left in the surface may be misconstrued as inherent porosity in the sample. These are but a few cases, but they serve to exemplify a typical artifact incurred by metallographic preparation.

Even small quantities of finely particulate minerals (21), fibers, textiles, and papers can be prepared by metallographic methods. It is often expedient to study a polished mount of a material rather than to attempt to cut the sample into thin sections. The plane of section is not difficult to control, and if a transparent mount is made, it is sometimes convenient, by looking into it, to view the surface of the specimen and relate it to the internal structure visible at the plane of section. The epoxy resins, in particular, Epon 828* catalyzed with triethylene tetramine, have been found quite satisfactory in mounting soft materials prior to sectioning, grinding, and polishing. Frequently these samples must be impregnated with the medium before mounting and sometimes this can be done by vacuum impregnation. Impregnation is also possible by an adaptation of embedding techniques used in the preparation of biological specimens for electron microscopy (22). By this method, the sample is soaked in a liquid which is a solvent for the epoxy monomer, then in a solution of monomer in this solvent, and later in catalyzed monomer which is subsequently hardened by polymerization.

Most metals and some minerals are sufficiently reflective to produce images of high contrast when etched, and this is a common

* Available from Shell Chemical Company.

metallographic procedure (20, 21). Even textiles have been etched. However, when reflectivity is low, image contrast has been improved by metallization.

Metallization technique (7) consists of the vacuum evaporation of metal onto the specimen. The metal is evaporated from a heated filament, and during the evaporation travels in straight paths from the filament to the surface of the specimen where it deposits only on the exposed portions. If the specimen is inclined to the direction of evaporating metal, a shadow effect is produced. The asperities receive a heavier metal coating and the pits less or none. The difference in reflectivity and resulting image contrast is expressed in terms of surface topography. Even when metallizing is done at normal incidence, and no shadow effect is produced, a more contrasty image will be seen by vertical illumination. Surface relief is present in some specimens in the polished condition due to differences in rates of abrasion among specimen constituents. Metallization has been used extensively in electron microscopy of surface replicas (23).

Replication plays an important role in the microscopical examination of surfaces in a wide variety of industrial problems. Replicas may be made from plastic, most often cellulose acetate in the authors' laboratory, and they are employed to reproduce surface structure. An impression or imprint is made by pressing the surface of a plastic sheet, softened by solvent, onto the surface of a sample. The plastic is allowed to dry while in contact with the sample. When they are separated, the plastic retains a negative imprint of the sample; that is, the topography of this replica is a mirror image of the sample. Not always is it necessary to metallize replicas to achieve adequate contrast. Enough light is sometimes reflected, by surfaces bearing no metal, to give instructive images. Artifacts most commonly found in replicas are bubbles resulting from incomplete contact while taking the imprint. It is

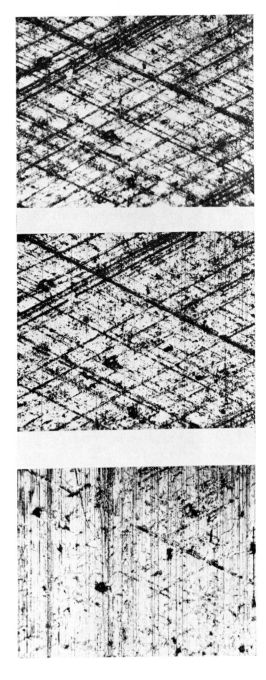

FIG. 4. Photomicrographs of replicas of an area on a cylinder liner showing progressive damage during a wear test. Top, Step 1; Center, Step 5; Bottom, Step 6.

of interest to note that when replicas are metal shadowed, there is a lack of contrast in structure within the shadows. This artifact may be avoided, if necessary, by shadowing from opposite directions.

The most widespread application for replicas is in the study of surfaces of opaque specimens; however, they are also useful in confining observation to the surface structure of transparent materials. Surfaces of curved objects, large objects which cannot be removed for examination, or parts of an intact mechanical device can be studied by the replica method. Replicas from curved surfaces, especially from cylinders, can be flattened without seriously distorting the structure rendered. An example of the replication of a curved surface in a mechanical device, which was not dismantled, is the study of scuffing and wear on the cylinder liners in a diesel engine (24). The progress of the wear was followed by replication. An engine test run was interrupted at certain intervals and replicas were taken of the cylinder-liner walls. Because it could not be anticipated precisely where the most significant scuffing would appear, the entire wall was replicated. These replicas were compared after the test was completed, and areas of interest were selected and studied more critically. Figure 4 illustrates that most of the wear in one of these selected areas took place catastrophically between Steps 5 and 6 and very little occurred between Steps 1 and 5. This type of retrospective study offers many advantages.

Specimen Preparation for Transmitted Light. Objects viewed by transmitted illumination are usually transparent and are studied by means of a biological-type microscope. The specimen preparation is ordinarily held on a microscope slide and covered with a cover-glass. In fact, as was previously mentioned, the objectives of the microscope employing transmitted light are corrected for use with a cover-glass. Very often the specimen is surrounded by a mounting medium, such as balsam, placed between the slide and cover-glass. The refractive index of the mounting medium often determines what is visible in a specimen. For example, if the external features of a transparent subject are to be visible, the refractive index of the mounting medium must differ from that of the subject. If, on the other hand, the internal structure is to be studied, confusing external features may be made invisible by placing the specimen in a medium having a matching index of refraction. Figure 5 shows an example; e.g., a sodium chloride crystal which was mounted in a matching medium to reveal brine inclusions.

Because different levels are visible in transparent or semitransparent specimens, it becomes necessary to make thin specimens so as to confine observation to a thickness within the range of the depth of focus of the objective. Otherwise, out-of-focus structure detracts from the image quality. Small particles and liquids are easily made into thin preparations, but reducing the thickness of large rigid specimens poses somewhat of a problem. Thin sections of materials of the proper consistency to be cut can be produced with a microtome, or sections of minerals and ceramics can be made by modified metallographic techniques (25). The latter involves cutting slices of the sample as thin as possible with a cutoff wheel, attaching the slice to a microscope slide and thinning it further by grinding and polishing the exposed side. If the section is mounted in a medium with a matching refractive index, distracting surface irregularities are invisible. Only the internal structure is visible. When transmitted and vertical illumination can be employed simultaneously, a suitably highly polished and/or etched surface is not covered with a mounting medium or cover-glass.

Thin sectioning with a microtome has been well established in microscopical science

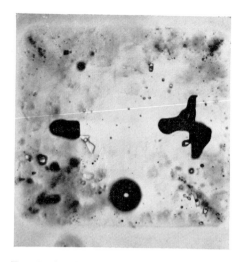

FIG. 5. A salt crystal mounted in a matching refractive index medium to reveal brine inclusions. 130×.

for many years; however, renewed interest in the development of refined techniques for the purpose of electron microscopy has pointed the way to extending those for light microscopy. Especially the embedding of materials in plastics has been found applicable to microtomy for light microscopy. The glass knife, also used routinely by many in electron microscopy, has been found useful in cutting thicker sections for light microscopy of materials embedded in these plastics. Sections of paper and textiles as thin as 3 microns have been cut routinely by these techniques. Figure 6 shows a typical 3-micron section of paper. Embedding procedures can be modified according to the nature of the material. In this respect, often it is possible to become less inhibited as to the embedding procedures than in the case of biological specimens. Many materials can withstand higher temperatures or solvent and chemical actions which are ordinarily avoided in embedding procedures. For example, the procedure used in the authors' laboratory for embedding paper commences by soaking it in alcohol. In fact, when the paper was first soaked in water, a swelling

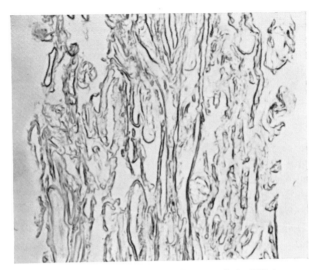

Fig. 6. A thin section of newsprint. 500×

of the fibers occurred and persisted throughout the embedding process. This swelling was undesirable from the standpoint of the study being made; but prior perfusion with a solvent was necessary to promote impregnation of the paper by the plastic; therefore, alcohol was chosen as a suitable substitute.

Deformed structure constitutes most of the artifact found in thin sections, and frequently it can be recognized by examining and measuring the sample both in the embedded and unembedded condition.

In conclusion, it is apparent that the successful application of microscopy depends upon a great many factors which are controlled by the interaction of the microscopist with his instruments. It should again be emphasized that the realization of significant results depends upon the broad experience and ingenuity of the worker, and in his interest in applying various techniques, both orthodox and unorthodox, the latter especially tailored to the problem.

REFERENCES

1. SHILLABER, CHARLES PATTEN, "Photomicrography in Theory and Practice," John Wiley & Sons, Ltd., London, 1944.
2. ALLEN, RAY M., "Photomicrography," Second Edition, D. Van Nostrand Company, Inc., Princeton, New Jersey, Toronto, New York, London, 1958.
3. BENNETT, ALVA H., OSTERBERG, HAROLD, JUPNIK, HELEN, AND RICHARDS, OSCAR W., "Phase Microscopy," John Wiley and Sons, Inc., New York, 1951.
4. WINCHELL, A. N., "Elements of Optical Mineralogy, Part I. Principles and Methods," 5th Edition, John Wiley & Sons, Inc., New York; Chapman & Hall, Ltd., London, 1951.
5. WAHLSTROM, E. E., "Optical Crystallography," 2nd Edition, John Wiley & Sons, Inc., New York, 1951.
6. KRAJIAN, ARAM, A., "Histological Technic," C. V. Mosby Company, St. Louis, Mo., 1940.
7. WILLIAMS, R. C., AND WYCKOFF, R. W. G., "Applications of Metallic Shadow-Casting to Microscopy," J. Applied Physics, 17, 23–33 (January, 1946).
8. ROSSI, BRUNO, "Optics," Addison-Wesley Publishing Company, Inc., 1957.
9. STOVES, J. L., "Fibre Microscopy," National Trade Press, London, 1957.
10. CHAMOT, EMILE, AND MASON, CLYDE, "Handbook of Chemical Microscopy," Vol. 1, Third Edition, John Wiley and Sons, Inc., New York, 1958, and Vol. 2, 2nd Edition, 1953.
11. FEIGL, FRITZ, "Spot Tests, Volume I, Inorganic Application," Elsevier Publishing Company, New York, 1954.
12. EVANS, B. S., Analyst, 69, 368 (1944).
13. GERDS, A. E., AND MELTON, C. W., "New Etch Spots Leaded Steels," Iron Age, 178, No. 9, 86 (August 30, 1956).

14. Oskr, Gerald and Pollister, Arthur W., "Physical Techniques in Biological Research," Vol. 1, Academic Press, Inc., 1955.

15. Jelley, E. E., *J. Royal Microscope Soc.*, **56**, 101 (1936).

16. Authors' unpublished work.

17. McCrone, Walter C. Jr., "Fusion Methods in Chemical Microscopy," Interscience Publishers, Inc., New York, 1957.

18. Haitinger, "Die Fluoreszenzanalyse in der Microchemil," E. Hain & Co., Leipzig, 1937.

19. Kehl, G. L., "Principles of Metallographic Laboratory Practice," McGraw-Hill Book Co., Inc., New York, 1949.

20. Greave, Richard H., and Wrighton, Harold, "Practical Microscopic Metallography," Fourth Edition, Chapman and Hall, Ltd., London, 1957.

21. Dillinger, Lee, and Sclar, Charles B., "A Method of Mounting Minute Particulate Samples of Opaque Ore Minerals for Quantitative Microscopic Analysis," *Economic Geology*, **55**, 187–191 (1960).

22. Newman, S. B., Borysko, E., and Swerdlow, M., *J. Res. Nat. Bur. Standards*, **43**, 183 (1949).

23. Wyckoff, Ralph W. G., "Electron Microscopy, Technique and Applications," Interscience Publishers, Inc., New York, 1949.

24. Young, A. P., and Schwartz, C. M., "A Replica Method for Examining Wear and Scuffing in Cylinder Liners," to be published.

25. Weatherhead, A. Petrographic microtechnique (thin sectioning), A. Barron, London, 1947.

C. W. Melton and C. M. Schwartz

MICROSCOPISTS AND RESEARCH MANAGEMENT

There is no question but that industry needs microscopy. It is a tool of science that enables us to get closer to things and obtain a better understanding of the how and why of nature. It must be remembered, however, that it is only a tool and that a scientist is needed so that the human brain can interpret what is seen by the eye. One question to be discussed is whether the use of microscopy is best accomplished by a trained specialist called a microscopist or by a scientist with microscopical training. Another question relates to the position of the specialist in industrial research.

The specialist learns a great deal about a limited area of science and in our present world certainly some specialization is necessary to solve the complicated problems of science. But on the other hand, a knowledge within several disciplines often is the key to the solution of problems. In some cases there is a point of no return in knowing more and more about less and less.

It is not important whether the microscope is used by a scientist called a microscopist or by a physical, organic, bio, inorganic, etc., scientist who is well informed on its use potential. The important factor is that the scientist have the knowledge to solve the problem; knowledge in the fundamentals of optical science so that he can use the microscope and all its accessories to their best advantage; knowledge from experiences which can be correlated with experimental observations; knowledge to relate what he sees to the theory of what could be the mechanism of a reaction or the physical structure of a material; knowledge which makes the scientist a specialist.

In our industrial research organizations, advancement has been up an administrative ladder. Each step requires supervision of more people. In research organizations a general scientific knowledge of all the work being supervised is expected of the leader. This means that administrative personnel cannot specialize but must broaden their knowledge. The eventual desire for administrative positions is probably one reason why it has been difficult to interest college students in a profession as specialized as microscopy. On the face of it, it would appear that it does not have a great financial future.

A number of research organizations, recognizing that the future of the specialist was being lost in such an administrative hierarchy, have developed professional as well as administrative ladders. This makes it possible to develop or grow in a professional way without going into administrative work. Cyanamid has such a program so that we are able to recognize the ability of the specialist and reward him accordingly.

In designing such a program, the question arose: What kind of program can we design that will retain, develop and reward a creative scientist in his field of competence and not force him into manager ranks as the only means of obtaining these rewards? If the administrative progression is the only way for advancement, then we may lose a good creative scientific specialist and obtain a poor manager. Many scientists can and should become managers, but those who have neither the desire nor the ability should not be forced to become managers in order to advance in their profession.

One way to accomplish this is to change the conditions which force many scientists to become administrators in order to get more money and recognition. We know from attitude surveys that more money alone is not the answer to the problem. The professional scientist is interested in the nature, scope and structure of his assignment and the relationship with his scientific colleagues, both within and outside his own company. He wants and has the professional right to an opportunity to contribute to scientific journals, participate in technical conferences and to expand his scientific horizons. He wants to know how his supervisors view his present performance and competence and what his future possibilities are in the organization.

In setting up a new program for professional growth at Cyanamid, we began by establishing certain minimum requirements or standards for competence. Within these broad standards were various levels of performance, knowledge, experience and potential through which the scientist would grow at various stages of his career. These levels of competence are in turn related to salary. It is possible for a man to move up from level to level without changing his job. He is not limited or hemmed in by a series of compartmentalized job descriptions. These new levels of professional accomplishment measured against the existing levels of managerial accomplishment form the basis for Cyanamid's Professional Development Program. Here the man is evaluated, not the job. Growth possibilities depend upon the ability of the man, not the confines of a job.

Figure 1 shows the progression of development in Cyanamid's Central Research Division. The B.S. graduate enters at level 1 as a Scientist (i.e., Chemist, Physicist, Biologist, Chemical Engineer, etc.). After a minimum of one year's experience, it is possible for the outstanding man to reach level 2. This level has qualifications similar to that for the M.S. degree, and the M.S. from college enters at this level. After a minimum of five years' experience from graduation the outstanding man can reach level 3, and at such time he is advanced to Research Scientist.

The Ph.D. enters into the organization near the top of level 3. The outstanding Ph.D. moves into level 4 after one year of experience. A minimum of five years after receiving his Ph.D. he may move into level 5 and advance to Senior Research Scientist. The outstanding B.S. or M.S. in science or engineering can progress through the same levels. For those who wish to develop further professionally there are the higher levels of Research Associate, Research Fellow and Senior Research Fellow.

On the management side the Group Leader is the first position, and these are chosen from levels 4 and 5, depending upon the responsibilities of the position. The advancing positions in this program are Manager of a Section and Director of a Department. It is possible to move from the professional side to the management side and vice versa. It is no longer necessary for research scientists to become managers to enjoy status or income.

A word here about the concept of expe-

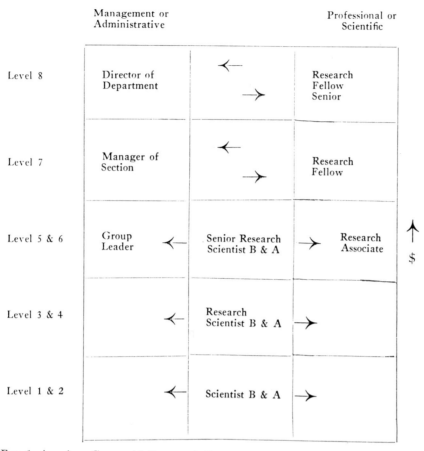

FIG. 1. American Cyanamid Company's Research Division Development Program.

rience in professional work. One year older does not necessarily mean that one year of experience or development has been gained. It should be clear that five years in a repetitive job might mean one year of similar experience repeated five times rather than five years of new and broadening experience.

The scientist who grows professionally may advance through the professional development program until he reaches the level equivalent to his maximum knowledge, experience and potential. He will have to content himself with this growth level unless he is able to get more knowledge or experience. Sometimes the work done by a man may not utilize his full abilities. If he has the potential, it may be advisable for him to study

more or transfer to a more challenging assignment.

It is research management's responsibility to utilize all personnel at their highest potential and make sure that the work being done stimulates rather than impedes, a man's creativity and progress. Proper placement is our goal and, although it is not easy to achieve, we recognize this and work toward it at all times.

The levels which have been discussed are related to compensation. Realistically speaking, compensation—whether at the professional or hourly level—is based on certain general characteristics. No management has yet been able to come up with a method of administration which can function in a vacuum, independent of what is generally paid by other firms.

Accordingly, as in most management practice, the top level of each research salary range is determined by surveys in cooperation with similar research organizations. Once the broad salary ranges have been established, it is possible to fit in the various levels of competence required in research work. Here again despite numerous experiments, psychologists and testing experts have never been able to come up with a screening method which can evaluate the ability of professional personnel independent of the two major factors of education and experience. For this reason, the compensation for new research personnel coming directly from the university is based on their level of education.

In attempting to fulfill its responsibility of utilizing personnel at their highest potential, our research management has developed a combined evaluation and counselling program. This involves the use of a Counselling Guide and a Performance Review form, in conjunction with two employee interviews.

The objective of this method of review of an employee's performance is twofold:

1. For Management: To provide the immediate supervisor and higher levels of management with a means of evaluating the performance and potential of each employee and of summarizing this information in reports.

2. For the Employee: To enable him to review his own performance objectively, both alone and with his supervisors; to learn how he is doing and where he is going, and to insure that he has the fullest opportunity for maximum improvement and development.

The Counselling program involves five general steps to complete the review of an employee's performance through forms and interviews. They are:

1. Distribution and explanation of forms to employee.

2. Completion of the forms, insofar as possible, by both the employee and his supervisor, independently, prior to the counselling interview.

3. The counselling and performance review interview between the employee and his supervisor.

4. Discussion of the completed forms by the supervisor and the next level of supervision.

5. An interview between the employee and his second-level supervisor to discuss results of the evaluation and the interview with the employee's immediate supervisor.

Why do we suggest distribution of these forms to the employees as a first step? Primarily, because we know that people tend to dislike and distrust what they do not understand. By giving them an opportunity to look over the forms at their leisure—and by suggesting that they make an attempt at a self-analysis, we believe some normal psychological resistance may be removed.

The Counselling Interview is probably the most difficult step in the over-all Counselling Program because the supervisor and employee meet face to face to discuss personal opinions. The supervisor should conduct the interview skillfully and with great tact so that criticism will remain factual and constructive rather than subjective and emotional. The two persons should meet in an atmosphere of mutual respect and with the same objective of further developing professional or administrative ability.

In conclusion, I want to make it clear that the specialist or professional we are talking about is a scientist who is advancing his knowledge and not just going along on his own experience. He does not know all the answers and will try new approaches and experiments to try to solve even old problems. The specialist who knows all the answers is not growing in his profession, he is a technician getting more proficient doing things over and over again with exacting skill.

GEORGE L. ROYER

MICROTOMY

Thanks to the contributions of the German physicist Abbe the efficiency of the light microscope was rapidly improved in the latter half of the 19th century. This development in turn implied that completely different demands had to be made on preparation of specimens. In order to make use of the increased resolution power of the microscope, it was necessary to employ thin sections in the study of biological material. In this way the development of microtomy was started. This development was both a consequence and a necessary precondition of modern light microscopy. The limit for the most important property of the microscope, the resolving power, is determined by the wave length of the light employed. As far as the light microscope is concerned, we can therefore only expect technical improvements in the future. Regarding the technique for making microscopical preparations, it seems however justified to hope for considerable progress.

Today the routine work in human pathology constitutes the overwhelming part of light-microscopical work on biological material. The cutting technique for this purpose is well developed, and generally known, and further information is therefore not needed. Contrary to this, severe problems are encountered, in quantitative morphological and cytochemical work. Like the other steps in the preparation of sections, cutting distorts the native tissue. If this is not taken into consideration, errors may arise in quantitative work. The aim of the present article is to illustrate these problems.

The Microtome. When classical histology was developed, the demands with respect to precision which were made on a microtome corresponded to the best which could be produced. Today the situation is different. The progress of modern precision industry makes the production of good microtomes an easy task. Only in the production of ultramicrotomes for cutting of material for electron microscopy are modern resources fully exploited. In principle a microtome produces two different movements between the knife and the preparation: (1) the cutting movement occurring in the cutting plane, and (2) the feeding movement perpendicular to this plane. In a microtome of good quality both these movements must be as precise as possible. The true feeding should not deviate more than 0.1μ from the microtome setting, when the latter is in the range $1–20 \mu$. Measurements on various slide and rotation microtomes show that this demand is met by most microtomes from well known firms. It is thus not the microtome which causes the problems in the cutting for quantitative analysis.

The Knife. Besides a good microtome it is also necessary to have a knife with optimal qualities. Ever since the cutting of biological material began, much work has been devoted to getting as good knives as possible. A large selection of suitable kinds of steel is available, varying from pure carbon steel to various types of multialloyed and specially hardened stainless steel. Three qualities of the steel are of special importance (1) the hardness, (2) the toughness and (3) the corrosion resistance. Unfortunately these parameters do not vary in a parallel manner. A very hard steel is brittle and increased addition of stainless metals reduces the hardness. Knife steel therefore represents a compromise which, however, thanks to modern metallurgy meets exacting demands.

The edge of the knife is the section line between the two facet surfaces. In order to understand which qualities the edge must possess it is necessary to illustrate schematically how cutting is performed (Fig. 1). During cutting, a distortion of the tissue occurs, causing the thickness of the section t_2 to be larger than the feeding of the block t_1. For the cutting three angles are of importance, (1) the rake angle (r), (2) the bevel angle (b), and (3) the clearance angle

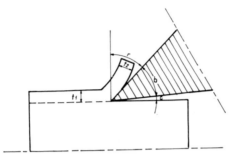

Fig. 1. Schematic illustration of sectioning at an angle of 90° between the cutting direction and the edge line. c = clearance angle, b = bevel angle, r = rake angle, t_1 = the feed of the microtome, t_2 = section thickness.

(c). The sum of these three angles is 90°. The larger the rake angle employed, the slighter the distortion of the section, i.e., the more the ratio t_2/t_1 approach 1. It is therefore desirable to have the clearance and the bevel angles as small as possible. However, the clearance angle cannot be smaller than 6°, if the risk of compression of the tissue block is to be avoided. The possibilities of decreasing the bevel angle are also limited, because of the difficulties involved in producing a sufficiently even edge line. If the facet surfaces meet in a small angle, even minimal abrasions may cause rather serious irregularities in the edge line. The solution must therefore be a compromise. To produce a bevel angle of 20°, e.g., which meets precise demands on the evenness of the edge line, a disproportionately large amount of work is required, while it is easy to make a good edge if the bevel angle is allowed to exceed 50°.

The sharpening of a microtome knife involves imparting to the two facet surfaces such a planarity and finish that their line of sectioning is exactly even. Fig. 2 shows an interference microscopical picture of facet surfaces produced by different methods. The shape of the interference fringes reveal the irregularities of the surface. The interfringe distance represents a profile depth of 0.27 μ. The rate of removal of the various methods

is, of course, inversely proportional to the resulting surface finish. The treatment of the facet surface, therefore, has to be made stepwise; the last step generally consists of lapping against glass in an immersion medium. To prevent this step from becoming too time-consuming, it is necessary that the facet surfaces be pretreated with coarser methods. Unfortunately, stropping is still widely used as the last step in the sharpening of microtome knives. As indicated in Fig. 2b, the facet surface exhibits a rather good finish after stropping and the edge is therefore sharp. However, the decreasing distance between the interference fringes as the edge line is approached shows that the facet surface is curved, so that the bevel angle is considerably larger than the original one, and is not well defined. The other angles also are unknown, and accurate cutting becomes undependable. Stropped knives therefore are to be avoided.

The control of the knife edge is a frequently neglected detail in microtomy. It is still customary to judge the sharpness by hair cutting or by passing the thumb over the edge. These procedures are unworthy of the instrumental equipment which we possess today. A microtome knife used for quantitative biological work ought to be well defined with respect to the bevel angle and to the width of the facet surfaces, and the evenness of the edge line should be controlled in incident dark-field microscopy at 700 times magnification.

Measurement of Section Thickness. In all investigations intending to supply quantitative morphological and cytochemical information, in which sectioned material is used, it is necessary to know the thickness of individual sections. This determination is often difficult. The lack of hardness in the sectioned tissue means that not even a minimal measuring pressure may be applied to the surface of the section without causing plastic deformation. Secondly, to control what is being measured, the method em-

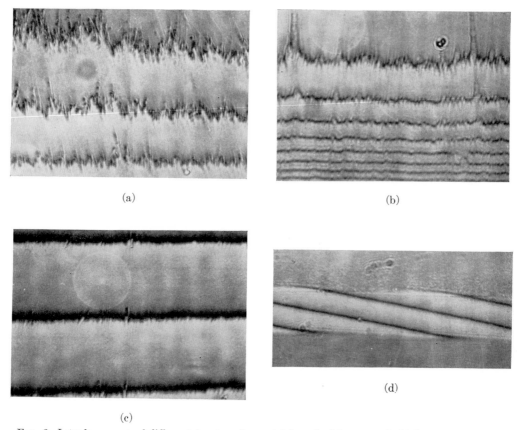

(a)

(b)

(c)

(d)

FIG. 2. Interferograms of different facet surfaces. (a) honed; (b) stropped; (c) lapped against cast-iron; (d) lapped against glass. (Hg-light, 300×). The interference fringes reveal irregularities in the surface. The distance between two fringes represents a profile depth of 0.27 μ.

ployed must possess the horizontal resolving power of the light microscope, as well as the vertical resolving power required for thickness determination. In Fig. 3 is shown an apparatus for thickness determination which meets these demands. It consists of a commercial microscope for incident light. To increase the focusing accuracy, a thin metal wire has been mounted in the plane of the field iris. By means of a special arrangement with off-central incidence of the light, this wire produces a shadow in the object plane which moves back and forth across the field of view during focusing and defocusing. The line of symmetry for this movement is indicated with a hair cross in the eyepiece, and it is therefore possible to reproduce the focusing with great accuracy. The vertical movement of the objective during focusing is registered by means of a mechanical measuring device. In this way it is possible to determine the thickness of a section by focusing first on the upper surface of the slide, and then on the upper surface of the section. By means of a special construction of the microscope stage, the slide may be moved in the horizontal plane with very small vertical deviations. If plane parallel slides are used, it is possible to perform topographical analysis of sections. Under ideal conditions the instrument permits measurements with an accuracy of 0.1 μ.

Thickness Variations in Sections. For anybody planning to use sectioned material

FIG. 3. Apparatus for thickness measurements of microtome sections.

for quantitative work the following questions arise. What are the optimal conditions for sectioning? Is there any difference between the thickness of the section and the feeding of the microtome? How large is the thickness variation within and between sections? It would be an easy task to select from the literature several papers, the value of which may be questioned, because the authors have neglected these questions. During an investigation comprising more than 15,000 thickness determinations of sections, the problem of cutting distortion has been analyzed from various points of view. On the basis of this investigation it is possible to answer the questions stated above.

The type of microtome employed is unimportant as long as it is of good quality. It is likewise of minor consequence whether it is driven by hand or by a motor, whether or not it is run continuously, and whether the rate of cutting is varied within rather wide limits. The type of tissue is also of little importance, except of course in the case of mineralized tissue. Among the embedding media employed the distortion is less with plastics than with paraffin. Indirect measurements indicate that the greatest risk of distortion exists with freeze sectioning.

The properties of the knife are of decisive importance for the qualities of the sections. If the bevel angle is above 50°, if facet surfaces more than 10 μ wide are used, or if the edge line in 700 $\times$ magnification is uneven, a rapid increase is observed in the ratio $t_{2/t1}$ as well as in the thickness variation within and between sections. If a stropped knife is employed, the distortion equals that obtained with a knife having a 70° bevel angle. Even when the cutting conditions are optimal with respect to the properties of the knife, to the type of microtome, and to the preparation of tissue—a rare event—considerable distortion may be anticipated. First of all, an increase of the thickness occurs, which seldom is less than 10 per cent. Secondly, thickness variations arise within and between sections, and these are so large that they cannot be neglected in quantitative work. The coefficients for the variation within and between sections in a series of 5 μ paraffin sections are not less than 6 and 30 per cent, respectively. For frozen sections the corresponding value for variation between sections is 45 per cent.

Duplication of Sections. A complete correction for thickness variations of sections would require a topographical survey of each individual section. This is impossible, because the necessary equipment is lacking in most laboratories; moreover, such a procedure would be extremely time-consuming, and the cytochemical and morphological analyses of the sections seldom permit them to be mounted on plane parallel slides for thickness determination. Since the variation between sections entirely dominates the

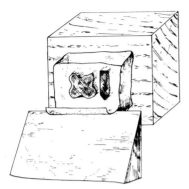

FIG. 4. Schematic representation of tissue and plastic bar molded into same block.

FIG. 5. Schematic representation of tissue in plastic hollow cylinder chucked for freeze-sectioning.

thickness variation of sections, it is highly important to correct for this factor. It is possible to do this by means of plastic duplicates.

A plastic bar (Fig. 4) made of butyl and methylmethacrylate (15 and 85 per cent, respectively) is used for embedded material. This is formed and embedded in intimate contact with the tissue to be sectioned. For frozen material a hollow cylinder is used, made of butylmethacrylate, which is filled out with the tissue (Fig. 5). In this way one obtains simultaneously a tissue section and a plastic duplicate which may be separated and measured independently, e.g., with interference microscopy. The error committed by allowing the setting of the microtome to indicate the thickness of the section is in this way reduced to about one half for em-

bedded material and to one third for freeze-sectioned material.

REFERENCES

ABBE, E., *Sitz.-ber. Jen. Gesell. Med. Naturw.*, **71**, 207 (1880).

ABBE, E., *J. Roy. Micr. Soc.*, Ser. II, **1**, 680 (1881).

APÁTHY, S. VON, "Neuere Beiträge zur Schneidetechnik", *Z. wiss. Mikr.*, **29**, 479 (1912).

ARDENNE, M. VON, *Z. wiss. Mikr.*, **56**, 8 (1939).

BAILEY, A. J., "Precision Sectioning of Wood", *Stain Technol.*, **12**, 159 (1937).

BEREK, M., *Sitz.-ber. Gesell. Beförd. ges. Naturwiss.*, (Marburg) **62**, 189 (1927).

BISHOP, F. W., "New Automatic Sharpener for Microtome Blades", *Rev. Sci. Instr.*, **25**, 1190 (1954).

BRATTGÅRD, S.-O., "Microscopical Determinations of the Thickness of Histological Sections", *J. Roy. Micr. Soc.*, **74**, 113 (1954).

DEMPSTER, W. T., "Distortions Due to the Sliding Microtome", *Anat. Rec.* **84**, 269 (1942).

DEMPSTER, W. T., "Properties of the Paraffin Relation to Microtechnique", *Michigan Acad. Sci.*, **29**, 251 (1943).

DEMPSTER, W. T., "The Mechanics of Paraffin Sectioning by the Microtome". *Anat. Rec.*, **84**, 241 (1942).

DEMPSTER, W. T., "Paraffin Compression Due to the Rotary Microtome", *Stain Technol.*, **18**, 13 (1943).

EKHOLM, R., HALLÉN, O. AND ZELANDER, T., "Sharpening of Knives for Ultramicrotomy", *Experientia*, **11**, 361 (1955).

FANZ, J. I., "An Automatic Microtome Knife Sharpener and Methods for Grinding and Honing the Knife Satisfactorily", *J. Lab. Clin. Med.*, **14**, 1194 (1929).

HALLÉN, O., "A New Method for Sharpening Microtome Knives", *Lab. Invest.*, **5** (1956).

HALLÉN, O., "On the Cutting and Thickness Determination of Microtome Sections", *Acta Anatomica, Suppl. 25*, 26 (1956).

HALLÉN, O., "Quantitative Analysis of Sectioned Biological Material". (In press).

HEARD, O. O., "The Influence of Surface Forces in Microtomy", *Anat. Rec.*, **117**, 725 (1953).

HILLIER, J., "On the Sharpening of Microtome Knives for Ultrathin Sectioning", *Rev. Sci. Instr.*, **22**, 185 (1951).

JOHNSTON, C., "Some Aspects of Microtome Knife Sharpening", *J. Med. Lab. Technol.*, **10**, 131 (1952).

KISSER, J., *Z. wiss. Mikr.*, **43**, 361 (1926).

KISSER, J., *Z. wiss. Mikr.*, **44**, 452 (1927).

LANGE, P. W. AND ENGSTRÖM, A., "Determination of Thickness of Microscopic Objects", *Lab. Invest.*, **3**, 116 (1954).

LENDVAI, J., *Z. wiss. Mikr.*, **26**, 203 (1909).

LÖW, W., *Z. wiss. Mikr.*, **48**, 417 (1931).

MALONE, E. F., "Sharpening Microtome Knives", *Anat. Rec.*, **24**, 97 (1922).

MOHL, H. VON, *Bot. Z.*, **15**, 249 (1857).

NAGEOTTE, J., *Bull. d'Hist. Appl.*, **3**, 258 (1926).

RICHARDS, O. W., "The Effective Use and Proper Care of the Microtome", Spencer Lens Co., Buffalo, N. Y., 1942.

SCHMERWITZ, G., *Die Umschau*, **36**, 827 (1932).

SSOBOLEW, L. W., *Z. wiss. Mikr.*, **26**, 65 (1909).

UBER, F. M., "Microtome Knife Sharpeners Operating on the Abrasive-Ground Glass Principle", *Stain Technol.*, **11**, 93 (1936).

OLLE HALLÉN

PLASTICS

In comparison with metals and fibers, microscopic investigation of plastic materials is still in its infancy. It is true that more has been done in this field in recent years, but there is still no question of extensive research. Microscopic methods are applied to plastics for: (a) examining fillers with a view to homogeneous dispersion; (b) examination of the mixing of various plastics; (c) studying fracturing of plastic materials; (d) stress investigation; (e) penetration and distribution of plasticizers.

Investigation can largely be carried out with intact materials, but study of fracture and stress should be effected with sections or films. All microscopic methods are suitable for examining these materials. The normal light microscope is used for observing dispersion of fillers. Sections or films are used for this purpose. For very finely ground fillers and for investigating the occurrence of cracks under the influence of filler particles, a phase contrast microscope is used. Differences in refractive index, occurring particularly in mixing various plastics, can be successfully investigated with a phase contrast microscope for the purpose of qualitative examination. Quantitative examination of these mixtures can best be effected with interference methods.

For plasticizer penetration the interference methods are excellent, and it is often advisable to make use of so-called ciné photographs.

The polarizing microscope is mainly useful for investigating stresses in plastic products and the occurrence of spherulites and oriented structures. This method is especially important for polyethylene and polystyrene investigation. The thickness of most plastic objects makes it necessary to use compensators which also compensate large phase differences. Ehringhaus' rotary compensator, of the Calcspar type, can be recommended.

In examining a mixture of two plastics it may be advantageous to incorporate a fluorescent dye, so that dispersion can be examined with a fluorescence microscope.

In plastics research, surface techniques have a fairly wide range of application. The normal reflection microscope, both bright and dark field, is used for appraising surface irregularities and for examining surfaces of breaks. In the latter case the purpose may be to examine the breakage phenomena as such, and in the case of highly filled plastics, dispersion of the filler can also be easily appraised.

The interference methods, both double and multiple beam, may be important aids to surface and fracture examination.

Electron microscope techniques are still comparatively uncommon. Their range of applications is in examining fine structures. Fields where this method has already been applied are the investigation of spherulite formation in polyethylene and nylon films and the examination of break surfaces by means of replicas.

The grain structure of suspension polymers can successfully be investigated with the electron microscope using ultra thin sections.

Sectioning of Plastic Materials

Hard plastics, such as polystyrene and methacrylates can most suitably be cut without further preparation, by means of a stable sledge microtome. The specimen holder must be as vibration-free as possible; the specimen may protrude only slightly outside the holder and the knife must be secured in a heavy knife block. Moreover, only that part of the knife which is close to the point where it is secured should be used.

Sometimes vibration cannot be entirely avoided. Especially in phase contrast or interference microscopic examination, care should be taken not to appraise specimens too quickly. As a rule, vibration becomes troublesome only when a number of successive specimens is to be used for spatial reconstruction. With such objects the blade of the knife soon gets damaged and grooves occur in the cut surface. Every slice must therefore be judged immediately with the aid of a dissecting microscope, so that a different part of the knife can be used at once if any damage is found to have been started by the knife.

The knife must be of higher quality than is required for cutting biological material. The blade must be very accurately ground. All slices tend to curl up. As soon as the sections are obtained they should be temporarily unrolled with a couple of small artists' brushes. They can be fully extended by placing them on a drop of xylene. This is usually sufficient to obtain a completely flat specimen.

The specimen can be mounted in Aquamount or Canada balsam.

Elastic plastic materials, such as polyethylene, are cut with a freezing microtome; here again the sledge type is used. The requirements for cutting hard materials apply also to elastic materials. Vibration resulting from cutting is noticeably less than with hard material. Artifacts due to cutting with a damaged knife blade are found, however.

Regular inspection of the slices immediately after cutting reduces the adverse effects of this. Here again the sections can be stretched on xylene after the slices have first dried. This is a successful method especially for polyethylene and polypropylene.

The production of thin sections for investigating filler dispersion is preferable to the melting method (see below). Cutting with a microtome does not alter the distribution of the fillers. Large aggregates do not disintegrate, nor are new ones formed. It is also possible to examine a spatial arrangement by means of a series of sections. Moreover, the influence of spherulite structures on filler dispersion can be appraised only from sections.

Examination of Films Obtained by Melting

Small pieces of plastic are heated until they have just melted. They are then pressed between two microscope slides until they are the desired thickness. These films, after mounting in Aquamount or Canada balsam, can be used for microscopic examination. This method is fairly widely used for examining filler dispersion in plastics. Its drawbacks are:

(1) Spatial distribution of the fillers can no longer be determined. There are fairly strong lines of flow in the specimens and no opinion can thus be formed regarding the uniformity of dispersion.

(2) Fillers often form a very labile system with the plastic. The big risk in melting is that the dispersion found in the films may not be the same as it was originally. Large aggregates may disintegrate and smaller granules may cake together.

(3) Orientation effects are no longer found. The filler granules are often oriented in the plastic. This orientation is lost.

(4) The influence of spherulite structures on filler dispersion can no longer be ascertained. The spherulites are either destroyed or in any case deformed. These structures

have a considerable effect on the uniformity of filler dispersion. Hence it is very important to keep them intact.

(5) If a mixture of two different synthetic components is to be examined, correct appraisal of the dispersion is very important. Disturbance of the original distribution is undesirable.

Appraisal of Plastic Films with the Polarizing Microscope

Most plastic films have a molecular orientation, even though they are not deliberately elongated. Even rolling causes a certain amount of double refraction. The intersection of molecular strands gives rise to a film texture. Elongation in the main direction of the strands soon causes a parallel structure, but elongation perpendicular to this direction widens the angle of intersection of the strands. In many films this film structure is demonstrable with a phase contrast microscope. In other cases, in which the refractive index difference between strands and surrounding material is slight, the phenomenon will hardly be visible with a phase contrast microscope. In these cases it can often be rendered visible by staining with $I_2 \cdot KI$ solution or iodine tincture. The film is then examined in its elongated state under a polarizing microscope, the axis of elongation of the specimen being rotated from the diagonal position to the orthogonal position. When the axis of the specimen forms an acute angle with the orthogonal position, the molecular strands of the one axis fade out while those of the other axis do not. In this way the microscope shows a "herringbone structure." This structure, which is regular in most films, also occurs in nearly all synthetic fibers, although the round or irregular sections of these fibers renders examination difficult. Exact examination can therefore only be made with longitudinal sections. With synthetic fibers $I_2 \cdot KI$ staining is also to be recommended. The texture occurring with the fibers may be:

(1) Regular single herringbone structure. This corresponds completely to the film texture and can be further divided into coarsely fibrillary and finely fibrillar.

(2) Irregular single herringbone structure. No clear arrangement of molecular strands. Both the angle of intersection, strand thickness and strand distance vary from place to place.

(3) Regular film structure. The angle of intersection, distance of molecular fibrils and strand thickness show a regular variation from outside to inside, but from place to place the herringbone structure may still be regular.

(4) Irregular film texture. The general character of the fibrillar structure is different on the outside of the fiber and in the middle. But the structure is everywhere irregular.

(5) Mixed film texture. The outer layer of the fiber shows a regular herringbone structure, while the pith has an irregular texture, or vice versa.

(6) Branched film texture. When the fiber is examined with its axis roughly corresponding to the orthogonal position, a fine secondary film texture may sometimes be visible in the light bands, having a slightly different orientation from the main direction. The secondary fibrils are noticeably thinner than the principal fibrils.

The above system applies in the first place to synthetic fibers, but is also found with films—though to a less extent.

Investigation of Spherulite Structures

For examining spherulite structures it is usually advisable to use thin films.

Many high polymers form spherulite structures when they crystallize from the melt. The number of spherulites formed depends upon the number of crystallization nuclei present and the speed of cooling. They may be very suitably examined with phase contrast and polarizing microscopes. The finest structures, however, become visible only with an electron microscope.

We can distinguish these crystal structures microscopically according to (1) their type and (2) their shape. The most common types are described below.

Single Spherulites. The polarizing microscope shows these as round to ellipsoid particles with a distinct polarization cross, the arms of which are not uniformly thick. If the spherulite is rotated this cross often splits into two hyperbolas. If these crystal structures are ellipsoidal the bigger axis is in the direction of elongation.

Dendrite Spherulites. Spherulites with a pronounced radial main structure. The radial fibrils have pronounced featherwise branches. This branching is also clearly visible with an electron microscope.

"Peacock"-Spherulites. Spherulites are sometimes found that show an alternation of concentric bands. These bands have alternate positive and negative birefringence. Electron microscopic examination suggests that this is a mixed structure of the single and dendrite types. The negative bands are said to be formed by the branched fibrils and the positive ones by the unbranched pieces with their purely radial orientation.

A pattern resembling the preceding one is found with polyethylene, in which spherulites occur with alternate negatively birefringent rings and isotropic bands. This gives a "peacock" effect under the polarizing microscope.

Irregular Spherulites. These are understood to be structures without any of the above-mentioned regularly geometrical fibril orientations. Sometimes zig-zag structures are found, while in other cases there is no regularity at all (e.g., Terylene).

A classification of spherulites according to their shape includes the following:

Regular Spherulites. Round to ellipsoid in shape these have originated independently and have not been obstructed in their growth.

Obstructed Spherulites. The structure is still regular, but the purely spherical or ellipsoid form is no longer attained. This is usually because the individual spherulites have impeded one another's growth.

Misformed Spherulites. If there are very many nuclei in the melt, the spherulites may obstruct one another to such an extent during growth that no regular structures can arise. In this case it is often very difficult to recognize the above-mentioned types.

Melting Point Tests with High Polymers

To determine the melting points of various plastics the ordinary melting point microscope can be used. It should be borne in mind that pieces of polymer are usually very poor conductors of heat. Only very small granules, 10–15 μ, are therefore used as specimens. If bigger pieces are used it is often found that the granules are already melted on the outside, while the inside does not melt until a higher temperature is reached, as shown by the thermometer in the microscope heating plate.

Even with very small granules the temperature must be allowed to rise only very slowly. It is advisable not to increase it by more than 2°C a minute.

Surface Examination

Examination of the surface of fractures causes little difficulty on the whole. With transparent plastics it may happen that cracks continuing to several microns below the surface cause interference colors.

If it is desired to examine filler dispersion from fracture surfaces, it is often advisable to use polarized light. For many plastics a specific angle of incidence can be determined at which polarized light depolarizes when reflected. As depolarization does not occur with the filler particles or occurs at a different angle of incidence, filler particle dispersion can be effectively studied with an analyzing filter. It should be remembered that surface unevennesses cause pronounced shadows which make appraisal difficult. Hence this method is applied only if filler dispersion cannot be appraised from sections or if it is desired to know the direct cause of the fracture.

Examining Plastic in Non-Plastic Materials

For investigating the presence of polymers in textile or leather materials, fluorescence microscopic methods are used.

If the material containing the plastic fluoresces only slightly or not at all, microtome sections can be examined direct by fluorescence microscopy. Most plastics fluoresce bright blue-white or yellow-green. This method is very exact on the whole.

Fluorescence microscopic examination of plastics in natural textile fibers is not usually directly possible because most natural fibers have a fairly strong fluorescence of their own. As these fibers generally have fairly strong hydrophilic properties, however, it is very simple to use fluorochromes. Staining with a mixture of coriphosphine 0.1 % and Rhodamine 6 GD 0.1 % for 15 minutes, thorough washing in distilled water and drying, followed by fluorescence microscopic examination, enables the plastic coating of the fibers to be rendered clearly visible in nearly all cases.

J. ISINGS

PULP AND PAPER

Among the methods for investigating pulp and paper, microscopic examination occupies an important position. Microscopic techniques are used for: (a) identifying paper fibers; (b) investigating coatings on paper; (c) investigating sheet formation by the fibers; (d) investigating fillers; (e) morphological examination of fibers.

In the practice of paper technology, identification of the various paper fibers is of primary importance. As a rule it is sufficient to use a normal light microscope. With a total magnification of 60 and 200 × stronger magnification is usually superfluous. Coatings can also be most suitably examined from their cross sections with a normal light microscope. These cross sections are usually made with a Hardy microtome or a freezing microtome. The pulp condition of the various fibers can most suitably be studied by examining the fibers in aqueous suspensions with a phase contrast microscope. This method has been very widely applied, especially in recent years. Birefringence of fibers with a polarizing microscope is not determined; this method is usually limited to investigating fillers.

The same can be said of the x-ray microscope. Although it is possible with this method to see the mutual coherence of the paper fibers it is especially important for examining filler distribution. Good results can be achieved, particularly with the x-ray projection microscope (q.v.) as there is no need to make cross sections for this. The fact that stereo photographs can easily be made with it makes this method still more attractive.

Fluorescence microscopy is still infrequently applied for paper fiber investigation. An indication of the usefulness of this method is to be found in Herzog, who noted a fairly pronounced difference in fluorescence color between soft wood sulfite and soft wood sulfate pulp. More important than the fluorescence of the pulp itself however, is the method whereby the coloring of fibers with fluorochromes is used. Definitive data regarding this are not available in the literature, although it is clear that straw and esparto pulp can easily be distinguished by this method.

Lastly, electron microscopy must be mentioned as an important method of paper investigation. This method is particularly important for exact investigation of the fibrils of pulped fibers. These can be examined with replica techniques under an ordinary electron microscope or with thin sections, the contact zone between the pulped fibers being chiefly examined. The reflection electron microscope has also been used with great success. It seems that still more results can be achieved in this direction with electron scanning techniques.

Paper Fiber Research

Preparation Techniques. The techniques used for preparing specimens for paper investigation are usually very simple. First, fiber suspensions are investigated which are obtained by shaking pulp or paper in water, possibly with the application of heat, after which it readily disintegrates. For x-ray microscopic examination the paper can remain intact, but for contact microradiography sections about 50 microns thick are used. The cross sections for examining coatings are made with a Hardy microtome (see Fibers (Textile)-Techniques). The specimens are usually embedded in a mixture of equal parts of water and glycerin. For the electron microscope normal replica techniques are used, while evaporated suspensions are suitable, after shadowing, for examination with a reflection microscope. Full details of this can be found in Emerton.

Staining Techniques. The main stains for paper fiber investigation are:

(1) Zinc chloroiodide solution in water (see Fibers (Textile) Techniques, p. 344).

(2) Solution of iodine in potassium iodide ($I_2 \cdot KI$). Both normal staining and $I_2 \cdot KI$ staining followed by treatment in glycerin-sulfuric acid give good results in paper investigation. The formulas are given in the article on Fibers (Textile)-Techniques (p. 346).

(3) Staining according to Lofton and Merrit with fuchsine and malachite green. Composition of the stain:

2 parts by volume of aqueous 1% fuchsine solution.
1 part by volume of aqueous ½% malachite green solution.

The solution will keep for about eight days. A paper fiber mash is freed from water as much as possible and stirred with the solution on a slide. After removal of the solution the specimen is treated for 10 to 30 seconds with 3 to 4 drops of 0.1% HCl and rinsed. *Result.* Unbleached sulfite wood pulp: purple red; unbleached soda and sulfate wood pulp: blue with a fairly pronounced red haze. Ground wood: stains like unbleached soda and sulfate pulp.

(4) Staining according to Graff (TAPPI standard method). Two stains are suitable for paper examination. The most widely used is Stain C:

Solution I: 40 g aluminum chloride in 100 cc water S.G. 1.15 at 28°C.
Solution II: 100 g $CaCl_2$ in 150 ml water S.G. 1.36 at 28°C.
Solution III: 50 g dry zinc chloride in 25 ml water S.G. 1.80 at 28°C.
Solution IV: 0.40 g dry KI 0.65 g dry I2 in 50 ml water S.G. 1.80 at 28°C.

The mixture for use is 20 ml of solution I, 10 ml of solution II, 10 ml of solution III and 12.5 ml of solution IV. A precipitate is allowed to form, the clear top liquid is pipetted. Add a crystal of I_2 and store the mixture in the dark. The results for the various pulps are listed in Table 1.

Paper Morphology

The fibers used in paper manufacture are of three kinds:

(1) Rags originating from textile material.

(2) Wood, straw, esparto, etc., pulp.

(3) Highly lignate fibers obtained by grinding wood.

In all three cases there are unpulped and pulped fibers.

Rag Fiber. *Cotton.* Cotton is nearly always very easy to identify as a fiber in paper. Even with thorough pulping, it is hardly ever possible to split all the fibers into the highly deformed single dimensional fibrils. The twisting of the ribbon-shaped fiber is a clear means of identification.

Flax and Hemp. Both flax and hemp may be used as paper fiber. As they are usually found in only small quantities in rag paper and are, moreover, greatly deformed by pulping, it is very difficult to estimate their

TABLE 1. STAINS FOR PULPS (GRAFF C)

	Unbleached (Colors in order of lower lignin content)	Bleached
Rags		claret
Ground wood	yellow	bright yellow orange
Soft wood pulp		
sulfite	yellow—green yellow pink gray	bright purple gray—pale red purple
refined sulfite	pale brown—blue gray	light reddish orange—dull red
sulfate	weak green yellow, strong yellow brown—mild yellow green—dark yellow gray	dark blue gray—dull purple
Hard wood		
sulfite	dull yellow green	weak purple blue—bright purple gray
refined		red orange—dull red
soda and sulfate	light blue green—dark blue-green— dark red gray	dull blue—dull purple
Manila	yellow gray—light blue—purple gray	
Jute	bright orange yellow bright yellow green	
Straw, esparto	bright green gray, dark blue gray—purple gray	
Kotzu	pale pink green	
Gampi	bright green yellow—light blue green	

Besides the C stain, stain A as modified by Sutermeister can also be used. This stain is obtained by mixing 45 ml of solution II from stain C with 5 ml solution IV from stain C and storing this in a dark colored bottle, a crystal of I_2 being added. Table 2 shows the colors that then occur for the various pulps. In appraising these, however, Graff's color chart is important.

percentage alongside the other rag fibers. Only large, hardly damaged pieces of flax are clearly recognizable from the displacements. It is usually more difficult to identify hemp fibers in paper from their morphological characteristics. The fiber tends very greatly to fibrillation and little can be seen of the large lumen. For the characteristics of the fibers when unpulped or only slightly pulped see the section on the Morphology of Textile Fibers, p. 350.

Hard Wood Pulp. The hard woods used for pulp are chiefly poplar, birch, eucalyptus and beech. Chestnut, maple, willow and ash are used to a less extent. Hard wood pulp consists of vessels, vascular tracheides, fiber tracheides, libriform fibers and parenchyma constituents. In the eucalyptus there are also secretion canals. In pulp it is often difficult to distinguish the various parts. Characteristics distinguishing them from other pulps are mainly the large vessels. As far as the

paper industry is concerned it is usually of importance only to know whether a pulp consists of hard wood or soft wood. Furthermore, in the case of a mixed pulp the percentage of hard wood usually has to be determined. The type of hard wood is less important.

Beech (Fagus sylvatica). The large vessels are usually fairly long and vary in width from 18 to 80 μ. The ends are cut off obliquely and are usually digitaliform at one end. The pits are easy to see. The thinner vessels are usually scalariform. The number of scalar rings is 6 to 20. Sometimes the rings are broken, but even with fairly thorough pulping they can still be identified. The types of pits are:

(1) Simple (small, scattered in medulla)

(2) Bordered (close together and small— the "border" is usually difficult to distinguish).

(3) Large medulla (closely defined and in rows).

Libriform fibers are the main constituent of pulp. There are many wide, short pits on the cell wall. The tracheides are very broad and have wide simple pits. The border of these is difficult to see. There are invariably many parenchyma elements in the pulp. These are elongated, thin-walled and very porous.

Birch (Betula alba). The vessels are characterized by bordered pits very close together. The border is not visible. The wood tracheides show simple pits, likewise very close together. The cell wall is only moderately lignate. Parenchyma cells are very thin and occur only sporadically.

Poplar (Populus alba). Bordered pits with hexagonal simple pits without a border and large pits in crosswise rows. The vessels have large, pronounced end-protrusions. The pits of the fibers are not arranged in long rows. Some fibers have no pits. The parenchyma elements are often elongated.

(3) **Soft Wood Pulp.** In the soft woods one must distinguish between the fiber tracheides, the medulla tracheides and the parenchyma elements. The fiber tracheides are 4 or 5 sided thick-walled elements. On

all walls. Semi-bordered pits are also found locally, i.e., where the tracheides border upon the parenchyma cells. Their walls are thicker in places and in cross and tangential sections these often look like tangential bars. The medulla parenchyma has ordinary pits on the walls adjoining other parenchyma cells. The walls adjoining the tracheides have semi-bordered pits.

In sulfite pulp the parenchyma cells also have pronounced resin particles. These particles, which are easily identifiable, are important in distinguishing between sulfite and sulfate pulp.

The surface of the primary wall of the Spring tracheides is greatly wrinkled during pulping of the wood and subsequent drying, while cracks also occur in it. Moreover, small fibers readily split off. This effect is particularly easy to see in sulfite pulp. In Autumn tracheides this crazing effect is far less pronounced.

Sulfate pulp is usually obtained from firs, the bordered pits appearing as large, square holes. Besides the above differences between sulfite and sulfate pulps the following may apply:

	Sulfite pulp		Sulfate pulp	
	Unbleached	Bleached	Unbleached	Bleached
Zinc chloroiodide	blue violet reticulated	blue violet	brown violet no reticulation	brown violet no reticulation
I₂.KI	green yellow	no color	weak green yellow	no color
Lofton and Merrit	purple red	no color	red violet	no color
Graff C solution	green yellow	purple gray	yellow brown— yellow green	blue gray

two walls they have large round bordered pits in rows. Besides these large bordered pits, the Spring tracheides, which have a wide lumen, show also small, ordinary pits irregularly distributed over the wall. The width of these tracheides is about 75 μ. The Autumn tracheides have only bordered pits. Their width is about 40 μ. The medulla tracheides have small, round bordered pits on

Straw pulp. Straw pulp consists mainly of bast fibers somewhat resembling flax fibers. Unlike flax, however, they are always present in paper almost undamaged. Furthermore, the X-shaped displacements are lacking. In addition there are large, round parenchyma cells without any contents. To a less extent annular, spiral and reticular vessels are found. Of primary importance to fiber identification are the strongly pebbled, crenelated skin cells.

Esparto pulp. This pulp is made from the leaves of *Stepa tenacissima* and *Lygenus spartus*. This pulp consists mainly of short, thin bast fibers closely resembling flax. But, here again like straw, the X-shaped displacements are lacking, while the fibers are hardly damaged even when pulped. These bast fibers are considerably thinner than those of straw. Small, sac-like skin cells are found throughout the specimen. The parenchyma cells, which are also present to a considerable extent, are usually badly damaged by pulping. The specimens also contain pieces of annular and spiral vessels and also short bits of hair, shaped like commas, which are very useful for a diagnosis.

It is difficult to estimate the percentage of esparto pulp mixtures which also contain straw pulp. After staining with Rhodamine 6 GD/Coriphosphine, an estimate is possible with the aid of the secondary fluorescence. Straw pulp fibers give a yellow green color and esparto a brownish green color.

Ampar (Bagasse). This pulp is made from the sugar-cane waste. Characteristics of this paper material are finely porous parenchyma cells and differentially formed sclereides. The bast fibers have the following forms: (a) greatly thickened, fairly wide fibers (approx. 20–30 μ). (b) short, uniformly wide fibers with thin walls. (c) narrow, tapering fibers largely resembling straw fibers.

The skin cells differ greatly in size and are not frequently found; they are usually badly damaged.

Ground wood. The ground wood mostly found is soft wood. In Italy ground poplar is often also incorporated in paper. Under the microscope the normal image of soft wood or hard wood anatomy is recognizable in the ground wood particles.

Ground soft wood is characterized by the wide fiber tracheides with their almost round bordered pits. Crosswise to these tracheides are the medullary rays built up of narrow and fairly long parenchyma cells. The droplets of resin characterizing soft wood are usually easy to see. Characteristic of ground hard wood are the large vessels and the absence of pits.

Pulped Fiber. The morphology of fibers is greatly changed by pulping, the extent depending upon the degree of pulping and on the type of pulping machine. On the whole the changes are fairly great in the case of rags, hard wood and soft wood. Straw and esparto pulps change to a less extent. In the case of highly pulped material it may often be difficult to distinguish the various kinds with a microscope. Staining methods are then often fairly difficult and are consequently of little value as evidence.

TABLE 2. STAINS FOR PULPS (A)

	Unbleached (Colors in order of lower lignin content)	Bleached
Soft wood (sulfite)	gray green—pink brown	red violet—red brown
sulfate and soda	green—gray green—gray violet	violet—blue violet
Hard wood		
sulfite ⎫		
sulfate ⎬	gray—blue violet—violet	blue violet—violet—light pink violet
soda ⎭		—blue
Rags		red brown—brick red—lilac
Straw, esparto,	gray green—green	
Bamboo		
Manila	gray blue—blue	gray blue—blue
Jute	yellow	yellow green
Ground wood	yellow	

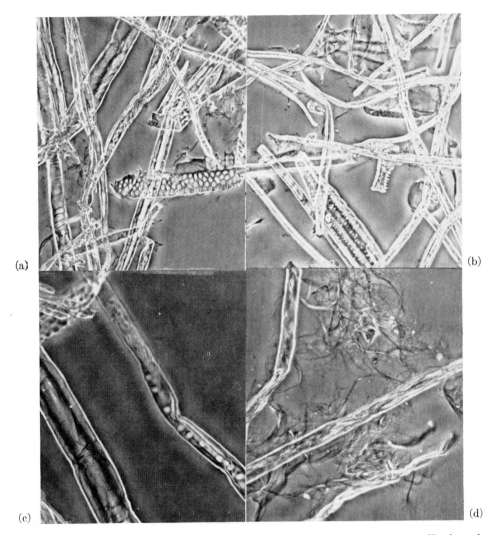

(a)

(b)

(c)

(d)

Fig. 1. Pulps. Lower left: Soft wood sulphite pulp, phase contrast, 300×. Upper left: Hard wood pulp beaten in hollander to 57° S. R., phase contrast, 300×. Lower right: Cotton rags beaten in hollander to 50° S. R., phase contrast, 200×. Upper right: Straw pulp beaten in hollander to 38° S. R., phase contrast, 350×.

When pulping is less thorough it is usually possible to identify the constituent fibers. In the case of rag fibers pulping causes in the first place internal fibrillation often attended by cross fracture. Despite this fracture, however, the typical fiber characteristics, such as the X-shaped displacements in the case of flax, usually remain fairly visible. This internal fibrillation is followed by external fibrillation, whereby a network of fine fibrils arises. Cell wall membranes are not found.

In the case of hard wood fiber, too, pulping causes considerable fibrillation. In the first instance, similarly to rags, this is internal. Besides this there is greater damage which loosens membranes, both from the fibers and the vessels, which lie as two-dimensional fibrils in the fiber suspension. These membranes are clearly visible only with a phase contrast microscope. With a normal microscope these fibrils are visible as structureless slime. The fibers are often so badly affected by pulping that they can be distinguished only by staining methods. The large vessels are also torn apart. Often, however, the fragments of these vessels are sufficient for identification.

On the whole, soft wood pulp shows a similar picture. Here again it is mainly the occurrence of two-dimensional fibrils that distinguishes them from rag fiber. As a rule, soft wood fiber disintegrates more than hard wood fiber. For strongly pulped specimens, pieces of tracheides with the typical single row bordered pits are important for identification, in addition to staining methods.

Pulping of straw and esparto fibers has much less effect. Straw fibers are only very slightly affected (Fig. 1b). Comparatively slight internal fibrillation, in addition to external fibrillation of the ends of the fibers to fibril bundles is the sole result, even after protracted pulping. The skin cells show a strong tendency to crumble, while the parenchyma cells are badly torn and pulped into large pieces. Difficulties in identification are hardly ever caused by pulping.

REFERENCES

HERZOG, "Handbuch der Mikroskopischen Technik für Fasertechnologen," Berlin, 1951.
HERZOG, "Mikrophotographischer Atlas der Technisch-wichtigen Pflanzenfaser," Berlin, 1955.
STOVES, J. L., "Fiber Microscopy," London, 1957.
WOLFF, TOBLER, F.v.G., "Mikroskopische Untersuchung Pflanzlicher Faserstoffe," Leipzig, 1951.

J. ISINGS

HISTORADIOGRAPHY. *See* X-RAY MICROSCOPY

INDUSTRIAL HYGIENE MICROSCOPY (INCLUDING REFRACTIVE INDEX MEASUREMENT)

The microscope is used as a qualitative instrument in the field of industrial hygiene to determine whether the type of dust prevalent in the working environment of the industrial worker is of a toxic nature and thus may be injurious to health. Determination of the amount of the toxic dust in the air is also usually necessary to evaluate the degree of hazard. Approximate percentages, such as in the case of quartz dust, can sometimes be determined with the microscope. However, in most instances, use of wet chemical analysis or additional instrumentation such as the spectrograph or x-ray diffraction is also necessary for more accurate quantitative results.

Following this preliminary qualitative and quantitative investigation, the microscope is used for counting the number of dust particles in the air and determination of their particle size. Results obtained may indicate that a definite health hazard exists. For example, Threshold Limit Values adopted at the yearly meetings of Governmental Industrial Hygienists state that in the case of dust containing more than 50% free silica, the number of dust particles in the breathing area of the worker should not exceed five million particles per cubic foot of air. This is particularly important in the case of small particle size dust which presents a greater health problem. Microscopic examination indicates that in pneumoconiosis, the particle size of dust in the lung is mainly below 5 microns in size, the largest not exceeding 10 microns.

Information obtained as a result of microscopic investigation is usually reported to the Medical and Safety Departments of the company involved. In the case of conditions exceeding the Threshold Limit Value, an exhaust system to remove the dust from the worker's breathing area may be recommended. If an exhaust is already present, results may indicate that it is inadequate in size or not operating efficiently.

Qualitative and Quantitative Analysis

Identification of the dust is not always necessary since in many industrial operations, the nature of the product is known. However, many materials such as abrasives, polishing and buffing compounds are sold under trade names with little information as to their chemical constituents.

Prerequisite to microscopic examination, spectrographic analysis is often of value for determination of the elements present. For example, if it is found that the sample is largely silicon, there is the possibility that it is primarily silicon dioxide. Confirmation as to whether the material is silicon dioxide and its molecular form can be made with the microscope. Determination of molecular form is important since investigation has served to indicate that crystalline forms of silicon dioxide such as quartz, cristobalite and tridymite are more toxic than crypto-crystalline and amorphous forms.

Preliminary microscopic examination should be made with the petrographic microscope (Fig. 1) or with a laboratory microscope equipped with polarizing accessories (cap analyzer and disc polarizer). Examination of the sample should be made with the analyzer and sub-stage polarizer in a crossed position. Particles observed will appear bright or dark on a dark background indicating whether they are single refracting (isotropic) or double refracting (anisotropic). Fig. 2 shows two forms of silicon dioxide as

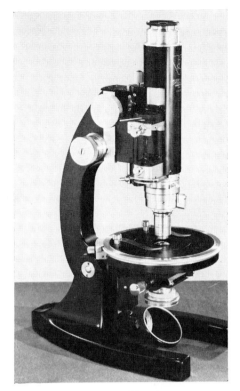

Fig. 1. Petrographic microscope.

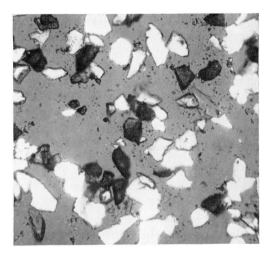

Fig. 2. Mixture of quartz (bright particles) and opal (dark particles).

observed with the petrographic microscope. Amorphous opaline silicon dioxide appears dark due to the fact that the ray of light

401

emitting from single refracting particles is rejected by the analyzer located above the specimen. Quartz in the same preparation appears bright. This is explained by the fact that double refracting particles divide the ray of light from the polarizer into two rays (ordinary and extraordinary ray). As in the case of the opal, the ordinary ray is rejected by the analyzer but the extraordinary ray, vibrating at right angles to the ordinary ray, is transmitted through the analyzer. As a result, the quartz particles appear bright on a dark background.

This preliminary microscopic examination serves to classify the unknown as to whether it belongs to the isotropic or anisotropic group of chemicals and minerals. Additional optical properties such as refractive index or indices are necessary for identification. In view of the possibility that the bright anisotropic particles (Fig. 2) might be crystalline quartz, a Handbook of Chemistry or Textbook of Mineralogy is consulted. Information obtained indicates that quartz has two refractive indices, 1.544 for the ordinary ray and 1.553 for the extraordinary ray.

Determination as to whether the unknown has these refractive indices can be made by use of a petrographic microscope illuminated with a sodium light source. The sample is mounted under a cover glass in a liquid of refractive index 1.544 for yellow light, and examined with the analyzer and polarizer of the microscope in a crossed position. The stage of the microscope is rotated until a particle being observed appears dark. The analyzer is then removed and the index of the particle with respect to the liquid is determined by the usual Becke line procedure. Using this method, a halo of bright light may be observed moving into or away from the particle as the focus of the microscope is slightly changed from exact focus. If the halo moves into the grain on the up focus, the particle has a higher index than the liquid; movement of the halo away from the particle into the index liquid signifies a

lower index. Complete disappearance of the particle being examined, indicates that it has an index of 1.544 for yellow light, the index for the ordinary ray of crystalline quartz.

The analyzer is now reinserted and the stage rotated to the second extinction position and estimation made on the same particle as to whether the refractive index for the other component vibration is higher than 1.544. If examination by the Becke line method proves this to be true, the above described procedure, as used for the 1.544 index, is now repeated using a liquid of 1.553. Disappearance in this liquid indicates that the particle in question has a second index of 1.553 for the extraordinary ray and can thus be considered crystalline quartz. Additional identifying procedures such as examination of interference figure and determination of optic sign used by the petrographer for mineral specimens are difficult or not possible on small particle size dusts.

A simplified procedure for the identification of dust particles is to examine the sample with a dispersion staining dark-field microscope. This method (1) of illumination is obtained by the addition of the accessories shown in Fig. 3 to a laboratory type microscope. For small particle size dust, a combination of a 20× (10.25mm) 0.40 N.A. objective with a 20× hyperplane eyepiece is suggested. The condenser employed is a 1.40 N.A. achromatic condenser but with the top element removed to give an N.A. of 0.59. The diameter of the dark-field stop used below the condenser is very critical, a diameter of 17 mm usually giving good results. Use of a cap analyzer over the eyepiece is of value for the identification of anisotropic dusts such as quartz.

As in the usual petrographic method described above, the sample is placed in a refractive index liquid which in the case of quartz would be 1.544 for yellow light. In place of a sodium lamp, a 6 volt—108 watt ribbon filament lamp is used for illumination. Using this dark-field method, yellow light

FIG. 3. Microscope accessories for dispersion staining.

for which the quartz and liquid are equal in refractive index will pass straight through the particle oblique to the optic axis of the microscope and thus not enter the objective. Blue and red light for which the quartz is not equal in refractive index are refracted at the particle-liquid interface to a degree as to enter the objective. Due to the greater bending of blue light as compared to red, the particle when equal to the liquid for yellow light appears largely blue with a trace of red. If the small amount of red is somewhat difficult to observe, increased visibility can be obtained by very slightly decentering the dark-field stop.

Success with this method, especially in the case of small particle size dust, is based on the use of index liquids of much greater dispersion than the sample examined. The greater the difference in dispersion between the sample and the liquid, the more brilliant the colors. For the identification of quartz, styrene stabilized with *tert*-butyl catechol has proved to be of value. It has an unusually high dispersion for its refractive index of approximately 1.544. As examined in this liquid with the dispersion staining dark-field

microscope, using a cap analyzer over the 20× hyperplane eyepiece, quartz particles oriented for the ordinary ray, 1.544 appear largely blue with a trace of red. Particles oriented for the extraordinary ray, 1.553 appear blue with a large amount of red or are homogenously red in the case of very small particle size. Rotation of the cap analyzer 90 degrees results in particles oriented for the ordinary ray (appearing blue with a small amount of red) to change in color to blue with a large amount of red, or all red. Particles oriented for the extraordinary ray, change in color to those significant for the ordinary ray.

Additional dispersion colors can be observed which are of value for identification. In place of a 1.544 index liquid, a 1.553 liquid equal to the extraordinary ray of quartz can be used and notation made as to the change in color on rotation of the cap analyzer. Dispersion colors can be observed indicating whether the dust sample is above or below the index liquid in refractive index. A pure blue with no trace of red is obtained when the particle is slightly lower in index than the liquid; light blue signifies a still lower

403

index. A large amount of red indicates a slightly higher index than the liquid and orange and yellow a still higher index. If solid and liquid are very far apart in index, dispersion colors will not be observed, the sample appearing white. To determine as to whether the white appearance indicates an index difference far above or far below, the dark-field stop must be removed and the Becke line method of index determination employed.

This same procedure of dark-field illumination can be used for the determination of other toxic dusts such as isotropic opal (Fig. 2). This form of silicon dioxide having only one refractive index shows no change in color as the cap analyzer is rotated since it has the same optical properties in all directions. Positive identification of opaline silica is more difficult than other forms of silicon dioxide since it has a variable refractive index. That index can vary from 1.41 to 1.46 depending on the amount of water present ranging from 1 to 20 per cent. Another problem with the lower index dusts such as opal, cristobalite and tridymite is to find identifying index liquids that have a much greater dispersion than the sample such as to give brilliant dispersion colors in the case of small particle size. In general, the lower index liquids have low dispersion, in some cases having a dispersion only slightly exceeding that of the sample examined. This problem can be largely solved by the use of ethyl cinnamate. Like styrene, it has a high dispersion for its index of 1.557. When mixed with ethyl phosphate, a series of liquids ranging in index from 1.410 to 1.557 can be prepared having higher dispersions than the index liquids commonly used for the Becke line method of index determination.

As indicated in the first part of this article, determination of the approximate amount of the toxic dust can in some instances be made by use of the microscope. This analysis is sometimes made on ledge or rafter samples which although collected close to the work-ing area may not always represent accurate information as to the amount of toxic dust breathed by the operator. For more accurate results, the sample can be collected in water or alcohol in a Greenburg-Smith or Midget impinger at the breathing area of the operator.

After collection, the impinger tube is placed in a water bath to evaporate off the water or alcohol leaving the dry dust in the impinger tube. A small amount of index liquid such as styrene, used in the identification of quartz, is placed in the impinger tube and thoroughly mixed with the dust sample. A rubber policeman is of value for both mixing and transferring the sample to a microscope slide. The preparation is covered with a cover glass and inspection made using the dark-field dispersion staining microscope to determine the approximate percentage of toxic dust such as quartz present in the preparation. More accurate quantitative results can be made by comparison with a standard sample containing a known amount of toxic dust. Two microscopes can be used in this determination. The stage of one microscope contains the unknown sample and the stage of the second microscope the known sample. The eyepieces of both microscopes are connected by means of a comparison eyepiece (Fig. 4) which permits examination of both samples in a circular field of view divided vertically, one half being the unknown sample and the other half the known.

Other methods of quantitative microscopic analysis of mixtures are described by Chamot and Mason (2). Ross and Sehl (3) describe a method for determination of the percentage of quartz in a mixture using the usual Becke line methods of identification. Employing this procedure, particles are counted and assigned weights dependent on their size as compared to the size of squares of a Whipple disk placed in the eyepiece of the microscope. This procedure should be more easily and accurately done by use of dispersion staining. By proper selection of

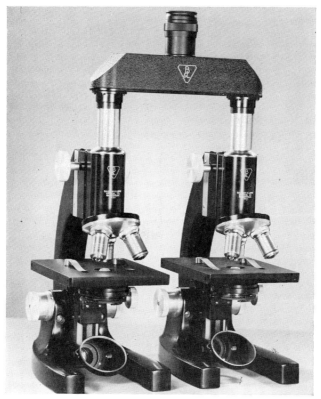

Fig. 4. Comparison eyepiece.

refractive index liquids, the toxic dust such as quartz could be observed in one color, material not quartz in other colors of the spectrum or white if far removed in refractive index.

A variation in the impinger method of collection is to use the identifying index liquid as the collecting liquid in place of water or alcohol. In this case, liquids of less volatility than styrene should be used. Index liquids commonly employed are a mixture of two liquids which may differ slightly in vapor pressure. As a result, during the procedure of collection of the sample, there may be greater evaporation of one of the constituents resulting in a slight change in refractive index. For accurate results, after collection of the dust sample, a drop of the collecting liquid should be checked on a refractometer and adjustment of its index made if necessary by addition of either a small amount of the lower or higher index components. Using the identifying liquid as the collecting medium, evaporation on a water bath is not necessary. The impinger sample can be stirred with a rubber policeman and a drop transferred to a slide for microscopic examination.

Quantitative results obtained should not be based on the examination of one sample. Although dispersion staining is probably the simplest method of microscopic examination, considerable experience is required in the case of small particle size dust. It has been our experience that more reliable information can be obtained by preliminary examination of a known sample, such as quartz, previous to examination of the unknown, in order to determine exact dispersion colors on rotation of the cap analyzer. The unknown is examined in the same way to determine whether particles present show the same shade of col-

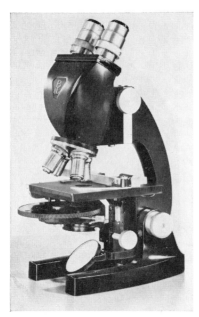

FIG. 5. Phase microscope.

ors as the known. Both samples should be examined at approximately the same temperature because the refractive index of a liquid changes with a change in temperature. For many liquids, the rate of change may have a value of around 0.00045 for each degree centigrade of variation.

This temperature factor is of value in some cases to obtain brighter dispersion colors which aid in increasing the visibility of small particle size dust. For example, if the preparation containing quartz is examined in a warming stage in a liquid of 1.544 adjusted to that index at 25 degrees centigrade, increasing the temperature will decrease the index of the liquid. As a result, quartz particles appearing blue with a trace of red can be made to appear homogeneously red, orange or yellow dependent on the temperature used. Consideration must be made, that although the contrast on a dark background is greater, identification by dispersion colors other than blue with a trace of red results in decreased accuracy. However, this possible error is reduced provided a sample of known material is simul-

taneously examined with the unknown by means of comparison dispersion staining microscope, comparing the change in color of both samples as the temperature is increased.

Counting Dust Particles

The number of dust particles in the air is usually determined by first collecting the dust in an impinger tube using water or alcohol as the collecting liquid. After collection, a 1-mm aliquot of the sample is placed in a dust counting chamber such as a Sedwick-Rafter or Dunn cell and counted under the light-field microscope employing a 10× objective in combination with a 7.5× or 10× eyepiece. Higher magnification oculars can be used but the resulting magnification should not exceed 1000 times the numerical aperture of the objective.

An objection to the use of the light-field microscope is the fact that dust particles of small size, having little or no color and close to the index of the collecting liquid, will be difficult or impossible to see. For this reason, we have suggested (4) the use of the dark contrast phase microscope (Fig. 5) for counting dust particles which results in greater accuracy and ease in counting. Fig. 6 is a comparative photomicrograph of magnesium fluoride dust in isopropyl alcohol as observed by both light-field and phase microscopy. It is rare that dusts of such low index and proximity to the index of the collecting liquid will be encountered in the usual working atmosphere. However, these photomicrographs serve to illustrate the effectiveness of the phase microscope for rendering visible dust particles having a refractive index differing only slightly from the refractive index of the examination liquid. According to Chamot and Mason (2), the use of the phase microscope gives values to an additional decimal place beyond that obtained by the usual Becke line method.

A number of papers have been published in the last few years suggesting the use of molecular filters in preference to the impinger method for collection of dust. Molecular filters are cellulose ester gels resembling ordinary filter paper in appearance but have a pore size such that they can retain dust particles of small particle size. One of the main advantages of their use, as pointed out by First and Silverman (5), is the fact that there is negligible penetration of the filter. Dust particles are deposited on the surface in the same state in which they existed when suspended in air.

In using these filters, the usual procedure is to place the filter in a holder designed for that purpose and collect the dust in the air at 0.1 to 0.5 cubic foot per minute using an electrically driven pump, Freon-powered equipment, or hand pump. After collection, the filter or a section of it is placed dust side down on a clean slide or on the ruling of a counting chamber such as a hemacytometer. Since the filter is opaque and transmitted light using the light-field microscope has been the usual method of counting, it is necessary to render the filter transparent by application of a drop or two of liquid equal to the refractive index of the filter.

A major objection to the above procedure, as pointed out by Drinker and Hatch (6), and by Paulus, Talvitie, Fraser and Keenan (7), is the fact that toxic dust particles such as quartz and diatomite close to the index of the clearing liquid will not all be included in the count, especially if of small particle size. A solution to the problem, as in the case of the impinger method of collection, is the use of the phase microscope. The superiority of phase illumination as compared to the usual light-field method is illustrated in Fig. 7 of diatomaceous earth particles collected on a molecular filter (Millipore type AA). The filter was rendered transparent by application of a drop of liquid of 1.507 at 25°C and covering with a cover-glass. Employing the phase microscope, the liquid used should be equal or very close to the index of the filter in the third decimal place

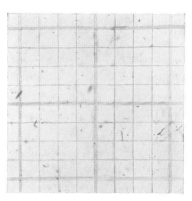

Fig. 6A. Magnesium fluoride. Light-field illumination.

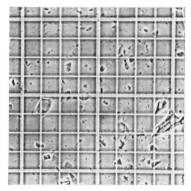

Fig. 6B. Exactly the same area as figure 6A. Phase illumination.

in order that the texture of the filter will not be revealed. Fig. 8 is a photomicrograph of diatomaceous earth collected on a Millipore Filter, type AA using a liquid of index 1.515 as the clearing liquid such as has been suggested for the usual light-field method. Although satisfactory for the light-field technique of counting, it cannot be used with phase illumination. As noted in the photomicrograph, it is difficult or impossible to differentiate small diatom particles from the texture of the filter.

The liquid used for clearing must have no solvent effect on the filter. Molecular filters are soluble in certain ketones, esters and methanol. A mixture of light mineral oil with Aroclor 1242 adjusted to an index of 1.507 on a refractometer at 25°C has proved

407

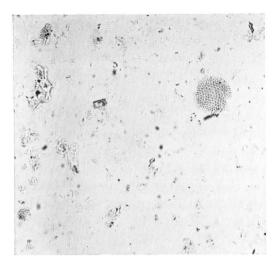

FIG. 7A. Diatomaceous earth particles on a Millipore type AA filter. Cleared in a liquid of refractive index 1.507. Light-field illumination.

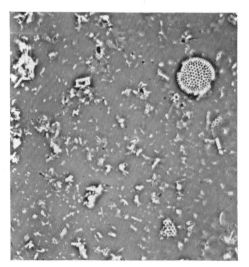

FIG. 7B. Exactly the same area as figure 7A. Phase illumination.

satisfactory. Another possibility if this 1.507 liquid is not available, is isoamyl salicylate. It is a colorless liquid with pleasant odor, has no solvent effect on the filter and its refractive index is usually close enough to 1.507 at 25°C as to render the filter quite transparent. In using these liquids, consideration must be made as previously mentioned, that the refractive index of liquids vary with temperature. Slight differences are not important but use of a 1.507 clearing liquid corrected for that index at 25°C and used at a much lower or higher temperature may result in some objectionable visibility of the filter.

Determination of Particle Size

Determination of the particle size of the dust at the approximate breathing area of the worker can be made by examination of the impinger sample collected for the purpose of making the dust count. If a hemacytometer was used as the counting chamber, some idea of the particle size can be obtained by comparison with the ruled areas of known size. Increased accuracy is obtained by use of a micrometer disc in the eyepiece or a Filar Micrometer eyepiece (Fig. 9). Before use, the divisions of the micrometer must be calibrated by use of a stage micrometer having a scale of known area, the smallest division being .01 mm (10 microns). Calibration of the eyepiece disc is made by first focusing on the stage micrometer. The stage micrometer is then moved to a point so that one line of it coincides with a line to left center of the eyepiece scale. Count is then made

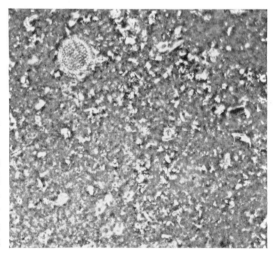

FIG. 8. Diatomaceous earth particles on a Millipore type AA filter. Cleared in a liquid of refractive index 1.515. Phase illumination.

across the eyepiece scale to the right from this point to another point where a line of the eyepiece scale coincides with a line on the stage micrometer scale.

If a large number of dust samples are to be examined, use of a micro-projector (Fig. 10) has proved to be the preferred method. In this case, the dust sample is projected onto a screen. Particle size distribution is determined by comparing the size of the projected images with a ruled area on the screen of known size. Another procedure is to measure the projected particles with a millimeter rule. Knowing the magnification, the value in microns for each division of the rule can be determined. For example, if the choice of optics and projected distance is such as to give a magnification of 1000×, a particle having a diameter of 1 mm as measured with the rule has an actual size of 1 micron.

In preparation of a particle size distribution curve, the total number of grains measured may vary from 200 to 2000 dependent on whether the dust sample contains a few sizes or many sizes. The number of each micron size counted is multiplied by the cube of the diameter to obtain the relative amount of that size present in the sample and the percentage of the total amount is calculated for each micron size. To obtain an accumulative curve, the percentage of the total sample larger than each size is plotted against the diameter in microns.

Considerable variation in the sizes obtained can result dependent on the method of collection. For example, disintegration of particles by high-velocity impingement may give an excess of fine particles. The use of liquid collecting medium such as water may result in solution of many particles. As previously indicated, due to proximity in index of the collecting liquid and the dust, small particle size material as examined by the usual light-field microscope will be difficult or impossible to see. As a result, these particles will not be included in the preparation of a particle size distribution curve.

FIG. 9. Filar micrometer

FIG. 10. Micro-projector.

Drinker and Hatch (6) suggest the use of the Molecular Filter and Thermal Precipitator for collection of dust for particle size determination. Collecting efficiency is high over the entire range of interest and the particles are deposited without being subject to physical stress. In the case of molecular filter samples, as previously described, a liquid of approximately 1.507 refractive index must be used for rendering the filter transparent. Approximate information as to size can be made by comparison with the rulings of the hemacytometer and more accurate information by use of a calibrated eyepiece micrometer. As in counting, the use of phase microscopy should increase the accuracy in determination of particle size. According to Richards (8), more precise measurements can be made with phase microscopy owing to the sharp edges of specimens free from indefinite diffraction patterns. Also, because of their definite edges, one can more readily determine whether a particle is single or aggregate.

A limitation of the usual particle size distribution curve obtained by use of the optical microscope, is the fact that particle size below its resolution is not included. Also the fact that little or no information is usually obtained as to the size of various constituents of a mixture. For example, particle size information on dust consisting mainly of clays and quartz sand in a ceramic plant may indicate that a large percentage of the dust is below 3 microns in size. It is important to know whether the small particle size dust is mainly quartz or clay. If present as quartz, the degree of hazard is considerably greater than in the case of small particle size clay.

Simultaneous measurement of particle size and identification of the particles measured can be made in many instances by use of the dispersion staining dark-field microscope. Unfortunately, samples collected on molecular filters cannot be used for this determination due to the fact that the index liquid employed must be selected for the purpose of rendering the filter transparent rather than for the purpose of identification of the particulate material collected. An exception is the rare case when the dust on the filter has an index equal to or very close to the index of the clearing liquid. Samples collected by other methods can be measured by use of the dispersion staining dark-field microscope. For example, in the case of dust from the ceramic plant containing primarily quartz sand and clay we are mainly interested in the size of the quartz particles. If examined in styrene, the quartz particles measured will appear blue with a trace of red changing in color on rotation of the cap analyzer to blue with a large amount of red or homogeneously red dependent on their particle size. Clay particles such as kaolinite present in the preparation, having different indices, appear in other colors of the spectrum or white and are thus readily distinguished from quartz.

REFERENCES

1. CROSSMON, G. C., "New Developments in Dispersion Staining Microscopy as Applied to Industrial Hygiene", *Am. Ind. Hyg. Assoc. Quart.*, **18**, 341 (1957).
2. CHAMOT, E. M. AND MASON, C. W., "Handbook of Chemical Microscopy", 3rd Ed., John Wiley & Sons, Inc., New York, (1958).
3. ROSS, H. L. AND SEHL, F. W., "Determination of Free Silica-Modified Petrographic Immersion Method", *Ind. Eng. Chem., Anal. Ed.*, **7**, 30 (1935).
4. CROSSMON, G. C., "Counting of Dust Particles by Phase Microscopy", *A. M. A. Arch. Ind. Hyg. Occup. Med.*, **6**, 416 (1952).
5. FIRST, M. W. AND SILVERMAN, L., "Air Sampling with Membrane Filters", *A. M. A. Arch. Ind. Hyg. Occup Med.*, **7**, 1 (1953).
6. DRINKER, P. AND HATCH, T., "Industrial Dust", 2nd Ed., McGraw-Hill Book Co., New York, N. Y. (1954).
7. PAULUS, H. J., TALVITIE, N. A., FRASER, D. A., AND KEENAN, R. G., "Use of Membrane Filters in Air Sampling," *Am. Ind. Hyg. Assoc. Quart.*, **18**, 267 (1957).
8. RICHARDS, O., "Photomicrography with the Phase Microscope," *Photographic Soc. America J. Sec. B.*, **16**, 94 (1950).

GERMAIN CROSSMON

INFRARED MICROSCOPY

The design requirements of infrared microscopes, or more accurately infrared microsampling attachments, have been rather thoroughly explored in recent years. All have the common property of measuring, as a function of wavelength, the infrared absorption of minute samples. The resulting absorption spectra are similar to the infrared spectra of macroscopic samples so that the well known applications of infrared (see Encyclopedia of Spectroscopy)—qualitative and quantitative analyses and molecular structure investigations—are possible. Infrared microscopes have unique importance where (a) the amount of sample is small, (b) the dimensions of the sample are small and (c) the sample is not homogeneous. As little as 0.1 microgram of sample in the field of the microscope can yield useful spectra.

Samples which have been studied using such equipment include natural and synthetic fibers, single crystals, biological tissue sections and bacterial cultures. Instruments of this type allow the study of liquid extracts and solutions in cells of extremely small volume. This means that it is now possible to use samples of compounds separated by *chromatography*. The technique for compressing finely ground samples mixed with KBr powder into optically clear pellets of optimum dimensions is now a very useful sampling procedure for infrared microspectrophotometry. Polarization effects permit investigation of molecular orientation in dichroic samples.

In the Perkin-Elmer infrared microscopic attachment (4) to their infrared spectrometer, energy from the exit slit of the monochromator is incident on a field mirror which directs it upward and forms a reduced image of the pupil of the monochromator (Littrow mirror) near the convex mirror of the condenser, so that radiation from the entire useful slit is directed to the condenser, which

forms a reduced image of the exit slit at the sample space. The objective collects the energy which has passed through the sample and forms a magnified image of the sample at an adjustable diaphragm. The energy then passes to a second field mirror which forms an image of the Littrow mirror near the center of curvature of the thermocouple condenser, which forms a reduced image of the slit on the thermocouple detector.

The microscope can be placed in the spectrometer either between the source and the entrance slit of the monochromator, or between the exit slit of the monochromator and the detector; the latter avoids difficulties in samples sensitive to heat or photochemical effects. Special precautions may be taken to eliminate absorption from atmospheric water vapor which may seriously interfere with spectra for very small specimens (5).

A Cassegrain-type condenser permits the substitution of photoconductive cells, photomultiplier tubes or other types of detectors in place of the thermocouple.

In practice the required thickness of the sample is about the same as for macroscopic work, frequently about 25 microns. The minimum sample area is that required to provide sufficient energy for satisfactory detection—that is, inversely proportional to source brightness, the transmission efficiency, the detector sensitivity and the square of the effective numerical aperture of the microscope objective. Thus the area may be decreased by the use of such intense sources as carbon arcs, zirconium arcs or tungsten glowers. Other controllable instrumental factors of course provide limits of size. If the sample does not cover the entire field of the microscope, some radiation will reach the detector without being subjected to absorption by the sample. This "dilution" of the spectra is also increased by aberrations and diffraction introduced by the ob-

411

jective. It is important to avoid impurity radiation in quantitative work on long, narrow samples such as fibers. A number of excellent infrared spectra made with the microscope attachment have been published, including tissue sections, single fibers (17–20 μ), liquids in short lengths of AgCl capillary tubing (3), and single crystals (6, 8, 9).

The determination of optical constants in the infrared especially for metals is a special contribution of Beattie and Conn (1, 2). Military surplus infrared image electron converter tubes continue to find application for the infrared examination of opaque dyes and pigments, and silicon ingots. In the latest work according to news reports the infrared microscope is adaptable to the examination of substances which can be differentiated on the basis of their specific infrared emissivity and reflectivity, as well as absorption (7).

REFERENCES

1. BEATTIE, J. R., *Phil. Mag.*, **46**, 235 (1955).
2. BEATTIE, J. R. AND CONN, F. K. T., *Phil. Mag.*, **46**, 222 (1955).
3. BLOUT, E. R., PARRISH, M., BIRD, G. R., AND ABBATE, M. J., *J. Opt. Soc. Am.*, **42**, 966 (1952).
4. COATES, V. J., OFFNER, A., AND SIEGLER, E. H., *J. Opt. Soc. Am.*, **43**, 984 (1953).
5. FRASER, F. D. B., *J. Opt. Soc. Am.*, **43**, 929 (1953).
6. LOWENTHAL, S., *Rev. Opt.*, **34**, 29 (1955).
7. MARESH, C., COVEN, G., AND COX, R., *Anal. Chem.*, **30**, 829 (1958).
8. NOMARSKI, G., *Rev. Opt.*, **34**, 29 (1955).
9. NORRIS, K. P., *J. Sci. Inst.*, **31**, 284 (1954).

G. L. CLARK

INTERFERENCE MICROSCOPY

FIBERS (TEXTILE). *See* **GENERAL MICROSCOPY, p. 343.**

INDUSTRIAL RESEARCH, APPLICATION TO. *See* **GENERAL MICROSCOPY, p. 363.**

INSTRUMENT CLASSIFICATION AND APPLICATIONS

Interference microscopy is a technique for the microscopic observation of specimens, whereby two superimposed fields of view are presented to the observer. One field contains an image of the specimen and is called the "image field"; the other (the "reference field") differs from the image field in some way, but the two fields are mutually coherent at every point. Contrast is produced by the effect on the interference phenomena of the path-differences caused by the optical thickness (for transparent objects) or surface contour (for reflecting objects) of the specimen.

It will thus be seen that interference microscopy makes use of the same properties of the specimen as does phase contrast microscopy. The advantages of the interference method are that certain artefacts (the "phase-contrast halo") are avoided, that measurements of path difference can be made precisely, and that the nature of the contrast can usually be altered by varying the overall path difference between the two interfering fields to obtain the best conditions for the detail being studied. A further advantage is that in some types of interference microscopes the aperture of illumination is not restricted.

Classification of Instruments

It is convenient to classify interference microscopes by the way in which the image and reference fields differ from each other. Three classes can be recognised, as follows:

I. The reference field is formed by light which has had no contact with the object.

II. The reference field contains an image

of the object which is out of focus or which has suffered very heavy aberrations.

III. The reference field contains an image of the object which is displaced laterally.

Each of the above three classes can also be divided into instruments for transparent or for opaque objects. As all these types of instruments possess both advantages and disadvantages, the selection of a type suitable for a given kind of work is a matter requiring some care.

In instruments of Class I the information given by the interference pattern is quite explicit, i.e., the relationship between intensity and optical thickness of the object does not depend on the properties of the object at points other than the one being considered. This may be contrasted with the state of affairs in phase-contrast microscopy where the intensity is related to the mean optical thickness in the neighborhood of the object point.

This is not necessarily the case in instruments of Class II, where an effect similar to that seen in phase-contrast microscopy may arise due to the influence of the image in the reference field. The effect of this image may be removed, however, by suitable design, as described later.

In instruments of Class III the information may be explicit if the object is so small that the images in the two fields do not overlap; otherwise the intensity is a function of the difference of optical thicknesses at two points at a distance apart equal to the separation of the two images. If this distance is made very small the two images will appear almost as one and the intensity will then very nearly be a function of the gradient of optical thickness in the direction of the displacement of the two images.

The Formation of Contrast

In order that the image and reference fields should be coherent it is necessary to fulfil two requirements. Firstly, both fields must be illuminated by light from the same cross-section of the light beam from the source and which is distributed in exactly the same way in the two fields. Secondly, the two fields must be aligned so that points in each field which correspond from the point of view of the source are superimposed with an accuracy which, it can be shown (1), is equal to the resolving limit of a perfect objective of aperture equal to that of the illuminating condenser. For good fringe contrast it is also necessary that the intensities of the two fields be equal.

Under these conditions, if there is a path difference p between the two fields, which are taken each to be of unit intensity, the intensity given by the combined fields is given by

$$I = 2(1 + \cos 2\pi p/\lambda) \qquad (1)$$

where λ is the wavelength used. If a detail in the topography of the specimen introduces an additional small path difference dp, the corresponding change, dI, in intensity is

$$(4\pi/\lambda)dp \sin 2\pi p/\lambda.$$

The contrast C is then given by

$$C = \frac{dI}{I} = -\frac{2\pi dp}{\lambda} \tan \frac{\pi p}{\lambda} \qquad (2)$$

It is evident from (2) that the contrast at any point can be brought to the best value by suitable adjustment of p, the "background" path difference. The contrast will be greatest when p/λ is an odd multiple of λ, but will not in practice become infinite because of parasitic light in the instrument. In general, however, such values of p will not give the best conditions, for then the intensity will depend on the square of dp, giving reduced weight to details with small values of dp and concealing the sign of the path-difference variation. Furthermore, as these values of p correspond to dark-field conditions, the intensity of the image is greatly reduced. It is generally better to depart somewhat from these conditions to obtain a more nearly linear variation of intensity with path difference and retain a reasonable image brightness. It can be seen from (2) that either positive or negative values of C can be obtained.

If white light is used color contrast is also present, which in many cases is useful in resolving the ambiguity which occurs if the optical thickness of a specimen exceeds one wavelength. It also can give rise to images of great beauty.

Interference Microscopes for Transparent Objects

Instruments of Class I. Some types of instrument designed for opaque objects can be used for transparent objects and fall into this class. One of these is the Linnik (2) microscope which consists of a Michelson interferometer with a microscope objective built into each arm (Figure 1). The transparent object is placed on a plane mirror and is imaged by one objective; the other images a plane mirror only. This arrangement has some advantages; the optical arrangement of the Michelson interferometer allows good control of the background conditions, giving the possibility of introducing fringes of controllable width into the field and of varying the background path difference, and the intensity in the two beams can be controlled for good contrast of the fringes.

Against this, the two beams pass through physically separate optics, which must be selected for equality of aberrations and chromatic dispersion of path difference. Also, as the beams are widely separated, the instrument is very sensitive to vibration. In consequence it must be built into a very

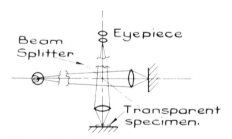

FIG. 1. Linnik interference microscope.

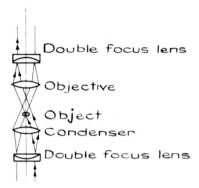

FIG. 2. Smith's interference microscope with double focus lenses.

heavy and rigid stand, which is necessarily costly, and cannot be used for path-difference measurements of great precision. A further difficulty which arises when using this instrument for transparent specimens is caused by the finite distance between the specimen and its image in the mirror.

Other instruments in this class will be described under the section on "Instruments for Opaque Objects."

Instruments of Class II. Instruments of this class have the great advantage that both beams traverse the same optics and are never very widely separated. This confers considerable immunity from the effects of vibration and also eliminates the necessity for matching optics for aberrations and path difference. It is very desirable that splitting and recombination take place in the space between condenser and objective.

One instrument of this class is the polarizing interference microscope of Smith (3) (Figure 2). Double-focus lenses of birefringent material are placed in conjugate planes as shown, forming two axially separated images of the light source; the object is placed in one of these, and the two beams are re-combined after passage through the objective.

Two images of the object are seen, one of which is out of focus and causes an effect similar to the "phase-contrast halo," making a measurement of optical thickness at a point depend on the mean path difference over a surrounding area equal to the out-of-focus disc corresponding to the axial distance between the two images. This effect would not be serious if this distance could be made large, but in practice it is limited by considerations of aberrations of the back focal plane of the objective, so path differences measured by this instrument should be treated with some reserve.

To avoid this effect another type of polarizing microscope due to Dyson (4) (Figure 3) employs two thick plates of Iceland spar cut parallel with the axis, one above and one below the object, the working distance of the objective being increased by a suitable optical system. The out-of-focus disc is now strongly astigmatic. As both splitting and recombination take place in the object space the limitations on the size of the disc are removed and it can be made larger than the field of view, which considerably reduces its effect on the uncertainty of measurement.

As both these instruments make use of beams which are polarized in mutually perpendicular directions, polarimetric means may be used to measure the path difference with considerable accuracy.

The effect of the out-of-focus disc may be removed entirely by another instrument due to Dyson (1) (Figure 4). Two glass plates, one or two millimeters thick and partially silvered on both surfaces, replace the Iceland spar plates shown in Figure 3. The ray paths are similar to those in a Jamin interferometer and the out-of-focus disc can be made

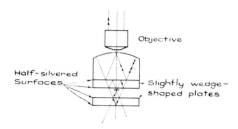

Fig. 4. Dyson's interference microscope with half-silvered glass plates.

many times the diameter of the field. As the reflecting system introduces a small central stop, a dark center, which can be made larger than the field, occupies the center of the out-of-focus disc, which therefore has no influence on the measurement, which is quite explicit.

The background path difference and the number of fringes in the field are both varied by making the two plates slightly wedge-shaped. The number of fringes is varied from zero (uniform field) to a maximum by rotation of one plate about the microscope axis, and the path difference by translation of the other plate by means of a micrometer screw. By means of a photometer eyepiece measurements of path difference may be made with an accuracy of $\lambda/300$. The highest powers of objectives can be used and the aperture of illumination is unrestricted.

As the separation of the images is so large, the leveling adjustment of the plates is quite critical, and the instrument is therefore more difficult to adjust than the others in this class. This is the price paid for unambiguous measurement and freedom from optical artifacts.

Instruments of Class III. Instruments of this class are usually known as "shearing" microscopes. An early instrument due to Lebedev (5) (Figure 5) made use of two Iceland spar plates cut at 45° to the optic axis, with an intervening half-wave plate to interchange the planes of polarization. Two images are thus seen, sheared laterally with respect to each other, one being somewhat

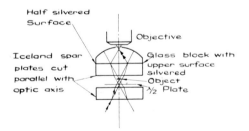

Fig. 3. Dyson's interference microscope with crystal plates.

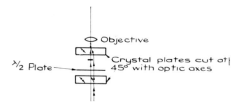

FIG. 5. Lebedev's microscope.

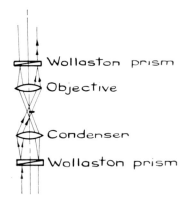

FIG. 6. Smith's shearing interference microscope.

astigmatic. A similar principle has been used by Smith (6) for a high-power instrument, replacing the lower plate by a plate of quartz of increased thickness, the half-wave plate being no longer required. This is of importance in high-power instruments where very large convergence angles are employed. The amount of shear is restricted by the thickness of the plate which can be employed, so both images appear in the field. In consequence only a limited area of the edge of a large specimen can be examined without overlap and loss of explicitness. On the other hand, the limited shear makes for increased ease of adjustment.

A critique of this and the Dyson instrument in Figure 5 has been published by Davies (7).

Another type of shearing microscope has been described by Smith (3), (Figure 6), using two Wollaston prisms in conjugate planes as shown. This avoids the astigmatism of one of the images, but this time the shear is limited by aberrations of the con-

jugate planes. It is interesting to notice that the lower Wollaston may be dispensed with if the condenser aperture is reduced to a narrow slit parallel with the apex edges of the prism, but this will of course give rise to some deterioration of the image quality.

The shear is produced in an instrument due to Françon (8) by means of a Savart plate just below the eyepiece, using slit illumination.

Shearing microscopes of low power have considerable advantages of simplicity and stability, making them perhaps the best instruments for the important field of the measurement of thin films, as described later.

Interference Microscopes for Opaque Objects

The distinctions between the three classes of instruments for opaque objects are if anything of greater significance than in the case for transparent objects, for path differences produced by reflection are usually greater than those produced by transmission.

Instruments of Class I. The Linnik instrument described above is typical of this class, and the discussion of this instrument as applied to transparent objects applies here also.

It is possible to construct microscopes of this class in which both beams traverse the same objective. An instrument due to Dyson (9) (Figure 7) uses a small reference flat separated axially from the specimen, with a splitting plane midway between them. The

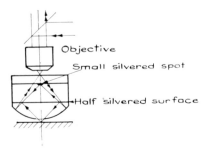

FIG. 7. Dyson's interference microscope for opaque objects.

image is transferred with a small magnification to the image plane of a conventional objective by means of a mirror system. This instrument can be used with the highest powers, but application to low powers is not easy without restricting the field of view.

An instrument due to Krug and Lau (10) (Figure 8) uses an oblique splitting surface below the objective with a reference surface out to one side. This is suitable for low powers and, in fact, cannot be used with high powers because of the large space required by the oblique splitting surface.

Several low-power instruments have been described which form fringes between the specimen surface and a partially reflecting plate pressed into contact with it. By suitable selection of the reflectivity multiple-beam fringes can be obtained, giving an enhancement of sensitivity, but in such instruments control of the fringe position is difficult.

The instruments so far described in this class are optically satisfactory, but the fact that the mechanical connection between specimen and reference surface is via the microscope limb and slides makes the direct measurement of path difference somewhat difficult because of thermal drift and vibration. (The magnetic adjustment incorporated in the instrument shown in Figure 7 helps a little in this respect.) For this reason, fringe measurements are better made from a photograph.

In many cases met with in engineering the sensitivity of the interference method is too high; thus, an ordinarily machined surface gives a confused mass of fringes which is difficult to interpret. A method was devised by Zehender (11) to deal with this situation A replica of the surface is made in a transparent plastic, which is then examined by transmission in a low-power interference microscope. A suitable instrument is that described by Dyson (12), in which a modified Mach-Zehnder interferometer is built into a microscope stage and very low powers are

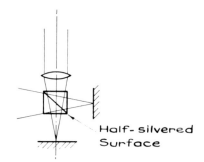

Half-silvered Surface

Fig. 8. Interference microscope of Krug and Lau for opaque objects.

used. By immersing the replica in a liquid of suitable refractive index, the sensitivity can be lowered as far as may be desired. Thus, using polymethyl methacrylate as the replica material and water as the liquid, each fringe corresponds to a height difference of 0.00013″ which is a suitable value for engineering purposes.

Instruments of Class II. An instrument of this class, using an out-of-focus image of the specimen as the reference field, would be very promising, as it would be free from the mechanical troubles mentioned above. However, reflecting objects usually introduce large phase differences over their whole surface and this would have an effect similar to that of placing a piece of ground glass in the reference beam at a point distant from the focal plane, thereby very seriously reducing the fringe contrast.

It is for this reason that instruments of Class II are conspicuous by their absence.

Instruments of Class III. Because of the fact that in this class of instrument the path difference measured is that between two points of the specimen separated by the distance of shear, the applications of such instruments are limited to the examination of small areas of imperfection on otherwise regular surfaces. An important class of such observations is that of the determination of the thickness of thin films by measurement of the height of the step formed at the edge of such a film laid on a reflecting surface.

417

For this application low powers are desirable for two reasons. First, it is sometimes not easy to make the film of constant thickness right up to its edge, so the distance of shear is required to be larger than the width of the imperfection; the required large shears are more easily obtained in low-power instruments. Secondly, parasitic effects, such as aberrations of the rear focal planes of objectives, are usually less pronounced in low-powered optics so these give interference effects of higher contrast.

Polarizing instruments such as the shearing microscopes of Smith and Françon described above can be modified in an obvious manner for opaque specimens and are particularly suitable for this type of measurement. By suppressing the image altogether and virtually converting the microscope into a polarimeter, Dyson (13) has shown that it is possible to make settings with an error not greater than one Angstrom unit of thickness.

It is evident from this review that the situation is less satisfactory for opaque objects than for transparent objects. No instrument is available for opaque objects which allows the use of a full range of powers on any type of object and also makes possible the precise measurement of path difference.

Applications of Interference Microscopy

Biological Applications. The interference method is useful for qualitative observations in biology because of the freedom from optical artefacts which it gives. Thus, a slow variation of optical thickness across a cell would probably pass unnoticed when observed by phase contrast methods, but is immediately evident by interference contrast.

A great impetus to the use of interference microscopy was given, however, by Davies and Wilkins (14) and Barer (15), who discovered independently the possibility of measuring the dry weight of a biological object, such as a cell, by measurement of its area and optical thickness.

Assume that the cell is a parallel-sided disc of thickness t and area A, its refractive index being μ_c, immersed in water of refractive index μ_W. Its optical thickness is then

$$p = (\mu_c - \mu_W)t \qquad (3)$$

The quantity $\mu_c - \mu_W$ is equal to 100 αc, where c is the concentration of dry substance in cell and α is the quantity known as specific refraction. The total weight M of dry material in the cell is equal to cAt, and from equation (3) can be given as

$$M = Ap/100\alpha \qquad (4)$$

The value of α is remarkably constant for the types of substance which are found in cells, and so from equation (4) a good approximation to the dry weight can be obtained in spite of the fact that the cell contents constitute a heterogeneous mixture.

As the cell has not in fact the elementary shape suggested above it is necessary to replace Ap in equation (4) by an integral of path difference over the cell surface. This integral can be evaluated by a number of methods. The path difference can be measured at a number of equally spaced points, using a graticule in the eyepiece, or a photograph can be taken. By setting the background path difference approximately midway between the values for maximum and minimum brightness, the intensity can be made very nearly a linear function of path difference for values of the latter small against a wavelength; hence the path difference can be found by densitometry on the negative, with appropriate corrections for the emulsion characteristics.

Methods are also available, due to Davies and Deeley (16) and Mitchison et al. (17), whereby the dry mass can be evaluated immediately by photo-electric means at the microscope without the necessity of taking photographs.

An excellent and exhaustive account of this subject with an extensive bibliography has been published by Davies (8). It is also treated extensively by Hale (18). Both these accounts discuss the errors which may be encountered in this work.

In biological applications it is usually necessary to make use of the highest possible powers, so only instruments which allow this can be used. In particular, instruments in which slit illumination is used are of little value.

The nature of the object may also have a bearing on the type of microscope to be used. If the object is in the form of small isolated patches, such as a widely scattered distribution of cells or groups of cells, each small as compared with the diameter of the field, a shearing type of instrument can be used, such as that described by Smith (6). If, on the other hand, the object is of the same size as the field or somewhat larger, the Dyson (1) microscope may be more useful. If the object is not too thick, interference contrast can still be obtained even if the object occupies the whole cross-section of the reference beam. Under these conditions it is still possible to make meaningful measurements of the path difference. The reason for this is that the object in the reference beam is so far out of focus that the effective background path difference does not vary appreciably over the limited area of the cell being measured.

Applications to Opaque Specimens

The literature on the use of interference microscopy to opaque specimens is much less extensive than that covering biological applications. However, it is being used to an increasing extent for the measurement of surface finish in engineering (12) and to the control of the groove profile of diffraction gratings.

For opaque specimens the interference method has considerable advantages over the phase contrast technique. It is funda-mental in phase contrast that the surface of the specimen acts as part of the optical train which images the illuminating annulus on to the phase ring, and it obviously will be quite unsuited for this purpose if the surface introduces large path differences, as for example in the case of a machined surface. Even if the surface is relatively smooth, a spherical or cylindrical object will introduce obvious difficulties.

In addition, in view of the large phase differences commonly observed in reflecting specimens, the image seen by phase contrast may bear very little resemblance in detail to the actual surface topography. An example of this (a diffraction grating) is shown in Reference 9.

Interference microscopes of Class I are immune to both these difficulties.

An investigation has been made by Tolmon and Wood (19) of an error which may arise in any high-power interference microscope, but which is most often met with in connection with opaque specimens. This concerns the relationship between the fringe spacing and the angle of slope of the surface; they show that errors of the order of 10% may arise if the angle of obliquity of the reflected beam is not taken into account.

A discussion of the micro-interferometry of opaque objects with a description of several instruments is given by Perry (20).

REFERENCES

1. Dyson, J., *Proc. Roy. Soc.*, (*London*), **A204,** 170–187, 1950.
2. Linnik, W., see Kinder, W., *Zeiss Nachr.*, August, 1937.
3. Smith, F. H., British Patent No. 639,014, June 21, 1950.
4. Dyson, J., *Nature*, **171,** 743 (1953).
5. Lebedev, A. A., *Rev. Opt.*, **9,** 385 (1930).
6. Smith, F. H., *Research*, **8,** 385–395 (1955).
7. Davies, H. G., in "General Cytochemical Methods," Ed. J. F. Danielle, New York, pp. 55–161, Academic Press, 1958.
8. Françon, M., "Le Microscope à Contraste de Phase et le Microscope Interférentiel." Paris: Editions du Centre National de la Recherche Scientifique, p. 113, 1954.

9. DYSON, J., *Proc. Roy. Soc. (London)*, **A216,** 493–501 (1952).

10. KRUG, W. AND LAU, E., *Ann. Phys.*, **6** (8), 329 (1951).

11. ZEHENDER, E., see KOHAUT, A., *Werkst. u. Betr.*, **86** (12), 725–732 (1953).

12. DYSON, J., *Engineering*, **179,** 274–276 (1955).

13. DYSON, J., *Physica*, **24,** 532–537 (1958).

14. DAVIES, H. G. AND WILKINS, M. H. F., *Nature*, **169,** 541 (1952).

15. BARER, R., *Nature*, **169,** 366 (1952).

16. DAVIES, H. G., AND DEELEY, E. M., *Exp. Cell Res.*, **11,** 169 (1956).

17. MITCHISON, J. M., PASSANO, L. M., AND SMITH, F. H., *Quart. J. Micr. Sci.*, **97,** 287 (1956).

18. HALE, A. J., "The Interference Microscope in Biological Research," E. and S. Livingstone Ltd., Edinburgh and London, 1958.

19. TOLMON, F. R. AND WOOD, J. G., *J. Sci. Instr.*, **33,** 236–238 (1956).

20. PERRY, J. W., *Research*, **8,** 255–261 (1955).

J. DYSON

PLASTICS. *See* **GENERAL MICROSCOPY, p. 390.**

PULP AND PAPER. *See* **GENERAL MICROSCOPY, p. 394.**

THEORY AND TECHNIQUES

Although interference of light waves has long been used for high precision measurements in physics and technology, only recently has it been applied to any large degree in microscopy. The invention and widespread success of the phase microscope emphasized the point that much could be gained by application of the principles of physical optics. One result has been the development of a number of interference microscopes which allow three dimensional study of objects, both qualitatively and quantitatively.

Opaque objects can be examined by interference microscopes employing reflected light. Transparent objects, normally invisible in an ordinary microscope, can be studied by transmitted light. As in the phase microscope, this permits living material to be examined without staining or other special preparation.

Both the phase and interference microscopes function by causing light waves to interfere. In each the waves are first split apart so that they follow different physical paths; they are then treated differently; and finally they are brought together to interfere. With the phase system irregularities in the object itself cause some of the light to deviate from its original direction. These deviated rays are then treated differently by the phase plate than are the undeviated rays. Thus the resulting image is characteristic of irregularities and discontinuities in the specimen.

In the interference microscope the light ray separation is accomplished by means of a beam-splitter. The object modifies one beam with respect to the other by retarding or advancing it. The image which results when the beams are recombined is therefore characteristic of the light-retarding properties of the object. An area of uniform optical path appears with a uniform brightness, or if white light is used the color is constant.

The really distinctive feature of the interference microscope is that it allows measurements of the optical path to be made. From these measurements information on the thickness of objects, the index of refraction of solids and liquids, the concentration of protein solutions, and the mass of cells can be deduced.

Interference of Light

The constructive and destructive interference of waves, illustrated in Fig. 1, follows certain fundamental laws. First of all, the two beams must be coherent, which in practice means that they must have come from the same source. Second, they must have the same wavelength. Third, if the beams are plane polarized, they will not interfere when the planes of polarization are mutually perpendicular, but only when they are brought to the same plane.

The concept of a wavefront is very useful. For the common plane wave, the wavefront

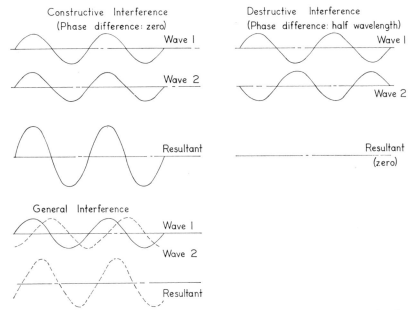

FIG. 1. Examples of interference of two waves of equal amplitude. In constructive interference, where the waves are in phase, the amplitudes add at each point. The resultant amplitude is twice the original, as shown on the third line. In destructive interference, the phase difference is one-half wavelength, and the algebraic sum of the two waves is zero at each point. In the general case, where the phase difference is neither zero nor a half-wavelength the resultant can also be obtained by adding algebraically the amplitudes of the two waves at each point.

is a plane perpendicular to the direction of propagation, over which the phase is everywhere the same. For a wave diverging from a point source or converging toward a point image the surface of constant phase is spherical.

The optical path between two points is the product of the physical distance and the index of refraction of the medium. If there are several different media along the light path the total optical path is the sum of the optical paths through each medium, measured along the path followed by the ray. In interferometry, where two beams are separated and later recombined, the optical path difference, or OPD, is just the difference in total optical paths encountered by the two beams while they were separated.

Several types of interference microscopes use polarized light but in a manner somewhat different than in the polarizing microscope. In the latter, one beam of plane polarized

light is incident on the specimen. On entering a birefringent specimen, plane polarized light is broken into two components, which are in phase with each other as they enter the specimen (Figs. 2a and 2b). If the optic axis of the specimen lies in the plane perpendicular to the original direction of the light one of the beams consists of vibration parallel to, the other perpendicular to, the optic axis of the specimen. These two beams travel through the birefringent specimen at different velocities, so that they emerge out of phase (2a). In general their resultant is no longer plane polarized light, but it is elliptically polarized (1). This light cannot be extinguished by an analyzer. Therefore in the polarizing microscope, such a specimen appears bright in the field.

In interference microscopes which utilize polarized light, relatively thick plates of birefringent material are used to separate physically the two beams, as shown in Fig.

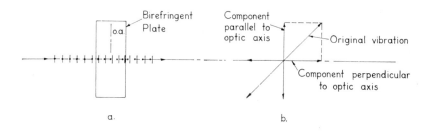

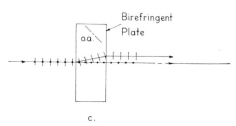

FIG. 2. Action of birefringent plates on polarized light. (a) Optic axis parallel to face of plate. The incident polarized light has a component vibrating parallel to the plane of the paper, indicated by the dashes, and a perpendicular component indicated by the dots. Before entering the birefringent plate they are in phase. On entering the plate the parallel component moves at a higher velocity, so that on emerging the parallel component is ahead of the perpendicular component. (b) The resolution of the incident plane polarized vibration into two components which occurs at the entrance face of the plate, as seen by an observer viewing the oncoming light. (c) Optic axis inclined with respect to the surface. In this case not only is there a phase difference introduced between the two components, but one component is refracted differently than the other. Crystals of calcite (Iceland spar) found in nature exhibit this effect, which results in a double image of everything viewed through the crystals.

2c. The two beams emerging from such a plate are not capable of interfering even if they are brought into coincidence, because their planes of polarization are mutually perpendicular. They can be brought to the same plane of polarization by means of an analyzer with its transmission axis at 45° to the plane of vibration of each beam. It can also be done by means of various compensators which permit the precise determination of the phase difference between the two components.

Another birefringent device frequently used is a half-wave plate. As shown in Fig. 3 it retards one component of polarized light by one-half wavelength relative to the other component. The net effect is to rotate the plane of polarization from azimuth $-\alpha$ to $+\alpha$.

The action of a quarter-wave plate is shown in Fig. 3b. If the incident plane-polarized light is oriented at 45° to the optic axis, the two components formed at the first surface are equal in magnitude. When they emerge, 90° out of phase, the resultant vibration is circularly polarized.

Principles of Commercially Available Interference Microscopes

Multiple-beam. The multiple-beam system can be set up with as little equipment as a standard microscope, a slide and cover glass with partially reflecting coatings, and a pinhole at the first focal plane of the condenser (2, 3, 4). A typical system (5) is a 0.5 mm diameter pinhole at the focal point of a 25 mm objective. Monochromatic light, such as the green radiation of a mercury arc isolated by a suitable filter, is used to illuminate the pinhole. Light is partially transmitted and partially reflected at each metallized surface, as shown in Fig. 4a.

In areas where the optical path difference between successive transmitted rays is an integral number of wavelengths, constructive interference occurs, and a bright fringe is seen in the field. A single fringe therefore traces out a contour line of equal optical path, and the deviation of a fringe as it passes through a specimen can be used to measure the optical path of the specimen.

The higher the reflectance of the metallized surfaces, the sharper is each fringe (6). For biological work with living specimens, an important requirement is that non-poisonous metals such as inconel or titanium be used. If the index difference between specimen and mounting medium is considerable, additional multiple reflections may occur

which add complexity to the fringe pattern (7, 8).

For the examination of surfaces and steps on flat surfaces the system can be used in reflection, through the use of a vertical illuminator. If the surface to be tested does not have sufficient reflectance it can be overcoated with silver, which contours the surface (9). For highest precision, such as in measuring glass or metal polishing defects or the thickness of evaporated films, fringes of equal chromatic order are often used (10, 11). As shown in Fig. 4b, a white light source is used and the image of the specimen is projected onto the slit of a spectrograph. The continuous spectrum is crossed by dark fringes, and the displacement of a particular fringe as it crosses the specimen is a direct measure of its physical height. Precisions of

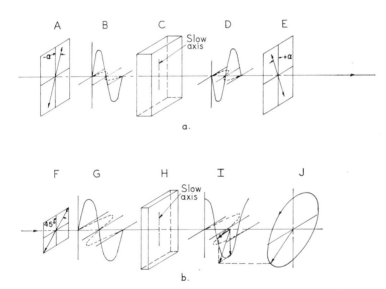

FIG. 3. Effects of wave-plates on plane-polarized light. (a) Half-wave plate, C, rotates the plane of polarization from azimuth $-\alpha$ (at A) to azimuth $+\alpha$ (at E). At B are shown the components of the incident light which are parallel (solid wave) and perpendicular (dashed wave) to the slow axis of the crystal. At D the parallel component has been retarded one half wavelength relative to the perpendicular component. The sum of these two vibrations gives a vibration which lies along the line shown at E. (b) A quarter-wave plate, H, converts linearly polarized light at F to circularly polarized light, shown at J. The two components of incident light, shown at G, are equal and in phase. After passing through the waveplate the components are out of phase by one quarter wavelength (I). As these two waves cross a reference plane, their instantaneous sum can be found by vector addition as shown by the arrows at I. As the wave progresses across the reference plane the tip of the vector traces out a circle, as shown at J.

423

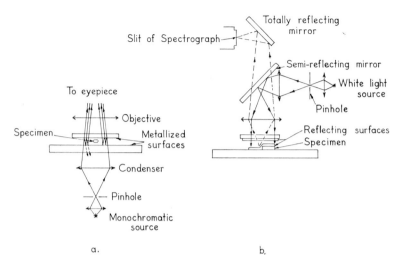

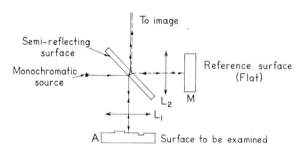

FIG. 4. Multiple-beam interference schemes. (a) The system used for transparent specimens. Although the condenser collimates the light from the pinhole, the rays are shown here at an angle so that the interreflections can be displayed. (b) One system used for opaque specimens. Rays incident on the interferometer are shown by solid lines and those reflected toward the spectrograph are shown by dashed lines. Both the angle of the reflected rays and the height of the specimen are greatly exaggerated.

FIG. 5. The essential components of the Linnik interference microscope. For best contrast the source should be conjugate to the specimen surface, and the objectives L_1 and L_2 should be interferometrically matched.

a few Angstroms can be obtained by this method.

Two-beam Interference Microscopes for Examination of Surfaces. The system shown in Fig. 5 was described in 1933 by Linnik (12). It is essentially a Michelson interferometer with a microscope objective in each arm. A normal image of the surface, A, under test is formed by objective, L_1. The coherent reference beam returning from the flat reference mirror, M, combines with the object beam to produce interference contrast in the image. Irregularities in the

surface under test are thereby revealed and can be measured.

More recently a system due originally to Mirau (13) has been modified and developed (14, 15). As shown in Fig. 6 it employs only one objective and a relatively small interferometer path, which has certain advantages in stability. The vertical illumination mirror R directs the monochromatic light down through the objective. At the top surface of plate T the beam is divided by a semi-reflecting coating. The transmitted component is reflected from the surface A which is under test. The light reflected from T strikes a fully silvered spot, S, which is located at the same optical distance from T as is the surface A. The two components are

recombined at Y and travel through the objective together.

These two-beam systems are somewhat easier to use than the multiple-beam methods. However, the two-beam precision is lower, being the order of $1/10$ fringe, or 0.025 micron.

Two-beam Interference Microscopes for Examination of Transparent Objects. *The Dyson Interferometer Microscope.* The Dyson interferometer microscope (16), manufactured by Cooke, Troughton, and Simms, Ltd., utilizes semireflecting coatings for beam-splitters. As shown in Fig. 7 the upper surface of plate A transmits part of the incident beam, which then proceeds through the object. The reflected portion of the incident beam is again reflected by the lower surface of plate A. This reference beam then passes through an area of the slide away from the specimen.

Plate B serves to reunite the object and reference beams. The fully silvered spot on the upper surface prevents rays having small values of γ from reaching the objective. The reason is that for these rays the reference beam is so close to the object beam that both may pass through the specimen.

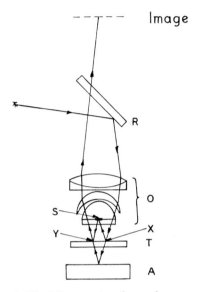

FIG. 6. The Mirau system for surface examination. *R:* Partially reflecting mirror, *O:* objective, *T:* glass plate with semi-reflecting surface, *S:* fully silvered spot, *A:* surface under test, *X* and *Y* are, respectively, the points at which the beam divides and recombines.

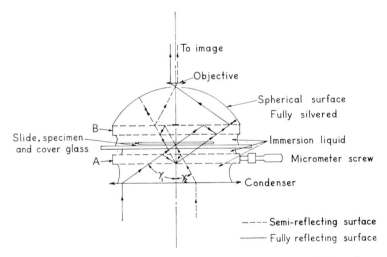

FIG. 7. The Dyson interferometer microscope. Plates A and B are very slight wedges, and the wedge directions can be aligned either in the same or opposite directions to give a fringe field or uniform field, respectively. Plate A is movable transversely for measurements.

The spherical mirror together with the upper surface of plate B is essentially a unit-power relay system which increases the working distance of the microscope objective. An image of the object is formed by this relay system below the objective and is magnified in the usual fashion by the objective and eyepiece.

As can be seen by comparing the solid and dashed paths, the distance between the reference and object beam depends on the angle, γ, of the incident ray. Thus when a full cone of light is incident from the condenser, the reference beams are passing through various portions of the slide surrounding the specimen.

In order to eliminate poor contrast and errors due to nonuniformities in the slide and coverglass, immersion fluid is used in the three places shown in Fig. 7.

For quantitative measurements, several methods are available. If plates A and B have their wedges aligned in opposite directions the field is uniform, except for the specimen. As plate A is moved laterally by means of the micrometer screw the field goes through maxima and minima of luminance. The micrometer dial is turned to obtain minimum luminance in the specimen and then in the background immediately adjacent to the specimen. The difference in micrometer readings is proportional to the optical path difference between the specimen and the surround. If the plates A and B have their wedges aligned other than exactly opposite, the field is crossed by fringes. Their spacing depends on the relatively angle between the wedge directions, and they move as plate A is adjusted laterally. The micrometer dial is turned until a dark fringe is located first in the specimen and then in the background immediately adjacent to the specimen.

Another method of measuring is to photograph the field with uniformly spaced fringes. Photographic photometry can then be used (17).

A photometer eyepiece is also available.

With it visual settings are made by matching the luminance in the specimen or surround with that of a reference spot superimposed in the field.

The above methods measure only the fraction of a wavelength of optical path. If the OPD is greater than one wavelength, or if it is not certain whether the path difference is positive or negative, the use of white light and the fringe field can usually settle the question.

The advantages and disadvantages of this microscope have been discussed by Hale (18).

The AO-Baker Interference Microscope. The AO-Baker interference microscope (19, 20) utilizes a birefringent plate located above the condenser as a beam-splitter. Plane polarized light incident on the birefringent plate is divided into two mutually perpendicular polarized beams, as described earlier. The extraordinary beam, consisting of vibrations in the plane of the optic axis, is the object beam.

In the shearing system, shown in Fig. 8a, the optic axis is in the plane of the paper but inclined at an angle of about 45° to the surfaces of the plate. This causes the object beam to be refracted to the left, or sheared, as shown. The reference beam, the ordinary beam, passes through the plate as ordinary light passes through a glass plate.

On passing through the half-wave plate both beams have their planes of polarization rotated by 90°. This allows the beams to be reunited by a second birefringent plate placed before the objective. It is identical in thickness and orientation with the first plate. As shown in Fig. 8a one beam has passed through the object while the other has passed through an adjacent area of the slide. After being reunited by the second birefringent plate these beams travel together through the objective and to the image. In general there is a phase difference between the beams. It represents the optical path encountered by the object beams minus that

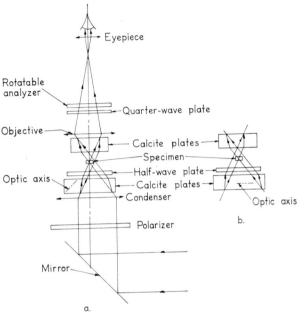

FIG. 8. The AO-Baker interference microscope. (a) The shearing system. The transmission axis o the polarizer is set at 45° to the axis of the first calcite plate. The calcite plates are essentially cleavage sections, similar to those found in nature. Each ray is split into two components as shown in Figure 2c. The half-wave plate axis is parallel to the polarizer axis, as is the quarter-wave plate axis. Measurements are made by rotating the analyzer. (b) The double-focus system. The only difference from the shearing system is that here the axes of the calcite plates are parallel to the faces of the plates.

encountered by the reference beam in the region in which they were separated.

In the double-focus system shown in Fig. 8b, the optic axis of the birefringent plate A is parallel to the surfaces. For a set of object rays passing through the specimen, the corresponding reference rays pass through an area above the specimen. As before, the phase difference between the two beams after they are reunited represents the difference in optical path encountered by the two beams.

In both systems the method for detecting and measuring this phase difference is shown in the upper part of Fig. 8a. A quarter-wave plate is oriented with its effective optic axis at 45° to the plane of polarization of the object beam. The two beams are thereby converted into circularly polarized light, one rotating clockwise, the other counter-clockwise. The resultant of these two vibrations

is simply plane polarized light. If the two beams are in phase, the plane of polarization is parallel to the axis of the quarter-wave plate, which may be called zero azimuth. Otherwise, the azimuth angle of the plane of polarization is just half the phase difference between the object and reference beams.* If the object beam is behind the reference beam, as in the case of a phase retarding specimen, the plane of polarization is rotated counter-clockwise from the zero azimuth. The opposite is true in case the surround has a greater optical path than the specimen.

If an analyzer is oriented perpendicular to the zero azimuth the background, where the optical paths are equal, will appear dark or black. Objects having greater or less op-

* Phase difference is often measured in degrees, 360° corresponding to one wavelength of phase difference.

tical path than the surround will appear bright. If the analyzer is turned until it is perpendicular to the plane of polarization in the image of the specimen, the specimen will have a minimum of luminance. The orientation of the analyzer is then read from a scale to determine the optical path in the specimen.

As in the other two-beam systems, if white light is used the specimen appears in color contrast. The colors change as the analyzer is turned. This is often useful in studying and photographing complex specimens.

For measurement of optical path, monochromatic light is necessary. The half- and quarter-wave plates are made for the green radiation emitted by a mercury arc. This wavelength, 546 mμ, was chosen partly because it is very near the peak of spectral sensitivity of the eye and partly because convenient, very bright mercury arcs are available and the green radiation can be isolated easily by means of gelatine, glass, or interference filters.

The human eye has great sensitivity for comparing the luminance of adjacent portions of a field of view. In order to take advantage of this sensitivity half-shade eyepieces have been designed for use with this polarizing type of interference microscope (21, 22). For half-shade eyepieces employing the optimum half-shade angle (23) and used with the $100\times$ shearing system, analyzer settings reproducible to 0.5° standard deviation can be obtained on specimens with areas of uniform path difference.

The object is set so that its image straddles the dividing line. As the analyzer is turned the two halves of the specimen image change in luminance relative to each other. At the match setting, the analyzer orientation, θ_1, is noted. Then the analyzer is turned until a match is obtained in the background adjacent to the specimen, and the reading, θ_2, is noted.

The optical path difference between the specimen and surround is computed according to the equation

$$\phi \equiv \text{OPD} = \frac{\theta_1 - \theta_2}{180}\lambda$$

where λ is the wavelength of the light used. θ_1 and θ_2 are in degrees, ϕ is in units of length e.g., millimicrons. The same equation applies for the analyzer orientations θ_1 and θ_2 determined by the half-shade method or by the extinction method described earlier.

If the object has a path difference greater than one wavelength, the above procedure will yield only the fraction by which ϕ is different from one, two, etc., full wavelengths. To determine the correct order number a convenient method is to use a quartz wedge eyepiece and white light illumination. Colored fringes cross the field, one of which appears blackest. The wedge is moved across the field and the black fringe is seen first in the specimen and then in the adjacent surround. The number of full wavelengths of path difference in the specimen is equal to the number of dark fringes which pass the specimen in this operation. For specimens with considerably different dispersion than the surround, the precautions mentioned by Faust and Marrinan (24) should be observed.

Françon Interferential Eyepiece (25). This system, like the multiple-beam method, permits interference contrast to be obtained with an ordinary microscope. An illuminated slit below the condenser is the effective source.

In the eyepiece, light of one polarization is sheared with respect to light of the opposite polarization. This could be accomplished by a single plate of birefringent material, as shown in Fig. 2c, except that there is then a large path difference between the beams and they cannot interfere, at least with the light sources normally used in microscopy. Equalization of path differences is accomplished by using two plates of equal thickness as shown in Fig. 9a. The combination is known as a Savart plate. The ray which is extraordinary in the first plate becomes the ordinary ray in the second plate, and vice-versa. The two rays can then be caused to interfere by bringing their vibrations into the same plane by an analyzer oriented at 45° to each.

The amount of shear is determined by the thickness of the plates and is selected according to the needs of the user. A small shear shows essentially gradients in optical path in the specimen, as shown in Fig. 9b. It is useful for producing contrast at the edges of objects or at gradients within the specimen. A large shear (9c) produces a double image and can be used for measurement of the optical path in isolated objects.

Numerous other uses for the Savart plate and its modifications, as well as the Wollaston prism, have been described by Françon and Nomarski (26).

The NIFE Interference Microscope. This system, first described by Johansson and

Afzelius (27), employs a modification of the Françon interferential eyepiece which allows measurements of optical path to be made. As shown in Fig. 10, a glass wedge at the image plane can be rotated in its own plane. Through a hole in the wedge the object to be measured is viewed. With white light illumination, the color of the object will depend on the phase difference, ϕ, between the two wavefronts from the specimen (Fig. 9). As the glass wedge is turned the phase difference between the two background wavefronts is changed, becoming a maximum when the direction of the wedge is parallel to the direction of shear. The viewer turns the wedge until the color of the background matches that of the object. An alternate method is to have the image of the specimen fall on the wedge rather than on the hole. Then the wedge is turned until the color in the specimen matches that in the hole. Ingelstam (28) has discussed the errors in this

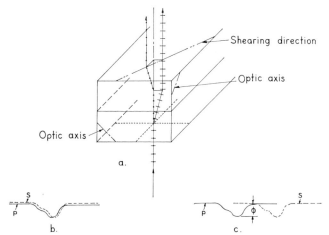

FIG. 9. The Savart plate. (a) Schematic diagram showing the action of a Savart plate. The component of incident light vibrating in the plane of the paper is sheared to the right by the first plate. The perpendicular component is sheared perpendicular to the plane of the paper by the second plate. The resultant shear is in the direction shown. (b) The differential method. Here the two wavefronts shown have been sheared by a small amount, by means of a thin Savart plate. The wavefront polarized parallel to the plane of the paper is designated by p, the wavefront polarized perpendicular by s. (c) The total doubling method. The two wavefronts shown have been sheared by a large amount, by means of a thick Savart plate. In order to produce interference in either case b. or c. the incident light must be plane polarized and the two emergent wavefronts must be brought to the same plane of polarization, as by an analyzer.

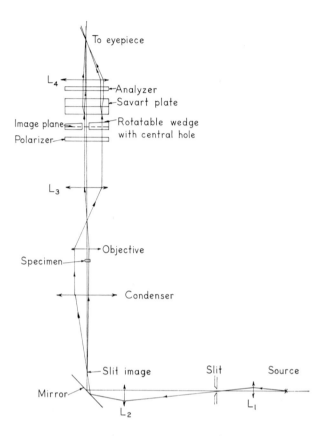

To eyepiece

L_4

Analyzer

Savart plate

Image plane

Rotatable wedge with central hole

Polarizer

L_3

Objective

Specimen

Condenser

Slit image   Slit   Source

Mirror

L_2 L_1

FIG. 10. The NIFE interference microscope. Except for the slit, an ordinary microscope may be used up to lens L_3. This lens collimates the light for passage through the Savart plate, which is between crossed polarizer and analyzer. The wedge and the specimen image are reimaged by lens L_4, the new image being doubled because of the Savart plate.

color matching technique and the advantages of the slit source.

Leitz Interference Microscope. A recent addition to the commercially available interference microscopes is the Leitz Interference Microscope (29). See Fig. 11. In the condenser light is divided by means of a prism system. Two identical objectives are used, one to view the object, the other to receive light transmitted through a reference slide. Six tiltable compensator plates are used to adjust the interference fringe pattern. Another prism system unites the two beams before the eyepiece. Measurements are made either visually by means of a wedge com-

pensator or by photographic photometry. The accuracies obtained are 1/70 and 1/200 wavelength, respectively (29).

A major advantage of this system is the complete removal of the reference beam from the specimen area. That is, there is no error due to part of the reference beam passing through the object or through an unknown area of the slide, and there is no out-of-focus image in the field. In return for this advantage it is necessary that objectives be carefully matched by the manufacturer. The user must compensate for the slide—mounting medium—coverglass system by proper adjustment of the tiltable compen-

divider in the condenser system, the numerical aperture of the illuminating bundle is relatively small, about 0.12.

Calculations

The optical path difference, ϕ, measured by any of the preceding methods, can be used to calculate a number of other quantities. The OPD is given by

$$\phi = t(n_2 - n_1) \tag{1}$$

where t is the thickness of the object, n_2 its index, and n_1 the index of the medium through which the reference beam passed, the mounting medium.

Thickness can be determined directly from equation (1) if the index difference is known. If the object is spherical, cylindrical, or some other regular shape so that its thickness can be determined by lateral measurements, then the *index difference* can be measured from equation (1).

If one is free to change and to measure independently the index n_1 of the mounting medium without changing that of the specimen, a second equation can be obtained.

$$\phi' = t(n_2 - n_1') \tag{2}$$

Then both *thickness* and *index*, n_2, can be determined simultaneously.

$$t = \frac{\phi - \phi'}{n_1' - n_1} \tag{3}$$

$$n_2 = \frac{\phi n_1' - \phi' n_1}{\phi - \phi'} \tag{4}$$

Since these equations utilize the differences between measured quantities, care must be taken that the desired precision is not lost.

A sensitive method for determining the *index* of a specimen is to change the index of the mounting medium until the object has no interference contrast, i.e., until $\phi = 0$.

Of major importance for biological studies is the general rule that the index of a solution of protein in water increases linearly as the concentration and that the specific refractive

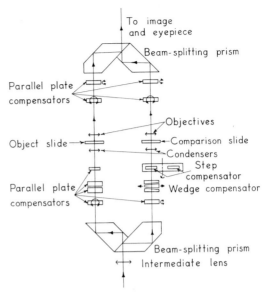

To image and eyepiece

Beam-splitting prism

Parallel plate compensators

Objectives

Object slide — Comparison slide

Condensers

Step compensator

Parallel plate compensators — Wedge compensator

Beam-splitting prism

Intermediate lens

FIG. 11. The Leitz interference microscope. In this system the object and reference beams are completely separate and pass through separate condensers and objectives. The horizontal distance between these two complete microscopes is 62 mm. Coarse adjustment of the optical path is provided by the step compensator. This is a rotatable disc on which ten glass plates are arranged so that they can be swung into path of the reference beam. The wedge compensator provides fine adjustment and measurement of the optical path. The motion of the center wedge is measured by a micrometer.

increment, α, is essentially the same for all proteins (30). The latter is defined by the equation

$$\alpha = \frac{n_s - n_w}{C} \tag{5}$$

where n_s is the index of the solution, n_w the index of water, $n_w = 1.33$, and C the concentration in grams of dry material per 100 ml of solution. For proteins the average value of α is 0.0018.

If the specimen of thickness t is mounted in water, the measured OPD is related to the above quantities by

$$\phi = (n_s - n_w)t \tag{6}$$

Therefore

$$\phi/\alpha = Ct. \tag{7}$$

431

The quantity Ct is the *dry mass per unit area of the specimen.*

The *total dry mass* of cells or nucleii can therefore be determined by integrating the dry mass per unit area over the area of the specimen. If the thickness, t, can be measured by one of the methods described earlier, then the *concentration*, C, can be determined from equation (7). Or if the index n_s can be measured as described, equation (5) can be used to determine concentration.

Precautions and Precision

The greatest potential source of random and systematic errors is the observer himself. In the extinction method it is difficult and treacherous to set the object at minimum when the background is changing luminance simultaneously. The tendency often is to set on maximum contrast rather than on extinction. The half-shade or photometer eyepieces help to overcome this difficulty by changing the task to one of matching. In this method the observer should adjust back and forth through the match position several times in order to avoid errors due to after-image effects. For the most exacting work it is desirable to have an iris or other diaphragm which can be adjusted to limit the field of view to the specimen.

In the discussion of optical path and thickness measurements it was assumed for simplicity that the rays all passed through the specimen parallel to the optical axis of the microscope. In interference microscopes of the Leitz, Dyson, Linnik, Mirau, and Baker types a cone of rays is incident on the specimen. Oblique rays generally receive a different retardation than normal rays.

In transmission microscopes a ray incident at an angle γ_1, on a flat plate-like specimen receives a retardation of

$$\delta = t(n_2 \cos \gamma_2 - n_1 \cos \gamma_1)$$

relative to the corresponding reference ray (31). Here n_2 and n_1 are the indices of the sample and of the immersion liquid; γ_2 and γ_1 are the respective angles of the rays measured from the optical axis. Averaging this quantity over the whole cone of rays gives approximately

$$\delta_a = t(n_2 - n_1) \left[1 + \frac{(NA)_c^2}{4n_1 n_2} \right]$$

where δ_a is the measured, average path difference, $(NA)_c$ is the numerical aperture of the condenser system used, which may be different from that of the objective.

Up to $(NA)_c = 0.4$ this expression is accurate to 0.1 % or less and may be used to correct for obliquity errors. The equation suggests two ways to reduce the error. A low condenser NA produces less error, but it also reduces resolution and image luminance. Whenever the sample permits, one should use the highest possible index n_1 of immersion medium, thus reducing obliquity error without sacrificing resolution.

It is interesting that for objects of index greater than the surround the transmission microscopes give a measured optical path which is slightly too large. Whereas in the reflection interference microscopes it has been found that the readings are slightly too small (32, 33).

For precision work it is necessary to pay as much attention to the path taken by the reference beam as to that of the object beam, since measurements involve them both. For the Dyson system methods have been given (18) for assuring that the reference area which is mostly outside the field of view, is sufficiently free from inhomogeneous material. In the shearing systems (AO-Baker, Françon, Johanssen and Afzelius) the reference beam passes through an area which is within the field of view, and the slide should be rotated if necessary to make sure this area is clear. As seen in the eyepiece of an AO-Baker shearing microscope the sharp image is at B (Fig. 12). An out-of-focus image is seen at A. This means that the reference beam for area A went through the specimen, which is a distance d to the right of area A. Hence the reference beam for area B goes through an area C, which is a distance d to the right of B. This area C should be kept clear when making measurements in area B.

Because of the separation of the object and reference beams, any non-parallelism such as a wedge in the slide, coverglass, or mounting medium becomes part of each reading. However, since the optical paths are determined by subtracting a reading in the surround from a reading in the object, the contribution of a uniform wedge drops out. In order to be safe the reading in the surround should be close in distance and in time to the reading on the object. To detect such a wedge the slide may be turned, preferably by means of a circular stage, and any change in luminance of the background noted.

In the systems employing polarized light a birefringent specimen should be aligned with its optic axis parallel to the vibration direction of the polarized light (parallel to the direction of shear). For many biological specimens the birefringence is too small to cause appreciable error. For highly birefringent specimens, methods have been described by Faust (34).

It has been shown (22) that with the AO-Baker shearing system there is a condenser aperture which produces the best contrast. The user can determine this condition of best contrast either by qualitative observations or by the use of a photomultiplier.

With the above precautions precisions of from one tenth to one three-hundredth of a wavelength can be expected, depending on the system used, the size and uniformity of the specimen, and the care of the observer.

Special-Purpose Modifications

As mentioned earlier, the *total dry mass* of cells or nuclei can be determined by integrating the measured dry mass per unit area over the area of the specimen. In cases where the measurements must be done quickly or

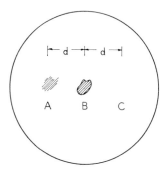

FIG. 12. The field of view of an AO-Baker shearing microscope. The object has a sharp image at B, a blurred image at A. Area C should be kept free of material which would cast a blurred image on area B.

the specimen is very irregular, it may be possible to employ an automatic integration technique (35, 36, 37). In the system of Mitchison, Passano, and Smith (36) the integration is done optically, but care must be taken that the maximum optical path difference is less than about $\lambda/8$.

The *index of liquids* available only in small quantities can be measured by a technique developed by Smith and Iverson (38). The liquid is allowed to fill a small wedge, and the interference bands seen in the image are measured.

The *optical absorption* of specimens can be determined by employing a modification of the AO-Baker system (39). If the object beam passes through an absorbing specimen but the reference beam does not, the emerging beams will be unequal in amplitude as well as in phase. Polarimetric techniques, including a sensitive half-shade device and/ or photoelectric comparison, yield both the amplitude ratio and phase difference. Measurements at various wavelengths in the visible spectrum are possible.

REFERENCES

1. DITCHBURN, R. W., "Light," p. 360, Blackie and Son, Ltd., London, 1952.
2. MERTON, T., *Proc. Roy. Soc. (London)*, **A189**, 309 (1947).
3. MELLORS, R. C., KUPFER, A., AND HOLLEN-

DER, A., *Cancer*, **6**, 372 (1953); **7**, 779, 873 (1954).

4. RICHARDS, O. W., *J. Biol. Photogr. Assoc.*, **19**, 7 (1951).

5. OSTERBERG, H., "Phase and Interference Microscopy," in G. Oster and A. W. Pollister, "Physical Techniques in Biological Research," Vol. 1, p. 378, Academic Press, New York, 1955.

6. JENKINS, F. A., AND WHITE, H. E., "Fundamentals of Optics," 3rd ed., p. 270, McGraw-Hill, New York, 1957.

7. GLAUERT, A. M., *Nature*, **168**, 861 (1951).

8. LINDBERG, P. J., *Optica Acta*, **4**, 59 (1957).

9. TOLANSKY, S., "Multiple-beam Interferometry of Surfaces and Films," p. 63, Clarendon Press, Oxford, England, 1948.

10. ibid., p. 96.

11. KOEHLER, W. F., *J. Opt. Soc. Am.*, **43**, 743 (1953); **45**, 1011, 1015 (1955).

12. LINNIK, W., *C. R. Acad. Sci. URSS*, **1**, 18 (1933).

13. DELAUNAY, G., *Rev. optique*, **32**, 610 (1953).

14. *The Microscope*, **11**, 163 (1957).

15. *J. Sci. Instr.*, **35**, 189 (1958).

16. DYSON, J., *Proc. Roy. Soc. (London)*, **A204**, 170 (1950).

17. DAVIES, H. G., WILKINS, M. H. F., CHAYEN, J., AND LACOUR, L. F., *Quart. J. Micro. Sci.*, **95**, 271 (1954).

18. HALE, A. J., "The Interference Microscope in Biological Research," E. & S. Livingstone, Ltd., Edinburgh and London, 1958.

19. LEBEDEFF, A. A., *Rev. optique*, **9**, 385 (1930).

20. SMITH, F. H., *Research*, **8**, 385 (1955). The objectives and condensers made for this interference microscope by C. Baker, Ltd., London, are used on the AO-Baker microscope of the American Optical Co., Buffalo 15, N. Y.

21. SMITH, F. H., *Nature*, **173**, 362 (1954).

22. KOESTER, C. J., *J. Opt. Soc. Am.*, **49**, 560 (1959).

23. INOUÉ, S., AND KOESTER, C. J., *J. Opt. Soc. Am.*, **49**, 556 (1959).

24. R. C. FAUST AND H. J. MARRINAN, *Brit. J. Appl. Phys.* **6**, 351 (1955).

25. FRANÇON, M., *Rev. opt.*, **31**, 65 (1952). Manufactured by Barbier, Benard, et Turenne, Paris, and Optique et Precision de Levallois, Paris.

26. FRANÇON, M., *J. Opt. Soc. Am.*, **47**, 528 (1957).

27. JOHANSSON, L. P., AND AFZELIUS, B. M., *Nature*, **178**, 137 (1956). Manufactured by Jungnerbolaget, Stockholm 14, Sweden.

28. INGELSTAM, E. & JOHANSSON, L., *Optica Acta*, **2**, 139 (1955). E. INGELSTAM, *Exp. Cell Res. Suppl.* **4**, 150 (1957).

29. GREHN, J., *Leitz Mitt. Wiss. u. Techn.*, **1**, 35 (1959).

30. BARER, R., *Nature*, **169**, 366 (1952); DAVIES, H. G., AND WILKINS, M. F. H., *Nature*, **169**, 541 (1952).

31. INGELSTAM, E., AND JOHANSSON, L. P., *J. Sci. Instr.*, **35**, 15 (1958).

32. TOLMON, F. R., AND WOOD, J. G., *J. Sci. Instr.*, **33**, 236 (1956).

33. INGELSTAM, E., JOHANSSON, L. P., AND BRUCE, C. F., *J. Sci. Instr.*, **36**, 246 (1959).

34. FAUST, R. C., *Quart. J. Micro. Sci.*, **97**, 569 (1956).

35. DAVIES, H. G., AND DEELY, E. M., *Exp. Cell Res.*, **11**, 169 (1956).

36. MITCHISON, J. M., PASSANO, L. M., AND SMITH, F. H., *Quart. J. Micro. Sci.*, **97**, 287 (1956).

37. SVENSON, G., *Exp. Cell Res.*, **12**, 406 (1957).

38. SMITH, F. H., AND IVERSON, S., *Quart. J. Micro. Sci.*, **98**, 151 (1957).

39. KOESTER, C. J., OSTERBERG, H., AND WILLMAN, H. E., JR., *J. Opt. Soc. Am.*, **50**, 477 (1960).

C. J. KOESTER

LIGHT (OPTICAL) MICROSCOPY

COMPARISON MICROSCOPES. *See* **ENGINEERING MICROSCOPES**, p. 438.

DESIGN AND CONSTRUCTION OF THE LIGHT MICROSCOPE

Base and Illuminator. The traditional horseshoe base with mirror has generally been supplanted by a base in the form of a hollow casting enclosing some form of built-in illuminator. Mirrors for use with external sources or natural lighting are available optionally, but the trend is toward the convenience and ease of operation resulting from the permanently correct alignment of a built-in source of illumination (See Fig. 1).

In some instances, instead of building the source into the base, an attachable source is made available which is interchangeable with the mirror. Such sources are generally of somewhat lower intensity than the built-in sources, sufficient for most visual (bright-field) tasks, but inadequate for photomicrography, or special requirements, such as dark-field or phase contrast. They are less expensive than the built-in source and easier to use than the mirror, since alignment is fixed.

The built-in source, on the other hand, is generally a very brilliant source, suitable for photomicrography, darkfield, and phase. A low wattage compact coil filament lamp is employed using the traditional Koehler illumination system, in which the lamp condenser is imaged in the field, and the coiled filament in the aperture of the system. Filters and variable voltage taps on the transformer provide means of controlling the intensity of the illumination.

The Arm. The traditional arm with inclination joint for tilting the microscope has in large measure been supplanted by a rigid non-tilting arm, which indeed is frequently an integral part of the base casting. The arm is normally hollow, enclosing the focusing mechanisms. At its upper end, it is frequently made in the form of a ring support permitting mounting of interchangeable microscope bodies, and rotation of the bodies to any desired orientation.

Bodies. Tilting the microscope on an inclination joint has generally been supplanted by the use of inclined body tubes, giving the same comfort of viewing, but without the attendant undesirable tilting of the stage.

The trend is toward inclined binocular bodies with their more natural fatigue-free type of viewing. Some manufacturers supply binocular bodies, which maintain a constant tube-length despite changes in the inter-pupillary setting. The advantage of this is that it keeps the objectives working accur-

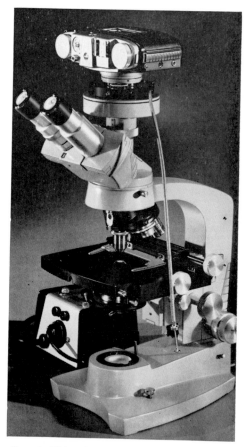

FIG. 1. This microscope depicts a good many of the trends in the modern microscope, such as built-in illumination, inclined binocular body, built-in means for photography, and low position coarse and fine adjustment. (*Photo courtesy American Optical Co.*)

ately under nominal tubelength, and rigidly maintains the factory setting for objective parfocality.

The so-called 'Triocular' body (Fig. 1) is also becoming more popular. This is an inclined binocular with a third (vertical) eyepiece tube for photomicrography. These contain either a removable prism for directing the light to either visual or photographic systems, or a beam-divider, which directs a portion of the light to each system.

Built-in Cameras. Small built-in cameras are finding increased favor over the larger external photomicrographic cameras.

435

These are normally 35 mm cameras, with their own eyepiece system built-in. Like the trend toward built-in illumination, they represent the outcome of a demand for quick convenient photography, resulting from the permanently correct alignment built-in at the factory. Focusing the picture is done either via the binocular viewing system, or by means of a small focusing viewer system.

Coarse Adjustment. The ancient and honorable rack and pinion persists as the most popular means of coarse focusing. One major difference in the modern microscope is that many stands now focus the stage rather than the body tube. The position of the coarse adjustment has accordingly been lowered to a more convenient height, permitting operating it with the hand resting on the table surface. In some stands the coarse and fine focus controls are made concentric for greater ease, and rapidity of operation.

Fine Adjustment. Like the coarse adjustment, the fine adjustment is almost universally located in a low position permitting use with the hand resting on the table surface. On many stands it is now made concentric with the coarse adjustment. Unlike the coarse adjustment, the fine adjustment has undergone many changes through the years, and no consistent design pattern exists among various manufacturers.

Most microscope makers have, however, adopted ball bearings not only for the focusing slide, but for the thrust bearings on the rotary control. Another trend, is to the use of mechanisms, which permit using a single focusing slide for both coarse and fine focus, rather than the older style of a slide carrying a slide.

The basic mechanism which produces the fine focusing motion is generally one of the following:

1. Screw and nut with reducing lever.
2. Screw and nut with reducing cam.
3. Screw and nut with worm wheel.
4. Cam and lever, friction clutch on pinion.

5. Planetary ball-bearing drive.
6. Face cam with limits which engage coarse adjustments.

None of these has established a clear-cut superiority over the others, and accordingly, there seems to be no trend toward conformity among microscope manufacturers in this design feature.

Stages. As has already been mentioned, the stage in the modern microscope has been made the focusable member, supplanting the focusable body tube, and making feasible the low position concentric coarse and fine adjustment.

Mechanical stages for accurately moving and locating the specimen are supplied either as accessory attachments or as built-in devices.

In some cases both the 'east-west' and 'north-south' motion are accomplished by sliding the specimen slide across the plain stage surface. In others, this is true for only one of these motions, the other being accomplished by moving the entire upper stage surface.

Another means of moving the specimen is offered in the so-called 'Glide Stage', in which the entire upper stage surface is movable by finger pressure in any direction. The plate slides on a film of grease, and can be moved with quite good precision as desired.

Substages. The simplest substage equipment, used on student microscope, consists of a rotatable metal disc containing a number of different apertures, used to control the N.A. of the illuminating beam. An iris diaphragm supplants this disc in a slightly better student model.

Another simple form of substage contains a 2-lens abbe condenser with iris diaphragm, held either in a fixed focus mount, or a helical focusing mount, in which focusing is done by rotating the condenser.

Once beyond the student level, however, most microscope substages employ rack and pinion focusing for the condenser. The condenser is normally clamped in a sleeve mount, usually factory precentered. An iris diaphragm is always available for control of the illuminated N.A.

Nosepieces. The rotating nosepiece, used to interchange objectives, is a remarkably precise mechanism. Repeatability of centering is commonly held to within 0.00005″, a value attained chiefly by a precisely fitted bearing and a sturdy and well designed click-stop. The bearing may be either a central cone bearing, or a peripheral ball bearing. The click stop may be either a V-shaped spring clicking onto a peripheral ball stop, or a spring-loaded rotatable ball clicking into a notch on the rim of the nosepiece. In either case, the spring is a very flat leaf spring, having good rigidity in its wide dimension to hold centering precisely, but yielding smoothly in a radial direction to give just the correct force to click the stop mechanism home.

Objectives. Objectives are almost universally threaded in conformance with the Royal Microscopical Society standard, so that objectives of one manufacturer may be interchanged with those of another in a nosepiece. The virtue of this standardization is somewhat lessened by the fact that the objectives are not standardized for shoulder to specimen distance, hence the convenience of parfocality is lost when intermixed objectives are used on a multiple nosepiece.

The lens elements are commonly burnished into individual cells, which in turn fit into a common bore in the objective barrel. The fit of cells into the bore and the centration of lens elements in their cells is the most difficult part of making a good objective, the tolerances being unbelievably tight.

Eyepieces are not greatly different in the modern microscope than in the microscope of 50 years ago. The simple 2-lens Huygens construction has stood the test of time and is still the most widely used eyepiece in microscopy. Probably the most significant change in eyepieces is the requirement for better centering today because of the increasing percentage of binocular models. To get proper results binocularly requires quite

good centration of the optics, although eyepiece centration is still much less critical than objective centration.

JAMES R. BENFORD

ENGINEERING MICROSCOPES

There are many applications of standard and specialized microscopes to the field of engineering in production and testing of manufactured articles. A few of the important examples are cited to show the great importance of microscopy in engineering.

Surface Examination. Perhaps the most direct application is the examination of surfaces particularly of metallic specimens, for the detection of flaws and cracks and for the distinction of surface finish. When a crack is of the order of 0.0001 in. in width, or when a surface structure is equivalent to a series of rulings of the order of 10,000 to the inch or less, a microscope is required. A conventional microscope discloses the extent or width of markings in a plane view, but depth measurement requires a special type of microscope, the Schmaltz Profile Microscope discussed in a later section. Requirements are adequate illumination of the sample, preferably from a vertical illuminator; and adequate resolving power (R.P.) of the optical system (see Optical Theory of Light Microscope). This R.P. or the minimum distance between two points which appear as two separate images is given by R.P. = $0.61\lambda/NA$, when λ is the wave length of light used and NA is the numerical aperture, which is a measure of the maximum cone of light which the microscope objective can take in and refract to the observer's eye. For the majority of cases of examination of machined surfaces the microscope is suitably fitted with a $\frac{2}{3}$ m. objective of NA 0.28 and an eyepiece of power 20×. The laboratory microscope is suitable when specimens are not too large, but in other cases special workshop microscopes of rugged design are available.

Hardness Tests. A special case of surface examination is the determination of the diameter of the depression formed in the test piece during a hardness test of the Brinell type. The depression is illuminated by a vertical illuminator and the magnified image formed in the focal plane of the eyepiece can be measured in two ways. The simplest is by comparison with a glass scale mounted in the focal plane of the eyepiece upon which the image of the indentation is focused and the diameter measured, as though the scale were an ordinary rule, down to 0.01 mm. The magnified image may be measured more accurately with a micrometer eyepiece. Two wires at right angles are mounted on a slide in the focal plane of the eyepiece, and the slide is moved by a micrometer screw from one side to the other of the indentation image. It is easily possible to measure within 0.001 in. on the magnified image which with a magnification of $10\times$ means 0.0001 in. in the actual depression. Excellent equipment is available in which the microscope is built into the hardness testing machine.

Comparison Microscope. In the estimation of surface finish by comparison with standards, the conventional microscope suffers from the disadvantage that only one specimen can be viewed at a time and appearances have to be memorized. It is not practicable to arrange specimen and standard side by side for simultaneous viewing, so that special comparison microscopes have been designed, the objects being well separated while the images are formed in adjacent positions in the eyepiece. This is done with prisms which form semicircular images on each half of the eyepiece.

Projection Microscope. It is possible to make comparisons of specimen and standard by projection in which a screen takes the form of a photographic plate. The two objects are not viewed simultaneously but a photographic record is made of each separately and thus the choice of the eyepiece magnification is determined by the resolving power of the photographic emulsion instead of the acuity of the eye. This of course is a special case of photomicrography (q.v.)

Schmaltz Profile Microscope. It has been shown that in surface examinations the conventional microscope is not able to make possible depth measurements. If a normal section of the specimen could be cut the depth could of course be measured directly as a simple lateral measurement. In the Zeiss Schmaltz Microscope this section cutting is effected by optical means. A line of light is focused on to the surface by means of an illuminating unit inclined at an angle of 45° to the surface inspected. This line of intersection is then viewed with a microscope also inclined 45° to the surface and 90° to the illuminator. The appearance in the eyepiece consists of a band of light running across a black background. The microscope is focused on one edge of this band, and the image thus forms a magnified contour of the surface. If the magnification is M, then the pitch or frequency of variations along the band is magnified M times, and the departure from straight lines, representing depths, $\frac{1}{2}$ M times. Measurements are made with a micrometer eyepiece. The instrument is suitable for measurement of surface finish of turned, bored and ground surfaces in which the scratches all run in one direction.

The Introscope. The examination of the interior surfaces of long tubes such as rifle bores and gun barrels is a problem for which the conventional microscope is unsuited. The Introscope design for this purpose consists of a low-power microscope with built-in illuminator, and a special copying system of lenses which enables the objective at some adjustable distance down the tube to be well separated from the eyepiece at the end of tube. The objective forms an image of I_1 of part S of the surface under examination; light from the lamp scattered from S reaches the lens after reflection by a prism. Copying units consisting of pairs of collimating lenses successively transfer the image to I_2, I_3, I_4

and finally to I_5, where it is viewed by the eyepiece.

Stereoscopic Microscope. Since the eyes are separated on the average by 64 mm, each sees an object from a different viewpoint, and the images formed on the respective retinas are correspondingly different. By the stereoscopic process the brain combines the two images into one composite picture with an accompanying sense of solidity or depth. So the stereoscopic microscope objectives form two images and each eye views one with an eyepiece. A prism system permits correct adjustments of the stereoscopic image. For high-power microscopes two objectives are not practicable so that two viewpoints are secured by using the light refracted by $\frac{1}{2}$ of the objective to form the image for one eye, and light from the other half to form the other image, the division being accomplished by a prism close behind the objective.

Measuring Microscope. For various measurements in machine shops for example, requiring the highest attainable accuracy, a considerable number of microscopes of various types are available which utilize glass scales or micrometer eyepieces. The Zeiss Universal Measuring Microscope and Vertical Comparator employ glass scales for the measurement of length. A scale is viewed with the microscope and subdivision is effected by means of a spiral micrometer eyepiece. The master scale is graduated in 0.05 in. divisions; a fixed glass scale or *graticule* in the microscope divides the image of one division into tenths or 0.005 in. Thus small divisions are further divided into hundredths, or 0.00005 in. by means of a special graticule graduated on a separate glass disk and rotated around a center to one side of the microscope axis. The microscope on a measuring machine as an optical vernier is also an optical pointer, which may take the form of a bent microscope as in the case of that used as jig borers, tool-room millers and other precision machines, as well as in pro-

file grinding machines designed to finish-grind regular and irregular forms of all types. Thus in one type of grinder a drawing of the required form is made 50 times size, and the outline is followed with the stylus of a pantograph. A microscope is fitted to the short arm of the pantograph which reduces 50/1, and thus the microscope cross-lines trace out the required form in the plane of the work. An accuracy of at least 0.0004 in. or better is possible. Manufacturers can provide details on a wide range of screw and profile projectors and travelling microscopes for the toolmaker, workshop microscopes for inspection processes, and many closely related optical instruments employing principles of the optical lever and interference effects (for example, for the evaluation of surface flatness).

Heating Microscope. Of both engineering and chemical interest are microscopes which provide necessary information concerning the behavior of materials at elevated temperatures. In some types hot stages of various designs are provided directly on the microscope, especially for fusion analysis of crystals at relative low temperatures and similar observations. In other cases the heating microscope consists of 3 principal units mounted on an optical bench comprising (1) a light source; (2) electric furnace with specimen carriage; and (3) observation and photo-microscope.

Fuel ashes, slags, ceramics, glazes and the like are more or less complex mixtures of the most diverse inorganic compounds. Being non-homogeneous substances, they do not have clearly defined melting points, but fuse and soften as they are heated and melt over a more or less wide temperature range depending upon their chemical composition before finally reaching the liquid state. In order to establish the typical softening and melting behaviors small samples of the material to be examined are pressed into specimens of specific shapes and the characteristic physical changes determined as the specimen is heated.

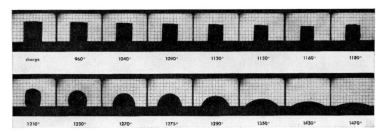

FIG. 1. Microscopic silhouettes of ash sample at increasing temperatures.

With the aid of the heating microscope the individual phases of the process may be observed and recorded photomicrographically.

The image of the specimen located in the electric furnace is magnified by the microscope and projected onto a ground glass screen, where it is observed. The characteristic phases are easily photographed. Thus the entire cycle can be observed, the series of photomicrographs giving an impression of the behavior pattern of the material being investigated. By evaluating the volume changes of the specimen a melting curve in relation to temperature is easily plotted.

One of the principal advantages of this method of investigation is that the specimen at no time is subjected to pressure by a probing rod. Thus, since no load is applied to the specimen, not only the softening process, but also any desired phase of the alteration in shape of the specimen can be investigated and recorded, such as the swelling of such material as ashes as well as the "melting point," the so-called hemisphere point.

In Figure 1, a series of photomicrographs made with a Leitz instrument showing silhouettes of the specimen, the individual characteristic alterations in shape necessary for judging the thermal behavior pattern of fuel ashes are clearly seen. The original shape of the specimen is shown in the first photomicrograph of the series. The next ones show that sintering occurs between 960° and 1160° C; the fact that both diameter and height of the specimen are reduced shows that sintering and not softening has taken place. At 1180° C the outlines of the silhouette have changed noticeably, indicating that the ashes of this stage have passed into the softening phase. The softening temperature, i.e. the temperature at which softening commences is thus found to be between 1160° and 1180° C. After swelling slightly at 1210° C. the specimen eventually melts. The photomicrograph made at 1270° C. shows the "hemisphere point," the officially accepted melting point. At 1430° C the ashes begin to liquefy and at 1470° C they have flowed uniformly to all sides. (From a brochure published by Ernst Leitz, Wetzlar, Germany.)

REFERENCES

1. HABELL, K. J., AND COX, ARTHUR, "Engineering Optics," Pitman and Sons, Ltd., London, 1956, pp. 411.

G. L. CLARK

MAGNETOGRAPHY: THE MICROSCOPY OF MAGNETISM*

Although the phenomena of magnetism have been known for many centuries and

* Reprinted by permission from the *Bell Laboratories Record*, 35, No. 5, pp. 175–8, 1957. Photographs courtesy of Bell Telephone Laboratories.

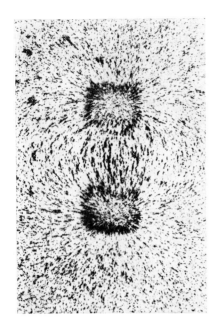

FIG. 1. Iron filings oriented along the magnetic lines of force around and between the poles of a small horseshoe magnet placed under surface shown.

their forces applied to practical problems with tremendous advantage, they have defied study by ordinary visual methods. One of the early methods of observing magnetic effects was to sprinkle iron filings above a magnet and allow the filings to orient themselves along the paths of magnetic force. As illustrated in Figure 1, the filings are aligned with the greatest concentration near the poles. It was with this demonstration and the simple compass test that every student of elementary physics encountered the law —"like poles oppose and unlike attract." This method of study, although interesting from the gross viewpoint of the external forces, gave no light on the internal forces that must be present and in equilibrium.

The first relatively successful attempts toward "seeing" magnetization, or visually appraising the forces that occur in the individual crystal of a ferromagnetic material, were not made until recent years. In 1931–32, Professor Francis Bitter of the Massachusetts Institute of Technology described a

method by which it was possible to see the separate so-called "magnetic domains" in a specimen. When a piece of ferromagnetic material is demagnetized, a nearby compass needle will be unaffected, and iron filings sprinkled on the sample will not indicate the presence of magnetic fields. When the sample is examined microscopically, however, it is found to consist of small regions, each of which is magnetized to saturation in a certain direction. These regions are called "magnetic domains".

In using Bitter's method, which was later used and greatly improved by W. C. Elmore of Swarthmore College, and L. W. McKeehan, formerly of Bell Telephone Laboratories, a suspension of colloidal magnetite is employed. This is an extremely fine iron oxide in a soap solution. When a drop of the colloidal suspension is placed on a freshly polished magnetic surface and covered with a thin glass disc, the magnetic particles are attracted by the strong flux at the domain boundaries. A metallurgical microscope which magnifies about 100–200 diameters is used to see the outlined domains, and the specimen is studied with either "brightfield" or "darkfield" illumination.

In the brightfield system, the light rays from the source are directed through the microscope objective lens to illuminate the specimen. On return, the reflected light from the specimen passes through the objective lens, thence to the eyepiece to form the final image (Figure 2). In the darkfield system,

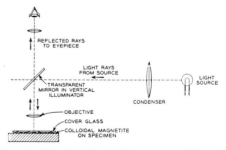

FIG. 2. The "brightfield" system of illumination. Reflected light returns through the objective lens, transparent mirror and eyepiece to the observer.

used most frequently by the Laboratories, the rays from the light source are directed around the objective, strike an annular mirror or condenser, and illuminate the specimen. This is illustrated in Figure 3. Since a polished magnetic specimen is highly reflecting, all incident rays striking the surface are reflected away from the objective, and the field in the microscope appears black. However, the small colloidal magnetite particles, which have already aligned themselves along the domain boundaries, are illuminated by the light impinging on their irregular sur-

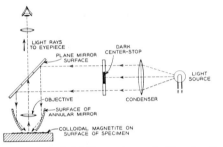

FIG. 3. "Darkfield" system of illumination. Light is reflected from the specimen surface through the microscope lens system to the eye.

faces. Since no light emanates from the background, the reflecting particles appear white. This provides maximum visual or photographic contrast as illustrated in the domain micrograph (Figure 4).

Over the years, the colloidal magnetite method has been used extensively. In this work, through the efforts of W. O. Baker and F. Winslow of the Laboratories, further refinement in the preparation of colloidal magnetite made it possible to see the more delicate delineations of the domains, and to observe the changing domain patterns over a much longer period of time.

Of particular interest was the change in domain patterns caused by various physical influences such as inclusions or small surface defects. It was further observed that irregularities in specimen preparation, such as surface straining, would cause a type of domain pattern that was not representative of the underlying structure. In addition to presenting a static picture of domains under the influence of an applied magnetic field, these domains would move with a change in field

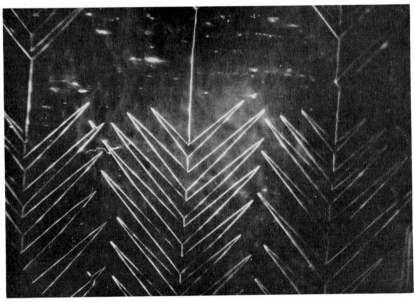

FIG. 4. Magnetic domain patterns obtained on silicon iron by H. J. Williams using the colloidal magnetite method with darkfield illumination.

intensity or direction. As a result, the domain patterns could be photographed and recorded in still or motion pictures. (The latter were taken by F. Tylee in collaboration with H. J. Williams and J. G. Walker.)

Although much was gained in the study of magnetic effects with colloidal methods, which are still used to great advantage, there are certain inherent restrictions. Among these limitations are the time required for the particles to collect along the domain walls and the failure to delineate the fine structure that the microscope can resolve.

During the latter part of the nineteenth century, a useful effect was observed by the Scottish scientist, John Kerr. He found that, when a beam of polarized light is reflected perpendicularly from a surface that is magnetized normal to itself, the plane of polarization of the light is rotated. The direction of rotation depends upon the polarity of the reflecting surface. Thus, if the north pole of a material rotates the plane in a clockwise direction, the south pole will rotate the plane in a counter-clockwise direction. It was thought that a study of the domains in a magnetic material might be possible using this effect. The phenomenon, known as the Kerr magneto-optic effect, was in 1950 applied to the microscopical study of magnetic domain structure in cobalt by H. J. Williams, E. A. Wood and the author.

In 1938, L. V. Foster of the Bausch and Lomb Optical Company described an illuminating system for a metallograph, using a cut and cemented calcite prism as a polarizing illuminator. Later, a polarized light compensator was developed to be used in conjunction with this metallograph for the study of opaque minerals. The combination of these two illuminating devices is shown in the diagram of Figure 5.

With this device, either the north or south poles in the surface of the specimen can be made to appear bright while the other set remains dark. This is done by adjusting the elliptical and rotation compensators, shown in Figure 5, to extinguish the light from one set of domains. When there is no compensation, both sets of poles or domains have the same intensity and they cannot be distinguished.

By means of this polarizing attachment for the metallograph, it was believed that the Kerr magneto-optic effect could be used to study the domain structures in magnetic materials. In the initial studies, using this effect, a single crystal of cobalt was selected. Subsequently, a cobalt crystal was made in the form of a half disc. With this shape crystal it was possible to observe domains between positions parallel to the c-axis, or easy direction of magnetization, to positions perpendicular to this axis. To minimize the possibility of a disturbed surface of cold worked material, the crystal was carefully electropolished.

Cobalt has a hexagonal structure. In this element, the domains tend to lie with the direction of magnetization in either a positive or negative sense along the c-axis. The photomicrographs that are shown in Figure 6, starting with a displacement of 4 degrees

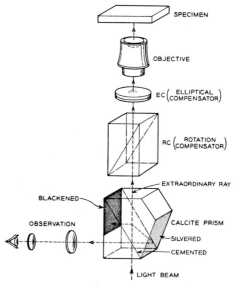

FIG. 5. Adaptation of elliptical vibration compensator used in conjunction with metallograph for studies of domains in magnetic materials.

from the c-axis and advancing through positions to 20 degrees, 49 degrees and 70 degrees, illustrate the change of domain patterns from rosettes to elongated areas. On the surface perpendicular to the c-axis (Figure 6) the magnetization forms small regions having poles of opposed polarity. This gives rather complex domain patterns on the surface, as can be seen in the comparison photomicrograph, Figure 7. Photomicrograph Figure 7, left, shows a collection of magnetite

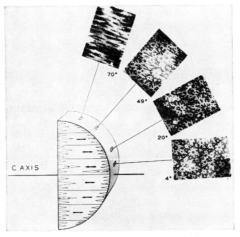

FIG. 6. Domain structure in a cobalt crystal cut in the form of a half disc. Arrows show directions of magnetization in the domains. No magnetic field applied.

particles (darkfield illumination) and Figure 7, right, is a direct view (polarized light) of the polished surface. The latter shows many fine details that cannot be seen in the colloidal magnetite picture.

In the microscopy of the magnetic domains of cobalt it has been found that the contrast is very low and, at times, has caused considerable difficulty in visual study. Photomicrography with high contrast emulsion films and special development has further aided this study.

Recently, B. M. Roberts and C. P. Bean of the General Electric Research Laboratories have studied the ferromagnetic intermetallic compound manganese-bismuth. This also has a hexagonal crystal structure with the direction of easy magnetization along the c-axis. In this compound, a much greater contrast is achieved with the domain patterns appearing virtually black and white. A study of this compound is currently in progress at Bell Telephone Laboratories; a domain pattern showing rosettes that indicate a surface normal to the c-axis is shown in the reference on page 440. Such patterns are an aid in determining the orientations of the crystallites in a polycrystalline specimen.

The importance of microscopy as an aid in the fundamental studies of magnetic do-

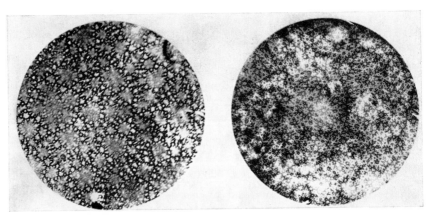

(Old) Pattern obtained using colloidal magnetite

(New) Polarized light pattern showing greater detail on same area of the cobalt crystal.

FIG. 7. Comparison of techniques.

mains cannot be overlooked. The colloidal magnetite method has long been established and has become an important adjunct as a microscopical method applied to magnetism. This method gives strong delineation of the domain patterns with a minimum of specimen preparation and outlay for specialized equipment. On the other hand, the polarized light method has the advantage that it yields instantaneously to field intensity or directional changes, and employs no surface additives. Also, it may be possible to use this method to study specimens at elevated temperatures. It is believed that with further development of the polarized light method a more intensive study of the geometrical configuration of the magnetic domain will be possible.

F. GORDON FOSTER

MEASURING MICROSCOPES. *See* ENGINEERING MICROSCOPES, p. 439.

OPTICAL THEORY OF THE LIGHT MICROSCOPE

Magnification

The light microscope is an optical instrument which produces highly enlarged images of very small objects. The microscope achieves its magnifying power in two stages. The *objective* performs the first stage of the magnification, forming a magnified image of the object near the top of the microscope tube. This image is further enlarged by the eyepiece, which acts as a magnifier. Objectives range in power from about $2\times$ to $100\times$. Eyepieces range in power from about $5\times$ to $25\times$. Thus the total magnification, being the product of objective and eyepiece magnification, ranges from about $10\times$ to $2500\times$.

Fig. 1 is a ray diagram of a typical microscope, and illustrates the two stages necessary to achieve the final magnification. The first (or objective) stage results in the "primary image", shown near the top of the microscope, and the second (or eyepiece) stage results in the very large "virtual image" shown near the bottom. Fig. 1 also is helpful in showing how the mirror directs the entering light upward toward the condenser, which in turn concentrates the light into a brightly illuminated spot on the object.

Resolving Power

The statement that the magnification of the light microscope ranges from about $10\times$ to $2500\times$ raises the question as to why it cannot be extended beyond $2500\times$. Actually it is quite possible to do this, but very little is gained by doing so, due to the limit in resolving power imposed by the finite size of light waves. Thus resolving power is in the final analysis the fundamental quality which imposes a practical upper limit on the magnifying power of the microscope.

Resolving power is a measure of the ability of the microscope to distinguish fine detail. It is, in quantitative terms, the distance between two points in the object which can just be detected as being separated and not single. The resolving power of a microscope depends generally on the design of the objective. An objective capable of utilizing a large angular cone of light coming from the specimen will have better resolving power than an objective limited to a smaller cone of light. This is demonstrated in Fig. 2, where the same specimen area has been photographed with two different objectives of quite different designs as indicated below each photomicrograph.

The quantity $N \sin U$ in Fig. 2 is called the Numerical Aperture (N.A.) of an objective. By definition:

$$NA = N \sin U$$

where N is the lowest refractive index between the specimen and the objective, and U is the half-angle of the cone of light as shown in Fig. 2. The objective shown at the right has a higher N.A. and has the superior re-

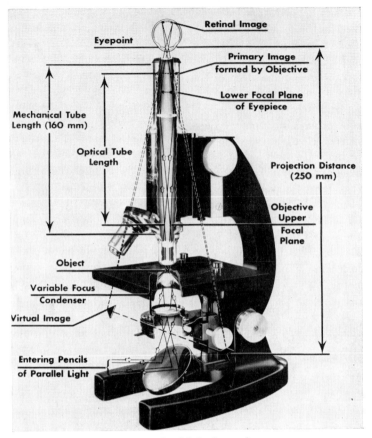

FIG. 1. The path of light in a microscope.

solving power. The smallest detail h which can be resolved by an objective is given by the formula $h = \lambda/2\,N \sin U = \lambda/2NA$.

As the above formula indicates, there are three ways in which to decrease the least resolvable separation h. The first is to decrease λ, the wavelength of light; the second is to increase the angle U in the object space; and the third is to increase the refractive index N in the object space.

The wavelength can be decreased to a rather modest extent by using the blue-violet region, the short wavelength end of the white light spectrum. Still further shortening of the wavelength is possible by using the ultraviolet region. This, however, requires a completely different optical system from the light microscope.

Increasing the angle U in Fig. 2, increases resolving power in proportion to the sine of the angle. Highly complex objective lens systems result in values of $\sin U$ as high as about 0.95, and this value represents about the maximum attainable limit for the N.A. of a top-quality dry objective. Normally however 0.65 N.A. represents a practical limit for the great majority of microscopes (see Fig. 3).

To go still further in resolving power "immersion objectives" are used, giving a value of N greater than unity in the formula

$$h = \lambda/2N \sin U$$

Immersion objectives, using oil as an immersion fluid, result in N.A.'s as high as 1.40, although 1.25 is more common. Monobromo-

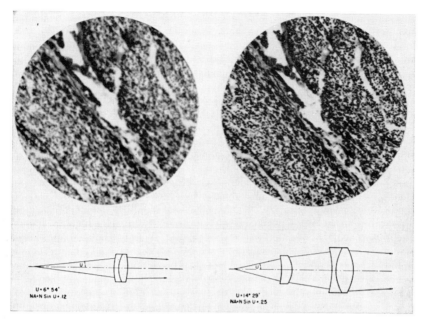

FIG. 2. The dependence of resolving power upon numerical aperture. The same object is here photographed with two different objectives. The picture at left was obtained with a 0.12 N.A. objective. The much sharper and better resolved picture at right was taken with a 0.25 N.A. objective.

naphthalene immersion objectives with N.A.'s of 1.60 have been made, but they are very uncommon, and are difficult to use.

Depth of Focus

At any given focus setting of a microscope only a limited thickness of the specimen appears in sharp focus. This thickness is called the "depth of focus" and, like resolving power is largely dependent on the objective design. The depth of focus is (approximately) inversely proportional to the square of the N.A. of the optical system, and is extremely small for high N.A. systems, e.g., a 1.40 N.A. objective has a depth of focus of about $\frac{1}{2}$ wavelength of light (0.00025 mm).

Aberrations

A first-class microscope is remarkably free from aberrations, or image defects, at least in the central portions of the field. However, some understanding of the seven different basic lens aberrations is essential to the

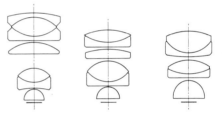

FIG. 3. Objective types. The objective at the right is a 4 mm, 0.65 N.A. Achromat having 5 glass elements, and no fluorite. The central objective is a 4 mm, 0.85 N.A. semi-apochromat, having 5 glass lenses and 1 fluorite lens. The objective at the left is a 4 mm, 0.95 N.A. apochromat, having 5 glass elements and 2 fluorite lenses.

proper selection and intelligent use of a microscope and its accessories; hence a brief discussion of the aberrations as they apply to a microscope is given here.

(1) *Spherical aberration* exists where light from a single object point on the axis is more strongly refracted by either the inner or the outer portion of the lens aperture, resulting in failure of the light to come to a common

447

focus. The visible effect is a loss of contrast. Well made objectives are normally quite well corrected for spherical aberration. High N.A. dry objectives, however, are quite sensitive to the effect of cover-glass thickness on spherical aberration. Most objectives are designed to work with 0.18 mm cover-glass thickness, and even small departures from this nominal value will result in loss of contrast in the image in high N.A. dry objectives. The experienced microscopist uses cover-glasses very close to 0.18 mm for optimum image quality. Immersion objectives are much less sensitive to cover-glass thickness, since immersion oil is quite close to the glass cover slip in refractive index and forms essentially a homogeneous optical medium between specimen and objective.

(2) *Astigmatism* is the defect whereby the image of a point is drawn out into two separate line images at 90° to each other. In a well made microscope, astigmatism will sometimes be present to a minor extent near the margin of the field, but not at the center.

(3) *Coma* is the lens defect in which different circular concentric zones of the lens system have different magnifications. It results in a comet-shaped image of a point object. Like astigmatism, in a well made microscope it will sometimes be present to a minor extent near the margin of the field, but not at the center.

(4) *Curvature of field* is the defect in which a flat object is imaged as a curved surface. This defect is the most difficult one to deal with in a microscope design. The high-power objectives in particular tend to have strongly curved fields, so that when the central image is in sharp focus the marginal image is out of focus, and vice versa. A certain amount of compensation for the objective curvature of field is possible by optimum choice of eyepiece, and in this regard the microscopist is well-advised to follow the manufacturer's recommendations on objective and eyepiece combinations.

Normally, curvature of field is more ob-jectionable in photomicrography where eye-accommodation and re-focusing in scanning the field are not possible. Special flat-field objectives are sometimes used here, and also special negative lens systems can sometimes by used to replace the eyepiece, to improve the performance of regular objectives.

(5) *Distortion* is the lens aberration in which straight lines are imaged as curved lines. This aberration is generally under good control in a microscope.

(6) *Chromatic aberration* is the defect which causes light of different wavelengths to be brought to different foci. Chromatic aberration is normally under good control in a microscope, particularly in the highly complex "apochromatic" objectives (see "Objective Types").

(7) *Lateral color* results in light of one color being imaged at a greater magnification than light of another color, causing the image of an off-axis point to be spread out into a tiny spectrum. This defect is greatest in the higher-power objectives. It can be compensated by proper choice of eyepiece, and again the manufacturer's recommendations should be followed.

Objective Types

Three types of objectives are normally made available by microscope manufacturers. These are called "achromats", "semiapochromats", and "apochromats", named in order of increasing excellence and complexity (see Fig. 3). The achromats are the simplest and least expensive. For most purposes achromats do an adequate job, and consequently they are popularly used on most medical and laboratory microscopes. The achromat is corrected for chromatic aberration at two wavelengths, one in the red and one in the blue, and is fully corrected for spherical aberration at one wavelength in the yellow-green. At other wavelengths in the visible spectrum the correction is good, but not complete.

By combining fluorite lenses with glass

lenses it is possible to get better color correction in an objective. The semi-apochromat uses fluorite to a limited extent, and represents a compromise between the achromat and apochromat in performance. The apochromat uses several fluorite lenses in combination with glass lenses, to achieve a very high degree of correction. Correction for chromatic aberration is achieved at three wavelengths in the red, green, and blue respectively, and spherical aberration is also held under closer control throughout the visible spectrum than is possible in the achromats. Apochromats are also normally higher in N.A. than corresponding powers in the achromats.

Eyepiece Types

Far and away the most popular eyepiece for general microscopy is the Huygens eyepiece. This comprises two separated simple plano-convex lenses, with field diaphragm located between the lenses. Despite its simplicity and inexpensive construction it is well corrected for lateral color and works quite well with low and intermediate power objectives.

For use with higher-power objectives, eyepieces of more complex form are superior to the Huygens eyepiece. These more complex eyepieces compensate the lateral color aberrations of the higher power objectives, and are particularly suitable for use with apochromats. These eyepieces are sometimes called "compensating" eyepieces, and in other instances are given specific trade names. The various manufacturers recommend optimum combinations of eyepieces and objectives to achieve best correction, particularly in regard to lateral color.

For photomicrography special negative (dispersive) lens systems are available, which markedly improve the correction of the image for flatness of field. These negative systems cannot be used as visual eyepieces, but are strictly for photomicrography.

Illuminating Systems

Brightfield Illumination. Most microscopy is done with "brightfield illumination" in which the illuminating beam is a solid cone of light concentrated on the specimen by a condenser lens system, mounted directly beneath the specimen. This lens system is called a "substage condenser" and is normally equipped with an iris diaphragm to allow the observer to control the angular cone of the illuminating bundle. This control on the light permits one to attain the optimum compromise between contrast and resolving power. This setting will be found to differ depending on the nature of the specimen.

Sometimes the light source will be external to the microscope, but the tendency is toward built-in sources, for obvious reasons of convenience and fool-proof operation. However, whether the source be built-in or external, the principle of Koehler illumination is normally employed in this system, the light source is imaged by a "lamp condenser" into the substage condenser. The latter images the lamp condenser onto the specimen. The virtue of this system is that it results in a nice even field of illumination, even though the source is of uneven brightness, as for example a coiled filament lamp. A small amount of diffusion is sometimes added to completely even out the illumination. Fig. 4 compares Koehler illumination with the formerly much-used critical illumination.

The most commonly used condenser is the two lens "Abbe condenser", having an N.A. of 1.25 or 1.30 (see Fig. 5). The upper element is a plano-convex hemisphere, and the lower element is bi-convex in shape. While the aberrations of this system are sizeable, it nonetheless does a very creditable job of illumination for any normal routine tasks. It is sometimes made with the lower element independently focusable as shown in Fig. 5 to provide better illumination of large fields in low-power work.

449

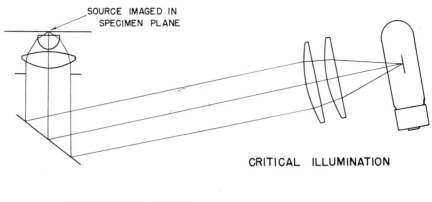

CRITICAL ILLUMINATION

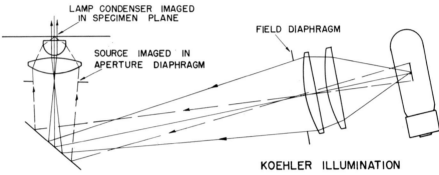

KOEHLER ILLUMINATION

FIG. 4. Ray-paths in critical and Koehler illumination. The Koehler form of illumination is most widely used, since it gives even illumination despite lack of uniformity in the source.

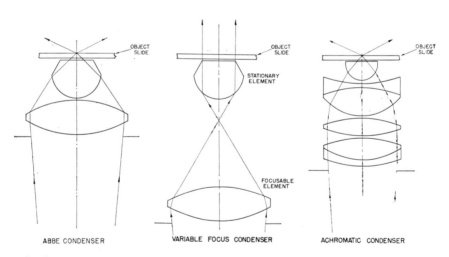

FIG. 5. Condenser types. The simple Abbe type at the left and the modified variable focus Abbe in the center are the most commonly used forms. The more complex achromatic form however gives more color-free illumination and higher N.A.

For more exacting work in microscopy or for photomicrography, an achromatic 1.40 N.A. condenser is often used. This is quite well corrected for spherical and chromatic aberration and permits more accurate control of the illuminated field and aperture, as well as giving more color-free illumination than is possible with the Abbe condenser. Its construction is shown at the right in Fig. 5.

Darkfield Illumination. This is another common system of illuminating micropreparations. In this system the illuminating cone is again concentrated on the specimen, but in this case is hollow, having a dark central core, as shown in Fig. 6. The objective lies in this dark central core, and "sees" only objects which scatter light onto it. The clear background appears black, and the specimen shines bright against this dark background. This very striking form of illumination is useful on very small transparent living objects such as spirochetes, bacilli, etc.

The most common form of darkfield illuminator is the Paraboloid Condenser, shown at the left in Fig. 6. A somewhat more complex, and slightly superior design is the Cardioid Condenser, shown at the right in Fig. 6. The Paraboloid delivers a hollow cone lying between the approximate N.A. values 1.15

and 1.40. The cardioid delivers a somewhat better concentrated hollow cone lying between the approximate N.A. values 1.20 and 1.40. Since in both cases the N.A.'s exceed unity, it is obvious that the condensers must be oil-contacted to the glass object slide. Since the objective N.A. must not be great enough to accept any of the direct cone of light, it is necessary to either use objectives lower in N.A. than about 1.0, or else reduce the N.A. to about 1.0 by a small baffle, called a "funnel stop", which fits into the back of an objective.

The effectiveness of a darkfield system is dependent on the use of an intense, nondiffused, light beam from the lamp condenser. Carbon arcs, ribbon filaments, or compact coil filament lamps are normally employed as the light sources. Extreme care must also be taken to get the object slide and cover glass clean, since any foreign objects will scatter light and destroy the contrast.

To carry the darkfield principle to its extreme, a very intense beam of light may be directed onto the object at approximately right angles to the optical axis. Such an arrangement is called an *ultramicroscope*, the name being derived from the fact that it is possible with this instrument to see particles which are well below the resolving power of

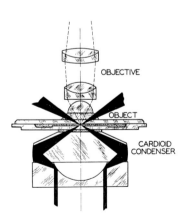
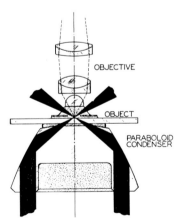

FIG. 6. Two forms of darkfield condensers. Note that, in each case, the direct light from the condenser is not picked up by the objective. The scattered light from the object, indicated by the dashed rays, produces a bright image seen against a dark background.

451

the microscope. The shape or nature of such particles cannot, of course, be determined, but they can be detected, and some estimate made of their size by inference from their brightness, and the speed of their Brownian movement, if the particles are suspended in a liquid.

Since the limitation on the smallest particle which can be made visible is imposed by the level of energy of the illuminating beam, the ultramicroscope uses an extremely bright light source, such as a carbon arc, and concentrates the light energy by means of a medium-power microscope objective into a horizontal beam at right angles to the

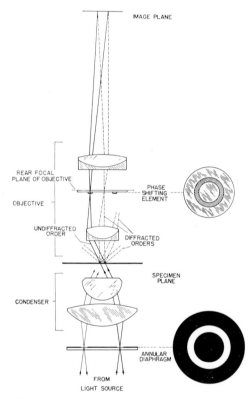

FIG. 7. The phase contrast microscope. The illumination is restricted to a hollow cone by the Annular Diaphragm, which is imaged into the Phase Shifting Element by the lenses. Interference, producing a visible image, occurs between the diffracted light passing around the Phase Shifting Element, and the direct light passing through this element.

microscope optical axis. The object slide is of special construction to admit this concentrated beam from the side.

Phase Contrast. Phase contrast is another form of illumination useful on transparent objects, and in particular on live preparations. The normal microscopic object is seen because it has regions of different opacity. In brightfield illumination a completely transparent specimen is very difficult to see in any detail, as all parts are equally dense. Darkfield illumination shows up border effects in such specimens, due to edge scattering, refraction, and diffraction. Phase contrast, is of more value with transparent media, due to its ability to reveal internal detail. This method has found extensive use in the study of transparent living preparations.

Phase contrast is really more than just a change in the form of illumination. It is basically a method of separating the diffracted and undiffracted parts of the light, treating them differently, and then re-combining them under conditions such that they produce controlled visible interference effects. The scheme produces a visible image of an otherwise almost invisible object.

The arrangement necessary for phase contrast is shown in Fig. 7. A clear annulus in the focal plane of the condenser is imaged at infinity by the condenser, and then re-imaged by the objective in its upper focal plane. The undiffracted light all passes through this image, and, by means of an annular phase pattern located in this focal plane, is both reduced in intensity and given a quarterwave phase shift with reference to the diffracted light. The end effect of these two changes in the undiffracted light, when combined with the diffracted light passing around the phase annulus, is to simulate the phase and intensity distribution which would be present in the objective focal plane if the specimen had density variations rather than refractive index variations. As a consequence, the image formed by the interference of the diffracted and undiffracted portions simulates that of a specimen having density variations.

For a more thorough understanding of phase contrast the reader is referred to "Phase Microscopy", by Bennett, Jupnik, Osterberg and Richards.

Polarized Light is another method of bringing out visible structure in transparent materials. Light energy is transmitted by transverse waves, generally vibrating in *any* direction at right angles to the direction of the light ray, but it is possible by means of devices known as "polarizers" to restrict the vibrations to a single plane. If two such polarizers are inserted in the light beam in such a manner that the second one transmits in a plane at right angles to the first, the light will be extinguished. Such an arrangement is called "crossed polarizers". The lower element is called a "polarizer"; the upper one the "analyzer". In practice, the polarizer is located beneath the microscope condenser, and the analyzer just above the objective. If now, in between these crossed polarizers we insert an object which is crys-

talline in nature, it will appear bright against the dark background caused by the crossed polarizers. Furthermore, if the crystal is rotated about the optical axis of the microscope, it will alternately brighten and darken every 90°, usually with attendant strikingly beautiful changes of color. The reason for this is that crystalline materials have different properties in different directions, and as a consequence they alter the state of polarization of the light, and thereby effectively "uncross" the polarizers.

Polarized light has long been a mainstay in the study of crystals, minerals, chemicals, and fibers. Special microscopes called "petrographic" or "chemical microscopes" are used for any serious work in these fields. These are equipped with accessories for making quantitative measurements of the polarizing characteristics of the material under study. Fig. 8 shows a typical Petrographic Microscope. It is equipped with a circular rotating stage, divided in degrees, with a vernier permitting reading of crystal orientation of 0.1°. The objectives are mounted in centerable mounts, since it is necessary

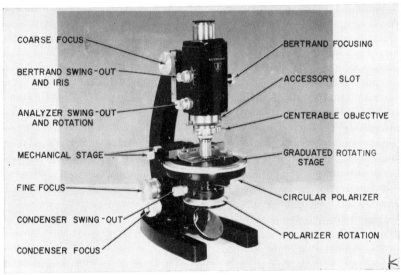

FIG. 8. A Typical Petrographic Microscope. This specialized microscope for use in the study of crystalline materials differs in many respects from the conventional microscope, as indicated by the many special control knobs in the figure.

to have the specimen stay accurately on center as it is rotated. The polarizer, mounted beneath the substage condenser, and the analyzer mounted above the objective are rotatable, and provided with circular scales to read their orientation.

Beneath the analyzer is an accessory slot, in which one may insert measuring accessories, such as a quarterwave plate, a sensitive tint plate, a quartz wedge, or a tilting calcite plate compensator. The first two of these devices are used to categorize crystals into one of several classifications. The quartz wedge refines this classification into semiquantitative sub-classifications, while the tilting calcite plate gives actual quantitative measurements for more refined classification.

Above the analyzer is an important element of the Petrographic Microscope, known as the 'Bertrand Lens'. This lens forms an image of the back aperture of the objective in the eyepiece focal plane, so that the observer sees the aperture rather than the field of the microscope system. A crystal, located between high N.A. condenser and objective, is traversed by polarized light in many directions. In each direction, its properties differ, and it accordingly transforms the state of polarization differently, so that between crossed polarizer and analyzer the crystal exhibits a characteristic light pattern which varies with direction. Looking at the aperture of the objective, one sees this pattern of light and shade, known as the "interference figure", and gains a clue as to the nature of the crystal.

The interference figure of a crystal may be further investigated in a quantitative manner by means of an accessory called the 'Universal stage'. This device, located on the stage of the microscope, permits turning and rotating the crystal about several different axes. Crystals have either one or two directions called 'optic axes' in which they behave as non-crystals. By means of the Universal Stage, the positions of these optic axes may

be determined, giving a very good clue as to the composition of the crystal.

For a more complete understanding of polarized light microscopy, the reader is referred to the following texts: "Crystallography and Practical Crystal Measurements", A. E. H. Tutton. "Microscopic Character of Artificial Minerals", A. N. Winchell. "Handbook of Chemical Microscopy", E. M. Chamot and C. W. Mason. "Optical Mineralogy", Rogers and Kerr.

JAMES R. BENFORD

ORIGIN AND HISTORY

Development of Optics and Microscopy from About 1600 to 1723

During the first years after the invention the words "perspicillum" or "conspicilium" were used both for the telescope and the microscope. What was meant in each case had to be understood from the context. For the microscope also "smicroscope" was used or "engyscope" and other words. Eventually the names familiar to us were accepted about 1615. They originated with the Academica dei Lyncei which had been founded in 1603. Allegedly the names were invented either by Giovanni Faber or Giovanni Desmicianus, who were both members of the Academy and whose names appear in writings from that time.

Johannes Kepler (1571–1630) is better known for his achievements in astronomy but he also studied intensively optical phenomena. In his *Paralipomena*, printed in 1604, he treated the nature of light and color, the position of images, refraction, function of the eye, and other subjects. Color is explained as light partially buried in the material of the medium which can vary in density, transparency, opacity and the various degrees of "the light inherent in the material." Kepler labored hard to determine the law of refraction. He experimented with many transparent media, as air, water, glass, turpentine, vinegar, wine, several oils, and others. He established the fact that refraction does not depend on the intensity of light. Quantitatively, he thought that for the ratio of the angles of incidence and refraction a relation involving the secant of the angle of incidence would hold.

The anatomical structure of the eye was unknown at Kepler's time. He made the discovery that the image of an object observed is focused on the retina by the refractive power of the crystalline lens. He is also among the first to arrive at distinct prescriptions for defective vision, namely convex lenses for farsightedness and concave lenses for shortsightedness.

In 1611 the *Dioptrice* was published, which is a "demonstration of those principles which relate to vision and visible objects on account of those glasses only lately invented." In the preface the author states that the book was inspired by the wonderful astronomical discoveries which Galilei had made with his telescope and reported in the preceding year 1610. The book brings some new results in all fields. The critical angle of total internal reflection is defined in the chapter dealing with refraction.

Kepler used the camera obscura for studying experimentally the properties of some lenses in order to confirm the results of his mathematical considerations. Kepler arrived at the conclusion that the internal surface of the crystalline eye lens must be a hyperboloid for the best focusing conditions on the retina, thus anticipating Descartes. Kepler discussed combinations of convex and concave lenses both for each kind in itself and with the other kind, which includes the Galilean telescope; what we call today the astronomical or Keplerian telescope is described. However, no reference to the use of a combination of lenses as a microscope is made, although the mathematical treatment of lens properties is quite thorough. It includes for example also an investigation of spherical aberration.

René Descartes (1596–1650) published his famous *Discours de la Méthode* in Holland in 1637. It is in its main part a philosophical treatise which established the fame of its author all over Europe but it contains also essays on geometry, meteors, and optics in which applications the usefulness of his method is demonstrated. In the optical part, called *Dioptrice* or *Dioptrique*, Descartes strives at a deeper understanding of optical experiments from mechanical considerations. Already Hero of Alexandria had felt the necessity of explaining the law of reflection by assuming that it was a property of light always to take the shortest path between two points. Kepler tried to understand the path of the reflected ray from the specific resistance which the light finds in the dense media.

Descartes, however, tried to establish a complete system of optics on mechanical principles based on the assumption of an ethereal fluid penetrating all bodies and the space around them extending throughout the whole universe. The particles of this fluid were thought to be very small and to act like balls bouncing off other bodies. In this way Descartes explains the equality of the angles in reflection as a plausible mechanical phenomenon. By suitable assumptions on impact and resistance of those balls impinging on the surface of optical media he arrived at the law of reflection which he properly formulated as the constancy of the ratio of the sines of incident and reflected angles.

Descartes does not mention the names of any other investigators in this connection. Usually the law of refraction is ascribed to Willibrord Snell, 1591–1626, a professor of mathematics at Leyden University, who had taught about his law in his courses on optics. He had prepared a publication but it was never printed. Huygens is reported to have seen the manuscript in which the law of refraction was expressed in mathematical terms, stating that for two different optical media the ratio of the cosecants of the incident and the refracted angles stays constant if the angle of incidence varies. Later, also by Descartes, this law was expressed by the respective sine functions.

The publication of Descartes' *Dioptrique* was followed by a violent controversy which continued even after Descartes' death. The theoretical derivation of the law was assailed. Descartes had stated that the velocity of light in the denser medium was increased, whereas his opponents argued that it would be retarded. Hero had argued for the law of reflection that a ray would follow the shortest path. For the law of refraction, Fermat assumed that a ray following an intrinsic law of nature would travel that path in a denser medium which requires the shortest time. For this argument it must be assumed then that the velocity of light would be reduced in a denser medium. In the eighth chapter of the *Dioptrique* Descartes showed how the aberration of a spherical lens could be avoided by non-spherical surfaces as for example ellipsoids or hyperboloids. He gave detailed instructions how to grind and polish this kind of lens and found one or two glass makers who tried to make them, but without much success.

Descartes suggested also an application of nonspherical lenses for single lens microscopes. One lens was to be mounted in the vertex of a spherical concave mirror so that it would protrude a little through a hole in the mirror, the object being held at its focus by means of a prong. The whole apparatus had to be held close to the eye and aimed at the sun. The light rays would illuminate the object and it would appear greatly magnified if observed through the lens. This instrument was intended for hand use only.

Descartes described another more refined one to be mounted on a high stand in the same way as telescopes are mounted. A parabolic mirror is provided, in the focus of which the object has to be held. The illumination is enhanced by means of a convex lens in front of the object. It is observed from the back through a compound microscope the tube of which is put through a hole in the vertex of the mirror. An interesting feature of this scheme is Descartes' proposition to use a Galilean type arrangement of one convex and one concave lens, both of which have to be hyperboloid.

Still another proposition of Descartes has the purpose of diminishing spherical aberration in a unique way. He suggested putting a water-filled tube with a membrane at one end right at the eyeball. The membrane would then adapt itself and its shape to the contour of the eyeball. The other end of the tube would be closed with a curved glass disc shaped similar to the eye curve. The effect would be to increase the depth of the aqueous humour of the eye because the refractive indices of this liquid and of water are about the same. From such an arrangement Descartes expected larger images of the objects observed, but he realized the inconvenience in practical use. He suggested replacing the water-filled tube by a long glass cylinder with a suitably curved surface at both ends, or a hollow tube with lenses at both ends. Their surfaces had to be shaped in a special way as required by his idea of increasing the effective depth of the human eye humour by optical means.

Athanasius Kircher, 1601–1680, wrote the book *Ars Magna Lucis et Umbrae* the first edition of which was published in Rome 1646 and the second edition in Amsterdam 1671. It contains one section "*De Mira Rerum Naturalium Constitutione per Smicroscopium Investiganda.*" The word *Smicroscopium* used here comes from the Ionian dialect in which Herodotus wrote. Kircher is the only author using this word. It fell out of use in later years. In his book he gives an account of all the microscopes of his day:

(1) Two convex lenses are used.

(2) Glass spheres filled with water are used as single lenses.

(3) Tiny glass spheres at the end of a tube are used with the object to be put right on it.

(4) One lens is used which has one spherical and one hyperboloid surface.

(5) Two hyperboloid glasses are used, one convex and one concave, as described also by Descartes.

Gaspar Schott (1608–1666) wrote *Magia Universalis Naturae et Artis* with a chapter: "Microscopes and Their Wonderful Power in Revealing the Constitution of Natural Objects" which appeared in 1657. In this book the author gives a classification of microscopes of his day:

(1) A short tube with a flat glass at one end and a glass sphere at the other end. The object had to be put inside of the tube on the flat glass.

(2) A glass vase into which small objects are put at the bottom and the neck of which is closed with a crystalline lens of a spherical shape.

Other examples for microscopes are given which repeat what Kircher had listed previously.

Peter Borelius made in 1655 a contribution to microscopy of historical importance in his book *De Vero Telescopii Inventore*. He collected important evidence concerning the inventors of the microscope which is used in the foregoing text. He also gave a classification of the microscopes of his time:

(1) Two glasses are put at the ends of a small tube. One is convex with spherical surfaces and the other is plane and carries the object. When this was a fly "enlarged to the size of an elephant", the instrument was called "conspicilium muscarium", or fly glass. But it would be "conspicilium pulicarium" or flea glass when the object was a flea enlarged "to the size of a camel", much to the enjoyment of the observer.

(2) One single spherule was mounted at the end of a tube. At the other end would be a small glass box containing sundry tiny objects.

(3) Two convex lenses were used with much superior properties.

(4) Several coaxial tube parts were mounted in such a way that the whole could be lengthened and shortened. It would contain three or four different lenses.

Borelius mentioned also the names of some of the more important opticians of his time and described the manufacture of their instruments, including the grinding and polishing of lenses.

In another part of his book Borelius gave a record of microscopical observations intended to be a guide to those who "wished to study the Majesty of God in minute creation and an offering of respect to the worthy citizens of Middelburg among whom the microscope had been invented." Listed are milk, blood, vinegar, two kinds of lice, fleas, six kinds of worms, spider eyes and eggs, pimples, ants, moss, ferns, caterpillars, butterflies and other objects up to one hundred exactly.

The attitude of Borelius demonstrated in his work and the details both of his instruments and observations classify him more as an amateur of optics; he was a physician at the court of Louis XIV.

Several other writers in the 17th century were delighting in listing the innumerable objects of the new world invisible to the naked eye. Among them was Robert Hooke, who gave a list of some 60 microscopical observations in his *Micrographia*, written in English and published in 1665. This book is remarkable because it also contains a detailed description of his compound microscope which had two convex lenses and, what would be called later, a field lens which he had learned to use with advantage for some observations. He also built a special illuminator in order to get brighter images of his objects. He complained about the unavoidable smallness of the objective lens which will not "admit a sufficient number of Rayes to magnifie the Object beyond a determinate bigness." He mounted on a stand an oil lamp, then in the proper distance, "a pretty large Globe of Glass fill'd with exceeding clear Brine," and a convex lens. With the flame of the lamp, the glass ball and the lens coaxially lined up he at first got enough light, "but after a certain degree of magnifying they leave us again to the lurch."

In one of his models Hooke used two lenses and filled the space between them with water. Such an arrangement was an improvement of Descartes' water tube described about 30 years before. Hooke praised the brightness of the image obtained in this way, but he did not use it much "for other inconveniences." The pictures in Hooke's book are considered by some historians the first precise and detailed technical observations depicted which we possess.

Another important microscopist of this time was Johannes Hevelius, (1611–1687) a German astronomer who devoted much time to the study of other scientific fields. His *Machina Coelestis* was printed in two volumes, the first of which, published in 1673, contains descriptions of his microscopes. He expressed his admiration for the English microscopes, probably of Hooke's design, but improved it by his invention of a micrometric fine focusing device. It consisted in a vertical screw-threaded rod, rotating in a spherical nut which pushed a sliding sleeve along another rod upon turning of the screw. The body of the microscope was fastened to the sleeve which, upon traveling along the rod, would gently lift or lower the microscope tube. With this "fine adjustment" microscope design made another important advance.

In the following century further progress in design and applications of the microscope was made with substantial participation of amateur microscopists, among whom Antonj van Leeuwenhoek must be mentioned as the most famous and successful. He lived all his life from 1632–1723 in Delft, Holland, where he was active in business on a small scale as a haberdasher, draper, Chamberlain to the Sheriffs, and surveyor. He was an amateur without any scientific education and special-

ized in optical lens grinding and polishing, in which art he acquired a high professional skill. All his observations and discoveries were made with homemade single lens microscopes, but no description of the manner of manufacturing or of using them was left by Leeuwenhoek. He never divulged his secret methods with which he could outperform all other microscopists for at least a century.

However, a few of his original microscopes are still in existence and have been studied. They have all very small double-convex lenses mounted in a socket between two metal plates, about 1.5 × 3.5 centimeters, riveted together. The object was held by a needle near the socket by means of which the object could be brought into the proper position. The lenses had a focal length of from fractions of a millimeter to about five millimeters, and a magnifying power from about 50 times to 270 times. Coarse and fine focusing were accomplished by means of two screws, one longer and vertical and another shorter and horizontal, the latter being fastened crosswise on the former by a nut piece which held the object needle. Upon proper operation of these two screws, the object could be accurately focused and rotated.

Twenty-six of Leeuwenhoek's microscopes were bequeathed to the Royal Society, where they all vanished about a century ago. The rest Leeuwenhoek left with his daughter when he died. After her death in 1745, they were auctioned off and scattered; most of them were acquired by Dutchmen. From the sales-catalog Leeuwenhoek seems to have left 247 complete microscopes with lenses and objects still in place and in addition to these 172 lenses mounted in their plates. Three lenses were made from quartz. The plates were mostly made from silver but three were of gold and sold by weight.

His observations and discoveries Leeuwenhoek described in letters (165 of them) mostly directed to the Royal Society in

London, which made him a Fellow in 1618. His letters have been translated from the old-fashioned Dutch which was Leeuwenhoek's mother tongue into English and Latin; many of them were published in the *Philosophical Transactions* from 1673 to 1723. A complete edition of Leeuwenhoek's letters was never published, but a collection of them appeared from 1695–1719 under the title *"Arcana Naturae ope microscopiorum detecta"* or "Mysteries of Nature Discovered by Means of Microscopes."

Some historians blame Leeuwenhoek for his naive ignorance; others praise him as the founder of bacteriology and protozoology. By the end of the 17th century Leeuwenhoek was the only earnest and scientific microscopist in the world. He seems to have been the first to really see and describe "animalculae" (the "little animals"), including spermatozoa and bacteria.

There were many contemporaries and followers of Leeuwenhoek who tried to imitate him but they were seriously hampered by the low quality of the optical lenses available at that time. Neither had they the excellent mechanical skill for making their own lenses as Leeuwenhoek had done, nor did they have the exceptional keenness of his eye. There is no wonder then that this whole area was not quite respectable among scientists and remained so for quite a long time. Numerous indications of this attitude can be found, for example in the *London Encyclopedia* in 1829 in an article entitled *"Optics:"*

"Microscopes, though but toys compared with telescopes, nevertheless deserve to be rendered as perfect as possible; for they yield not to them in the quantity and variety of rational amusement which they are capable of introducing to us, though not of the sublime description of the wonders of the heavens. Compound microscopes, though not so much to be depended upon for the purposes of discovery and philosophical investigation as single lenses, are still best adapted for recreation."

The preference of single lenses expressed in this article over compound microscopes has its reason in increasing awareness of aberrations, of which especially chromatic aberration is very harmful to the quality of the images attainable with a compound microscope. The so-called spherical aberration, brought about by the use of spherical lenses, could be remedied to a large extent, as Newton had shown in his *"Optics,"* published 1704. But he also thought that the chromatic abberation was unavoidable because the production of colors by dispersion seemed to be inseparable from the refraction necessary for the formation of images by lenses. This had been found by Newton experimentally. He also derived a mathematical formula for dispersion which was criticized by Euler in 1750 and a new formula was proposed. However, about 80 years later, Cauchy showed that Euler's formula was untenable and suggested another. This field of mathematical optics has been worked on by many other scientists and mathematicians up into modern times.

Many experimental and theoretical investigations were made in the 100 years following the publication of Newton's "Optics" and it was found that the dispersion and refraction change in a different way in going from one medium to another and the problem was recognized to consist in finding the proper combination of two or more optical media.

Development of Microscopy from 1723 to Modern Times

The problem of manufacturing achromatic lenses, at first for telescopes only, was solved by several amateurs and scientists, either entirely or partially independently. Among them were Ch. M. Hall in 1729, a barrister and amateur in optics; L. Euler, a mathematician, in 1747; S. Klingenstierna, a mathematician, in 1755; J. Dollond, an optician, in 1755. The latter was producing lenses with reduced chromatic aberrations on a commercial scale from that time on.

The decisive experiments had been made by Hall, who found that flint glass differs only slightly in refractive power from ordinary crown glass, though its dispersion is more than twice as large. This led to a co-axial combination of a strong positive crown glass lens with a weaker negative lens of flint glass, which compensates the chromatic aberration of the other lens but reduces its magnification to only about one-half. This is the type of lens which Dollond brought on the market for telescopes from about 1760 on. The difficulty in making perfect chromatically corrected lenses for the microscope seemed unsurmountable because of their necessary exceedingly small size.

Only very few experimenters were successful in their efforts at that time. An example is an achromatic microscope objective in the possession of the Utrecht University Museum which had been made by an amateur in 1791. He was a cavalry colonel, named F. Beeldsnijder. Even professional opticians, such as Fraunhofer in Munich, Amici in Modena, Charles in Paris, and others, were failing in the first quarter of the 19th century. However, as early as 1807, Harmanus van Deijl, optician in Amsterdam, Holland, had produced satisfactory achromatic objectives for sale and had published his efforts and results. Obviously, it had been impossible for a long time to learn from his experiences.

In 1824 a new principle for making higher-powered achromatic objectives for the microscope was introduced by the French physicist Selligue, who suggested screwing several low-powered achromatic lenses together. In this way, a higher magnification was obtained without grinding and polishing lenses with very short focal length. This principle was used and improved by the commercial opticians of that time, Chevalier in France, Amici in Italy, and Lister in England.

The method of finding the best combinations of lenses for the desired effect was more or less trial and error, leading to a tremendous waste, and it was Carl Zeiss in Jena, Germany, who was no longer willing to accept this situation. In order to bring to an end "das ewige bei uns Optikern gebräuchliche Probieren" meaning "the eternal trying out of lenses so customary with us opticians," Zeiss formed a partnership with Ernst Abbe, a young physicist at the University of Jena, who cleared the theoretical background and calculated better and better lenses in the future. From 1883 on apochromatic objectives were made which were corrected both for achromasy and for spherical aberration at three different wave lengths. Because glass with new optical properties was needed, Schott's Optical Glass Works were founded at Jena. It produced all the optical glass needed by Zeiss. This cooperation turned out to be so advantageous that the Dutch and English monopoly in optics was no longer unchallenged after the second half of the 19th century.

An important contribution to the optical art was made by Abbe in 1878 by the design of immersion objectives, the principles of which had been well known for about 200 years. In the 17th century Hooke had made the observation that he got much clearer pictures of the "animalcules" living in water when the front lens of his microscope touched the water so that there was no air between the lens and the object. The explanation is that the resolving power of an objective is proportional to its aperture or to the vertex angle of the cone of light which the front lens admits. This aperture is much reduced by total reflection of the light coming from the object and going in one case, either through water and air or, in the other case, through water, a cover glass, and air into the front lens.

In Hooke's experiments this loss was avoided because the interspace between the object and the front lens of his microscope was entirely filled with water. Hooke naturally did not know this explanation but Amici in 1850 tried to make use of this principle. Obviously the effect would be the more useful the more similar the refractive power of the medium of the interspace between the object and the front lens came to the refractive power of glass. Amici tried other liquids, e.g., glycerin and oil, with some success.

These problems were brought to the attention of Abbe by English friends with a request for investigations. He complied only hesitantly because the great amount of work necessary did not seem to him to be justified by only limited applicability, as for instance in metallurgy. But he measured and tried a great number of liquids, about 300, and found the best to be cedar oil. The next step was to modify the objective lens so that it would be better adjusted to the optical data of the oil. In this way the old idea of Descartes of optically homogenizing the path of light through several media, which he had tried with his crude water tube, found a revival in a refined manner in modern times.

With apochromatic and homogeneous immersion systems the optical microscope was approaching the limit of its power of resolution, which is about 250 millimicrons for visible light, permitting the observation and identification of most bacteria. This limit was shown by Abbe to be determined by the wave length of the light used for observation.

About the results of his experimental and theoretical investigations Abbe reported in a great number of publications beginning in 1869. His complete theory of the microscope appeared in periodicals from 1888–1895.

Recent Lines of Development

The microscope had been found to be an instrument with a very wide general applicability in many fields of research and developmental technology. It could be expected that with the further growth of these fields needs would arise which would demand special requirements of diversified applications leading to detailed specializations of microscope design and methods of use which deviate more or less from tradition.

Examples of this development are such fields as interference microscopy, polarizing microscopy, X-ray microscopy, and the so-called flying spot microscopy. Also belonging in this group are the reflecting microscope, the fluorescence and the phase contrast microscope, which are briefly described in the following.

The Reflecting Microscope. The principles of a reflecting microscope were first described by Isaac Newton (1672) in a letter to the Royal Society in London. He might have realized that the objective of his reflecting telescope, described twenty years before, could be used as a microscope objective of long focal length if the light travel through the instrument would be reversed. In the following 100 years other inventors tried this principle also on the other reflecting telescope types known at that time. However, about 1824 this line of development practically came to an end because of the introduction and further improvements of achromatic lenses.

A new phase began in 1931, induced by the important advantages which reflective systems have over refractive systems for special applications. These are the absolute achromatism, the long working distance, and its unlimited applicability for a very wide range of wavelengths. Depending on the special conditions several distinct groups have been developed during the last 30 years.

For single mirror objectives materials like quartz, lithium fluoride and other synthetic inorganic crystals are used for the ultraviolet and the infrared region. The practical use of these systems was found to be awkward in some cases because the customary microscope stand and its accessories, which had their own long line of development, usually could not be used. Active in this field were men like R. Smith, 1738; K. Schwarzschild, 1905; H. Chrétien, 1922; B. K. Johnson,

1934; A. H. Linfoot, 1938; D. D. Maksutov, 1944; J. D. Dyson, 1949; A. Elliot, 1950; and others.

In two-mirror objectives a concave mirror is used for compensation of the aberrations of a second, convex, mirror. This principle was refined by the application of immersion and non-spherical systems, monochromators, interferometers, and spectroscopes. Workers in this field were Hershgorin and associates in 1941; D. R. Burch, 1943; E. M. Brumberg, 1943; A. H. Bennett and associates, 1948; W. E. Seeds, 1949; D. L. Wood, 1950; E. R. Blout and associates 1950; D. W. Dewhirst, 1951; S. Miyata, 1952; and many others.

In solid objectives several reflecting surfaces are used but the space between them is filled with glass, or, in some cases, quartz. Some authors feel that further development of this type of optical systems might well improve the standards of the old microscope construction as they are followed at the present time. Contributors to the field of solid objectives were D. D. Maksutov, 1932; D. G. Wynne, 1952; A. Bouwers, 1952, and others.

Fluorescence Microscopy. The advantage of this special field of microscopy which was first mentioned in publications in 1929 is the possibility of making visible or studying finer details of the structure of living protozoa or cells of tissues which might differ from their surroundings in fluorescing power under illumination by ultraviolet light. This necessitates the use of special optical systems, as for example lenses made from quartz and aluminized mirrors. Also special optical filters were used for a better definition and a suitable choice of a particular section of the spectrum. Contributions to this field were made by M. Haitinger, P. Ellinger; 1929, J. Smiles, 1933; J. Dyson, 1949; J. R. Benford, 1947; B. K. Johnson, 1949; F. Bräutigam and associates, 1949; C. A. Thorold, 1954, and others.

Phase Contrast Microscopy. The founder of this field of microscopy, F. Zernike, used a principle known from the study of diffraction gratings. This principle was at first used for the testing of telescope objectives. In 1942, the discoverer recognized its importance for microscopy and the number of its applications grew with every year.

In the usual microscopic observation the objects are visible due to their stronger or weaker absorption, in other words, the reduction of the amplitude of the light waves. In the optical system of a phase contrast microscope another property of the object material is used which consists in shifting the phase of the light waves more or less depending on the material constants. Upon leaving the object the light does not appear to be changed in any way when observed with the usual optical means. However, when it is combined again with another part of the original light bundle which has suffered a fixed change of its phase by a so-called phase plate, interference occurs which renders visible details of the image which could not be seen under a traditional microscope.

An especially important field of this technique is the observation of details in living cells which must not be harmed or changed by the usual methods of selective staining.

Those interested in the development of the mathematical theory and the contributions to optics of men like Descartes, Newton, Huygens, Gauss, Hamilton, Maxwell, Seidel, Helmholtz, Abbe, Gullstrand, and T. S. Smith are referred to articles in the proper periodicals as for example published by the Royal Microscopical Society in London. A comprehensive article, 22 pages, about the theory of optical systems was published by M. Herzberger in *Zeitschrift für Instrumentenkunde* Vol. 52, 1932.

Historical Review

In the course of the development of microscopy from its origin to modern times, distinct periods can be recognized. They are usually initiated by a technical breakthrough, followed by a whole series of discoveries in new fields not accessible by the optical means in use before.

This mode of progress is well known from other fields of technical and scientific endeavor but it is especially intriguing to outline the respective phases in the development of a field the study of which was denied so long to unaided human senses. In the field of microscopy the following periods can be recognized, in each of which the technical progress and the achievements are named:

First Period: From about 1600 to 1723. Invention of the microscope. Discovery of the law of refraction by Snell and Descartes, 1637. Establishment of geometrical optics by Fermat, Newton, Huygens and Euler. *Achievements:* Discovery of the capillaries by Malphigi in 1660. Discovery of plant cells in fossil wood by Hooke in 1664 and the first magnified drawings of small animals, the flea and the louse, by the same in 1665. Discovery of the mammalian ovarian follicle by De Graaf in 1672. Descriptions by Leeuwenhoek of protozoa in 1674, striation of muscle fibers in 1682, bacteria in 1676, spermatozoa in 1672, yeast cells in 1688, leukocytes in 1689, axon and sheath of nerve fibers in 1717.

Second Period: From 1723 to 1830. Almost no progress from Leeuwenhoek's death at the beginning of this period until the end. This was the high time of the hobby microscopist, best exemplified by the title of a book which appeared in 1763. It is Ledermüller's "Mikroskopische Gemüts- und Augenergötzung," which might be translated by "Microscopical Pasttime for Eyes and Soul."

Third Period: From 1830 to 1878. Invention and further improvements of achromatic lenses. *Achievements:* Fermentation is explained from the action of living cells by Cagniard de la Tour in 1837. The first clear description of the division of the cell nucleus is given by Leyden in 1848. Anthrax bacteria

discovered by Pollender in 1849. Establishment of histology as a special field by Kölliker in 1852. The first microtome was designed by Welcker in 1856. Lactic acid bacteria were discovered by Pasteur in 1857. Introduction of antisepsis based on microscopial evidence by Lister in 1864. Methods of selective staining developed for tissues by Gerlach in 1858 and for bacteria by Weigert in 1875.

Fourth Period: From 1878 to 1931. Introduction and further development of the homogeneous immersion. *Achievements:* Gonorrhoea cocci found by Neisser in 1879. Leprosy germs seen by Hansen and typhus germs by Ebert in 1880. Malaria parasites seen within red blood cells by Laveran in 1880. In the two decades from 1880 to 1900 numerous other pathogenic protozoa and bacteria were discovered, as tuberculosis and cholera by Koch in 1882, plague by Kitasato in 1894, tetanus by Nicolaier in 1884, Syphilis by Schaudinn in 1905, of foot and mouth disease using ultraviolet light by Frosch in 1924.

Fifth Period: From 1931 to the present time. Invention and development of the electron microscope. Further development of the light microscope into numerous new models for special applications. *Achievements:* The first micrographs of virus corpuscles, not visible with the light microscope, were made by Kausch and Ruska of the tobacco mosaic virus in 1939.

It is obvious that these periods overlap each other widely and many a discovery might just as well be assigned to the preceding or the following period. However, a general pattern is certainly recognizable.

REFERENCES

Magie, W. F., "A Source Book in Physics," McGraw Hill Book Co., New York, 1935.

Sarton, G., "A History of Science," Harvard University Press, 1. vol. 1952, 2. vol., 1959.

Sarton, G., "Ancient and Medieval Science," University of Pennsylvania Press, Philadelphia, 1953.

"Moments of Discovery" ed. by G. Schwartz and Ph. W. Bishop, Basic Books Inc., New York, 1958.

King, H. C., "The History of the Telescope" Sky Publishing Corp., Cambridge, Mass., 1955.

"Modern Methods of Microscopy" ed. by A. E. Vickers, Butterworth Scientific Publications, London, 1956.

Rooseboom, M., "Microscopium," Leiden, 1956.

Dobell, C., "Antony van Leeuwenhoek and his Little Animals," Russell and Russell, Inc., New York, 1958.

"Origin and Development of the Microscope" as illustrated by the Catalogues ... of the Royal Microscopical Society. ed. by A. N. Disney. The Royal Microscopical Society, London 1928.

Hoppe, E., "Geschichte der Physik," F. Vieweg AG, Braunschweig, 1926.

Rosenberger, F., "Geschichte der Physik," (3 vols.), F. Vieweg AG, Braunschweig, 1890.

Dannemann, F., "Die Naturwissenschaften in ihrer Entwicklung und in ihrem Zusammenhang," 2. ed. W. Engelmann, Leipzig, 4 volumes, 1920–23.

Articles in *Isis, Scientific American, American Journal of Physics, Science, Forschungen zur Geschichte der Optik, Zeitschrift für Instrumentenkunde,* and others.

E. K. Weise

PARTICLE SIZE AND SHAPE MEASUREMENTS AND STATISTIC (*See also* pp. 406, 408)

Particle Size Methods

The microscope for making particle size measurements should be equipped with a graduated mechanical stage, achromatic or apochromatic objectives including an oil immersion objective, a substage condenser, and a graduated fine focusing adjustment. A revolving nosepiece is desirable which can be used to attach three or four objectives, preferably parfocal, to the microscope. A monocular microscope is preferable to the binocular for highly critical work. A phase contrast microscope is often useful for measuring particles of low contrast, and a polarizing microscope is useful when differentiation among various types of particles or identification of particles is desirable. The light source should be equipped with a condensing lens and a field diaphragm, and should be focusable.

A number of accessories are either necessary or highly convenient. Particle diameters are generally measured with eyepiece (ocular) micrometers which consist of scales to be placed in the focal plane of the ocular. A number of types are available and the type used depends somewhat on the definition of diameter which is employed. If the diameter is defined in terms of actual dimensions of the particle, a linear scale is desirable. "Globe and circle" micrometers are convenient for rapid sizing, the diameter being defined as the diameter of a circle whose area is equal to the projected area of the particle. Filar micrometers have either a movable scale or a movable cross hair and fixed scale. Ocular micrometers must be calibrated for every combination of objective, ocular, and tube length used, and the calibration is usually accomplished with a stage micrometer with linear rulings.

Another useful accessory is the dark field condenser, which often provides increased contrast. A condenser with central stop is useful for fairly large particles, but the "Cardioid" condenser is preferred for particles having diameters close to the limit of resolution of the microscope.

Special devices which produce uniform illumination of opaque objects by reflected light are often very helpful. The illumination may be vertical or annular.

Particle size distributions are sometimes made from photomicrographs. Advantages are less eyestrain and a permanent record of the appearance of the particles; disadvantages are the additional time-consuming steps and less flexibility in the examination of a field. Microprojection equipment is often useful, especially if the images can be projected on a disposable screen such as a sheet of white paper. The images can be checked off as measured, thus avoiding duplication.

The proper preparation of slides to produce representative, well-dispersed samples is especially important. It is, of course, necessary to start with a small representative sample of the powder, a few milligrams of which are usually dispersed in a drop of liquid on a clean slide. A wooden toothpick is a convenient dispersing tool which has the advantage over glass or steel that it is not apt to crush or shatter the particles. The suspension is spread over the glass slide as a thin film and covered with a clean cover glass to complete the preparation. The following are a few of the many liquids which have been used for dispersing powders.

Water	Butanol
Water and ammonia	Dammar
Water and potassium citrate (2%)	Turpentine
Water and Calgon (0.1%)	Duco cement
Glycol	Glucose syrup
Glycerol	Xylene
Ethanol	Polymethylmethacrylate
Acetone	Polystyrene
Cyclehexanol	Solutions of surface-active agents

Considerable experimentation with different liquids is sometimes required before one is found which is satisfactory for a given powder.

A sufficiently large number of particles must be measured so that the size distribution obtained is representative of the original powder. Usually at least 200 particles are measured. If the size distribution is very wide there may be hundreds or thousands of small particles for each of the large ones. In this case it is often helpful to measure all the larger particles in a relatively large area with a low-power objective and all the small particles in a much smaller area with a high-power objective; the results are combined arithmetically for any arbitrary area.

The number of fields which should be examined depends largely on the number of particles per field. The choice of fields can be random or according to a pattern, but should be made prior to observing the fields through the microscope in order to avoid unconscious preferential selection.

When measuring the sizes of particles whose diameters are close to the theoretical limit of resolution of the microscope, proper alignment and illumination are particularly important. Thus, when illuminating with transmitted light ("brightfield" illumination) critical or Kohler illumination should be used to obtain the full benefit of the capabilities of the microscope.

Images of particles observed with the microscope are larger than the particles by an amount approximately equal to the limit of resolution of the microscope. The amount of this enlargement varies somewhat with the illumination, the type of material, and the ability of the observer to distinguish various degrees of contrast. Some microscopists subtract the limit of resolution from the measured diameters when determining particle sizes which are close to the limit of resolution.

The thickness of particles can be measured with the fine-focusing adjustment. The graduations on this adjustment must be calibrated and this is readily accomplished with small beads or cylindrical fibers. The diameter of the bead or fiber is measured with an ocular micrometer and the microscope is focused on the glass slide and then on the top of the fiber or bead, noting the readings on the fine adjustment. The difference in readings corresponds to the diameter. Obviously the thickness of an irregular object can then be obtained by focusing on the slide and on the top of the object and noting the difference in readings.

Many special techniques are available for determining particle sizes and size distributions. Electronic methods have been developed for scanning the image formed by a microscope. For example, a television rastor can be placed at the ocular of the microscope so that a minute spot of light scans the particle field on the microscope slide, while the transmitted light is picked up by a photo-multiplier tube. A similar result can be achieved by illuminating the sample with a very narrow fixed beam of light and scanning the sample by automatically moving the stage. The beam, after passing through the sample, passes through the microscope and into a photomultiplier tube. In each case the signal from the photomultiplier tube is analyzed electronically and presented as a size distribution.

Equipment has been developed for obtaining photomicrographs of aerosol particles without having to remove them from the air or other gas. Actual images of the particles are obtained in one technique, while in others diffraction patterns are obtained whose intensities are functions of the particle sizes. Such methods are especially useful for obtaining the size distributions of particles such as fog droplets which might be changed during a collection process.

Particles which are smaller than the limit of resolution of a microscope can be observed as unresolved dots of light using the ultra-microscope. A mean particle size can be determined by suspending a known weight of powder in a known volume of some liquid and determining the number of particles per unit volume. A hemacytometer-type cell is often convenient for holding the suspension during the counting process. The bottom of the cell is ruled off into squares and "snap counts" are made of whether there are none, 1, 2, 3, etc., particles per square at any moment.

Theory and Statistics of Analysis.[*] The word *particle*, in its most general sense, refers to any object having definite physical boundaries, without any limit with respect to size. Particles varying from about 0.01 to 1000 microns are considered in this discussion. The term is often ambiguous unless carefully defined for a specific case. For example, the particles in a soil may be con-

* From "Encyclopedia of Chemistry Supplement," Reinhold, New York. 1958, p. 210.

sidered to be the loose aggregates, the "ultimate" particles of which the aggregates are composed, or even individual mineral grains in the ultimate particles.

The term *particle size* is also usually ambiguous unless defined for each type of application. Particle size is usually described in terms of rather artificially defined "diameters" which generally fall in one of two classes. Diameters of one class, called statistical diameters, are defined in terms of the geometry of the individual particles and are determined for a large number of particles. Definitions of some statistical diameters are:

(1) Martin's diameter: the distance between opposite sides of the particle, measured crosswise of the particle, and on a line bisecting the projected area.

(2) The diameter of the circle whose area is the same as the projected area of the particle.

(3) The shorter of the two dimensions exhibited.

(4) The average of the two dimensions exhibited.

(5) The average of the three dimensions of the particle.

(6) The distance between two tangents to the particle, measured crosswise of the field (for example, of a microscope), and perpendicular to the tangents.

Diameters determined by sieving are also statistical diameters.

Diameters of the other class are defined in terms of the physical properties of the particles. Examples are diameters determined by sedimentation or elutriation.

Numerous definitions of the mean particle size of a powder may be used, the choice depending largely on the use to which the data are to be applied. It is convenient to define such means in terms of data which have been classified into groups (classes) which are defined by means of particle size limits called class boundaries. The midpoint of each interval is called the class mark (d_i), the number of particles in each interval is called the frequency (f_i), and the total number of particles measured is denoted by n. The following table is a summary of the definitions of various means.

Name	Symbol	Definition
Arithmetic mean	$\bar{d}$	$\dfrac{1}{n} \sum d_i f_i$
Geometric mean	d_g	$(d_1^{f_1} d_2^{f_2} d_3^{f_3} \cdots d_n^{f_n})^{1/n}$
Harmonic mean	d_{na}	$\left[\dfrac{1}{n} \sum \left(\dfrac{f_i}{d_i} \right) \right]^{-1}$
Mean surface diameter	d_s	$\sqrt{\dfrac{\sum f_i d_i^2}{n}}$
Mean weight diameter	d_w	$\left(\dfrac{\sum f_i d_i^3}{n} \right)^{1/3}$
Linear mean diameter	d_1	$\dfrac{\sum f_i d_i^2}{\sum f_i d_i}$
Surface mean diameter	d_{vs}	$\dfrac{\sum f_i d_i^3}{\sum f_i d_i^2}$
Weight mean diameter	d_{wm}	$\dfrac{\sum f_i d_i^4}{\sum f_i d_i^3}$

The median and the mode are also often used as a measure of central tendency. The median is the middle value (or interpolated middle value) of a set of measurements arranged in order of magnitude. The mode is the measurement with the maximum frequency. The mode is sometimes reported with the arithmetic mean or the median to give an indication of the skewness of the distribution.

Some quantitative indication of particle shape is often desirable. Harold Heywood has suggested the following method. The particle is assumed to be resting on a plane in the position of greatest stability. The breadth (B) is the distance between two parallel lines tangent to the projection of the particle on the plane and placed so that the distance between them is as small as possible. The length (L) is the distance between parallel lines tangent to the projection and perpendicular to the lines defining the breadth. The thickness (T) is the distance between two planes parallel to the plane of greatest stability and tangent to the surface of the particle. Flakiness is defined as B/T and elongation as L/B.

The sizes of particles in a powder or other particulate system may be represented by some mean value, as indicated above. Usually some indication of size distribution or spread is desirable and can be provided by the standard deviation,

$$\sqrt{\frac{1}{n} \sum (d_i - \bar{d})^2 f_i},$$

or by means of quartiles if the median is used as the measure of central tendency. Quartiles are the values completing the first 25% and the first 75% of the values when they are arranged according to increasing order of magnitude. However, it is often necessary to provide a more complete indication of the particle size distribution. Classified data can readily be represented by a bar type of graph called a histogram. The position of the bar locates the class interval and the length of the bar corresponds to the frequency.

Suppose that in preparing the histogram an infinite number of particles are measured and the class intervals made to approach zero. The ends of the bars would become a smooth curve, called the size frequency curve. The function describing the curve is the distribution function. Probably the most familiar distribution function is the normal distribution, defined by the equation

$$f(d) = \frac{1}{s\sqrt{2\pi}} \exp\left[-\tfrac{1}{2} \left(\frac{d - \bar{d}}{s} \right)^2 \right]$$

where s is the standard deviation. The standard deviation for particles which are distributed normally is such that the interval

$(d - s)$ to $(d + s)$ includes about 68 % of the particles.

Other functions which fit distributions often encountered are (1) the log normal distribution:

$$f(d) = \frac{1}{\log s_g \sqrt{2\pi}} \exp\left[-\tfrac{1}{2}\left(\frac{\log d - \log d_g}{\log s_g}\right)\right]^2$$

(2) the Rosin-Rammler function:

$$\frac{dw}{d(d)} = 100 c b d^{c-1} \exp(-bd^c),$$

(3) $$f(d) = a \exp(-bd^c),$$

and

(4) $$f(d) = ad^{-c}$$

where s_g is the standard deviation of the logarithms of the diameters, $dw/d(d)$ is the weight falling within a narrow size range $d(d)$, and a, b, and c are constants.

Cumulative curves are often used to represent particle size distributions graphically. These are curves which result from plotting the percentages of particles greater than (or less than) a given particle size against the particle size. The ordinate can represent the percentage of total surface or of total weight instead of the percentage of the number of particles. When the diameters are normally or log normally distributed the cumulative curves are straight lines when plotted on "probability" or "log probability" graph paper, respectively. Such paper is commercially available.

A very large number of methods have been proposed for determing the sizes of particles, but most of them are based on one or more of a small number of principles. Optical microscopy is often used for particle size determination. It has the advantage that the particles are observed directly and that the basic equipment is relatively inexpensive. However, it is a very tedious method if accurate results are to be obtained and is subject to large sampling errors unless adequate precautions are taken.

RICHARD D. CADLE

PLASTICS. *See* GENERAL MICROSCOPY, p. 390.

PROJECTION MICROSCOPES *See* ENGINEERING MICROSCOPES, p. 438.

PULP AND PAPER. *See* GENERAL MICROSCOPY, p. 394.

SCHMALTZ PROFILE MICROSCOPE. *See* ENGINEERING MICROSCOPES, p. 438.

STEREOSCOPIC MICROSCOPE. *See* ENGINEERING MICROSCOPES, p. 439.

METALLOGRAPHY

INDUSTRIAL RESEARCH, APPLICATIONS TO. *See* GENERAL MICROSCOPY, p. 363.
TRANSMISSION ELECTRON MICROSCOPY OF

METALS—DISLOCATIONS AND PRECIPITATION. *See* p. 291.
WEAR AND LUBRICATION. *See* ELECTRON MICROSCOPY, p. 308.

MICROMETRON AUTOMATIC MICROSCOPE

The micrometron is a new microscope which provides a fully automatic stage traverse mechanism combined with accurate photoelectric observation of the microscopic images. It is often necessary to scan systematically over large areas of tissue section in order to reveal a simple central truth relative to normal or pathological state, or to

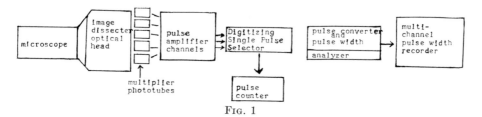

Fig. 1

count a number of blood cells, for example, in a much larger field than is provided by observation of a single area through the microscope.

As several authorities have pointed out, large numbers of single, quantitative observation events which can be gathered at great speed by an automatic microscope have a total content of significant information that a human observer simply cannot obtain in any reasonable length of time. The basic principle of operation is a quantitative digitized pulse enclosing the whole desired element of measurement within a single instrument-selected or instrument-processed pulse, which becomes the information signal. The advantage of the digital-computer automatic microscope lies in the fact that it can measure, compute and interpret at the rate of thousands of single observations per second as compared with 50 or 100 observation events that the microscopist can study in a reasonable period. The operation of these electronic circuits is a consequence of the radiation-observing properties of Geiger, proportional and scintillation counters. The block diagram of the first commercially produced instrument, the Micrometron (Optronic Research, Inc., Cambridge, Mass.) is shown in Figure 1.

Routinely it can count 10,000 blood cells in 10 to 20 seconds. When used as a counter it can take the place of 6 to 10 hematology technicians with an accuracy equivalent to the averaged result of the count of 20 human observers working simultaneously on the blood specimen from a single patient.

As a research instrument it can establish unequivocal diagnostic indices or basic standards of toxicity levels, or study fluorescence of nuclei of cells or their spectral absorbance under widely varying conditions. Unquestionably also a wide variety of inorganic and industrial materials may be routinely observed, measured and controlled by such a technique. In the words of Rovner, one of the developers of the micrometron, "It is exciting to realize that the individual blood cells have the qualities of a digitized scanning modality, probing into contact with every living cell in the human organism, and that we can now study them in large enough numbers to learn a great deal more of what they are trying to say."

REFERENCE

1. ROVNER, LEOPOLD, "Microscopy: Automatic," *Medical Physics*, Vol. III, p. 369, Year Book Publ. Inc., 1960.

G. L. CLARK

MICRORADIOGRAPHY. *See* X-RAY MICROSOCOPY, p. 561

Optical Mineralogy (Petrographic Microscopy)

Optical mineralogy utilizes the theory and methods of optical crystallography for the description, classification, and identification of opaque and nonopaque minerals, especially by observations under the polarizing microscope. Prior to about 1900 the polarizing microscope was used principally for the determination of the texture and mineralogy of rocks, and emphasis was placed on the identification of minerals by properties that could be measured in thin sections mounted on glass slides. Since 1900 instrumentation and techniques have improved rapidly, and examination of minerals under the polarizing microscope by a variety of methods has become routine procedure in many fields of science and technology.

An ultimate purpose of optical mineralogy is the accurate correlation of optical properties of all minerals with crystal structure, chemical composition, and other physical properties, and to arrive at an understanding of the influence of various physicochemical factors on the optical properties. With such information the optical technique is a valuable tool for identification of mineral substances, estimation of chemical composition, and determination of the natural history of crystallization. Optical studies, together with x-ray examinations and crystallochemical investigations within a large range of pressures and temperatures provide a complete and powerful approach to the study of the nature and genesis of minerals.

The physical properties of a mineral in equilibrium with its environment are constant and correlate directly with the chemical composition. The physical properties of a mineral of the same chemical composition which is not in equilibrium differ from those of the equilibrium mineral to an extent depending on the departure of the atomic configuration of the crystal structure from that for the equilibrium state. For example, two mineral specimens of identical gross chemical composition, but with different thermal histories, commonly show noteworthy differences in their optical properties.

Very few minerals are "pure" in the sense that the chemical composition can be expressed by a formula in which the ratios of the numbers of the atoms can be expressed in simple, whole numbers. Isomorphism is common in most minerals and comes about from mutual substitution (diadochy) of atoms or groups of atoms in crystal structures. For example, monoclinic amphiboles have a generalized formula which can be expressed as $W_3(X, Y)_5Z_8O_{22}(OH, F)_2$, in which $W = Ca$ and Na; $X = Mg$, Fe'', and Mn; $Y = Al$ and Fe'''; and $Z = Si$ and Ti. Each element contributes more or less to the optical and other properties depending on its relative amount in a crystal, the properties of the individual atoms, and their positions and manner of coordination in the crystal structure.

Correlation of optical properties with chemical composition and physical state differs in complexity from one mineral series to another. Quartz, for example, has a crystal structure that, within ordinary temperature ranges, is incapable of accepting foreign atoms except in trace amounts. Accordingly, the optical properties of quartz are constant from specimen to specimen, and are diagnostic. Minerals in which isomorphism (diadochic substitution) is characteristic show wide variations in optical properties. Some appreciation of the contributions of individual elements or radicals to optical properties is gained from a study of the specific refractive energies (Jaffe, 1956) or specific refractive capacities (Allen, 1956), particularly as the amounts of the elements or radicals in crystals influence the refractive indices.

A convenient method for showing how optical properties vary with composition is afforded by plotting data of various kinds on charts. In simpler mineral series, such as the olivine series, [(Mg, Fe)$_2$SiO$_4$], the composition of a particular member of the series can be expressed in weight or molecular proportions or percentages of Mg$_2$SiO$_4$ and Fe$_2$SiO$_4$. Using Mg$_2$SiO$_4$ and Fe$_2$SiO$_4$ as "end members" simple diagrams can be prepared which show how the optical properties vary with composition. Mineral series for which compositions can be expressed in terms of three "end members" are plotted on triangular diagrams, and so on. However, mineral series with more than four end members require polyhedral plots, and the difficulty of plotting data and interpreting diagrams becomes very great, if not almost insurmountable. In complex mineral series an effort generally is made to group similar end members in such a way that data can be plotted on simple diagrams, and it is understood that compositions determined from optical data plotted on the diagrams are only approximations.

Laboratory investigations in optical mineralogy are of three general kinds: (1) study of crystals or fragments in liquid immersions, (2) examination of single crystals or aggregates in petrographic thin sections ground to a thickness of 0.03 mm and mounted on a glass slide, and (3) examination of opaque substances in polished sections by reflected light, together with systematic etching and microchemical analysis. All techniques employ the polarizing microscope as more or less modified for a specific purpose. The theory and practice of the immersion method (Wahlstrom, 1960), the thin-section method (Moorehouse, 1959), and the polished-section method (Short, 1940, and Freund, 1954) are reviewed in several books and in numerous articles in chemical, mineralogical, and geological journals. Summaries of properties of nonopaque minerals (Winchell and Winchell, 1951; Larsen and Berman, 1934) and

of opaque minerals (Short, 1940) are found in standard referances and handboods.

The fundamental optical properties of nonopaque minerals are the principal refractive indices measured for one or more reference wave lengths of light, the crystallographic orientation of the vibration directions of light corresponding to each of the principal refractive indices, and the amount and manner of absorption of light for various directions of vibration and transmission of light by a crystal. All other optical properties can be calculated or predicted if the fundamental properties are known.

The immersion technique permits accurate measurement of refractive indices by comparison of the mineral with liquids of known refractive indices, observation of the manner of absorption of transmitted light, and, under favorable circumstances, determination of optic orientation. Other properties can be calculated or can be measured with special optical accessories. In special applications of the immersion technique crystals or fragments are observed on special multiaxis auxiliary stages that permit rotations of preparations into any desired position. Valuable additional equipment is a monochromator for varying the wave length of the source of illumination, and temperature control apparatus.

In the thin-section method refractive indices are not measured directly, but optic orientation and differential absorption of light can be determined by direct observation. Other diagnostic properties are noted or measured with the aid of a variety of optical measuring devices. As in the immersion method a multiaxis stage assists in many measurements.

Polished sections of opaque minerals are examined in reflected light from a vertical illuminator attachment. Various optical effects are noted, and properties such as reflectivity, color, and rotation of polarized light may be estimated visually or measured with spectrophotometric equipment. In practice mineral identification is expedited by systematic etch tests with corrosive reagents and by microchemical and x-ray analysis of powder scratched from the surface of the polished section.

For simple determination of minerals by optical techniques apparatus requirements are not great, but for investigations of new minerals or for the purpose of establishing accurate correlation of optical properties with composition, crystal structure, and genetic history, extensive facilities are required. A well-equipped laboratory for the examination of minerals by the methods of mineralogy, including optical mineralogy, should include the following:

(1) *Polarizing microscope* with rotatable stage, attachable 4-axis and 5-axis universal stages, and attachable vertical illuminator for examining polished surfaces of opaque substances. Appropriate optical accessories and lenses.

(2) *Temperature control equipment.* This should include apparatus for varying temperature of stage and hemispheres of universal stage and a heating stage that can be attached to the microscope stage. A high-temperature furnace may be useful for studies of certain thermal effects.

(3) *Light sources.* Included should be a white light source, a monochromator, and a series of color filters. Also useful are a sodium-vapor lamp, mercury-arc lamp, and a hydrogen-discharge tube.

(4) Spectrophotometric equipment for analyzing colored light transmitted by microscope. This equipment should be designed also to permit measurement of ellipticity of transmitted or reflected light, measurement or rotation of plane of vibration of reflected light, and measurment of reflectivity of opaque specimens.

(5) *Photomicrographic apparatus* suitable for photographing specimens by transmitted or reflected light.

(6) *Counting or measuring stage attach-*

ments such as Chayes point counter or Rosiwal stage.

(7) *Index liquids for immersion studies.* A complete set includes liquids in the index range 1.40 to 2.0, approximately. To standardize liquids an Abbe-type refractometer with temperature control suffices for the index range 1.40–1.80. Higher index liquids are standardized in a hollow prism mounted on a spectrometer.

(8) *Equipment for sample preparation and physical analysis.* Included should be all apparatus necessary for cutting, grinding, and polishing thin sections and polished sections and placing in appropriate mounts for microscopic examination by transmitted or reflected light. Crushing equipment and screens or elutriation equipment for particle-size separation or analysis are useful.

(9) *Equipment and reagents for microchemical analysis,* particularly for use with polished sections of opaque substances.

(10) *Miscellaneous laboratory equipment,* including reflecting goniometers for crystal-angle measurement. Stereographic and equal-area nets for plotting crystallographic data, including optical data.

(11) For correlation of optical data with chemical composition and crystal structure facilities should be available for quantitative chemical analysis, spectrographic analysis, and x-ray study of single crystals and powders. Occasionally useful are differential thermal equipment, an electron microscope, and an electromagnetic or electrostatic separator for separation of mineral fractions.

(12) For correlation of optical properties with complex mineral series, comparison with synthesized minerals is useful. Synthesis commonly requires apparatus capable of generating high pressures and temperatures and, at times, withstanding the effects of corrosive fluids.

REFERENCES

ALLEN, R. D., "A New Equation Relating Index of Refraction to Specific Gravity," *Am. Mineralogist,* **41,** 245–257 (1956).

FREUND, H., "Handbuch der Mikroskopie in der Technik," Vol. II, Umschau Verlag, Frankfurt, a. M., 1954.

JAFFE, H. W., "Application of the Rule of Gladstone and Dale to Minerals", *Am. Mineralogist*, **41**, 757–777 (1956).

LARSEN, E. S. AND BERMAN, H., "The Microscopic Determination of the Nonopaque Minerals," U.S. Geological Survey, Bull. 848, 1934.

MOOREHOUSE, W. W., "The Study of Rocks in Thin Section," Harper and Bros., N.Y., 1959.

SHORT, M. N., "Microscopic Determination of the Ore Minerals," *U.S. Geological Survey, Bull.* 914, 1940.

WAHLSTROM, E. E., "Optical Crystallography," 3rd Ed., John Wiley and Sons, N. Y., 1960.

WINCHELL, A. N. AND WINCHELL, H., "Elements of Optical Mineralogy, Pt. II," "Descriptions of Minerals," John Wiley and Sons, N.Y., 1951.

ERNEST E. WAHLSTROM

PETROGRAPHIC THIN SECTIONS

The industrial chemist often has to deal with hard or brittle solids which are essentially transparent. In the microscopy of such solids, the ground thin sections developed by the petrographer for the study of rock specimens (1) may be used to good advantage, either alone or in conjunction with other sampling methods (2). Such thin sections are particularly useful in developing the following information: number and population of the various species which are present; the structure of the specimen and the spatial distribution of the entities of which it is composed; evidences of physical and chemical changes which have occurred in the specimen; microscopic characteristics of the specimen in specific orientation.

Typical industrial materials which are well adapted to thin section microscopy are: abrasive wheels, coal, charcoal, ceramics, refractories, clinkers and slags, glass, resins, scales and deposits, pelleted and molded materials, catalysts, caked and cemented solids, and solid raw materials. Literature references to several of these applications are given by Chamot and Mason (2).

The petrographer's standard procedure for thin section preparation involves the following basic steps: preparation of a slice or chip of suitable area and $\frac{1}{8}$ inch or less in thickness; grinding of one side of the slice to provide a smooth, though not polished, surface; cementing of the smooth surface to a glass slide; grinding of the other side of the slice with progressively finer abrasive until the desired thickness (usually .02–.03 mm) is reached and the free surface is smooth; cementing of a cover glass on the section unless it is desired to polish the surface and combine polished section and thin section microscopy in the same slide (3). Poorly consolidated materials are embedded in a suitable resin before grinding and either water or a hydrocarbon, depending on the solubility characteristics or the specimen, is used as a grinding lubricant. Typical basic equipment includes: a diamond or carborundum saw, a variable speed mechanical grinder with interchangeable lapping plates for coarse and fine abrasives, a flat glass plate for fine lapping, and an adjustable hot plate or oven. Rogers and Kerr (1) describe these techniques in detail and Chamot and Mason (2) list a wide variety of modern cementing and embedding media.

The petrographer's standard procedures may usually be applied to any thermally stable industrial materials. Modification, as dictated by the specific case, is required for extension to organic and thermally unstable inorganic samples. This involves specific choice of the combination of cementing and embedding media, abrasive, lubricant and general conditions based on the chemist's knowledge or best guess concerning the interaction of these factors with the sample. For instance, excessive temperatures must be avoided during grinding and handling of the specimen and a lubricant must be chosen which will not dissolve it. Thin sections of samples which are soft enough to retain abrasive during the customary wet grinding but which, for any reason, may not be sectioned by microtomy may sometimes be ground suitably by substitution of a graduated series of garnet and emery papers for the usual lubricated, powdered abrasives. The use of a low curing temperature and a somewhat viscous cementing agent will minimize solution of the specimen. For instance, a liquid epoxy resin, such as Shell "Epon" 815 with a room-temperature curing agent such as diethylenetriamine, may be used for the embedding and cementing at room temperature of materials such as urea and Bisphenol A which would readily dissolve in and react with the resin at higher temperatures. Some compromise with desired refractive index and penetration of the specimen may be involved.

The petrographer's use of the standard thickness of .02–.03 mm for his thin sections not only insures adequate transparency for most nonopaque rock specimens but is also indispensable to his direct identification of mineral species in the section (1). In many industrial studies, particularly those in which the species are identified or characterized through microscopy of separate, powdered portions of the specimen or those in which only the structure of the sample is of interest, the thickness of the section is not critical and may be dictated only by the transparency of the material and the diameter of the smallest feature which is of interest. In some cases the section may be 0.25 mm or more in thickness. On the other hand, for semi-opaque materials such as cements (4) and filled plastics (5, 6) the section must be as thin as .01–.015 mm; in such cases the microscopist may elect to use, where applicable, the metallographer's polished sections or, for soft materials, the petrographer's "peels" (7).

The ceramics and refractories industries have probably drawn more heavily than other industries upon petrographic thin sections in their microscopic studies. Typical applications are illustrated by Insley and Frechette (4) and by Norton (8). Wright and Wolff (9) describe the use of thin sections in the study of the degeneration of alumina-silica firebrick during use in the thermal cracking of natural gas to hydrogen and carbon. Free and combined silica in the bricks were being reduced to volatile silicon monoxide, leaving corundum as a granular residue. Changes in the pattern of the attack from level to level in the checkerwork as revealed by thin sections indicated carbon, rather than hydrogen or carbon monoxide, to be the principal reducing agent.

Other typical industrial applications of thin section microscopy, taken from actual experience, are described briefly below.

Catalyst Degradation Studies. A clay-bonded, diatomaceous catalyst carrier was subjected to a corrosive environment in which blackening of the pellets, due to carbonization of organic reactants, and eventual disintegration of the pellets took place. Examination of the used pellets in thin section revealed distinguishable crystalline species, resulting from attack of the clay binder, which were not present in the virgin catalyst. The species were either identified or characterized by microscopic examination of the powdered, used catalyst and further details concerning the degradation were developed through systematic study of thin sections of pellets taken from selected locations in the catalyst bed. Clusters of carbon were definitely associated with an iron-containing crystalline species and the disintegration of the pellets was tentatively tied to the observed disparity between the large diameters of the clusters of new crystals and the smaller diameters of the skeletal pores.

Deposition of Silica Gel on Catalyst Carrier. Attempts to deposit a uniform coating of silica gel on the component particles of a catalyst carrier consisting of bonded quartz fragments yielded a product which did not have the desired surface properties. Examination of thin sections of these grains revealed that the deposited silica gel was merely plugging the large external pores of the grains and was not distributed uniformly over the full carrier surface (Figure 1).

Structure of Urea Prills. In one case, the reason for the abnormal weakness of urea prills was sought. Thin sections revealed that the crystal bundles of which the individual prills were composed did not, in the case of the weak prills, meet along uniformly narrow contact zones in the normal manner but were irregularly separated by relatively wide void spaces (Figure 2). This observation could be correlated with operating conditions. In another case, the prill structures of a number of competitive brands of urea were examined by means of thin sections. In three brands, round cross-sections and compact structures characteristic of prills cooled directly from the melt were observed. In the fourth brand, the cross-section was irregular and the rather loosely bonded urea crystals showed a strong peripheral alignment; it was deduced that these prills were probably formed by mechanical means.

Examination of Heat Exchanger Deposit. A thick scale removed from a heat exchanger tube was found through thin section microscopy to consist of a single, readily identifiable species in definite, even bands. The interpretation of the observed structure was that the scale was deposited during discrete intervals between which neither erosion nor deposition of scale occurred. These observations could be correlated with plant operating conditions.

Internal Structure of Crystals. In an investigation of the effects of environmental conditions on the crystallization of ammonium sulfate, internal twinning and other imperfections were studied by means of thin sections.

Strain Patterns in Resin Test Pieces. Thin sections were helpful in the study of strain patterns in deformed resin test pieces, since (1) strain patterns which were too intense for resolution in the full thickness of the specimen were easily resolvable at reduced thickness and (2) patterns could be

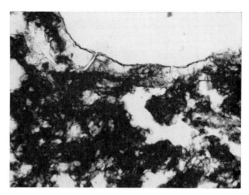

FIG. 1. Silica gel plugging. Coarse catalyst carrier pores. (×100).

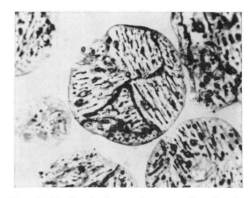

FIG. 2. Mechanically weak urea prills. (×40).

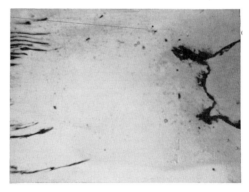

FIG. 3. Strained Izod specimen—end of notch. Ordinary transmitted light. (×14).

studied in any desired orientation of the specimen. Figure 3 shows, in ordinary transmitted light, a portion of a section approximately .25 mm in thickness of the notch area of a notched Izod impact test specimen

475

Fig. 4. Same field as Figure 3. Polaroids crossed.

of transparent resin which had been placed in the Izod test vise and hit with the test hammer only hard enough to deform the specimen slightly without breaking it. Observe (1) the incipient tears at the notch corners and (2) the two sets of fracture cracks on the left. Figure 4 shows the same field between crossed Polaroids. The intense strain pattern, due to plastoelastic deformation, is divided into two sections, each of which converges on one of the incipient tears at the notch corners. The fracture cracks extend into the strain patterns but distort them only very slightly. In the full ⅛-inch thickness of the specimen, these features were not readily resolvable but the adjoining strain patterns of lower order due to elastic

deformation, which were obliterated in grinding to the .25-mm thickness, were fairly readily resolvable. At half-thickness of the specimen, the latter patterns were quite clear and the former was just beginning to emerge.

REFERENCES

1. ROGERS, A. F. AND KERR, P. F., "Optical Mineralogy," McGraw-Hill, New York, 1942.
2. CHAMOT, E. M., AND MASON, C. W., "Handbook of Chemical Microscopy," Chapter 5, John Wiley & Sons, New York, 1958.
3. KENNEDY, G. C., "The Preparation of Polished Thin Sections," Econ. Geol., 40, 353–59 (1945).
4. INSLEY, H. AND FRECHETTE, V. D., "Microscopy of Ceramics and Cements." Academic Press, New York, 1955.
5. ROCHOW, T. G., "Microscopy in the Resin Industry," Ind. Eng. Chem. Anal. Ed., 11, 629–34 (1939).
6. ROCHOW, T. G. AND GILBERT, R. L., Chapter on "Resinography" in Volume V of Matiello's "Protective and Decorative Coatings," John Wiley & Sons, New York, 1946.
7. WEATHERHEAD, A. V., "A New Method for the Preparation of Thin Sections," Mineralog. Mag., 25, 529–33 (1940).
8. NORTON, F. H., "Refractories," McGraw-Hill, New York, 1946.
9. WRIGHT, R. E. AND WOLFF, H. I., "Refractory Problems in the Production of Hydrogen by Pyrolysis of Natural Gas," J. Am. Ceram. Soc., 31, 31–38 (1948).

R. E. WRIGHT

PHASE MICROSCOPY (*See also* pp. 365, 452)

ANOPTRAL MICROSCOPE*

In 1944 the author began searching for possible means of detecting more clearly in the microscope the structure of living cells and tissues. Most excellent microscopes have been in use for nearly a hundred years,

* Exerpt from paper in *Mikroskopie*, 9, 1954, Nos. 1–4, pp. 80.

and they reproduce very well the structure of objects which are fixed and stained and usually embedded in Canada balsam. However, there are certainly many unknown fundamental facts that can only be revealed by studying the living preparation directly. Life is sometimes characterized much better by motion, growth, propagation and exchange of the cellular constituents than it is

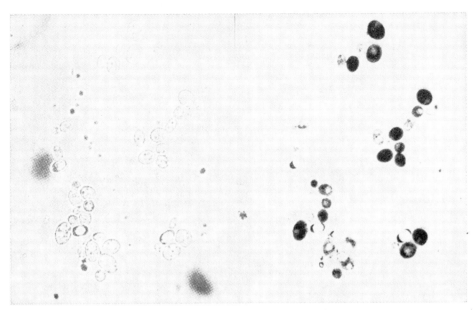

FIG. 1. In the left-hand picture living yeast cells were photographed by means of an ordinary microscope objective (Reichert achromat 60X); in the picture to the right the same specimen is shown with the objective treated as described in the text. In the latter picture the cells with a good nutritional status appear dark while others remain more or less pale (old, degenerating, poorly nourished cells). There are no halo effects around the cells as there would be with an ordinary phase contrast.

by the multiplicity of structures. There are, however, difficulties in the way of studying unstained preparations.

All those who have worked with the microscope must be aware of the fact that a normal stained biological preparation provides an excellent picture when viewed through a microscope with large objective and condenser apertures, whereas in the absence of staining very little if anything can be seen since the details are only distinguishable then by their refractive power. Not until the illuminating aperture has been reduced, e.g., by stopping down the iris diaphragm, do the details begin to appear one after another, but even then they are surrounded by concentric diffraction fringes which have a detrimental effect in that they reduce the resolving power.

Nor does dark-field microscopy help very much. Abrupt changes in the refracting properties of the details of the object certainly show up clearly, but small differences

or gradual changes in the refractive index remain invisible.

These drawbacks led the author to undertake extensive experiments with the "schlieren" method discovered by Töpler nearly a hundred years ago, and to apply them to microscopy. It was soon discovered that an annularly defined aperture in both the condenser and the objective was the most suitable one. The realization of annular defined apertures in objectives, however, was very difficult. After experimenting with thin coatings of silver, without much success, the author tried coatings of soot applied by repeatedly exposing the surfaces of an objective lens to a candle flame.

A microscope modified on the above lines provided much better images of living specimens viewed through it. The obvious course, then, was to proceed on purely empirical lines.[1] It was soon evident that excellent re-

[1] It is interesting to note that Leeuwenhoek was not familiar with the theory of optics. He was

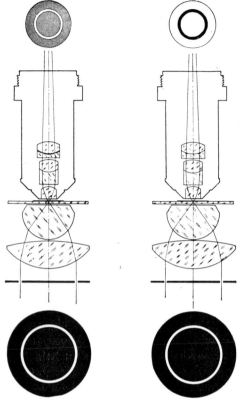

FIG. 2. The first contrast pictures (Fig. 1.) were made by using a circular aperture in the condenser and a likewise circular, clear area on a lightly-sooted objective lens surface. The left hand picture shows the path of light in the system; above and below are the objective and condenser apertures in a perpendicular view. In the picture to the right is shown the anoptral method developed later. The non-diffracted rays penetrate a heavily light-absorbing, non-reflecting area in the objective.

sults could be obtained by using an annular diaphragm opening in both the condenser

not college-trained, understood only Dutch, and did not even write his own language like an educated man. The microscope consisting of objective and eyepiece had been discovered and used before Leeuwenhoek was born, but he never possessed one. He saw blood corpuscles, sperm-cells and even bacteria with his instrument, which contained only a single tiny lens. Yet he was able to make such a number of microscopical observations which he communicated to the Royal Society of

and the objective, the transmission of the objective diaphragm being 50 per cent. Living specimens such as yeast cells appeared very clear and sharply defined with this system, and had an agreeable brownish tint on a bright background. The cells showed darker the more the refractive power of their content exceeded that of their surroundings, i.e., the better their state of nourishment (Fig. 1).

Later the author found that the phase-contrast microscope, developed on a theoretical basis by Zernike, had been constructed by the Zeiss Optical Works. When the author looked into a phase-contrast microscope for the first time he was surprised to note the similarity of the images obtained with it and with his own equipment. Both of them certainly had annular condenser apertures, but the phase-contrast objectives had light-absorbing annuli whereas the author's had an absorbent coating recessed in the form of a ring. But the effect produced by the images was not identical. Round each light-refracting detail the phase-contrast microscope exhibited haloes which had no counterpart in reality. The author's microscope showed none of these haloes, and the gradation of the different intensities of contrast, depending on their light-refracting properties, was agreeably soft.

During his first experiments the author made an observation which was afterwards to prove significant. If the coating of soot in the objective was not recessed in the form of an annulus, but complementarily applied so that the light coming from the condenser diaphragm passed through this annulus, an image was obtained which exhibited the opposite properties (Fig. 2). The author resumed his experiments in this direction in

London that the Dutch have recently published them in four large volumes. Nor were the inventors of the first achromatic microscope objectives, Aepinus and Beelsnyder, professional opticians. The former was a Privy Councillor and the latter a cavalry officer (see also p. 458).

1952, partly because the available phase-contrast microscopes had not been developed further. The halo effect in them, mentioned above, continued to prove disturbing, and often led to false interpretations.

When attempts were being made to improve this second method it became clear that increasing the light absorption of the soot ring to over 90 per cent gave a particularly well contrasted image with a golden-brown background against which the details of the object usually appeared bright (because of their higher optical density), but were surrounded by narrow, darker zones. The image was, so to speak, the reverse of an ordinary phase-contrast image, with dark borders instead of the bright haloes. The golden-brown tint of the image was a happy chance, for it is agreeable and restful to the eye—a fact long known in art photography. The question is now: Are the dark shaded zones of the picture less disturbing than the bright haloes of ordinary phase-contrast microscopy?

The answer is a definite affirmative. We recognize the shape of most objects better if we see them lighted as they usually appear in our everyday surroundings. The objects are not as a rule presented in transmitted light, or as silhouettes, but appear in our visual field illuminated mostly from above, from the side, or from several directions at the same time. The diffuse light from the sky is probably the most original and natural form for the human eye. If we look at a stone on sandy ground under this mode of illumination we can see a lightly shaded zone around it. If we saw the same thing as a negative, in which the half-shadow borders were replaced by haloes, it would be difficult to apprehend the shape of the object.

The normal image of the stone on the sandy ground bears the same relation to the negative as the microscopic image produced by the author's second method has to the image obtained by "positive" phase-contrast. The disturbing haloes—simulating phosphorescent edges—of the latter, are converted into a virtue by their reversal, since this half-shadow bordering assists the apperceptive faculty and produces an almost plastic effect. (Fig. 3).

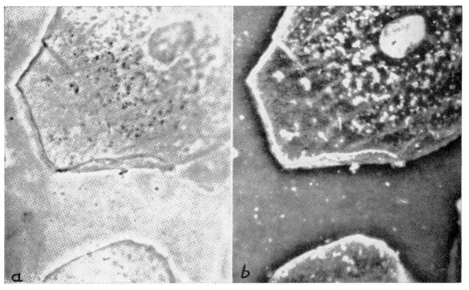

FIG. 3. Parts of two (2) epithelial cells from the oral mucosa seen by ordinary phase contrast (a) and by the anoptral method (b). From the latter we obtain an illusion of third dimension (depth) which is due to the shadow-effects around the cell borders. Reichert achromats 100✕. Magnification 1350✕.

479

The writer has also been able to familiarize himself with the "negative" phase-contrast objectives of different makes. The image effects obtainable with them are of course somewhat similar to those obtained by the author's second method, but the pictures give rather a cold impression because of their grayish-white color accompanied by a metallic sheen and a strange fogginess. As the phase annuli are made by vacuum evaporization and especially as metals are used, the light-absorbing layers tend to introduce reflecting surfaces into the system. Since the degree of absorption of the phase annuli must be considerable in order to obtain a very high degree of contrast, it is no wonder the stray light from these reflections becomes nearly equal in brightness to the image itself. The soot surface, on the contrary, reflects very little. For the commercial production of the new objectives, the coating of soot, as it is not very resistant, must be replaced by other suitable substances which produce the same effect. Messrs. Optische Werke C. Reichert A. G., Vienna, Austria, have solved this problem by using means available only to a large firm of microscope makers. They are now manufacturing these objectives and their accessories on a commercial basis under the name of "Anoptral Contrast Equipment" (anoptral = nonreflecting).

A. WILSKA

POLARIZING MICROSCOPE (*See also* CHEMICAL MICROSCOPY, pp. 21, 31, 52; INDUSTRIAL HYGIENE MICROSCOPY, p. 400; OPTICAL MINERALOGY, p. 470)

BASIC DESIGN AND OPERATION. *See* OPTICAL THEORY OF LIGHT MICROSCOPE, p. 453.

DESIGN FOR MAXIMUM SENSITIVITY

General Description

The polarizing microscope is a compound light microscope used for studying the anisotropic properties of objects and for rendering objects visible according to their optical anisotropy. To this end a polarizing microscope is generally equipped with a polarizer and an analyzer (or "polars" following the terminology of Swann and Mitchison, 30), strain-free condenser and objective lenses, compensators, a Bertrand lens or a telescopic eye piece, and a graduated revolving stage. Both transmitted light and vertical illumination are used and the image may be studied orthoscopically as in ordinary microscopy or conoscopically by viewing the interference pattern at the back aperture of the objective. Depending on its application a polarizing microscope may also be called a petrographic microscope, a metallographic microscope, a chemical microscope, etc. Many types of interference microscopes are also essentially modified polarizing microscopes. The general principles and application of regular polarizing microscopes can be found in several texts (1, 2, 4 to 7, 17, 22 to

28, 32, 33; see especially 5 for general reference and 33 for a thorough theoretical treatment of the polarizing microscope).

This article will give special attention to methods and devices for obtaining maximum sensitivity with the polarizing microscope. As described later, the combined sensitivity, resolution, and image quality of the polarizing microscope has been vastly improved in the past few years, and retardation (coefficient of birefringence × thickness) of 0.1 Å unit can be detected on objects 0.2μ wide. These advances now permit application of polarization microscopy to new realms such as analyses of fine structure in living cells, or experimental studies of rigorous diffraction theory of the kind which could not be performed with equipment available in the past.

Specification of the System for Obtaining Maximum Sensitivity

For the sensitive detection of birefringence (BR) and dichroism, precise measurement of retardation, optical activity (rotation of plane-polarized light), extinction angle, etc., detectable contrast must be introduced with only minimal differences in a parameter. Contrast is maximized for a given object by reducing stray light in the system (11, 30), and by using appropriate compensators or half-shade plates (3, 7, 11, 13, 15, 18, 27, 28, 30, 31). The degree of success in reduction of stray light, or increase in extinction factor (EF), can be expressed numerically as EF = intensity of light with parallel polars, divided by intensity of light with crossed polars (30). The effect of various components on the EF is discussed in the next section.

The ability of the eye to perceive contrast is drastically lowered at low levels of image brightness, a condition which prevails at high EF's. A maximally bright light source is therefore required. Contrast discrimination can also be improved by darkening the room and by masking off unwanted sources of bright light in the image (e.g., retardation can be measured to $\lambda/1000$ with a quartz wedge when the regions outside of the dark fringes are masked).

Specification of the Components

Polars. Modern sheet polaroids (general properties outlined in 21) can, but do not always, have EF as high as 3×10^5 for green light at normal incidence. For most work EF of this magnitude is adequate, but two additional factors should be borne in mind for critical application. The parallel transmission of a pair of high extinction polaroids is of the order of $10 \sim 15\%$, hence a considerable light loss takes place. Most sheet polaroids have microcrystalline textures or inclusions which can cause "hot spots" affecting the diffraction image.

Calcite polars coated with a low reflection film may show virtually no light loss (parallel transmission $\fallingdotseq 50\%$) and an extremely high EF ($\sim 3 \times 10^6$). Of the various types of calcite prisms available (17, Lambrecht 20 has supplied excellent quality prisms), the square-ended Glan-Thompson prisms appear to be the most effective. The optical quality and EF of calcite prisms depend to a great extent on the skill of manufacture and subsequent care of handling since the soft calcite surfaces are prone to scratching and pitting. The beam passing through the analyzing calcite prism should be made parallel by the stigmatizing lenses to minimize the astigmatism resulting from the double refraction of calcite.

Condenser and Objective Lenses. All optical components lying between the polarizer and the analyzer must be scrupulously clean. Not only may any dust particle, greasy surface, etc. scatter enough light to lower the EF and seriously reduce object contrast, but by acting as loci having high transmittance, such entities would give the effect of oblique illumination and distort the diffraction image.

The deleterious effect of large amounts of strain BR in the condenser and objective

481

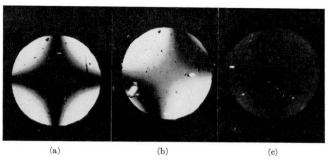

(a)   (b)   (c)

FIG. 1. Appearance of the back aperture of a 97 × 1.25 NA strain-free coated objective with and without rectifiers. The condenser, which is identical with the objective, is used at full aperture. Collimated mercury green light (546 mμ) used for illumination. (a) Crossed polarizers, no rectifier. (b) Polarizer turned 2°, no rectifier. (c) Crossed polarizers, with rectifiers in both condenser and objective. Photographs a, b, and c were given identical exposures. From Inoué, S. and W. L. Hyde (12).

lenses has long been recognized and polarizing microscopes are generally furnished with "strain-free" lenses. The magnitude of strain BR in these lenses is frequently still considerable and for realizing the utmost sensitivity, lenses with exceptionally low strain BR must be selected. The procedure for selecting these follows.

Preparation for the Test. Provide a polarizing microscope with a very high intensity light source, such as a high pressure mercury arc lamp (General Electric A-H6 or Osram HBO 200) or other lamp of equivalent brightness. The components of the microscope should be adjusted or repaired so that the EF of the system without the lenses is greater than 10^5. Close down the field stop and use Köhler illumination, employing a nominally identical objective as the condenser. It is convenient to screw the test lens into an objective holder which in turn is placed inverted on the rotating stage and centered to the optical axis. This acts as the condenser (or objective in an inverted system as in Fig. 2) and the selected mate remains fixed. In addition prepare a removable rotating mica compensator of the order of λ/20 to be placed in the slot above the objective or between the condenser and the polarizer.

Test for Freedom from Strain BR. When the pair of lenses is aligned, the polars crossed and the image of the field stop properly focused a dark cross (Fig. 1a) should appear at the back aperture of the objective. In the absence of strain BR the cross is observable with objectives of NA as low as 0.1 with no object lying between the condenser and objective lenses. The cross must be symmetrical and very dark between crossed polars and should open symmetrically into two hyperbola-like fringes the "V's" (Fig. 1b) when the polarizer or analyzer is rotated. The arms of the V's should remain dark until they disappear beyond the edge of the aperture. If the lenses are free from local and lateral strain these dark fringes remain undistorted when the stage is rotated and the test lens is examined at various orientations.

Some lenses seemingly passing the above test may still suffer from radially symmetric (strain) BR. This is checked by inserting the mica compensator. When the lenses are free from radial as well as lateral BR the cross loses contrast and fades away with little change in its shape or position when the compensator is rotated. If lenses possess radial BR the cross will open into two V's as though with a strain-free lens the analyzer had been turned.

Rectifiers. Lenses selected for freedom from strain by the methods described can give extremely high EF at low NA's (e.g., 3×10^5 at condenser NA = 0.1). However, they still exhibit a dark cross which becomes progressively more prominent as the NA is increased (Fig. 1a). Light from the areas between the arms of the cross is introduced by rotation of the plane of polarization at glass air interfaces in the lenses and in microscope slides. The rotation is a result of differential reflection losses of the parallel and perpendicular components of polarized light and may be as large as $7° \sim 8°$ for high NA objectives even after low reflection coating and oil immersion (2, 10, 33). This lowers the EF ($\sim 10^2$ for $NA_{objective} = NA_{condenser} = 1.25$) and furthermore distorts the Airy diffraction pattern (14, 19). Much of the rotation and therefore light giving rise to the cross can be eliminated by the use of "polarization rectifiers" built into the objective and condenser lenses (Fig. 2R). The rectifier consists of a $\lambda/2$ BR plate which reverses the above mentioned rotation and a zero power meniscus which introduces sufficient additional rotation to cancel out the reversed rotation (12).

Suitably rectified objectives and condensers used with a proper microscope (last section) give very high EF (2×10^4 for $NA_{condenser} = NA_{objective} = 1.25$) and make detectable very small BR (< 0.1 A°) of objects which in themselves are barely resolvable with the light microscope ($\leq 0.2\mu$). The objective back aperture being uniformly dark (Fig. 1c), spurious diffraction is reduced to a minimum and the image is therefore more reliable (12, 14). Determination of the polarization angle and other parameters can be made with great accuracy by using rectified optics whereas such measurements with ordinary polarizing microscopes contain inherent and significant errors (33).

Compensators. Many types of compensators and half-shade plates have been used for increasing the sensitivity and precision in determining the ellipticity of polarized light, polarization angle, etc. Their construction, sensitivity and operation may be found in references 3, 4, 7, 9, 11, 13, 15 to 18, 23, 24, 25, 27, 28, 30, 31, 33. As mentioned above, the property of the eye or other detectors influence their performance. Photoelectric or photographic photometry can also aid in increasing the sensitivity.

When algebraic computation of compensator actions are difficult, e.g., when more than two anisotropic components lie between the polars, advantage can frequently be taken of the geometrical construction available with the Poincaré sphere or its two dimensional analog (16, 29).

Optical Layout of a Polarizing Microscope with Exceptional Sensitivity. Figure 2 shows the essential optical layout of a transilluminating polarizing microscope designed to give maximum sensitivity and image quality. The system illustrated is inverted with the light source S on top and detectors (EM and E) at the bottom.

Light from the bright source is filtered and is focused by L_1 and L_2 onto a pinhole aperture A_2. This restricts the size of the source image so that after projection by L_3 it just covers the condenser aperture diaphragm A_6. The polarizing Glan-Thompson prism POL is placed behind the stop A_4 away from the condenser COND, to prevent light scattered by the polarizer from entering the condenser. Half-shade plates are placed at the level of A_5, and compensators COMP above the condenser. Both the condenser and the objective OBJ lenses are rectified by R_1 and R_2 and are low reflection coated. The image of the field diaphragm (A_3 or A_5) is focussed onto the object plane OB by the condenser, whose NA can be made equal to that of the objective.

Stigmatizing lenses St_1 and St_2 are low reflection coated on their exteriors while their backs are cemented directly onto the analyzing Glan-Thompson prism ANAL to protect the surfaces of the prism. Aperture stops A_1–A_8 are placed at critical points to minimize scattered light from entering the image forming system. The final image is cast by OC_1 on a photographic or photoelec-

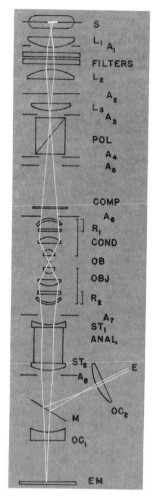

FIG. 2. Optical layout of an inverted transilluminating polarizing microscope designed to give maximum sensitivity and image quality. See last section of text for details.

tric sensor EM or to the eye E via a mirror M and ocular OC_2.

This optical system was used for developing and testing the rectified objectives mentioned earlier and may be considered to be the basic system necessary and ample for obtaining maximum sensitivity and resolution with the transilluminating polarizing microscope.

REFERENCES

1. AMBRONN-FREY, "Das Polarisationsmikroskop, seine Anwedung in der Kolloid-forschung in der Färberei," Akademische Verlag, Leipzig, 1926.

2. BARER, R. in MELLORS, R. C., "Analytical Cytology" Chapt. 3, McGraw-Hill, New York, 1955.

3. BEAR, R. S. AND SCHMITT, F. O., "The measurement of small retardation with the polarizing microscope," J. Opt. Soc. Am., 26, 363–364 (1936).

4. BENNETT, H. S., "The microscopical investigation of Biological materials with polarized light," in McClung: Handbook of Microscopical Technique, p. 591, P. B. Hoeber, Inc., New York, 1950.

5. CHAMOT, E. M. AND MASON, C. W., "Handbook of Chemical Microscopy," John Wiley and Sons, New York, 1949, second edition, Vol. 1.

6. GIBBS, T. R. P., "Optical Methods of Chemical Analysis," McGraw-Hill, New York, 1942.

7. HALLIMOND, A. F., "Manual of the Polarizing Microscope," Cooke, Troughton and Simms, York, England, 1953.

8. HSÜ, H. Y., RICHARTZ, M., AND LIANG, Y. K., "A generalized intensity formula for a system of retardation plates," J. Opt. Soc. Am., 37, 99–106 (1947).

9. INOUÉ, S., "A method for measuring small retardation of structures in living cells," Exptl. Cell Research, 2, 513–517 (1951).

10. INOUÉ, S., "Studies on depolarization of light at microscope lens surfaces. I. The origin of stray light by rotation at the lens surfaces." Exptl. Cell Research, 3, 199–208.

11. INOUÉ, S. AND DAN, K., "Birefringence of the dividing cell," J. Morph., 89, 423–456 (1951).

12. INOUÉ, S. AND HYDE, W. L., "Studies on depolarization of light at microscope lens surfaces. II. The simultaneous realization of high resolution and high sensitivity with the polarizing microscope." J. Biophys. Biochem. Cytol., 3, 831–838 (1957).

13. INOUÉ, S. AND KOESTER, C. J., "Optimum half-shade angle in polarizing instruments," J. Opt. Soc. Am. 49, 556–559 (1959).

14. INOUÉ, S. AND KUBOTA, H., "Diffraction anomaly in polarizing microscopes," Nature, 182, 1725–1726 (1958).

15. JERRARD, H. G., "Optical compensators for measurement of eliptical polarization," J. Opt. Soc. Am., 38, 35–59 (1948).

16. JERRARD, H. G., "Transmission of light through birefringent and optically active media: the Poincaré sphere," J. Opt. Soc. Am., 44, 634–640 (1954).

17. Johansen, A., "Manual of Petrographic Methods," McGraw-Hill, New York, 1918, second edition.

18. Köhler, A., "Ein Glimmerplättchen Grau I. Ordnung zur Untersuchung sehr schwach doppelbrechender Präparate," Z. wiss. Mikroskop., **38,** 29–42 (1921).

19. Kubota, H. and Inoué, S. "Diffraction images in the polarizing microscopes," J. Opt. Soc. Am., **49,** 191–198 (1959).

20. Lambrecht, K., See Catalogue "Polarizing Optics." (4318 N. Lincoln Ave., Chicago 18, Ill.)

21. Land, E. H., "Some aspects of development of sheet polarizers," J. Opt. Soc. Am., **41,** 957–963 (1951).

22. Oster, G., "Birefringence and Dichroism," in Oster and Pollister: "Physical Techniques in Biological Research," Vol. I, Chapter 8, Academic Press, New York, 1955.

23. Pfeiffer, Hans H., "Das Polarisationsmikroskop als Messinstrument in Biologie und Medizin," Friedr. Vieweg and Sohn, Braunschweig, 1949.

24. Rinne, F. W. B. and Berek, M., "Anleitung zu optischen Untersuchungen mit dem Polarizationsmikroscop," Leipzig, 1953.

25. Ruch, Fritz, "Birefringence and Dichroism of cells and tissues," in Oster and Pollister: Physical Techniques in Biological Research, Vol. III, 149–176 Academic Press, New York, 1956.

26. Schmidt, W. J., "Die Bausteine des Tierkörpers," F. Cohen, Bonn, 1924.

27. Schmidt, W. J., "Die Doppelbrechung von Karyoplasma, Zytoplasma und Metaplasma," Bd. II, Protoplasma-Monographien, Berlin, 1937.

28. Schmidt, W. J., "Die Doppelbrechung des Protoplasmas und ihrer Bedeutung für die Erforschung seines submikroskopischen Baues," Ergeb. Physiol., **44,** 27 (1944).

29. Skinner, C. A., "A universal polarimeter," J. Opt. Soc. Am., **10,** 491–520 (1925).

30. Swann, M. M. and Mitchison, J. M., "Refinements in polarized light microscopy," J. Exp. Biol., **27,** 226 (1950).

31. Tuckerman, L. B., "Doubly refracting plates and elliptic analyzers," Univ. Nebraska Studies, pp. 173–219 (1909).

32. Wahlstrom, E. E., "Optical Crystalography," John Wiley and Sons, New York, 3rd. Ed., 1960.

33. Wright, F. E., "The Methods of Petrographic Microscopic Research," (Carnegie Institution of Washington, Washington, D.C., 1911).

Shinya Inoué

FIBERS (TEXTILES). See GENERAL MICROSCOPY, p. 343.

INDUSTRIAL RESEARCH, APPLICATION TO. See GENERAL MICROSCOPY, p. 363.

PLASTICS, See GENERAL MICROSCOPY, p. 390.

PULP AND PAPER. See GENERAL MICROSCOPY, p. 394.

Refraction of Light, Refractometry and Interferometry*

ANGLE REFRACTOMETRY (See also p. 400)

The direct application of Snell-Descartes' law led to the design of many prismatic instruments utilizing angular measurements— the so-called transmission refractometers.

* Objections may be raised that this topic is not properly included within the framework of Microscopy. However, the fundamental phenomenon of optical refraction of light in microscope lenses, the microscopic measurement of refractive index,

The subsequent discovery by Augustin Fresnel of the quantitative relationship between refraction *on* a surface, reflectivity *by* this surface and absorption by the medium, fi-

and the intimate relationships between microscopes, refractometers and interferometers as optical instruments, completely justify inclusion of the four articles extracted from an exhaustive monograph and prepared expressly for this Encyclopedia by Dr. Raymond Jonnard.—Ed.

nally led to the design of another type of refractometer adapted to the study of opaque substances, namely, reflective refractometers. The following account of this field of measurements is intended to serve as a guide. In each case it is imperative to refer to the original references, giving the exact detailed procedure to be followed. (For references, refer to article "Historical Introduction.")

Transmission refractometers include: the Abbé simple and double types (26)* from which are derived the various designs of "dipping refractometers": the Pulfrich refractometer (27); the Lob instrument (28); the Pfund total reflexion device (29) and its modification by Countryman (30); the Ferry hollow prism refractometer; the Jelley refractometer (31); the Jelley-Fischer (35) instrument adapted for observations on molten substances; the Nichols double reflection instrument (32) and its modification for microanalysis (33), both of which must be used conjointly with a microscope; the Hilger ultraviolet refractometer designed after the original instrument of Ch. Henri (34); the Fredriani instrument (36), really a modification of Jelley's; the recording modification of Ferry's design used by Cruikshank and Fairweather (37) in their chemical work; the photoelectric multiple reflection device of Karrer and Orr (38); the Emmons spherical refractometer for solids (39); the recording refractometer of Barstow (40); the "chemical refractometer" of Barnes (41); the Jacobsohn instrument for opalescent fluids (42); the Stamm *et al.* differential recording instrument (43), using either three Wernicke hollow prisms, or a double Zenger hollow one; the Clamann pneumatic refractometer for gases (44), in which a beam of light is deflected at the interface of two gas phases, imparted with a parallel rapid laminar flow; the Broumberg refraction monochromator, which can be adapted to refraction measurements (45); and a few others mentioned elsewhere.

On the principles of angular measurements embodied in the instruments listed are based also a number of *methods* which can be carried out with such conventional instruments as the microscope, the goniometer and the photometer. These methods include: the Becke lines displacement, the Christiansen effect, the Merwin (46) and the Emmons methods for crystals, and the Wood and Ayliff method for solids in general.

Prismatic refractometers utilize either one of the two basic properties of transparent media: (1) the existence of a minimum deviation angle of emergent light, or (2) the existence of a critical angle.

Instruments based upon the determination of the *minimum deviation angle* have only an historical interest. Their passing into oblivion is perhaps unjustified, for it is now possible to measure—and to record or continuously monitor—with them small angular deflections with an approximation better by several decimal places than was possible half a century ago. Such instruments, being basically extremely simple, might be worth reconsidering for certain industrial applications. For these reasons, additional comments on the goniometric method and of that of Biot and Arago are given.

Methods of Newton, and of Biot and Arago. Only in rare instances is it possible to measure the angle of refraction directly. Such measurements, of limited accuracy, are convenient when working with properly shaped transparent solids. They are easily effected with a goniometer, sometimes called a "spectrometer." The conventional goniometer is described in practically every textbook. More elaborate instruments of the "transit" type, when equipped with reflection or internally illuminated auto-collimation devices, are usable for this purpose.

In all cases the measurement method is based upon the property of a prism of exhibiting a minimum deviation angle. The existence of this angle is a direct consequence of the critical refraction angle. The method originally designed by Newton, and by Biot and Arago is still valid. The original prism of Arago and Biot was large, yielding directly the absolute n value of gases or liquids relatively to vacuum.

The apex angle is conveniently made 143°. (Instruments of this type are no longer commercially available.) The path of light is first determined with the prism either evacuated or filled with dry air. In a second operation, one measures with the specimen filling the prism.

Refractive Index Measurement with the "Autocollimator." A small instrument constructed especially for the measurement of small angles or small defects of parallelism in mechanical parts and machines, known as the "Tuckerman Autocollimator"[*], can also be used for the measurement of the refractive index of transparent substances.

The autocollimator consists essentially of a highly corrected objective lens, in the focal plane of which is a high-precision reticle. Part of this reticle is illuminated to form a fiduciary object. The parallel light emerging from the lens can be reflected by any external plane surface back into the instrument, and the reflected image can be made to fall on the main scale of the reticle.

The position of the reflected image of the reticle is a function of the orientation of the mirror, and this can be measured by means of another scale in the fiducial image, which acts as a vernier to the main scale of the reticle. An eyepiece is provided to observe the images. The distance from the mirror to the instrument does not affect the readings, so that the instrument can be used to measure the degree of parallelism between two plates separated by a transparent medium. If two such plates form a small angle a (unknown), the interposed medium having a refractive index n, the measured angle being d, one has:

$$a = \frac{\text{arc sin } (\sin d/n)}{2} \qquad (7)†$$

---

[*] Mfd. by Aminco, Silver Spring, Md.
† (For equations 1–6 see next article).

Conversely, if a and d are known, one calculates n:

$$n = \sin d/\sin (2a) \qquad (8)$$

The Goniometer. For the measurement of small angles involved in a number of methods mentioned herein, it is often convenient to use the goniometer. The goniometer method is based upon a property of the refracting prism already described, i.e., the existence of a minimum deviation angle. The determination of the refractive index n requires measuring the minimum deviation angle. This involves moving both the prism and the telescope, as in the Biot and Arago method. However, a greater accuracy is possible with the goniometer by rotating the prism on the turntable so as to give it successively two exactly symmetrical positions.

A modification of the method permits measurements on liquids. Instead of a solid prism, the goniometer is equipped with the double rectangular liquid compartment of Hallwachs. The table is oriented so that light falls at grazing incidence on the plate of glass separating the two fluids and one observes the angular deviation relatively to the direction of the rays when the two compartments are empty:

$$\sin^2 \theta = n_1^2 - n_2^2 \qquad (9)$$

(n_1 and n_2 are indices of the fluids filling the two compartments, respectively). By using a double switching method and taking readings in two opposed directions at 180°, differences of refraction of the order of 1.5×10^{-6} can be measured.

Other Methods of Angular Measurements. A number of refractometric methods involving angular measurements to be carried out with non-specialized instruments have been developed primarily for the analytical chemist. The required implements are usually a microscope, a goniometer, or a simple type of photometer.

Microscopic methods utilizing the Becke lines displacement are described in textbooks of microscopy. They were critically reviewed by Saylor (47). The utilization of the Christiansen effect falls into the same category. In general, such methods have been brought to a high degree of perfection mostly for the requirements of petrographic studies (48 49, 50). They culminated in the very perfect microscope stage for crystallography designed by Emmons and Winchell (39). The measurements can be extended to any substance exhibiting metallic reflection (51), as well as to plastics and to resins (52). The basic procedures remain those of earlier investigators (53, 54, 55, 56, 57) and others. Several of these procedures can be combined with the "immersion method" familiar to microscopists (46, 58, 59). The Merwin method for crystallography has long been standard. Those of Wood and Ayliffe (60), and of Wood, Ayliffe and Williams (61) are rather general for all solid specimens.

The procedure of Kienle and Stearns (62) for computation of refractive indices of opaque specimens from iso-reflectance diagrams and the Fresnel's formulas are illustrative of the use of a spectrophotometer (American Cyanamid Co. automatic recorder) for such a purpose.

Refractometric measurements by means of the microscope are considered by Addey (63).

The Critical Angle Refractometer: Abbé Instrument. Measuring instruments of this type are based upon Snell's formula (1). The measurement consists in observing the critical angle of emergence r_c with light falling at grazing incidence (i practically equal to 90°) upon the boundary of two transparent media, one of which has a known refractive index, n_g.

The simplest instrument of this category is the Abbé refractometer. It is essentially formed of a flint prism whose angles are respectively 90, 60, and 30 degrees. A slightly convergent beam of light is furnished by a suitable condenser and falls at grazing incidence upon the hypotenuse face of the prism which also supports the specimen under investigation. A suitable telescope is placed on the small side of the prism, near its right angle. This telescope is mobile around an axis perpendicular to the plan of refraction of the rays of light, and centered around the right angle of the prism. It is attached to a graduated circle, so that the angle of emergence of the refracted rays can be measured. When the direction of emergence is found, the field of the telescope appears divided into two zones: one bright, and one completely dark if the incident light is monochromatic.

The original Abbé refractometer was improved to permit measurements on both transparent and opaque liquids as well as on solid specimens. To the hypotenuse face of the original Abbé prism a second prism exactly identical is attached. The hypotenuse face of this second prism, in contact with that of the former, is finely ground and is provided with a small cylindrical cavity where the specimen under investigation is placed. To this combination is added a trapezoidal piece of glass of such a shape that the incident ray of light falls upon the surface of the specimen.

The methods available for measuring the characteristic constants of the critical angle refractometer are often successfully used in setting up other types of optical instruments, such as spectrometers. The original Abbé refractometer has been modified and improved in numerous ways by ingenious manufacturers. Precision type instruments are currently manufactured in this country by Bausch & Lomb Optical Co., American Optical Co., Precision Scientific Co., Industro—Scientific Co., and by the Gaertner Co. The latter, originally developed by Jacobson is suitable for turbid fluids. The Ostwald refractometer (Zeiss Mfg.) is a differential instrument based upon the same principle.

The Fery Refractometer. A different version of the application of the principle of the critical angle to the measurement of refractive indices is embodied in the Fery refractometer. In this instrument, the refracting prism is a hollow body to be filled with the liquid under investigation. The faces comprising the refracting angle are made of two half-lenses. This body is mobile transversely to the path of light, so that a narrow beam of collimated light can be made to pass through it at various distances from its refracting angle a. A telescope provided with a cross-air reticule permits one to observe the apparent position of another reticule disposed inside the collimator tube. This apparent position depends upon the refractivity of the liquid contained in the prism. The image of the collimator reticule is brought back in coincidence with that of the reticule of the telescope by moving the prism by means of a micrometric screw. This displacement is a simple function of the refractive index of the liquid.

This instrument really makes use of a "variable refraction angle prism." It has known a very prolonged success in chemistry, probably because of its low cost of construction and its ease of operation, but is less satisfactory than the Abbé refractometer.

The Dipping Refractometer. The "dipping refractometer" has received very wide acceptance in industry. Since it can be applied to measurements even in flowing fluids, it is the nearest thing, in its class, to a truly industrial apparatus.

The dipping refractometer is designed on the principle of the Abbé refractometer. The refracting prism is similar to the upper prism of the Abbé apparatus, but there are provided usually six interchangeable prisms of various indices covering the range of measurements from 1.32539 to 1.54409.

The telescope is of conventional design but of longer focus. The dividing line between the two halves of the field is formed in the plane of a divided scale and its position is read directly; no moving parts are involved. A single Amici prism is provided for correcting (and approximately evaluating) the dispersion.

Various attachments, which need not be mentioned here, permit one to adapt the instrument for measurements on either bulk liquids, single drops, properly cut transparent solids, or opaque liquids.

The accuracy of the measurement is of the order of 0.00003 to 0.00004, according to the position of the dividing line in the field of the telescope.

The Pulfrich Refractometer. This device utilizes the *total reflection principle*. A glass prism of high refractive index has two polished faces perpendicular to one another, one of them being horizontal. This horizontal face has a small glass cell cemented to it for retaining the liquids to be examined. The beam of incident light is directed so as to strike the prism at *grazing* incidence after traversing the liquid. The emergent beam passes through the vertical face of the prism. It is sharply outlined by those rays which actually graze the prism surface. The sharp boundary is observed with a telescope attached to a divided circle and vernier. Readings are possible to 6 seconds of arc. For accurate temperature control, the optical parts of the instrument are surrounded by a water jacket.

The instrument is intended for measurements on liquids, the refractive indices of which are lower than that of the glass of the prism. To extend the range of measurements, interchangeable prisms of different indices are available. The accuracy on the refractive index of liquids is about 0.00001. It reaches 0.00002 on the measurement of the dispersion with monochromatic lights.

Solid samples must be cut so as to present two perpendicular faces meeting at an unbroken line, while one of the faces must be fairly well polished. Optical contact is obtained in the usual way.

For convenience, the manufacturers supply tables giving the value of n vs. the measured angle i, for various spectral lines.

489

Lob and Pfund Refractometers. The principle of the Lob refractometer is identical with that of the Pulfrich refractometer, but all the readings are made with the same telescope used for indicating the direction of critical emergence. The eyepiece is fixed, and it includes an accessory prism for compensating the spectral dispersion. Instead of the Pulfrich prism, a double Abbé prism is used.

The Pfund refractometer utilizes the principle of the total reflection of light at normal incidence at the boundary of two different media. A convenient instrument of this type for the study of the solidification process of varnishes and lacquers has been described by Countryman and Kunerth (30).

Other Prismatic Refractometers. An early modification of the Abbé refractometer was the Fery instrument, already mentioned. In this instrument the curved faces introduce "caustics" which produce greater uncertainties on the readings. Despite this defect, this instrument has been used for an extraordinarily large volume of data relative to organic chemistry.

Cruikshank and Fairweather (31) have modified the Fery refractometer to adapt it for continuous recording.

The Nichols (32) double reflection microscope attachment for refraction measurements in reality must be classified with the prismatic refractometers. It has been adapted to microanalytical work by Alber and Bryant (33). This instrument, requiring only 5 to 10 mm^3 of fluid, may be operated at high temperature (melting point refractivity) and is most convenient for chemical studies. Its sensitivity can be considerably increased by using an interference method for measuring the displacement of the two beams of light. It is possible to place a double Young's slit over the conventional microscope condenser. If the aperture is limited to the production of the so-called marginal rays, then the emergent light is coherent, and suitable for the production of inter-

ferences. A Nichols refractometer placed on the stage of such a modified microscope then becomes a small interferometer, the beam spacing of which depends upon the refractive index of the substance under study.

For work in the ultraviolet, M. M. Hilger manufactures a photographic angle refractometer which appears to be but a commercial version of an instrument originally designed by Charles Henri (34).

The chemical micro-refractometer of Jelley (31) is intended for the rapid determination of the refractive index of immersion liquids used for the identification of crystals by one of the immersion methods employing the Becke lines or the Christiansen effect. The essential part of the instrument is a small glass wedge of refractive index n_g, supported by a plate. The wedge supports a drop of the specimen, forming a liquid prism of index n_e and of refracting angle a. This prism is about 1 mm thick. A narrow slit is adjusted so that a thin beam of light falls upon the prism about the middle of the wedge. An observer sees a sharp virtual image of the slit formed upon the scale which is graduated directly in terms of refractive indices.

The instrument can also be used conjointly with a heating device for measuring the refractive indices of melted substances, up to about 300°C.

The Jelley refractometer is particularly well adapted to chemical studies when a modest sensitivity is required. Its commercial version, the Jelley-Fisher refractometer, described by Edwards and Otto (35), is currently used to measure indices at the melting point. For measurements at still higher temperatures (up to 300°C), one can use Fredriani's modification (36), which permits simultaneous observation of the melting points.

Broumberg's focal refraction monochromator (45), although not using a prism, is based upon Snell-Descartes' formula, and therefore it may be considered in the same light as the prismatic refractometers. In fact, it can be used for refractometric measurements.

Extensive data relative to the refractivity of organic substances and the application of such measurement methods to the problems of organic analysis have been collected (64–68). Applications of refractometry to chemical production control became really practical with the advent of rugged recording types of instruments. One of the early designs is the multiple reflection instrument of Karrer and Orr (38), now obsolete. It was based upon the principle of Fery's hollow prism. The Barnes recording refractometer (41) is now superseded by the commonly used industrial instrument of Barstow (40).

At present there is a tendency to extend a renewed interest in differential types of instruments. A differential refractometer prism is described by Kegeles (69). It consists of two identical, hollow rectangular prisms of refracting angle A adjacent on their hypotenuse faces. One compartment is used for a reference fluid of index n_0, the other receives the test solution of index n. Parallel light enters normal to one of the small faces, passing through the test fluid first, and is deflected from the normal by an angle given by Snell-Descartes' law. Similar prismatic refractometers have been described by Thovert (70), Zuber (71), Longworth (72), Debye (73), and others.

The advantage of such a design lies in its small size, so that sufficiently rugged measuring cells may be built for direct measurement of sedimentation equilibrium in the ultracentrifuge (Kegeles (74)), by a modification of Lamm's schlieren scale method (75), with the introduction of suitable corrections indicated by Kegeles. With sufficiently high prismatic channels and suitable optics, it is possible to observe directly a two-dimensional refractive index distribution in a heterogenous—say, for instance, refraction increment dn, vs. a concentration gradient. Greater deflections may be obtained by auto-collimation. The two-dimensional plot may be directly projected on a screen, or it may be magnified.

The Grauer angle refractometer is an interesting adaptation of a two-prism system employed at the National Bureau of Standards for the study of solid specimens (76). It could be easily adapted to the study of fluids.

"The instrument consists of a light source with a horizontal filament, a collimator, a diaphragm, a pair of 45-degree-90-degree cemented prisms forming a 90-degree hollow at the upper half and a parallel plate at the lower half, a filar micrometer, and a telescope. All the components are centrally aligned along a common axis."

Compensation of the Spectral Dispersion. In the preceding discussion it was assumed that the incident light was monochromatic. With composite light, white or variously colored, the critical angle of refraction varies with the wavelength. If such light is used for the measurements, the boundary line seen in the telescope appears as a hazy colored band, the colors being arranged symmetrically in the two halves of the field. The dispersion of the light in the instrument is due to the combined action of two factors: (a) the constant effect of the prisms, the physical dimensions of which are fixed, and (b) the variable effect of the specimen under investigation. The first factor could be corrected once for all; the second requires adjustment for every specimen investigated.

In order to cancel out this phenomenon, the modern refractometers are provided with two composed Amici prisms disposed inside the telescope. These prisms are cut at a suitable angle so that the light from the sodium D_{Na} lines passes undeviated.

A rough estimation of the spectral refractive dispersion of substances under investigation can be derived from the conventional expression:

$$d = n_D - 1/(n_F - n_C) \qquad (10)$$

where the n's are the refractive indices successively measured with the light from the D_{Na} line of sodium, the C_H line of hydrogen, and the F_H line of hydrogen, respectively.

For this measurement, the two Amici prisms of the refractometer are mounted in such a way that they can be rotated in opposite directions about the optical axis of the telescope, their respective positions being read on an arbitrary scale.

With all types of critical angle refractometers, certain factors limiting the accuracy of the measurements are not entirely controllable by the operator. These factors are:

(1) The extreme temperature sensitivity of the instrument, producing a hazy, shifting, dividing line, even when a thermostatic jacket is provided.

(2) The difficulty in setting the exact incidence and proper convergence for the light. This factor affects the contrast at the dividing line in the field of the telescope and limits the reproducibliity of the settings.

(3) The limited power of the dispersion compensation prisms. These prisms are efficient only for the D lines of sodium light, and they exactly correct images that are formed only near the center of the field. With liquids of high refractive indices (oils, etc.) the boundary is always somewhat broad and iridescent.

(4) The accuracy on the reading of the divided circle (critical angle). This last point is discussed in physics textbooks.

Some of these difficulties are reduced by designing refractometers covering certain limited ranges of indices, for special industrial applications (oils, sugars, resins, wines, etc.), and by using readily interchangeable monochromatic sources of radiant energy, now commercially available at reasonable price and directly operated from the power line (filtered carbon arc, mercury arc, helium and hydrogen tubes, Na, Sr, K, Cd, Kr, Ne, lamps, etc.). A convenient table for the selection of suitable radiation sources will be found in an article by Tilton and Taylor (79).

Microscopic Methods Based on Change of Focus. The method of determination of the true thickness of an immersed object by means of the microscope was originally invented by the Duc de Chaulnes, and was completely discussed by Johannsen (53), the Winchells (54), Addey (63), Blunck (65), and summarized by Chamot and Mason (58). This method is very widely used in chemistry.

A glass plate is provided with a hollow cell 0.5 to 2.0 mm deep and about 3 mm in diameter. The bottom of the cell is polished with parallel faces and scratched. The cell is filled with a liquid to be studied and covered with a cover glass, itself scratched. The apparatus is placed under the microscope, and the apparent vertical distance between the virtual images of the scratches is measured with the micrometric adjustment of the microscope. The true distance between the two faces of the cell is also measured in the absence of liquid in the cell ($n = 1$). The refractive index of the liquid is given by the relation:

$$n = \text{true thickness/apparent thickness} \quad (11)$$

The micrometric adjustment of the microscope can be calibrated directly in terms of refractive indices by the use of liquids of known refraction.

When the solid specimen available is too small (powders), the above mentioned crystallographic methods cannot be applied. It is, however, possible to evaluate the refractive index of these solid specimens by immersion in liquids of convenient refractive index. When the index of the immersion liquid equals that of the immersed specimen usually some sharp modification of the microscopic image of the latter can be observed. The refractive index of the liquid is then measured by one of the methods described. The equality of the indices can be ascertained by the microscopical observation of either one of the following phenomena: (a) the displacement of the Becke lines; (b) the Christiansen effect.

The Becke Lines. The displacement of the Becke lines when a crystal is immersed in a liquid is explained as follows. When a crystal is seen through the microscope, the image of the edge will move away from the crystal when the objective is moved upward, and its index is smaller than that of the immersion fluid. It will not move at all when the refractive indices are equal.

The method applies also to crystals other than those of the cubic system. In this case, several Becke lines are visible, but, by adding a polarization attachment to the microscope, all but one of these lines at a time can be immobilized and the corresponding refractive index thus determined. With positive uniaxial crystals one index, n_w, the lowest, is the same in all directions of the crystal. The other index varies between the value above and a maximum value n_e. The inverse relationship holds for negative uniaxial crystals.

With biaxial crystals, both indices n_w and n_e, respectively, vary with the direction, but a maximum and a minimum value also can be recorded when a mixture of crystals of various sizes is observed. However, in this case the final interpretation requires another set of observations with conoscopical light (convergent polarized light).

A very complete discussion, including all operational details and bibliography, will be found in Chamot and Mason (58).

The Christiansen Effect. The Christiansen effect takes place when two contacting media (a crystal immersed in a liquid) have the same refractive index for a given wavelength, but a different spectral dispersion; the Becke lines then have the aspect of small bright spectra. The image of the object is surrounded by colored fringes moving in one direction or the other with the movements of the microscopic objective.

Observation of the Christiansen effect leads to very valuable information concerning the spectral dispersion of the material under investigation, if that of the immersion liquid is known.

Extensive lists of immersion liquids which have proved their worth exist in the literature (46, 56 58). Let us mention only the tetrasodium dioxypentathiostannate of Jelley, which, being soluble in water, is valuable for the study of water-insoluble organic materials.

The methods available for adjusting the refractive index of the immersion liquid to equal that of the immersed specimen are: (a) the dilution method, utilizing known mixtures of liquids (tedious, but very accurate); (b) the Merwin (46) method. Use is made of the different spectral dispersions exhibited by the liquid and by the sepcimen. A monochromator is used to change progressively the wavelength until the Becke lines seen in the microscope disappear; (c) the Emmons method, using the different relationship existing for the immersion liquid and the specimen, between the refractive index and the temperature: the microscope must be provided with a hot-stage attachment; the method can also be combined with method (b); (d) the Leitz-Emmons hemispherical refractometer, which fits over any standard microscope. The specimen and immersion liquid are enclosed in a small hemispherical cell together with a concentric hemispherical hollow rotatable from outside, and having a different diameter. When the indices of the liquid and specimen, respectively, have been matched by adjusting the temperature of the hot stage, the refractive index of the liquid is immediately determined by rotating the hemispherical hollow until the position of total reflection of light is found; the apparatus serves as its own refractometer.

The crystallographic immersion methods described here are applicable to metallographic and metallurgical specimens. Most of them can be carried out on rough speci-

493

TABLE 1

	dn	Wavelength
Nichols refractometer	.001	Na
Jelley	.001	Na
Edwards-Otto	.002	Na
Microscope	.003	Na
Beck lines	.003	Na
Christiansen effect	.003	Na
Pfund	.0001	Na
Henry	.0004	Na
Barstow (recording)	.0004	Na
Cruikshank-Fairweather	.0004	Na
Fery	.0005	Na
Tuckerman (auto-collimator)	.0005	Na
Abbé	.00001	Na
Abbé	.00002	(White)
Pulfrich	.00002	Na
Grauer	.00004	Na
Dipping (B. & L.)	.00004	Na
Lob	.00005	Na
Interferometers	.0000401	Na
Phase-contrast interferometers	.000000005	Na-594

mens in a few minutes, and for these reasons are widely used industrially.

Selection of a Refractometric Technique. The last significant figure of relative refractive index obtained with the available instruments serves as a guide in selecting the proper refractometric technique. Routine figures currently accepted for some commercially available instruments are given in the Table 1.

REFERENCES

See next article.

R. JONNARD

HISTORY OF LIGHT REFRACTION (*See also* p. 454)

The term "refraction" refers to the change of direction, or "breaking" of the rectilinear path of light at the surface of separation of two transparent media.

This paradoxical phenomenon has attracted the attention of philosophers since early Greco-Latin antiquity, and it was cor-

rectly opposed to the rectilinear propagation observed when light travels through unobstructed space. It is worthy of note that the word *Optikos* ("I see") existed only in the Greek language. Thus, the study of optics appears to be an intellectual phenomenon properly Greco-Latin in origin, arising sometime toward the end of the Hellenic period of history (1).

The historical development of knowledge relative to the refraction of light encompasses the whole of geometric optics as well as the nature of light and the mechanism of vision. Reflection phenomena, linked with rectilinear propagation were well described in Plato's "Times" (427–347 B.C.), in Euclid's "Optica", Vol. VII (2), (circa 325 B.C.), in Appollodorus's "Philosophy" (3), and in Claudius Ptolemy's "Physics" and "Catoptries" (2nd century A.D.). All these authors knew the elementary laws of optical reflection.

Simultaneously with the development of knowledge about the reflection of light, the apparently contradictory notion of *refraction* was neatly distinguished by the peripatetician of Chalcis, Aristotle (322–284 B.C.) in his "Rhetoric" and "Meteorology." His views were extended by the Stoic Posidonius, of Apamee (135–50 B.C.). Lucius Annaeus Seneca's "Natural Questions" (circa 25 A.D.) contains abundant allusions to the consequences of the refraction of light through flasks, bottles, glass, menisci and the like. In fact, Mediterranean antiquity knew how to utilize these effects practically.

The full significance of these discoveries appeared after Aristotle, referring to the fifth century (B.C.) philosopher Empedocles, postulated that light is a vibrational phenomenon traveling with a finite velocity through fluids of definite densities. Such views were subsequently expounded by Aristoxene of Tarente (circa 4th century B.C.), to be finally developed by the Arab Averrhoes in the 12th century A.D.

As early as the 10th century A.D. one

finds a most explicit mathematical theory of refraction in the Ibn-Al-Haitham's "Treatise of Optical Geometry" after this author, recognizing the limitations of Ptolemy's elementary law, discovered the principle of the inverse return of spherical waves, which is the basis of modern prismatic refractometers. During the Middle Ages the laws of light refraction were widely applied. For instance, Roger Bacon in his "Opius Maius" (1270) describes glass lenses without stating their basic properties. Indeed, one finds in Al-Hazem's Treatise all necessary fundamentals which might have been desirable at the time. Thus, contrary to a common assertion and to the opinion of Joseph Bertrand, the discovery of refraction considerably preceded Tycho-Brahe, Vitellio (circa 1270), and Kepler.

Johannes Kepler (6) must be credited with what may be considered the first practical refractometer. Its principle is well described in his "Dioptrice," published in 1611. The instrument permits one to determine the relationship between the ratio of length of the shadows and the ratio of incidence and of refraction angles, the two rays traveling through air and an unknown medium, respectively. Although Kepler labored under the wrong assumption that light has an infinite velocity, it is with such an instrument that he discovered the important phenomenon of the internal total reflection in glass for an angle of about 42°. Thus, Mees (7) erred when he stated that Kepler did not know the law of refraction.

There is some evidence that Robert Hooke (8), in England, also invented a refractometer of some kind, but no trace of Hooke's instrument has been discovered.

The 17th century continued to labor under the assumption of an infinite velocity for light. To Descartes (9), light was simply a "pressure transmitted to the eye," with an infinite velocity which could "still be greater" when traveling in denser media than in lighter ones. Despite this error, he was able, in 1644, to interpret correctly Willibrod Snell's experiment (Leyden, 1621) and to formulate the basic law of refraction which summarizes so well most of geometric optics:

$$\sin i/\sin r = n = Cte \qquad (1)$$

where n is the refractive index characteristic of the medium traversed. This law made modern optics possible.

Thus, the early history of the refraction of light can be traced from early Greco-Latin antiquity, along two main lines of thought. One is concerned with the studies derived from the reflection of light, running from Empedocles (5th century B.C.) through Aristotle, Plato, Euclid, Apollodorus, Ptolemy, Bacon, Magnus, Kircher, Snell and Descartes. The other is concerned with the phenomena related to the non-linear propagation of light, from Aristotle again, to Aristoxene, Posidonios, Cleomede, Lucretius, Seneca, Ibn-Al-Haitham, Averrhoes, Bacon, Tycho-Brahe, Vitellio, Kepler, Hooke, Snell and, again, Descartes.

For the remaining conformal picture fragments, the historical development, the reader is referred to the classical works of Leonardo da Vinci (10), Huygens (11), Fresnel (12), Arago (13), Mach (14), and others. A very clear exposition of the phenomena of refraction from the standpoint of geometric optics is given by J. W. Forest in O. Glasser's book (15), while the references in Reymond's book (16) somewhat fill up some lacunae in Wile's basic work. Other important reference works include: Delambre (17), Doublet (18), Marion (19) and Tannery (20).

Almost simultaneously with the publication of Descartes' momentous synthesis, Pierre de Fermat showed that the "sine law" could be deduced from the philosophical principle of "optical extremum path." The principle proved much broader than the experimental data then available, and its influence in science may be felt in the work of Leibnitz, Kant, Hamilton, Gauss, and even of Mach. This lends support to a remark made by Destouches (21) that "the essential, in order to build a theory, is to possess simple and schematic ideas, of origin rather intuitive than purely experimental, and a long work of the mind is required."

de Fermat's principle is often expressed mathematically as a "stationary time integral":

$$\rho \int n \, ds = 0 \qquad (2)$$

where n is the cartesian refraction index, ds is the geometric path length, and the quantity nds defines the optical path length.

It is interesting to note that a very similar principle of optimum path length was already proposed in the third century by Hero of Alexandria who implicitly admitted a finite light velocity (22). The principle is sometimes more useful in the equivalent form:

$$\rho \int ds/d\lambda = 0 \qquad (3)$$

In all its forms, the principle states that the sum of *all* optical path lengths followed by the light rays through any succession of isotropic, homogeneous transparent media separated by stigmatic surfaces, is stationary, that is, two such adjacent rays differ in optical length only by an infinitesimal quantity at least of second order. The principle never states whether this length is a maximum, a minimum, or an inflexional quantity, but only that it is constant. The writer, among others, has cautioned about the indiscriminate interpretation of this principle (23). The argument can be summarized as follows. In the relatively simple case of a beam of parallel rays of light, the algebraic sum of all of the partial path lengths of incident plus reflected rays remains constant regardless of the angle of incidence on a given surface, be it an ellipse, an hyperboloid or a parabola.

It is obviously important to know the where abouts of the rays ultimately emerging from the optical system considered. This is given by Malus' theorem, according to which all the rays issued from a point source S, after undergoing multiple reflections and/or refraction, remain normal to a family of parallel surfaces E, each point of which is equidistant from S (conjugate) by the same optical length L. The surface defines the "wave-front surface" or surface of equal phase. It is that which is reached by light after a unique time T (equations *3* and *4*) from *all* the possible trajectories so that:

$$T = L/C = \Sigma(l/V) \qquad (4)$$

where l is the geometric path length. This is in strict conformity with de Fermat's principle. A bundle of light rays satisfying such conditions is said to form a congruence of normals when their direction of propagation is defined by a series of parameters (X, Y, Z) which depend upon at least two independent variables (such as V, U, etc.). In the limited case of geometric optics ($n = Cte$) with only one variable, one has a totality of curves orthogonal to a family of wave surfaces instead of a congruence. Huygens construction (1690) is merely a convenient geometric demonstration of this theorem.

It is perhaps clear to those conversant with Huygens' work that the ideal stigmatic surface of a given optical system may differ from the actual physical surface of its dioptic elements. Thus, three situations may arise, according to which the actual surface is either tangent, internal, or secant to the stigmatic surface. Accordingly, the optimum path length of de Fermat is either a maximum, a minimum, or an inflectional quantity, respectively, and in the order given above.

The implications of de Fermat's principle pervade much of contemporary physical-chemistry. Almost simultaneously with its publication, Pierre Maupertuis showed, independently, that when a "material point in action" is analyzed, the sum of all the energies involved is stationary, the representative equation being:

$$\rho \int \sqrt{(U + E)\, ds} = 0 \qquad (5)$$

where U is the potential energy,
E is the kinetic energy
ds represents the distances involved.
It remained for the genius of Sir William Hamilton to discover the analogy between equations (3) and (5) and to bring it forth by postulating:

$$\sqrt{(U + E)} = n \qquad (6)$$

The fundamental importance of Maupertuis' discovery is perhaps clearly stated in the following citation: "Thus, the refractive index n expresses the force function or field existing in matter, which results in slowing down the velocity of light and determines the trajectory of rays or streams of information, to use modern terminology. In this sense, n is a measure of interaction between matter and light, and its determination contributes to a knowledge of the structure of matter. The abstract concept of a field of forces remains only a convenient but arbitrary form of language to explain the properties of space and to predict the future behavior of the material particles, the local sources of the physicists, or points of particular chemical interest contained in space. Thus, field of forces, space properties, and the chemical properties of the elements are theoretical views of the mind that become real, like shadow of a tree, only when some interaction takes place. One sees that the concept of generalized interaction is contained in that of field, as was perceived by Paul Langevin when he wrote in 1903: 'It is always matter which contains the charges whose field divergence becomes different from Zero.' In the absence of matter, indeed,

$$\sqrt{(U + E)} = 1,$$

and it is the nature of the sources that determines the properties of the field: if there is no matter, there are no charges, no sources, no force, and no field in space." (1)

Following this discovery, the great amount of experimental work stimulated by the theories of T. Young, A. Fresnel, and C. Maxwell, all based upon the fundamental concept of "field of force," revealed that, in fact, the refractive dispersion of transparent substances is fully governed by their ability to absorb radiant energy. It is possible to develop newer, more satisfactory theories of electromagnetism *without* utilizing the abstract concepts of field of force and of action at distance (24) but the antiquated *field* remains a convenient means of expression.

Today, it is admitted that the proposition represented by equation (5) is valid if n varies *little* and *continuously*. The "rays" considered are no more than trajectories of electromagnetic energy, and de Broglie remarks (25) that, in this case the treatment is compatible with *both* Newton's strangely modern corpuscular theory and Fresnel's undulatory theory. But, if n varies suddenly, diffraction takes place and the concept of "ray" vanishes. However, that concept of refraction in the sense of Hamilton's equation remains valid. It is apparent from the foregoing, that the determination of refractive indices may be accomplished essentially in two ways: (a) by application of Kepler-Descartes formula, involving angular measurements, (b) by application of de Fermat's principle, involving velocities, or phase, measurements. The first method involves all the prismatic refractometers and derived procedures. The second method concerns all the interferometric, differential methods. From this point on it is a matter of textbook record that the instrumental development based upon one method or the other fluctuated with the fortunes and temporary relative importance of the underlying theories of light.

REFERENCES

1. JONNARD, R., "Optics, a Greco-Latin Miracle," Sigma-Delta-Epsilon Lect., N. Y. Academy of Sciences, Jan. 20, 1958.
2. TEUBNER, S. H., "Euclidis Optica," Heidelberg, 1895.

3. Wilde, H., "Geschichte der Optik, Berlin, 1838.

4. de Tonquedec, J., "Critique de la Connaissance," G. Beauchesne, Paris, 1929.

5. Jonnard, R., "Principles of Rationalization in Biology and Medicine," Proc. 7th Nat. Conf. I.S.A., Cleveland, O., Sept. 1952.

6. Kepler, Johannes, "Ad Vitellianem Paralipomena quibus astronomiae pars optica traditur," I, p. 20, Frankfort, 1604; Also: Dioptrica, Frankfort, 1654.

7. Mees, C. D., and Baker, J. R., "The Path of Science," J. Wiley & Sons, New York, 1946.

8. Hooke, Robert, "Micrographia, or Some Physiological Descriptions of Minute Bodies Made by Magnifying Glasses, with Observations and Inquiries Thereupon," London, 1664.

9. Descartes, René, "Dioptrique," 1637; "Discours de la Method: Principa Philosphae," 1644.

10. da Vinci, Leonardo, "Ueber die Malerei," German ed. by Ludwig.

11. Huygens, C. v. Z., "Traité de la Lumière," Leide, 1690.

12. Fresnel, A., "Oeuvres Complètes," Paris, 1858.

13. Arago, F., "Oeuvres Complètes," Paris, 1865.

14. Mach, E., "Principles of Physical Optics," transl. Anderson, J. S. and Young, A. F. A. Dover Publications, N. Y., 1926.

15. Forrest, J. W., "Refractometry," cf. in Glaser, O., "Medical Physics," Year Book Publ., Chicago, 1944.

16. Reymond, A., "Histoire des Sciences Exactes et Naturelles dans l'Antiquité Gréco-Romaine," A. Blanchard, Paris, 1924.

17. Delambre, J. B., "Histoire de l'Astronomie Ancienne," Delagrave, Paris, 1817.

18. Doublet, E., "Histoire de l'Astronomie," Doin, Paris, 1922.

19. Marion, F., "L'Optique," L. Hachette, Paris, 1869.

20. Tannery, P., "Mémoires Scientifiques: Sciences éxactes et naturelles dans l'Antiquité," Gauthier-Villars, Paris, 1912.

21. Destouches, J. L., "Méthodologie de la Physique Théorique Moderne. Notions de Logistique," Tournier et Constans, Paris, 1946.

22. Hero, "Dioptra," ed. by Schöne, H. Teubner, 1903.

23. Jonnard, R., "Random Selection System for Automatic Dynamic Biochemical Analysis," Ann. N. Y. Academy of Sciences, 87, 669–728, (1960).

24. Moon, P., and Spencer, D. E., "The Coulomb Force and the Ampere Force," J. Franklin Inst., 257(4), 305–315 (1954); Am. J. Physics, 3, 120–134 (1954); J. Franklin Inst., 257(4), 369–382 (1954).

25. de Broglie, L., "Matter and Light, the New Physics." Dover, New York, 1946.

26. Abbé, E., "Neue Apparate Zur Bestimmung des Brechungsund Zerstrenungsver Fester und Fluessiger Koerper," Naturwiss., 8, 96–174 (1874).

27. Pulfrich, C., "Ein Neues Refraktometer," Zeitschr. f. Instr., 7, 16–27 (1887).

28. Lob, P., "Eine Neue Universal Refraktometer mit Innenablesung," Zeitschr. f. Instr., 53, 27–30 (1933).

29. Pfund, C., J. Opt. Soc. Am., 24, 121–125 (1934).

30. Countryman, A., and Kunerth, W., "The Construction and Use of a Pfund Parallel Plate Refractometer," J. Opt. Soc. Am., 24, 25–28 (1934).

31. Jelley, E. E., "A Microrefractometer and its Use in Chemical Microscopy," Proc. Roy. Microscopic. Soc. London, 54(3), 234–245 (# 535, 317-8-XVI) (1934); "The Preparation and Constitution of Thiostannates. II: tetra- and octa-dioxypentathiostannates," J.A.C.S., 78, 1076 (1934).

32. Nichols, L., "Double Reflexion Refractometer," Nat. Paint Bull. 1, 12–13 (1937); 1, 14–16 (1937).

33. Alber, H., and Bryant, J. T., "Systematic Qualitative Organic Micro-analysis. Determination of the Refractive Index of Liquids," Ind. Eng. Chem. Anal. Ed., 12, 305–307 (1940).

34. Henri, Ch., "Etudes de Photochimie," Gauthier-Villars, Paris, 1919.

35. Edwards, A. E., and Otto, C. E., "A Microrefractometer of Simple Design. Laboratory Construction," Ind. Eng. Chem. Anal. Ed., 10, 225–226 (1938).

36. Fredriani, H. A., "Refractive Index Measurements at and Above the Melting Point of Solids," Ind. Eng. Chem. Anal. Ed., 14, 439 (1942).

37. Cruikshank, C., and Fairweather, W., Brit. Pat. 555,928, Sept. 13, 1943.

38. Karrer, E., and Orr, R. L., "Recording Photoelectric Refractometer," J. Opt. Soc. Am., 36, 42–46 (1946).

39. Emmons, R. C., and Winchell, A. N., "Some Methods for Determining Refractive Indices," Am. Mineral., 11, 115–118 (1928).

40. BARSTOW, O. E., "A New Recording Refractometer," *Instr.* **23**(4), 396–398 (1950).

41. BARNES, R. B., "Refractometer for Chemical Reactions," U.S. Pat. 2,413,208, Dec. 24, 1946.

42. JACOBSON, S., U. S. Pat. 237,1625, May 20, 1945.

43. STAMM, R. F., MARINER, TH., BARNES, R. B., AND STRYKER, CH. R., U. S. Patent 258,-3973, Jan. 29, 1952.

44. CLAMMANN, E., "Pneumatic Refractometer," *Instr.*, **26**(5), 740–742 (1953).

45. BROUMBERG, E. M., "Une Nouvells Methode Pour Rendre la Lumière Monochromatique," *C.R.U.R.S.S. Acad. Sci.*, **2**, 464–469 (1935;) *Rev. d'Opt. Theor. et Experim.*, **15** (2), 69 (1936).

46. MERWIN, H. E., AND LARSEN, C. S., "Mixtures of Amorphous Sulfur and Selenium as Immersion Media for the Determination of High Refractive Indices with the Microscope," *Am. J. Sci.*, **34**(4), 42–47 (1956).

47. SAYLOR, CH. P., "Accuracy of Microscopical Methods for Determining Refractive Indices by Immersion," *Nat. Bur. Std. J. Res.*, **15**, 277–294 (1935).

48. TSUBOI, S., "A Dispersion Method of Determining Plagioclase in Cleavage Flakes," *Mineral. Mag.*, **20**, 108–122 (1923).

49. TSUBOI, S., "A Dispersion Method of Finding the Principal Refractive Index of Crystals in Powders," *J. Geol. Soc. Tokio*, **32**, 1–6 (1925).

50. TSUBOI, S., "A Dispersion Method of Discriminating Rock Constituents and its Use in Petrographic Investigations," *J. Fac. Sci. U. Tokio*, **1**(2), 139–140 (1926).

51. VALASEK, J., "Optical Constants of Substances Which Exhibit Metallic Reflexion," "Int. Crit. Tables," **5**, 248.

56. WEST, C. D., "Measurement of Refractive Indices of Resins and Plastics," *Ind. Eng. Chem. Anal. Ed.*, **10**, 627–628 (1938).

53. JOHANNSEN, A., "Manual of Petrographic Methods," p. 238. McGraw-Hill, N. Y., 1914.

54. WINCHELL, N. H., AND WINCHELL, A. N. W., "Elements of Optical Mineralogy," p. 69, J. Wiley & Sons, N. Y., 1922.

55. OLLIVIER, H., "Cours de Physique Générale," p. 252, Hermann, Paris, 1923.

56. WRIGHT, F. E., "The Methods of Petrographic Microscopic Research," *Carnegie Inst. Wash. Publ.*, **158**, 95 (1915).

57. WRIGHT, F. E., "Measurement of the Refractive Index of a Drop of Liquid," *J. Wash. Acad. Sci.*, **4**, 269–279 (1914).

58. CHAMOT, E. M., AND MASON, C. W., "Handbook of Chemical Microscopy," Vol. 1, 2nd Ed. p. 358. J. Wiley & Sons, N. Y., 1938.

59. MARTIN, L. C.,, "Optical Measuring Instruments," p. 164, Blackie & Sons, Phila., 1924.

60. WOOD, R. G., AND AYLIFFE, A., "Method of Analyzing Small Crystals for Optical Properties," *J. Sci. Instr.*, **12**, 299 (1925); *Phil. Mag.*, **21**, 321 (1936).

61. WOOD, R. G., AYLIFFE, A., AND WILLIAMS, G., "Method of Analyzing Small Crystals for Optical Properties," *Proc. Roy. Soc. London*, **A-177**, 140 (1940–41).

62. KIENLE, R. H., AND STEARNS, E. I., "Adaptation of Automatic Spectrophotometer for Special Measurements," *Instr.*, **20**(11), 1057–1063 (1947).

63. ADDEY, F., "A Note on the Measurement of the Vertical Dimensions by Use of the Graduated Fine Adjustment of the Microscope," *J. Qekett Micros. Club (2)*, **14**, 279 (1922).

64. BENEDETTI-PICHLER, A. A., AND SPIKES, W. F., "Introduction to the Microtechniques of Inorganic Qualitative Analysis," Douglaston, N. Y., 1935.

65. BLUNK, G., "Quantitative Bestimmung Physikalische Chemischer Eigenschaften Mikroscopish Keiner Mengen," *Zeitschr. wiss. Mikros.*, **37**, 138–40 (1920).

66. EVERSMANN, TH., "Bemerkung zur Mittelbaren Langennessung mit Distanz faden nach Reichenbach," *Zeitschr. f. Instr.*, **52**, 525–528 (1932).

67. KIRK, P. L., AND GIBSON, C. S., "Refractive Index Measurements in Qualitative Organic Microanalysis," *Ind. Eng. Chem. Anal. Ed.*, **11**, 403 (1939).

68. REIMERS, F., "Investigations of Microchemical Methods. IV Identification by Means of Microdetermination of Refraction," *Dansk. Tids. Farm.*, **15**, 81–99 (1941).

69. KEGELES, G., GOSTING, L. J., HANSEN, E. M., AND MORRIS, M., "Equipment and Experimental Methods for Interference Diffusion Studies," *Rev. Scient. Instr.*, **20**(3), 209–215 (1949).

70. THOVERT, —., *Ann. Chim. Phys.*, **2**(9), 369 (1915).

71. ZUBER, R., *Z. Physik.*, **79**, 280–290 (1932).

72. LONGSWORTH, L. G., "Optical Methods in Electrophoresis," *Ind. Eng. Chem. Anal. Ed.*, **18**, 249–269 (1946).

73. DEBYE, P., "A Photoelectric Instrument for Light Scattering Measurements and a Dif-

ferential Refractometer," *J. Appl. Phys.*, **17**(5), 392–398 (1946).

74. KEGELES, G., AND GUTTER, F., "Determination of the Sedimentation Constants from Fresnel Diffraction Patterns," *J.A.C.S.*, **69**, 1302–1305 (1947); **73**, 3770–3777 (1951).

75. LAMM, O., "Measurements of Concentration Gradients in Sedimentation and Diffusion by Refraction Methods. Solubility Properties of Potato Starch," *Novo Acta Regiae Soc. Sci. Upsaliensis*, IV, **10**(6), 1–115 (1937).

76. GRAUER, B., "Prismatic Refractometer," *Nat'l. Bur. Std. Tech. News Bull.*, **37**(9), 535 (5953).

77. TILTON, L. W., AND TAYLOR, J. K., "Refractive Index Measurements," in: BERL, W. C., "Physical Methods in Chemical Analysis," Vol. 1, Academic Press, N. Y., 1950.

78. LAUER, J. L., AND KING, R. W., "Refractive Index of Liquids at Elevated Temperatures," *Anal. Chem.*, **28**(11), 1697–1701 (1956).

79. ROTHEN, A., "Optical Properties of Surface Films," *Ann. N.Y. Acad. Sci.*, **153**, 1054–1064 (1951).

80. DAYHOFF, E. S., "Correction in High Accuracy Fresnel Region Microwave Interferometry," *N. B. S. Tech. Rep. 4514* (Feb., 1956).

81. RAVEAU, C., "Etude des Franges des Lames Crystallines au Moyen de la Surface des Indices," *Bull. Soc. Fr. de Mineral.*, **34**, 5–12 (1911); "Sur la Visibilité et les Singularités des Franges d'interférence," *Resum. Comm. Soc. Fr. de Phys.*, p. 40, (April, 1901).

82. LOWRY, T. M., AND ALLSOPP, C. B., "A Photographic Method of Measuring Refractive Indices," *Proc. Roy. Soc. London*, A-**126**, 165 (1929).

83. LORD RAYLEIGH, "On Some Physical Properties of Argon and Helium," *Proc. Roy. Soc. London*, **59**, 200–217 (1896).

84. WILLIAMS, W. E., "Studies in Interferometry," *Proc. Phys. Soc.*, **45**, 699–727 (1933). "Applications of Interferometry" Methuen, London (1928).

85. HIRSH, P., "The Refractometer and the Interferometer," *Z. Nahr. Genuscm.*, **43**, 65–78 (1922); "Die Abderhalden-Reaktion Mittels der Quantitativen Interferometrischen Methods," *Deutsch. Klin. Wchnschr.*, **4**, (1365–1366 (1925); *Deutsch. Klin. Wchnschr.*, **4**, 1560–1562 (1925).

86. COTTON, A., "L'Interféromètre de Jamin à Faisceaux Polarisés," *Rev. d'Opt. Théor. et Instrum.*, **5**, 153–166 (1934).

87. BRILLOUIN, M., "Recherches sur l'ellipticité du Géoide," *C. R. Acad. Sci.*, **137**, 786–788 (1903); "Mémoires des Savants Etrangers," **23**(3) (1908).

88. BARCHEWITZ, P., "Etude sur l'interféromètre à rayous Polarisés de Jamin," *Rev. d'Opt. Théor. et Instrum.*, **5**, 167–178 (1934).

89. SMITH, F. H., U. S. Pat. 2,601,175, June 17, 1952.

90. SAGNAC, G., *Le Radium* (July 8, 1911).

91. RAMSAY, B. P., "A grating interferometer" *J. Opt. Soc. Am.*, **24**, 253–268 (1934).

92. BARUS, C., "Elliptic Interferences," *Carnegie Inst. Wash. Publ. No. 149:* (1911–1914).

93. MARTON, L., "Electron Interferometer," *Phys. Rev.*, **85**(4), 1057–1058 (1952).

94. MARTON, L., SIMPSON, J. A., AND SUDDETH, J. A., "An Electron Interferometer," *Rev. Scientific Instr.*, **25**(10), 1099–1104 (1954).

95. SIMPSON, J. A., "Electron Interference Experiments," *Rev. Modern Phys.*, **28**(3), 254–260 (1956).

96. MARTON, L., "Electron Physics," *Nat. Bur. Std. Circ. 527.*

97. JONNARD, R., "Réfractometrie Interférentielle et Structure du Sérum Sanguin," Maloine, Paris, 1937.

98. JONNARD, R., "Réfractomètre Interférentiel Pour Usages Biologiques," *Rev. d'Opt. Théor. et Instrum.*, **15**, 425–430 (1936).

99. DUFFIEUX, N., "Fente Simple Pour Spectrographies," *Rev. d'Opt. Théor. et Instrum.*, **15**, 298 (1936).

100. LENDEL, E., ZIMMER, A., AND FEHLOW, W., *Munch. Med. Wchnschr.*, **37**, 1–16 (1927).

101. BRUINS, H. R., *Rec. des Trav. Chim.*, **50**, 121–128 (1931); *Koll. Zeitschr.*, **54**, 265–271 (1931); **54**, 272–275 (1931); **57**, 152 (1932); **59**, 263 (1932).

102. JONNARD, R., "Automatic Electronic Recording Interferometer. II-Performance," O. N. R. Technical Report, March, 1957.

103. OLLIVIER, H., "Cours de Physique Générale," **3**, 252, Hermann, Paris, 1923.

104. JONNARD, R., "The Orthoptic Microscope Interferometer. Theory, Standardization, Applications to Precision Interferential Refractometry." Proc. 7th Nat. Conf. I.S.A., Sept. 8–12, Cleveland, O., 1952.

105. JONNARD, R., U. S. Patent 2,858,728, Nov. 4, (1958).

106. STOCKBARGER, D. C., AND BURNS, L., "Line Shape as a Function of the Mode of Spectrograph Slit Irradiation," *J. Opt. Soc. Am.*, **23**, 379 (1933).

107. JONNARD, R., "Random Selection System for

Automatic Dynamic Biochemical Analysis," Ann. N. Y. Acad. Sci. Conf. on Automatic Analysis, Nov. 12, 1959.

108. FERRANTI, A., Brit. Pat. 760321, 1958.

109. PECK, E. R., AND OBETZ, S. W., "Wavelength or Length Measurements by Reversible Fringe Counting," *J. Opt. Soc. Am.*, **43**(6), 505–509 (1953).

110. INGELSTAM, E., "A Phase Contrast Refractometer With High Accuracy for Gases and Liquids," *Ark. f. Fysik*, **6**(29), 287–316 (1953).

111. JONNARD, R., "Recent Advances in Interferometry." *Trans. N. Y. Acad. Sci. II*, **15**, 269–280 (1953); "Biological Applications of Interferometry," Seminar, Brooklyn Polytech. Inst., Dec. 1953; "The Nature of Biological Information," *Chem. Eng. News*, **32**, 595 (1954).

112. HUNTOON, R. D., WEISS, A., AND SMITH, J. R., "Electronic Fringe Interpolation for an Optical Interferometer," Nat. Bur. Std. Report 1228, May 15, 1952; *J. Opt. Soc. Am.*, **44**(4), 264–269 (1954).

113. DECKER, M. M., AND MUELLER, H., "Transmitting Data by Light Modulation," *Control Eng.* (July, 1957).

114. JONNARD, R., "Automatic Electronic Recording of Refractive Dispersion by Interferometry," Proc. First Internat. Instrum. Cong. and I.S.A. Conf. Sept. 13–23, Phila., Pa., 1954.

115. JONNARD, R., "Automatic Electronic Recording Interferometer. I-Design and Construction O. N. R. Technical Report," August, 1956.

116. JONNARD, R., "Adventures in Laboratory Automation," *Cybernetica*, **2**(3), 152–188 (1959).

117. JONNARD, R., L'analyse des Composés Lourds par Réfractométrie Interférentielle. *Bull. Soc. Chim. Biol. de Paris*, **21**, 1185–1193 (1939).

118. LORENTZ, H. A., "Ueber die Beziehung Zwischen der Fortplanzungsgeschwindigkeit des Lichtes und der Korper Dichte." *I. Wiedmann Ann. des Phys. und Chem.* **9**, 641–665 (1880).

119. GIBSON, R. E., AND KINCAID, J. F., "The Influence of Temperature and Pressure on the Volume and Refractive Index of Benzene." *J.A.C.S.*, **60**, 511–518 (1938).

120. KURTZ, S. S., AND WARD, A. L., "Refractivity Intercept and the Specific Refraction Equation of Newton. I. Development of the Refractivity Intercept and Comparison with Specific Refraction Equations," *J.*

Franklin Inst., **222**, 563–592 (1936). II. The Electronic Interpretation of the Refractivity Intercept and of the Specific Refraction Equations of Newton, Eykman and Lorentz-Lorenz. *J. Franklin Inst.*, **224**, 697–728 (1937).

121. SWIETOSLAWSKI, W., "Atomic Refraction." *J.A.C.S.*, **42**, 1945–1951(1920).

122. LAGEMANN, R. T., "A Relation Between Viscosity and Refractive Index." *J.A.C.S.* **67**, 498–499 (1954).

123. DEBYE, P., "Polar Molecules." *Chem. Cat.*, N. Y., N. Y., (1929).

124. NUTTING, P. G., "Dispersion Formulas Applicable to Glass," *J. Opt. Soc. Am.*, **2**, 61 (1919).

125. WRIGHT, F. E., "The Petrographic Microscope in Analysis." *J.A.C.S.* **38**, 1647–1658, (1916). *J. Opt. Soc. Am.* **5**, 389–395 (1921).

126. CHAUDRON, P., "Gaseous Equilibria Measurements." Thesis, Univ. of Paris, fac. Sc. Mason, Paris (1921).

127. THOMPSON, W. R., HUSSEY, R., TENNANT, R., AND CAMPBELL, N. O., "Effects of Radiations on Biological Systems. I. Studies in Respiration." *J. Gen. Physiol.* **16**, 207–220 (1932).

128. BELL, F. K., AND KRANTZ, J. C., JR., "An Interferometer Method for the Assay of Nitrous Oxide." *J. A. Pharm. Assoc.*, **29**, 126–130 (1940).

129. SCHÖNROCK, L., "Refractivity of Sucrose Solutions." Int. Critical Tables, **2**, 336.

130. RAW, R., "The Control of Fractional Distillation by Means of Refractive Index Measurements." *J. Soc. Chem. Ind.*, **66**, 451 (1947).

131. KIRK, P., "Density and Refractive Index. Their Application in Criminal Identification." A. Thomas, 1951.

132. JONNARD, R., "Determination of Total Nitrogen in Proteins and Their Hydrolyzates." *Ind. & Eng. Chem.* **17**, 246–248 (1945).

133. PAIC, M., AND DEUTSCH, V., "Dosage Réfractometrique des Protéines Sériques." C. R. Ac. des Sc., **199**, 1306–1308, 1934.

134. CLEASON, S., *Ark. Kem. Mineral. Geol.* **23**-A(1), (1946).

135. TISELIUS, A., AND CLEASON, S., "Adsorption Analysis of Amino Acids and Peptides," *Arkiv. Kemi. Mineral. Geol.*, **15**-B(6), 18–23 (1941).

136. HOLMAN, R. T., AND HAGDAHL, L., "Tiselius-Cleason Interferometric Absorption Apparatus," *Anal. Chem.*, **23**, 794–797 (1941).

137. SVENSON, H., "Some Improved Forms of the

Differential-Prismatic Cell." *J. Opt. Soc. Am.*, **44**(2), 140–146 (1954).

138. KEGELES, G., "A New Optical Method for Observing Equilibrium." *J.A.C.S.*, **69**, 1302–1305 (1947).

139. GIBERT, R., *J. Chim. Phys.*, **44**, 37–39 (1947).

140. CALVET, E., AND CHEVALERIAS, R., "A New Interference Method for Studying Diffusion in Liquids," *J. Chim. Phys.*, **43**, 37–53 (1946).

141. COULSON, C. A., COX, J. T., OGSTON, G. T., AND PHILPOT, J. St. L., *Proc. Roy. Soc. London*, **A-192**, 382 (1948).

142. GUILLAUMIN, CH. O., "Remarques Techniques sur l'interféromètre de Zeiss et la Méthode de Hirsch." *Bull. Soc. de Chim. Biol.*, **15**, 1393–1414, 1933. La Réaction Sérointerférométrique de Hirsch. Conf. Soc. Pharm. Paris, June 6, 1934.

143. JONNARD, R., "Titration des Antigènes et des Anticorps par Réfracométrie Interférentielle." *C. R. Soc. Biol.*, **127**, 418–421 (1938).

144. JONNARD, R., "La Titration du Serum Antifièvre Scarlatine par Réfractométrie Interférentielle." *C. R. Soc. Biol.*, **128**, 263–265, 1938. La Titration des Antigènes Microbiens et des Sérums Immunes par Réfractométrie Interférentielle. *Biol. Med.*, **28**, 469–512 (1938).

145. JONNARD, R., AND LOUVIER, R., "L'affinité du Sérum Sanguin Pour les Hormones Sexuelles Déterminée par Réfractométrie Interférentielle." *Rev. Pathol. Comp. et Hyg. Gén.*, **512**, 1–4 (1939).

146. JONNARD, J. R., "L'analyse des Composés Biologiques Lourds par Réfractométrie Interférentielle." *Bull. Soc. Chim. Biol. de Paris*, **21**, 1185–1193 (1939).

147. INGELSTAM, E., DJURLE, E., AND JOHANSSON, L., "Precision Concentration Analysis of D_2O/H_2O by Means of Phase Contrast Refractometry." *J. Opt. Soc. Am.*, **44**(6), 472–77 (1954).

148. JONNARD, R., "Etude Interférométrique de la Réfraction du Sérum Sanguin en Fonction de la Concentration." *C. R. Ac. Sc.*, **203**, 124 (1936).

149. JONNARD, R., "Etude de la Stabilité du Sérum Sanguin." *C. R. Soc. de Biol.*, **121**, 841–843, (1936).

150. JONNARD, R., "Le Séro-Diagnostic Inter-

férométric Devant la Physique," *Rev. de Pathol. Comp. et Hyg. Gen.*, **483**, 1–7, 1936.

151. JONNARD, J., "Etude Interférométrique de la Réfraction du Sérum Sanguin en Présence d'électrolytes." *C. R. Soc. de Biol.*, **122**, 1305–1306 (1936).

152. JONNARD, R., AND ZUCKERKANDL, F., "Etude de la Réfraction du Serum Sanguin en Présence d'électrolytes." *C. R. Soc. de Biol.*, **122**, 1315–1316 (1936).

153. JONNARD, R., FAILLIE, R., AND ZUCKERKANDL, F., "Etude du Pouvoir Réactionel du Sérum Sanguin par la Méthode Réfractométrique." *Biol. Med.*, **28**, 1–23 (1938).

154. JONNARD, R., "Réfractométrie Interférentielle du Sérum de Cancéreux." *Bull. Soc. de Chim. Biol. de Paris*, **19**, 893–897 (1937).

155. JONNARD, R., "Individualidad Fisico-quimica de los Constituyentes del Suero Sanguines." *Bol. Inst. Med. Exp. Buenos Aires*, **43**, 529–436 (1937).

156. JONNARD, R., "Investigaciones Fisico-quimica Sobre el Suero de Cancerosos," *Bol. Inst. Med. Exp. Buenos Aires*, **44**, 141–158 (1937).

157. JONNARD, R., AND RUSKIN, S. L., "Studies in Calcium Metabolism." *Am. J. Digest. Dis.* **5**, 676–680 (1938).

158. JONNARD, R., AND RUSKIN, S. L., "Etude Physio-chimique Comparée du Gluconate de Calcium, du Cévitamate, et de la Vitamine C." *C. R. Soc. de Biol.*, **128**, 286–288 (1938).

159. SVENSON, H., AND FORSBERG, R., "A New Optical System for Simultaneous Recording of Refractive Index and its Gradient in Stratified Solutions." *J. Opt. Soc. Am.* **44**(5), 414–416 (1954).

160. CONN, G. K. T., AND EATON, G. K., "On a Systematic Error in the Measurement of Optical Constants." *J. Opt. Soc. Am.* **44**(6), 477–480 (1954).

See additional bibliography, p. 522.

R. JONNARD

INTERFEROMETRIC METHODS*

Besides the angle refractometer (q.v.) a second group of refractometric methods involves direct determination of the velocity variation which radiant energy undergoes

* The writer's experimental work with the recording interferometer was entirely supported by the Physics and Physiology Branches, Office of Naval Research, U. S. Navy, under a series of contracts granted to the Paterson General Hospital, Paterson, N. J. and Columbia University College of Physicians and Surgeons, New York, N. Y. from 1954 to date.

when traveling through transparent media. While absolute measurements of the velocity of light are difficult, evaluation of relative variations is relatively easy. The instruments used for this purpose are generally called interferometers.

Today, radiant energy is considered as an electromagnetic perturbation the two fields of which are normal to one another and also normal to the direction of propagation of the perturbation: the vibrational field is transversal. A monochromatic radiation is characterized by its *period*, T, or time in seconds required by one energy wave to effect a complete oscillation, or in Maxwell's theory for the corresponding line of force h to effect a complete rotation around the point O.

During this time T, the perturbation travels in a direction x with the velocity C (light velocity in a vacuum). The *distance* traveled is:

$$C \cdot T = \lambda \qquad (12)$$

this being called the *wavelength*, measured in Angström units.*

The period T is not directly measurable. Only in a vacuum, C being the same for *all* radiations, is λ directly proportional to T. The *frequency*, ν, of a radiation is the number of oscillations contained in the distance CT over a period of one second:

$$\nu = C/\lambda \qquad (13)$$

Frequencies are expressed in Fresnel units (10^{-12}). The *wave numbers*, $\tilde{\nu}$, are more conveniently handled than either λ or ν. They are the number of vibrations contained in 1 cm:

$$\tilde{\nu} = \frac{1}{\lambda} = \frac{1.10^8 \text{ cm}}{\lambda(\text{ in A})} \text{ (cm}^{-1}) \qquad (14)$$

The quantities C and λ vary with the *medium* traversed, but ν (and T) do not. The latter quantities characterize the conditions under which the radiation is generated (excited orbital, atomic number, temperature,

* See equations 1–11 in two preceding articles.

etc.). The quantity C (or λ), on the contrary, characterizes the conditions under which the radiation travels.

The value of C can be calculated in another way, by means of the classical dimensional equations.

Both Coulombic electrostatic and magnetic attraction forces between two unit charges e can be measured. For the electric attraction one has:

$$F = \pm \frac{1}{k_6} \cdot \frac{e^2}{d^2}$$

or

$$e = (K_0 F d^2)^{0.5} \qquad (15)$$

or in dimensional form:

$$[e] \equiv K_0^{1/2} M^{1/2} L^{3/2} T^{-1} \qquad (16)$$

Since a moving charge e generates a magnetic field, the latter may also be a measure of e:

$$[e] \equiv [M^{1/2} L^{1/2} \mu_0^{-1/2}] \qquad (17)$$

(since force = mass $\times$ acceleration $\equiv MLT^{-2}$, and $d^2 = L^2$). The two above quantities are *equal*:

$$[M^{1/2} \cdot L^{1/2} \cdot \mu_0^{-1/2}] \equiv [K_0^{1/2} M^{1/2} L^{3/2} T^{-1}] \qquad (18)$$

or

$$[LT^{-1}][\mu_0^{-1/2} \cdot K_0^{-1/2}] \equiv \frac{1}{\sqrt{K_0 \cdot \mu_0}} = V \qquad (19)$$

Hence, the quantity V found has the dimension of a velocity whose value is equal to the ratio of the e s u and e m u units. It was experimentally found equal to the velocity of light *in vacuo* (Weber, 1856): $C = 2.9986 \times 10^{10}$ cm/sec.

The value of C calculated above represents a maximum. It is not the only characteristic velocity of electromagnetic phenomena which needs to be considered. The group-velocities of Rayleigh are useful in interpreting the peculiarities of *refractive dispersion within an absorption band*, even when "monochromatic light" is used, for even the finest spectral lines have always a finite width within which the spectrum is continuous.

A discussion of group-velocities falls outside the scope of this article, except where the refractive index is concerned.

The group-velocity U is related to the refractive dispersion by the formula:

$$U = C/[n - (\lambda \cdot dn/d\lambda)] \qquad (20)$$

Since dn is large compared to $d\lambda$, U tends to become much smaller than C, which represents a maximum: the refractive index $n = C/U$ for the bundle becomes *greater* than that for any one of the radiations it contains.

The group-velocity concept has recently acquired a fundamental importance, as the cornerstone of a generalized theory of Refraction. This new theory is now capable of encompassing the situations arising when the radiation emitters are in fast motion relatively to the medium of index n. These phenomena include the emission of the Cherenkov-Vavrilov polarized radiation, the Doepler effect at super-light velocity, and others. They have an immense practical importance for the interpretation of all high-energy high-velocity phenomena involved in nuclear energy investigations. The complete theory of interferences at superlight velocities however, remains to be fully developed.

The optical pathway L_1 of light through a transparent medium is related to the time t required to traverse it by

$$t = L_1/V_1, \quad \text{or} \quad L_1 = t \cdot V_1 \qquad (21)$$

A similar relation holds for any other medium in which the velocity will be V_2. If during the same time t, light traverses a layer L_1 of medium 1 and a layer L_2 of medium 2, one can write:

$$L_1/L_2 = t \cdot V_1/V_2 \qquad (22)$$

Since $V_1/V_2 = n_2$ or relative index of medium 2 compared to medium 1, one has

$$L_1 = n_2 L_2 \qquad (23)$$

If one of the media is a vacuum ($n_0 = 1$), it results that the optical path length is the product of the geometrical length of a medium by its refractive index relative to vacuum (n_1). This important relation is the basis for the determination of relative refractive indices by the interferometric methods, involving a direct comparison of the products nL in two media, one of which is known.

In Huygens vibrational theory it is postulated that "something along the path of a light ray is vibrating according to a sinusoidal function of the general type:

$$L = A \sin 2\pi \left(\frac{t}{T} - \frac{x}{\lambda} + \alpha \right) \qquad (24)$$

The correctness of this theory became apparent when Thomas Young succeeded (1813) in composing the vibrations issued from two synchronous light sources (pinholes lighted from the same primary source) whose interference thus extinguished the light.

By application of Huygens theorem to the space between the primary source of radiant energy and the plan containing Young's twin apertures, it is possible to demonstrate that the rays issuing from these apertures are formed of synchronous vibrations. Such rays are said to be "coherent".

In this memorable experiment two synchronous point sources of light A and B, separated by a distance a produce two narrow beams of light falling upon the same area c on a screen placed at the distance d.

The amplitude L of the synchronous vibration λ issued from A and B is:

$$L = A_0 \sin 2\pi \left(\frac{t}{T} + \alpha \right) \qquad (25)$$

The difference ρ between the paths of the light rays Ac′ and Bc′ falling on c' ($c - c' = z$) is:

$$\rho = Bc' - Ac' = x_2 - x_1 \qquad (26)$$

and the difference of phase φ, of the two

superimposed vibrations in c' is equal to the difference of amplitude of the two vibrations falling in c' at the same time:

$$\varphi = L_2 - L_1 = \left[A \sin 2\pi \left(\frac{t}{T} - \frac{x_2}{\lambda} + \alpha \right) \right]$$
$$- \left[A \sin 2\pi \left(\frac{t}{T} - \frac{x_1}{\lambda} + \alpha \right) \right] \tag{27}$$

or:

$$\varphi = 2\pi\rho/\lambda \tag{28}$$

This value of φ is independent of α. The amplitude L resulting from the composition of the two vibrations arriving in c' with the difference of phase φ is practically equal to $L_1 + L_2$ if the angle γ is very small:

$$L = 2A \sin 2\pi \left(\frac{t}{T} - \frac{x_1 + x_2}{2\lambda} + \alpha \right)$$
$$\cdot \cos \pi \left(\frac{x_2 - x_1}{\lambda} \right) \tag{29}$$
$$= 2A \cos \pi \frac{\rho}{\lambda} \sin 2\pi \left(\frac{t}{T} + \beta \right)$$

and the intensity I_c of the light in c' is the product of a constant by the square of L or:

$$I_c = 4A^2 \cos^2 \frac{\pi\rho}{\lambda} = 4A^2 \cos^2 \pi q \tag{30}$$

where

$$q = \rho/\lambda$$

In other words, in c' the intensity of light is four times greater than that produced by either one of the sources alone. In summary, on a plan intersecting the common path of two *synchronous* rays, the light is distributed along a series of maxima and minima between which the intensity varies according to a simple periodic function.

A region of space answering to this definition constitutes a fringe system. Its symmetry may be either axial or radial, depending upon the instrument, but the fundamental relations are the same.

In the broader sense, an interferometer is an instrument capable of (1) splitting a monochromatic sinusoidal wave train of given frequency into two (or more) *coherent* beams, and (2) allowing these beams to become superimposed again after a variable path, in such a way that the resulting instantaneous sum sine wave amplitude can be detected. The principle of measurements with such an instrument is contained in the statement that the amplitude of the sine wave is a periodic function of the phase difference between the two component wave trains, with a period equal to 2π radians.

The above definition is sufficiently broad to encompass types of instruments in which the active coherent beams interfere once, those in which only a small sample of many wave trains interfere simultaneously (Fabry-Perrot type), and those in which the interfering waves are transported on another carrier wave.

In the latter case, the only requirement is that the wave under question be recoverable (by some demodulation process). In interferometry the nature of the transport mechanism need not be specified.

Such a definition is rather close to that adopted by Dayhoff (80).[*] Extended implications and practical applications in the microwave field will be found in the report of this author.

This definition is compatible with classifications of possible interferometers from several points of view. In every case, the basic information supplied by an interferometer is a *phase difference*. A knowledge of the phase difference is complete if its angle—or corresponding amplitude difference—and its algebraic sign are ascertained.

In equations (27) to (30), it is assumed that the rays of light travel from A and B to c and c' in an isotropic medium of refractive index 1. Obviously, equation (29) remains valid if two different media of refractive indices n_1 and n_2, respectively, are interposed on the trajectories Ac and Bc.

[*] See references on page 500.

In this case, the new values x_1' and x_2' will be the optical pathways $x_1' = x_1' \cdot n_1$, and $x_2' = x_2' \cdot n_2$, respectively, according to equation (23). Consequently, the measurement of I_c, at point c' should lead to the calculation of the refractive indices, n_1, for instance, if the other, n_2, and the values of: a, d, z, and λ are known. This determination can be effected more easily by considering only the distance from point c on the screen, of the points where the intensity I_c is either zero (minimum) or maximum ($4A^2$), thus avoiding photometric measurements. One demonstrates that the maxima of light (center of bright fringes) are located in the points where the difference of optical pathways $x_2 - x_1$ is either zero or an exact integer $K = 0, 1, 2, 3, 4$, etc., of the wavelength λ:

$$\rho = K \cdot \lambda \qquad (31)$$

Similarly, the location of the minima (center of dark fringes), where $L = 0$ for any value of t, is such that:

$$\cos \frac{\pi \rho}{\lambda} = 0, \quad \text{or} \quad \pi \left(\frac{\rho}{\lambda} \right) = \frac{\pi}{2} + k\pi,$$
$$\qquad (32)$$
$$\text{or} \quad \rho = (2K + 1) \frac{\lambda}{2}$$

One demonstrates that the locus of all the points satisfying equation (28) is a series of hyperboloids of revolution centered on A and B. Only for the lowest values of the order K of the black fringes are these fringes appearing straight in the zone where the observation plan on the screen c intersects the hyperboloids.

A last simplification is derived from the relationship existing between the difference of pathways ρ and the geometrical dimensions of the apparatus, a and d:

$$\rho = x_2 \cdot n_2 - x_1 \cdot n_1 = a \sin \theta = az/d \quad (33)$$

Combining (32) and (33), the distance from z to the centers of the black fringes (order $K = 1$) is given by:

$$az/d = (2K + 1) \lambda/2 \qquad (34)$$

or

$$z = \frac{(2K + 1)d \cdot \lambda}{2a}$$

Obviously, the distance h between the centers of two consecutive black fringes is

$$h = d\lambda/a \qquad (35)$$

If the geometrical dimensions: $Ac = Bc = l$ are constant but the two interfering beams of light rays traverse two different media of refractive indices n_1 and n_2, respectively, equation (33) becomes:

$$\rho = 1(dn) = a \cdot z/d \qquad (36)$$

The middle fringe (and also the whole system) moves away from the point c to another point c' which is distant from c by the width $2h$ of an interfringe when:

$$1(dn) = \frac{ad\lambda}{ad} = \lambda \qquad (37)$$

Therefore, a single measurement of the displacement of the fringes on the screen gives directly dn, if λ, a, and d are fixed.

The various interferometric methods differ by means utilized to produce two coherent beams of light. The selection of an instrument depends upon the application contemplated.

Classification of Interferometers

Several classifications of interferometers are possible, according to the predominant point of view.

If one considers mainly the utilitarian aspect, two broad groups can be distinguished: *Instruments with widely separated beams of light.* This group includes instrument types based upon the original experiment of Thomas Young, and those based upon the properties of semireflecting surfaces. The former type is realized in devices identified by their inventor's name: Young's, Fresnel mirrors, Fizeau, Soleil, Mascart, Billet's lenses and prisms, Desains, Rayleigh, Rayleigh-Williams (Hilger Mfg.), Le Chatelier,

506

Haber-Lowe, (Zeiss, Mgf.), some of C. Barus designs, our early model (Jobin-Yvon, Mfg.), and the newer orthoptic microscope interferometer (Aminco, Mfg.). The second type is realized in interferometers of Jamin, Michelson, Sagnac, the Zeiss-Opton interference microscope (1950), Lotmar, and a few others of fundamentally identical design used in microscopic interferometry. Thus, this first group includes both "narrow beam" instruments (the first type) and "broad beam" devices (the second type).

Instruments with superimposed beams. These include the Newton ring devices, the Fabry-Perot interferometers and its numerous variants, and the Dyson microscope interferometer. Instruments of this type are quite useful in metrology and for physical optics investigation, but are ill-suited to the study of transparent media.

Another classification can be arranged on the basis of the kind of information gained by the use of the interferometer. It is a rational classification based on the structure of the device used to produce the two required coherent light beams, and such considerations become of prime importance in evaluating original designs. One thus finds three classes: (a) instruments based on "phase splitting", (b) instruments based on "amplitude splitting", and (c) instruments based on "polarization separation".

This new classification is useful in generalizing the field of applicability of interferometric methods without limitation to any spectral region. Indeed, the principles previously summarized apply to practically all electromagnetic vibrations, from electronwaves and x-rays, to the visible and the infrared radiations and up to the longest radio waves.

Instruments based on "phase splitting." These are represented by the father of all—the Young interferometer—and the one best known commercially—the Rayleigh instrument. The first produces a spherical wave-front; the second, a cylindrical front.

Instruments of this type correspond to group (a) in the first classification. They are all of the "narrow beam" type, and this common appellation well describes their practical limitations. The real advantages of the phase splitting technique lie in the simplicity of design, the flexible requirements for the optical parts involved, and the relative independence of the performance from wavelength limitations, at least within the range of radiations within which the device producing the coherent pencils is practically realizable (UV to the middle of the IR range). These conditions are discussed in another article. It will be seen that the critical width and separation of the apertures used are also related to the wavelengths (in air) of the radiations utilized.

Instruments of the amplitude splitting type. Such instruments generally make use of semireflecting surfaces. Semireflecting beam splitters are effective only within certain narrow wavelength limits. No such really good device exists for the electron waves, the x-ray range or the extreme ultraviolet. In the visible range, silver, aluminum, chrome, titanium dioxide and "Inconel" castings are quite satisfactory.

In the infrared, the absorptive properties of the layer becomes prohibitive, although quite satisfactory mirrors may be made by evaporating selenium, tellurium, and even aluminum. Even under the best conditions the over-all efficiency is not very good, since the energy is always distributed between three fractions: reflected (R), transmitted (T), and absorbed (A). The latter may become preponderant at these wavelengths for which the first two fractions are equal to one another. This condition is found, for a λ of a few microns, by resolving Maxwell's equations, for the properties involved are independent of λ and the only variable is the surface electrical conductivity of the coating. For instance, when T equals R, the total A may represent 80 % of the incident flux.

Still another classification can be based on

the *shape of the wave-front* realized. This proved occasionally to be of considerable value in discovering newer applications of known arrangements. The wave front shapes involved are: (a) plane wave fronts, (b) curved wave fronts with spherical geometry, (c) irregularly curved fronts (Gouy).

The meaning of these distinctions will become apparent after a discussion of the diffraction phenomena taking place in every interferometer.

Finally, from a didactic standpoint, it is still convenient to follow the classical distinction of two groups of interferometers based upon the required means of observation, as is done in the next two sections: apparatus producing localized fringes, and apparatus producing non-localized fringes.

The practical implications of this last classification become apparent by considering the Raveau's rule: "when the two rays of light, resulting from the splitting of a single ray emitted from the center of a source S, after its passage through an interferential apparatus, are superimposed at a real point S', the fringes are visible at this point even if the source S is large."

Apparatus Producing Localized Fringes

The oldest apparatus of this category was conceived by Newton. The difference of optical path ρ, is given by:

$$\rho = 2n_1 \cdot \cos r \qquad (38)$$

the order of the fringes being:

$$p_1 = \rho_1/\lambda, \qquad p_2 = \rho_2/\lambda, \qquad \text{etc.} \dots$$

From this expression, it appears that the fringes will be apparent under two sets of conditions, both practically important: (a) with parallel light ($r = cte$) and variable l: the fringes will represent the zones of uniform thickness of layer L; (b) with an optically parallel plate ($l = cte$) and diffused light: the fringes then represent the locus of the impact of rays of identical incidence.

Fringes of Equal Thickness. A first type of interference produced by Newton rings has wide applications as a checking method in the manufacturing of all sorts of mechanical parts. The classical arrangement is still that originally proposed by Fizeau.

When the flint surfaces of the plane p are altered, Sleator and Martin (81) observed that a ring system with black center was obtained, although the conditions were such that a white centered system should be produced (flint index 1.72, lens index 1.53, oil medium index 1.62, in their experiment). This effect disappeared after re-polishing the flint. Conversely, this observation suggests the utilization of Newton's rings for the study of the superficial layers and of their alterations.

When the medium interposed between the plane p and the lens L is air ($n = 1$), a measurement of the diameter of the fringe gives the radius R of the lens as a function of k and d:

$$d^2 = 4Rk \qquad (39)$$

where k is the order of the fringes considered, and d is the fringe diameter.

If it is desired to measure the refractive index, the transparent medium whose refractive index is to be measured is placed between the lens L and the plane p, in optimal contact with both (for instance, a small closed cell is built to contain the liquid, and this cell is completely filled up). The method of measurement is based upon the fact that, while the square of the diameters of successive fringes of the same color (black, for instance) are as the order of the natural numbers, these diameters are related to the thickness l of the corresponding refracting layer, and to the radius R of the lens by the relation:

$$d^2/4 = 2Rl \qquad (40)$$

On the other hand, one has also:

$$2nl = k\lambda, \quad \text{or} \quad l = k\lambda/2n \qquad (41)$$

Combining (40) and (41) gives:

$$n = 4Rk\lambda/d^2 \qquad (42)$$

With this method, the measured diameter d varies only as the square root of the refractive index.

Fringes of Equal Incidence. The arrangement of the optical parts is similar to that used to produce Newton's rings, but there is no lens, and the plane p is formed of a parallel-face transparent plate of thickness l and index n. A large monochromatic light source is used (sodium lamp). The fringes are circular and centered around the point corresponding to the incidence of rays perpendicular to the plate ($r = 0$). The center of the system is black. The difference of pathway between the two reflected beams of rays is equal to $2\ nl$. The angular radius of the first ring is:

$$a_1 = n\lambda 2/p_0 \qquad (43)$$

the order of this first ring being:

$$p_0 = 2nl/\lambda \qquad (44)$$

The angular radius a of any ring of order k is given by:

$$a = n\lambda\ 2/p_0 \cdot k \qquad (45)$$

With thicknesses successively 0.1, 1.0, 10, and 20 mm, the following radii are found: 6′, 2′, 38″, and 27″, respectively.

Even with a plate deviating from parallelism by as much as 30″ (seconds of arc), the fringes are still visible, provided the zone observed is less than 0.5 mm in diameter (ocular $f = 60$ mm, objective $f = 30$ mm, magnification $\times 0.5$, with an ocular diaphragm of 1 mm forming on the plate a virtual image of 0.5 mm diameter).

This arrangement is very convenient the verification of optically parallel transparent plates: a variation of thickness of $dl = \lambda/2n = 0.18$ produces a variation of diameter equal to the thickness of one fringe. Continuous photographic recording is possible. This apparatus, as well as Fizeau's, is frequently used in dilatometric studies.

The standard ultraviolet refractometer of Lowry and Allsopp (82) uses the formation of fringes by a wedge comprised between two semi-platinized glass flats, mounted on the Hilger Co. stand. The separation of the fringes depends only on the wavelength and the index of the medium filling the wedge. The spectrograph is set at right angles to the fringes. The fringes' separation can be measured at any wavelength, on the spectrograms, by reference to a set of engraved lines. The theory of the fringes produced by a wedge is that of Fabry and Perot interferometer.

Instruments Producing Non-localized Fringes

Instruments of this type possess two well-separated beams of light. They are adaptable to measurements by application of equation (37). The first observations made along this line were those of Thomas Young. Since this memorable experiment, the procedure always involves producing two synchronous (coherent) pencils of light from one single narrow slit or a small circular aperture. From there on, the means employed to divide the light along these pencils vary.

The simple arrangement of the Fresnel double mirrors dates from 1816. Fresnel's double-prism setup, dating back to 1819, and his triple mirror interferometer of 1820, described in most textbooks, utilize the same principle. Other interferometers of the same general design were subsequently built by Lloyd (1837), by Haidinger (1849), by Fizeau, and by Mascart.

Billet's half-lens and his half-prism interferometers are based upon the principle of homo-focality, and date back to 1858. The apparatus of Dessains is of considerable historical interest for the metrologists.

The apparatus built by Jamin between 1856 and 1858 was established on the work of Brewster on the interferences produced by thick glass plates (circa 1817). In this apparatus the separation of the two light beams is obtained by successive reflections on the front and the rear face of a thick mirror. The writer had the opportunity to work with a reference instrument kept at the Paris Institute of Optics, in which the separation is 50 mm between beams. Despite the apparent simplicity, the adjustment of this apparatus is extremely laborious. If the mirror faces are not parallel to better than a small fraction of a wavelength, the fringes seen are due to defects in the mirrors, and the desired non-localized fringes vanish.

The interferometer built by Lord Rayleigh in 1896 is a direct adaptation of Young's experiment, to which was added an Arago Compensator. In the path of light were disposed narrow gas tubes, 40 cm long, terminated with parallel faced glass windows, for the study of gases. It is with this apparatus that Rayleigh discovered Argon (83).

The standard Rayleigh interferometer has proved its value in a voluminous literature. It has also proved its inherent encumbrance and difficulty of use. In order to obtain sharp fringes, this instrument requires an extremely powerful source of light and a very narrow entrance slit. Spectral dispersion measurements are difficult on account of the low luminosity.

A very important improvement was made by W. E. Williams (84), basing his work on the design of the Michelson star interferometer (an instrument of gigantic proportions with a 30-meter base, or interfering slit distance, used to measure the diameter of distant stars). In the Williams instrument, the interfering slits are extremely close together, thus permitting the use of a rather large, very luminous entrance slit. Increased separation between the two beams is obtained by means of an Albrecht rhomb. A similar, but reversed rhomb, placed before the telescope objective, re-combines the two beams and produces the interference pattern.

Another variant of the Rayleigh device is the Haber-Lowe interferometer, manufactured by Zeiss, and popularized by Hirsh

(85). Small size and portability are achieved by folding the Rayleigh interferometer and utilizing an auto-collimating optical system. Despite the apparent simplicity, the measurements are subject to numerous causes of error controllable only with great difficulty.

One drawback of Rayleigh's interferometer is its very low luminosity. Svenson found that considerable light gains accrue if the single entrance slit is replaced by a grating. To understand the production of interferences under these conditions, it must be remembered that all trajectories represented by the light rays are reversible. Thus, illuminated slits may take the place of the bright fringes in the plane of the normal interference pattern. One such slit in the position of the achromatic fringe produces an image in the place of the usual entrance slit. Another slit in the position of the fringe of order One will produce an image displaced laterally in the plane of the entrance slit. The required spacing of the entrance slits is easily calculated. The fringe width, L, is given by the fundamental formula:

$$L = f \cdot \lambda / d \qquad (46)$$

where d is the spacing of Young's slits, and f is the focal length of the collimator lens. The proper spacing S of the slit is

$$S = k \cdot L \lambda \qquad (47)$$

when k is a small integer.

Another variant of the Rayleigh interferometer is the Linnik instrument, recently manufactured in the USSR. This is a large size industrial device in which the phase separation system is ingeniously adapted to the verification of extended flat surfaces, a feat heretofore considered the prerogative of amplitude-splitting types of instruments.

Polarization Interferometers.

The laws of interference of polarized light had been formulated by Fresnel and Arago. To interfere, it is essential that the two rays of light, in addition to being synchronous, be polarized in the same plane; interference is impossible if the planes are at 90° to one another. For other relative orientations, all degrees of contrasts of the fringes are observed.

There is, however, one important exception to the general laws above. If a pencil of light is rectilinearly polarized, then split by one of the methods indicated herein, the resultant beams are polarized at 90° to one another, as is well known. Yet, when they are brought again to coincidence on a common plane, interference is still possible. Such splitting of an incident ray may be obtained by utilizing the phenomenon of double refraction in certain crystals. If the incident light is white, in this case the emergent rays are no longer so. Furthermore, one must be cognizant of the fact that one of the emergent rays suffers a retardation, relatively to the other, of one-half wavelength.

In an instrument based upon this principle and built by Jamin in 1868 the separation of the rays was obtained by two very large spar crystals. The original memoir had been completely forgotten when, in 1934, A. Cotton (86) accidentally discovered the original apparatus in a pile of discarded antiques.

The essential feature of this instrument is that it can produce both localized and non-localized fringes. If the incident light is exactly parallel and if the two crystals are also exactly parallel, the two beams of light are superimposed and one observes only a uniform color depending upon the orientation of the half-wave plate. Non-localized fringes appear if the observation is made with a telescope adjusted *ad infinitum*, according to Raveau's rule. If the two crystals are not exactly parallel and if the light source is a very small pin hole, the fringes become visible on a distant screen, without any telescope. In addition, there is another system of localized fringes, near the emergent face of the last crystal, and due to the defects of the latter.

Instruments built on this principle have had some practical use. The one designed by Brillouin in 1903 (in complete ignorance of Jamin's work) was used to detect extremely small displacement of a galvanometer frame supporting the second crystal. In 1930 Lebedeff (Optical Inst. of Leningrad) built another polarization interferometer in which the two beams were not exactly separated but only slightly so. Used conjointly with a polarization microscope, the apparatus served for the measurement of the refractive index of very small crystals suspended in a liquid, and for the study of heterogeneities in solution.

The use of the Jamin apparatus as a precision colorimeter must be mentioned. The complete modus operandi was developed by Barchewitz (87).

An interference microscope built by F. H. Smith (88) and utilizing a plurality of birefringent coaxial elements constitutes an interesting extension of the principles embodied in Jamin's polarization interferometer.

Amplitude Splitting Interferometers

The prototype in this class is the well known Michelson Interferometer. The two instruments built by Sagnac (89) in 1911 and 1914 are, similarly, based upon the property of semireflecting "beam splitting" surfaces.

The Michelson beam-splitting system has been modified in numerous ways to satisfy particular technical requirements. One of its chief advantages is the wide separation obtained. Usually the two coherent beams are at 90° to one another.

The "Zeiss-Opton" interference microscope is a good example of an instrument based upon the amplitude-splitting principle. It utilizes a collimated parallel incident light. The interferometer attachment to the Chapman research polariscope is based on the same principle. The Twyman-Green interferometer and the so-called Penn-modified Twyman instrument, utilize collimated incident light, too, but they differ from Michelson's device in that they produce a plane wave front resulting in a fundamentally different performance.

The Lotmar interferometer for the study of electrophoresis phenomena effects a compromise between Jamin and Michelson designs. It must be mentioned here that, in general plane-reflecting surfaces can be replaced by plane gratings in most instruments listed above. This was originally done by Ramsay (91) for the Michelson interferometer. A very extensive study of this new class of instruments is due to Barus (92). Such modified devices function as their own monochromator. Indirectly, these experiments extended the field of interferometric measurements to both the very short and the very long wavelengths. The application to electron diffraction spectra is due to Marton (92-93, 94, 95, 96). In the infrared domain, it is no longer possible to separate the production of interferences from polarization phenomena, for all "beam-splitters" are gratings which act as good polarizers. Several infrared interferometers are due to Robinson and a commercial device is available from Baird Associates.

The details of construction of a Rayleigh type interferometer were previously discussed by the writer (97–98). A device built accordingly by Jobin-Yvon Co. still enjoys the favor of European biochemists. The key to success is a correct design of the collimator. An entrance slit that meets Duffieux criterion (99) is still the best from the standpoint of fringe contrast. Other factors to be considered include the slit length, dioptric power, radius of curvature and focal length of the lens, spectral transmission and dispersion, minimum spherical aberration tolerance, chromatism, surface reflection and astigmatism. A slit which is 20 to 50 times larger that calculated by the Schuster factor is still satisfactory, in the visible spectrum. Best results are obtained with small lenses, for only the diffraction fringe of zero-order is useful in such an instrument.

The construction of the twin diffracting apertures presents no difficulties, provided one keeps in mind that there are several particular combinations of aperture width, spacing and focal length for which interference is impossible. Fluid cuvettes of the type built by Jamin were later modified by Lendel (100), but are extremely costly. The cuvettes of the Kern-Lotmar interferometer could be adapted to the Rayleigh interferometer. The type of cell designed by the writer proved the most practical for serial determinations. This design minimizes the effects of temperature gradients and sudden variations, the role of glass dispersion, and the errors due to defect of parallelism. These cuvettes have been redesigned to allow continuous fluid flow with good frontal characteristics, for recording purposes. They may then be used also for continuous diffusion experiments by the method of Bruin (101). The improved design of fluid cuvettes and a more compact construction of the instrument now make it practical to consider interferometric measurements for continuous industrial plant monitoring and control.

Observation of the fringe displacement may be visual or photoelectric (automatic). Visual measurements are best made with a magnifier (about 20×) and an adjustable bifilar micrometer or graticule. Greater accuracy is obtained if, instead of observing the fringes shift one uses a compensator and null method. The original Arago compensator was made of two movable glass wedges. Its precision was poor. The parallel plates compensator of Jamin represents a remarkable improvement, despite its disturbing chromatism. Rotatable glass prisms are sometime used to compensate for this defect (Haber-Lowe).

Modern interferometers are equipped with two symmetrical, rotatable parallel glass plates (Rayleigh compensator) permitting a larger range of measurements with a smaller chromatic error. It is convenient to have a linear relationship between the retardation introduced by the compensator (or the corresponding dn) and the angular rotation observed. This is obtained by means of a "tangent screw" mechanism. Fairly good linearity can thus be obtained within a rotation range of about 20° on each side of the zero-position. The range of measurements depends primarily upon the angular setting of the plates. An increased range can be achieved by the introduction of thin stationary plates, in a manner amounting to a true optical zero-suppression method.

The optical devices available for pointing the fringe system in its zero-position require some comment. In general, a micrometer offers definite advantages over a simple cross-hair or other fiduciary reference marks (Brillouin) (87) provided the correct technique is employed. Pointing may be effected either with a telescopic ocular, or with a low-power microscope. Photography of real fringes does not present unusual problems. The accuracy of the pointings is always limited by the sine distribution of energy in the fringes, among other factors. It is usually limited to $\frac{1}{5}$ of the interfringe spacing. Increased accuracy is obtained if a small slit is placed in the focal plane of the viewer and the light is modulated at 15 cps. Such a flicker method, previously described (102) raises the reproducibility of the pointings to $\frac{1}{20}$ of one fringe. Still greater accuracy is possible by electronic recording (v.i.). The accuracy of final pointing of zero-position of the fringes is a problem quite apart from that of making accurate visual refraction measurements. These measurements involve tracking the fringes from their extreme shift position back to the zero-position. This latter problem is complicated in monochromatic light by the uniform appearance of the fringes: the "middle reference fringe" is unrecognizable. In polychromatic light, the middle "achromatic" fringe is theoretically recognized by its symmetrical chromatism. In practice, this aspect is marred by the disturbing effect of the spectral dispersion of the compensator plates and of the layer of examined fluid, and rather complicated correction formulas

must be introduced. Certain combinations of refractive dispersion value result in the presence of several achromatic fringes ("sprung" phenomenon). This is likely to occur with strongly colored fluids with sharp absorption bands. A complete discussion of such disturbing dispersion phenomena was given by Ollivier (103). Corrective methods have been proposed from time to time. Even when only one achromatic fringe is present, Grunwald and Berkowitz (88) remark that the compensator dispersion still introduces a small residual error whose exact correction is very involved. The practical correction method proposed long ago by the writer (97) still remains valid and sufficient in a large number of cases.

The developments summarized above are embodied, with utmost condensation, in a small low-cost portable interferometer built by the writier in 1953—the so-called orthoptic microscope interferometer (104). This last publication and a patent (105) give the basic principle employed, the details of construction and a complete functional analysis. The instrument utilizes the microscope's bundle of marginal rays, which are parallel and sufficiently coherent—hence, the instrument's name. The device fits on any commercial microscope. These same publications also offer a practical approach to the correction of the errors inherent in most interferometric measurements on liquids: (1) the fluid layer thickness, (2) the fluid compartment parallelism, (3) the error on wavelength determination, (4) the variation of apparent color temperature of the light source when polychromatic measurements are contemplated, (5) the pointing errors, (6) the compensator calibration error, (7) the scale reading error, (8) the effect of ambient temperature changes, and (9) the role of temperature gradients within the measuring compartment.

Illumination Systems

Optimum performance of all types of refractometers depends a great deal on correct illumination. This generally neglected problem is not as simple as often assumed. However, it is possible to formulate a few recommendations of general value. The physical structure of the light source is important. Usually it is the exit aperture in the source housing which acts as the real, primary radiation source, and not the heated filament of the lamp. The constructor of an optimum condenser must take this fact into consideration. Surprisingly, optimum performance is not necessarily realized when the source is exactly focused on the entrance aperture of the instrument.

The so-called field-type illumination (source imaged onto the collimator lens) is essential for most photographic applications. For photoelectric measurements, it is preferable to use the Twyman-Simeon mounting, as discussed by Stockbarger and Burns (106). However, if a monochromator is interposed between the source and the measuring instrument, the desired spectral resolution enters into the calculations and the general solution requires that only approximately one-half of the monochromator collimator diameter be utilized (thus sacrificing much of the available radiant power). In this last case, much is regained by substituting mirrors for lenses in the illumination system. A more complete discussion, with relations derived from the application of the spatial frequency analysis method, was given in a previous publication (107).

Continuous Recording in Interferential Refractometry

The practical value of interferometric measurements is greatly enhanced by the availability of automatic, continuous recording methods. Photographic and cinematographic recording have long been successfully used. However, deciphering the films is a time-consuming procedure. A considerably faster procedure utilizes electronic fringe counters, several models of which exist. A simple system includes only a scanning slit in the plane of the fringes, a photocell and a pulse-type amplifier followed by a mechanical counter. The Ferranti system (108), although designed for counting the "moire" fringes produced by crossed gratings, utilizes this principle. Direction discrimination is achieved by simultaneously inspecting two points on the pattern separated by an odd-number of quarter-wave lengths. An electronic binary counting system has also been successfully operated with a modified Michelson interferometer by Peck and Obetz (109). Such double scanning systems present certain difficulties. If both the amplitude of the fringe shift and its direction must be recorded, it is necessary to arrange the apparatus so that a photo-electric signal proportional to the first quantity is produced. Then a phase modulation related to the second quantity (direction) is introduced. The operation amounts to effect an automatic differentiation of the fringe energy distribution curve, including extraction of the differentiation sign. The desired result can be achieved with two photomultiplier tubes in a bridge circuit, as proposed by Ingelstam (110). A general approach to the problem was discussed in a previous publication (111). Considerable instrumental simplification results from the use of a single radiation receptor and a scanning mechanism operating at a fixed frequency. Similar advantages accrue by modulating the output amplified signal in relation to the direction of fringe shift.

The fringe interpolator developed at the National Bureau of Standards (112) for use with a Pulfrich-type interferometer introduces a modulation at the fundamental frequency of a tuning fork on one of the light beams. A similar system is employed in the Glennite Co. interferometer, which thus could be easily adapted for continuous recording. Other modulation methods must be considered for special applications. For instance, magnetostriction of the short nickel cylinder (attached to one of the elements of an interferometer) with a pulsed magnetic field of about 50 oersteds provides a modulation amplitude of only a fraction of one fringe. The Kerr magneto-optic effect is also usable for this application (Decker (113)). The writer has discussed several other modulation systems applicable to the Rayleigh interferometer (114). The modulation can be directly applied to one of the compensator plates. Further improvement is derived by the use of a feedback servomechanism acting on the compensator to maintain the fringes on zero. Recording then merely requires translating the rotation of the compensator shaft into a corresponding variable voltage of suitable magnitude and sign, which can be continuously monitored by a commercial strip chart recorder. One such system has been fully described (115). The chief advantage is the ability to obtain a continuous record of fringe shifts in terms of an optical retardation which remains linearly proportional to the corresponding refractive index variations. Time variations or refractive dispersion can be conveniently recorded in this manner.

In all cases successful recording depends in great part on the performance of a suitable amplification system associated with the phase-sensitive circuit. A highly satisfactory differential AC amplifier developed for this purpose and exhibiting great zero-stability, has been described at length (116).

REFERENCES

See references for the second article of this series (History of Light Refraction), p. 497.

R. Jonnard

REFRACTOMETRIC APPLICATIONS

In the preceding articles the principal techniques of refractometric measurements —angle refractometry and interferometry— have been presented. Many other facets of such refractometric measurements must necessarily be omitted, among them the numerous "schlieren" methods, striascopy, the refractivity of anisotropic media, that of continuously variable media (of importance in astronomy), measurements at very long wavelengths in relation to nuclear magnetic resonance phenomena, the refractivity of semiconductor materials, the relationships between refraction and production of Cherenkow-Vavrilov radiation at super-light group velocities, phase-contrast microscopy, and measurements with the phase-contrast interferometer and with the three-slit interferometer. The latter methods open the way to measurements of relative refractive indices of the order of 10^{-9} with possible applications in the field of isotopes analysis— a point discussed by the writer in 1939 (117).

Refractive index measurements find application in many fields of analytical chemistry, and even a reasonably complete bibliography of applications is beyond the scope of this article. Crystallographic and mineralogic applications were briefly mentioned in the preceding articles. Refraction offers a positive means of identifying both organic and inorganic crystalline substances. The combination of refraction and melting point determination is often very specific in organic analysis, in the study of alloys and melts of many kinds and in the study of phase equilibria. Metrological applications too fall outside the limits assigned to this article. It will suffice to mention the possibility of measuring—and now recording— very small angular rotations or displacements, such as those of micro-balances, dilatometers, thermal equilibrium or magnetic balances and reference galvanometers, either by a method derived from the prismatic refractometer principle, or by one of the interference methods. For instance, C. Barus applied his modification of Michelson interferometer (p. 511) to small mirror rotations, and the writer once transformed his instrument into a sensitive "static" galvanometer.

The subordination of the refractive index, n, to chemical structure was suspected by

Newton, who based upon such evidence his opinion that water and diamond must "contain both some kind of combustible substance". Refractive indices, being affected by many factors, are not additive. Therefore, they are seldom used directly, although in solutions of a single solute an empirical relation linear with respect to concentration C:

$$(n - n_0)/C = Cte \qquad (48)*$$

is often usable. The refraction-density relationship of Newton:

$$r_g = (n^2 - 1)/d \qquad (49)$$

(where d is the density), although often sufficient, is not general. J. H. Gladstone and I. P. Dale (1858), and later Landolt (1864) showed that another empirical relation is much less dependent on temperature and concentration changes:

$$r_g = (n - 1)/d \qquad (50)$$

This is known as the specific refractivity ($n - 1$ being the refractivity). A theoretical derivation, made independently by Lorenz (of Copenhagen) and Lorentz (of Leyden) in 1880 (118) is called the theoretical specific refractivity or specific refraction:

$$r_g* = (n^2 - 1)/d(n^2 + 2) \qquad (51)$$

This relation is more general. It applies regardless of the physical state of matter, and it is valid at all wavelengths, although a correction for spectral dispersion is required in each case. The constant 2 often needs to be adjusted in particular cases. For gases, particularly hydrocarbons, Eykman, and also Gibson, (119) prefer the value 0.4. Yet Zehnder and his associates found that a factor of the form: $(n - 1)$ in the above formula followed more closely the experimental data relative to the effect of pressure on gases. A convenient rule—which is not always valid—is to use a formula of the $(n - 1)$ form (Newtonian type) when dealing with the effects of physical factors on refrac-

* Equations 1–47 in preceding articles.

tivity, and a Lorencian formula in $(n^2 - 1)$ when dealing with concentration and chemical effects; the reverse is more often correct, however, when dealing with substances in the glassy state. In either case, a simple calculation can be used to find relative proportions (by weight) of mixtures of nonpolar substances in which insignificant volume changes take place (most gases and many very dilute solutions):

$$100(n - 1)/d = [p_1(n_1 - 1)/d_1] \\ + [(100 - p_1)(n_2 - 1)/d_2] \qquad (52)$$

(or the corresponding $(n^2 - 1)$ quantities for a "Newtonian" case, or $(n^2 - 1)/(n^2 + 2)$ for a "Lorencian" case). If, in a more general case, the volume variation c is known and expressed by the relation:

$$c = [(v_1 + v_2) - V]/(v_1 + v_2) \qquad (53)$$

the relation may be further improved:

$$[100(n - 1)/d] \cdot [(1 - ac)/(1 - c)] = \\ [p_1(n - 1)/d_1] + [(100 - p_1)(n_2 - 1)/d_2] \qquad (54)$$

(the factor a usually varies with the wavelength).

Referring again to pure substances, the empirical specific molar refractivity Mr_g, is given by:

$$Mr_g = M(n - 1)/d \\ = M(n - 1) \cdot v = V(n - 1) \qquad (55)$$

(where M is the molecular weight, v is the specific volume and V is the molar volume: $V = Mv = M/d$.) Similarly, one calculates a molar refraction derived from the non-Newtonian formula:

$$Mr_g* = M(n^2 - 1)/d(n^2 + 2) \\ = M(n^2 - 1)v/(n^2 + 2) \qquad (56)$$

(and the variants mentioned above). It is often more convenient to convert (56) to its decimal log form:

$$\ln Mr_g* = \ln r_g* + \ln M - \ln d \qquad (57)$$

(ln is given directly in five-decimal log tables). More recently Kurtz and Ward (120) modified the formula, replacing the figure 1 by an empirical constant b of such value that: $(n - b)/d = 0.5$. The slope-intercept form is more convenient: $n = b + (d/2)$. It is found that b is often constant in homologous series, thus having a practical usefulness for the qualitative identification of organic chemicals and of their mixtures. Care must be taken inasmuch as molar refractivities are only partly additive, under restricted conditions.

A comparison of data for a large number of compounds of known chemical composition has led to the step of attributing additive values of a so-called atomic specific refraction, Ar_g, to the atoms. Such values are affected by the nature of the specific groups in which the atoms are involved. This work, initiated by Bruhl (1880), was further developed by Eisenlohr (1913) and by Swietoslawski (1920) (121). The sum of the Ar_g's plus that of the particular linkages should aggregate the Mr_g^* value of the molecule, but there is often complete disagreement in the case of electrolytes, with strongly polar molecules, and with most moderately concentrated solutions. The confusion is greatly increased by the diversity of values attributed to some of the elements, e.g., about 30 different values are known for nitrogen.

Another practical formula is Lagemann's relation (122) between Mr_g^* and Sounders viscosity constant $I\eta$ in homologous series:

$$I\eta = a \cdot Mr_g^* + b = M(\lg_{10} \eta + 2.9)/d \quad (58)$$

(where η is the viscosity in millipoises). Tables of the constant a are available. As a first approximation, a is usually very close to 12.

The Lorentz-Lorenz formula is strikingly similar to the relation giving the molar polarization derived from Clausius-Mosotti equation, as a function of the dielectric constant ϵ:

$$P = M(\epsilon - 1)/(\epsilon + 2) \quad (59)$$

One demonstrates that, theoretically ϵ should equal the square of the specific refraction at infinite wavelength (zero-frequency), assuming that then the molar polarizability factor, which enters into the calculations, is constant. Despite this limiting assumption, the relation offers a convenient means of qualitatively distinguishing between polar and nonpolar molecules. The practical interest of such measurements is found in the observations and the theories relating the refractive index to the dielectric constant in the radiofrequency domain, to the London vibrational energy of dipoles at the zero-energy point, and to a number of other phenomena related to the polarization and/or polarizability of molecules under the influence of electromagnetic fields. A more complete discussion was given by Debye (123).

It is clear from the foregoing that refraction measurements cannot be divorced from a consideration of the wavelengths used. Yet, the relationships between refraction and wavelength are often confusing. When measurements are made in a region where absorption is low, the Cauchy formula may be used:

$$n = A + B/\lambda^2 + C/\lambda^4 \cdots \quad (60)$$

(where A and B are constants). A plot of n vs $1/\lambda^2$ is then very close to a straight line. The Nutting relation (124) is often more convenient:

$$1/(n - 1) = C + (D/\lambda^2) \quad (61)$$

Both formulas are valid only within relatively narrow spectral limits, but the values of the constants are often characteristic of the substances under investigation. Other empirical formulas, such as that of Wright (125):

$$n - n_D = a(n_F - n_C) - b \quad (62)$$

the Hartman equation:

$$n = n_0 + C/(n_0)^a \quad (63)$$

or that of Waldmann:

$$(n_D - n_C) = k(n_F - n_C) \quad (64)$$

are useful in calculating the "specific dispersion": $(n_F - n_C)/d$, but they too, break down with substances of high refractive index, high absorbance, high dispersion, or when applied over too large a spectral range. Yet, the specific dispersion thus defined is practically useful for the rapid determination of aromatic content of gasolines and naphthas.

The more general formulas of Maxwell and Sellmeyer, or that of Helmholtz and Ketteler, are more involved and are based upon a number of simplifying assumptions. The fact that contemporary quantum and wave theories generally substantiate these assumptions does not remove their indeterminate character. This indeterminacy mostly stems from the lack of accuracy of refraction measurements outside the visible spectrum. In the vicinity of absorption bands the calculations usually become complicated. Their intricacy places them beyond the attainment of the average chemical laboratory, and they are then casually referred to as problems of "anomalous dispersion". It must be emphasized, however, that anomalous dispersion is the rule, rather than the exception, for all substances, in the vicinity of absorption bands, anywhere in the spectrum, and that its determination as a measure of the "chemical exaltation of refractivity" acquires a meaning complementary to that of spectrophotometric absorption.

High-precision refractometry has been impeded by the scarcity of suitable reference standards. Measurements referred to dry air are ambiguous, for the relative index of air is not exactly proportional to its density. The correction factor in the Sellmeyer formula used to improve the comparison itself varies with the wavelength. Air is also subject to a very large temperature coefficient. Solid standards for use with prismatic refractometers are now available from the National Bureau of Standards, as well as from several firms.

Agreement on liquid standards is not so easily reached. Distilled water occupies first place, but what is distilled water? and how to keep it so? Specially purified toluene, 2,2,4-trimethylpentane and methylcyclohexane are also recommended. Their indices are known to the 5th decimal place, but this is often insufficient. We have had quite a satisfactory experience with purified sodium chloride, zinc sulfate and potassium alum, within moderate concentration ranges. In general, the range of indices available, the temperature ranges and the wavelength spectra covered by the standards at present available are not quite sufficient to meet the needs of this rapidly expanding branch of technology.

The analysis of gases and the study of gaseous equilibria (by interferometry) were pioneered by Lord Rayleigh, Le Chatelier, and more recently by Chaudron (126). Pressure variations may be used as a means of compensation. Multicomponent mixtures require a more elaborate set-up. Nevertheless, a method devised by Thompson (127) has been applied to the study of respiration. Anesthetic mixtures have also been monitored by refractometry (Bell and Krantz (128). The Bruin method (101) for the determination of diffusion constants of large molecules has been mentioned. A refractometric method for the measurement of colloidal particles size has been published.

Refractometry is still a basic method in the sugar industry, using Schonrock (129) calibration tables. Applications in the petroleum industry stem from the observation that the specific refractivity as well as the specific dispersion are often constant for many types of distillates. More recently, detailed studies of the refractive dispersion in the near ultraviolet range served to characterize many hydrocarbons (130).

Refractometry is an empirical but convenient means of checking the quality of soaps, fats and oils. In the case of soaps, above 70°C the value obtained in solution is identical with that obtained on the solid. Refractive index of oils and fats is closely related to their acid value and their iodine number, and it is a sensitive index of mild oxidation.

Criminological applications have been detailed by Kirk (131). Empirical methods of analysis based on refractometry may be developed on a purely experimental basis. For instance, chemical titrations of weak polyelectrolytes, in dilute nonaqueous solutions without indicator, are possible with unambiguous end points. The method is often more sensitve than high-frequency titrimetry (Q-analysis), and polar solvents are no contraindications.

Biochemical applications have long been limited to the quantitative determination of total blood serum proteins, following the work of Reiss in 1904. The refraction increment k, per gm % of proteins as determined by a suitable Kjeldahl nitrogen analysis (132) averages 0.00184, according to Paic and Deutsch (133).

Numerous biochemical investigations, conducted by similar empirical methods, have involved the construction of special refractometers and interferometers for the study of streaming fluids, notably by Cleason (134), Tiselius and Cleason (135), Holman and Hagdall (136), Svenson (137), Kegeles (138), Gibert (139), Calvet and Chevalerias (140), Coulson, Cox, Ogston and Philpot (141), and others. Other empirical applications deal with the voluminous body of work on the "Abderhalden ferments" (142). The phenomenon is real, but it still lacks a satisfactory explanation. In general, high precision continuous recording refractometry is well adapted to enzymological studies, to kinetic investigations and to the detection of reaction intermediates.

Many other biological problems can benefit from high sensitivity refractometric measurements. The successful titration of highly diluted antigen-antibody systems was found possible, although no detectable precipitate was formed (143–144). Some rather complex systems of this kind have been resolved by

this method (144). Some attempts at detecting antihormones by refractometry (145) should be mentioned. The study of isotope exchanges in biological systems was cursorily tried by the writer (146) in 1939. A contemporary renewal of interest in this field is manifest (147).

Still another fruitful field of investigation is the study of binding power of proteins and of other products of biological and medical interest. It seems that the refraction increment of blood proteins can be markedly abnormal in certain diseases. So can the extent of its deviation from linearity at serum concentrations lower than 10 % in isotonic saline solution (148–150). Heavy metal binding to proteins, because of its specificity for certain functional groups, has long found analytical applications. But the binding of smaller ions (Na, K, Rb, F, Mn) also can be readily demonstrated by interferometry (151–156). Similarly, the binding of organic molecules (ascorbic acid (157–158), cholesterol (153)) seems to be demonstrable. Another large field of biochemical applications involves the measurement of refraction gradients by the "schlieren" method, as in electrophoresis experiments.

Finally, the complementary character of reflection, refraction and transmission phenomena of electromagnetic waves make these measurements of particular importance in the newer technology of dielectric films and of semiconductors (Conn and Eaton: (160)).

REFERENCES

See references for the second article of this series (History of Light Refraction), p. 497.

Addendum and Bibliography Supplement

In recent years the volume of published work on refractometry and interferometry has reached proportions defying the capability of any single investigator. The following notes added after setting of the galleys represent an almost futile effort to reconcile the content of these articles with the publication date.

Refinements to the prismatic refractometer continue to appear. Svenson (161) extensively studied several forms of this refractometer. This type of instrument lends itself to automatic direct reading (Johnsen and Schnelle: 162) as well as to self-balancing techniques (Penther and Noller: 163).

Considerable effort is currently devoted to refractometric measurements in the infrared radiation domain. The dispersion of Standard dry air in this region is now extensively tabulated, together with the depolarization factor of atmospheric gases and Rayleigh's scattering cross-section (Penndorf: 164). Spectrometric methods are available in this domain (McAlister *et al.*: 165), as well as an arsenic trisulfide glass hollow-prism instrument (Jaffe and Oppenheim: 166), and a modified goniometer (Traub and Osterberg: 167). Accurate observations made with a Capehart-Farnsworth IR image converter tube—a method proposed, but not used, by the writer in 1954—have now been reported (Carlan and Paul: 168). By far the greatest advances in the infrared region have been gained by the use of interferometric methods which permit both the frequency calibration of spectrometers (Brodersen: 169, Polster: 170) and the measurement of secondary wavelength standards (Rank *et al.*: 171). The Greenler instrument (172) appears particularly well adapted to these measurements. A simple filter device has also been used by Kagarise and Mayfield (173); a modified Fabry-Perot etalon was proposed by Oppenheim (174) and a modified Ebert monochromator with interferometric modulation has been used by Strong (175) in the far-infrared. The Casey-Lewis filter (176) is, in reality, an infrared interferometer. As a result, a dispersion formula for air in the near infrared more exact than that previously given, was recently published by Schlueter and Peck (177). Phase-contrast

refractometry was extended to the infrared by Rodney and Djurle (178).

Direct refraction measurements on the atmosphere have now been extended to the radio-waves domain. Basic computations were given by Johnson (179). Straight refractometric methods (Crain: 180, Crain and Deam: 181), phase-shift techniques (Tolbert and Straiton: 182), diffractometry (Bachynski and Bekefi: 183) and interferometry (Artman: 184) are now currently used for such measurements.

The introduction of Information Theory in optics leading to new advances in this field (Linfoot: 185), a better understanding of certain limitations of optical elements (Jones: 244), and a mastery of wave fronts (Zernicke: 186) and of their use in image reconstruction (Kirkpatrick *et al.*: 187), are developments which must be recorded. Some of these advances are embodied in new instruments such as the Kapany fiber-glass refractometer (188) based upon the properties of coated dielectric cylinders (Kapany and Pike: 189). A commercial version suitable for industrial control is now described in the chemical literature. The fiber-glass refractometer is really making use of the critical angle phenomenon. The instrument of Forrest and Straat (190) for glass production control falls in this category. An exhaustive study of errors in this type of measurements is due to Forrest (191).

Previously clear-cut delineation between the fields of microscopy, refractometry and interferometry tend to disappear in contemporary technology. For instance, the "schlieren" refraction technique has now been adapted to the measurement of microscopic particles (Meyer-Arendt: 192), and the Polanyi diffractometer (193) yields the number, volume and index of red blood cells in suspension. The interferometric study of living cells has been reported by Barer (194) while the polarization interference microscope has been extensively investigated by Françon (195). Such hybrid techniques are now the topic of large international symposia (Françon: 196).

The technical advances of recent years have been made possible by parallel advances in theoretical optics. For instance, a revised, more general theory of the Fabry-Perot interferometer was offered by Vander Sluis and McNally (197), and a fruitful vector theory of the Mach-Zehnder interferometer was completed by Bennett and Kahl (198). Many technical refinements become possible by introducing the concept of partial coherence (Thompson: 199) on a solid mathematical basis (Thompson and Wolf: 200).

In recent years the Jamin Interferometer has been modified in many ways (Lotman: 201). The introduction of a total reflection prism led to the construction of the Riken instrument (Namba: 202) for isotope analysis. Similarly, corner-mirrors are used by Peck (203) in a variant of the industrial beam-splitter interferometer. A further simplification ("common-path" interferometer) of this industrial instrument is due to Dyson (204). The variable pressure gas compensator is enjoying a renewed popularity (Rank and Shearer: 205), simultaneously with the development of hybrid measurement methods such as that combining interferences with the "Schlieren" method (Temple: 206). This path was also explored by Ingelstam (207). The Fizeau method also has been further improved (Osterberg and LaMarre: 208).

The Mach-Zehnder interferometer continues to be modified in many different ways to suit specific purposes (Price: 209). A special construction is available for measurements on volatile liquids (Caldwell, Hall and Babb: 210), for heat transfer study (McLean, Scherrer, Nanney and Faneuff: 211), and for aerodynamic investigations (Blue and Pollack: 212).

The newer "series" or "in-line" interferometers for industrial applications, whose theory was developed by Saunders (213) are multiple beam devices based upon the properties of crystalline films but Fabry-Perot etalons can also be used in the same manner (Post: 214, Primak: 215). Application to the refractive index of liquids was carried out by Bakarat (216), who built a specialized form of the instrument for this purpose (Bakarat and Nooh: 217).

All interferometric methods have common problems. Variable contrast between fringes of different order presents difficulties (Price and Wedaa: 218). Correlating readings and wavelength is another problem (Hirschberg and Kadesch: 219). Apparent fringe width variability has received special attention (Leadon and Werner: 220–221, also Winkler: 222). Various spectral effects have been considered by Kahl and Sleator (223), and by Koester (224).

Recording techniques are now currently used conjointly with such diversified interferometers as the Riken type (Namba: 225), the Fabry-Perot type (Biondi: 226) and the beam-splitter type (Hasa and Smith: 227). In the device of Peters and Stroke (228) the exit beam is divided by a Wollaston polarizer and is modulated by a rotating polaroid. Directional counting of fringes has been obtained by the use of four phototubes (Eisner: 229). An exhaustive evaluation of the recording problems in interferometry is due to Stroke (230).

Concerning the use of Rayleigh type interferometers for measurements on fluids, the dispersion error was extensively evaluated by Grunwald and Berkowitz (231). They devised an elaborate correction method which does not seem to offer many advantages over that previously mentioned.

The list of applications continues to grow. A combination of interferometric and spectrometric methods has been used by Ellis (232) to study plastic films. Precision analysis of D_2O-H_2O mixture is due to Ingelstam and co-workers (233), using a phase-contrast method, and by Schneider (234), using a mica plate interferometer. Many contemporary applications are, of course, concerned with semiconductor surfaces. Multiple reflection interferometers incorporating such surfaces lend themselves to a great diversity of measurements (reflectivity, conductivity, flatness, thickness, etc.) as shown by Belk, Tolansky and Turnbull (235). Germanium has been extensively studied by such optical methods (Rank, Bennett, and Cronemeyer: 235), and so was tellurium (Hartig and Loferski: 237). Limitations of the methods were evaluated by Berning (238), and by Smith (239).

An unexpected application of interferometry is the analysis of flames by interferometry (Harned and Ginsburg: 240).

Detailed calculations and actual measurement techniques with the various types of interferometers—including the Fabry-Perot etalon, the "echelon" type, and several commercial comparators—are found in Candler's book (241). Applications to the control of grating ruling engines are striking. The use of two Fabry-Perot etalons in tandam is shown to permit the measurement of the refractive index of an interposed gas. By contrast, rather more detailed theoretical developments relative to the same topics are found in Tolansky's book (242), in that of Ditchburn (243) and a paper by Jones (244).

BIBLIOGRAPHY SUPPLEMENT

161. Svenson, H., "Some Improved Forms of the Differential Prismatic Cell," *J. Opt. Soc. Am.*, **44**(2), 140–146 (1954).

162. Johnsen, S. E. J., and Schnelle, P. D., "A Precision Recording Refractometer," *Rev. Scient. Instr.*, **24**(1), 26–35 (1953).

163. Penther, C. J., and Noller, G. W., "Self-balancing Laboratory Differential Refractometer," *Rev. Scient. Instr.*, **29**(1), 43–46 (1958).

164. Penndorf, R., "Tables of the Refractive Index for Standard Air and the Rayleigh Scattering Coefficient for the Spectral Region Between 0.2 and 20.0 mµ and Their Application to Atmospheric Optics," *J. Opt. Soc. Am.*, **47**(2), 176–182 (1957).

165. McAlister, E. D., Villa, J. J., and Salzberg, C. D., "Rapid and Accurate Measurements of Refractive Index in the Infrared," *J. Opt. Soc. Am.*, **46**(7), 485–487 (1956).

166. Jaffe, J. H., and Oppenheim, U., "Infrared Dispersion of Liquids by Critical Angle Refractometry," *J. Opt. Soc. Am.*, **47**(9), 782–784 (1957).

167. Traub, A. C., and Osterbert, H., "Brewster Angle Apparatus for Thin Film Index Measurements," *J. Opt. Soc. Am.*, **47**(1). 62–64 (1957).

168. Carlson, A. J., and Paul, F. W., "Refractive Index Measurements in the Near Infrared," *Rev. Scient. Instr.*, **27**, 772–773 (1956).

169. Brodersen, S., "Interferometric Frequency Calibration of Infrared Spectrometers," *J. Opt. Soc. Am.*, **46**(4), 255–258 (1956).

170. Polster, H. D., "The Parallel Plate Interferometer for Wave Number Calibration of Infrared Spectrometers," *Rev. Scient. Instr.*, **25**(6), 503 (1954).

171. Rank, D. H., Bennett, J. M., and Bennett, H. E., "Measurement of Interferometric Secondary Wavelength Standards in the Near Infrared," *J. Opt. Soc. Am.*, **46**(7), 477–484 (1956).

172. Greenler, R. G., "Interferometric Spectrometer for the Infrared," *J. Opt. Soc. Am.*, **47**(7), 642–646 (1957).

173. Kagarise, R. E., and Mayfield, J. W., "Simple Interferometer for Dispersion Measurements of Liquids in the 2-22 mµ Region," *J. Opt. Soc. Am.*, **48**(6), 430–431 (1958).

174. Oppenheim, U., "Semireflecting Silver Films for Infrared Interferometry," *J. Opt. Soc. Am.*, **46**(8), 628–633 (1956).

175. Strong, J., "Interferometry for the Far Infrared," *J. Opt. Soc. Am.*, **47**(5), 354–357 (1957).

176. Casey, J. P., and Lewis, E. A., "Interferometer Action of a Parallel Pair of Wire Gratings," *J. Opt. Soc. Am.*, **42**(12), 971–977 (1952).

177. Schlueter, D. J., and Peck, E. R., "Refractivity of Air in the Near Infrared," *J. Opt. Soc. Am.*, **48**(5), 313–315 (1958).

178. Rodney, W. S., and Djurle, E., "Infrared Phase-contrast Refractometer," *J. Opt. Soc. Am.*, **48**(4), 388–389 (1958).

179. Johnson, W. E., "An Analog Computer for the Solution of the Radio Refractive Index

Equation," *J. Res. W. B. S.*, **51**(6), 335–342 (1953).

180. CRAIN, C. M., "Apparatus for Recording Fluctuations in the Refractive Index of the Atmosphere at 3.2 cm. Wave-length," *Rev. Scient. Instr.*, **21**(5), 456–457 (1950).

181. CRAIN, C. M., AND DEAM, A. P., "An Airborne Microwave Refractometer," *Rev. Scient. Instr.*, **23**(4), 149–151 (1952).

182. TOLBERT, C. W., AND STRAITON, A. W., "A Phase-shift Refractometer," *Rev. Scient. Instr.*, **22**(3), 162–165 (1951).

183. BACHYNSKI, M. P., AND BEKEFI, G., "Study of Optical Diffraction Images at Microwave Frequencies," *J. Opt. Soc. Am.*, **47**(5), 428–435 (1957).

184. ARTMAN, J. O., "A Microwave Fabry-Perot Interferometer," *Rev. Scient. Instr.*, **24**, 873–875 (1953).

185. LINFOOT, E. H., "Recent Advances in Optics," Clarendon Press, Oxford, England, 1955.

186. ZERNIKE, F., "Latest Wave in Physical Optics," *J. Opt. Soc.*, **47**(6), 466–468 (1957).

187. KIRKPATRICK, P., AND EL-SUM, H. M. A., "Image Formation by Reconstructed Wave Fronts. I. Physical Principles and Methods of Refinement," *J. Opt. Soc. Am.*, **46**(10), 825–831 (1956).

188. KAPANY, N. S., "Fiber Optics. Part I—Optical Properties of Certain Dielectric Cylinders," *J. Opt. Soc. Am.*, **47**(5), 413–422 (1957); "Part II—Image Transfer on Static and Dynamic Scanning with Fiber Bundles," *J. Opt. Soc. Am.*, **47**(5), 423–427 (1957).

189. KAPANY, N. S., AND PIKE, J. N., "Fiber Optics. Part IV—A Photorefractometer," *J. Opt. Soc. Am.*, **47**(12), 1109–1117 (1957).

190. FORREST, J. W., AND STRAAT, H. W., "Refractometer for Glass Control," *J. Opt. Soc. Am.*, **46**(7), 488–489 (1956).

191. FORREST, J. W., "Shielding Errors in Critical Angle Refractometry," *J. Opt. Soc. Am.*, **46**(8), 657–660 (1956).

192. MEYER-ARENDT, J. R., "Schlieren Method for Mass Determinations in Microscopic Dimensions," *Rev. Scient. Instr.*, **28**(1), 28–29 (1957).

193. POLANYI, M. L., "Volume and Index Measurements of Blood Cells with Recording Diffractometer," *Rev. Scient. Instr.*, **30**(8), 626–632 (1959).

194. BARER, R., "Refractometry and Interferometry of Living Cells," *J. Opt. Soc. Am.*, **47**(6), 545–557 (1957).

195. FRANÇON, M., "Polarization Apparatus for Interference Microscopy and Macroscopy of Isotropic Transparent Objects," *J. Opt. Soc. Am.*, **47**(6), 528–535 (1957).

196. FRANÇON, M., "Contraste de Phase et Contraste Par Interference," Collog. Comm. Internat. d'Optique, May 1951; Rev. d'Opt. Theor. et Instrum., Paris, 1952.

197. VANDER SLUIS, K. L., AND MCNALLY, J. R., JR., "Fabry-Perot Interferometer with Finite Aperture," *J. Opt. Soc. Am.*, **46** 1), 39–46 (1956).

198. BENNETT, F. D., AND KAHL, G. D., "A Generalized Vector Theory of the Mach-Zehnder Interferometer," *J. Opt. Soc. Am.*, **43**(2), 71–78 (1953).

199. THOMPSON, B. J., "Illustration of the Phase Change in Two-beam Interference with Partially Coherent Light," *J. Opt. Soc. Am.*, **48**(2), 95–97 (1958).

200. THOMPSON, B. J., AND WOLF, E., "Two beam Interference with Partially Coherent Light," *J. Opt. Soc. Am.*, **47**(10), 895–902 (1957).

201. LOTMAR, W., "An Interferometric Micro-electrophoresis Apparatus," *Rev. Scient. Instr.*, **22**(12), 886–890 (1951).

202. NAMBA, S., "Analysis of D_2O/H_2O by the Interferometer," *Rev. Scient. Instr.*, **27**, 872–873 (1956).

203. PECK, E. R., "Uncompensated Corner-reflector Interferometer," *J. Opt. Soc. Am.*, **47**(3), 250–252 (1957).

204. DYSON, J., "Common Path Interferometer for Testing Purposes," *J. Opt. Soc. Am.*, **47**(5), 386–390 (1957).

205. RANK, D. H., AND SHEARER, J. N., "Linear Gas Mass Flow Device with Applications to Interferometry," *J. Opt. Soc. Am.*, **46**(6), 463–464 (1956).

206. TEMPLE, E. B., "Quantitative Measurement of Gas Density by Means of Light Interference in a Schlieren System," *J. Opt. Soc. Am.*, **47**(1), 91–100 (1957).

207. INGELSTAM, E., "Some Quantitative Measurements of Path Differences and Gradients by Means of Phase Contrast and New Interferometric Devices," *J. Opt. Soc. Am.*, **47**(6), 536–544 (1957).

208. OSTERBERG, H., AND LaMARRE, D., "Modified Method of Fizeau Fringes for Thickness Measurements," *J. Opt. Soc. Am.*, **46**(10), 777–778 (1956).

209. PRICE, E. W., "Initial Adjustment of the Mach-Zehnder Interferometer," *Rev. Scient. Instr.*, **23**(4), 162 (1952).

210. CALDWELL, C. S., HALL, J. R., AND BABB, A. L., "Mach-Zehnder Interferometer for Diffusion Measurements in Volatile Liquid Systems," *Rev. Scient. Instr.*, **28**(10), 816–821 (1957).

211. McLEAN, E. A., SCHERRER, V. E., NANNEY, C. A., AND FANEUFF, C. E., "Interferometer Used to Study Transient Heating of Water," *Rev. Scient. Instr.*, **29**(3), 225–227 (1958).

212. BLUE, R. E., AND POLLACK, J. L., "An Interferometer—Schlieren Instrument for Aerodynamic Investigations," *Rev. Scient. Instr.*, **23**(12), 754–755 (1952).

213. SAUNDERS, J. B., "In-line Interferometer," *J. Opt. Soc. Am.*, **44**(3), 241–242 (1954).

214. POST, D., "Characteristics of the Series Interferometer," *J. Opt. Soc. Am.*, **44**(3), 243–249 (1954). "Multiple-beam Fringe Sharpening with the Series Interferometer," *J. Opt. Soc. Am.*, **48**(5), 309–312 (1958).

215. PRIMAK, W., "Fringe Sharpening in Divided Beam Interferometers," *J. Opt. Soc. Am.*, **48**(6), 375–379 (1958).

216. BAKARAT, N., "Interference Fringes with Cylindrically Curved Thin Films," *J. Opt. Soc. Am.*, **48**(2), 92–94 (1958).

217. BAKARAT, N., AND NOOH, H., "Principle of an Interference Refractometer," *J. Opt. Soc. Am.*, **48**(2), 90–92 (1958).

218. PRICE, E. W., AND WEDAA, H. W., "Contrast and Color in Interference Fringes," *Rev. Scient. Instr.*, **24**, 332–334 (1953).

219. HIRSCHBERG, J. G., AND KADESCH, R. R., "Synchronous Wavelength Sweep of a Diffraction Grating and Fabry-Perot Interferometer," *J. Opt. Soc. Am.*, **48**(3), 177 (1958).

220. WERNER, F. D., AND LEADON, B. M., "Very Accurate Measurement of Fringe Shifts in an Optical Interferometer Study of Gas Flow," *Rev. Scient. Instr.*, **24**(2), 121–124 (1953).

221. LEADON, B. M., AND WERNER, F. D., "Fringe Spacing Changes in Accurate Measurements of Interferometer Fringe Shifts," *Rev. Scient. Instr.*, **25**, 923–924 (1954).

222. WINKLER, E. H., "Very Accurate Measurements of Fringe Shifts in an Optical Interferometer Study of Gas Flow," *Rev. Scient. Instr.*, **24**, 1067–1068 (1953).

223. KAHL, G. D., AND SLEATOR, D. B., "Spectral Effects in Interferometry," *J. Opt. Soc. Am.*, **48**(8), 525–530 (1958).

224. KOESTER, CH. J., "Phase Shift Effects in Fringes of Equal Chromatic Order," *J. Opt. Soc. Am.*, **48**(4), 255–260 (1958).

225. NAMBA, S., "Photoelectric Recording Interferometer for Gas Analysis," *Rev. Scient. Instr.*, **30**(8), 642–645 (1959).

226. BIONDI, M. A., "High Speed Direct Recording Fabry-Perot Interferometer," *Rev. Scient. Instr.*, **27**(1), 36–39 (1956).

227. HARA, K., AND SMITH, D. S., "Length Measurement by Fringe Counting," *Rev. Scient. Instr.*, **30**(8), 707–710 (1959).

228. PETERS, J., AND STROKE, G., "Electronic Location of Interference Fringes," *J. Opt. Soc. Am.*, **43**(8), 668–671 (1953).

229. EISNER, R. L., "Reversible Photoelectric Fringe Counting," *Rev. Scient. Instr.*, **29**(6), 521–523 (1958).

230. STROKE, G. W., "Photoelectric Fringe Signal Information and Range in Interferometers with Moving Mirrors," *J. Opt. Soc. Am.*, **47**(12), 1097–1103 (1957).

231. GRUNWALD, E., AND BERKOWITZ, B. J., "Rayleigh Interferometer for the Analysis of Liquid," *Anal. Chem.*, **29**(1), 124–129 (1957).

232. ELLIS, R. H., "Measuring Refractive Index of Plastic Films," *Rev. Scient. Instr.*, **28**(7), 557–558 (1957).

233. INGELSTAM, E., DJURLE, E., AND JOHANSSON, L., "Precision Concentration Analysis of D_2O-H_2O by Means of Phase-Contrast Refractometry," *J. Opt. Soc. Am.*, **44**(6), 472–477 (1954).

234. SCHNEIDER, S., "Interferometer for Analyzing Mixtures of Hydrogen Isotopes," *Rev. Scient. Instr.*, **29**, 623–624 (1958).

235. BELK, J. A., TOLANSKY, S., AND TURNBULL, D., "Use of Multilayer Films for Surface Topography Interferometry," *J. Opt. Soc. Am.*, **44**(1), 5–10 (1954).

236. RANK, D. H., BENNETT, H. E., AND CRONEMEYER, D. C., "The Index of Refraction of Germanium Measured by an Interference Method," *J. Opt. Soc. Am.*, **44**(1), 13–16 (1954).

237. HARTIG, P. A., AND LOFERSKI, J. J., "Infrared Index of Refraction of Tellurium Crystals," *J. Opt. Soc. Am.*, **44**(1), 17–19 (1954).

238. BERNING, P. H., "Note Concerning Multiple Reflections Within Absorbing Thin Films," *J. Opt. Soc. Am.*, **46**(10), 779–783 (1956).

239. SMITH, S. D., "Design of Multilayer Filters by Considering Two Effective Interfaces," *J. Opt. Soc. Am.*, **48**(1), 43–47 (1958).

240. HARNED, B. W., AND GINSBERG, N., "Analysis of Interference Fringes From a Flame," *J. Opt. Soc. Am.*, **48**(3), 178–183 (1958).
241. CANDLER, C., "Modern Interferometers," Hilger and Watts, Ltd., publ. London, 1951.
242. TOLANSKY, S., "An Introduction to Interferometry," Longmans, Green and Co., London, 1954.
243. DITCHBURN, R. W., "Light," Interscience, New York, 1952.
244. JONES, C. R., "On Reversibility and Irreversibility in Optics," *J. Opt. Soc. Am.*, **43**(2), 138–144 (1953).

R. JONNARD

RESINOGRAPHY

Definitions and Scope

Resinography, as the name implies, is the *graphic* part of the study of resins. The term "resin" stands for natural *resins*, such as rosin, and also for high *polymers*. High polymers may be natural, regenerated, modified or synthetic; for examples, respectively: cotton, viscose, cellulose acetate and polyacrylonitrile. High polymers may be thermoplastic or thermoset. Characteristically a high polymer is in the rubbery, glassy and/or crystalline state. Examples of exceptions are silicone oil and its "bouncing putty." Inorganic glasses, especially their fibers, may also be studied resinographically.

Resinography is an integral part of the analytical and synthetical studies of such materials. For examples, as discussed later in more detail regarding Figure 8, a resin was found to have higher impact strength than could be fully explained by the chemical-physical history. Resinographic examination revealed the presence of two coexistent physical phases. Their separate properties and the effects of their combination were correlated with the sizes, shapes and distributions of the physical phases as well as with the over-all chemical composition.

Resinographic studies are made not only on static samples but also on dynamic ones. That is, behavior is studied as well as architectural design and construction. All parts of the complete, cyclic studies are not only connected but interrelated as suggested in Figure 1.

The term "resinography" is analogous to, but distinct from "metallography" and from studies of other *plastic* materials such as metals, waxes, mastics and plasters. The analogy stems from similarities and distinctions among properties and methods of fabrication. "Continents," boundaries and "bridges" in the world of plastic materials are fancifully mapped in Figure 2.

Resins and high polymers like the other plastic materials suggested in Figure 2 are characterized by properties which permit manufacture by plastic deformation such as pressing, pushing, pulling, pounding, plaiting, punching, pinching, pruning, planing, polishing, pasting, plastering, or packing into position.

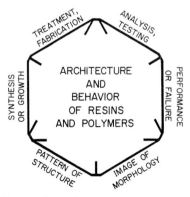

FIG. 1. Some facets of resinography.

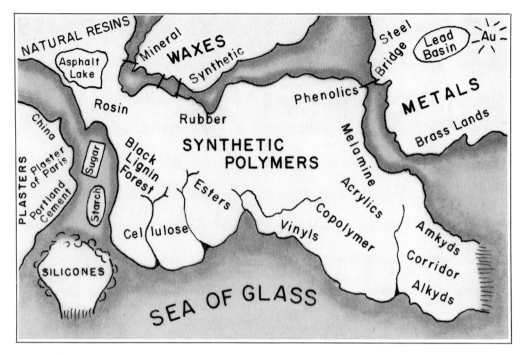

FIG. 2. A fanciful map to chart the relationships in the world of plastic materials.

High polymers also differ from metals in that the molecules of high polymers are huge and may vary in effective sizes, assumed shapes and internal configurations and conformations. High polymers differ from waxes in that the former may be of much higher degree of polymerization and/or they are not always predominantly crystallized. High polymers can be of only one phase or state and yet be plastic; mastics and plasters are plastic only while solid particles are moving around in a second, liquid phase.

Solid metals are always crystalline and waxes are essentially crystalline. In metals the crystalline grain is the primary unit involved in fabrication, use, fatigue and failure. For example: One speaks of inter- or intra- granular diffusion, corrosion or fracture; precipitation may be along grain boundaries; deformation takes place in each grain according to its own crystallographic orientation. On the other hand, in polymeric

materials at least four types of units appear (9) to be at play in the construction and behavior as indicated in Table 1.

Type I. By classical definition, the smallest descriptive and functional unit which is characteristic of a material phase is the molecule. In resins such as rosin, when the molecules are monomeric or nearly so, they are far from visible in the electron-lens microscope; in low polymers there are macromolecules, but even these are too small to be resolved. In some high polymers heterogeneities of macromolecular order are revealed, e.g., as spheroids (Figure 4), ellipsoids or fibrils near the limit of visibility.* The dimensions are small, generally varying between the lower microscopical limit (10 or 20 A) to 100 or 200 A, but precision of measurement is hampered by relatively broad, fuzzy boundaries. Details such as the

* "Visibility" pertains to both resolution and contrast.

TABLE 1. VISIBLE UNITS OF ARCHITECTURE IN POLYMERS AND RESINS

Type	Origin	Unit	Visible with
I	Polymerization; stereo-arrangements.	Effect of macromolecules.	Electron-lens microscope, in some instances.
II	Coagulation; peptization.	Colloidal particle.	Electron-lens microscope, generally.
III	Formulation; processing.	Amorphous, oriented, or crystalline phase.	High powered light microscope, generally.
IV	Molding; casting; drawing; laminating.	Amorphous and/or crystalline material.	Light microscope, hand lens, or eye alone.

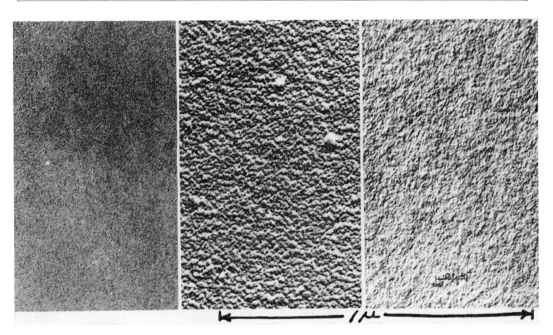

FIG. 3. Linseed oil in various stages of polymerization. Electron micrographs at same magnification, showing particles of Type I. Self-supporting films, metal-shadowed simultaneously.

coils, appendages and links generally are not resolved. Nevertheless, information concerning macromolecules has been obtained which explained variations during synthesis (8) and/or analysis (Figure 3).

Demonstration of macromolecular boundaries is the least developed and most difficult part of resinography. Besides the problems of preparing specimens, obtaining and maintaining highest electron microscopical visibility, there are problems of interpreting images near such limits and of explaining

results which are practically or theoretically unexpected.

Type II. Many kinds of polymers manifest *colloidal sizes* in connection with physical-chemical history and practical properties (Figures 5A and B). During polymerization, gelation is often a step in the process and colloidal particles are revealed microscopically. The particulate boundaries apparently are also involved in tests such as fracturing (Figure 6) or etching and in performance such as strength, wear and toughness. Sim-

527

FIG. 4. Polyacrylonitrile as thin, self-supporting film cast from dilute solution in ethylene carbonate. Shadowed at 10° with U and electron micrographed. Shows Type I particles some as monolayers partially covering holes (broken bubbles) in the film. 72,000×

ilarly in natural or synthetic latices, emulsions and suspensions, the colloidal particles are involved in failures such as by freezing, in consolidation such as by smoking natural rubber latex or in performance such as in painting or printing. Particles of Type II may be perceptible light microscopically and generally are perceptible electron microscopically.

Type III. These may be aggregates of Type II particles. (Figure 7) More and more resins are being formulated to meet useful specifications by "alloying" two or more phases of the same or different component (monomer) in a *system*. For example, a latex may be added sometime during the polymerization of styrene to make a more impact-resistant material. (Figure 8). During the consolidation with polystyrene the rubbery colloidal particles may be greatly enlarged or a rubbery phase may be milled into an adhesive to give resilience to the finished joint. A crystalline phase may be introduced to a system to give rigidity. That is particles of Type III may be amorphous or crystalline and of the same or different stereoisomer. The amorphous phase(s) may be in the rubbery and/or glassy states (Figure 9).

Type III particles and parts are generally visible in the light microscope. It should provide illumination as bright-field or dark-field, by transmitted or reflected light, polarized or unpolarized, as needed. Ability to change from one kind of illumination to another should be quick and easy (1, 2).

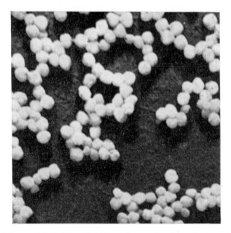

FIGS. 5(A) Emulsion polymerized polyacrylonitrile, as dried and electron micrographed. Type II particles, useful as a latex or in consolidation. 34,000×.

(B) Same polymer after pressure-molding and fracturing. Positive electron micrograph of replica shows that resin came apart between same type of particles as were molded together. 34,000×.

Type III units of each phase not only can be related to their origin and functions by their light microscopic morphology, but also by their optical properties such as relative and specific refractive indices, and kind and degree of double refraction. Some other physical properties can generally be determined such as softening temperature, scratch and indentation hardness. Such tests usually can be done on the discrete phase *in situ* ("intangible isolation (6)"). Some other destructive tests can be devised if the discrete phase is tangibly separable from a sufficiently large sample.

Type IV. This may be a system of phases of the whole material. The phase(s) may be amorphous, continuous or discontinuous, rubbery or glassy, crystallizable or noncrystallizable. If a grafted part shows a boundary with the original polymer, it is best described as a separate unit of Type IV. So are other coatings and layers of one phase each. For example, there may be a precoating of phenolic resin on each of two anodized aluminum sheets with an intermediate layer of rubber in between (1). In every case, each unit has its own physical-chemical origin and purpose, and it is important that each be observed separately during process-control and development of use.

Fibers and foils are special examples of Type IV; they are so important that there are special technologies, societies and schools to study them. Yet the study of fibers and foils must be considered as resinography. They are highly polymeric in origin, have important uses in resins as reinforcing parts, have characteristic directional morphology and many optical properties. These properties are generally those of particles of Type I or II which have been oriented to some extent, usually by the application of external stress or by artificial conditions (e.g., spinning and drawing a fiber; casting a film) (Figure 10).

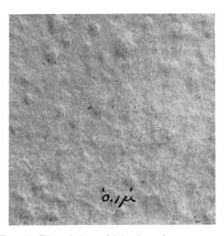

FIG. 6. Phenol-formaldehyde polymer, experimental fracture surface. An electron micrograph of a positive replica. The larger type of particle is classified as Type II and the smaller is probably Type I.

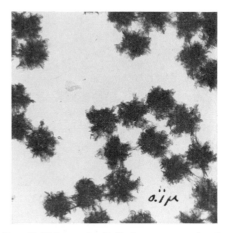

FIG. 7. Polyacrylonitrile in a very early stage of bulk polymerization. An electron micrograph showing particles of Type III composed of particles of Type II (5).

Crystals on the other hand are composed of macromolecules (Type I) which *grow* by their own attractive forces into geometric or skeletal shapes of characteristic habit and phase. The crystalline habits of any one phase are characteristic of variations in crystallizing conditions. Transformation of one crystalline phase into another is far less common than it is among metallic alloys.

529

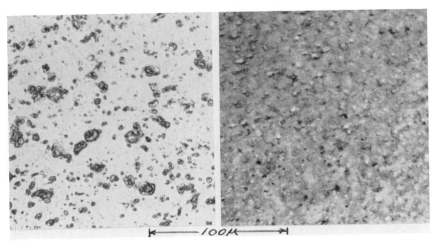

Fig. 8. Two "alloys," high in polystyrene containing small amounts of synthetic rubber as particles of Type III, illustrating also two methods of preparation and two methods of lighting. Left: Polished and etched (benzene in methyl alcohol ca. 1:4); bright-field reflected illumination. Right: Microtomed thin section; bright-field, slightly oblique, transmitted illumination.

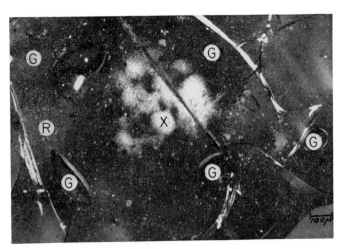

Fig. 9. Polystyrene varying across the field in proportion of isotactic (crystallizable) and atactic (non-crystallizable). Light micrograph of unstirred sample between partially crossed polars, by transmitted illumination. Melt quenched in air, warmed slowly until glassy phase, such as (G) was almost entirely transformed to continuous rubbery (R) phase, held at slightly lower temperature to form some colonies (X) of crystals, quenched again to freeze the 3 co-existent phases, not in equilibrium. Some cracks are isotropic (shown black); some are anisotropic (shown white).

The crystalline parts of Type IV are generally *aggregates* of unicrystals (Types II & III) (Figure 11). Such aggregates have their characteristic habit (e.g., spherulitic), origin (e.g., self-nucleating), optical properties (e.g., undulate extinction between crossed polars), and practical properties (e.g., intergranular fracture). There is some evidence that at least some kinds of aggregates are a combination of crystalline (internal) forces and applied (external) stress. Starch grains are natural aggregate units quite characteristic of the botanical species.

Paper sheets, woven or nonwoven fabrics, roving threads, tire cords, and reclaimed rubber are examples of systems of phases or materials that may be only part of the fabricated whole. It may be very important to recognize their areas and boundaries and to determine how they may be reacted with or anchored to the contiguous materials. Conversely, fibers, foils, sheets, tubes, fabrics and so forth may have another resin phase attached by grafting, impregnating or coating.

A very important kind of Type IV is the *molded grain*. This is generally supposed to represent the material of the molded piece and to contain the resin, fibrous and/or particulate fillers, pigments, lubricants, etc. Yet after molding, the original pellets of the molding grains can be seen before or after preferential relief polishing, etching, staining or breaking at grain boundaries.

The resinographic problem can be complicated. For instance, starch grains may be incorporated into a urea-formaldehyde adhesive binding cellulosic and metallic sheets. To differentiate the starch grains from the synthetic resin would one examine thin sections (with reflected light) or thick sections (with transmitted light)?

Combination with Other Materials. If the resin is combined with metal the method

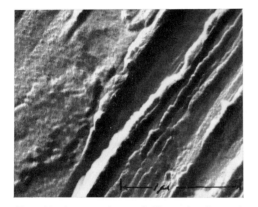

FIG. 10. An experimental fiber of polyacrylonitrile. A positive electron micrograph of a silica replica. The fiber represents a unit of Type IV. The ridges of the "bark" running parallel to the fiber-axis apparently contain both Types II and I particles. So does the core, exposed in the upper left part of the micrograph but here the particles are less ordered.

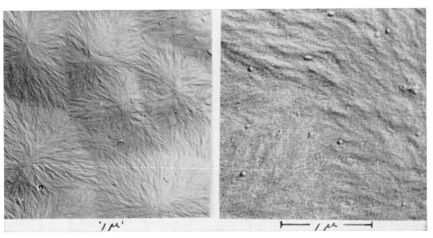

FIG. 11. Commercial foil (Type IV material) manifesting three types of particles. Electron micrographs of positive replica of rougher side, no shadowing metal. Left: Spherulitic grains (Type III) composed of crystallites (Type II). Right: Higher magnification. Apparently there are small particles (probably Type I) arranged roughly in line within the variously oriented crystallites.

531

of examination of the combination would probably follow the techniques of metallography and microscopy by reflected light. If the resin is combined with rock, mineral or ceramic, the techniques would be related to petrography and transmitted light, or mineralography and reflected light.

If common amounts of pigments or fillers are added to the resin, the product is generally so opaque that reflected light is the only light-microscopical illumination feasible. It is very satisfactory.

Equipment

If the resinographer is in a narrow field of making, fabricating, testing or using resins, his microscopical equipment, accessories and techniques may be definitely specified. If, however, the resinographer is in research, development, consulting or a very broad field of manufacture or use, he will need a wide variety of equipment, accessories, techniques, experience and personal help. Furthermore, the manufacturer of resins which are to be sold for many purposes may have a much broader interest in the texture, structure and combination of a resin than the fabricator or consumer who has a specific interest. Indeed, the resinographer of a primary manufacturer has broad interests and responsibilities of health, safety, competition, "security" and fundamental research; his microscopical equipment must be as versatile as he is.

Away from his laboratory the experienced resinographer finds that he can recognize and study resins a great deal better with a simple magnifier (3) than with the unaided eye. For example, a $10\times$ pocket magnifier, correct for aberrations, can be carried at all times. It gives an erect, virtual image that is easy to interpret. Its chief disadvantage is that it must be held close to both the object and the eye. This simple magnifier or a pocket compound microscope (3) is recommended for field work, within limits and within the experience of the resinographer,

to examine the surfaces of Type IV particles, inserts, laminates, possible cracks and voids, etc. of fabricated, cut or fractured surfaces during manufacture, test or use. Only morphology is revealed and such information is limited; optical properties or patterns cannot be studied without provision for polarizing the light.

In the resinographical laboratory three general kinds (2) of compound microscopes will be essential if all 4 types of units are to be considered. These microscopes, in the recommended order of their acquisition are:

(1) *Stereoscopic, biobjective (Greenough)* light microscope for preliminary work and some units of Types IV and III (q.v., p. 538).

(2) *Monoobjective, polarizing* light microscope equipped for both transmitted and reflected illumination for more precise work with units of Types IV and III and some units of Type II.

(3) *Electron* microscope, especially for seeing morphology of units of Type II and, at highest powers and best performance, some units of Type I.

Stereoscopic Microscope with Polars. The kind of microscope recommended for preliminary examination, preparation, micromanipulation, and experimentation on resinous materials is the Greenough type, biobjective, stereoscopic microscope fitted with polars (2). This type of microscope is generally excellent for the examination of particles (IV) of moldable or molded grains, crystalline aggregates, some fillers, most inserts, many foreign particles, most laminates; some single crystals, multi-phase systems, most cracks, many voids. The objectives have such long depth of focus (*ca.* 25 μ) that the object might be studied as it is or after fracturing, cutting, sawing, and/or abrading into thick or thin sections to reveal all of the pertinent views.

Reflected illumination, whether directional, or symmetrical, is typically darkfield in the Greenough microscope. That is, the illuminator is outside the objectives, and light gets into the microscope and eye as a result of scattering by the object. Consequently, paper, for example, appears white and a glass slide appears dark. Dark-field images by reflected light are the easiest to interpret because they are of the same type as received by the unaided eye.

Transmitted illumination is typically bright field in the Greenough microscope. Paper, for example appears dark and a glass slide appears bright.

Reflected and/or transmitted light may be used with adequate control and inexpensive lighting. With the simultaneously rotatable polars and transmitted light, double refraction can be detected and studied during heating or cooling under stretch or compression, or with other physical-chemical treatments.

With its two objectives and an eyepiece for each, the Greenough microscope is two compound microscopes, one for each eye at about the angle for maximum stereoscopic effect. There should be little eyestrain or fatigue, provided that the prisms are in adjustment. The Greenough microscope has reinverting prisms so as to give erect images. This feature is especially convenient in micromanipulation and experimentation: Something pushed "north" and "east" does not seem to go "south" and "west." Erect images are interpreted as they would be with the eye unaided: If a texture is bright on the side toward a lamp the texture is an elevation, not a depression.

The two stereoscopic objectives have long working distances so that physical or chemical operations may be performed on the object; for examples: scratch or impression hardness testing; tensile or compression testing; electric, magnetic or electrophoretic experiments; chemical reactions; etching or staining.

The commercially available stands are versatile and interchangeable. The microscope on the simple mount can be placed directly on flat objects such as sheets, boards,

walls, floors and table-tops, so as to examine them without destructive sampling. Special stands may be improvised.

The biobjective (Greenough) microscope has inherent limitations of resolving power. The two objectives must be so close and at such an angle that their numerical aperture is not much over 0.1. In fact, objectives of all available magnifications have about this same numerical aperture, which is not much, if any, greater than a hand lens. Therefore the stereoscopic microscope cannot reveal structure separated by much less than 5 μ (0.005 mm). The kinds and quantities of properties are limited not only by the objective and focusing device but also by the illuminating systems.

Therefore, the resinographer's next microscopical requirement would probably be a high powered, polarizing light microscope.

Polarizing Light Microscope of High Power. In resinography a light microscope of moderate power and quality of image is required for the smaller sizes of Type IV units (Figure 12, right). The highest powers and qualities may be needed for Type III; they certainly will be needed for Type II whenever such small units can be made visible with light. In order to cover the whole range of samples from transparent to opaque, high powers must be available by either transmitted or reflected illumination (2). That is, there must be both a substage condenser and a vertical illuminator and each should be of high aperture, of good image quality and with a polarizer. The analyzer can be common to both illuminators. A binocular eyepiece (so much used by biologists) is not used with polars and so is not recommended for resinography.. The combination (2) of "petrographic" and "ore" microscopes is recommended. The "petrographic" part with its condenser and polarizer for transmitted illumination is used for emulsions, suspensions, fibers, films, mounted grains and prepared thin sections (Figure 8, right). The "ore" part with

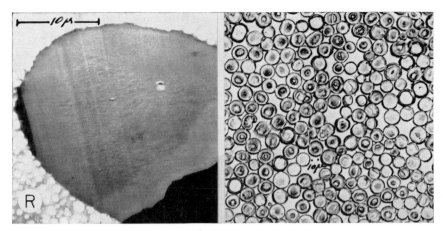

FIG. 12. Experimental fibers of polyacrylonitrile showing variation in cross-sectional texture. Left: Electron micrograph of ultrathin section cut after coating with a resilient polyacrylate latex (R) and then mounting in methacrylate (4). Right: Light micrograph of a thin section showing that these experimental fibers varied in the number of rings.

vertical illuminator and polarizer is used for surfaces, opaque grains, polished thick sections, opaque inserts, and optical sections of transparent objects (Figure 8, left).

Along with other optical methods for enhancing contrast, darkfield illumination by either transmitted or reflected illumination is handy, if not required. Dark field by reflected light permits the distinction of pigment or streak color from specular color. In general, images by dark-field reflected illumination are easier to interpret because they are more natural than bright-field images.

Among high polymers and resins observation and measurement of optical properties are important adjuncts to descriptive and interpretive morphology or texture. In order to observe most optical properties the light microscope must have variable apertures from low to very high, in both objective and condenser, the polars must be crossable and uncrossable, and their directions of vibrations must be known. There should be a rotatable object-stage.

With transmitted illumination specific or critical refractive indices may be measured. Double refraction can be detected and measured. Distinction can be made among the

origins of the double refraction, such as single crystals, crystal aggregates, strain (Figure 9), deformation, orientation of anisotropic particles of resin, or orientation of tiny rods or plates of isotropic particles in an isotropic medium of different refractive index (2). The direction(s) of vibration of slower component(s), the sign of elongation or the optical sign can be determined directly. The two or three specific refractive indices may be determined with a compensator and crossed polars.

With only one polar and knowing its vibration direction, pleochoism and sign of color absorption can be determined qualitatively and quantitatively in colorful, dyed or stained materials such as fibers.

Rotated between crossed polars the behavior of a polymeric specimen may be very different from that of a single, unstrained crystal. Examples are: crystalline aggregates, such as spherulites; natural aggregates, such as starch grains and natural fibers; synthetic aggregates such as special polarizing films, wrapping foils and textile fibers.

Crystals and other orientations of highly polymeric particles have characteristic diffraction patterns (interference figures) which are separate sources of determinative and interpretive information from transmitted light.

By reflected light, interference patterns (polarization figures) are being studied on ore minerals, but such a study on resins is to date only suggested.

Electron Microscope. High polymers, alone or simply formulated with plasticizers, curing agents and/or stabilizers are composed generally of very small particles (Types II and I). Such particles are smaller than the wavelengths of light and, for this reason, are not observable with a light microscope. A stream of *electrons* at a potential of 55 kv has a wavelength of about 0.05 A and even though the numerical aperture of an electron lens is extremely low (about 0.02) a resolution as relatively poor as 100 A is more than ample to separate colloidal particles (Type II). Electron microscopes, of or over 50 kv in potential, somewhat corrected in astigmatism, clean and in good operation, can resolve distances of 20 to 10 A or, perhaps, smaller. This kind of resolution should resolve macromolecular particles (Type I) of above approximately 20,000 in molecular weight. The remaining problem is to obtain adequate contrast in the boundaries or among loci of influence.

If the surface of a high polymer or its resin is to be examined electron microscopically, a negative, positive, or pseudo replica will probably serve the purpose (Figures 5B, 6, 10, 11, 14). In any kind of replication of a high polymeric material, the primary replicating medium must not modify or stick to the material. Therefore, replicating media are generally limited to aqueous media, such as a "solution" of gelatin, methyl cellulose or polyvinyl alcohol. Control samples of the replicating and photographic media should be compared with the electron micrograph of the specimen.

A "surface" of a polymer is generally an interface of the polymer with air, liquid or solid, and the electron microscopical image must be considered as such even when the fabricating interface may be unknown— for example, with commercial fibers, foils, laminates and moldings.

The internal texture may be entirely different from the external one. The problem of representing the interior of the specimen may be very difficult. Since the area needed is small, a small part of a fracture surface may be sufficiently flat (Figures 5B, 6, 14). For such purposes *fracturing* is generally simple when the sample is cooled to brittleness. Even a film can be fractured in a planar section if the substance can be obtained as a liquid and used as an adhesive between halves of two L-shaped pieces of sheet iron or steel. After the "adhesive" is hardened and cold-embrittled it is usually fractured by holding one "leg" of the composite L in a vise and striking the other leg sufficiently with a hammer. The fracture-surface is then replicated as usual.

In a corollary manner a replica can be made of a single microtomed surface of fibers, foils, films or other soft materials. Grooves will probably appear in the replica but these are readily related to microscopic nicks in even the best cutting edge. A glass cutting edge and a cantilever rocking microtome may be preferred to rotary microtome and a steel knife.

Mounting specimens for microtomy is even more important in electron microscopy than in light microscopy. Special precautions may have to be taken to avoid distortion, chattering and other effects. A very successful method for fibers is to treat them with a synthetic rubber latex before embedding in methacrylate (4) (Figure 12, left).

The most direct method of examining a high polymer is to cast it into a film which is sufficiently thin for electron microscopy (Figure 4). This presupposes that the specimen is obtainable in a fluid state, which will flow to a thin film and cure or dry to a film which is self-supporting and able to withstand the incidence of the electron beam. Linseed oil cast on water can be prepared

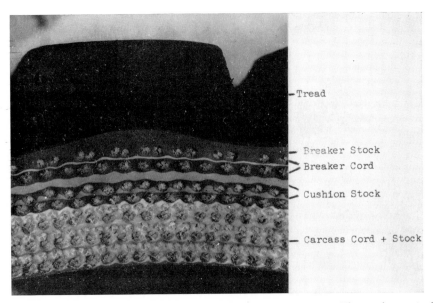

FIG. 13. A cross-section of an automobile tire of unknown manufacturer. The section, cut with a wet razor blade, was photographed by oblique, reflected light. Shows the kind, numbers and distributions of the layers and indicates places to sample for identification of the kinds of rubbers and fibers.

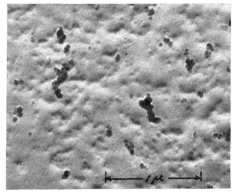

FIG. 14. Natural rubber tire tread stock filled with carbon black (shown as black round areas and also as commensurate depressions and elevations). An electron micrograph of positive replica; no shadowing metal. Matrix also manifests tiny rubber particles of Type I(7).

this way (Figure 3). Cellulose esters (e.g., collodion) and some vinyl polymers (e.g., "Formvar" polyvinyl acetal) meet the requirements so well that they are used as replicating media. Gelatin, polyvinyl alcohol and cellulose ethers are hydrophilic and are used as replicating media when organic solvents

are detrimental. These organic replicating media and substrates are high polymers and as such they could manifest particulate texture as large as that of the specimen. Instead, carbon, silica and other inorganic replicating media should be considered. With any replicating medium or substrate, "blanks" should be run. For similar reasons "blanks" should be run on all photographic materials.

The general techniques of electron microscopy and replication are described in detail elsewhere in this encyclopedia, and limitations as well as advantages of the electron microscopy have been published (2, 3). The specific advantage of the electron microscope is that it makes visible practically all particles of Type II and significant ones of Type I. The limitations are related to the problems of representing the texture, gaining sufficient contrast and avoiding polymerization, scission or any other change due to the electron beam or vacuum.

There are also the general limitations of resinography with respect to its infancy.

536

The technology is almost certain to develop as the microscopy, interpretations and conclusions develop.

Nature of Information Obtained Microscopically

The nature of resinographical information has been discussed in terms of four kinds of architectural units and four kinds of microscopes. In conclusion, reference is made to the finished product, in terms of fabrication, end-use and gross-texture (1). These can only be suggested because of restricted space.

In rubber tires, for example, (Figure 13) one may be interested in the thickness of tread or retread, occurrence of reclaimed rubber, distribution of carbon or white reinforcing agent, layers of gum-stock, number of plies of cord, kinds of cordage fibers, construction of bead, etc. In these and other rubber products one may be interested in variations in texture of the rubber due to poor distribution of accelerator, retardant or antioxidant. The distributions of sizes and shapes of pigments, fillers or abrasives may be important in rubber products, (Figure 14) writing boards, floor and table coverings, pavements, and paints.

Related to paints is the resinographic examination of inks, lacquers, polishes, adhesives, mastics and casting resins. Moldable resins are generally solids, as powders, grains or preforms. Some polymeric cements and adhesives are also marketed dry.

In painted, inked, varnished or lacquered surfaces there may be the question of number, thickness, uniformity and adherence of layers. There are similar problems with laminates of wood, paper, cardboard, fabrics, polymeric foils and adhesive tapes. Coatings may also be important on leather, fabrics, and other materials of decoration, safety, clothing, upholstery, housing, packaging and industry. Resins and/or high polymers are an inherent part of non-woven fabrics and papers of high wet and dry strength.

Whatever the state of fabrication and use of the resin or high polymer the resinographer must be prepared to show the texture and structure of its units *in situ*.

REFERENCES

1. ROCHOW, T. G., AND GILBERT, R. L., "Resinography," Chap. 5, Vol. *V*, "Protective and Decorative Coatings," edited by J. J. Mattiello, Wiley, New York, New York (1946).
2. CLARK, G. L., Editor-in-Chief, "The Encyclopedia of Chemistry," pp. 220–3, Reinhold Publishing Corporation, New York, (1957).
3. CHAMOT, E. M., AND MASON, C. W., "Handbook of Chemical Microscopy," Vol. I, 3rd edition, Wiley, New York, (1958).
4. BOTTY, M. C., FELTON, C. D., AND ANDERSON, R. E., "Microscopy of Experimental Fibers," *J. Textile Research Institute* (1960).
5. THOMAS, W. M., THOMAS, A. M., AND DEICHERT, W. G., "Microscopical Study of Heterogeneous Polymerization," International Symposium on Macromolecules (International Union of Pure and Applied Chemistry), Wiesbaden, Germany, October, 1959.
6. SAYLOR, C. P., "The intangible isolation of contaminants within purified substances," Gordon Research Conference on Separation and Purification, 1954, *Science* **119**, 6 (Apr. 16, 1954).
7. ROCHOW, T. G., ROCHOW, E. G., "The Size of Silicone Molecules," *Science*, **111**, 271–275 (1950).
8. MOORE, L. D., PECK, V. G., "Study of Particles Present in Some High Pressure Polyethylenes," *J. Polymer Sci.*, **36**, 141–153 (1959).
9. ROCHOW, T. G., THOMAS, A. M., BOTTY, M. C., review on "Electron Microscopy," *Anal. Chem.*, **32**, 99R (1960).

T. G. ROCHOW

Stereoscopic Microscopy (*See also* p. 532)

BASIC DESIGN, OPERATION AND USE

The stereomicroscope differs from the conventional compound laboratory microscope in several respects:

(1) it is actually *two* compound microscopes aimed at a common object;

(2) the image is erect and non-reversed;

(3) the image is truly stereoscopic, or three-dimensional, as contrasted with the binocular body of a conventional microscope which presents identical images to both eyes, and hence is not stereoscopic;

(4) the useful magnification limit is much lower, generally 100 to 150×, as contrasted with 1000 to 1500× in a normal compound microscope.

From the foregoing, it is apparent that the stereomicroscope gives an image which is much more easily interpreted than those obtained with the laboratory microscope. The low magnification is a factor in this easy interpretation, since one sees a good deal of the actual object, and can easily gain the impression of simply being brought closer to a familiar object.

True stereoscopy is also a potent factor in creating realism in the image. The observer sees the depths and heights standing out clearly and quite naturally, and the transition from normal viewing to microscope viewing is easily made. The stereomicroscope has quite a large depth of focus, so that the sense of depth perception is heightened accordingly.

The erect and non-reversed image also creates a natural and easily understood image. It also permits one to easily manipulate the specimen on the stage, without the attendant frustration involved in attempts to do the same thing on the laboratory microscope. This permits use of the stereomicroscope in many applications where very precise manipulations must be made, such as micro-dissection of biological material, or assembly of tiny electronic components in the industrial field.

Structure of the Stereomicroscope

Figure 1 shows the basic structure of a simple stereomicroscope. The left and the right microscopes aim toward a common object field. Each microscope comprises an objective, a prism-erecting system, and an eyepiece. Each prism system is mounted on a bearing concentric with the objective axis, around which it may be rotated to adjust it to the observer's interocular distance.

Normally the angle between the two microscope axes is in the neighborhood of 10°, which is about the normal convergence angle for viewing an object at 15 inches distance.

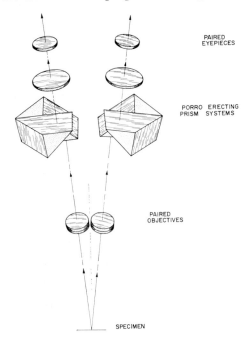

PAIRED EYEPIECES

PORRO ERECTING PRISM SYSTEMS

PAIRED OBJECTIVES

SPECIMEN

Fig. 1. The basic optical elements of a stereomicroscope in its simplest form. The Porro prisms serve not only to erect the image, but provide a simple means for changing the interocular distance to suit the observer.

The eyepieces are normally three-element construction, with external focal plane. They have about 25% larger fields than conventional microscope eyepieces, and are often termed "widefield" eyepieces.

The objectives are each achromatic doublets. To change power, another objective pair of different focal length must be substituted. This is normally done by mounting several objective pairs on a sliding or revolving nosepiece.

Instead of changing objectives, it is possible also to change lenses within the body of the microscope to achieve a power change. One such system employs parallel light beams beyond the objectives, into which small Galilean telescopes are inserted in either normal or reversed direction. A 2× Galilean system, so used, multiplies the power by either 2 or ½, depending on its orientation. A second pair of Galilean telescopes may similarly give 3× and ⅓×.

A more elaborate power changing system is to make the objectives continuously variable in power. Such systems are known as "zoom" lenses. With these, the field of view is never lost during power change, so that there are no blind spots in converting gradually from low to high power. This is an important point, particularly in teaching, where the student may more easily grasp the relationship of the part to the whole in a biological specimen.

Figure 2 shows a side view of the optical system of a zooming stereomicroscope. The complete system, of course being actually two such systems, arranged to aim at a common object point, as in Figure 1. The zooming lens system comprises three pairs of doublet lenses, the upper two pairs being accurately cam-driven to hold the image in focus as the power is changed.

Figure 3 shows a front view of the cam system used to drive the movable lenses. The power change knob has a gear on its mounting shaft which drives two identical gears on two identical cam shafts. Thus the

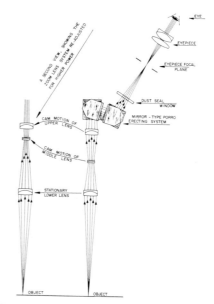

FIG. 2. The optical system of a continuously variable power stereomicroscope. The movable lenses are shown in the two limiting positions of their cam driven motion.

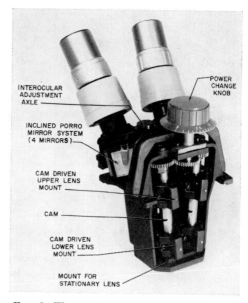

FIG. 3. The mechanical structure of the microscope shown in Figure 2. A single knob drives both cams, thereby synchronizing the power change in both left and right sides of the microscope.

cam-driven lenses move in accurately synchronized motions so that left and right

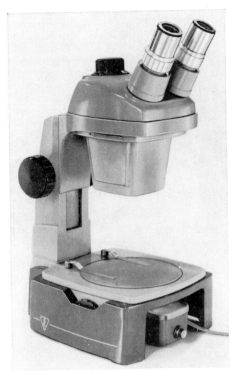

FIG. 4. The assembled zooming stereomicroscope, with built-in fluorescent lamp illuminator.

images are always matched for power, and maintain a constant focus as the image is zoomed. An interesting psychological phenomenon occurs when one zooms such a microscope, in that the image definitely appears to approach at high power and recede at low power, despite the fact that on the grounds of pure physics or geometrical optics, the image lies in the same plane at any power setting. A small insect placed on the stage and viewed at low power assumes a somewhat frightening aspect as one zooms to high power, making the insect appear to be a large creature approaching at a startling rate of speed.

Stereomicroscopes are supplied with a wide variety of stands to hold them and focus them on a great variety of objects, large and small. Also various forms of illumination are made available, such as fluorescent lamps for illumination of transparent objects or spot-light forms of illumination for top or oblique lighting of paque specimens. Figure 4 shows a typical arrangement for a stereomicroscope intended mainly for transmitted light work. The substage illuminator contains two small fluorescent lamps, with a frosted screen to even out the lighting on the specimen.

Historical Background

Early attempts to make stereoscopic microscopes concerned themselves more with the binocular properties than the stereoscopic properties. Indeed many early designs, such as those of Cherubin d'Orleans (*ca.* 1660) were actually pseudoscopic systems, i.e., the left image went to the right eye and vice versa. Wheatstone in 1852 wrote a treatise on binocular vision which stimulated increased interest in the stereomicroscope. Wenham, 1860, is credited with the construction of the first truly stereoscopic microscope, but the forerunner of the modern systems was the twin objective system (Fig. 1) devised by H. S. Greenough in 1897. Improvements in the 1900's consisted of opening up the fields of view and making power change more convenient, culminating in the continuously variable power system introduced in 1959.

J. R. BENFORD

ENGINEERING MICROSCOPE. *See* LIGHT (OPTICAL) MICROSCOPY, p. 439.

"SOLID-IMAGE" MICROSCOPE

For many purposes, such as tracing networks of neural structure in the brain, a normal microscope has the serious limitation that only a thin layer of the specimen can be studied at one time, owing to the limited depth of focus of microscope objectives. When a thin section is examined, only those structures which happen to lie in the plane of the section can be observed. This plane may be confused by such objects as fibers coming away from or toward the plane of the section. A microscope which gave a large

Fig. 1. Gregory "solid image" microscope: left, microcsope in which slide is mounted on steel tuning fork (not shown); right, screen mounted on matched tuning fork upon which synchronous vibrating image is projected. The 2 processes thus provide scanning of specimen in depth giving a "solid image."

depth of field, and which presented the image as a solid in a luminous block in which the structures could be observed in depth would have important advantages over existing optical microscopes. We have designed and constructed a primitive prototype of an instrument giving such a "solid image". It is possible to observe this from any position and to see the structures with appropriate parallax.

The instrument involves two processes. (1) The focal plane of the objective is effectively made to "scan" up and down through the depth of the section. In the prototype instrument, this occurs at a rate of 50 double scans/sec. The slide is mounted on a steel fork tuned to 50 c./s. which is driven by a polarized solenoid energized by a 50 c./s. sine wave. Thus the slide is carried up and down through the focal plane of the objective 50 times/sec. (2) The image is projected on to a screen mounted on a second tuned fork which vibrates at the same rate and in the same phase as the slide carrying the specimen.

Scanning serves to extract the information in depth from the specimen; the second process reconstitutes it in depth, giving a "solid image" in the space swept by the screen. Its frequency of vibration is greater than the fusion frequency for the eye, so that little or no flicker is observed.

Figure 1 is a photograph of the apparatus, in which the tuning fork does not appear. In improved designs an aperiodic drive is superior to the power-economizing tuned fork, for this will not drift in phase with temperature changes as does the tuned fork. The vibrating screen is replaced by a helix driven by a synchronous motor, the image to be projected on a sector near the edge of the helix. A solid glass helix or "circular wedge" is being experimentally tried for changing the focal length of the objective to give scanning without physical movement of the objective or the specimen. With a sinusoidal scan, as used now, it is essential (a) to modulate the intensity of the light by using a high-pressure mercury lamp off mains, and to phase this with velocity; and (b) to chop the light at each half-scan, to cut out the image produced either by the upward or downward scan to prevent the possibility of mis-registration of the 2 sets of images given by a phase error or by asymmetrical wave form of the scan. The substage condenser is extremely important; it must be of high N.A. (numerical aperture) and correctly adjusted.

The instrument was exhibited for the first time in London on May 23, 1960.

REFERENCE

Nature, **182,** 1434 (1958).

Richard L. Gregory

TELEVISION MICROSCOPE

A very simple principle is the basis of the television microscope. In photomicrography a real microscopic image is formed on the photographic emulsion; here it is formed on the receptive surface of the tube of a television camera. In other words, in comparison with the customary manner of using a television camera, the microscope takes the place of a photographic objective as imaging system. The advantages of such an arrangement are due to the characteristics of the television installation and the principles upon which it is based. Thus the application of electronic image transmission permits a spatial separation of the object and the microscope on one hand and the reproduction of the image on the other hand. This at the same time makes it possible to show the microscopic image to any number of observers, also of such objects as are in rooms which for various reasons may not be entered by the observers. This for example can be the case when microscopic images of infectious material are to be shown, or conversely, to avoid the danger of observers carrying infection to tissue cultures. The television microscope can also be advantageously used in the microscopic examination of radioactive objects or objects subjected to radioactivity.

Application of the television microscope in the morphological branches of natural science and medicine have brought about a substantial advance. It is generally recognized that microprojection is a most valuable and almost indispensible aid in these subjects. This is specially true today where the number of instructors stands in a progressively less favorable ratio to the increasing number of students. The size of the projection screen must be increased with the size of the lecture hall and the average distance of the observers from the screen in order that details of the microprojection image be visible from all parts of the auditorium. However, since the brightness of the image decreases as the square of the magnification, a corresponding increase in the intensity of illumination of the object is required to obtain sufficiently bright projected images. Even in lecture halls of average size the limits of a permissible illumination load for the object are already reached with medium microscopic magnifications. Nevertheless, one often encounters the erroneous opinion that the determining limit for microprojection is given by the efficiency of available light sources.

One often encounters the false conception that it suffices, for protection of the object, to filter out the invisible light, especially the heat radiation. However, it is to be kept in mind, at least in microprojection of biological objects with transmitted light, that the illumination load on the object is decisive. A structurally determined absorption by the object is the presupposition for production of image contrast in the most commonly employed bright-field illumination with transmitted light. Independent of its wavelength, the total radiation absorbed by the object is finally converted into heat. If now one compares the size of the receptive surface of a television camera tube having an effective image diagonal of about 15 mm with the diameter of the customary microprojection image of about 1–1.5 mm, and if one further considers that the illumination intensity required on the receptive surface for operation of the camera tube is very low, then it is understandable that one arrives at requirements for illumination of the object which are not substantially greater than those for direct subjective observation.

Herein lies the basis for the decided advantages of the television microscope. As a consequence of the slight illumination load on the object and the possibility of a large

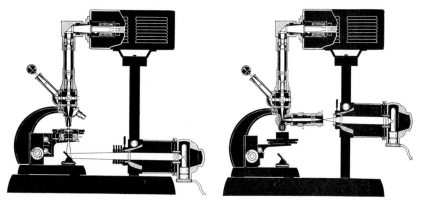

Fɪɢ. 1. Diagram of the path of rays in the Zeiss-Siemens television microscope. Left with transmitted, right with incident light.

number of viewing screens, practically everything visible in the microscope can be shown simultaneously to an audience of any size. Naturally that holds not only for microscopic imaging in bright field with transmitted light, but also for the various imaging procedures with unfavorable light yield, as for example dark-field, phase contrast, or epimicroscopy.

This optical system projects the microscopic image at suitable magnification on the receptive surface of the television camera tube and provides for a continuous magnification regulation in the ratio of 1:3.2 without change of optics as shown in Fig. 1. For incident illumination an auxiliary lens is inserted in the front opening of the lamp carrier in place of the quadruple filter holder. Unexceptionable maintenance of the Koehler illumination principle is assured in each case. The imaging beam is deflected at a right angle from the projective to the television camera by a prism located in an adapter which is screwed into the threaded objective ring of the television camera. A light-excluding tube provides for lightproof connection between adapter and projective.

Operation of the Ziess-Siemens microscope takes place in customary manner. A small remote control desk is located on the table for regulating the television installation.

Cables pass from it as well as from the camera to the central power supply of the television installation. The control monitor with its 17-cm picture tube, set up on the table, is likewise connected with the central power supply. Additional viewing apparatus of optional screen size, number, and distance, and also a television projection receiver are connected by means of a coaxial cable optionally to the central power supply or to a control receiver. Up to three television cameras can be directly connected to this central power supply. They can be applied in a most diversified manner. Since the Siemens television installation is equipped with a so-called automatic gain control, its operation is restricted to switching on and off, and the occasional refocusing of the camera tube and regulating the image brightness of the receivers according to the brightness of the room. This means that during actual use its operation is essentially restricted to manipulation of the microscope and consequently is simpler than that of a microprojection apparatus. Basic considerations and the experience gained thus far indicate unequivocally the advantages of the television principle of microscopy. Adapted from an article by Helmut Haselmann in *Zeiss Werkzeitschrift*, No. 29, p. 42 (Sept., 1958).

G. L. Cʟᴀʀᴋ

543

ULTRAMICROSCOPY

DESIGN AND OPERATION. *See* OPTICAL THEORY
   OF THE LIGHT MICROSCOPE, p. 451.

ULTRASONIC ABSORPTION MICROSCOPE

The desire to explore the world of small scale structure (e.g., biological systems) has furnished at least a portion of the incentive for the development of such devices as the light microscope and the electron microscope. In each case much new information on the microstructure of the system or material studied has resulted.

The light microscope (absorption type) exhibits certain structural features of cellular and subcellular biological organization by means of the contrasting pattern of light and shade resulting from the absorption of electromagnetic energy to different extents by various parts of the structure under examination. The use of various selective staining materials such as dyes, which display different affinity for acidic and basic parts of the tissue structure, permits other aspects of structure to be detected and also raises the possibility of correlating morphology, not directly observable in unstained material, with chemical properties. With the advent of phase contrast microscopy it became possible, without an increase in resolving power, to identify structural features not observable with the light microscope employing the absorption principle.

With the arrival of electron microscopy, new details of cellular structure could be detected because of the higher available resolving power and suitable impregnation methods for producing contrast. These selective impregnation methods result in the retention of salts of heavy metals at certain sites in the structure and thus produce contrast in electron transmission because the scattering power of the elements increase as the atomic number becomes larger (1).

Consideration of the propagation characteristics of acoustical energy in tissue or suspensions of biological material suggested the development of an instrument which can be expected to yield information on the structure of biological systems not obtainable from either light or electron microscopy studies (2, 3). This follows from the fact that the interaction of the sound waves with the tissue structure is of a different nature from that of light or electrons. Experimental results (4, 5, 6) indicate that the protein constituents of tissue are largely responsible for the magnitude of the absorption of acoustic energy in the ultrasonic frequency range. This work also shows that *some* different types of protein molecules, at equal concentrations, absorb sound at different rates (7). Therefore, a suitably designed acoustic instrument could yield information on both spatial distributions and identification of types of protein in tissue. Since this device is only in the early stages of development, this article is concerned with outlining the principles of operation, briefly describing results of measurements on filament models at low resolution, and indicating the results of theoretical calculations of attainable resolution (2, 3).

The results of an approximation analysis of the resolving power of this device are given below. The details are included in reference (3) in which formulas are derived permitting a calculation of the maximum resolving power attainable with present technology. It should be noted here that considerable additional knowledge of tissue structure can be expected from an examina-

544

tion by an "ultrasonic microscope" of less resolving power than that of the light microscope. This follows from the fact that many structural components of biological materials or systems, with different ultrasonic absorption coefficients, may not be detectable at all by the light microscope. There is no *a priori* reason why materials with greatly different ultrasonic absorption coefficients should have either detectably different absorption coefficients or indices of refraction for light.

The principle of operation of the ultrasonic microscope is illustrated in Fig. 1. High frequency sound waves are generated in a "coupling" medium by a piezoelectric crystal vibrating in a thickness mode. The coupling liquid, which fills the irradiation chamber, serves to conduct the sound to and from the movable specimen which is interposed between the crystal and a small thermoelectric probe. (An array of probes can be incorporated for more rapid acquisition of data). The piezoelectric crystal is excited electrically at a mechanical resonant frequency by voltage pulses with a rectangular temporal envelope (carrier frequency equal to the mechanical resonant frequency) of short duration. The small probe detects the acoustic energy level of the sound which passes through the portion of the specimen in its immediate neighborhood. The variation in this transmitted energy level, as a function of the position of the specimen relative to the probe constitutes an acoustic image of the ultrasonically detected structure.

Two mechanisms are involved in the detection of the ultrasound by the thermoelectric probe (8, 9, 10). First, an increase in the temperature of the wire results from the conversion of acoustic energy into heat by the viscous forces acting between the wire and the imbedding fluid medium. Second, acoustic energy is converted into heat by the absorption of sound in the body of the coupling medium which surrounds the

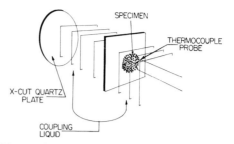

FIG. 1. Schematic representation of the ultrasonic microscope showing the transducer plate which is excited to produce pulses of ultrasound in the coupling liquid, the specimen under examination which is movable in the coupling liquid, and the thermocouple probe whose junction is placed immediately adjacent to the specimen.

probe and specimen. The thermoelectric emf of the probe acts as the input to a DC chopper amplifier (noise level less than 0.01 microvolt), the output of the latter driving the vertical deflection plates of a cathode-ray oscilloscope (see Fig. 2). Thus, when the sound source is driven by a suitable radio frequency pulse, the cathode-ray beam is transiently deflected from its equilibrium position and the magnitude of this deflection is a measure of the relative amount of acoustic energy detected by the probe. As the specimen is moved parallel to the radiating face of the crystal through the pulsed acoustic field, the changing deflection of the cathode-ray beam is observed and recorded. The data are then plotted and a contour "picture" of the disturbance to the sound field distribution, caused by the presence of the specimen, is obtained. The contour picture constitutes an acoustic image of structure in the specimen.

The electronic instrumentation used in the first model of the ultrasonic absorption microscope is illustrated in the block diagram of Fig. 2. A commercial signal generator is used to obtain the radio frequency energy of predetermined frequency. The signal generator is controlled by a keying unit which activates the generator to produce a pulsed output. The keying unit is, in turn, controlled by a digital timing device which

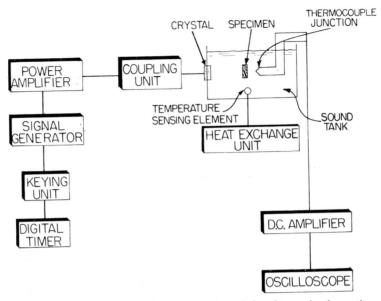

FIG. 2. Block diagram of the electronic instrumentation of the ultrasonic absorption microscope.

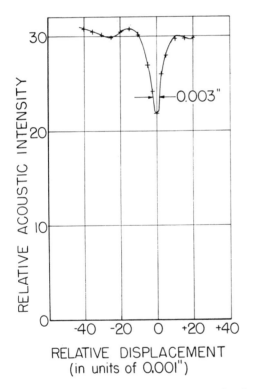

FIG. 3. The detection of the presence, in the coupling liquid, of a 0.003 in. nylon filament by the ultrasonic microscope operating at a frequency of 12 mc/sec.

permits accurate duplication of the duration of the acoustic pulse. A power amplifier stage, driven by the signal generator, is used to provide the power required to drive the piezoelectric transducer. A coupling unit is placed between the power emplifier and the transducer element in order to obtain electrical impedance matching. The electronic driver system must be stable in frequency and amplitude so that artifacts are not introduced into the "picture."

An example of the type of data obtained at relatively low resolution using filament models as test specimens is shown in Fig. 3. Here, a nylon monofilament 0.003 inch in diameter is moved in a plane between the sound source and the probe (which has a maximum dimension of 0.0005 inch in the vicinity of the junction) starting from a position in the field where its presence does not appreciably influence the level of acoustic energy detected by the probe. The direction of movement is parallel to the crystal face and perpendicular to the filament axis. During this motion, the quartz plate is excited to radiate pulses of 12 mc/sec ultrasound with a duration of 0.1 sec. The abscissa of the figure indicates the position of the filament specimen in the plane of movement parallel to the crystal face. The ordinate indicates the relative acoustic intensity detected by the probe, the scale being in units of deflection on the oscilloscope screen. The minimum in the curve corresponds to the position of closest approach of the nylon filament to the probe as the specimen traverses the acoustic field. The presence of the filament at the position of closest approach causes a reduction of 30% in the acoustic intensity below the undisturbed level. At half of this reduction, the curve is 0.007 inch wide and the width is equal to the filament diameter (0.003 in.) at 0.8 of the total reduction. Not all of the observed reduction is produced, in this case, by absorption of sound within the nylon. Since there is a mismatch in acoustic impedance between the coupling liquid and the filament of at least 10%, some of the incident acoustic energy is scattered. In addition, some of the sound energy is converted to heat at the interface between the nylon filament and the coupling liquid as a result of the viscous forces acting there.

Measurements similar to those shown in Fig. 2, but obtained with copper filaments of 0.001 inch diameter in the field, demonstrate that at an operating frequency of 12 mc/sec, model structures of this type with a diameter of 25 microns can be resolved.

An approximation analysis (3) (based on formulas derived to describe the behaviour of a thermoelectric probe in a pulsed acoustic field) (8, 9, 10) of the operation of the ultrasonic microscope indicates that a structure with a "radius" of 0.4 micron and having an acoustic intensity absorption coefficient per unit path length differing from the average value of the specimen by 5% should be detectable if the following acoustic and other parameters are employed: frequency—1,000 mc/sec., ultrasonic intensity—1,000 watts/cm², acoustic pulse duration—0.1 microsecond, and thermocouple lead diameter-0.1

micron. A convenient pulse repetition rate for rapid assimilation of data would be 1000 pps. The "radius" of the structure is defined to be that distance from its center at which the deviation of the absorption coefficient from the average value of the surroundings is down to 0.7 of the maximum deviation. If the absorption coefficient of the structure differs from the average by a greater percentage, then a smaller structure can be detected.

Note added in proof:

Since the preparation of this article, techniques have been developed for producing sound fields of appreciable amplitude in high absorption liquids to 500 mc–sec and for fabricating thermoelectric detectors having maximum dimensions in the vicinity of the junction of 5 microns (11).

REFERENCES

1. See appropriate sections of this encylopedia for comprehensive descriptions of light, phase-contrast and electron microscopy.
2. DUNN, F., AND FRY, W. J., *J. Acoust. Soc. Am.*, **31**, 632–633 (1959).
3. FRY, W. J., AND DUNN, F., "Physical Techniques in Biological Research," ed. W. L. Nastuck, Academic Press, New York (to be published, 1961).
4. CARSTENSEN, E. L., AND SCHWAN, H. P., "Ultrasound in Biology and Medicine," ed. E. Kelly, Am. Inst. Biol. Sci., Washington, D. C. (1957).
5. SCHWAN, H. P., AND CARSTENSEN, E. L., WADC Tech. Rept. 56-389, Wright Air Development Center (1956).
6. CARSTENSEN, E. L., AND SCHWAN, H. P., *J. Acoust. Soc. Am.*, **31**, 185–189 (1959).
7. CARSTENSEN, E. L., AND SCHWAN, H. P., *J. Acoust. Soc. Am.*, **31**, 305–311 (1959).
8. FRY, W. J., AND FRY, R. B., *J. Acoust. Soc. Am.*, **26**, 294–310 (1954).
9. FRY, W. J., AND FRY, R. B., *J. Acoust. Soc. Am.*, **26**, 311–317 (1954).
10. DUNN, F., AND FRY, W. J., I.R.E. Trans. on Ultrasonic Engineering, PGUE-5, 59-65 (1957).
11. DUNN, F., *J. Acoust. Soc. Am.*, **32** (1960).

FLOYD DUNN AND WM. J. FRY

Ultraviolet Microscopy

BASIC PRINCIPLES AND DESIGN

The wavelength region of the visible spectrum is 400 to 700 mμ. The adjacent shorter wavelength region (100 to 400 mμ) is the (invisible) ultraviolet region. Below 100 mμ, air absorption restricts the transmission of ultraviolet, and this region is called the "vacuum ultraviolet" region.

Inasmuch as resolving power is proportional to wavelength, it is possible to resolve finer structure in ultraviolet than in visible radiation. Also, since many biological materials have absorption bands in the ultraviolet, their microstructure may, by the use of the ultraviolet microscope, be rendered visible without resort to staining.

The ultraviolet microscope differs from the conventional light microscope in that it includes means for converting the invisible ultraviolet image into a visible image. Furthermore, since optical glasses do not transmit ultraviolet, other materials, notably fluorite and fused quartz, are used for lens elements, and mirror systems often are used in place of refracting optics. These same differences also apply to the illuminating system, and of course, the source itself is different, since it must emit in the ultraviolet rather than the visible, and cannot be enclosed in a glass envelope, since glass absorbs the ultraviolet.

Conversion of the ultraviolet to visible energy is accomplished by (1) photography, (2) fluorescence, (3) television type receptor tubes, (4) flying spot television techniques, or (5) photoemissive image-converter tubes.

Early History. Koehler (1) developed the first optical systems for ultraviolet microscopy in about 1904, his work being aimed toward the goal of increased resolving power due to the use of shorter wavelengths. Microscopes made in accordance with Koehler's design were made by the Zeiss firm. The objectives were monochromats, i.e., corrected for only one wavelength in the ultraviolet. Photography was used to render the image visible. Work with this instrument was difficult, and apparently very little real application was made of it.

Spectral Absorption. In the 1930's, interest in ultraviolet was revived by the work of T. Caspersson (2, 3) in Sweden, and J. Loofbourow (4, 5) in the United States, in studying the spectral absorption properties of various biochemicals. With ultraviolet, these men found that it was possible to photograph live unstained tissue sections and tissue cultures, and to differentiate various normal and abnormal cells by their absorption characteristics.

Objective Designs. Studies of this nature led to a re-activation in the field of ultraviolet microscope design improvement. L. V. Foster (6), described in 1946, an achromatic objective composed of fused quartz and fluorite for use in a sufficiently broad range in the ultraviolet, so that a fluorescent screen could be used for focusing. Interest in spectral absorption studies, however, led to the demand for still greater wavelength range, and mirror type objectives were designed by Brumberg (7), Burch (8), and Grey (9) to fulfill this requirement.

The most widely used of these are the Grey designs, which employ a combination of reflecting and refracting optics to achieve good correction over a large wavelength range with very little central obscuration by the mirror system. The refracting elements are of fused quartz and fluorite Fig. 1, shows the construction of the 0.72 N. A. Grey design as made by Bausch & Lomb. This objective is corrected for the complete spectral range from 254 mμ to 700 mμ, hence is useful in applications where focusing is accomplished in the visible for photography in the ultraviolet.

Sources of Ultraviolet Energy. The noisy and odorous cadmium spark, originally used as the source for ultraviolet, has been replaced by the quartz-jacketed mercury arc. Combination glass and liquid chemical filters have been replaced by the grating monochromator, which provides simple and convenient means for changing and selecting desired ultraviolet wavelength regions.

Viewing Systems. Perhaps the most difficult technical problem in the design of the ultraviolet microscope has been that of achieving a receptor to permit seeing the image. All of the early work used photography with trial and error search for best focus. Later the fluorescent screen was employed, but the image was generally too grainy and dim for much useful work.

The advent of high-speed processing of photographic film led to the possibility of only a very short time delay between exposure of the film and seeing the image. The "color translating microscope" developed by the Polaroid Corporation utilized this technique. Three adjacent frames of ultraviolet sensitive film were exposed rapidly in sequence to three pre-selected wavelengths in the ultraviolet. The film was rapidly developed, fixed, and projected onto a viewing screen. Each frame was projected through a primary color filter, and the images, optically superimposed on the screen, formed a composite three-color image. This instrument was, of course, extremely expensive, and its use, accordingly, severely restricted.

Television image scanning techniques have also provided means for seeing ultraviolet images. Two basically different approaches have been used in applying television apparatus and methods. In one, called the "flying spot microscope" (q.v.) an ultraviolet-emitting cathode ray tube face is located in what is normally the image plane of a photomicrographic set-up. The microscope, acting in reverse, forms a greatly reduced image of the cathode ray tube face

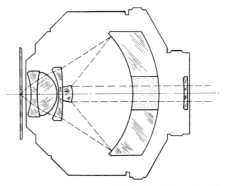

Fig. 1. The 53X, 0.72 N.A. Catadioptric objective for ultraviolet, designed by D. S. Grey and manufactured by Bausch & Lomb. Refracting elements are of fluorite and fused quartz.

on the specimen. An ultraviolet sensitive photomultiplier tube picks up the signal transmitted by the specimen, as it is scanned, and the energy signal from the photomultiplier is converted to a visual image on a conventional cathode ray tube, which is tuned to the same sweep frequency as the illuminating cathode ray tube. The particular virtue of this "flying spot" system is the low dosage of ultraviolet concentrated on the specimen, since prolonged exposure to ultraviolet is lethal to most living specimens. Its disadvantage is the technical difficulty of attaining a satisfactory means of varying the wavelength of the ultraviolet emitted from the cathode ray tube.

Another television type solution to the problem is to use a conventional ultraviolet source and monochromator to illuminate the microscope, and to pick up the image on an ultraviolet sensitive image-orthicon, and by means of a closed circuit television sending and receiving set-up, view the image on a conventional television screen.

Both of these television systems share the basic problems of the color translating microscope, that is, they are extremely costly and elaborate to build, and require considerable training and skill to keep in good operating condition. Because of the complexity of these systems, their use has been

549

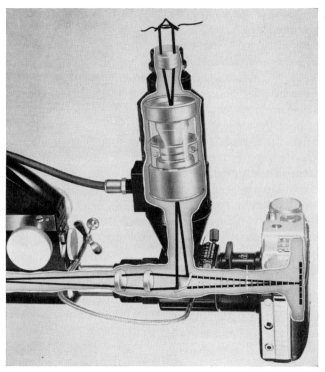

Fig. 2. The RCA "Ultrascope" image-converter tube used as an ultraviolet viewer and pre-focusing device for photography in the Bausch & Lomb Ultraviolet Photomicroscope.

limited to a very small number of research organizations.

In 1959, RCA introduced an ultraviolet image converter tube, which greatly simplified the technique and equipment needed to see an ultraviolet image. The tube called an "Ultrascope", employs a photoemissive cathode, a single-stage electron imaging system, and a fluorescent screen to convert the ultraviolet image into a light image. The double conversion is thus ultraviolet to electrons to visible.

Figure 2 shows the manner in which this converter tube is mounted on an ultraviolet microscope. A small removable mirror deflects the ultraviolet image to the Ultrascope tube, or when withdrawn permits photography of the image, as seen and focused by the Ultrascope tube. This equipment represents a tremendous simplification over previous ultraviolet viewing systems, and gives promise of creating new and expanding interest in this field of research.

REFERENCES

1. *Zeit. f. Wiss. Mickros.*, **21**, 129, 273 (1904).
2. *Skand. Arch. Physiol.*, **73** (1936).
3. *Nature*, **143**, 602 (1939).
4. *Bull. Basic Sci. Res.*, **5**, 46 (1933).
5. *J. Opt. Soc. Am.*, **29**, 535 (1939).
6. *J. Opt. Soc. Am.*, **38**, 689 (1948).
7. *Bull. Acad. Sci.*, USSR, **6**, 32 (1942).
8. *Proc. Phys. Soc.* (*London*), **59**, 41 (1947).
9. *J. Opt. Soc. Am.*, **39**, 719, 723 (1949).

J. R. Benford

COLOR TRANSLATING TV ULTRAVIOLET MICROSCOPE

Aim of the New Design. The electronic color translating TV ultraviolet microscope, designed by scientists of Neutronics Research Company, is the most recent means for studying the topography, chemical similarities and dissimilarities, and the absorption spectrum of cellular components, synthetic and natural fibers, crystals, and amorphous substances. Its usefulness enters fields of investigation in biology, medicine, physics, and metallurgy as well as organic, inorganic, and physical chemistry.

Operation. The Model ME-101a TV ultraviolet microscope essentially consists of a triple monochromator system, which sequentially illuminates a specimen at three easily preselected ultraviolet wavelengths down to 2400A. The microscope proper provides coarse and fine adjustments for the condenser and objective, which consist of $53\times$ apochromatized catadioptric lenses furnished with the microscope. The objective fine focus is in steps of one micron. The specimen slide rests on a microscope stage, which allows circular and x–y movements. The three sequential UV beams are then picked up by the projection eyepiece ($3.5\times$ and $10\times$) which projects the absorption images of the specimen on to the three UV-Vidicon tubes of the color television cameras. The UV wavelength separation is achieved by means of a rotating mirror system. Each vidicon is associated with a primary color in a closed loop color television system. The presence of a specific color in the image on the 15″ television monitor screen indicates transmission of the corresponding ultraviolet wavelength. A camera is provided to obtain color photographs of the television monitor screen display. Magnifications from specimen to screen of about $4,000\times$ to $25,000\times$ are possible. Resolution, under favorable conditions, is of the order of 0.3 micron. Variations in hue correspond to differences in transmission spectra and thus indicate differences in chemical composition. Variations in optical density (with no color difference) indicate various amounts of material of the same absorption spectrum in the light path.

The line analyzing microspectrophotometer simultaneously displays the point-to-point absorption variation for any selected ultraviolet wavelength by extracting any one of the horizontal scan lines in the color television monitor for display on the line analyzer 5″ screen. A dry processing camera is provided to obtain permanent records of the transmission curves.

Since specimen illumination for any wavelength is not continuous but occurs in the form of about 14 millisecond long pulses, the problem of irradiation damage to cells is minimized.

The use of three TV cameras overcomes the serious problem of color carry-over.

Applications. The microscope is intended for quantitative and qualitative investigations from 2400A to 6000A. To a major extent, investigations to date have been in the medical field in the examination of cells (living, stained, or unstained) for determining chemical similarities and dissimilarities of objects within the specimen as well as the structure and topography of the cell. Microchemical analysis can be performed by this technique. Unstained and living specimens, which are entirely colorless when viewed in visible light, give results comparable to a selectively stained sample. For instance, at 2800A, absorption coincides closely with areas rich in proteins containing amino acids, which would take an acid stain such as eosin; on the other hand, areas which absorb heavily at 2600A often correspond to those that take basic stains indicating the presence of nucleic acid.

Focusing and area selection are performed as in ordinary microscopy except that eye strain is reduced to a minimum since the operator need only watch the color TV screen during these operations.

G. L. CLARK

551

IMAGE FORMATION BY A FRESNEL ZONE PLATE*

This article describes experiments in the use of a new type of Fresnel zone plate for image formation with visible light and ultraviolet radiation. Tests with visible light and ultraviolet down to 2537 A are described below followed by a description of our plans to extend these tests down to about 100 A. There is good reason to believe that the same zone plate will operate over a large range of wavelengths from the soft x-ray region through the infrared because its transparent zones are completely open. Therefore, it is opportune to speculate on the possibility of using the zone plate to focus even other radiations and particles. First, however, let us consider the motives that prompted us to construct this zone plate for soft x-ray and extreme ultraviolet radiation.

Early research in the means of focusing light was motivated in part by interest in the construction of microscopes and telescopes. These instruments were, after all, the earliest "space probes" into both the intermolecular and extragalactic worlds. Later, the properties of the electromagnetic spectrum outside of the visible region prompted natural extensions of image-forming devices into the near infrared and the ultraviolet.

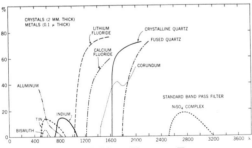

TRANSMISSIVITY (I/I₀) OF VARIOUS TRANSPARENT SUBSTANCES

FIG. 1. The transmissivity of several materials in the ultraviolet. The crystalline materials that might serve for lenses cease to show any appreciable transmission below 1000 A. The thin metal films could serve as filters.

---

* See also "X-Ray Telescope for 1–100 A Region," in "Encyclopedia of Spectroscopy," p. 778.

Today similar motives exist for the construction of microscopes and telescopes to work in the soft x-ray and extreme ultraviolet (hereafter referred to as euv) region. While no definite bounds exist for the euv region we shall limit our study to wavelengths from 10 A to about 1000 A. Although the developments in x-ray microscopy and microradiography have already been responsible for two international congresses (1, 2), the new interest in telescopes that can operate in the soft x-ray and euv regions stems chiefly from discoveries in astrophysics.

Rocket experiments have already demonstrated that solar, stellar and interstellar sources of euv exist (3), but the earth's atmosphere prevents most of the radiations shorter than 3000 A from reaching its surface. The advent of rocket and satellite-borne experiments justifies serious consideration of telescopes and spectrographs sensitive to wavelengths between 1 A and 3000 A.

We distinguish between instruments, such as lenses and mirrors, whose main function is to form optical images and those such as prisms and gratings, whose purpose is to produce dispersion. Our interest for the present is primarily in image formation. The classical means of focusing visible light for image formation involve reflection (mirrors) and refraction (lenses). Proper choice of materials allows the use of reflectors and refractors in the ultraviolet from 3000 A to about 1000 A. Between 1000 A and 10 A refraction is out of the question because most materials are opaque to radiation in this region. Special types of glass (4) have been developed which can transmit about 70 per cent at 2200 A through a thickness of 1 mm. But this is exceptional since the transmission of most types of glass drops essentially to zero below 3000 A. Although transmission of wavelengths below 10 A does occur, the index of refraction is so close to unity that refraction is impractical.

The transmission of several materials is shown in Fig. 1 (5). Except for thin films

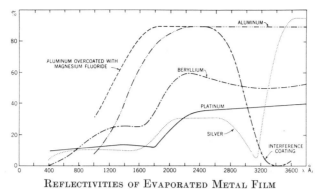

REFLECTIVITIES OF EVAPORATED METAL FILM

FIG. 2. Normal incidence reflectivities of various materials in the ultraviolet. Aluminum overcoated with magnesium fluoride gives useful reflectivity even below 1000 A. Below 400 A there is a dearth of experimental information on reflectivity.

of aluminum, tin, indium, and bismuth, as shown, (22) the materials of which lenses might be made cannot transmit below 1000 A. Below this wavelength, then, lenses are apparently not worth considering.

How about mirrors? Anastigmatic image formation with a single mirror requires good reflectivity at normal or near-normal incidence. Recently Hass (6) and his co-workers have developed coatings of evaporated metal films which, when deposited on glass or other materials, produce high reflectivities down to fairly short wavelengths. Fig. 2 (5) summarizes the characteristics of some of the best coatings. The data show trends rather than authoritative values. For these the reader is referred to the modern literature.[6, 21] For wavelengths shorter than 585A the Fresnel zone plate may find application as a recurring device. Nevertheless, one must not exclude the possibility of using very large mirrors with very low reflectivities.

For angles of incidence close to 90° it becomes convenient to speak of the "grazing incidence angle," that is, the complement of the usual angle of incidence, which is the angle subtended by the incident ray and the normal to the reflecting surface. For x-rays, the phenomenon of total reflection at grazing incidence is well known (7, 8). The reflectivity is 100 per cent because the index of refraction for most materials is less than unity. Point-to-point grazing-incidence systems for forming images have been built by Kirkpatrick and his students (9, 10, 11), but reflection from a single curved mirror at grazing incidence is highly astigmatic and can be corrected only by the difficult technique of crossed mirrors. Systems of this type have not been developed for wavelengths as long as 100 A but they may have to be considered.

If we restrict ourselves to the less formidable process of image formation by normal incidence reflection at a single surface, we can probably conclude that a region exists, somewhere between 10 A and 1000 A, where image formation by reflection or refraction is either difficult or impossible.

Zone Plate for Focusing Extreme Ultraviolet and Soft X-Radiation

Diffraction offers still another way of bending light to produce focusing. Several such methods have been suggested (12, 13) but even the simplest, the Fresnel zone plate (14, 15) has not received serious use in any region of the spectrum, let alone that between 10 and 1000 A. Several writers have noted that Fresnel zone plates might be used for image formation in this difficult region, but no successful attempts to build a zone plate for x-rays or euv have come to this author's attention.

This paper describes the construction and

use of a Fresnel zone plate whose opaque bands are made of thin gold and whose open bands are completely transparent to radiation between 10 A and 1000 A, because they are empty.

A Fresnel zone plate consists of alternately opaque and transparent bands bounded by circles of radii

$$r_n = r_1\sqrt{n}; \qquad n = 1, 2, 3, \cdots \quad (1)$$

Its principal focal length, f, obeys the simple relation

$$f\lambda = r_1^2, \qquad (2)$$

where λ is the wavelength, and r_1 is the radius of the central circle.

In considering the focusing of x-rays for microscopy we see that the product $f\lambda$ can be disturbingly small. For example, in an x-ray microscope one might consider $f = 1$ cm and $\lambda = 1$ A. This requires $r_1^2 = f\lambda = 10^{-8}$ cm^2 or $r_1 = 10^{-4}$ cm or one micron. By Eq. 1 we find that the width of the nth zone is

$$s_n = (\sqrt{n+1} - \sqrt{n})r_1, \qquad (3)$$

which, for large n is approximated by

$$s_n = \frac{r_1}{2\sqrt{n}}, \qquad (4)$$

If, for example, $n = 25$ and $r_1 = 10^{-4}$ cm, then $s_n = 10^{-4}/2\sqrt{25}$ cm $= 10^{-5}$ cm or 0.1 micron. Since the best photographic emulsions (e.g., Eastman 649 spectroscopic plates) have a resolution of about a micron, a zone plate made to these specifications looks impossible indeed. The product $f\lambda$ needs to be considerably larger before zone plates look feasible. Fortunately, the current interest in the use of x-rays and euv in microscopy and astrophysics can lead to larger values of both f and λ.

Consider λ first. Wavelengths much longer than 1 A are important for different reasons. In x-ray microscopy, for example, there has been a trend towards wavelengths approaching 100 A because microscopic objects of biological interest have low atomic numbers and their differential absorption is therefore greater in this region (16). On the other hand, the wavelengths from 10 to 100 A, which are very long x-rays, are considered very short compared with the wavelengths of ultraviolet radiation, and are of potential interest in astrophysics. Also, the lines around 150 A and 300 A emitted by the sun's corona would be of interest as sources for telescopic image formation (19).

Now consider the focal length, f. In microscopes we want f to be small, but in a telescope a long focal length is an advantage; in fact, a focal length of 100 cm would be practical and one of 1000 cm, though somewhat large, is not completely beyond possibility if we could build the right kind of platform. The reader must bear in mind that the ultimate platform for telescopes operating in the soft x-ray and extreme ultraviolet regions must be a satellite orbiting above the earth's atmosphere.

To choose figures of the right order of magnitude, consider $f = 100$ cm and $\lambda = 100$ A. Using $n = 25$ we get $s_n = r_1/2\sqrt{n} = 10^{-3}$ cm or ten microns. This value is about ten times the resolving power of the finest-grained photographic films and makes the construction of a zone plate for soft x-rays seem feasible.

However, a zone plate made by exposing a photographic film would be useless in the region between 10 and 100 A because the base on which the emulsion rests, and even the emulsion layer itself, are practically opaque to these wavelengths.

Recently we have succeeded in producing a zone plate whose opaque elements are thin concentric bands of gold made self-supporting by the use of thin radial struts (see Fig. 3). The streaks in the photograph are imperfections in the form of very thin filament-like pieces of gold. The outer diameter of the zone plate is 0.2596 ± 0.0002 cm. The central circle has a diameter of 0.0426 ± 0.0002 cm. The bands are bounded by circles whose radii obey the relation $r_n =$

$0.0213\sqrt{n}$, $n = 1, 2 \cdots 38$. For a zone plate with a large number of rings the more precise formula for r_n would be needed,

$$r_n = \sqrt{fn\lambda} \; \sqrt{1 + n\lambda/4f}. \qquad (5)$$

The narrowest band was designed to measure 0.0017 cm in width. Actually it varied between 0.0010 and 0.0020 cm. The zone plate was made for us by the Buckbee Mears Company of St. Paul, Minnesota. As far as we know this is the first zone plate with transparent regions that are completely open (except for the supporting radial struts). The images formed are very sharp, comparing favorably with those made by lenses of similar focal length and aperture (see Fig. 9). We may suggest one explanation for the good quality obtained with these zone plates as compared with that of the photographically based zone plates. The phase condition that requires an increment of exactly one wavelength between successive transparent bands must be difficult to meet with a film base many microns thick that is not held to optical flatness. This condition is probably less difficult to meet with the new zone plate that has no film base at all.

Since the transparent regions of the zone plate are completely clear they should transmit radiation of all wavelengths. The gold bands are practically opaque to all radiations between 10 and 1000 A; therefore, the zone plate should be able to focus soft x-rays and euv in this region. Of course, it can also operate in the visible and infrared regions. It should also work with particles having wave-like characteristics of the proper wavelength, but our present interest is in the soft x-ray and euv region.

Our first zone plate, with which all the tests reported in this article were made, was designed to have a focal length of about 400 cm at 100 A. At 4000 A its focal length is 10 cm; it thus lent itself very conveniently to tests with visible light. All the tests described below with the exception of those at 2537 A were made with visible light. We

FIG. 3. An enlarged photograph of the self-supported gold zone plate used in these experiments. The diameter of the outer circle is 0.2596 ± 0.0002 cm. The central circle has a diameter of 0.0426 ± 0.0002 cm. The thickness of the gold is estimated as 10 microns. The white bands representing the transparent regions are completely open and hence will transmit electromagnetic radiation of all wavelengths.

plan to continue tests at 100 A and 1000 A with newly acquired sources.

Resolution

Theoretically, the smallest angular separation, $\theta_{\min}$, between two monochromatic point sources at infinity that can just be resolved when imaged by a zone plate, can be shown (14) to obey the Rayleigh criterion for a lens:

$$\sin \theta_{\min} = 1.22 \; (\lambda/D). \qquad (6)$$

Here λ is the wavelength and D the diameter of the outermost circle of the zone plate. To test this relation we used fine mesh screens as objects, illuminating them by transmission as shown in Fig. 4. In Eq. 6 we could vary λ, the wavelength being used, but not D, as all our zone plates had the same diameter, approximately 0.26 cm. A zone plate is a highly chromatic device, having a focal length that is inversely proportional to the wavelength. We used filters to monochromatize the radiation or

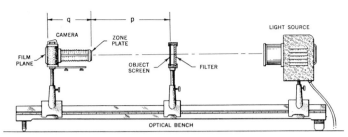

FIG. 4. The layout of the apparatus on the optical bench. The light source consisted of a tungsten filament lamp and a condensing lens system. For the experiments at 2537 A the source was a 4-watt General Electric germicidal lamp, No. GT4/1. The filters are described in the text. The zone plate was mounted at the open end of a bellows extension. The camera was an Exakta VX IIa. Eastman Kodak Microfile Contrast Copy film was used throughout, processed in D 19. Object and image distances are labeled p and q, respectively.

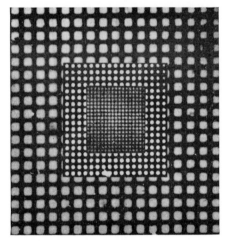

FIG. 5. Pictures of a mesh with 4 lines per mm taken with the zone plate at three different wavelengths. Working out from the center we see pictures taken at 6700 A, 4358 A, and 2537 A, in sizes proportional to the original image sizes obtained with a fixed object-to-zone plate distance of 47 cm. The shorter wavelength results not only in a longer focal length and hence a larger image size but also in improved resolution. See also Fig. 6.

exhibit the improvement in resolution from red light to ultraviolet. For example, in Fig. 5, three pictures of the same object mesh made with the zone plate are shown superimposed on one another to exhibit the ratio of the sizes in which the original pictures appeared when taken with red (6700 A), blue (4358 A) and ultraviolet (2537 A) light. The increase in image size results from the fact that the focal length of the zone plate increases as the wavelength decreases, while the object distance, p, remains fixed at 47 cm. This increase in image size alone, can bring about an improvement in signal-to-background ratio, but notice that an improvement in resolution has also taken place. The ultraviolet picture is not only the largest; it is the best resolved because it was made at the shortest wavelength.

To exhibit this improvement in resolution apart from the change in magnification, the pictures of Fig. 5 were enlarged photographically so that the distance between squares remained constant. The improved resolution becomes clearer. In Fig. 6 (left), p equaled 47 cm and q was adjusted to 7.2 cm, a value that produced the best focus experimentally for a wavelength of 6700 A. A gelatin filter was used with a pass band of about 400 A. The object mesh had 4 lines per mm. The angle subtended at the zone plate by two successive centers of open mesh

relied on the strength of a spectral line, as in the case of the 2537 A source, to produce approximately monochromatic radiation. The object distance, p, and the image distance, q, (Fig. 4) were chosen to exhibit the improvement in resolution that accompanies the use of shorter wavelengths. We operated in a region close to the limit of resolution. The parameters were purposely chosen to

was 0.00053 radian, which is 1.68 $\theta_{\min}$ for that wavelength.

The center picture of Fig. 6 was made at $p = 47$ cm, $q = 12.5$ cm, at a wavelength of 4358 A. A Baird interference filter with a total pass band of about 100 A was used. Here the angular separation between adjacent centers is 2.59 $\theta_{\min}$. An improvement in resolution is apparent.

Fig. 6 (right) shows an image of the same mesh taken at 2537 A. The value of p remained fixed at 47 cm, q was 27 cm and the angular separation between object centers was now 4.44 $\theta_{\min}$. The source was a General Electric germicidal lamp number GT4/1. The manufacturer states that this lamp yields 60 % of its energy at 2537 A. A filter was used to remove the visible radiation, but the monochromatic effect at 2537 A is due only to the relative intensity of this line. This demonstrates a point about zone plate focusing that may be useful in ultraviolet and x-ray astronomy: a relatively intense and isolated spectral line may preclude the use of filters. These pictures lead us to believe that the resolution will continue to improve in a predictible way as we go down first to 1000 A and later to 100 with our zone plate.

Comparison of Zone Plate with Pinhole and Lens

Next we compared the image-forming qualities of our zone plate with those of a pinhole. The pinhole size was calculated to give the optimum resolution for the chosen values of λ, p, and q. The optimum diameter for such a pinhole is given by the expression (17)

$$d = 2 \sqrt{\frac{0.9pq}{p+q}}. \qquad (7)$$

This may also be written $d = 2\sqrt{0.9 f\lambda}$ which, interestingly enough, is very close to the diameter of the innermost circle of a zone plate that gives good focus at the same distances and for the same wavelength. In

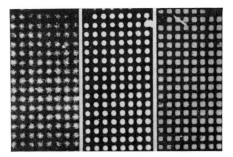

FIG. 6. The pictures of Fig. 5 are here enlarged to produce equal image sizes. From left to right, they were made at 6700 A, 4358 A, and 2537 A. The angles subtended at the zone plate by two adjacent midpoints of the open area of the object mesh were 1.68 $\theta_{\min}$, 2.59 $\theta_{\min}$, and 4.44 $\theta_{\min}$, where $\theta_{\min}$ is the theoretical minimum angle of resolution computed at the respective wavelengths. The improvement in resolution with shorter wavelength is apparent.

other words, the pinhole behaves like a zone plate with a single circular opening.

Fig. 7 is a picture of a mesh with 4 lines per mm framed by the lines of a coarser screen with 0.7 lines per mm, made with the pinhole at a wavelength of 4358 A. With the same screens as an object and all other factors the same, a picture was taken with the zone plate instead of the pinhole, with the results shown in Fig. 8. The angular separation, at $p = 26.7$ cm, between adjacent centers of the smaller screen pattern was 5.3×10^{-4} radian or 4.5 $\theta_{\min}$, as computed for the zone plate. Theoretically, the improvement in resolution of the zone plate over that of the pinhole is a factor $\sqrt{n}$ or 6.23 for our zone plate of 38 rings. The actual improvement as demonstrated in Figs. 7 and 8 is quite apparent.

The zone plate has another advantage over a pinhole in that the light flux reaching the image is greater with the zone plate, so that much less exposure time is required if all other factors have been left unchanged. In our notation, n stands for the number of circles in the zone plate pattern. Hence $n/2$ is the number of open zones or bands. The expected improvement in exposure should

557

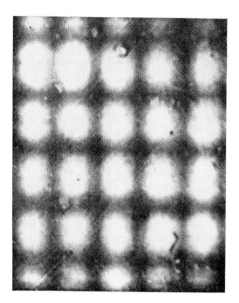

FIG. 7. An object consisting of a coarse grid, one rectangle of which measures 1.43 mm by 1.72 mm, within which there is a fine mesh with 4 lines per mm, photographed through a pinhole whose aperture was chosen to produce the optimum resolution for the wavelength and distances involved. Only the coarse grid is resolved. Compare this with Fig. 8.

be $n/2$ since all the zones have equal areas. For our zone plate, $n/2 = 19$. The actual exposure time used for the pinhole was 40 times greater than that required for the zone plate. Since the densities of the plates were compared only by eye the experimental values do not seem out of line.

Next we compared the resolution of our zone plate with that of a lens of similar focal length, of aperture equivalent to that of the zone plate. For both the lens and the zone plate $f = 10.2$ cm and $D = 0.26$ cm. Fig. 9 (right) shows the image of a screen with 4 lines per mm photographed with the lens, and Fig. 9 (left) shows the same screen photographed with the zone plate. Adjacent centers of the object screen subtended an angle equal to 2.6 θ_{min}. Other constants were $p = 47$ cm, $q = 13$ cm, and $\lambda = 4358$ A. The lens had a simple plano-convex form. If a highly corrected camera lens had been

chosen the comparison might have favored the lens, but since it was stopped down to $f/18$ and the field covered was not very large, it was not subjected to undue demands

FIG. 8. The object of Fig. 7 photographed through a zone plate, with all other factors fixed except the exposure. The exposure time required for the pinhole picture was about 40 times greater than that used for the zone plate picture.

FIG. 9. Comparison of a lens and a zone plate as image forming devices near the limit of resolution. On the left is a picture of a fine mesh screen taken with a zone plate. On the right is a picture of the same screen taken with a plano-convex lens of similar aperture and focal length. All other factors were kept the same except the exposure which was 20 times greater for the zone plate. The wavelength used was 4358 A. If the exposure comparison had been made at 1000 A the results would have been much more favorable for the zone plate.

as an image-forming device. We can conclude that the zone plate image compares favorably with that of the lens.

The zone plate was about 20 times slower than the lens for the following reason: in the vector diagram representing the amplitude of the waves that pass through successive Fresnel zones, the continually changing phase produces a spiral (Fig. 10). In Fresnel's treatment of the contributions of successive circular zones, the amplitude of the contribution due to one zone is represented by the vector AB. The length of the arc ABC, starting at A and ending at C, would be proportional to the amplitude produced by two zones of a lens (since the lens has the property of orienting all the infinitesimal vectors in the same direction). The ratio of these amplitudes is approximately π. The ratio of intensities would be π^2. This argument would hold for a perfect zone plate, that is, one in which the width of an opaque band never exceeded the mathematically computed value of s_n.

With the real zone plate, the widths of all the gold bands are greater than the theoretical value of s_n, thereby reducing the intensity of the light gathered at the focus. A perfect zone plate introduces the factor π^2 and inaccuracies in manufacture introduce a factor of about 2, making the ratio approximately $2\pi^2$ which is about twenty. This means that a single zone plate is not a very efficient gatherer of light when compared with a lens. However, with sufficiently intense sources it can produce images with good resolution. Certainly the resolution and light gathering power are much better than those of a pinhole. We conclude that the zone plate is much better than a pinhole both in resolution and light-gathering power; it is comparable to a lens in resolution but about twenty times slower than a lens of similar aperture when used with visible light.

To overcome the intensity limitation the method of superposition of images could be

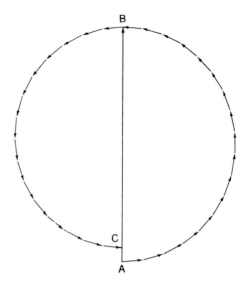

FIG. 10. The vector AB represents the resultant of the infinitesimal vectors contributed by the sub-zones of one open Fresnel zone in a zone plate. The *length* of the arc ABC represents the amplitude of the contributions due to two successive Fresnel zones in a lens. The continuously changing thickness of a lens causes the infinitesimal vectors to line up since they all have the same phase. The ratio of the length of the arc ABC to the length AB is approximately π.

used. It has been shown (18) that n pictures of the same object each exposed for a time t (where t would yield an underexposed negative) give negatives which when superimposed produce an image comparable in exposure to that of a single picture exposed for a time nt. Intead of photographic recording some form of electronic readout might be used to integrate the signals from n zone plates and produce an exposure in t seconds that ordinarily would have required nt seconds. Because noise increases along with the signal, the advantages in resolution are not simply multiplied n times. Nevertheless, a gain does result from this technique and since zone plates may eventually be produced fairly cheaply, it is conceivable that the signals received simultaneously from many zone plates could be integrated advantageously.

559

Conclusion

In summary, then, we have produced a Fresnel zone plate consisting of a set of gold bands supported by radial struts, leaving alternate bands almost completely empty, thereby making possible the transmission and focusing of soft x-rays and extreme ultraviolet radiations. We have tested it in visible light and in the ultraviolet only as far as 2537 A. All tests indicate that the experimental resolution and transmissivity are what one would expect from simple theoretical considerations. This means that from the point of view of resolution and exposure the zone plate is a great improvement over a pinhole. It compares favorably in resolution, but not in speed, with a simple lens, if we make the comparison in the visible region. Below 1000 A, however, the speed of the zone plate would be thousands or millions of times greater than that of a lens made of any known material. All the experimental evidence now in existence seems to indicate that there is a region in the euv where the zone plate could serve as the only practical focusing device, because the reflectivity and the transmissivity of known materials would make the use of lenses or mirrors at normal incidence either difficult or impossible.

The lines of future research now seem clear. First, experiments to focus soft x-rays and euv radiation between 10 A and 1000 A should be made since in this region the conventional methods of image formation seem likely to break down. Next, as the zone plate is a highly chromatic device, sources of essentially monochromatic radiation must be found for it. Several schemes suggest themselves at once. For example, limiting stops placed strategically can absorb the radiation of one wavelength while almost all else proceeds essentially unaffected. If we could precede the circular zone plate by similarly self-supporting diffraction gratings, new types of euv spectrographs with

little or no astigmatism might become feasible.

The uses to which these zone plates may be put in the astronomical telescopes of the future will be determined by the problems that need to be explored in astrophysics. Because of the great intensity available from the sun some early solar experiments would probably be in order. The isolated lines at around 150 and 300 A in the spectrum of the sun's corona (19, 20) seem ideal for an experiment with a zone plate telescope "tuned" to one of these lines. Next in intensity—and in possible interest—might be the moon and the planets. The present limitations on speed indicate that we must develop means of greatly increasing the effective speed of a zone plate device before it can be useful in gathering euv and x-rays from the stars (18).

REFERENCES

1. Symposium on X-ray Microscopy and Microradiography, Cambridge, England, August 16–21, 1956. The proceedings of this conference were published in the following work. V. E. Cosslett, Arne Engstron and H. H. Pattee, Jr., "X-ray Microscopy and Microradiography." Academic Press, Inc., New York, 1957.
2. Second International Symposium on X-ray Microscopy and X-ray Microanalysis, Stockholm, June 15–17, 1959.
3. JASTROW, R., J. Geophys. Res., 64, 1647 (1959).
4. KOLLER, L. R., "Ultraviolet Radiation," Chap. 5, p. 146, John Wiley and Sons, Inc., New York, 1952.
5. WHIPPLE, F. L., AND DAVIS, R. J., Astron. J., 65, 285 (1960).
6. HASS, G., AND TOUSEY, R., J. Opt. Soc. Am., 593 (1959).
7. RIESER, L. M., JR., J. Opt. Soc. Am., 47, 987 (1957).
8. COMPTON, A. H., AND ALLISON, S. K., "X-rays in Theory and Experiment," 2nd ed., Chap. IV, p. 305 et seq., D. Van Nostrand Co., Inc., New York, 1935.
9. KIRKPATRICK, P., AND BAEZ, A. V., J. Opt. Soc. Am., 38, 766 (1948).
10. KIRKPATRICK, P., AND PATTEE, H. H., JR., X-ray Microscopy. Handbuch der Physik.

Encyclopedia of Physics. Vol. XXX (Edited by S. Flugge, Springer-Verlag, Berlin, 1957).

11. Cosslett, V. E., Engstrom, A., and Pattee H. H., Jr., "X-ray Microscopy and Microradiography," Academic Press, New York, 1957.

12. Baez, A. V., *J. Opt. Soc. Am.*, **42**, 756 (1952).

13. Gabor, D., *Proc. Roy. Soc.*, **A197**, 454 (1949).

14. Myers, O. E., Jr., *Am. J. Phys.*, **19**, 359 (1951).

15. Strong, J., "Concepts of Classical Optics," W. H. Freeman & Co., 1958.

16. Henke, B. L., Seventh Annual Conference on Industrial Applications of X-ray Analysis, University of Denver, 1958.

17. Mack, J. E., and Martin, M. J., "The Photographic Process," McGraw-Hill Co., Inc., 1939.

18. Kirby, D. S., *Pubs. Astron. Soc. Pacific*, **71**, 334 (1959).

19. DeJager, C., *Ann. de Geophysique*, **II**, 1 (1955).

20. Giacconi, R., and Rossi, B., *J. Geophys. Res.*, **65**, 773 (1960).

21. Berning, P. H., Hass, G., and Madden, R. P., *J. Opt. Soc. Am.*, **50**, 586 (1960).

22. Walker, W. C., Rustgi, O. P., and Weissler, G. L., *J. Opt. Soc. Am.*, **49**, 471 (1959).

Albert V. Baez

X-RAY MICROSCOPY

BONE STRUCTURE AND AGING BY CONTACT MICRORADIOGRAPHY. *See* MEDICO-BIO-LOGIC RESEARCH BY MICRORADIOGRAPHY, p. 591.

CONTACT MICRORADIOGRAPHY

Microradiography is the name applied to the oldest and simplest type of x-ray imaging, which is accomplished by placing the specimen in direct contact with a recording material, exposing to x-rays, and subsequently viewing the image with a microscope. No direct x-ray magnification is obtained, and the maximum resolution is therefore limited by the granularity or structure of the recording material. Although the earliest uses of the basic method go back several decades (1–3), it was not until the introduction of the Lippmann type photographic emulsion, with grain size under a micron, that high optical magnification of the x-ray image became useful. Many discussions of this technique are in the literature (4–8) and additional applications will be found elsewhere in this volume. We shall limit our discussion to the technical requirements for microradiography, and to a description of some of the newer modifications and extensions of the basic method.

Basic Geometry of Contact Method

The great simplicity of the contact image geometry is an obvious advantage when the other possible systems of x-ray imaging are considered by comparison. Less obvious are the advantages in speed, resolution and width of field which are obtainable with the contact method. The author has indicated (16, 20) how this method may offer superior potentialities in these respects than the other techniques of x-ray microscopy now known.

To realize these advantages for a given specimen size and thickness requires the proper choice of source size and source location with respect to the specimen. In general, the source-to-specimen distance should be small to give maximum intensity, but it must not be so small that the source penumbra limits the resolution or that the obliquity of the rays causes image distortion or uneven illumination over the desired field. For the fixed source diameter of a standard x-ray tube and average specimen thickness (10–

100 microns), the maximum allowable penumbra usually determines the minimum source-to-specimen distance. However, if a variable focus microbeam x-ray source is available the optimum choice of source diameter and source-to-specimen distance will be determined by both the desired resolution and width of field. Since the maximum permissible loading on microfocus tubes increases approximately inversely as the source diameter (9, 10), it is an advantage in speed to use the closest source to specimen distance that will illuminate the entire specimen evenly, and the largest source diameter which, at that distance does not cause penumbral blurring above the desired minimum resolving distance.

For example, referring to Figure 1, if we have a specimen of thickness b, located a distance a from a source of x-rays of diameter s, then the maximum possible penumbral width P will be given by $P = (b + c)s/a$, where c is the thickness of the recording material. This penumbra may be made arbitrarily small by decreasing s or increasing a, but only with a corresponding decrease in intensity. It is also obvious that the desired minimum geometric resolving distance for a given specimen and recording material thickness determines only the ratio s/a and not the scale. Because of the aforementioned inverse relation of source loading to source diameter the maximum intensity at the detector for a constant ratio s/a is obtained as s and a are made as small as possible. However, under these conditions the area of the specimen which is evenly illuminated also becomes small. In practice, a certain width of field is desired for a given specimen and this determines the smallest useful values of s and a. In general, the useful width of field is about $\frac{1}{2}$ a, although a wider field can be imaged adequately for qualitative work if the lower intensity at the margins can be tolerated.

It should be emphasized that if exposure time is not an important consideration, and if good specimen contrast can be obtained using wavelengths of 2.5 A or shorter, a standard diffraction tube with millimeter focal spot size, properly arranged, can give results equal in quality to those of much more complicated systems. For thin sections of biological material, on the other hand, the use of ultrasoft x-rays is a necessity for good contrast, and therefore special effort must be made to achieve adequate intensity. For this reason, at wave lengths of about 5 A and longer, microfocus tubes are a distinct advantage.

Selection and Production of Proper X-ray Spectrum

The determination of a suitable wavelength for a given problem is much less difficult than producing the desired spectrum at a useful intensity. For qualitative observation it is normally sufficient to choose an average wavelength which will be neither too strongly absorbed nor too strongly transmitted by the specimen. For maximum accuracy one may use the criterion that the wave length should be chosen so that $1/\mu$ is equal to the specimen thickness (11).

For quantitative measurements of absorption, the production of sufficiently monochromatic radiation is more difficult.

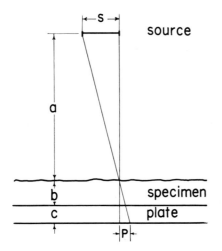

FIG. 1. Geometry of contact image (see text).

This is especially true in the ultrasoft x-ray region where suitable target materials are scarce and where intensities are discouragingly low. Three general approaches to monochromatization may be used, generally in combination. First, the target material may be chosen to yield emission lines as near the desired wavelength as possible. Second, filters may be interposed in the beam to selectively suppress the remaining unwanted portions of the spectrum. A filter may be of the direct absorption type which sharply attenuates the unwanted wave length near the short wave length side of the characteristic absorption edge of the filter element (12, 13); it may consist of a grazing incidence reflector which eliminates all the x-rays shorter than a critical wave length, but with a cut-off which is not sharp (14, 15); or it may be a crystal reflector which achieves practically complete monochromatization, but only with such a considerable loss of intensity that it is not likely to be useful for normal image production.

Finally the response of the detector may be used to eliminate unwanted wave lengths either by failing to absorb the harder components (16, 17) or by discriminating between different x-ray energies as in the case of proportional counters (18, 19). These methods of monochromatization are covered in detail in the references given. Their proper use will depend on the specific application and the type of information required.

Recording and Detecting Materials

Since both penumbral blurring and diffraction effects may be reduced to practically negligible amounts by proper contact image geometry (20), the resolution of the method is limited by the grain or structure of the recording material or by the optical system which is used to view the recorded image. For enlargement with the light microscope there are several recording materials with background structure which is visible only under the highest magnification, and some which show no background structure at all. For electron optical enlargement, on the other hand, the resolution is limited by the structure of the recording material. We shall describe briefly some of the existing materials useful for contact x-ray image recording and indicate their range of usefulness.

Photographic Materials. Most standard photographic films are designed for normal enlargement, which is seldom greater than 10 or 20 times in linear magnification. Consequently they have a resolving power in the range of 50 to 150 lines/mm. For photomicrographic magnifications of 200 or 500 times an order of magnitude higher resolution is essential. The films most commonly used for these high magnifications are Gevaert "Lippmann", Agfa "Mikrat", and Eastman Kodak "Type 649" and "Maximum Resolution Plate". These materials have a resolution of approximately 1000 lines/mm, or better, depending on conditions of use and of measurement. In spite of the very small individual grain diameters of these emulsions (0.05μ) they nevertheless exhibit visible granularity after development which often limits their usefulness for optical magnifications over 500×. They are also too thick for the optimum optical enlargement, being about ten times the depth of field of a microscope with a N.A. of 1.0. This thickness may be necessary to efficiently absorb x-rays of wave length shorter than 2A, but it is a disadvantage when the recording of only the ultrasoft x-ray components from a continuous spectrum is desired. Several experimental emulsions have been made (21, 22) to try to improve the qualities of these emulsions for contact microradiography. The adaptation of ultra-fine grained photographic emulsions for electron optical enlargement has also been considered by Recourt (23).

Fluorescent Screens. Instead of forming a permanent optical image directly from the x-ray exposure, it is possible to convert the x-rays to visible light by means of a fluorescent screen. The image may then be viewed directly with a microscope or photographed for permanent recording. The production of a visible microfluoroscopic image requires a fine-grained fluorescent screen, an intense microfocus source of x-rays, and a well-designed, high-aperture optical viewing system. An instrument comprising these features is illustrated in a later section. The fluorescent screens themselves may be produced by vacuum evaporation of a suitable phosphor, such as Zn_2SiO_4, onto a thin, optically polished substrate. Methods for producing such screens are described by Feldman and O'Hara (24) and Pattee (16). Also commercial screens have been obtained on special order (25).

A general comparison between direct photographic recording and the x-ray conversion with the fluorescent screen is not simple to make. Certainly in problems where motion or change in the specimen occurs in short intervals of time the fluoroscopic method of viewing is superior. On the other hand when a permanent record of an extensive area of a specimen is desired, the direct photographic recording is the best choice. For observing a small region of a specimen at the highest resolution it is not easy to make the choice without trying both methods. The fluorescent screen has less granularity than some batches of type 649 plate, but at the same time the intensity and contrast of the direct fluorescent image may not be as good as that obtained in viewing a direct contact photographic image.

For quantitative absorption measurements, again there is no clear-cut choice. The intensity of the fluorescent image may be measured directly with a photometer so that no errors of photographic recording or development enter. Measurements may also be made more rapidly on the fluorescent image. Nevertheless, a permanent record of the image is a great strategic advantage in any quantitative work since one may check

or add to the original measurements should any doubts or questions arise. There are, of course, possibilities of photometric errors, but although they are different for each method the effort necessary to correct them is about the same in both cases.

There is one great advantage of the fluorescent recording which should be mentioned, although it falls under the topic of monochromatization rather than image recording. Because of the method of fluorescent screen production it is possible to control the screen thickness and uniformity with great accuracy down to sub-micron thicknesses. This makes it practical to design the screen to filter out effectively all but the ultrasoft components of the x-rays by not absorbing them. Photographic emulsions may also be made uniformly thick, but only with difficulty at submicron dimensions.

Other Recording Methods

There are many possibilities for x-ray recording materials besides the conventional silver halide emulsions. It is well known, for example, that some ionic crystals take on a characteristic color as a result of irradiation (26). Another well known effect of irradiation on plastics is a change in solubility produced by cross-linking or change of polymer length. This effect has been used by the Ladds (27) to produce microradiographic images for electron optical enlargement, and by Warnes (28) for ordinary light optical magnification. Common plastics such as vinylidene chloride (saran) will give visible x-ray contact images without development of any kind, although a clearer image is produced by washing the exposed plastic in a solvent.

A third type of x-ray record may be produced by photoreactive dye derivatives which become dyes on exposure to sufficiently energetic radiation. Many of these materials are used in light photography for low speed copying. One material of this type has been described by Chalkley (29) for recording the ultraviolet spectrum at wave lengths shorter than 3200 A. A similar material, pararosaniline leuconitrile (30), has also proved useful for high resolution contact x-ray images (31). This dyestuff may be dissolved in several materials including gelatin and nylon, and since it is insensitive to light the problems of specimen mounting are greatly simplified. Furthermore, the x-ray image may be viewed as it is produced during the exposure, provided that a suitable optical system is available.

This dye shows no granularity under the highest possible optical magnification. The resolution at the samples tested so far is limited by the thickness of the sensitive layer which greatly exceeds the depth of focus of the enlarging microscope.

A fourth type of contact x-ray recording, recently reported by Auld and McNeil (32), makes use of the xerographic process, in which the x-ray image is produced by electrostatic variations on a semiconducting surface. In this case the charge "picture" is made visible by depositing fine opaque particles on the exposed surface. The charged regions of the surface collect the largest number of particles thereby producing visible contrast. Although this method also suffers from grain structure, it requires considerably less exposure time for a given resolution than for any of the photographic materials.

Materials Useful for Electron Optical Enlargement

All the materials previously described have resolutions of a micron or better, and therefore they approach the resolution limit of the optical microscope by which they are enlarged. A few of the materials have sufficiently small background structure that no graininess is visible even at the highest optical resolution. Therefore to carry the contact method to its potential limit of resolution requires finding x-ray recording materials which permit enlargement by electron optical systems.

Although several promising techniques have been studied none of them, at this stage, may be considered as more then experimental methods. Much development work must be done before any reliable quantitative results may be expected. We shall only mention the various approaches to this problem to illustrate the difficulties and possibilities.

An x-ray sensitive material which gives a good electron image must have certain peculiar characteristics. It must be thin enough to form an electron image of reasonable resolution and contrast, and at the same time it must be thick enough to absorb the x-rays in the initial recording process. For all but the ultrasoft x-rays these two requirements are incompatible in the same material. The Ladd technique (27) overcomes this difficulty by forming the x-ray image on a thick sheet and then replicating the topographic x-ray image with a thin material which is viewed in the electron microscope. This method may be used with any topographic method of image formation, however for an electron image contrast which corresponds to x-ray absorption the same recording material should be used for both x-ray exposure and electron imaging. For x-ray wave lengths from 4 to 8 A it is possible to use films of micron thickness, although speed is lost from incomplete x-ray absorption and resolution will suffer from too much electron scattering. For wave lengths of 12 to 24 A the situation is much improved and recording films of 1000 A or less are practical.

The mechanism of image formation which has shown the most promise from the work of Asunmaa (33) is photoreactive staining which is produced in a uniform, low atomic weight substrate by the combined action of the x-rays and a heavy atom stain. The stain is more chemically reactive under irradiation so that electron density is decreased where the x-ray photons are absorbed in the substrate.

Even if an ideal recording material were found, the ultimate resolution of this method would be limited by the range of the photoelectrons ejected by the incident x-rays. This distance is about 100 A in low atomic number materials for 500-volt electrons.

A system for the direct conversion of x-rays to electrons, analogous to the microfluorographic technique for light optical magnification, has been investigated by Mollenstedt and Huang (34) and by Huang (35). In this system the x-rays fall on a thin structureless foil in the object plane of an electron optical system. The specimen is in contact with the foil on the x-ray side while the other side serves as a type of photocathode in the electron system. The initial photoelectrons have too large an energy spread to allow high resolution focusing, however they give rise in the foil to tertiary electrons of much lower energy which can be uniformly accelerated and focused. The

ultimate resolution of such a system will again depend on the range of the initial photoelectrons.

Contact Microradiographic Apparatus

For many applications good quality microradiographs may be made using standard, sealed-off diffraction x-ray tubes, and a simple film holder for a camera. However for wave lengths longer than about 2.5 A or for difficult problems, special apparatus may be required. At present the only commercial apparatus specifically designed for soft x-ray contact microradiography is manufactured by N. V. Philips of Holland (36). This instrument, designated the CMR-5, is illustrated in Fig. 2. The sealed-off beryllium window x-ray tube projects from the side of the case which houses the filament and high voltage supplies and their controls. Maximum anode voltage is 5 Kv and the useful spectrum ranges from about 3 to 12 A wavelength. With an anode voltage of 3 Kv the peak of the continuous spectrum

FIG. 2. Philips contact microradiographic apparatus, CMR-5. The x-ray tube, shown in Fig. 3, is mounted in the housing projecting from the case. The case contains all of the power supplies and controls for operation.

is at 6.5 A, which is useful for a wide range of histological specimens. Figs. 3 and 4 show cross sections of the x-ray tube and camera.

Many tubes for contact microradiography have been specially constructed, and the details of their operation may be found in the references. Efforts have concentrated on achieving focal spots smaller and more brilliant than standard diffraction tubes, as in the Ehrenberg and Spear microfocus tube (37), or in reaching the ultrasoft wavelengths as in the tubes described by Engström and Lindström (38) for historadiographic analysis, and by Engström *et al.* (39) and Henke (13) for wave lengths in the 20 A region. Other tubes and cameras for microradiography are described by Fitzgerald (40) Ely (41), Salmon (42), Greulich (43), and Recourt (23).

For realizing the optimum conditions of intensity and resolution for the contact x-ray image the source must have an adjustable diameter as well as a variable spacing from the specimen and recording material, as previously pointed out. Also for good contrast in different specimen materials or thicknesses the target material should be easily changeable and the anode voltage adjustable.

In many specific applications such refinements are not worth the effort. However, for microfluoroscopic viewing the maximum intensity must be available for a clearly visible image. This requirement led to the design of an instrument shown schematically

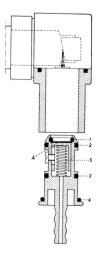

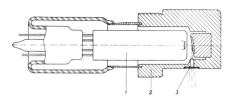

FIG. 3. Cross-section of x-ray tube for microradiography between 1.5 and 5 kV. *1*, cathode with tungsten filament; *2*, anode with tungsten target; *3*, beryllium window 50 microns thick. The tube is 8 cm long. The (effective) size of the focal spot is 0.3 × 0.3 mm.

FIG. 4. The target end of the x-ray tube, showing attached cylinder into which the film-holder is inserted. Underneath is the film-holder itself, loaded with film, specimen and specimen carrier. The pressure plate is in the form of a plunger which, under the action of a spring *5*, keeps the film, specimen and specimen carrier (*A*) pressed against a rubber ring *1*. The other rubber rings (*2*, *3* and *4*) ensure a good seal, making it possible to evacuate the film-holder by attaching a vacuum line (a water-jet pump provides sufficient vacuum) to the nozzle provided for the purpose.

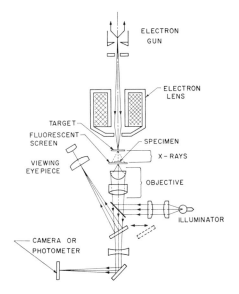

FIG. 5. Schematic diagram of the microfluoroscope.

567

F<small>IG</small>. 6. Photograph of the microfluoroscope. The variable microfocus x-ray source is shown at the top center. The viewing microscope is in position for mounting a specimen or changing target. For viewing or exposure the microscope is moved on the short optical bench until its objective axis is coincident with the axis of the microfocus tube.

in Fig. 5 (16). The electron gun and lens can produce a 10–100 micron beam at the aluminum foil target with a specific loading of up to 10^4 watts/mm². The target also serves as the vacuum window. The specimen and fluorescent screen are mounted on the mechanical stage of an inverted metallurgical microscope. Target to screen distance may be adjusted from 1 cm down to 50 microns. A photograph of the instrument is shown in Fig. 6. The viewing microscope is mounted on a short optical bench so that it can be displaced, as shown, to allow changing targets and specimens. This arrangement has proven valuable for ordinary microradiography as well as for the experiments with x-ray sensitive materials which may be enlarged in the electron microscope (33).

REFERENCES

1. H<small>EYCOCK</small>, C. T., <small>AND</small> N<small>EVILLE</small>, F. H., *Trans. Chem. Soc. London*, **73**, 714 (1898).
2. G<small>OBY</small>, P., *Comptes Rend.*, **156**, 686 (1913).
3. D<small>AUVILLIER</small>, A., *Comptes Rend.*, **185**, 1460 (1927).
4. C<small>LARK</small>, G. L., <small>AND</small> B<small>ICEK</small>, E. J., in "Medical Physics," 2nd ed., p. 902, Glasser, O., ed., Year Book Publishers, Chicago, 1950.
5. E<small>NGSTRÖM</small>, A., in "Progress in Biophysics and Biophysical Chemistry," Butler, J. A. V., and Randall, J. T., eds., Academic Press, New York, and Butterworth-Springer, Ltd., London, 1950, p. 164.
6. See also "Bibliography on Microradiography and Soft X-ray Radiography," prepared by Eastman Kodak Company, X-ray Division and Kodak Research Laboratories, Rochester, New York.
7. E<small>NGSTRÖM</small>, A., this volume.
8. S<small>HARPE</small>, R. S., this volume.

9. Oosterkamp, W. J., *Philips Research Repts.*, **3**, 49, 161, 303 (1948).

10. Müller, A., *Proc. Roy. Soc. London*, **A132**, 646 (1931).

11. Henke, B. L., Lundberg, B., and Engström, A., "X-ray Microscopy and Microradiography, Cosslett, V. E., Engström, A. and Pattee, H. H., eds., Academic Press, New York, 1957, p. 240.

12. For absorption theory and data see Compton, A. H., and Allison, S. K., "X-rays in Theory and Experiment," 2nd ed., Van Nostrand, New York, 1935, Chapt. VII, Secs. 7 and 8.

13. For application of this method see Henke, B. L., in "X-ray Microscopy and Microradiography," Cosslett, *et al.*, eds., Academic Press, New York, 1957, p. 76.

14. For curves of reflected x-ray intensity vs. angle of incidence see Rieser, L. M., *J. Opt. Soc. Am.*, **47**, 987 (1957), and Hendrick, R. W., *J. Opt. Soc. Am.*, **47**, 165 (1957).

15. For application of this method see Ref. 13 above, p. 82.

16. Pattee, H. H., *Science*, **128**, 977 (1958).

17. Pattee, H. H., in "X-ray Microscopy and X-ray Microanalysis," Cosslett, V. E., Engström, A., and Pattee, H. H., eds., Elsevier, Amsterdam, 1960, p. 79.

18. Duncumb, P., *ibid.*, p. 374, 617.

19. Rosengren, B. H. O., *Acta Radiol.* Supplement 178, Stockholm, 1959.

20. Pattee, H. H., in "X-ray Microscopy and X-ray Microanalysis," Cosslett *et al.*, eds., Elsevier, Amsterdam, 1960, p. 56.

21. See Ehrenberg, W., and White, M., in "X-ray Microscopy and Microradiography," Cosslett *et al.*, eds., Academic Press, New York, 1957, p. 214.

22. Eastman Kodak Company Research Laboratories, Rochester, New York has made experimental emulsions for microradiography similar to Type 649, but none is yet commercially available.

23. Recourt, A., in "X-ray Microscopy and Microradiography, Cosslett *et al.*, eds., Academic Press, New York, 1957, p. 234.

24. Feldman, C., and O'Hara, M., *J. Opt. Soc. Am.*, **47**, 300 (1957).

25. Evaporated fluorescent screens have been obtained by the author from the Liberty Mirror Division of Libby-Owens-Ford Glass Company, Brackenridge, Pennsylvania.

26. See, for example, Seitz, F., *Rev. Mod. Phys.*, **18**, 384 (1946).

27. Ladd, W. A., Hess, W. M., and Ladd, M. W., *Science*, **123**, 3192 (1956).

28. See discussion by Pattee in "X-ray Microscopy and Microradiography," Cosslett *et al.*, eds., Academic Press, New York, 1957, p. 387.

29. Chalkley, L., *J. Opt. Soc. Am.*, **42**, 387 (1952).

30. Experimental samples of this material were obtained through the cooperation of Dr. E. Ryskiewicz of the International Business Machines Research Laboratory, San Jose, California.

31. Pattee, H. H., in "X-ray Microscopy and X-ray Microanalysis," Cosslett *et al.*, eds., Elsevier, Amsterdam, 1960, p. 61.

32. Auld, J. H., and McNeill, J. F., *ibid*, p. 5.

33. Asunmaa, S. K., *Nature* **186**, 1036 (1960).

34. Möllenstedt, G., and Huang, L. Y., in "X-ray Microscopy and Microradiography, Cosslett *et al.*, eds., Academic Press, New York, 1957, p. 392.

35. Huang, L. Y., *Z. Phys.* **149**, 225 (1957)

36. Combée, B., and Recourt, A., *Philips Tech. Rev.*, **19**, 221 (1957/58).

37. Ehrenberg, W. and Spear, W. E., *Proc. Phys. Soc. London*, **B64**, 67 (1951).

38. Engström, A., and Lindström, B., *Biochim. et Biophys. Acta*, **4**, 351 (1950).

39. Engström, A., Greulich, R. C., Henke, B. L., and Lundberg, B., in "X-ray Microscopy and Microradiography," Cosslett *et al.*, eds., Academic Press, New York, 1957, p. 218.

40. Fitzgerald, P. J., *ibid.*, p. 49.

41. Ely, R. V., *ibid.*, p. 59.

42. Salmon, J., *ibid.*, p. 465.

43. Greulich, R. C., in "X-ray Microscopy and X-ray Microanalysis," Cosslett *et al.*, eds., Elsevier, Amsterdam, 1960, p. 273.

H. H. Pattee

DIFFRACTION MICROSCOPY*

A technique for indicating the changes in metal crystals upon deformation was proposed in 1945 by Barrett as a kind of microscopy (1). From many examples applied to single crystals and polycrystalline metals one example is selected. Figure 1a diagrammatically illustrates the technique, which consists in directing the x-ray beam at a small grazing angle on the surface of the specimen, while the film is arranged above the surface, as shown, so as to register any beams re-

* Adapted from publications by C. S. Barrett and Y. Cauchois.

flected by grains at the proper Bragg angle with respect to the incident beams of given wavelength. For an entirely unstrained material there will appear magnified images of these grains (the greatly inclined reflections produce streaked images as in Fig. 1b for commercial aluminum strip electropolished). When the strip is elongated 20 per cent and again electropolished, these uniform grain images break up into an intricate array of fragments (0.005 mm in size) as shown in Fig. 1c. Even 1 per cent elongation shows easily apparent distortion of the internal structure.

Mlle. Cauchois has constructed a microscope with a curved crystal of mica (2). The x-ray beam undergoes regular Bragg reflections from crystal planes, but these serve the same purpose as curved mirrors, and an image of a specimen, itself serving as the source of x-rays or bathed by a beam of rays, may be formed as indicated in Fig. 2 and enlarged in accordance with the same principles and equations as apply to light optics. Guoy, von Hamos, and others mentioned in Mlle. Cauchois's paper anticipated the development of optics with plane and bent crystals.

Fig. 3 shows the x-ray image spectrograph devised by von Hamos, employing a curved crystal which focuses secondary fluorescent radiation to true monochromatic images of the specimen in accordance with the equation

$$2X = 2R \sqrt{\left(\frac{2d^2}{n\lambda}\right) - 1}$$

where $2X$ is the distance between corresponding points in the sample to the image in the film, R is the radius of the bent-crystal surface, and n (order of reflection) λ (wave length) and d (crystal interplanor spacing) in the Bragg equation. The intensity of the image, which is an enlarged representation of the distribution of the chemical elements in the specimen whose secondary characteristic rays are registered, is measured with a microphotometer. This permits a true microanalysis of a very small specimen. For example distinct zinc peaks are produced for only 0.2 γ of zinc in the area of the thin microtome section of pancreas 200 μ thick, exposed to

FIG. 1. (a) Barrett diffraction microscope technique for enlarging grain images. (b) Patterns by Barrett technique of polycrystalline aluminum before application of tensile stress, showing enlarged unrestrained grains. (c) Patterns by Barrett technique of polycrystalline aluminum after elongation, showing sensitive detection of strain.

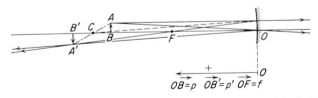

FIG. 2. The production of optical images from a bent crystal (Cauchois). O, bent crystal; F, focal point, AB, specimen; $A'B'$ image.

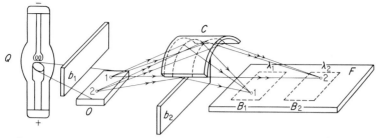

Fig. 3. X-ray image spectrograph for microanalysis by fluorescent emission (von Hamos). Q, x-ray tube; O, sample to be analyzed; F, photographic film; b_1b_2, diaphragms; C, bent crystal; B_1B_2, spectral images of specimen from focused monochromatic rays.

copper primary x-radiations; and a similar amount of iron in a spleen section 80 μ thick exposed to chromium radiation. Thus microscopy and microanalysis are possible both by the emission and diffraction analysis with bent crystals of characteristic radiation, and by the absorption in the specimen of monochromatic or polychromatic beams.

REFERENCES

1. Barrett, C. S., *AIME Tech. Publs.*, 1865; *Metals Technol.*, April, 1945.
2. Cauchois, Y., "Sur la formation d'images des rayons X," *Rev. opt.*, **29**, 151 (1950).
3. Clark, G. L., "Applied X-rays," 4th ed., McGraw-Hill Book Company, N. Y., pp. 107, 702, 1955.
4. von Hamos, L. and Engstrom, A., *Acta Radiol.*, **25**, 325 (1944).

G. L. Clark

EYE RESEARCH APPLICATIONS

X-ray microscopy has been applied to the eye in order to delineate the eye's two main types of channels: the vascular system and the aqueous outflow apparatus.

The Vascular System

The technique of x-ray microscopy has been useful in examining the blood vessel patterns in the relatively thick and opaque sections necessary for their demonstration. Many have contributed to this field which has been called historadiography, microradiography and microangiography. The main development work has been at the Nuffield Institute for Medical Research, Oxford, England, by the late Alfred Barclay (1) and in the Department for Physical Cell Research, Karolinska Institutet, Stockholm, Sweden, under the direction of Arne Engström (2).

Because of the transparency of the retina, its vascular pattern may be studied in the light microscope after injection of an opaque material such as India ink. Such a method is not feasible with the thicker and more opaque tissues of the eye. In such areas x-ray microscopy is probably the most suitable method. François, Neetens and Collette (3, 4) applied this method to the eye. Thorotrast was injected as a contrast medium. They used a Machlett A2 tube with an iron target and a beryllium window. "Lippman" emulsion film (Gavaert) was used. The parts of the eye taken for examination were dissected under the dissecting microscope and the fixed wet samples were supported between thin plastic sheets.

Studies were made of the retina, choroid, ciliary body, iris (3) and optic nerve (4). Some of the major findings were:

(1) At the level of the peripapillary portion of the retina anastomoses exist between capillaries originating from the optic nerve and the retinal capillaries proper.

(2) The intraocular portion of the short ciliary arteries nourishes the choroid only.

571

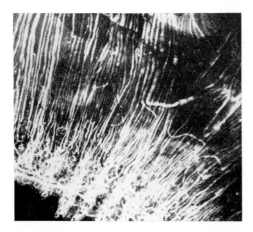

FIG. 1. View of ciliary body, ciliary processes, pars plana and transition zone toward the choroid (×9). (From Fig. 14—Francois, Neetens and Collette, Ophthalmologica 129: 155 (1955).)

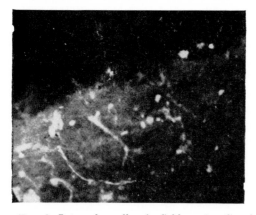

FIG. 2. Internal wall of Schlemm's Canal (×100). Streaks are the canals leading to the white dots which represent the mouth of the openings into the canal. (From Fig. 8—Francois, Collette and Neetens, Etude Microradiographique de la parof interne du canal de Schlemm. J. Belge. de Radiol., 38, 11 (1955).

(3) There are no anastomoses between the greater arterial circle of the iris and the choroidal arterial meshwork so that there are no arterioles in the pars plana. This appears to be at variance with the work of Wybar (5) in 1954.

(4) The existence of two basic vascular patterns in the vessels of the optic nerve was established:

(a) Transverse, having the form of a pentagon, encircling single nerve bundles at regular distances.

(b) Longitudinal, running in the interfascicular spaces in between the bundles from front to back.

An example of this work is given in Fig. 1, which shows the detail afforded by this technique.

X-ray microscopy of the vascular system of the eye has been useful and informative, uniquely in the areas other than the retina.

Aqueous Outflow Apparatus

Two separate groups of investigators, François, Collette and Neetens (6) and Pattee, Garron, McEwen and Feeney (7), have used x-ray microscopy in an attempt to visualize the outflow channels of the human eye. Other investigators (e.g. Cohan 8, 9), have used ordinary radiographic techniques for the visualization of radio-opaque material injected into the anterior chamber of the eye. Their results mainly indicated that standard roentgenologic techniques were not suitable and that a further step to microradiography was necessary in order to obtain delineation of some of the structures of the outflow apparatus.

François et al. (3, 4) used essentially the same technique as they used for their vascular studies. Figure 2 shows the details achieved by this method.

Refinements of the method were carried out by Pattee et al. (7). The contrast medium (Thorotrast) was perfused through freshly enucleated eyes under a controlled pressure of less than 25 mm Hg. The eyes were frozen in liquid nitrogen. Small sections were excised from the frozen specimen and lyophilized in order to obtain greater contrast. The x-ray apparatus consisted of a Machlett

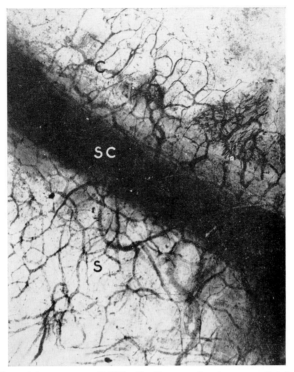

FIG. 3. Limbal region of human eye (×32). C—Cornea showing superficial vascular arcade. SC—Schlemm's canal. S—Sclera showing deep and superficial vascular arcade. (From—Pattee, Garron, McEwen, Feeney—Steromicroradiography of the Limbal Region of the Human Eye. X-Ray Microscopy and Microradiography. Academic Press, N. Y., 1957. Eds. Cosslett, Engstrom and Pattee.)

AEG-50 tube with vanadium target and a beryllium window. The tube was operated at 12.5 KV at a distance of 100 cm and the path was filled with helium. Both Lippman film (Gevaert) and type 649 spectroscopic plate (Eastman) were used. Exposure time was about one hour. Stereo images were produced by tilting the specimen and photographic plate 15° with linear translation. An example of the results achieved by this method is given in Fig. 3. It is apparent that good visualization of channels has been obtained. The location in depth of the vascular network is obtained by viewing the photographs steroscopically.

The results of both François et al. (6) and Pattee et al. (7) are in essential agreement that holes exist between the anterior chamber and Schlemm's canal and the episcleral vessels show many anastomoses and interesting vascular patterns.

REFERENCES

1. BARCLAY, ALFRED, "Micro-arteriography," Charles C Thomas, Springfield, Ill., 1951.
2. BELLMAN, S., "Microangiography," Acta Radiol. Suppl. 102 (1953).
3. FRANÇOIS, J., NEETENS, A., AND COLLETTE, J. M., "Microangiographie oculaire," Ophthalmologica, 129, 145–159 (1955).
4. FRANÇOIS, J., NEETENS, A., AND COLLETTE, J. M., "Vascular supply of the optic pathway. II. Further studies by micro-arteriography of the optic nerve," Brit. J. Ophthal., 39, 220–232 (1955).
5. WYBAR, K. C., "Vascular anatomy of the choroid in relation to selective localization of ocular disease," Brit. J. Ophthal., 38, 513–527 (1954).
6. FRANÇOIS, J., COLLETTE, J. M., AND NEETENS, A., "Etude microradiographique de la paroi interne du canal de Schlemm," J. Belg. de Radiol., 38, 1–15 (1955).

7. PATTEE, H. H., JR., GARRON, L. K., McEWEN, W. K., AND FEENEY, M. L., "Stereomicroradiography of the limbal region of the human eye," in "X-ray Microscopy and Microradiography," Academic Press Inc., N. Y., 1957, pp. 534–538, Cosslett, V. E., Engström, A., and Pattee, H. H., Jr., Eds.
8. COHAN, B. E., "Radiography of Aqueous Humor Outflow," *A.M.A. Arch. Ophth.*, **60**, 110–115 (1958).
9. COHAN, B. E., "Aqueous humor outflow: An experimental study using opaque materials," *A.M.A. Arch. Ophth.*, **55**, 793–799 (1956).

W. K. McEWEN
M. L. FEENEY
L. K. GARRON

GEOLOGICAL, MINERALOGICAL AND CERAMIC APPLICATIONS OF MICRORADIOGRAPHY

Some of the first microradiographs ever obtained were probably of fossils and minerals (1) but such applications do not appear to have been very common. However, an interest is developing in uses of microradiography for the examination of industrial minerals, concentrated ores and related materials such as refractories and ceramics. Thus, applications to ores have been described by Kirchberg and Möller (2) and to mineral concentrates by Cohen and Schloegl (3). Other examples on ores by Jackson (4) and Niskanen (5) have been published and considerable work (6, 7, 8, 9) has been done on sintered iron ores. In the field of refractories the work of Cockbain and Johnson (10) indicates further potentialities for the method.

A technique for microradiography by reflection has been suggested by Trillat (11) and by Pospisil (12) where secondary emission of electrons or x-ray fluorescence is responsible for producing the image. This method appears to have no advantages over the more usual technique using transmission apart from the obvious one of not having to make a thin section. This can be quite difficult for some of the specimens considered in this section.

Figs. 1 and 2 show the differences between the optical and x-ray transmission of a thin section of iron ore. The ground mass of siderite (iron carbonate) containing quartz inclusions shows up much more clearly on

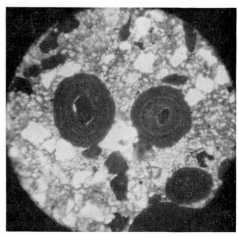

FIG. 1. Section of Jurassic Ironstone showing ooliths surrounding angular quartz grains. The matrix contains some quartz grains embedded in siderite. Thin section photomicrograph—ordinary light. ×27.

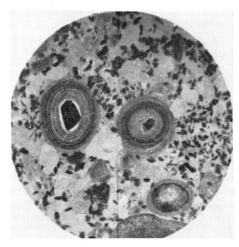

FIG. 2. Microradiograph of the same area as Fig. 1 which now clearly shows the variation of iron content in the concentric layers of the ooliths. The angular shape of the quartz grains is much more precise than in the photomicrograph. ×27

the radiograph than optically. So, also, does the fine structure of concentric layers characteristic of the ooliths. The latter are often built around a quartz fragment and contain layers of varying iron content, most probably in the form of a hydrous iron-alumino-silicate.

The presence of films of minerals with strong optical absorption or of staining within grains can give a false impression of the relative amount of opaque and transparent material in a section. If in the case of iron ores, say, the iron content is judged by the amount of opaque material then clearly the estimate will always be high. Figs. 3 and 4 show a photomicrograph and a radiograph of an iron ore which demonstrates this effect. Some of the ooliths are transparent to both light and x-rays and must contain little iron. Others which are opaque to light do in fact contain some iron but, as can be clearly seen in the radiograph, the iron is very thinly distributed and the total iron is still very small compared to the siderite matrix.

Figs. 5 and 6 show a similar ore of marine origin which consists of ooliths of iron silicate clay minerals etc. along with fossil fragments embedded in a fine grained matrix of crys-

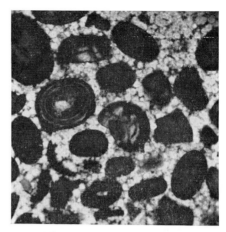

FIG. 4. Microradiograph which reveals the iron content of the ooliths to be low and generally dispersed. The matrix of siderite strongly absorbs the Cu radiation and hence shows white. ×45

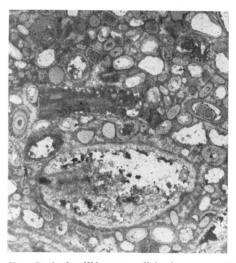

FIG. 5. A fossiliferous oolitic iron ore. The matrix is iron carbonate and the ooliths mainly iron alumino-silicate. The bivalve shell in the lower part is completely replaced by iron carbonate. Photomicrograph—ordinary light. ×17

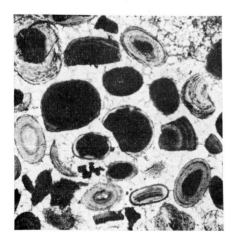

FIG. 3. Iron ore showing opaque and transparent ooliths embedded in siderite matrix. Photomicrograph—ordinary light. ×45

talline iron carbonate. The lower half of the section contains the fossil of a bivalve shell and shows the internal loop-like structure very well. The whole of the shell has been replaced by iron carbonate and a part of the internal cavity has become filled with siderite mud, some crystalline siderite and

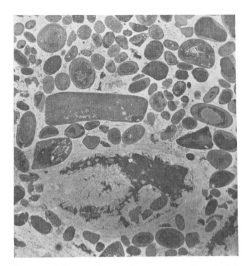

FIG. 6. Microradiograph corresponding to Fig. 5. ×17

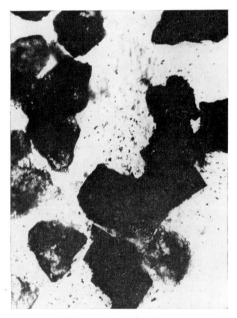

FIG. 7. Tailings from a lead-zinc ore containing galena, sphalerite and pyrite as the heavy minerals. Photomicrograph—ordinary light. ×75

a few ooliths. Well developed rhomb-shaped crystals of iron carbonate can be seen in the cavity and in general the radiograph provides a much crisper picture of the structure than the photomicrograph.

Another application in the field of industrially important ores is in the examination of tailings and hence the assessment of the efficiency of mineral dressing operations. The difficulties associated with different opaque minerals and of fine particle size are again the main ones in optical work but Figs. 7 and 8 show the improvement obtainable by radiography. The material is a lead-zinc ore containing the sulfides of lead (galena), zinc (sphalerite) and iron (pyrite) as the heavy constituents. The galena is easily distinguished by its cubic cleavage but the zinc and iron sulfides are not readily differentiated. It would be possible, however, to get some change in contrast for these two sulfides by changing the radiation from, say copper or nickel to iron radiation.

The specimens for this type of examination were made of a single layer of particles mounted on a cover glass with Canada Balsam. Provided the particle size was less than about 100 micron diameter and of

FIG. 8. Corresponding radiograph clearly shows the cleavage of the galena but does not differentiate between sphalerite and pyrite. ×75

fairly uniform grading good radiographs were obtained. Figs. 9 and 10 show tailings from a lead ore which were examined to assess the value of retreatment. The material consisted of fine transparent or translucent grains all more or less heavily iron stained. The valuable minerals were cerussite and mimetite, and these were almost indistinguishable from gangue minerals such as calcite, other carbonates, quartz, etc., because of the fine grain size iron staining and the general weathered condition of the material. The radiograph clearly shows the lead-bearing particles (white); assaying by particle counting was fairly easy on the radiograph but quite impossible directly on the sample. For example, a large irregular grain near the center of the field appears quite uniform but reference to the radiograph shows it to consist of almost equal amounts of gangue and lead mineral.

Fig. 11 shows a radiograph on gold ore tailings which shows the state of association of the gold. For example, some of the gold particles are free from gangue and should not have passed the concentration process. Others are associated with gangue and clearly could be recovered by further grinding and separation but the very fine dissemination of particles visible in some of the grains are clearly beyond the possibilities of physical separation methods. Distinguishing gold from accompanying pyrite is difficult optically and the radiograph offers a much better chance of detecting the odd grain or fine disseminations which are responsible for tailing losses.

The application of radiography to opaque materials is further exemplified by reference to investigations on the structure of sintered iron ores. Figs. 12 and 13 show radiographs of some sintered ore at different magnifications. The material is very heterogeneous but mainly consists of iron oxides embedded in a melilite type silicate. The irregular distribution of voids and pools of solidified silicate can be seen. Pin-point

x-ray diffraction analysis on the area in Fig. 13 showed the dendrites to be FeO grown from an iron-monticellite type silicate,

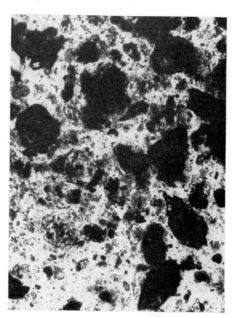

FIG. 9. Optical micrograph of lead ore tailings. ×113

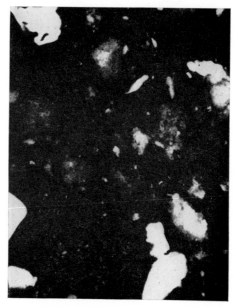

FIG. 10. Microradiograph of same area as Fig. 9 showing lead distribution (white). ×113

577

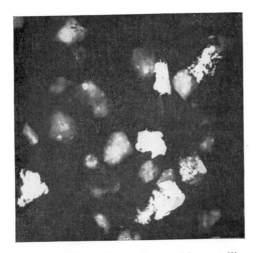

FIG. 11. Microradiograph on gold ore tailings showing three types of particles—those unattached to any gangue, those attached to quartz gangue which could be further separated and a very fine dissemination in pyrite which is beyond the possibilities of physical separation. ×75

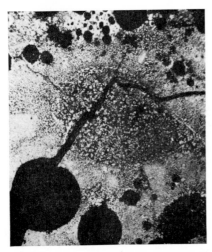

FIG. 12. Sintered iron ore. Heterogeneous structure of granular oxides (Fe₃O₄), holes and slag pools containing dendrites. Microradiograph Ni radiation. ×18

whereas the predominant oxide is usually Fe_3O_4 in a properly sintered ore. In order to carry out x-ray diffraction on a thin section, the use of any supporting material is very undesirable due to absorption, and specimens are usually impregnated with balsam

or cold-setting plastic to give mechanical strength. If, however, radiographs only are required, it is quite permissible to prepare the section on a microscope cover slide and take the radiographs with the specimen still mounted on it.

Figs. 14 and 15 show further radiographs on sintered iron ore where the conditions of operation have been altered to find the optimum conditions for sintering. This particular sinter contained a 20 % addition of flue dust which provided sufficient extra heat to give a general coarsening of the texture and large scale solution of iron as evidenced by the secondary dendrites and skeletal crystals of magnetite. The marginal break-up and recrystallization of large ore lumps also show the characteristic "shaded" cracks which are always found to precede the final break-up and recrystallization.

The examination of used steel plant refractories by microscopic methods presents difficulties due to the opaque nature of the parts where iron oxide has been heavily absorbed. Reflected light techniques are possible, particularly with diamond polished specimens, but even here the friable nature of the material makes the interpretation of

FIG. 13. Structure of dendrites of FeO in slag pool of Fig. 12. Microradiograph Ni radiation. ×180

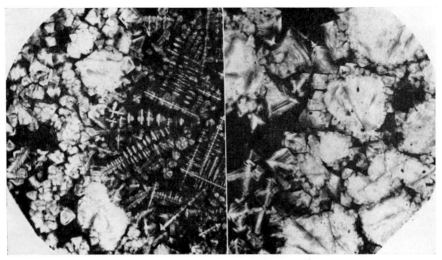

FIGS. 14 and 15. Sintered iron ore with 3% addition of coke and 20% flue dust showing extensive 're-crystallization of iron oxides around the periphery of original ore grains alone with primary dendrites of Fe_3O_4 in slag pool. Note the characteristic "shaded" cracking which is found to precede final break-up and recrystallization of ore grains. ×93. Microradiograph —Cu radiation.

the structures difficult due to falling out of parts of the surface.

The structure of a magnesite refractory uncontaminated by iron is clearly shown by radiography in Fig. 16. Here a large piece of "fused cast" magnesia is embedded in finer-grained magnesia. The whole structure is bonded by silicate which appears white on the radiograph due to the very low absorption of magnesium compared to the calcium associated with the silicate. The "fused cast" magnesia demonstrates the three dimensional aspect of radiography.

It is in the field of chrome/magnesite refractories, however, that microradiography has proved of even greater value by giving an understanding of the structures formed in service, in particular, in open-hearth furnace roofs. Figs. 17, 18 and 19 show typical radiographs on sections near the working face of such bricks. All the sections are completely opaque except for some tiny pools of silicate. The magnesia in Fig. 17 which has recrystallized into crystals elongated perpendicular to the working face is considerably lighter than in Fig. 16. This is due to the high iron content of the MgO which

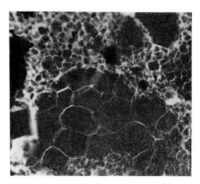

FIG. 16. Microradiograph of part of used magnesite brick with a large piece of "fused cast" magnesia embedded in a finer magnesia, the whole being bonded with silicate (white, because of Ca content). Note the three dimensional effect visible in the large grains. ×25 Ni radiation.

actually contains a fine precipitate of $MgO \cdot Fe_2O_3$—usually unresolved on the radiograph. In Fig. 18 a coarser precipitate is clearly resolved.

Both Figs. 17 and 18 show the intimate bonding between the chrome grains and the magnesia which often nucleates on the front of the grain during recrystallization. An iron rich spinel phase is found on the other side away from the furnace and grows as co-

579

lumnar crystals showing lighter on the radiograph. The absorption is greater because
the chrome grains contain MgO and Al_2O_3
as well as Cr_2O_3 and Fe_2O_3. Fig. 19 is a good
example of these long crystals of iron rich
spinel. Also, iron penetration can be seen
along cracks in the chrome grains and this
is often associated with diffusion of Al_2O_3

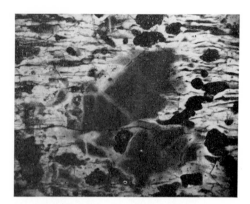

FIG. 19. Chromite grain embedded in collum-
nar iron-rich spinel showing porosity due to loss
of material by diffusion. Microradiograph—Ni
radiation. ×12.5

FIG. 17. Characteristic structure formed near
the hot face in used chrome magnesite roof bricks.
A remnant grain of chrome ore is surrounded by
recrystallized magnesia which itself contains a fine
unresolved precipitate of $MgO.Fe_2O_3$ and is therefore lighter than that of Fig. 16. The elongated
iron-rich spinel crystals behind the chrome grain
are just differentiated. ×18. Microradiograph—Ni
radiation.

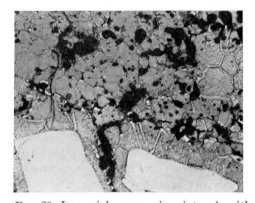

FIG. 20. Iron rich magnesia sintered with
chrome ore showing the nucleating effect of the
chrome spinel and the orientation of the iron bearing precipitate $(MgO.Fe_2O_3)$ in the magnesia.
×30. Microradiograph—Ni radiation.

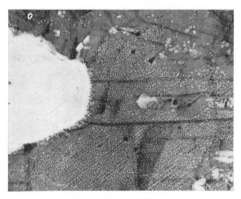

FIG. 18. Similar region to Fig. 17, but showing
resolution of the precipitate in the recrystallized
magnesia. Near the chrome grain the precipitate
has nucleated on the spinel grain leaving a margin
free from coarse precipitate. ×38. Microradiograph—Ni radiation.

away from the grain which leaves some pores
behind.

The effect of high temperature sintering
on magnesia containing iron oxide in the
presence of chrome is shown in Fig. 20. The
precipitate in the MgO is just resolved in
this case but the most striking feature is
the nucleating effect of the spinel crystals.

The study of porosity and iron distribution
in fireclay refractories has been helped by
radiography as is shown in Fig. 21 taken on
a section from a firebrick during work on
carbon disintegration, alkali attack and zinc

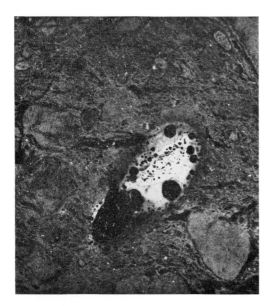

FIG. 21. Iron-rich spot in a firebrick derived from impurity in original clay. The iron oxide has melted during firing and reacted with the firebrick giving a silicate inclusion. This is not as detrimental as iron oxide itself since in the latter case the deposition of carbon from furnace gases may be catalysed. Microradiograph. Cobalt radiation. ×25

deposition which occurs when firebricks are used for blast furnace linings. Microscopical work on these materials is difficult due to the fine grain size and the optical properties of the altered products.

REFERENCES

1. GOLY, P., *Compt. Rend.*, **156**, 686 (1913).
2. KIRCHBERG, H. AND MÖLLER, H., *Mitt. Kaiser Wilhelm Inst. fur Eisenforschung*, **23** (part 17), 309–314 (1941).
3. COHEN, E. AND SCHLOEGL, I., To be published in proceedings of the second international conference on X-ray microscopy and microradiography held in Stockholm (1959).
4. JACKSON, C. K., pp. 623–627 of "X-ray Microscopy and Microradiography," (1957), Academic Press, New York. (Edited by V. E. Cosslett, A. Engström and H. H. Pattee, Jr.).
5. NISKANEN, E., *Norelco Reporter*, **VI**, No. 3, p. 70 (1959).
6. COHEN, E., *Metallurgia*, **41**, 227–233 (1950).
7. McBRIAR, E. MAUD, JOHNSON, W., ANDREWS, K. W., AND DAVIES, W., *J. Iron Steel Inst.*, **177**, 316 (1954).
8. JOHNSON W. AND ANDREWS, K. W., *Iron and Steel*, **31**, 437–444 (1958).
9. COHEN, E., *J. Iron and Steel Inst.*, **175**, 160–166 (1953).
10. COCKBAIN, A. G. AND JOHNSON, W., *Trans. Brit. Ceram. Soc.*, **57**, No. 8, 511–526 (1958).
11. TRILLAT, J. J., *Compt. Rend.*, **214**, 164–166 (1942).
12. POSPISIL, R., *Hutnike Listy*, **1** (9), 193–197 (1947).

W. JOHNSON

GRAINLESS MEDIA FOR IMAGE REGISTRATION (See also p. 564)

It was inevitable that attempts should be made in microradiography and historadiography to avoid the limitations imposed in enlargments of contact images by graininess of photographic emulsions. The solution of this problem has taken two courses, with very successful results. From among various x-ray-sensitive substances which will show no structure even in electron microscope ranges of enlargement, Ladd, Hess and Ladd (1) found that faces of ammonium dichromate crystals, and some polymers such as polyvinyl films were most useful. In both cases the solubility of the medium changes in proportion to the amount of exposure to the x-ray beam, with the result that the microradiographic image can be etched into a relief by suitable solvents. Anhydrous alcohols are used for developing the image on the dichromate crystals, and a 30 % solution of acetone in water the image on the plastic sheets, in which cross-linking between polymer molecules has resulted from absorption. A cast, thin enough to permit the passage of an electron beam is then made of the relief surface with silicon monoxide, carbon or other materials generally used for making replicas for electron microscopy. This replica is shadow-cast with metal vapors directed at an angle to the surface and then examined in the electron microscope up to 200,000 diameters magnification.

As discussed by Pattee in his article on Microfluoroscopy, almost grainless thin films of fluorescent materials can be produced, thus providing excellent resolution at high magnifications.

An important improvement in the polymer film method was announced in the July 25, 1960 number of *Chemical and Engineering News*. This was achieved by Dr. Saara Asunmaa, working under Dr. H. H. Pattee, Jr. in Stanford University's Biophysics Laboratory.

Dr. Asunmaa makes a contact x-ray micrograph on a sensitive film in which the absorbed radiation changes the electron density. This film is then used as a specimen in the electron microscope. The film that does the trick is made of cellulose nitrate activated with silver chloride. Dr. Asunmaa mixes lithium chloride and silver nitrate in an acidic medium with a 2% solution of cellulose nitrate in ethanol and ether. From this she casts the thin films—about 1000 A. thick—on glass slides, then ages them in a desiccator.

To make the micrograph she places the specimen in contact with the film and exposes it to x-rays from a microfocus tube for 10 minutes to one hour. The silver chloride particles act as radiation traps and are reduced to metallic silver. The reduced silver gives an image that is directly visible under a light microscope, but this optical contrast does not correspond to differences in electron scattering.

To get an image that is observable in the electron microscope, the structure of the film must be altered. The radiation absorbed by the silver chloride not only reduces the silver salt but also degrades the cellulose nitrate. Aqueous methanolic sodium cyanide dissolves the soluble low molecular weight fraction of the polymer, while the silver and unreduced silver salts are removed as cyanide complexes.

What is left is a relief image with electron optical contrast corresponding to x-ray absorption by the original specimen. This relief image can now be used as the specimen in an electron microscope. The enlargement here is limited only by the resolution obtained in the original x-ray micrograph. Using diatoms as test specimens Dr. Asunmaa has demonstrated resolution down to at least 600 A. and has produced electron micrographs with enlargements up to 40,000 diameters.

REFERENCE

1. Ladd, W. A., Hess, W. M., and Ladd, W. M., *Science*, **123**, 370 (1956).

G. L. Clark

HISTOLOGY BY THE PROJECTION MICROSCOPE

Historadiography (1) or the study of tissues and cells by x-rays, has to date been carried out almost exclusively by contact microradiography. Using preparation techniques generally identical with those used in optical microscopy, the thin tissue section is either placed upon or embedded in the emulsion of a fine grained photographic plate and exposed to soft x-radiation. The small x-ray picture or microradiogram so obtained at unit magnification is subsequently magnified optically.

A major problem (2) has been the attainment of adequate resolution, since ordinary cells measure only about 10 microns in diameter, and structures within the cells are less than 5 microns in diameter. So far as microscopy is concerned the contact method is limited by the grain size of the recording emulsion, size of the x-ray source, and resolution of the optical system used for viewing or enlarging the plate image.

The x-ray projection microscope has both theoretically and actually a high resolving power, and a resolution of 0.05 micron seems practicable in the near future. Tissue sections can be studied with the instrument using either the contact or projection method. In practicing the former method, advantage is taken of the ultra-fine focus and x-ray brilliance provided by the tube to reduce geometrical unsharpness and exposure time, while in the latter case full advantage is taken of the resolution and primary magnification afforded by the x-ray point source.

Histological sections can be examined with the x-ray microscope under atmospheric conditions by the projection method. Ordinary sections (10 –15 microns thick), mounted on thin Terylene or Melinex plastic film and deparaffinized with xylene and several changes of ethyl alcohol, when placed a short distance above the target (10 mm) give very contrasty low power projection micrographs ($1 \times$ to $20 \times$) on standard lantern slide emulsion (Ilford Contrasty plates). Such micrographs show the varying radiodensities of the different tissues and provide much useful microanatomical information. For example, transverse sections of human foetal neck (C.R. 161 mm) when so examined show the lining epithelium of the laryngeal cleft, mural constituents of the oesophagus, mature cartilage cells surrounding the primary ossific center of the vertebral body, as well as many other details of the cervical musculature, vessels and nerves. Or again, projection micrographs of the adult human lung demonstrate the terminal pulmonary anatomy almost diagrammatically, recording the respiratory bronchioles, atria and alveoli, as well as foreign inclusions such as mine dusts (e.g., tin).

However, tissue sections prepared by conventional methods considered adequate for optical microscopy are not suited to x-ray microscopy which, like electron microscopy, demands special attention to tissue preparation. Also absorption by the plastic mounting film and air column limit cellular definition, and require the use of a vacuum camera.

The vacuum camera used for high power studies of tissue sections resembles a funnel centered upon and threaded to the target assembly of the x-ray microscope. The interior of the camera is stepped in millimeter stages to give known target to specimen distances, and is fitted with specimen rings for the support of tissue sections. The sections (4–6 microns thick) are mounted on brass rings bearing a formvar film; nonmagnetic rings are essential since the section lies within the magnetic field of the objective lens polepiece. The formvar substrate is best dispensed with in order to eliminate extraneous absorption and sharpen cell definition. The upper part of the camera consists of a removable photographic plate chamber (4 cm high) that is evacuated by a vacuum pump. Ultra-fine grain emulsion, such as maximum resolution plates (Kodak) or Lippman film (Gevaert), should be used for recording tissue micrographs.

A certain primary magnification of $2 \times$ to $10 \times$ of unstained animal and human tissues and cells can be obtained rapidly ($\frac{1}{2}$–4 min) with the aid of such a camera, while operating the x-ray microscope at approximately 7 kv with a beam current of 4 to 100 microamperes and using a thin aluminum target (4 to 10 microns). Lower initial magnification is used in the interests of intensity and exposure time. Further useful secondary magnification up to $1100 \times$ can be made on fine grain emulsion (Kodak Microfile or Adox K.B. 14 or 17).

In projection microscopy, resolution depends upon the size of the x-ray source and hence also partly upon focusing accuracy. Focusing is unfortunately critical and difficult at the lower kilovoltages so essential to the production of reasonable contrast in tissue sections. It can however, as mentioned earlier, be facilitated by reducing the target-screen distance before viewing the test grid.

Other factors influencing sharpness of definition and contrast, are the choice, fixation, and preparation of the tissue. Tissues that undergo keratinization (skin) or mineralization (teeth, bone) give contrasty projection micrographs, as do those which accumulate chemical elements sufficiently to induce high x-ray absorption (thyroid). Most animal tissues are formed from elements of low atomic number, but curious and often inexplicable variations in cellular radiodensity occur. The chemical significance and interpretation of these microscopic areas of transparency and selective absorption await study.

Freeze drying and substitution have been found to give the best tissue fixation for x-ray microscopy, as well as the best contrast, since they produce few or no chemical changes and remove only water. Also, as in optical microscopy (3), it has been confirmed that flotation of tissue sections causes cytological changes and solution losses, and that both structural and density differences are readily detectable in comparison x-ray micrographs taken of serial sections after they have been either dry-mounted or floated out over water or saline (4). The latter may yield better pictures but are not representa-

tive of the tissue, and hence this point must also be considered in carrying out x-ray absorption analyses of tissue.

Unstained sections of animal and human tissues, both soft and mineralized, can be studied by x-ray projection microscopy, such as skin, hair, sebaceous gland, kidney, submaxillary gland, cartilage and bone. Micrographs of human skin clearly show the cells and intercellular boundaries of the stratified epidermis, and also the keratinized strands at the skin surface. The structure of hair and its appendages can be well visualized by projection microscopy owing to the presence of hard and soft keratin, both of which contain sulfur. Cross sections of human scalp show, for example, the process of keratinization among the cells of the inner root sheath of the hair follicle, and such details as the polygonal cells and stratum cylindricum of the outer root sheath of the hair follicle. The accumulation of lipid droplets within the cells of human sebaceous glands is strikingly recorded, appearing as dark radiolucent spherules which contrast markedly with the white x-ray absorbent cell membranes and cell nuclei (Fig. 1). Other micrographs show the manner in which the lipid droplets coalesce, forming a uniformly black cytoplasm about the white "doughnut-like" nucleus just before the mature cells break down.

Many of the differences which occur in glandular epithelium from organ to organ and within the same organ can be detected by x-ray microscopy. For example, projection micrographs of the submaxillary gland show terminal ramifications and cytoplasmic differences, such as the conglomerate appearance of the acinar cells and peculiar radiolucency of the cells of the granular tubules. Other features visible are the striations of the intralobular salivary ducts, epithelium and basement membrane of the intercalated ducts (Fig. 2). Projection micrographs of human foetal tissue such as the developing thyroid gland yield interesting details such

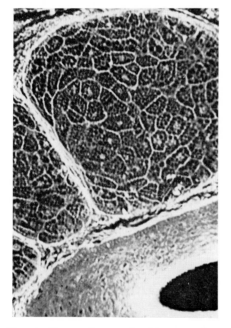

Fig. 1. X-ray micrograph of human sebaceous gland showing the cell boundaries and dark radiolucent lipid droplets within the cells. Part of a hair follicle is also seen. Mag. ×375

584

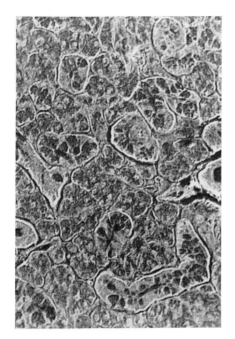

FIG. 2. X-ray micrograph showing the terminal ramification of the submaxillary gland in the rat. Note the conglomerate appearance of the acinar cells and dark radiolucent cells of the granular tubules. Mag. ×185

as the formation of the cell cords and follicles.

General microscopic structure, such as the glomerular and tubular pattern of the kidney, is readily recorded and in addition, even unstained sections reveal cytological features such as the distinctive cells of the collecting tubules and brush border of the proximal convoluted tubules.

Mineralized tissues, such as developing teeth, cartilage and bone are well suited to study by projection x-ray microscopy, yielding contrasty micrographs. Both low and high power views of ordinary or decalcified bone can be obtained, and the mineralization process and cells connected with osteogenesis readily studied. The region of the epiphyseal disc, for example, shows the zone of young proliferating cartilage, with its columns of wedge shaped cartilage cells separated by bundles of collagen fibers, giving

way to the zone of maturing and calcified cartilage, where the large cartilage cells undergoing dissolution are separated by partitions of calcified intercellular substance. Osteoblasts can be seen lining the adjacent marrow spaces, and also bone newly laid down on the persisting cores of cartilage matrix in the process of trabecular formation (Fig. 3). The blood vessels and other contents of the marrow spaces can be recorded, and fully formed and developing Haversian systems, as well as the trabecular patterns of normal and pressurized bone, can be clearly visualized.

The x-ray projection microscope is a particularly versatile laboratory instrument many applications of which have yet to be explored. It is particularly suited to microangiography and microlymphangiography, providing a good method of studying the

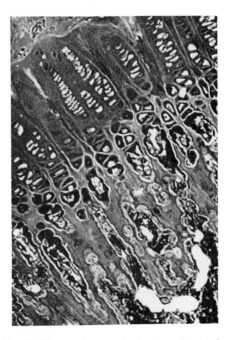

FIG. 3. X-ray micrograph showing the epiphyseal growth zones at the proximal end of decalcified rabbit tibia. Young, maturing and calcifying cartilage is seen, also marrow spaces, osteoblasts, and newly formed bone. The blood vessels in the marrow spaces contain Micropaque.

585

smallest blood and lymphatic vessels in either the dead or living animal. In the vascular field of human embryology and anatomy its future is assured.

The magnified images of unstained animal and human tissues, both soft and mineralized, exhibit much useful histological and cytological information. Stereoscopic visualization of internal structure and the interpretation of differences in absorption open new avenues to the microscopist.

The x-ray projection microscope lends itself to spatial localization and chemical determination on a microscopic scale. By utilizing the initial x-ray magnification, and applying the known laws of x-ray absorption and fluorescence, the intense x-ray point source afforded by the instrument offers as yet unrealized possibilities for the microchemical analysis of tissue areas but a few microns in diameter.

REFERENCES

1. LAMARQUE, P., *Radiol.*, **27**, 563 (1936).
2. ENGSTROM, A., In "Analytical Cytology," McGraw-Hill, New York, 1955.
3. HANCOX, N. M., *Exptl. Cell Research*, **13**, 263 (1957).
4. SAUNDERS, R. L. DE C. H. AND VAN DER ZWAN, L., Proc. 2nd International Symp. X-ray Microscopy and Microanalysis, Stockholm, 1959.

R. L. DE C. H. SAUNDERS

INTER-RELATION OF TECHNIQUES FOR THE INVESTIGATION OF MATERIALS

The fullest advantages are obtained from the use of microradiography when the results are associated with data or information derived from other sources such as the optical microscope, x-ray diffraction, etc. (1, 2). The diagram is intended to show how several different techniques are interrelated and help in various ways to build up reasonably complete understanding of the constitution and texture of materials. The scheme is perhaps particularly applicable to metallurgical and mineralogical samples, but has a more general interest. Techniques to the left of the diagram give the chemical analysis and indicate phases present, and those to the right give information about segregation effects and texture, but may also contribute to the identification of phases. Special x-ray techniques which give information about preferred orientation have been omitted in the interests of simplicity, while the identification of single crystals by x-rays (or other techniques) is probably outside the present terms of reference.

Chemical analysis and x-ray (powder) diffraction of bulk samples to establish the general chemical composition and phase constitution are often the first steps in a comprehensive investigation of a material. For the other techniques it is desirable to prepare thin sections cut from lump material and if it is intended to examine both, it is desirable to examine the same area of solid surface from which the thin section has been taken, and if possible to use the same thin section for optical examination as for microradiography. As the diagram implies, the use of a polished surface of a lump of material by reflection microscopy is characteristic of practice with metallurgical specimens and thin section microscopy is more typical of petrological examination. The examination of rocks, ceramics or other materials by reflection microscopy is not excluded. The electron microscope is indicated for either technique, but in fact transmission is most frequently employed. Foils or other thin specimens are generally used, or otherwise solid surfaces are represented by replicas. The scale of magnification in microradiography is, however, comparable to that of the optical microscope.

The diagram draws attention to a number of other points. For example, microradiography may contribute confirmatory evidence or even in certain circumstances provide the main evidence for the identity of certain phases and give information about grain

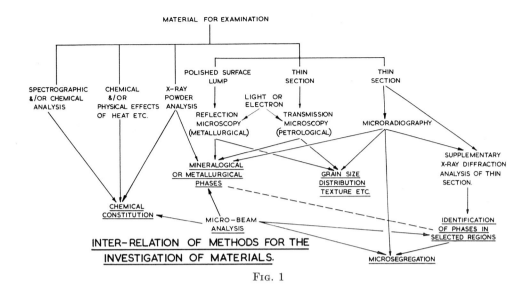

MATERIAL FOR EXAMINATION

INTER-RELATION OF METHODS FOR THE INVESTIGATION OF MATERIALS.

FIG. 1

size, distribution and shape. The use of x-ray diffraction analysis of the same thin section may be valuable in establishing the identity of phases in a particular region, "pinpointed" if necessary by reference to some fiducial marks on the specimen. Such patterns have been used for the identification of phases which have a characteristic appearance on the microradiograph (3) or under the microscope. When the identification of typical localized features is once established the microradiograph alone may then be sufficient for subsequent identification. Microradiography is also directly useful in revealing micro-segregation within grains or passing through grains, and may assist in the identification of inclusions as well as metallurgical phases (See next article).

The comparatively new technique of microbeam analysis (4, 5, 6) has a special place in such a scheme because it gives information about the chemical constitution in a small region and can therefore point to, or confirm, the identity of phases and indicate microsegregation. The technique does in fact employ spectrographic analysis of x-rays emitted from the small region referred to, the excitation being provided by an electron beam.

REFERENCES

1. ANDREWS, K. W. AND JOHNSON, W., "X-ray Microscopy and Micro-radiography," pp. 581–9, 1957, Academic Press, New York. (Edited by V. E. Cosslett, A. Engström and H. H. Pattee, Jr.).
2. JOHNSON, W. AND ANDREWS, K. W., *Iron and Steel*, **31**, 437–444 (1958).
3. McBRIAR, E. MAUD, JOHNSON, W., ANDREWS, K. W., AND DAVIES, W., *J. Iron and Steel Inst.*, **177**, 316 (1954).
4. CASTAING, R. AND DESCAMPS, J., *J. Phys. Radium*, **16**, 304–317 (1955).
5. PHILIBERT, J. AND CRUSSARD, C., *J. Iron and Steel Inst.*, **183**, 42–47 (1956).
6. MELFORD, D. A. AND DUNCUMB, P., *Metallurgia*, **57**, 159–161 (1958).
(See also chapter by P. Duncumb pp. 617–622 of the same volume as Reference (1) above.)

K. W. ANDREWS

IRON AND STEEL APPLICATIONS OF MICRORADIOGRAPHY

The application of microradiography to iron and steel does not usually involve serious difficulties in specimen preparation although cracking due to brittleness can occur, and specimens of the necessary thinness do in fact tend to curve slightly (1). A thickness of 0.002 inch has been found most satisfactory for steels. The preparation of specimens can follow one of the simple established procedures (1, 2, 3, 4).

For ferrous metal specimens the possible choices of radiation can be exploited to advantage, since a number of conventional alloy elements lie in the same row of the periodic table, and the usually available target metals for providing Kα radiations are in the same series. Thus nickel radiation is most heavily absorbed by iron itself, while differentiation of inclusions or other particles containing manganese in particular is facilitated by the high absorption of Cu, Co and Ni radiations and low absorption of Fe, Mn, and Cr radiations. The following figures (2) illustrate this point and bring out the possibility of reversal of contrast.

LINEAR ABSORPTION COEFFICIENTS FOR K
RADIATIONS

Coefficients	Co	Cr	Ni
μ_a Fe	470	903	3120
μ_b MnS	1445	670	1070
$\mu_b - \mu_a$	975	−233	−2050

Figures 1 and 2 show microradiographs of a piece of free-cutting steel which not only illustrate the reversal of contrast with MnS, but also bring out the ease with which the

FIG. 1. Microradiograph with cobalt radiation of free cutting steel showing manganese sulfide sometimes surrounded by lead (white areas). The black striations are cavities due to break up of inclusions during cold drawing. ×100

FIG. 2. Same region as in Fig. 1 but with chromium radiation. MnS regions now darker than matrix. Note: Lead is still represented by white areas. Some lead has squeezed into the cavities in the MnS. ×100

distribution of lead particles can be examined. Other examples of manganese sulfide or lead distribution have been referred to in the literature (1, 2, 3, 5). One of these refers to the presence of MnS inclusions which lie along cracks in broken fatigue specimens. The over-all segregation of manganese in a high manganese steel is represented by a pattern of relatively darker and lighter bands.

Figs. 3, 4, 5 also happen to illustrate the occurrence of manganese sulfide but are of interest in that, by taking advantage of the different absorption properties segregation of chromium is established, and some indication of the presence of other inclusions is obtained. These pictures illustrate a banded segregation of chromium which appeared to suggest that the maximum difference in chromium content might be over 5%.

Another kind of segregation is represented by Fig. 6 a photomicrograph and Fig. 7 a microradiograph of an alloy steel. The segregation is attributed to molybdenum which is present in considerably larger amounts in one phase (sigma) than in the other (ferrite). A notable case of this kind is shown in Fig. 8, the microradiograph of a high alloy steel containing molybdenum and niobium. Other

FIG. 3. Microradiograph. Iron radiation. 12% Cr steel with white streaks due to Cr segregation, containing dark specks due to MnS. ×75.

FIG. 4. Same area as Fig. 3. Cobalt radiation. MnS now also shows up white as well as the Cr segregation. Some dark areas associated with MnS may be cavities or silicate inclusions. ×75

examples of segregation of alloy elements into one phase or another or of segregation into dendrites or other cast structures have been given in the literature (3, 6, 7).

The radiations which are usually available and suitable for the microradiography of

FIG. 5. Same area as in Figs. 3 and 4. Chromium radiation. MnS and associated cavities or silicates are now dark. Cr segregation not revealed. White specks could be due to traces of lead or other heavy element. ×75

iron and steel are such that lead particles always appear lighter than the matrix (higher absorption) while alumina and other light inclusions appear darker (lower absorption). Similarly, graphite flakes show up very readily in cast iron (3, 5) and small graphite particles etc. can easily be detected in graphitized steels (8). Other applications include the study of interdiffusion between metals. A particular example is described by Goldschmidt (9) and concerns the changes which occur during the preparation of iron-chromium alloys by sintering powders.

An effect which is important with relatively coarse-grained ferrous materials (as indeed with any kind of metallic specimen) depends on diffraction. Different grains in a specimen will diffract the incident radiation to different degrees according to their orientation. This effect reduces the intensity of the transmitted beam and may lead to a reproduction of the grain pattern on the microradiograph which readily shows contrast reversals with different radiations or

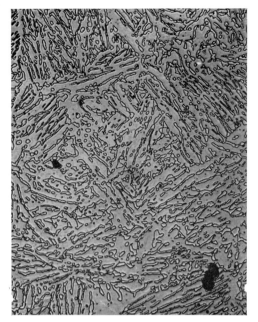 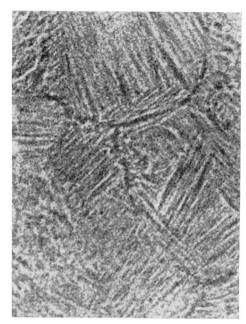

FIG. 6. Photomicrograph ×230   FIG. 7. Microradiograph ×230

Alloy steel (20%Cr, 7%Ni, 3½%Mo) showing sigma phase in austenite matrix after heating at 900°C. for 500 hours. Fig. 7 indicates segregation of molybdenum between the two phases.

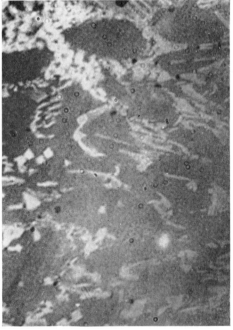 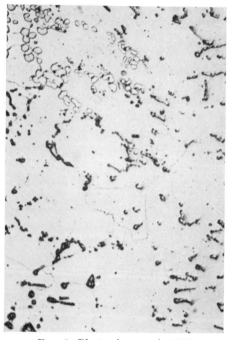

FIG. 8. Microradiograph ×160   FIG. 9. Photomicrograph ×160

Alloy steel (15%Cr, 18%Ni, 3%Mn, 2½%Mo, 7%Co, 2½%Nb). Contains carbides and intermetellic compounds. (Segregation of alloy elements was further elucidated by use of other radiations). Note: Effect of specimen thickness.

590

with the same radiation at different angles of incidence. Examples are given in the literature (5). If microradiography by projection is employed diffraction can produce images which correspond to a reduced intensity of transmitted radiation and simultaneous images from intensity diffracted in forward directions with Bragg angles less than 45° (10). This effect is similar to the phenomenon of diffraction from coarse grains in metal specimens giving mottling effects on macroradiographs (11).

REFERENCES

1. SHARPE, R. S., "X-Ray Microscopy and Microradiography," pp. 591–602, Academic Press, New York, 1957. (Edited by V. E. Cosslett, A. Engström and H. H. Pattee, Jr.)
2. JOHNSON, W. AND ANDREWS, K. W., *Iron and Steel*, **31**, 437–444, 1958.
3. BETTERIDGE, W. AND SHARPE, R. S., *J. Iron and Steel Inst.*, **158**, 185–191 (1948).
4. This Encyclopedia Section, p. 561, 574.
5. ANDREWS, K. W. AND JOHNSON, W., pp. 581–589 of Reference (1).
6. MORLEY, J. I., *Iron and Steel Inst. Spec. Report No. 43*, pp. 195–205. (Esp. Figs. 48–51 and p. 200).
7. KIRKY, H. W. AND MORLEY, J. I., *J. Iron and Steel Inst.*, **158**, 289–294, 1948 (Esp. Figs. 34–40).
8. CLARK, G. L. AND GROSS, S. T., *Ind. Eng. Chem. Anal. Ed.* **14**, 676–683 (1942).
9. GOLDSCHMIDT, H. J., "The Mechanism of Phase Transformations in Metals," pp. 105–119, 1956, The Institute of Metals, London. (Monograph and Report series, No. 18.)
10. VOTAVA, E., BERGHEZAN, A., AND GILLETTE, R. H., pp. 603–616 of Reference (1).
11. GLAISHER, W. H., BETTERIDGE, W., AND EBORALL, R., *J. Inst. Met.*, **70**, 81 (1944).

K. W. ANDREWS
W. JOHNSON

MEDICO-BIOLOGIC RESEARCH BY MICRORADIOGRAPHY

Theory and Technique

Microradiography in medico-biological research is that method by which a magnified radiographic image (microradiograph) of an object is obtained. It is desirable to bring the minimum magnification into this definition because there are many workers using powers as low as 2× or 3×, claiming such slightly enlarged radiographs to be microradiographs. On the other hand, the power may be called "micro" if it brings into view such structures as cells, thin fibers, capillaries, etc., which are not seen with the unaided eye or with the low power mentioned above. It is proposed to consider 35× to be this minimum power of a microradiograph.

Magnification of an x-ray image may be effected with different methods discussed in several articles of this book. Most of these are of recent proposition and are now in the experimental stage; only contact microradiography has been used in medico-biological research for more than 20 years (in relation to this research this method is sometimes called "historadiography"). In 1951 Cosslett and Nixon proposed their "x-ray shadow microscope", later termed "x-ray projection microscope" for use in medico-biological research. Theory and technique of the x-ray projection microscopy are described elsewhere in this book and will therefore not be discussed here. The method attracts with its possibility of obtaining a magnification of the radiographic image without interference from emulsion graininess. Principles of both methods are illustrated in Fig. 1.

Before it can be indefinitely applied in medico-biological research, however, the x-ray projection microscopy has to work out several problems of which the most important is that of the resolution of microstructures with x-rays 1 Å or longer. These rays have a very low effective intensity especially at the distance necessary for a magnified image. This intensity is increased in the contemporary x-ray projection microscopy by making use of higher kilovoltage and, consequently, harder x-rays.

Literature data on the x-ray projection microscopy show, however, that even these

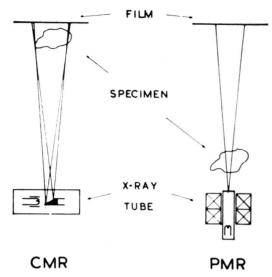

FILM

SPECIMEN

X-RAY
TUBE

CMR   PMR

Fig. 1. Scheme of contact microradiography (CMR) and projection microradiography (PMR). Dependence is shown in P.M.R. of magnification upon the distance: specimen—film.

hard projection micrographs (at 20–30 kv) are made at comparatively short distance because their maximum true magnification (not that achieved by the following photographic enlargement) is shown to be about 30×. This is much lower than the working magnification of contact microradiography (around 120–150×). However, this difficulty of PMR may be overcome through making use of ultra-sensitive emulsions and by carrying out microradiography in vacuum. To our knowledge these experiments are now in progress. There are some reasons to believe that they will be successful and the x-ray projection microscopy may soon be widely used in medico-biological research together with contact microradiography.

Microradiography can take its place in medico-biological research equally with other methods if it complies with the following requirements:

A. If it presents an image of details with satisfactory contrasts and sharpness which reduce the error to an admissible minimum.

B. If a possibility exists of increasing x-ray

absorption artificially via selective x-ray coloring.

C. If there is a facility of comparing microradiographical patterns of details with those obtained by other methods of microscopical anatomy.

It will be shown that all these requirements are fulfilled in microradiography.

Contrast and Sharpness in Microradiography (Terminology relevant to microradiography used in this article, mostly after Bronkhorst (37).

Contrast: The amount of precipitated silver in the emulsion layer of a radiographed and processed film or plate which can be measured in units of blackness. Color of black velvet comprises approximately 2.0 of these units, color of a sheet of white paper—zero units, with all transitions from black to white having a definite numerical expression in these units.

Difference in contrasts: Difference between two contrasts of any present in a microradiograph.

Range of contrasts: The number of contrasts present in a microradiograph. Microradiograph is poor in contrasts if their range is within the limits 20–30; 100 and more is the range of a microradiograph rich in contrasts.

Density: Transparency of a given microradiograph or part of it to the passing light.

Sharpness (definition or detail): The exactness in picturing of details. One point of the image corresponds to one point of the object in an ideally sharp microradiograph.

Marginal sharpness: Sharpness seen on margins of the image of a microstructure.

Depth sharpness: Sharpness of image of microstructures which are far from the emulsion layer during microradiography.

Unsharpness: Inexactness in picturing of details. It is revealed as blurring either of margins or of structural details of the image.

Brightness: Magnitude of light passing through the microradiograph.

Resolution of details: The visualization of structures invisible with the unaided eye.

Resolving power: Ability of an instrument (e.g., microscope), photoemulsion, x-rays, etc. to bring into view structures not seen with the unaided eye.

It is obvious that the resolving power of the microradiograph is closely connected with both contrast and sharpness (see further about the unsharpness due to "discontrasting effect" of the magnification).

Microstructures may be only then visualized in a microradiograph if they absorb a certain amount of x-rays and the effective intensity of rays which passed through these structures is sufficient to produce either a visible contrast within the emulsion layer or a conspicuous fluorescence of the screen. All these dependencies are well expressed in the equation:

$$I^{\text{pr}} = I^{\text{abs}} + I^{\text{eff}} \qquad (1)$$

The primary intensity comprises x-ray factor, the absorbed intensity depends mostly upon the object factor and the effective intensity produces the x-ray image. All these factors will now be discussed in detail.

X-ray Factor. X-rays may resolve in two ways: qualitative and geometrical. The first is the direct x-ray resolution; it is connected only with the quality of x-rays used. It will be discussed in this paragraph. The geometrical resolution is closely connected with the divergency of x-rays. Some data on this resolution will be found in this paragraph (focal spot size). Other data will be in the next paragraphs on object and image.

The direct resolving power of x-rays depends either upon their wave length, if rays are monochromatic, or upon the length of an effective wave, if rays are "white" or "continuous" (mixed). The diapason of wavelengths of soft and ultra soft x-rays (those longer than 4.2 Å) is quite large—from 0.5 to 100 Å. However, in microradiography only x-rays from 1 to 10 Å are used. These wave lengths of white radiation may be obtained at 12 kv and less in the x-ray tube with tungsten target according to the Duane-Hunt law:

$$\lambda_0\,(\text{Å}) = \frac{12{,}400}{V} \ \text{(approximately)} \qquad (2)$$

X-rays 1 Å long are absorbed by all microstructures containing a sufficient amount of an element occupying a high place in the atomic chart, e.g., by any tissue containing calcium or by blood vessels containing x-ray opaque media, artificially introduced. Eight kv which generate white x-rays with the effective wave length 1.55 Å appear to be the lowest tension which can resolve details mentioned above with the necessary contrast and sharpness. Harder rays (at 20–30 kv) produce a blacker image than necessary and do not effectively show certain differences in contrasts, e.g., those between calcium-rich and calcium-poor elements. On the other hand, the effective intensity of x-rays obtained at 3 kv and less may be too weak to produce any differentiation. If we take for example again the calcium-rich tissue, it should appear homogeneously white in an ultra-soft microradiograph.

Lamarque (81–83) has already pointed out that there is no essential difference between a microphotograph and a microradiograph of tissues and cells low in absorbing x-rays, and this assumption is supported to some extent by the following experiment of Bohatirchuk (unpublished): two plates of the same thickness (about 1 mm) one of lead (A) and the other of aluminum (B) were radiographed with x-rays of different penetrative power (Fig. 2). It is obvious that in the radiograph made with 6 kv x-rays (1) there is no difference in contrasts between images of both plates; in other words these soft x-rays are alike to light in their effect. The differentiation becomes visible at 9 kv, but only at 20 kv (2) is it quite clear. Certainly there is no proved indication in the

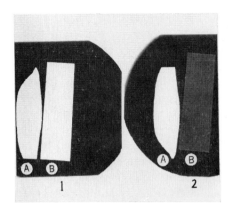

Fig. 2. Magnified radiograph of lead (A) and aluminum (B), both about 1 mm thick. Radiograph (1) is made with soft x-rays about 1.8 Å, radiograph (2) with 0.5 Å. The specific x-ray absorption is not conspicuous in the radiograph made with soft x-rays.

literature that some new or smaller details may be resolved with x-rays obtained at tensions lower than 3 kv. With 2.0 to 4.0 Å the following microstructures can be resolved as described by different authors: cell, i.e., cytoplasm, nucleus (sometimes even nucleolus), cell membrane, sometimes cytoplasm inclusions, fibers, some blood elements, etc. In other words, all structures can be resolved which may be seen within the limits of magnification of a microradiograph (see below). The resolution of such structures as chromosomes, Golgi apparatus, etc. depends more on the resolving power of the emulsion than on the qualitative and geometrical resolutions.

Therefore the tendency of some authors to use ultra-soft x-rays for every kind of microradiography does not appear sound from the point of view of micromorphology.

The beryllium window of the Machlett tube AEG-50A is about 1 mm thick. According to Lurie (86) (see Table 1) this window reduces by half the intensity of a beam of x-rays with the effective wavelength around 2.0 Å. It is therefore possible to get 2.0 Å x-rays out of this tube. However, mindful of the great absorption of these

rays by air (approximately 20 times more than of 1 Å rays) (110) one has to use a very short distance between the beryllium and the object-emulsion. At a longer distance the air between window and object has to be evacuated. X-rays with the wavelength longer than 2.5 Å are absorbed by 1 mm beryllium. According to Lurie, x-rays 4.2 Å long are absorbed by half, even by a beryllium plate as thin as 0.14 mm, which thinness can be achieved only under laboratory conditions. The industrial limit is now 1 mm. As was mentioned above, the air absorption of x-rays 4.2 Å and longer is very considerable. For example, according to Victoreen (110), this absorption for rays 4.2 Å long is almost 70 times more than those of 1 Å. Evidently, all microradiographs with rays longer than 2.5 Å must be done in vacuum and the tube window, if any, has to be very thin and made of metal which occupies a low place in the atomic chart. Aluminum of 50 μ thickness is used for this purpose by most workers. Lamarque pointed out that he used lithium but this metal, although a poor absorber of x-rays, is very difficult to handle. Lindemann glass (containing boron, lithium and beryllium instead of silicon, sodium and calcium of ordinary glass) is used in Europe for windows. This glass is hard and resistant to atmospheric pressure even in thin sections. However, the x-ray absorption by Linde-

TABLE 1

Wavelength (Å)	Half-Value Layer, in Millimeters	
	Air	Beryllium
.25	27400	23.8
.63	6440	15.1
1.0	1940	7.0
1.24	1040	4.05
1.54	550	2.41
1.93	287	1.26
2.5	136	.63
3.6	43.7	.21
4.2	30.6	.14
7.0	6.2	.026
9.9	2.3	.010

mann glass is a little greater than by beryllium. A scheme of the AEG-50A Machlett tube with the vacuum camera is shown in Fig. 3. The similar camera was made for our tube by R. H. Archer (Ottawa, Civic Hospital).

Until now we have discussed the continuous radiation produced by the tungsten target. Yet there is another way to obtain soft and ultra soft x-rays by using higher kilovoltages. These x-rays, so-called "characteristic", are emitted at a definite tension by a target made of a specific material. The above mentioned Duane-Hunt law (*2*) is not applicable to characteristic rays. Their wavelength depends upon other laws discussed in works on the subject where one can find both the target material and the necessary tension for the emission of this radiation. It is possible to make these characteristic rays monochromatic using special filters. Targets of chromium (λ 2.287 Å at 6 kv), iron (λ 1.935 Å at 7 kv) and copper (λ 1.539 Å at 9 kv) are producers of characteristic radiation most frequently used (38). This characteristic monochromatic radiation is especially important for precise quantitative and qualitative analyses. These, however, meet with many practical difficulties in their application to biological specimens. The detailed description of methods may be found elsewhere (Clark) (38).

The size of the focal spot is very important for obtaining sharp microradiographs. This size is 1.5 mm square in projection in the Machlett AEG-50A tube, and is 40 μ in the Hilger & Watt microfocus tube. It may be reduced to still smaller size through the application of the condenser and objective lenses as is done in the Cosslett-Nixon tube for x-ray projection microscopy or in the electron microscope.

The smaller the focal spot the more is the geometrical resolution of x-rays, i.e. the less is the penumbra formation. These dependencies are discussed in detail in special publications on the subject (11)(23)(38)(90)(99).

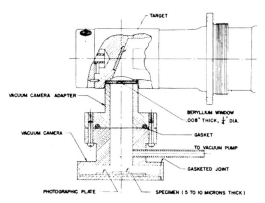

FIG. 3. Scheme of Machlett AEG-50A tube with vacuum camera, specimen and plate in place as given by Lurie (86).

The scattering in air of both kinds of secondary rays, modified and unmodified by the Compton effect, is quite considerable for soft rays used in microradiography (see equation *3*). However, the influence of scattered rays on image formation may be reduced to a minimum by using several diaphragms on the path between tube target and object. Lead pipes covering the entire distance between the tube target and the cassette cover may be used with the same effect. Such a pipe is shown in Fig. 23.

Object Factor. With a rough approximation the x-ray absorption (*m*) in biological tissues may be expressed in such an equation:

$$m = k\lambda^3 \cdot Z^4 \text{ (approximately)} + 0.2 \quad (3)$$

where λ is the wave length, Z (AN) number of element in atomic chart, k the constant and 0.2 the coefficient of scattering.

Hydrogen (Z 1), carbon (Z 6), nitrogen (Z 7), oxygen (Z 8) and calcium (Z 20) are the main elements present in animal (human) body in considerable quantities; sulfur (Z 16), iron (Z 26) and phosphorus (Z 15) comprise only a small percentage of body components. Zuppinger (116) gives for macroradiology the following data on linear coefficients of attenuation (Table 2). From

TABLE 2. LINEAR ABSORPTION COEFFICIENTS

(after table from Zuppinger)

Substance	Spec. Gravity	Chemical Composition	Linear Absorption Coefficient
Water	1.0	H_2O	2.506 λ^3
Protein		C 52%, H 7%, N 16%, O 24%, S 1%	1.78 λ^3
Fat (man)	0.9	C 75.6%, H 12.6%, O 11.8%	1.135 λ^3
Muscle	1.06	W 80%, Pr 18%, F 1%, Sa 0.9%	2.62 λ^3
Blood	1.06	W 80%, Pr 19.1%, Sa 0.9%	2.61 λ^3
Transudate	1.008	W 96.8%, Pr 2.4%, Ash 0.8%	2.72 λ^3
Exudate	1.02	W 93.3%, Pr 5.9%, Ash 0.8%	2.69 λ^3
Pus	1.06	W 90.6%, Pr 7.8%, F 0.8%, Sa 0.8%	2.67 λ^3
Tendon (conn. tissue)	1.1	W 62.9%, Pr 34.7%, F and similar subst. 1.9%, inorganic Sa 0.5%	2.37 λ^3
Fat tissue	0.92	W 11.7%, Pr 2.1%, F 86%, Ash 0.2%	1.37 λ^3
Calcium stone	2.6	$CaCO_3$	22.85 λ^3
Compact bone	1.9	W 26%, Pr 24.5%, F 2.3%, Ash 47.2%	13.24 λ^3
Liver	1.06	W 76%, Pr 20%, F 3%, Ash 1%	2.61 λ^3
Hairs	1.3	C 50.5%, H 6.4%, N 17.1%, O 20.7%, S 5%, Ash 0.3%	2.89 λ^3
Spleen	1.05	W 78%, Pr 16%, F 5%, Ash 1%	2.61 λ^3
Kidney	1.06	W 83.5%, Pr 15.7%, Ash 0.8%	2.62 λ^3
Lung		W 80.1%, Pr 16%, F 2.7%, Ash 1.2%	2.69 λ^3
Thyroid	1.06	W 82%, Pr 16%, Ash 1%, with I 0.016%	2.70 λ^3
Iron	7.86	Fe	107.7 λ^3
Nerves	1.03	W 76%, Pr 7%, Ch and Lipids 13.5%, Ash 1.5%, S 0.5%, P 1.5%	3.12 λ^3
		W—water, F—fat, Pr—protein, Sa—salts, Ch—Cholesterol	

this table one may see that x-ray absorption comprises in muscle 2.62 λ^3, blood 2.61 λ^3, liver and spleen 2.61 λ^3, kidney 2.62 λ^3; in other words they have equal or almost equal absorption coefficients. Only hairs (2.89 λ^3), thyroid and cartilage (2.70 λ^3), placenta (2.75 λ^3) and especially nerves (3.12 λ^3) possess more or less high coefficients distinguishing them from other tissues. One may find out from this table that some organs cannot be differentiated one from another in radiographs (for instance liver and spleen, or muscle and kidney, etc.); the difference of absorption between some tissues is so minute that they also have little chance to be differentiated (e.g., muscle from liver and spleen). The situation with absorption improves considerably in microradiography due to another factor of equation 3—λ^3. If, for instance, the difference in attenuation

coefficients between carbon and oxygen is 0.802 for 1 Å, this difference with 2.0 Å wavelength comprises 5.973, in other words it increases about 7 times (110). However, this possibility of improving the morphological differentiation has its limits in medicobiological research due to the very slight penetrative power of ultra soft x-rays (see above).

From the study of all these data one may conclude that the application of microradiography to the study of genuine (noncontrasted) body tissues encounters many difficulties which are partly unsurmountable at this stage of development in microradiographical technique. Only calcium-containing tissues possess an absorption coefficient so high that they can be differentiated in all their parts without the technique of coloring. One has not to forget, however, that contemporary histology was developed due to the introduction of coloring (or staining). The same possibility exists in microradiography.

Until now the object of microradiography made with white radiation was approached mainly from a morphological point of view. An analytical physico-chemical approach to such a microradiograph is also possible to some extent. This idea was suggested by Lamarque (81) and worked out by Engström (53), who proposed to radiograph simultaneously the specimen and, as the author calls it, the reference system. This consists of foils of nitrated cellulose having different thicknesses. The composition of cellulose is as follows: C—43%, O—41%, N—7% and H—5%, that is, it is quite close to the composition of protein. Fig. 4 shows how microradiography proceeds in this case. It is obvious that each thickness of foil produces a quite definite contrast which may be compared with those of tissue components. Consequently, according to this author, the mass (weight) of biological tissue may be determined. This interesting idea is connected, however, with some practical difficulties, limitations and possible errors, which are discussed in detail in the original works on this subject (see especially Brattgardt and Hyden) (36).

The coefficient of scattering in biological tissue seems to be quite considerable (see equation 3). It increases proportionally to the wavelength of x-rays and to the percentage of water in radiographed tissue. However, since specimens are mostly dehydrated, cut in thin sections and are in close contact with the emulsion during radiography, the influence of scattering on the formation of penumbras may be neglected.

The thickness of the object and its influence on image formation will next be discussed.

X-ray Image Factor. A microradiographical image is the result of complicated interrelations among the qualitative resolv-

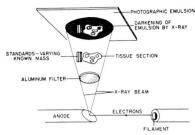

FIG. 4. Scheme of Engström's reference system radiographed with specimen. Standards produce image of various contrasts depending upon known mass of foil. Identical image contrasts of reference system and specimen have evidently the identical mass (from Fitzgerald) (63).

ing power of x-rays, absorption of x-rays by varied object components, geometrical resolution by x-ray beam, and the graininess of the emulsion. The last two items have a direct relation to the image formation and therefore will be discussed in this paragraph.

Geometrical Characteristics of the X-ray Beam. Let us imagine that the immobile specimen is radiographed with divergent x-rays emitted from the point-like focal spot, on a practically grainless emulsion of negligible thickness and with no interference of secondary radiation. Then the unsharpness will be directly proportional: (a) to the size of the focal spot discussed above, (b) to the thickness of the specimen and, connected with it, the superimposition of images of microstructures, and (c) the distance between specimen and emulsion (Fig. 5).

It is obvious that the influence of the second factor may be diminished by making the object as thin as possible; the best remedy for the third is the closest contact between specimen and emulsion.

There are many superimpositions of images of microstructures lying at different levels of a three-dimensional specimen as seen in a two-dimensional microradiograph. The thicker the specimen the greater is the number of these superimpositions and the less is the chance to obtain an image of microstructure free of them. It is observed that the unsharpness caused by superimposi-

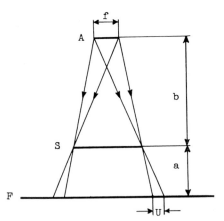

FIG. 5. Scheme of geometrical unsharpness (from Engström) (54). S—specimen, F—film, A—focal spot, b—distance specimen—focal spot, a—distance specimen—emulsion, U—penumbra. It is evident that penumbra (U) is the greater the farther the specimen is from emulsion. The closer it is, the less its image is blurred by divergent x-rays.

tions, even if it seems insignificant at low power, becomes more and more pronounced with increasing magnification. This loss of sharpness together with the "discontrasting" effect of magnification diminishes evidently the resolving power of the microradiograph.

No literature data are available on the ratio between the thickness of specimen and the maximum possible magnification of microradiograph. Cosslett (40) showed that the resolution of microstructures in an electron micrograph of a section cannot be more than one tenth of the thickness of the section. In other words, one cannot expect to see details smaller than one tenth of a micron in an electron micrograph of a section one micron thick. Although there are no direct indications in the literature, apparently a similar ratio exists in optical microscopy. However, the optical resolution of the microscope may be improved to some extent by making use of the micrometer. The use of this is very limited in the study of contact microradiographs. The micrometer may be applied only for the better viewing of parts of microradiographical image lying in different planes of the emulsion

coat. Evidently, the above-mentioned ratio has to be in microradiography other than 1:10 pointed out by Cosslett, probably 1:2 or even 1:1. According to our experience one may expect to obtain a sharp x-ray image of a microstructure, that is to say, an image which remains sharp at maximum magnification, if the radiographed section contains merely this structure or is at least no more than twice as thick as this structure. In other words, it is possible from the geometrical point of view to get a sharp image of a structure 5 μ in diameter only in microradiographs of sections 5 μ or at the most 10 μ thick.

The contact between the emulsion and the object is achieved by pressure on all parts of the object. This may be done with a film of some polyethylene resin (e.g. "Teflon," "Alathon" of DuPont) 0.00001 in. thick (or even thinner if available). These films only slightly absorb x-rays, are resistant to alkalies and acids, and are structureless as seen in microradiographs.

In the cassette used by us (Fig. 6) the plastic film is stretched on the interior (inferior) side of the upper cassette cover. When the cover is in place the plastic film presses the object which is put on a fine-grain plate in the middle of the cassette base. After the plastic has worn out it may be changed easily. In the middle of the cassette cover there is a round opening 1 in. in diameter over which a light-proof film is stretched which does not absorb x-rays. Aluminum is not good for this purpose because it is mostly transparent to light rays in thin sections and has a structure conspicuous in microradiographs. Light-proof films may be made in one's own laboratory by bathing celloidine film (about 0.00001 in thick) in an alcoholic solution (0.25%) of Sudan black. The entire upper part of the cassette is covered with lead 2–3 mm thick in order to protect the x-ray plate from any secondary radiation emitted by air. The

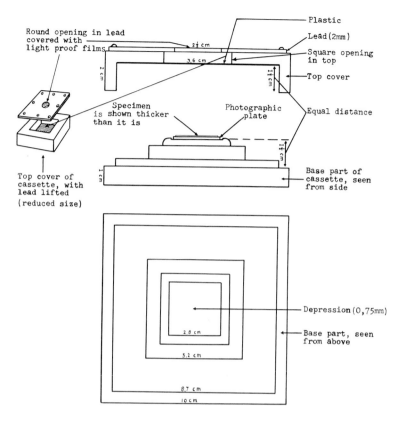

Scheme of Microradiographical Cassette

FIG. 6. Scheme of MRD cassette used by Bohatirchuk (explanation in text).

base and cover of the cassette are made of hard wood.

The cassette proposed by Sherwood (104) is much more complicated. In this "vacuum exposure holder for microradiography" the contact between specimen and emulsion is achieved through the evacuation of air between object and emulsion. This is performed with an air pump connected with the interior of the cassette (Fig. 7). Unfortunately, this cassette cannot be used in microradiography of medico-biological specimens because, owing to the vacuum inside the cassette, its cover has to be made of a hard and thick plastic material resistant to atmospheric pressure. Such a cover absorbs soft and ultra soft x-rays used in medico-biological microradiography.

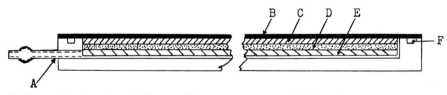

FIG. 7. Schematic drawing of Sherwood's vacuum exposure holder. A—vacuum pump connection B—opaque cover, C—specimen, D—photographic emulsion on glass plate, E, F—grooved trap (from Sherwood) (104).

The most perfect contact is easily achieved in microradiography of sections of undecalcified bone (see below); the most difficult is to get it in wet specimens. In the first case the bone section has a smooth, dry surface; in the second it may stick to the emulsion and the subsequent tearing off damages the emulsion. In other cases the emulsion is damaged by alkalis or acids present in wet specimens. Different methods are at hand to avoid this complication. Bohatirchuk (23) (26) (125) proposed to mount specimens on thin sheets of plastic (e.g., "Alathon"), and then place the mounted specimen plastic-down on the emulsion. Specimens mounted on plastic are prevented from shrinking; they may undergo coloring procedures and may be preserved for a long time. Engström (54) proposed to cover the emulsion with collodion, usually a few microns thick, prior to mounting the specimen. After radiography the collodion film is taken off easily and the plate developed afterward.

In some cases wet specimens may be dried by putting them between two pieces of fine blotting (or filter) paper which in turn are pressed between two glass slides. This simple method is very good, especially in handling thick sections.

It is quite obvious that the system x-ray tube: specimen: emulsion has to be held motionless during microradiography. The shrinking and the resulting motion of the wet specimen during long exposures, especially

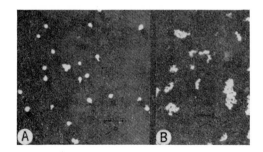

Fig. 8. Replica electron micrograph of unexposed and processed grains of a NTB emulsion (reproduced from Boyd) (35). A. before, B. after development (explanation in text).

under vacuum, may be avoided only through the shortening of the exposure time. Vibration of the building due to traffic or trembling of the tube due to boiling water in the cooling hoses are among the causes of unsharpness. They should be foreseen and avoided.

It is possible in some objects, e.g., bone and teeth, to cut sections serially in planes perpendicular one to another. This allows the reconstruction of micro-anatomical interrelations from their microradiographs.

It is necessary to mention here that the thickness (discussed in this paragraph) is considered to be equal in all parts of the object. This condition presents difficulties in microradiography of natural (not sectioned) objects. Evidently, a sharp microradiographical image may be obtained only of those parts of natural objects which are in close contact with the emulsion and are thin enough to permit the magnification of their image.

Graininess of the Emulsion. The mosaic character of x-ray image is due to the silver grains of the emulsion. The graininess is revealed even at comparatively low magnification in the usual emulsions of high sensitivity. The emulsion for microradiography must have the finest grain possible. Many firms and companies in Europe and America nowadays produce such emulsions. Only the properties of the most frequently used Kodak and Gevaert emulsions will be discussed here. Eastman Kodak (USA) manufactures fine-grain spectroscopic plates 649-O or GH and high resolution plates as well as other samples. Gevaert (Belgium) issues Lippmann films and Scientia 5e 56 plates. Emulsions of these samples of both companies have very much in common.

Regular size of grains of a fine-grain emulsion is within the limits of a few millimicrons (5–15 mμ). Grains acquire irregular shape after processing and their size increases (Fig. 8, reproduced from Boyd) (35). Even distribution of grains and dense concentration are prerequisites of a sharp image at high magnification. Unfortunately, these properties cannot be controlled easily and they vary therefore from one sample of emulsion to another, and even within the sample itself. There was an attempt to increase the density of grains in some experimental fine-grain emulsions (Blackett) (19). Although the microradiographs of this author made on this emulsion appear to be a step forward, there is no indication in the literature as yet that the plates coated with this emulsion are produced commercially.

Thickness of the emulsion coat varies in different emulsions, being in finest samples around 5–10 μ. Sensitivity of fine-grain emulsions is very low; if the sensitivity of an ordinary x-ray emulsion is taken for one, the sensitivity of Gevaert Lippmann emulsion will be 1/10,000 and that of No. 649-O or GH spectroscopic plates of Eastman Kodak about 1/15,000. Exposure time is therefore quite long, from 2 to 60 minutes, depending in inverse ratio on the kilovoltage used and on the thickness of the specimen. On the average, one tenth of a second exposure on x-ray film will require about 16 minutes on Lippmann film and about 25 minutes on Kodak 649 (see also below). Gevaert Lippmann films are more sensitive at lower kilovoltages than Kodak spectroscopic plates. "Scientia" 5e 56 plates issued by Gevaert not so long ago have very fine grain and approximately the same sensitivity as Kodak 649-GH samples.

Resolving power varies in different samples. Producers of fine-grain emulsions claim that the finest samples resolve about 1,000 lines per mm. This means that this finest emulsion may resolve structures of 1 μ size. However, what is right for an almost two-dimensional ruler-line is not always so in relation to a biological three-dimensional microstructure. A line is seen relatively sharp even in the presence of grains, but not the biological structure. Besides that, the resolution of objects 1 μ in size comes across the

limitation of geometrical resolving power mentioned above.

Processing of exposed fine-grain films and plates does not differ much from that of ordinary material but it requires meticulous cleanliness. All the solutions have to be filtered every day, the glass ware thoroughly cleaned. Washing has to be carried out with distilled water, the drying to proceed in exsiccators. Ready microradiographs have to be covered with cover glass for better preservation. In general, darkroom accessories must be as in a chemical laboratory where qualitative and quantitative analyses are performed. D-19 or usual x-ray developer produce good results (the latter 50% diluted). Time of development with these developers is from 3 to 5 minutes. No advantage was found with other developers recommended for fine-grain emulsions, in particular microdol. The time of development with microdol is much longer (10 to 12 minutes) and the achieved range of contrasts is rather poor.

A recipe for the preparation of a fine-grain emulsion in any laboratory is given in the paper by Bohatirchuk (125).

Each magnification of any photo-image has a somewhat "discontrasting" effect. This is due to the fact that silver grains, which seem to be solidly packed at a lower magnification, appear separated at a higher one. It is obvious that the smaller the grains of emulsion are and the closer they are packed in the emulsion layer, the less is the discontrasting effect.

It is accepted that the minimum difference in contrasts which may be observed in macroradiographs is about 30%. In other words, one cannot distinguish blackness 1.5 from 1.2; only 1.5 from 2.0 or from 1.0. This percentage is about 15–20% in microradiography in spite of the discontrasting effect of magnification. Cytoplasm and cell membrane, cytoplasm and nucleus may be differentiated though their difference in contrasts is even less than 15–20%. This is shown by the work of Lamarque, Turchini (83) and others.

It is necessary to mention here attempts to use for microradiography another material sensitive to x-rays. W. A. Ladd and M. W. Ladd (80) and Pattee *et al.* (95) found that a completely grainless x-ray image can be obtained on some plastic (e.g., vinylidene chloride) after a certain exposure time. Although its range of contrasts may be increased through bathing the exposed plastic in NH_4OH (10%) the image obtained remains very indistinct. Authors express hope, however, that they will succeed in improving these preliminary results.

Limit of magnification of microradiograph. It is obvious from the foregoing that the resolving power of a microradiograph depends upon three components: qualitative and geometrical resolutions by the x-rays, and resolution by the emulsion. Only then can one expect the maximum resolution in a microradiograph when each of these components produces, in harmony with the others, the best effect. Both qualitative and geometric resolutions are to some extent under the control of the researcher, but the resolution of the emulsion is not.

Summarizing the data discussed above one may conclude that the maximum magnification can be obtained if the microradiograph is made: (1) with x-rays 1 Å or longer, (2) of a section 10 μ and thinner and (3) on fine-grain emulsion like 649-O or GH sample. This maximum is around 300–336×, i.e., 20× objective and 15× eyepiece or 42× objective and 8× eyepiece. As was mentioned above the average (working) magnification is around 120× to 150×. Since the average thickness of sections used in microradiography is 10 μ, 5 μ size is the smallest microstructure of which a sharp and contrast image may be expected. Only in the exceptional case of a finest-grain emulsion may one observe a sharp and contrast image of detail 1 μ size, but this is possible only in microradiographs of sections 1 to 2 μ thick.

Apparently one cannot expect notable improvement of the above mentioned limit of magnification in microradiographs for the near future unless a new sensitive material to x-rays will become available.

One may consider that the little magnification possible in microradiography cannot reveal new data unknown to general micromorphology. This is wrong, as will be shown later, because microstructures are seen from a new and peculiar point of view which is presented due to selective x-ray absorption. After all, knowledge of micromorphology is not so perfect that this new possibility may be rejected.

One may conclude that both contrast and sharpness of contact microradiographs can be obtained sufficient for visualization of micromorphological structures within the limits of the method. These data can be used with certain reservations for qualitative and quantitative analyses of biological tissues.

Selective X-ray Coloring of Vessels, Canals, Cavities, and other Elements of Biological Tissues

After Baker, who proposed to use the term "coloring" instead of "staining" in histology, it was thought that the term "x-ray coloring" could well designate any procedure connected with the artificial increase of x-ray absorbing capacities.

Numerous x-ray coloring media (called here also x-ray opaque or contrast media, or simply OM or CM) are used in microradiography. Choice depends on the purpose of the research. Negative contrasting (through the injection of air) is not used in microradiography. Opaque media for microradiography may be introduced either in vivo ("vital injection") or post mortem. The introduction post mortem may be carried out in both humans and animals; vital injection is used only in experiments. There are two kinds of vital injection used in microradiography: (1) direct and (2) indirect. The direct method is called microvasography or microradiovasography (Bohatirchuk) (22) or micro-angiography (Bellman) (12). In this method OM is injected into the blood stream and is retained in the blood vessels of the whole body or of a single organ for the duration of the experiment. In the indirect method OM is also introduced into the blood stream but with this it is only transferred to some organs or tissues which absorb this OM. Post mortem coloring may also be of two kinds: (3) through direct injection of OM, and (4) through selective absorption of OM.

Direct Vital Injection of OM. Direct vital injection may be either total or local. The purpose of the total vital injection is to use the heart as a pressure pump for bringing OM to the minute vessels of any desired organ of the experimental animal. This method seems to be the most natural way of filling capillaries with OM. Accordingly, OM has to mix with the blood and must not cause any obstacle in the blood circulation, nor shock to the animal or immediate fatal effects. OM particles, if any, have to be much smaller than the diameter of the narrowest capillary (around 5–7 μ). The greater the particles are the greater is the danger of obstructing vitally important capillaries with sudden death of the animal resulting. One has to remember that particles of all OM have a tendency to stick together producing an embolus of larger size than one particle.

Thorotrast is the best OM for direct vital injection. It may be introduced into the animals blood in quantity up to 10% of its body weight. It does not irritate the walls of the blood vessels and does not provoke spasms as iodine frequently does. Thorotrast, due to the high number of thorium in the atomic chart (290), produces contrast images even in so weak concentrations as 1 or 2% (more details about thorotrast see further).

The experiment with direct total vital microvasography proceeds as follows:

(1) Blood is taken from the heart or aorta

in the maximum permissible quantity (Wiggers) (115).

(2) OM is administered. It is better to take out blood and inject OM by portions although it prolongs the experiment for 1 or 2 minutes.

(3) Pathological agent (cold, heat, drug, etc.) is applied.

(4) The animal is sacrificed no later than 5 minutes after the beginning of the experiment. The method of killing must not cause the displacement of the contrasted blood in capillaries. Therefore, death has to be achieved as fast as possible. Electric shock is probably the best method in this case.

(5) Desired organs are taken out and prepared for microradiography according to general rules.

Local vital injection is much easier to carry out. OM is introduced directly into the artery of a desired organ (e.g. kidney, ovary, etc.) and this is taken out after OM appears in vasa efferentia. Much greater concentrations of OM in the capillaries may be achieved with this method than in total vital injection. In addition to thorotrast other OM may be used (pantopaque, urocon, etc.).

Indirect Vital Injection of OM. This examination is used to visualize the elements of the reticulo-endothelial system (RES). It is known that any particles, especially colloidal ones, being introduced into blood, if not excreted (secreted) are at first adsorbed and then absorbed by RES cells.

Of all opaque media, "Thorotrast" (Heyden, Germany, and an American preparation under the same name) is mostly used for this study. Thorotrast is the trade name for the colloidal solution of thorium dioxide. It contains from 22 to 26% thorium by volume. Negatively charged particles of thorium are a few millimicrons in size. Thorotrast is well tolerated by animals, mixes with blood perfectly, and its pH is about 7.2. Another preparation of thorium is umbrathor. It has an acid reaction (pH about 2.3). It is not so well tolerated as

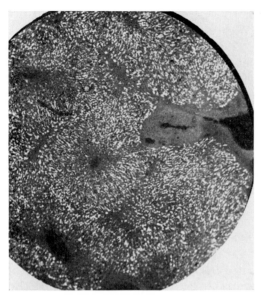

FIG. 9. MRD (microradiograph) of a normal rabbit liver in a case of indirect vital injection of thorotrast. Section 10 μ, 2 hours after injection, approx. ×80.

Typical distribution of thorotrast in RES elements of liver lobules.

All the microphotographs (called MRD) of this article are reproductions of original microradiographs, i.e. their maximum white color corresponds to the maximum absorption of X-rays in an object, the maximum black to the minimum absorption.

thorotrast and contains a little less thorium (about 22% by volume). Disadvantages of thorotrast are its slight radioactivity (half life about 25 years) and the perpetual retention in cells of RES. These drawbacks, however, are mostly of no importance in research with vital injections which last a short time.

Figures 9 and 10 present microradiographs of the liver and spleen of rabbit and dog (both normal) after vital injection of thorotrast: 10 cc to rabbit and 15 cc to dog, two hours before sacrificing the animals. One may see rows of Kupffer cells in the liver and histiocytes in the spleen packed with thorotrast (Bohatirchuk) (21) (24). These pictures suggest that the thorotrast impregnation of RES cells may be used not only

for the study of the morphology of RES elements but also for the examination of their function. Thorotrast disappears completely from the blood in 4 to 6 hours. If, for some reason, thorotrast is contraindicated, one may use the colloidal preparation of iodine: iodocol sol (Mulford Colloid Laboratories, Philadelphia, USA). A similar preparation "iodsolen" was made in Germany (Schering Co.) shortly before the war. Both these preparations are not radioactive and are excreted from the RES cells within 24 hours. However, the x-ray opacity produced by both colloids is very slight and may be detected only in very soft microradiographs.

In addition to liver and spleen small quantities of thorotrast are found after vital injection in the RES elements of lymphatic glands, kidneys and lungs. However, the data on these findings are very scanty.

There are a few indications that iron (Barclay) (6), bismuth (Lamarque) (82) were found in the lungs of experimental

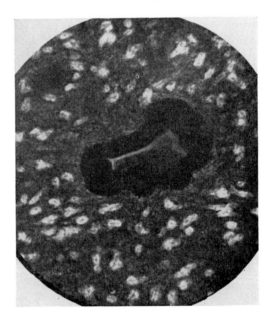

FIG. 10. MRD of dog spleen, 24 hours after indirect vital injection of thorotrast, approx. ×180, 10 μ.

Thorotrast within histiocytes. Observe that OM is only in cytoplasm, nuclei remain black.

animals. These data also remain unelaborated.

Montichelli *et al.* reported preliminarily that in some cases of hyperthyroidism increased absorption of iodine was found in the thyroid gland via microradiography. Unfortunately, neither a further report by these authors about their results nor information about the technique used is found so far in the literature.

OM is injected subcutaneously in the method called microlymphography. From this depot OM spreads into minute lymphatic vessels. After several hours the animal is sacrificed and the organ of which the lymphatic capillaries should be studied is taken out and prepared for microradiography in the normal way. Thorotrast is considered the best OM for this method (14) (39).

Some authors recommend stereo-microangiography and stereo-microlymphography. Since literature data do not mention any achievement in medical research accomplished by these methods their detailed description is omitted. Any one interested may find this not only in the works mentioned above but also in publications by Engström (55); Oden *et al.* (92); Pattee *et al.* (95).

Direct Injection of OM Post Mortem. There is a wide choice of OM with particles small enough to pass through the narrowest capillaries. Many iodine compounds (diodrast, pantopaque, uroconsodium, telepaque, etc.); colloidal solutions (thorotrast, umbrathor, colloidal bismuth, etc.); emulsions (micropaque, bismuth subcarbonate, etc.); various preparations of mercury and other OM are used for this purpose.

The administration of OM into arteries or veins is carried out along general lines, covered in textbooks on anatomical and pathological techniques. One should be careful to avoid any forcing during the filling of the vessels with OM. Extravasation caused by torn capillaries or aterioles can produce a non-existing contrast in a large area of the microradiograph. As was mentioned above,

it is also necessary to prevent the outflow of OM from the capillaries, which frequently happens during cutting. Mindful of this possibility it is better to use as dispersing media solutions of starch, dextrose or gum arabic, because these media are mostly converted into gels after formalin fixation of the specimen. It is also possible to prevent the outflow of OM by keeping the temperature of the section below freezing point for the whole time of exposure. For this purpose the interior of the microradiographical cassette has to be connected with the freezing gas. Although to our knowledge some researchers use such equipment it is not described in the literature relevant to microvasography. Sometimes the outflow of OM may be indirectly prevented by making use of thicker sections (up to 500 μ). Though microvasographs of these sections permit only low magnification they present a good picture sufficient for general orientation in the morphology of capillaries. Some instructions on the subject of technique may be found in works of Bellman (12); Barclay (7); Okawa and Trombka (93) and others.

Post Mortem Selective Coloring by OM. The first indication in the literature on the possibility of post mortem coloring may be found in the work of Clark (38) and Mitchell (89). It was pointed out that some OM are absorbed selectively by different biological tissues. As was mentioned above we prefer to use the term "adsorption" instead of "absorption" for the initial stages of OM consumption because OM is at first localized outside the cell membrane and only after some time may it be found within the cell as well.

In this method of coloring a section of biological tissue is immersed into OM solution for several hours, then washed, dried and radiographed. It was found that some embedding media (e.g., paraffin, celloidin) impede the normal adsorption of OM. Therefore, they have to be removed before immer-

Fig. 11. MRD of a normal rabbit heart after post mortem coloring with thorotrast, 25 μ, approx. ×35.

Selective absorption of thorotrast by contracting muscle substance is conspicuous.

sion. Besides that, paraffin absorbs x-rays and may produce erroneous images.

Bohatirchuk (unpublished) has immersed 15 μ (or thicker) frozen sections of cat spinal cord for 24 hours into the following solutions: thorotrast, neo-silvol (colloidal silver iodide, 24% of silver), iodocol sol (iodine 8%), ferrocol sol (colloidal iron 3.5%), sequestrol (colloidal lead, 6%) and Lange's colloidal gold solution (0.01%). The most conspicuous selective adsorption found in microradiographs was that of thorotrast. All other solutions were either adsorbed very little (neo-silvol) or could not be detected in microradiographs at all. Note, however, that microradiography in this experiment was done with 1.2 Å (8 kv) x-rays; it is possible that softer radiation would bring to view also tissues only slightly colored with OM (the description of morphological findings will be given later). Apparently, silver is selectively adsorbed by the same tissue elements as thorotrast. However, final conclusions on the adsorption (or absorption) of silver and other OM (with the exception of thorotrast) depend on further study.

Selective adsorption (or absorption) of OM depends probably upon the signs of electrical charges in both adsorbent (OM)

and adsorber (element of biological tissue). Adsorber and adsorbent must have opposite charges in order to be attracted. This assumption may be proved in the case of thorotrast adsorption by positively charged or amphoteric tissues. Fig. 11 shows a macroradiograph of heart muscle of rabbit after a section of it was immersed into thorotrast for several hours. It is obvious that the amphoteric contracting muscle substance selectively adsorbs OM. Another example is the adsorption of thorotrast by positively charged collagen. It is known also that thorotrast is never absorbed by negatively charged tissues such as cartilage, chromatin, etc. One should mention that biological tissues do not show any affinity for neutral OM (e.g., for barium and bismuth).

All these data support the old Ehrlich theory of coloring, according to which the sign of electrical charge is primarily responsible for the adsorption (or absorption) of dye (Baker) (5).

Summarizing data on x-ray coloring in general, we may say that this method can be used in microradiography and should bring, even with the limitations of magnification mentioned above, new data important for medico-biological research.

Comparison of Microradiographic Data with those of Other Methods used in Anatomy and Histology

As was mentioned above, a microradiograph presents usually a real image of a biological microstructure and not its "shadow" as many authors think (some of them even use such a strange term as "shadowgraph") (47). Only in an ordinary photograph does one see sometimes an object and its structureless shadow; in the microradiograph each image is full of structure. In addition to that, it is possible to color some microstructures, low in absorbing x-rays, with OM and to study their real image in microradiographs. The process of selective absorption of OM and the following visualization of microstructures is very similar to that in histology. No one, however, calls histological specimen "shadow" of the dyes used for their visualization. In order to avoid this misunderstanding we do not use the term "x-ray shadow" in our work, but call any radiograph of a structure an "x-ray image" of this. Resink (98) calls a real x-ray image of a real structure "supraliminae" contrary to "infraliminae" or unreal image caused by superimposition of images of other structures or by penumbras of other origin. If the microradiograph is made in accordance with the above rules its images will be mostly "supraliminae."

However, real microradiographic images are not always easy to interpret; they have too many peculiarities characteristic only for x-ray images.

The student of morphology as it is seen in microradiographs is able to compare radiographical images with known anatom-ical and histological patterns and to make the three-dimensional reconstruction of microstructures from their images in serial microradiographs (81) (82). It is necessary to emphasize the important works of Vincent (111) (112) (113) (145), Lacroix and Ponlot (79), who were the first to use microradiography, autoradiography and histological coloring of the same section of bone (bone was decalcified only for histology).

Bohatirchuk (30) proposed "stain histo-radiography" for simultaneous study of undecalcified bone together with surrounding soft tissues and bone marrow (unfortunately, it was impossible to call this method "color microradiography" because of possible misunderstanding). In this method a section of undecalcified bone, usually 10 μ thick, is radiographed with x-rays 1.0 Å long and subjected afterward to coloring procedures without previous decalcification or disembedding (Fig. 12).

A

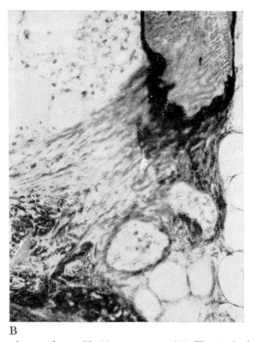

B

Fig. 12. A—MRD, B—Stained specimen of the same human bone, 72, 10μ, approx. ×256. The typical stain-historadiograph. The presence of decalcified tissue with cells is shown in those parts of specimen which do not reveal any calcium. Especially conspicuous this decalcified tissue is in those parts which are in close contact with the calcium-containing bone (dark black in microphotograph).

Practical Achievements

Microradiography of Biological Tissues Highly Absorbing X-rays. It is natural to suppose that microradiography of calcium-containing tissues (bones, teeth and various calcifications) would be the main subject in which the selective absorption of x-rays could prove its validity for medico-biological research, and yet there have appeared until recently comparatively few publications, probably because of the difficulty in obtaining thin slides of undecalcified calcium-containing tissues for which the grinding was commonly used. One can get thin pieces of calcium-containing tissues with this method. However, it is sometimes impossible either to get ground sections thinner than 50 μ (especially those of cancellous bone and pathological calcifications) or to obtain serial sections of calcareous material. These drawbacks, together with the complicated techniques of grinding, appear to be the main obstacles to a wider use of this method. The introduction of plastic as an embedding medium and the manufacture of bone microtomes with heavy knives made of extra hard steel, allow the cutting of undecalcified bone in serial sections 10 μ and less with minimal damage to calcareous material (about techniques of cutting see below in Supplement). This cutting together with microradiography of obtained sections allow much more complete qualitative and quantitative evaluation of calcium distribution than was possible before.

The first approach to the study of bone problems was made by Amprino and Engström (121) who used microradiographs of compact human bone as well as of bones from experimental material. Ground sections 20–50 μ thick were radiographed with x-rays 2.5 to 4.0 Å long. From their microradiographs these authors made at least two important conclusions: (1) they queried the validity of the Ebner-Gebhardt theory (114) which states that the cement substance is the only bearer of calcium salts in bone, because they think that fibers are also calcified; (2) they indicated that calcium impoverishment of bone during atrophic process goes on without, at least to some extent, the simultaneous destruction of the organic matrix. Contemporary findings, arrived at with the improved technique of microradiography, confirm data of this early work. The next year Engström and Engfeldt (57) demonstrated in microradiographs the different calcium content in neighboring lamellae of the osteon. However, their techniques did not permit a thorough analysis of this finding.

The different mineralization of lamellae was also found by Davies and Engström (43) in 1954. Again microradiographs were made of sections too thick to permit further conclusions on the structure of lamellae. Vincent, as mentioned above, combined microradiography with autoradiography (after administration of S^{32} to dogs) and histology (after previous decalcification). He confirmed the results of Amprino and Engström, Davies and Engström in part referring to different calcification of bone elements.

Stain historadiography (Bohatirchuk, 1957) (30) opened new possibilities in morphological bone studies. As was mentioned above, two properties differentiate this method from earlier ones: serial sectioning of undecalcified bone along with serial microradiography of the obtained sections, and the parallel coloring of the same sections with histological dyes. Accordingly the morphology of calcium-containing and calcium-free bone elements may be compared in microradiographs and histological specimens (the latter free of the artifacts caused by decalcification and disembedding).

Bohatirchuk (33) in 1959 published results of using this method in his studies on bone morphology. He showed that the main depot of calcium in fine-fibered bone is present in fibers or fibrils, which circle around

Haversian canals in compact bone or go parallel to the long axis in trabeculae of cancellous bone. Bundles of these clacified fibers comprise "x-ray opaque stratum." It alternates with another stratum called "x-ray rarefied." Both strata run parallel one to another. X-ray rarefied stratum consists of (1) thin calcified fibers crossing the bone in direction perpendicular or oblique to Haversian canal or to the long axis of trabecula and, probably, (2) of amorphous calcified ground substance in which intra-osseous lacunae are mostly located. These microradiographic data supplement and clarify those of electron microscopy and explain those differences in calcification of osteons which were seen by the above mentioned authors. The work presents new data on the localization of intraosseous lacunae which, according to previous authors (e.g., Weidenreich) (114), should be localized along non-calcified fibers (Fig. 13, 14).

Microradiographic studies of auditory ossicles were performed by Karlsson et al. (77). They showed that in the ossicles similar calcium distribution occurs as in fine-fibered bone of the human skeleton.

Another group of works using microradiography as a principal method comprise those studying bone pathology. They were published mostly by Swedish authors. Engfeldt and Zetterström (52) investigated osteodys-

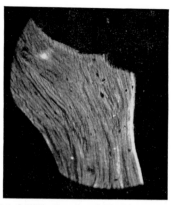

FIG. 14. MRD of undecalcified human bone, 72, 10 μ, approx. ×120. The pronounced stratification as well as disunited strata on the superior bone surface are clearly shown. In comparison with a young bone the aging bone appears to be blacker in MRD thus revealing the lesser content of calcium.

metamorphosis in one case of a ten months old child by microradiography and other methods (histology, autoradiography, microscopy with polarized light, etc.). A demineralization of the skeleton together with the presence of calcium in kidneys is well shown in their microradiographs. Their finding was also very important in the fact that collagen fibrils are not destroyed when calcium is lost from them. In other words, the results of these authors contradict the theory of bone resorption accepted by most in the literature (see below).

Two cases of Paget's disease were investigated by Engfeldt et al. (58) making use of x-ray diffraction and microradiography. They found a considerable difference in mineral content between normal and Paget's bone newly organized. This finding is in disagreement with the existing theory according to which no pathological bone is produced in Paget's disease, only normal processes of growth and resorption are exaggerated (Dible, 1950) (45). Of course, on two cases no one can make final conclusions but these results must encourage fresh investigations especially with the new improved technique.

Engfeldt et al. (51) investigated bones of 4 cases of osteogenesis imperfecta. Their findings

FIG. 13. MRD of undecalcified human bone, 27 years old, 5μ, approx. ×80. Stratification of fine-fibered bone, its elasticity are conspicuous.

contradict the view generally accepted that the growth of long tubular bones in length is not affected in this disease. Their microradiographs demonstrate clearly pathological changes in epiphysial plates and metaphyses.

We would like to emphasize especially the important work of Italian scientists in the field of bone microradiography. Orlandini *et al.* (94), using microradiography as the main method, investigated formation and evolution of callus of bone fractures, the changes in ear ossicles in the course of chronic inflammation of the middle ear, the bone changes in osteomyelitis, leukemia, etc. Starcich (108) proposed a new classification of myelomatous osteopathies based on his microradiographical observations. Prevedi and Margato (96) investigated the growth of bone. The main purpose of all the above work was to show the importance of microradiography in bone research, and this purpose was excellently achieved.

Microradiographic studies of resorptive processes in bone were initiated by Lacroix and Ponlot (79) with their work on posttraumatic osteoporosis, in which this method was used parallel with autoradiography and histology. This work demonstrated the importance of comparing microradiographs and histological preparations of the same specimen: large areas of the calcium-free fibrous tissue were found in histological specimens within the atrophic osteon. The same observation was made by Bohatirchuk in his works on aging bone atrophy (27) (28) (29) (126) (127) (128). Decalcified bone tissue was found by him everywhere in aging atrophic bone. According to the Albright-Pommer theory (1), this decalcified tissue is a new matrix produced by osteoblasts, and this matrix only failed to calcify. The same theory considers the complete destruction of the old matrix to be the prerequisite of any bone atrophy. However, stain historadiographs reveal that fibers of atrophic tissue are the exact continuation of bone collagen fibers; the only difference is that

the latter are calcified and the former not. Serial microradiographs demonstrate also fibers partially or completely decalcified. From these observations we suggest that the decalcification of bone fibers and not their destruction is the characteristic sign of aging bone atrophy. In other words, the old halisteresis theory is revived by stain historadiographical findings (Fig. 12).

It is proposed in the same work to differentiate between osteoporosis and bone atrophy using the first term only in case of pathological destruction of bone.

As mentioned above, the physicochemical approach is also possible in the study of "white" microradiographs of calcium-containing tissues and is effected by comparing x-ray absorption (1) of a standard wedge of which the thickness is increased step-wise, and (2) of the desired part of the specimen. Aluminum or collodion are used as material for wedges in this research. The Laboratory for Morphological Ultra Structural Research in Geneva uses this method (Baud) (10). The reference system of Engström and Lindström may also be used for this analysis (Amprino and Engström) (117). We are of the opinion, however, that change of bone density alone without some accompanying morphological changes cannot be accepted as a decisive diagnostic sign, especially in cases of bone atrophy, because individual variations are very great.

This quantitative approach to the determination of the calcium content via microradiography is especially well worked out in dental research. Even in 1936 Hollander (76) described an original x-ray microdensitometer for qualitative analysis of teeth calcium. The effective intensities were measured by a double ionization camera after x-rays passed through the desired part of the tooth and through the standard wedge of aluminum. The author considered the possible error to be only 0.3%. He worked with tooth specimens 300 μ thick and with x-rays obtained at 18 kv.

610

In a series of works on mineralized dental tissue Engfeldt *et al.* (49) used microradiography in combination with autoradiography. This work illustrates the importance of the combined method not only in quantitative analysis but also in the finding of morphological changes (with vitamin D deficiency, at teeth germs, in the study of dental tubules, etc.). All this work contributes to the better knowledge of calcification both normal and pathological in teeth and to the understanding of the resistance of teeth to decay. There is no doubt that after overcoming the technical difficulty with the serial sectioning of undecalcified teeth, microradiography will make further progress in dental research. We should also mention important morphological contributions to this research by Röeckert (101) and by Applebaum (2) (3) (4). The first studied the structure of dentine in microradiographs, the second the morphology of so-called "mottled enamel" which, according to his observations" happens to exist quite frequently in people using fluoridized water."

The research has only started in the microradiographical study of such calcareous tissues as tendon and ligament bones, larynx calcifications, etc. One tendon bone and several calcifications of larynx cartilages have been studied by Bohatirchuk. Both kinds of "calcifications" possessed the typical structure of fine-fibered bone: alternation of x-ray opaque and rarefied strata, typical distribution of intraosseous lacunae (colored specimens revealed even the presence of osteocytes within lacunae), calcification of fibers, typical bone canalization, etc. (Fig. 15). Here microradiography at once answers the question whether the hard tissue is organized bone or a formless calcification. In one case, the hard tissue inside a tumor was found to be true bone. The complete results of these observations will be published elsewhere. Reasons are not clear, however, why in one case true bone develops and in another a structureless calcium depot

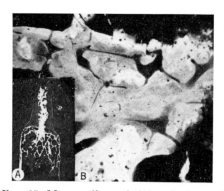

FIG. 15. Macroradiograph (A) and microradiograph (B) of ossifying human rib cartilage, 80, 25 μ ground section (courtesy of Dr. Bélanger), approx. ×80.

MRD presents the bone structure in the calcifying cartilage: intraosseous lacunae, stratification. In the right lower part of MRD several cartilage cells are seen with the partially calcified cytoplasm and cell membrane.

remains. We believe that microradiography will help to explain these problems.

Among other calcareous tissues urinary calculi were under study by microradiography. William H. Boyce *et al.* (34) found among other interesting data a striking resemblance between the stratified calcium impregnated fibers in fine-fibered bone and the similarly stratified calcium distribution in calculus stroma. This stratification is especially obvious in calcium oxalate stones. They point out that probably an affinity exists between fiber or fibril of connective tissue or collagen fiber and by hydroxyapatite crystals.

Sufficient has been said above to show that microradiography must be integral to research on calcareous tissues.

Microradiography of Tissues *per se* Low in Absorbing X-rays in Medico-Biological Research. As mentioned above, this microradiography encounters many difficulties, particularly in its application to the study of morphology. We know only a few of these morphological contributions. First the works of Lamarque and Turchini (83) should be mentioned, in which morphological description of microradiographical findings was given for normal and pathological human tissues. Special attention must be given to the work of J. Lamarque and Guilbert (81) where parallel histological and histo-radiographical study was carried out on three tumors: skin epithelioma, mixed tumor of breast in dog, and sweat gland epithelioma of the scalp. The authors gave several histo-radiographical signs typical for each of these neoplasms. They found, for instance, that all negatively charged parts of stroma or cells do not absorb x-rays (e.g., chromatin of the normal nucleus), but degenerated chromatin of cancer cells does absorb. They described also the microradiographical image of kerato-derma. But their data are very scanty as evidence on the importance of microradiography in this kind of research. Further studies are necessary. Godlewski in a series of works (71) (72) (73) described microradiographical image of some cancer cells, giant cells, etc. These works are very important but, again, observations are very scarce.

Other studies include those who apply the "reference system" proposed by Engström (53). The most important work on the subject was done in Sweden. The determination of the dry weight of cytological structures (Lindström, 1954) (84), the localization and amount of water in biological samples (Engström and Glick, 1956) (59), the distribution of mass and lipides in a single nerve fiber (Engström and Lüthy, 1949 and 1950) (61) (62), the changes in dry weight of squamous epithelium during carcinogenesis (Lindström and Moberger, 1954) (85) the composition of the nerve cell (Brattgard and Hyden, 1954) (36) are the contributions most widely known in which the reference system of Engström was applied. In the United States Fitzgerald (63) made use of the same method and has determined in several works the mass of cancer cells and found that their mass is much smaller than that of normal cells of the same organ.

Summarizing, one can say that despite some interesting contributions to our knowledge, microradiography of tissues *per se* has been too little used and then only with scanty material. Further research is necessary in this most important field.

Microradiography of Tissues Low in Absorbing X-rays with the Use of X-ray Coloring Media. *Microvasography (Microvasoradiography, Microangiography).* Some work has been done in normal morphology of blood vessels as seen in microvasographs. The first one was published by Priwes (97) in USSR on the subject of blood circulation in tubular bones. Making use of microvasographs, he refuted Lexer's data that epiphysial arteries are terminal and he brought evidence that epiphysial and diaphysial vessels anastomose. This work is important in understanding the aetiology of osteomyelitis. Subsequent years brought microvasographic data on normal liver, kidney and lungs by several authors, summarized by Barclay in his monograph on microarteriography (7). In the United States microvasography is under study by Tirman and Banker (109) and Meschan (88) with coworkers. The first presented microvasographical patterns of nearly all rabbit organs. It is necessary to stress here that these authors started microvasography with very simple means using ordinary diagnostic apparatus, and only later did they purchase special equipment. Meschan *et al.* conducted a thorough study of minute brain vessels.

A very detailed investigation of liver vessels was carried out in Portugal by Ayres de Sousa and Cruz (105). With microvasography they studied not only the morphology of liver vessels but were able to form some conclusions about their function. In Belgium, Blickman *et al.* (20) also investigated vascular patterns in the liver of rats as seen in microradiographs, and came to conclusions similar to those of Sousa and Cruz. They paid special attention to interrelations between hepatic artery branches and liver cells, and also between sinusoids and branches of the portal vein. They surmise that branches of the hepatic artery are capable of regulating the amount of blood brought to the sinusoids. Ayres de Sousa, Cruz and Morais (106) investigated also microvasographical patterns of lungs. A. and J. F. de Sousa (107) studied biliary capillaries after post mortem thorotrast injection into the common bile duct and gave patterns to these structures.

In Canada, Saunders (102) investigated microvasographical patterns of muscles. His important data offer some facts on the blood capacity of these organs. Saunders has investigated also vasographical patterns of tooth pulp in different ages (103). It is necessary to mention here that Saunders is alone on this continent in studying the application of the x-ray projection microscopy to medico-biological research (Cf. articles by Saunders).

The first publication on microvasography in pathological conditions appeared in 1943 (Bohatirchuk) (24). Several experiments were carried out in this work with direct vital total macro and microvasography. After the injection of thorotrast, such strongly acting agents as heat or cold were applied to some part of the body on one side, or introduced into the blood stream, e.g., adrenalin, etc. The reaction of the big vessels to the agent was first studied in serial macroradiographs. After that the animal was sacrificed and the capillaries of lungs, liver and other organs were studied. The action of the agents mentioned above on vessel tone was clearly demonstrated in microvasographs. It was shown that heat is a vasodilator and cold a vasoconstrictor and also at the considerable distance from the point of application.

Barclay and Bentley (1949 and 1951) (8) (9) injected silver iodide into arteries of stomach resected because of peptic ulcer and, for comparison, into those of normal cadaver stomach. They found in microradiographs a considerable scarcity of capillaries in the area of the stomach wall close to the ulcer and they explained this local ischaemia as due to the spastic contraction of the capillaries in the ulcer area. They think that the blood circulation in this case proceeds through atriovenous shunt in the submucous plexus and that the spasm of the mucosal capillaries in the ulcer area is caused by the blocking influence of sympathetic nerves which develops after the abdomen is opened. In cases where this influence was excluded no difference was found in the filling of capillaries with opaque medium in any part of the stomach wall. These authors consider the important advantage of microvasography to be the possibility of examining comparatively thick sections of gastric wall with its numerous capillaries.

Another explanation of the phenomenon mentioned above was given by Doran (46), who considered not the spasm but the scarcity of blood vessels on the lesser curvature to be primarily responsible for ulcer development (it is known that ulcers develop usually on the lesser curvature). The inverse picture was observed by him in the duodenum. However, he did not fill the vessels through a special device in which the pressure of the opaque medium was controlled by a manometer as Barclay and Bentley did, but exercized this control by hand. Bentley and Barlow (1951) (18) indicated that this "poor" technique is a cause of, as they said, Doran's "erroneous" conclusions.

The scarcity of mucosal vessels filled with OM was demonstrated also by Benjamin (1951) (15) (16) and by Benjamin, Wagner and Zeit (1953) (17), who injected at first 50 ml of 20% neo-silvol followed by 50–100 ml of 10% bismuth oxychloride. Neo-silvol passed into the venous system while particles of bismuth being too large to pass through the arterial capillaries, remained on the arterial side. These authors presented very persuasive microradiographs in support of their opinion. Their technique was used by Barlow, Bentley and Walder (1951) (9) in their further microradiographical studies of the atrio-venous shunt in stomach wall; 400 μ thick sections were used in this study. They re-asserted that shunts do exist and that their approximate size is 140 μ.

Serious objections to the conclusions of all the above authors were brought by Bellman (12) and especially by Herzog (74). Bellman (1953) injected vessels of a resected stomach 30 minutes after surgery. His microradiographical findings are in disagreement with the ones mentioned above. He found quite adequate filling of the mucosal capillaries in all his specimens. Herzog (1957) used 278 specimens of resected stomachs in his study. Blood vessels were injected with 15% silver iodide; 400 μ thick sections were studied of which 3,000 microradiographs were prepared. Herzog found the shunt mentioned above only in one case. He could not find definite changes either in number of capillaries or in their morphological properties. Herzog is rather pessimistic; he considers any conclusions about the vascular function via microradiography to be impossible. He thinks many of the findings are uncertain. Making use of some drugs with a strong spastic action Herzog could not find any break in the blood circulation in areas of the stomach wall close to the ulcer (drugs were injected either with silver iodide or before it).

The contradictory results of the workers mentioned above prove only the necessity of further studies in this important branch of gastric pathology. First of all the technique has to be identical if one would make conclusions of equal validity. In this technique everything counts: opaque medium used, the method of injection and type of OM, period of time between resection and injection and between injection and microvasography, type of narcosis used during surgery, histological and microradiographical techniques, etc. Such an equation with so many

unknowns cannot be solved by a few investigations.

Great progress was achieved through microvasography in the knowledge of the vascular supply of the optic pathways in the ophthalmological clinic of Liège University by works of François, Neetens and Collette (64) (65) (66) (67) (68) (69). Making use of thorotrast, for injection these authors studied the blood circulation of the chiasma, geniculate body, optic nerve and other parts of optic pathways at capillary level. All their conclusions are supported by precise microradiographs. They used comparatively thick sections (150–400 μ) in order to study large areas of the capillary bed.

In one of their works authors studied via microradiography the structure of Schlemm's canal (66). They found numerous pores in the inner wall of this canal through which communication occurs between the vitreous of the anterior chamber and the canal. These pores were seen in microradiographs after the injection of thorotrast or angiopac either into the anterior chamber or into Schlemm's canal. The authors surmise that the obstruction of the pores prevents free communication between the vitreous of the anterior chamber and Schlemm's canal with the resulting increase of intraocular pressure, and this leads to the development of glaucoma. A further contribution to glaucoma research was made by the same authors through their study of the influence of hyaluronidase on the pores (68). According to Barany large molecules of polymerized hyaluronic acid, which is known to be present within the wall, may block the narrow pores and consequently provoke glaucoma. This hypothesis was refuted by François et al, who found that on the contrary many new openings make their appearance after the injection of hyaluronidase into the anterior chamber or after treatment of the wall with this enzyme.

Morphological findings of François et al. were confirmed by Pattee et al. (1957) (95)

in stereo-microvasographical studies. These authors also injected OM into both the anterior chamber and Schlemm's canal and found free communication between these structures.

Tumor vessels were under study by Bohatirchuk (1943) (24) and Delarue *et al.* (1956) (44). Bohatirchuk investigated experimental tumors, mostly their metastases in Brown-Pearce rabbit cancero-sarcoma. Vital injection of thorotrast was used, in some cases complemented by post mortem filling. This author found that scarcity and irregularity characterize neoplastic blood vessels. Many sinuses, cavities and irregular canals are present in the tumor stroma through which evidently blood circulation proceeds. This work is in apparent contradiction to the work of Delarue *et al.* (44), who investigated the blood supply in tumors of the human large intestine. They found that the blood supply is abundant in tumors. However, the irregularity and scarcity of tumor vessels have only an indirect relation to the tumor blood supply. In one sinus or cavity there may be more blood than in many regular capillaries. In addition to that, the vital injection produces results more reliable than post mortem filling. The profuse hemorrhages which happen frequently in tumors of the large intestine are better explained by the presence of sinuses and cavities within the tumor stroma than by the presence of a plexus of regular blood vessels. Fig. 16 presents kidney metastases of Brown-Pearce tumor in which large cavities in tumor tissue are conspicuous. Of course, only two works on this subject are insufficient to give a complete answer to this interesting question.

A very promising and original method of studying blood vessels in situ was used by Bellman and Engfeldt (13) in their experiments on the action of gonadotropin on the ovarian blood vessels in the rabbit. The authors put a film wrapped in aluminum foil under the ovaries of the living animal,

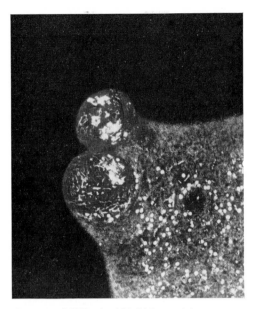

Fig. 16. MRD of rabbit kidney with metastases of Brown-Pearce tumor (two of these are seen on the kidney surface, approx. in center of the picture), direct vital thorotrast injection, 15 μ, approx. $\times 80$.

Large irregular cavities and vessels are seen within both metastases filled with thorotrast. Note the great amount of thorotrast in cavities which indicates that despite the poor development of regular vessels the blood supply of tumor stroma is ampler than in normal organ tissue.

after which OM was administered and one macroradiograph made, followed with gonadotropin injection and another macroradiograph taken on a new film. The considerable enlargement of vessels was found after gonadotropin. Microradiography confirmed their finding.

Bellman and Engfeldt (123) studied kidney lesions during hypervitaminosis D. Though changes in blood vessels are conspicuous in the microradiographs presented, the material is not enough to make any final conclusions.

Our review of works in microvasography is incomplete, yet it is adequate to show that with this method many problems of vascular morphology and of blood circulation may be

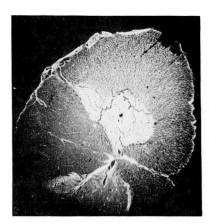

FIG. 17. MRD of cats spinal cord, PM thorotrast coloring, 10 μ, approx. ×20. The selective absorption of thorotrast by the white matter and fibers is shown.

studied in the normal as well as the pathological.

Indirect Vital Coloring with OM of Tissues Low in Absorbing X-rays. Although Gobi (70), Dauvillier (42) and Lamarque (82) suggested the possibility of indirect x-ray contrasting of organs and tissues via the blood stream, the first practical application of microradiography for this purpose was made by Bohatirchuk (1940) (22) who proposed the injection of thorotrast as a test to determine the function of RES. The idea of the test was that in case of stimulation or blockade of RES the adsorption of thorotrast has to be respectively accelerated or delayed and macroradiographs as well as microradiographs had to confirm this assumption. Although both acceleration and delay of x-ray opacity of organs and cells of RES was found in some experiments, they were discontinued due to the outbreak of war and were not renewed again.

Post Mortem Coloring with OM of Tissues Low in Absorbing X-rays. As mentioned above, sections of the cat's spinal cord after coloring with thorotrast show in microradiographs selective x-ray absorption. The amphoteric cytoplasm of typical motor cells of the ventral horn, cell membrane and proc-

esses become visible while as a rule nuclei (like nuclei of other kinds of cells) are not conspicuous. Sometimes, however, some x-ray absorbing inclusions are seen within nucleus, e.g., nucleolus. Fibers with opaque myelin sheaths are colored almost always and may sometimes be followed in microradiographs up to the periphery of the section. Fibrous network in neuroglia adsorbs thorotrast as do some glia cell elements. White matter generally adsorbs more thorotrast than gray matter (Fig. 17, 18). Not much is known about selective coloring of other normal tissues besides the few facts pointed out above.

Only one work was published on the practical application of this method in patholog-

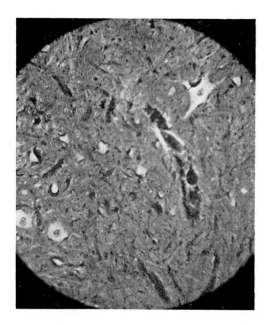

FIG. 18. Microphotograph of a frontal part of the anterior horn of MRD No. 17 at the higher magnification (approx. ×180). The selective thorotrast absorption nervous in cells, fibers and glia elements is shown. In the right upper part of the microphotograph a large neuron with several dendrites is conspicuous. Note some inclusions within the dark nucleus which selectively absorb thorotrast (similar inclusions are seen also in other nuclei). The origin of these inclusions is not clear as yet.

ical cases. Bohatirchuk (1955) (28) immersed sections 35–70 μ thick, both primary and metastatic from experimental and human tumors, into thorotrast for some time and radiographed them afterward. The selective adsorption of thorotrast by tumor tissue in case of liver metastasis (Fig. 19) is quite obvious (Brown-Pearce rabbit cancer). This increase of adsorption is conspicuous in spite of the fact that the normal liver tissue (RES elements) adsorbs OM selectively (see upper part of Fig. 19). It was also found that in some cases of liver metastases the adsorption of thorotrast was increased by liver tissue in which no cancer cells were present (Fig. 20). It is probable that this phenomenon is due to pre-cancerous changes in the liver parenchyma. This observation deserves attention because patho-histology has not

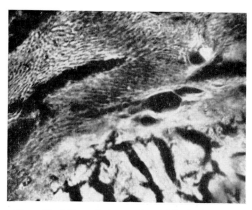

Fig. 20. Microphotograph of MRD No. 19 at the higher magnification (approx. ×200). Although the demarcation line between the tumor and normal liver tissue is conspicuous, many areas in "normal" tissue are seen (e.g. in the upper right corner) which absorb thorotrast selectively. It is believed that these areas represent the precancerous stage of the tissue.

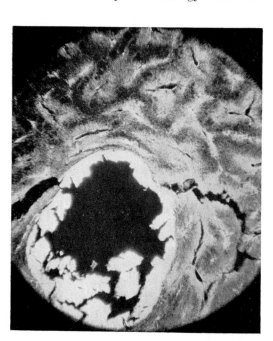

Fig. 19. MRD of rabbit liver with metastases of Brown-Pearce tumor. PM thorotrast coloring, 10 μ, approx. ×80. Large metastasis is conspicuous in the right lower part of the specimen. Note the selective absorption of thorotrast by tumor cells and sharp demarcation line between the normal and cancerous tissue.

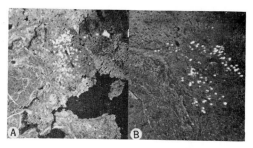

Fig. 21. MRD-s of cat's brain in case of injury. (A) in place of injury (frontal lobe), (B) in some neighborhood of middle brain. PM thorotrast coloring, 10 μ, approx. ×80. Selective adsorption of thorotrast by some elements of brain tissue is conspicuous not only in the place of injury but also at a considerable distance from it. The origin of elements selectively absorbing thorotrast is not clear as yet. It is believed however, that the degenerated myeline is this absorber.

quite a reliable method for the morphological determination of pre-cancerous changes.

In another work (unpublished) Auer and Bohatirchuk investigated the possibility of x-ray coloring technique in case of degenerated nerve fibers. Some signs were found of selective adsorption of thorotrast by these fibers (Figs. 21 A and B). However, results of these preliminary experiments await further study.

Future of Microradiography in Medico-Biological Research

All the advantages and disadvantages of microradiography relevant to medico-biological research are pointed out in this chapter. One may see from this description that only in a few fields has microradiography brought evidence of its validity. Many fields are not explored at all.

Research in calcareous tissues is one of the most promising fields for microradiography and this is shown by several works mentioned above. But even in this field microradiography only begins to explore its possibilities. The vast field of heterotopic bones and calcifications is only slightly investigated via microradiography although more exact knowledge of this deviation from normal is very necessary. Here stain historadiography in combination with serial cutting is applicable because it helps to understand the degree of participation of soft tissues and their cells in the process of ossification. Another field for the application of microradiography is bone growth. Much has still to be learned of the many interrelations between organic matrix and mineral deposits, e.g., between cartilage cytoplasm nucleus and calcium. Parallel processes of ossification and resorption in course of bone growth are also far from being clear from a morphological point of view, especially the participation of osteoclasts and osteoblasts in bone reconstruction (rebuilding). Canalization of bone is another field in which microradiography was tried only in a few works, while making use of obsolete techniques. No attempt is known from the literature to differentiate either between arterial and venous capillaries of bone or between canaliculi of intraosseous lacunae and bone blood vessels.

Bone pathology only starts to be investigated by microradiography. Here also microradiography in combination with coloring technique will be of great help. Differences of calcium impregnation have not been explored at all by microradiography in malign and benign neoplasms nor the process of bone resorption during malignant growth. In our short review many bone diseases have been indicated which also are a "must" for microradiographical research. Especially important is the study of calcium behavior during various dystrophic and fibrotic processes in bone.

Osteoporosis and bone atrophy were investigated only in a few papers which brought forward a new concept of the mechanism of calcium loss. This new approach to the understanding of bone atrophic process is very important for the study of aging bone. Obviously, microradiographical data cannot be generally accepted until they have been confirmed by other methods.

As was shown above microradiograph of bone presents a satisfactory image of calcium distribution even with comparatively low limit of magnification.

Microradiography of x-ray colored tissues is elaborated only in a few fields. Microvasography, for instance, has neither a uniform technique nor a generally accepted opaque medium. Every author tries his own method and this results in controversial conclusions as in the above cited works of Barclay and Bentley, Benjamin, Herzog, and others. The attempt to work out a satisfactory technique of injection is shown in works of Okawa and Trombka and Bellman. However, as was mentioned above, these authors left many questions unanswered. The most detailed study of microvasographical technique is also one of the "musts" for future research. One has to be always mindful that to discredit a method is much easier than to bring evidence of its validity.

Microradiography of biological tissues low in absorbing x-rays colored with OM is also an acute problem for future research. Here even less is done than in microvasography.

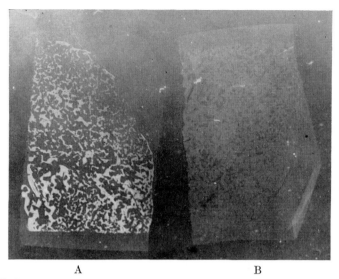

A   B

Fig. 22. Magnified macroradiographs of A—bone section fixed (neutral formalin), and B—bone section immersed into osmium fixative (see text) for 12 hours. The lack of calcium in osmium fixed bone is quite obvious.

The range of OM, methods of impregnation and the selective absorption of OM by different elements of biological tissues, healthy and diseased, these are only a few of the many problems which will confront the researcher. The change of behavior of cellular elements during neoplastic diseases appears to be one of the most promising fields as well as the study of degenerated nerve fibers. The further elaboration of methods is necessary which permit the comparative study of microradiograph and its colored replica. Stain historadiography is such a method. It has proven its validity in research on calcareous tissues. However, it is necessary to find a similar method also for other tissues low in absorbing x-rays. Ward's bio-plastic cannot be used as embedding medium in this case because it is too hard and cannot be cut with the usual microtome. It is therefore necessary to find some other embedding agent which (1) does not produce any image if radiographed, (2) is not too hard and (3) at the same time does not prevent any coloring with histological dyes. Coloring can be done also after the disembedding of radiographed sections but in this case there

will be some structural dissimilarity between embedded and disembedded sections. All these and other problems of technique have to be solved.

When starting to make use of microradiography one has first of all to be clear that the working magnification will be 120X–150X and only in rare cases 300X. Consequently there is no sense in trying to "squeeze out" of a microradiograph those details which can only be seen with a higher power. Comparative study of the colored and the microradiographed specimen will be of help in case the higher power is necessary because the colored specimen has the same limits of magnification as a histological slide.

Further research is necessary in microradiography of tissues *per se* which are low in absorbing x-rays. Here, first of all, the simplification of equipment and technique is necessary. The expensive and complicated equipment cannot be recommended to anatomy and histology laboratories especially if it requires a trained technical staff for its exploitation. A new, possibly grainless, emulsion is also one of the demands of microradiography of tissues low in absorbing x-rays. Intracellular components require a greater magnification for their visualization than that possible in microradiography.

The x-ray industry must understand that now together with macroradiology (diagnostic and therapy) there exists also microradiology (contact microradiography and x-ray projection microscopy) applied to medicobiological research.

Practical Suggestions for Starting Microradiography in a Laboratory

Choice of Equipment. The equipment depends on the kind of microradiographical research which one has in mind. The most complicated and expensive equipment is necessary for microradiography of non-calcareous tissues per se. This has to consist of a special tube with the inbuilt vacuum camera and a transformer which permits a tension so low as 3 kv (see above in "X-ray factor"). So far as we know this equipment is made only to special order and is not listed by any manufacturer (see equipment of Lamarque, Fitzgerald, Engström and others).

A much simpler equipment is possible for

FIG. 23. Tube stand (A), tube (B) and cassette (C) in position. X-rays pass through a cone (D). E—Diffraction unit.

microradiographical research of calcareous tissues, microvasography, etc. It has to consist of a tube and power supply. The above mentioned AEG-50A Machlett tube with 1 mm thick beryllium window may be used. The tube is supplied with hoses permitting cooling with flowing water from any water tap. A tube stand for this tube may be made in any workshop (Fig. 23).

The low voltage necessary for the AEG-50A tube may be obtained either from a diffraction unit or from a special microradiographical equipment made by some companies (e.g. Philips). In the latter the midget tube (with beryllium window and air cooling) is built into the transformer housing. The defect of this equipment is its low effectiveness due to the absence of water cooling and other reasons.

Diffraction unit produces stabilized, rectified secondary current. Kv range is from 5 to 50. It is costlier than the former but is more powerful. It works also with the Machlett tube.

One may obtain low voltage also from the usual diagnostic transformer. It is only necessary to regulate input to the primary coil of this transformer. It is known that the coefficient of transformation is in transformers of this continent approximately 500. That is to say, 20 v input produces approximately 10 kv. Since autotransformers of usual diagnostic apparatus cannot regulate so low an input, it is necessary to use an additional autotransformer for these low voltages. The switching of this autotransformer and the calibration of the resulting kv output can be done easily by any engineer or even a skilled electrician. Since any obsolete transformer may be used for the equipment this self-made microradiographical unit will be within the financial limits of any laboratory.

Cutting and Coloring of Calcareous Tissues. Specimens of calcareous tissues with surrounding soft tissue of the smallest possible size are removed after death and fixed in 10% neutral formalin for at least 1 week, followed by washing in running water for about half a day.

Dehydration and embedding proceeds as follows:

4 changes of acetone of at least 10 minutes each

10% bio-plastic in acetone for 24 hours

20% bio-plastic in acetone for 24 hours

30% bio-plastic in acetone for 24 hours

3 changes of 100% bio-plastic for 24 hours each.

Mold releasing compound (Ward's) is applied to the inner surface of a dish which aids in removing the block from the mold. When dry, fresh bio-plastic is poured into the dish and catalyst added (tertiary-butyl-hydroperoxide). The correct ratio between the amounts of plastic and catalyst is important; 25 cc of plastic and 7 to 8 drops of catalyst is used in this laboratory.

After the specimen has been immersed in the mixture it is allowed to polymerize at room temperature for 48 hours. When ready, the block is cut to approximately 2 cm² size with a zig-zag saw and afterwards sectioned with the Jung microtome (Fig. 24). The block surface is slightly moistened with water and after cutting the section is unrolled on a piece of plastic. The upper surface of the section is blotted, turned around with the aid of a probe and blotted again. Afterwards the sections are stored between two glass slides. Sections are usually strong enough to stand this handling if care is observed. After radiography the sections are colored. Presently good results are achieved with the following procedure:

Stain 5 to 10 minutes in 10 cc of sat. sol. Thionin (approx. 1%) in 50% alcohol and 90 cc of 1% phenol in water (Nicolle 1871)

wash in distilled water

remove excess stain bathing for 5 seconds in 25 cc of dist. water to which 1 drop of HCl has been added

wash well for few minutes

counterstain for 10 minutes or longer in ½% eosin in water

FIG. 24. Jung bone microtome type K. (Heidelberg, W. Germany).

Technical Data:

Knife.................. 3⅜″ x 4½″.
Length of rails........ 40 cm 16 inches.
Total vertical excursion. 30 mm 1⅕ inches.
Automatic adjustment of the thickness of the sections up to........ 50 microns.
in steps of............ 2 microns.
Maximum size of the objects to be clamped .. 80 by 55 mm
Ground space of the microtome............. 80 by 40 cm
Height of the instrument................. 40 cm
Weight................. 90 kg approx. 210 pds.

wash in distilled water

dip shortly in 70% alcohol (in and out)

differentiation is completed in absolute alcohol till clouds of stain cease coming out of the section

clear in xylene and mount in premount (Fisher Scientific).

With this coloring the bone appears rosy or red, soft tissues in different shades of blue.

This coloring is now used together with the previously reported Boehm-Oppel and Schmorl methods.

SUPPLEMENT

New Data

For the current and previous years several contributions to micro-biological research were made in which microradiography was used as a principal or partial method of examination, as well as many other publications appeared on the subject of microradiographical technique.

A new method of microradiography (alpharadiography) was described by Belanger (122) in which the author used Polonium 210 as a source of alpha particles. A histological slide is put on a fine-grain emulsion plate or film and both are placed in a camera obscura on the distance from 20 to 30 mm. After exposure from 4 hours to 4 days, the obtained alpharadiograph may be studied under the microscope as a usual microradiograph. The author showed several demonstrative alpharadiographs he made with this method. There is no doubt that this method will contribute to the medical research in the near future.

Bergandall and Engfeldt (123) described a review of various methods of preparing material for microradiography. They have especially elaborated methods of bone grinding, embedding, etc. Several critical remarks are made on x-ray projection microscopy. Some valuable suggestions for the preparation of undecalcified bone for microradiography was made by Pugh and Savchuk (137).

Vincent (113), Engfeldt (48) demonstrated the stratification of fine-fibered bone in microradiographs but did not give morphological explanation to this phenomenon. Bohatirchuk reported results of his microradiographic studies on the reversibility of atrophic process in aging bones to the IVth and Vth Gerontological Congress (127) (128). He showed in the first report that certain signs indicate that the calcium impoverishment of aging bones is to some extent a reversible process. Experimental results reported to the Vth Congress showed that the bone resorption and bone restitution proceed in aging humans and in rabbits along the same morphological lines, and that the experimental bone atrophy is also a reversible process.

Bohatirchuk (unpublished) made experiments with various bone fixatives used by some authors. Microradiographs show almost the complete decalcification of bone by osmium buffered with veronal up to 7.3 pH during 12 hours of fixation (Scott and Pease) (141). Despite some impregnation of bone and soft tissue by osmium, there is almost no absorption of X-rays typical when calcium is present in bone (Fig. 22). The same decalcification may be found after fixation with 30% glacial acetic acid after 4 hours fixation. Both these fixatives were used by some electron microscopists who claimed that they have studied the "undecalcified" bone. The advice given to electron microscopists and microradiographists is: before using bone for study, check its calcium content via microradiography.

Vascularisation of bone was the subject of microradiographic studies of Brookes (129) (130). Apparently this author has been the first who clearly demonstrated in his precise radiographs the large capillary bed in the rat bone proper under the normal and pathological conditions. Carreto (131), Trueta et al (143) and Vincent (145) studied partly via microradiography the calcification of bone organic matrix in endochondral type of growth. Trueta et al yet once more emphasized the role of giant cartilage cells and vessels in the process of calcification.

Two new contributions were made on the mass determination of cells by Grampp et al (136) and Rosengren (140) obtained by reference system of Engström mentioned above. Findings are in agreement with works on this subject previously cited.

Lagergren et al presented in two works (136) (137) microangiographical patterns of the inflammatory hypervascularity and those of fibromatous and fibrosarcomatous tumors. In the latter work authors point out the connection between malignancy of the tumor and its vascularity: according to their findings, the more vascular the more malignant. Amprino (117), (118), Strandh

622

(142) used microradiography in their studies of the process of bone remodelling. Amprino and Camanni (119), (120) studied microradiographical patterns of dental tlisues.

Cosslett (132), One Sing Poen (138), Grampp and Hallén (133), Istok et al (135) discussed several questions pertaining to the technique of the contact and projection microradiography.

Acknowledgment. The work on microradiography in general and on microradiography of aging bone in particular has been started with the financial and moral support of the University of Ottawa. Afterwards it was supported by grants of the Atkinson Charitable Foundation (Toronto, Canada), Canadian Arthritis and Rheumatism Society, National Research Council of Canada, James Picker Foundation, and is supported now by the USA Public Health Service (Research grant No. A-2298).

I express my sincerest gratitude to all these organizations.

REFERENCES

1. ALBRIGHT, F., "Osteoporosis," *Annal. Intern. Med.*, **27**, 861–882 (1947).
2. APPLEBAUM, E., "Mottled Enamel," *Dental Cosmos*, **78**, 969–980 (1936).
3. APPLEBAUM, E., "Grenz Ray Studies of the Calcification of Enamel," *J. Dental Research*, **12**, 181–190 (1938).
4. APPLEBAUM, E., HOLLANDER, CH. F., AND BOEDECKER, F., "Normal Pathological Variations in Calcification of Teeth as Shown by the Use of Soft X-Rays," *Dental Cosmos*, **75**, 1097–1105 (1953).
5. BAKER, J. R., "Principles of Biological Microtechnique," Methuen & Co., London, 1958.
6. BARCLAY, A. E., "Demonstration of Iron in Cells," *Brit. J. Radiol.*, **22**, 268–269 (1949).
7. BARCLAY, A. E., "Microarteriography," Ch. C Thomas, Springfield, Ill., 1954.
8. BARCLAY, A. E., AND BENTLEY, F. H., "The Vacularization of the Human Stomach," *Gastroenterology*, **12**, 177–183 (1949).
9. BARLOW, T. E., BENTLEY, F. H., AND WALDER, D. N., "Arteries, Veins, and Arteriovenous Anastomoses in the Human Stomach," *Surgery Gyn. Obst.*, **93**, 657–671 (1951).
10. BAUD, CH. A., "Radiographies et Microradiographies Osseuses Quantitatives," *Praxis*, **15**, 329–331 (1957).
11. BEETLESTONE, A., AND THURNER, G., "Some Considerations of Focal Spot Sizes," *Brit. J. Radiol.*, **31**, 492–497 (1958).
12. BELLMAN, S., "Microangiography," *Acta Radiol.*, Supplement 102 (1953).
13. BELLMAN, S., AND ENGFELDT, B., "A Microradiographic Study of the Effect of Gonadotropin upon the Blood Vessel System of the Ovaries of Rabbits," *Acta Radiol.*, **43**, 459–468 (1955).
14. BELLMAN, S., AND ODÉN, B., "Experimental Micro-Lymphangiography," *Acta Radiol.*, **47**, 289–307 (1957).
15. BENJAMIN, H. B., "The Neurovascular Mechanism of the Stomach and Duodenum," *Surgery Gyn. Obst.*, **92**, 314–320 (1951).
16. BENJAMIN, H. B., "The Neurovascular Mechanism of the Mucous Membrane of the Stomach," *Surgery Gyn. Obst.*, **93**, 672–675 (1951).
17. BENJAMIN, H. B., WAGNER, N., AND ZEIT, W., "Intragastric Temperature: Its Variations in Gastric Ulcers," *Surgery Gyn. Obst.*, **97**, 19–24 (1953).
18. BENTLEY, H. F., AND BARLOW, T. E., "Aetiology of Chronic Gastric Ulcer," *Lancet*, **260**, 470–471 (1951).
19. BLACKETT, N. M., "The Resolution Obtainable with a Commercially Available Microradiographic Unit," *Brit. J. Radiol.*, **31** 368–371 (1958).
20. BLICKMAN, J. R., RECOURT, A., AND KLOPPER, P. J., "Microradiographical Investigation of the Vascular Pattern in the Liver of Rats," *J. Belg. Radiol.*, **41**, 122 (1958).
21. BOHATIRCHUK, F., "Thorotrast-Test for RES." In: Works on Conference on Connective Tissue, *Acad. of Sciences of Ukr. S. S. R.*, Kiev., 1940.
22. BOHATIRCHUK, F., "Experimental Macro- and Microvasographic Investigations," Dissert., Kiev, 1940.
23. BOHATIRCHUK, F., "Die Fragen der Mikroröntgenographie," *Fortschr. Geb. Röntgenstrahlen*, **65**, 253–263 (1942).
24. BOHATIRCHUK, F., "Totale experimentelle Makro- und Mikrovasographie, etc.," *Fortschr. Geb. Röntgenstrahlen*, **68**, 159–180 (1943).
25. BOHATIRCHUK, F., "Makro- und Mikroröntgenographie der Blutgefässe bei experimentellen Geschwülsten," *Virchow's Ach. Path. Anat.*, **313**, 216–228 (1944).
26. BOHATIRCHUK, F., "Historoentgenography (Microradiography) of Impregnated Can-

cer Tissue," *Am. J. Roentg.*, **70**, 119–125 (1953).

27. BOHATIRCHUK, F., "Some Microradiographical Data on Bone Ageing," *Brit. J. Radiol.*, **27**, 177–182 (1954).

28. BOHATIRCHUK, F., "The Ageing Vertebral Column (Barclay Prize Essay), *Brit. J. Radiol.*, **28**, 389–404 (1955).

29. BOHATIRCHUK, F., "Ageing and Osteoarthritis," *J. Canad. Med. Assoc.*, **76**, 106–114 (1957).

30. BOHATIRCHUK, F., "Stain Historadiography." *Stain Technol.*, **32**, 67–74 (1957).

31. BOHATIRCHUK, F., "Applied Microradiography in Medical Research," In: "X-Ray Microscopy and Microradiography," Academic Press, New York, 1957.

32. BOHATIRCHUK, F., "Erfahrungen der letzten zwanzig Jahre in der Anwendung der Mikroröntgenographie in der medizinischen Forschung," *Fortschr. Geb. Röntgenstrahlen*, **87**, 44–56 (1957).

33. BOHATIRCHUK, F., "Microradiographical Data on Fine-Fibered Bone," *Anat. Record*, **133**, 203–217 (1959).

34. BOYCE, W. H., POOL, CH. S., MESHAN, J., AND KING, JR., J. S., "Organic Matrix of Urinary Calculi," *Acta Radiol.*, **50**, 544–560 (1958).

35. BOYD, G. A., "Autoradiography," Academic Press, New York, 1955.

36. BRATTGARD, S., AND HYDEN, H., "The Composition of the Nerve Cell Studied with New Methods," *Intern. Rev. Cytology*, **3**, 455–476 (1954).

37. BRONKHORST, W., "Kontrast und Schärfe im Röntgenbild," G. Thieme, Leipzig, 1927.

38. CLARK, G. L., "Applied X-Rays," McGraw-Hill Book Co., New York, 1955.

39. COLLETTE, J. M., "La Microlymphographie," *J. Belg. Radiol.*, **36**, 293–312 (1953).

40. COSSLETT, V. E., "How Thin a Section should be," *J. Biophys. Biochem. Cytol.*, **3**, 815–816 (1957).

41. COSSLETT, V. E., AND NIXON, W. C., "Projection Microradiography," **28**, 532–536 (1955).

42. DAUVILLIER, A., "Réalisation de la Microradiographie Integrale. Comptes rendus hebd. des Séances de l'Académie des Sciences," **190**, 1287–1289 (1930).

43. DAVIES, H. G., AND ENGSTRÖM, A., "Interferometric and X-ray Absorption Studies of Bone Tissue," *Exper. Cell Research*, **7**, 243–255 (1954).

44. DELARUE, J., MIGNOT, J., AND BULLIARD, A.,

"Etude sur la Vascularisation des Cancers du Gros Intestin," *Presse Med.*, **94**, 2164–2167 (1956).

45. DIBLE, H., "Pathology," J. & A. Churchill, London, 1950.

46. DORAN, F., "Aetiology of Chronic Gastric Ulcer," *Lancet*, **260**, 199–202 (1957).

47. EHRENBERG, W., AND WHITE, M., "Resolution in Contact Microradiography," *Brit. J. Radiol.*, **32**, 558 (1959).

48. ENGFELDT, B., "Recent Observations on Bone Structure," *J. Bone & Joint Surg.*, **40A**, 698–706 (1958).

49. ENGFELDT, B., BERGMAN, G., AND HAMMARSLUND-ESSLER, E., "Studies of Mineralized Dental Tissues," *Exper. Cell Research*, **7**, 381–392 (1954).

50. ENGFELDT, B., ENGSTRÖM, A., AND ZETTERSTROEM, R., "Osteopetrosis, *Acta Paediatr.*, **43**, 152–162 (1954).

51. ENGFELDT, B., ENGSTRÖM, A., AND ZETTERSTROEM, R., "Biophysical Studies of the Bone Tissue of Osteogenesis Imperfecta," *J. Bone & Joint Surg.*, **36B**, 654–661 (1954).

52. ENGFELDT, B., AND ZETTERSTRÖM, R., "Osteodysmetamorphosis, etc.," *J. Paediatr.*, **45**, 125–140 (1954).

53. ENGSTRÖM, A., "A New Differential X-Ray Absorption Method for Elementary Chemical Analysis," *Rev. Scient. Instr.*, **18**, 681–683 (1947).

54. ENGSTRÖM, A., "Microradiography," *Acta Radiol.*, **31**, 503–521 (1949).

55. ENGSTRÖM, A., "Stereomicroradiography," *Acta Radiol.*, **36**, 305–310 (1951).

56. ENGSTRÖM, A., BELLMAN, S., AND ENGFELDT, B., "Microradiography," *Brit. J. Radiol.*, **38**, 517–532 (1955).

57. ENGSTRÖM, A., AND ENGFELDT, B., "Lamellar Structure of Osteons Demonstrated by Microradiography," *Experientia*, **9**, 19 (1953).

58. ENGSTRÖM, A., ENGFELDT, B., KELANDER, C. G., WILTON, Å., AND ZETTERSTRÖM, R., "Paget's Disease," *Acta Pathol. Microbiol. Scandin.*, **31**, 256–261 (1952).

59. ENGSTRÖM, A., AND GLICK, D., "Localisation and Quantitation of Water in Biological Samples by Historadiography," *Science*, 27–28 (1956).

60. ENGSTRÖM, A., AND LINDSTRÖM, B., "The Properties of Fine-Grained Photographic Emulsions used for Microradiography," *Acta Radiol.*, **35**, 33–44 (1951).

61. ENGSTRÖM, A., AND LÜTHY, H., "Die Massenverteilung in der Markhaltigen

Nervenfaser, bestimmt durch Roentgenabsorptionsmessung," *Experientia*, **6**, 244–245 (1949).

62. ENGSTRÖM, A., AND LÜTHY, H., "The Distribution of Mass and Lipids in the Single Nerve Fiber," *Exper. Cell Research*, **1**, 81–91 (1950).

63. FITZGERALD, P., "Application of Soft X-Rays Methods to a Study of Normal and Neoplastic Cells," *Ann. New York Acad. Sciences*, **63**, 1141–1176 (1956).

64. FRANÇOIS, J., NEETENS, A., AND COLLETTE, J. M., "Etude Microradiographique de la Paroi Interne du Canal de Schlemm," *J. Belg. Radiol.*, **38**, 1–15 (1955).

65. FRANÇOIS, J., NEETENS, A., AND COLLETTE, J. M., "Microangiographie Oculaire," *Internat. J. Ophthalmol.*, **129**, 145–159 (1955).

66. FRANÇOIS, J., NEETENS, A., AND COLLETTE, J. M., "Microradiographic Study of the Inner Wall of Schlemm's Canal," *Am. J. Ophthalmol.*, **40**, 491–500 (1955).

67. FRANÇOIS, J., NEETENS, A., AND COLLETTE, J. M., "Vascularization of the Optic Pathway," *Brit. J. Ophthalmol.*, **39**, 220–232, 1955; **40**, 341–353; **40**, 730–741 (1956).

68. FRANÇOIS, J., NEETENS, A., AND COLLETTE, J. M., "Microradiographic Study of the Influence of Hyaluronidase on the Permeability of the Inner Wall of Schlemm's Canal," *Am. J. Ophthalmol.*, **41**, 651–657 (1956).

69. FRANÇOIS, J., NEETENS, A., AND COLLETTE, J. M., "Vascularisation des Voies Optiques Primaires. Problèmes Actuels d'Ophthalmologie, S. Karger, Basel, 1957.

70. GOBY, P., "Applications Nouvelles de la Microradiographie," *Bull. Soc. Française de Photogr.*, **5**, 196–197 (1914).

71. GODLEWSKI, M., PELISSIER, M., AND LEENHARDT, P., "Radiomicrographie des Cancers du Foie et des Voies Biliaires," *J. deRadiol. d'Electrol.*, **38**, 297–300 (1957).

72. GODLEWSKI, M., PELISSIER, M., AND LEENHARDT, P., "Radiomicrographie de quelques Cellules Géants," *J. de Radiol. d'Electrol.*, **38**, 296–297 (1957).

73. GODLEWSKI, M., PELISSIER, M., LEENHARDT, P., AND ROVIRA, R., "Radiomicrographie et Frottis Cytologiques," *J. de Radiol., d'Electrol.*, **37**, 969–971 (1956).

74. HERZOG, W., "Theorie der functionellen Durchblutungsstörungen beim Magengeschwuer," *Äerztl. Forschung*, **3**, 134–141 (1957).

75. HERZOG, W., "Zur Mikroangiographie,"

Fortschr. Geb. Röntgenstrahlen, **86**, 124–132 (1957).

76. HOLLANDER, F., "The Degree of Calcification of Teeth: What it means and how we Measure it," *Dental Cosmos*, **78**, 1143–1151 (1936).

77. KARLSSON, K., ENGSTRÖM, A., AND ENGSTRÖM, H., "Microradiographic Studies of the Auditory Ossicles (Malleus and Incus) and of the Osseous Labyrinth," *Acta Radiol.*, **42**, 381–391 (1954).

78. KEMP, F. H., AND NICHOLS, A. F., "Focal Spot Sizes," *Brit. J. Radiol.*, **31**, 486–489 (1958).

79. LACROIX, P., AND PONLOT, R., "Remarques sur l'Histopathologie de l'Osteoporose Posttraumatique," *Acta Medica Belgica*, J. Hilgers, Bruxelles, 1956.

80. LADD, W. A., AND LADD, M. W., "High-Resolution X-Ray Microscopy." In: "X-Ray Microscopy and Microradiography," Academic Press, New York, 1957.

81. LAMARQUE, J., AND GUILBERT, H. L., "Nouvelles Recherches Historadiographiques Appliquées à l'Etude des Tumeurs," *Bull. du Cancer*, **31**, 13–28 (1939).

82. LAMARQUE, P., "Historadiography," *Radiology*, **27**, 563–568 (1936).

83. LAMARQUE, P., AND TURCHINI, J., "Une Nouvelle Méthode d'Utilization des Rayons X: l'Historadiographie," *Montpellier Médical*, **2**, 1–34 (1937).

84. LINSTRÖM, B., "Absorption Spectro-Photometry with Extremely Soft X-Rays for the Quantitative Determination of the Dry Weight of Cytological Structures," *Exper. Cell Research*, **6**, 537–539 (1954).

85. LINDSTRÖM, B., AND MOBERGER, G., "Studies on the Qualitative Distribution of the Dry Weight in Squamous Epithelium during Carcinogenesis," *Exper. Cell Research*, **6**, 540–542 (1954).

86. LURIE, W. B., "A New Advance in Historadiography," *Cathode Press*, **6**, 26–27, 1949.

87. MARINELLI, L., FERLAZZO, G., FITZGERALD, P., AND FOOTE, G., "Historadiography of Thyroid Gland" (Abstract), *Am. J. Pathol.*, **25**, 811 (1949).

88. MESCHAN, I., POOL, CH., NETTELESHIP, A., WINER, M., AND ZEMAN, W., "The Radiomicrography of the Autopsy Brain," *Radiol.*, **65**, 770–777 (1955).

89. MITCHELL, G. A. G., "Microradiographic Demonstration of Tissues Treated by Me-

tallic Impregnation," *Nature*, **165,** 429 (1950).

90. NIXON, W. C., "X-Ray Microscopy," *Research*, **8,** 473–483 (1955).

91. NUERNBERGER, J., ENGSTROEM, A., AND LINDSTROEM, B., "A Study of the Ventral Horncells of the Adult Cat by Two Independent Cytochemical Microabsorption Techniques," *J. Cell. & Comp. Physiol.*, **39,** 215–254 (1952).

92. ODÉN, B., BELLMAN, S., AND FRIES, B., "Stereo-micro-lymphography," *Brit. J. Radiol.*, **31,** 70–81 (1958).

93. OKAWA, C., AND TROMBKA, J. I., "The Technic of Making Microangiograms of Rabbit Bone Marrow," *Am. J. Clin. Pathol.*, **26,** 758–764 (1956).

94. ORLANDINI, J., BASSINI, G., CASACCI, A., "La Formazione e l'Evoluzione del Callo Osseo di Riparazione delle Fratture," *Anali di Radiologia e Diagnostica*, **29,** 254–301 (1956).

95. PATTEE, H. H. Jr., GARRON, L. K., McEWEN, W. K., AND FEENEY, M. L., "Stereo-Micrography of the Human Eye." In: "X-Ray Microscopy and Microradiography," Academic Press, New York, 1957.

96. PREVEDI, G., AND MARGATO, M., "Studio Microradiographico sull'Accrescimento del Osso Frontale e del Parietale nel Feto Humano," *l'Ateneo Parmense*, **6,** 446 (1945).

97. PRIWES, M., "Blood Supply of Long Tubular Bones," *Vestnik Roentgenol.*, **20,** 175–198 (1938).

98. RESINK, J., "Roentgenogram of Fine Structure," *Acta Radiol.*, **32,** 391–403, 1949.

99. ROBERTSON, C. W., AND WATSON, G., "Precise Measurements of Focal Areas in Diagnostic X-Ray Tubes and Their Application in Tube Development." *Brit. J. Radiol.*, **31,** 489–492 (1958).

100. ROBERTSON, J. K., "Radiology Physics," D. Van Nostrand Co., New York, 1944.

101. ROECKERT, H., "Microradiographic Studies of Teeth," *Experientia*, **11,** 143 (1955).

102. SAUNDERS, R. L. DeC. H., "Microradiographic Studies of the Vascular Patterns in Muscle and Skin." In: "X-Ray Microscopy and Microscopy and Microradiography," Academic Press, New York, 1957.

103. SAUNDERS, R. L. DeC. H., "Microradiographic Studies of Human Adult and Fetal Dental Pulp Vessels." In: "X-Ray Microscopy and Microradiography," Academic Press, New York, 1957.

104. SHERWOOD, H. F., "Vacuum Exposure Holder for Microradiography," *Rev. Sci. Instr.*, **18,** 80–83 (1947).

105. SOUSA, A. DE, AND MIRABEAU CRUZ, J., "Microangiographia e Microcolangiographia. Relatorio Apresentado a IV Congresso dos Radiologistas de Cultura Latina," Bertrand (Irmaos), Lissabon, 1957.

106. SOUSA, A. DE, MIRABEAU CRUZ, J., AND BELLO DE MORAIS, J., "Microangiopneumographie," *Am. Radiol.*, **1,** 9–22 (1958).

107. SOUSA, A. DE, AND SOUSA, J. F. DE, "An Experimental Study in Microcholangiography," *Brit. J. Radiol.*, **29,** 377–381 (1956).

108. STARCICH, R., "Histopathological and Microradiographical Observations on Myelomatous Osteopathy," *Acta Haematol.*, **18,** 113–125 (1957).

109. TIRMAN, W. S., AND BANKER, H. W., "Further Studies in Microradiography," *Am. J. Roentgenol.*, **75,** 366–373 (1956).

110. VICTOREEN, J. A., "Absorption and Scattering." In: "Medical Physics," O. Glasser, edit., The Year Book Publishers, Chicago, 1944.

111. VINCENT, J., "Les Remaniements de l'Os Compact Marqué à l'Aide de Plomb," *Rev. Belg. Pathol. Méd. Expér.*, **26,** 161–168 (1957).

112. VINCENT, J., "Le Remaniement de l'Os Compact chez le Cercopitheque," *Arch. Biol.*, **68,** 561–579 (1957).

113. VINCENT, J., "Microradiographie des Lamelles de l'Os Haversien," *Arch. Biol.*, **69,** 561–575 (1958).

114. WEIDENREICH, F., "Das Knochengewebe." In: "Die Gewebe." In: "Möllendorf's Handbuch der speziellen pathologischen Anatomie und Histologie," J. Springer, Berlin, 1930.

115. WIGGERS, C. J., "Physiology in Health and Disease," H. Kimpton, London, 1949.

116. ZUPPINGER, A., "Die theoretischen Grundlagen und Möglichkeiten der Röntgendiagnostischen Weichteiluntersuchung," Georg Thieme, Leipzig, 1935.

117. AMPRINO, R., "Rapporti fra Processi di Reconstruczione e Distribuzione dei Minerali nelle Ossa," *Zeitschr. f. Zellforsch.*, **37,** 144–183, 1952.

118. AMPRINO, R., "Struttura Microscopica e Rimovamento delle Ossa," *Atti della Societa Italiana Pathologia*, **IV,** 9–68, 1956.

119. AMPRINO, R., CAMANNI, F., "Applicazione del Metodo Istoradiographico allo Studio dei Tissuti Mineralizzati del Dente," *Minerva Stomatology*, **6,** 1–24, 1956.

120. AMPRINO, R., CAMANNI, F., "Historadio-

graphic and Autoradiographic Researches on Hard Dental Tissues," *Acta Anat.*, **28**, 217–258, 1956.

121. AMPRINO, R., ENGSTRÖM, A., "Studies on X-ray Absorption and Diffraction of bone tissue," *Acta Anat.*, **17**, 1–22, 1952.

122. BÉLANGER, L., "Microradiography with a Polonium Alpha Source," *J. Bioph. & Biochem. Cytology*, **6**, 197–202, 1959.

123. BELLMAN, S., ENGFELDT, B., "Kidney Leisons in Experimental Hypervitaminosis D," *Amer. J. Rad.*, **74**, 288–294, 1954.

124. BERGANDALL, G., ENGFELDT, B., Preparing Material for Microradiography, "*Acta Pathol. & Microbiol. Scandinavica*," **49**, 30–38, 1960.

125. BOHATIRCHUK, F., "Uber Ergebnisse der Mikroröntgenographie," *Acta Rad.*, **27**, 351–365, 1953.

126. BOHATIRCHUK, F., Microradiographical Data on Aging Bone Atrophy as Seen in Microradiographs and Colored Specimens," *J. of Gerontology*, **15**, 142–149, 1960.

127. BOHATIRCHUK, F., "Reversibility of Bone Changes in Physiological Aging," Report to the IVth International Gerontological Congress, Merano, Venice, 1957. Tito Mattioli, Fidenza.

128. BOHATIRCHUK, F., "Experimental Bone Atrophy in Rabbits in Comparison with Bone Atrophy in Aging Humans as Seen in Historadiographs and Colored Specimens," Report to the Vth Int. Gerontological Congress, San Francisco, 1960 (in press).

129. BROOKES, M., "The Vascular Architecture of Tubular Bone in the Rat," *Anat. Rec.*, **132**, 25–47, 1958.

130. BROOKES, M., "The Vascular Reaction of Tubular Bone to Ischaemia in Peripheral Occlusive Vascular Disease," *J. Bone & Joint Surg. (Brit.)*, **42b**, 110–125, 1960.

131. CARRETO, L., "Contributo allo Studio della Matrice Ossea Neodeposta," Archive "Putti," X, 211–230, 1958.

132. COSSLETT, V. E., "Microscopy with X-rays," *Nature*, **183** 1423–1427, 1959.

133. GRAMPP, W., HALLEN, O., "Microphotometry in X-ray Contact Microscopy," *Exp. Cell Research*, **19**, 83–92, 1960.

134. GRAMPP, W., HALLEN, O., Rosenbren, B., "Mass Determination by Interference and X-ray Microscopy," *Exp. Cell Research*, **19**, 437–442, 1960.

135. ISTOCK, J. T., MILLER, C. W., CHAMBERS, F. W., LYON, H. W., "Historadiography of Hard and Soft Tissues, *U.S.A. Armed Forces Med. J.*, **11**, 497–506, 1960.

136. LAGERGREN, C., LINDBOM, Å., SÖDERGERG, G., "Hypervascularization in Chronic Inflammation Demonstrated by Angiography," *Acta Radiol.*, **49**, 441–452, 1958.

137. LAGERGREN, C., LINDBOM, Å., SÖDERGERG, G., "Vascularization of Fibromatous and Fibrosarcomatous Tumours," *Acta Radiol.*, **53**, 1–16, 1960.

138. ONG SING POEN, "Microprojection with X-rays," Martinus Nijhoff, The Hague, The Netherlands, 1959.

139. PUGH, M. N., SAVCHUK, W. B., "Suggestions on the Preparation of Undecalcified Bone for Microradiography," *Stain Techn.*, **33**, 287–295, 1958.

140. ROSENGREN, B. H. O., "Determination of Cell Mass by Direct X-ray Absorption," *Acta Radiol. Supplementu*, **178**, 1959.

141. SCOTT, B. L., PEASE, D. C., "Electron Microscopy of Epiphysial Apparatus," *Anat. Rec.*, **126**, 465–480, 1960.

142. STRANDH, J., "Microchemical Studies on Single Haversian System," *Exp. Cell Research*, **19**, 515–530, 1960.

143. TRUETA, J., MORGAN, J. D., "The Vascular Contribution to Osteogenesis," *J. Bone & Joint Surg., Brit.*, **42b**, 97–109, 1960.

144. VINCENT, J., "Correlation Entre la Microradiographie et l'Image en Lumière Polarisée de l'Os Secondaire," *Exp. Cell Research*, **12**, 422–424, 1957.

145. VINCENT, J., "Etude Microradiographique de l'Ossification Enchondrale," *Acta Anat.*, **40**, 121–129, 1960.

F. BOHATIRCHUK

MICROANGIOGRAPHY WITH THE PROJECTION MICROSCOPE

The use of x-rays for microscopy derives from the fact that x-rays have a shorter wavelength than light and therefore a greater penetration and higher resolving power. Contact microradiography (1, 2) has long been available to biologists, but it is only recently that the principles of reflection (3) and projection (4) have been applied to x-ray microscopy. The first x-ray projection microscope was reported in 1952 by Cosslett and Nixon.

The projection method of x-ray microscopy rests on the fact that a point source of x-rays casts an enlarged image of a nearby object on to a distant fluorescent screen or photographic plate with a resolution approximately equal to the size of the point source. The Cosslett-Nixon x-ray microscope operates on this principle and routinely provides a resolution of the order of a half to one micron. The best resolution obtained to date with this type of instrument has been about 0.1 micron. Since the magnification depends on the ratio of the target-object to target-plate distance, both of which are variable, a high primary magnification of up to ×200 is obtainable depending on the nature of the object under study.

Projection x-ray microscopy has many applications in biology, anatomy, and medicine. The first biological studies were made on drosophila (5) and insect flight musculature (6) with interesting results. In the vascular field it has been used to study the microscopic blood vessels of a variety of organs and tissues, including skin, muscle, bone, teeth, kidney, stomach, intestine, brain, spinal cord and nerves (7, 8, 9). In the field of histology it has recently been used to examine unstained sections of animal and human tissue (10) and is also being applied to the determination of the dry weight (mass) and elementary analysis of cellular structures.

Operation of the Instrument. The x-ray microscope resembles an inverted electron microscope in that it consists of two variable electro-magnetic lenses, termed the condenser and objective, which are mounted vertically above the electron gun. A v-shaped tungsten filament within the gun produces an electron beam which is accelerated at a selected kilovoltage. The objective lens is fitted with a special polepiece which produces a strong magnetic field that focuses the electrons onto a thin target of metal foil supported by a target assembly within the polepiece. The target gives rise to a beam of x-rays over which a fluorescent screen or specimen holder and camera can be placed as required. The total height of the instrument column is 80 cm (approx. 32 in.) and so the operator can remain seated while inspecting the fluorescent screen.

Preliminary alignment of the microscope column is carried out by lateral and axial adjustments of the two lenses, with the object of centering the electron beam upon a small circular viewing screen which is substituted for the target assembly within the polepiece of the objective lens. A greatly demagnified image of the electron source is first formed and focused to a point upon the viewing screen. This screen is then replaced by the target which consequently emits x-rays from what is virtually a point source, so avoiding the difficult problem of focusing x-rays. Further focusing is carried out upon a fluorescent screen placed above the target, with the aid of a small ×10 ocular or magnifier. In actual use the operator judges the sharpness of the enlarged x-ray image of a test grid placed upon the target while varying the lens current. A fine silver mesh grid (1500 mesh/inch) composed of 3 micron bars and 17 micron spaces is used for this purpose, as well as for determining the resolution and calibrating the magnification. When the grid image is as sharp as possible, the test grid is removed, and the instrument is ready for experimental purposes. No further lens adjustments are usually necessary during the course of the day, so that attention can be devoted to the experiments in hand. A specimen holder and camera can now be placed over the x-ray beam, an exposure made, and the plate developed.

The instrument has a variable kilovoltage (5–30 kv); hence it is possible to select that voltage which gives the optimum penetration and contrast. The choice of the target and the operating kilovoltage, are dictated by the study proposed. The target is interchangeable, and is simply punched out of a thin metal foil, 3 to 12 microns thick. Tungsten, gold, silver, and various other elements may be used depending on the characteritsic x-ray line deemed most suitable to the study. A target of thin copper foil, either 5 or 10 microns in thickness, used with an accelerating kilovoltage of 10 to 30 kv provides reasonably good resolution and adequate penetration for most vascular experiments upon animals. Remarkably contrasty and detailed projection micrographs can be obtained with such a target using standard lantern slide plates (e.g. Ilford Contrasty) while working under atmospheric conditions.

Histological sections however require x-rays of long wavelengths, such as produced by an aluminum target. Since better resolution is obtained with a thin target its maximum thickness should be 4 to 5 microns. An operating voltage of the order of 6 or 7 kilovolts or less is essential to the production of reasonable contrast in tissue sections, as is the use of a vacuum camera. Focusing is both critical and difficult at these lower kilovoltages owing to the low intensity and reduced image contrast, but it can be facilitated by reducing the target-screen distance before viewing the test grid. A new focussing aid has recently been developed which reduces the difficulties to a large extent (11).

A mechanical stage is placed over the target when viewing small objects under atmospheric conditions. The central aperture of the stage is large enough to allow a specimen cup to be moved mechanically in the two horizontal axes across the x-ray beam, and to be approximated to the target in order to obtain higher magnification. The bottom of the specimen cup is either covered with a thin supporting film of plastic (6 micron Mylar) or fitted with rings which give support to the specimen. All parts of the specimen are in focus at once, and owing to the great depth of field, stereographic views can be produced either by tilting the specimen at low magnification between two exposures or traversing the specimen across the x-ray cone at high magnification.

A simple stage of sheet plastic or metal, fitted with pressure clamps about a central aperture, is particularly helpful when examining large objects such as a gross section of brain, tissue flap, or the ear of a living rabbit. Both types of stage are used with a simple metal box camera (2.5 cm high) fitted with plate guideways which allow the selection of different target to plate distances. The open bottom of the camera rests upon the specimen stage, while a circular aperture at the top accomodates a fluorescent screen for visual checking of the object or vascular field prior to the introduction and exposure of a plate.

Specimen Preparation. Microangiography, or the x-ray study of microscopic blood vessels necessitates the use of a contrast medium of high radiopacity and small particle size, that is readily miscible with blood, and capable of traversing the capillary bed.

Excellent microangiograms of fresh surgical or cadaveric material, both animal and human, can be obtained with Micropaque. This is a colloidal suspension of barium with a particle size of half a micron and less, which is capable of entering the smallest capillaries. Its white color lends itself to anatomical dissection and makes it easy to determine, prior to x-ray microscopy, whether good filling of the blood vessel net has been obtained. A 10 to 25 % solution of Micropaque warmed to body temperature and injected intra-arterially until whitening of the venous return is detected, usually gives a clear demonstration of the vascular pattern of the tissue flap or organ under study. Attention should of course be paid to injection pressures especially in the case of delicate foetal vessels. This solution may even be injected into the living animal although eventual clotting of the blood is to be expected. Specimens injected with Micropaque can be fixed in formalin.

In the living animal the concentration, volume and toxicity of the contrast medium are important if vascular irritation and disturbance of circulatory dynamics are to be

629

avoided. The injection of contrast medium into small local arteries produces beautifully detailed microangiograms, but cannot be regarded as other than a blood displacement technique unrelated to the normal circulatory picture. X-ray microscopy used in conjunction with circulating contrast medium provides a new method of observing the vessels of the microcirculation.

The water soluble iodinated organic class of radiopaque compounds may be used for microangiography, but the best results in the living animal have been obtained with Thorotrast, which is a colloidal solution of 25% thorium dioxide. It is nonirritating to vascular tissue and owing to its small particle size (0.1 micron) readily enters all parts of the vascular network. Its high radiopacity, combined with the fact that it persists in the blood stream for several hours or more, makes it very suitable for imaging small blood vessels in the living animal by x-ray microscopy. The dose should be based on the estimated plasma volume of the animal to reduce circulatory disturbances, and given intravenously or intra-arterially at some point distant from the vascular field under study. A dye should be added to the Thorotrast to increase vessel visibility during operative procedures, since its accidental escape quickly opacifies a tissue area. Specimens injected with Thorotrast are not fixed by formalin, but can be fixed with alcohol or acids (12).

Vascular Results. Projection x-ray microscopy is highly suited to the study of the small vessels which go to make up the microcirculation. All the blood vessels remain in focus owing to the great depth of field of the x-ray microscope. This permits the visualization of the volume pattern of the blood vessels and also its rendition stereoscopically by simply moving the specimen laterally between two successive exposures. Such vascular patterns are unobtainable by light microscopy even with the aid of clearing techniques.

Conventionally fixed material, both animal and human, can be readily examined by the projection method, but it must be remembered that histological fixatives denature protein and appreciably alter x-ray transmission. Also no firm conclusions should be drawn regarding the functional status of the blood vessels prior to death since fixatives themselves produce vascular changes. The use of such microangiograms should therefore be restricted to the study of vascular anatomy.

The best projection micrographs are obtained from freshly injected but unfixed material, it being possible to record large areas of moderately thick (1–5 mm) specimens without a blurring of the superimposed vascular images such as limits conventional microradiography. For example, thick sections (taken from the kidney, stomach and intestine of the freshly killed albino rat, after retrograde injection of the aorta with Micropaque) showed that the glomerular tufts and intertubular capillaries of the kidney could be imaged without difficulty. The arteriolar, capillary and venular components of the mural plexuses of the intestine, including the capillary loops within the villi, could also be clearly visualized.

Projection studies of the rabbit ear in the freshly killed animal (following bilateral carotid injection with Micropaque) reveal the extraordinary complexity of the peripheral vascular network. The continuity of its small arteries and arterioles with the capillary bed and the draining venules are demonstrated with almost diagrammatic clarity. The central artery of the ear and its subsidiary branches are seen to give rise to smaller arteries that intercommunicate by a series of arterial arcades, so forming a coarse net or macromesh. Within this coarse peripheral net lies a more complex and finer network or micromesh formed by the arterioles, capillary bed and ultimate venous radicals. Micrographs of the ear margin show that the capillary loops and the small venules draining them form a dense palisade, whose venous tributaries drain in turn into the adjacent marginal vein and a coarse subcutaneous venous network (Fig. 1). Central areas of the ear (Fig. 2) show the coarse and fine vascular nets, and also short circuits or arterio-venous anastomoses connecting arterioles and venules. These structures appear as S-shaped side branches from the terminal arterioles which after a short tortuous course run directly into an adjacent venule.

Stereomicrographs of such tissue areas provide a three dimensional view of the blood vessels and help to verify the course and connections of the arterio-venous anastomoses. Also, since the size (diameter) of the vascular field and its magnification can be altered by varying the target specimen and target-plate ratio, it is possible to select and record arterio-venous anastomoses and other minute vascular features for detailed study and measurement (Fig. 3).

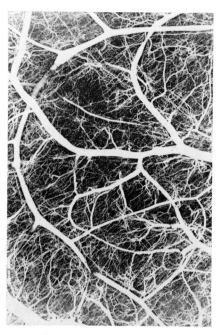

FIG. 2. X-ray micrograph of a more central area of a rabbit ear showing the vessels of the microcirculation. The fine vascular net or micromesh is formed by the arterioles, capillary bed and ultimate collecting venules. ×6.8

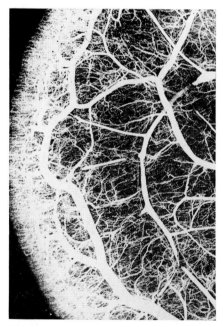

FIG. 1. X-ray micrograph of the margin of a rabbit ear showing the coarse arterial network or macromesh, fine capillary net or micromesh, and small marginal veins. ×5.3

An unexpected finding, possibly of physiological interest, was that both large and small peripheral nerves could be located by their vascular patterns. In the case of the rabbit ear the longitudinally disposed capillary vessels of the intrinsic vascular plexus of the great auricular nerve can be easily seen. The veins draining the nerve trunk are more conspicuous than the arteries of supply, and can be seen to pass in a regular segmental manner toward adjacent subcutaneous veins. Minor cutaneous branches of the nerve are likewise revealed by the vascular nets which lie about them (Fig. 4).

Projection x-ray microscopy can also be carried out on the living animal either by taking a microangiogram immediately after the regional injection of contrast medium (blood displacement technique), or by taking successive microangiograms following a single intravenous injection of contrast medium

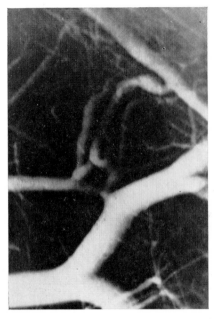

FIG. 3. X-ray micrograph of rabbit ear showing an arterio-venous anastomosis connecting a small artery to an adjacent venule. The artery lies to the right and the vein to the left. ×20

to record the pattern of the peripheral vascular bed during its transit (circulating slug technique). As aforementioned the dose or slug may be calculated so as to represent some known fraction of the total plasma volume, with a view to limiting circulatory disturbances. For example the blood vessels in the ear of the living rabbit have been studied over the x-ray microscope for periods up to two hours, after a single dose of Thorotrast corresponding to one-tenth of the estimated plasma volume (38 ml/kg), had been injected into the marginal vein of the contralateral ear. During this period the ear may be subjected to various experimental procedures such as trauma, freezing, or the injection of pharmacological agents. Areas of inflammatory reaction and the capillaries therein have been imaged, as well as sites of arterial spasm adjacent to the injured area. Constrictions indicative of localized arterial spasm have been recorded from the time of onset to their disappearance almost an hour

(e.g., 50 min.) later. Control micrographs should be taken of both ears prior to recording a series of vascular events. Vascular response to vasomotor drugs may also be observed by x-ray microscopy.

Lymphatic vessels can also be visualized in the living animal by x-ray microscopy. Good results have been obtained by the contact method, but the technical advances anticipated (13) for the projection method have recently been realized. Successive x-ray micrographs taken shortly after (1–45 min.) the injection of contrast medium directly into the subcutaneous tissue of the living rabbit ear, show the peripheral lymphatic capillary plexuses about the depot area of contrast medium (e.g., .01–.05 ml Thorotrast) as well as the collecting lymph channels draining the area (Fig. 5). Such micro-lymphangiograms also show the bead-like silhouette of the valves within the lymphatic

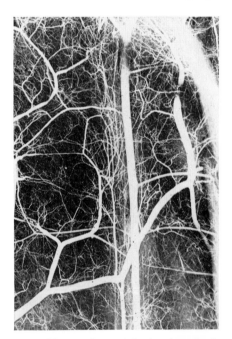

FIG. 4. X-ray micrograph showing the longitudinally disposed capillaries within the great auricular nerve of the rabbit. The nerve lies parallel to the central artery, and gives off small branches to right and left. It is drained by adjacent subcutaneous veins. ×4.8

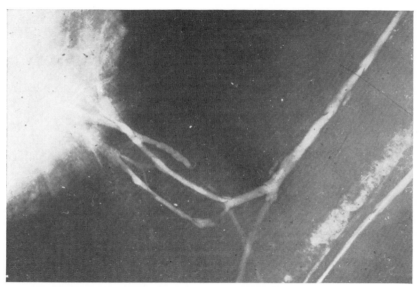

FIG. 5. Microlymphangiogram of living rabbit ear showing the peripheral lymphatic capillary plexus draining a subcutaneous injection of Thorotrast (opaque area on left). Note the numerous paired valves within the collecting lymph vessels. ×12

vessels, and the perivascular network of lymph vessels as they pass centrally along the branches of the auricular artery. Both blood vessels and lymphatics have been imaged simultaneously by combining microangiographic and microlymphangiographic techniques. Such techniques may be expected to add to our knowledge of the factors regulating lymph flow in the living animal.

Microangiography of human material by the projection method has included studies of the mode of vascularization of nerves, as well as of the brain and spinal cord. Knowledge of the deeply placed and microscopic vessels within the human brain and spinal cord is understandably limited, since neither dissection nor traditional histological methods permit the tracing of the cerebral arterial tree in its entirety. Using contrast media of colloidal dimensions, and the eye as a gauge of capillary filling, it has been possible to determine the course, connections, and volume pattern of the intracerebral vessels of the human brain, and record them stereoscopically (Fig. 6).

Interesting morphological features of the

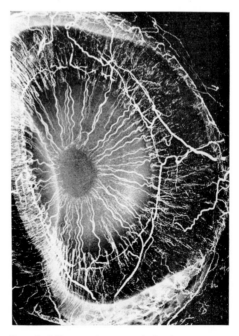

FIG. 6. Microangiogram of the human eye recorded by the contact method. The vessels of the iris can be used as an index of satisfactory injection of the brain. The pupil is surrounded by the vessels of the iris, ciliary body and choroid.

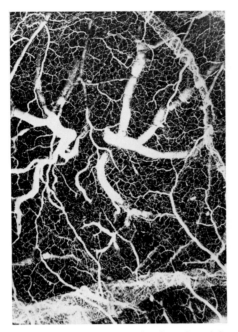

FIG. 7. Microangiogram showing the pial arteries, veins and capillaries on the surface of the human brain. The small club-like projections represent the commencement of cortical and transcerebral arteries which descend vertically into the brain substance. Foetus CR.14.5. ×5.5

cortical, transcerebral and central vessels of the cerebral microcirculation have been so recorded (14), for example the coarse distributor network and fine capillary bed formed by the pial vessels on the brain surface, as well as the myriads of small transcerebral arteries which arise therefrom to traverse the entire thickness of the brain (Fig. 7). These last terminate in a subependymal capillary plexus about the central cavity or lateral ventricle of the brain (Fig. 8). The vessels contributing to the intraspinal circulation such as the radicular, peripheral and central arteries of the spinal cord have been similarly recorded (Fig. 9).

The blood supply of human peripheral nerves, such as the sciatic nerve and its branches, has also been studied by projection microscopy. The vessels (arteriae nervorum) contributing to the extraneural and intraneural vascular pattern can be easily traced by taking successive micrographs along the length of the nerve trunk. The intraneural arterioles and capillaries, by repeated division and anastomosis, form a continuous network along the length of the nerve. In view of the size and multiplicity of these vessels it is not surprising that peripheral nerves bleed when severed.

The vascular pattern of developing and adult dental pulp vessels of the human tooth can be demonstrated by both contact (15) and projection methods (16), and viewed stereoscopically, without destruction of the vessels such as occurs in histological sectioning. The vessels within the foetal jaws and dental germs are prepared by retrograde aortic injection with Micropaque at low pressure, prior to excision of both foetal jaws and removal of the contained dental germs for x-ray microscopy. The dental pulp vessels of the extracted adult human tooth can be filled with Thorotrast by suction in-

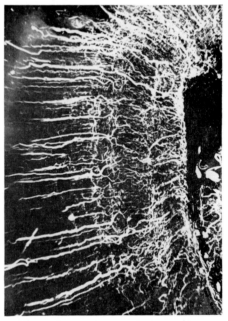

FIG. 8. Microangiogram of human brain showing the long transcerebral arteries passing through the brain substance and terminating in a subependymal capillary plexus about the lateral ventrical. ×17

jection. The tooth crown is drilled via the occlusal surface and the dentine penetrated until several of the blood filled capillaries of the subdentinal plexus can be seen and severed. Contrast medium is then aspirated through the pulpal vessels via the root canal vessels and the now ruptured capillary plexus.

After fixation and decalcification the softened tissue of the tooth can be shaved off so that the final preparation for x-ray microscopy consists of the entire pulp with supporting side walls of dentine. X-ray microscopy has provided the first complete pictures of the vascular networks lying within the dental papilla and about the dental sac of the developing human tooth; these have accordingly been named the intradental (intrapapillary) and peridental (perifollicular) plexuses respectively. Projection x-ray

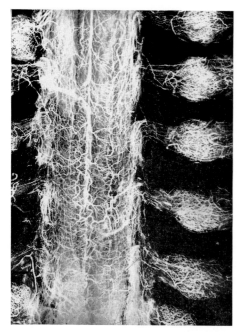

FIG. 9. Microangiogram of human spinal cord showing the peripheral system of blood vessels surrounding the cord. Within the cord can be seen the brush-like central arteries, branching to right and left of the midline. Note the radicular vessels in the nerve roots and the capillary bed within each spinal nerve root ganglion. Foetus CR. 19 cms. ×5

microscopy provides both overall and detailed pictures of the anatomy of the adult dental pulp vessels with facility. Moreover an intact specimen may be studied from different projections and viewed stereoscopically before commencing sectional studies. The pulpal vascular patterns of all the teeth of the adult dentition have been so demonstrated including the finest capillaries of the peripheral or subdentinal plexus.

REFERENCES

1. GOBY, P., *C. R. Acad. Sci.*, **46**, 686 (1913).
2. ENGSTROM, A., BELLMAN, S., AND ENGFELDT, B., *Brit. J. Radiol.*, **28**, 517 (1955).
3. KIRKPATRICK, P., *Nature*, **166**, 251 (1950).
4. COSSLETT, V. E., AND NIXON, W. C., *Proc. Roy. Soc.*, **B140**, 422 (1952).
5. COSSLETT, V. E., *Med. & Biol. Illus.*, **4**, 95 (1954).
6. SMITH, D. S., In "X-ray Microscopy and Microradiography," Academic Press, New York, 1957.
7. SAUNDERS, R. L. DE C. H., *Nature*, **180**, 1353 (1957).
8. SAUNDERS, R. L. DE C. H., Proc. Microscopy Symposium, McCrone, Chicago, 1958.
9. SAUNDERS, R. L. DE C. H., *J. Anat. Soc. India*, (June, 1959).
10. SAUNDERS, R. L. DE C. H., AND VAN DER ZWAN, L., Proc. 2nd International Symp. X-ray Microscopy and Microanalysis, Stockholm, 1959.
11. ONG SING POEN, "Microprojection with X-rays," Hoogland and Waltman, Delft, 1959.
12. BELLMAN, S., *Acta Radiol. Supp. 102*, I (1953).
13. BELLMAN, S. AND ODEN, B., *Acta Radiol.*, **47**, 289 (1957).
14. SAUNDERS, R. L. DE C. H., Proc. 2nd International Symp. X-ray Microscopy and Microanalysis, Stockholm, 1959.
15. SAUNDERS, R. L. DE C. H., In "X-ray Microscopy and Microradiography," Academic Press, New York, 1957.
16. SAUNDERS, R. L. DE C. H., Year Book, Goteborgs Tandlakare-Sallskap, Gothenberg, Sweden, 1957.

R. L. DE C. H. SAUNDERS

MICROFLUOROSCOPY. *See* CONTACT MICRORADIOGRAPHY, p. 561.

PLANT MICRORADIOGRAPHY

Plant cell research in recent years has contributed greatly beyond its own specific field to important developments in biology as a whole, such as bacteriology, virology, antibiotics, tissue cultures, tumors and genetics. And yet botanists have not utilized to any extent x-ray methods in their research work, with the possible exception of diffraction on membrane and fiber structure study. Generally plant cell mechanisms are better known because of greater cell size and resistance in plant tissues than is true for animal or human cells. Now with the development of the several techniques of x-ray microscopy, stimulated by the successes of electron microscopy including scanning and television recording of cell images, there are great possibilities of satisfying the needs of plant biology.

History. In the past half century physicists and chemists by their fundamental investigations have enabled development of x-ray apparatus, and have established the laws of penetration of x-ray beams through thin samples, the preparation of suitable specimens, the interpretation and comparison of images on photographic films, and diverse applications. To measure plant microradiographic progress since the first attempts, it suffices to survey the steps from 1913 to actual contemporary results obtained with thin sections. When Goby (1) announced both the origination and the purpose of a new technique by these words: "Microradiography must be able to permit observation of internal structures of small objects too opaque to be observed in the (optical) microscope", he proposed several potentially successful types of materials; among them a *Diatomea* was the first plant specimen microradiographed. The characteristics of his apparatus and technique, however, were not mentioned. The second successful accomplishment with plants was made by Dauvillier (1930) (2) with a Lipp-

mann photographic emulsion and exposure time "not as long as two hours". This author published a beautiful cross section microradiograph of *Sambucus* pith at a magnification of 600 diameters. The physicists Barclay and then Leatherdale (1948–1951) (3) discovered with soft x-rays spots in the leaves of many plants. These authors deduced facts on the distribution in autumn of mineral deposits of high atomic weight elements, and on the development of plant galls. This early work created a true interest in the application of the microradiographic technique to plant problems, but during this period of about 40 years metallurgical, zoological and medical progress was considerably greater than in the science of botany.

In the past decade workers have presented some plant examples indicative of decisive improvements. Following Lamarque (1936) (4) whose microradiographs attained high quality with x-rays generated at 7 to 10 kV, 80 to 100 mA and 10 to 30 min. exposure, mention is made of the application of a similar technique to materials similar to plant specimens, such as paper, by Pelgroms (1952) (7): contact method 3–15 kV, 10–20 mA, 5–60 min. exposure, $\times 50$ magnification, opacifying solution iodine, specimen thickness 30 μ. Clemmons and Aprison (1953) (5) undertook to develop the use of soft x-rays generated at still lower voltages especially in biological research. These authors devised apparatus so that vacuum was maintained around the specimen in order to reduce exposure time to a tenth of that ordinarily required and thus to enable the production of 10 or more historadiographs per hour. Moreover the excellence of the images permitted quantitative analysis of specimens.

Mitchell (1954) (6) used microradiography on natural samples such as elm leaves with galls and mineral deposits, and wheat grains infested by weevils. His advice was that results were no better than those of ordinary microscopy but quicker and more easily obtainable without laborious preparation. In addition, freeze-drying of green or moist specimens increases radiotransparency and permits shorter exposures. The operating conditions in this work were as follows: projection microscopy; magnification ×15, ×20 or ×260 by photographic enlargement, ×900 for high resolution film; 7 to 20 kV and 5 to 10 mA; Mo target and Be window; tube-object distance = 40 cm; vacuum in cassette; Lippmann film or Maximum Resolution plates; exposure times vary from second to hour, depending on object, distance, voltage, milliamperage, vacuum and speed of films; film employed depends on magnification wanted and influences exposure time.

At this same time Trillat in France asked a botanist to study with a physicist the common problem of a proper handling technique for plant biological researches. In order to approach histological field a survey was made to examine optimum conditions of exposure time, and microradiographic accuracy of very different specimens such as leaves, epiderms, algae, crystalline structures, salt and aqueous constitution of tissue. The detailed technique of a very simple contact method was described by Legrand and Salmon (1954) (8) and Salmon (1956) (9); additional details were given in following publications (10). Then work was undertaken with help of this equipment by Manigault and Salmon (1956) (10) concerning cancer plant tissue development, concurrently with staining and polarizing techniques. Results were satisfying enough to assure the great utility of this x-ray method in plant biology.

Histological Technique for microradiography (MR): A summary of details of this contact method is as follows: commercial sealed-off tube (Fig. 1, Pl. 1); chromium anode; wavelength 2.28 A; 15 to 20 kV and 20 to 15 ma; focus-specimen distance of 5 cm, the specimen being 1 cm from the Be window; 15 sec. to 1 min. for exposure; holder for object and film is a cylindrical camera moving in a tube at any desired distance from x-ray focus. The specimen is pressed against a flat fine-grain Lippmann film by a spring to a limiting aperture and a brass disk closes the camera (Fig. 4, Pl. 1). The use of a vanadium filter is not to be recommended in these conditions for it eliminates the useful CrKβ line and removes only a small amount of radiation of short wavelength. An automatic switch guards against a fall in pressure of the cooling water. Control arrangements in the generator ensure that it functions within the prescribed limits of voltage.

To obtain greater contrast it is also easy to employ in a few cases the small Philips generator (1 to 5 kV; 6 to 8 A; Cu anode; focus-specimen distance 1.5 to 2.5 cm, but the observable area is smaller than that for the tube described above; possibility to evacuate air around object; 1 to 10 min. exposure).

A monochromator can be added when a long exposure is not inconvenient. Relative to specimen preparation, it is better to cut it by freezing microtome in sections from 50 to 100 μ. Then sections are fixed preferably with Carnoy's solution during one hour. Serial sections are impregnated with increasing concentrations of alcohol, so that they are taken from absolute alcohol for radiography. Alcohol does not interfere with observations but it is necessary to drain the section before exposing to the x-ray beam without avoiding complete desiccation. The results are poorer with formalin fixation or from sections embedded in paraffin although these methods are usable in case of necessity. However a fresh test section must be compared in order to evaluate these different experimental procedures, especially to estimate the importance of the haze due to impregnation of water in plant tissue.

The development of film is made in the following solution during 1 min.:

Metol............ 1.5 gr
Hydroquinone.... 6
Sodium sulphite... 37
Sodium carbonate. 37
Potassium bromide 1
Water............ 1 liter

First trials can be made with fairly grainy film such as Kodalith and then the final microradiographs with fine-grain film such as Lippmann. After exposure the film is dried and mounted with Canada balsam between glass slides. Photographic enlargement is then possible by usual microscopic processes. Small magnifications are less easy to realize. It is frequently required to reproduce at ×10 a whole microradiographed section to compare it with a cell fragment included within, itself greatly enlarged several hundred times. These small enlargements are difficult to obtain in good quality. To achieve this the film to be photographed is placed between an objective with a diaphragm (f = 35 mm) and a divergent lens of 3 cm in diameter in the photographic mounting. In the other part usual magnifications with Lippmann film reach approximately ×300 without difficulty.

To complete the information given by contact microradiographs it is sometimes necessary to standardize with some macro- or microscopic experimental tests. Reference systems are numerous and depend upon the scale of chosen contrast and range from nitrocellulose foils to impregnated papers illustrated in Fig. 2, Pl. 1. In this case ashless paper of known thickness is observed with an increasing saline mass per unit area after evaporation and macroradiography. Fig. 7, Pl. 1 shows another system with saline solutions in small and long cylinders of identical diameter whose area is here visible. Comparative opacity measures the relative degrees of absorption.

After Clark (1955) (11) published excellent microradiographs of white oak sections, a botanical example was illustrated by Nixon (1956) (12) with the point projection system constructed by Cosslett and Nixon, using two electron lenses to obtain a high demagnification of the electron source (5–20 kV, ×1000). This was a bean section whose accuracy represents conspicuously a valuable quality of micrographs obtained by this method. Jackson (1956) (13) studied in the Cavendish Laboratory untreated specimens of obeche infected with a staining fungus and mahogany sections by means of projection microscope; then abnormal elm burrs sections were presented by the same process (point projection microradiography; target = copper foil 3 μ; accelerating voltage 10 or 15 kV; normal exposure time of 4 min.; target-plate distance = 6 cm).

By the projection method Ely (1956) (14) also studied crystals of *Rosa* leaves and their seasonal variations (7 to 15 kV; 200 mA; 15 sec. to 5 min. exposure).

Ong and Le Poole (1958) (15) by means of a technique based on projection microscopy but borrowing from electron microscopy the methods of shadowcasting and replicas, have obtained relief effects and interesting details concerning certain structures of paper fibers and a section of ashwood 50 μ thick, diatoms and the stigma of a leaf with crystals. This method permits enlargements up to ×520, with an ultimate possibility of ×1000 (anode voltage = 6–12 kV; 2–15 min. exposure with Al target, 10 sec. with Au white radiation).

The highest point of progress in microradiography of plant specimens is the remarkable work on extremely thin sections presented by Engström and co-workers (1950–1957) (16). To develope this method accessory techniques were studied. An example given by Greulich and Engström (1956) (17) and then by Engström and Lundberg (18) in plant field is *Allium* root tip sections; the onion is a Monocotyledon which therefore possess great cell size. Nu-

EXPLANATION OF PLATES (white areas on figures correspond to the most highly absorbing matter, black to little or no absorption).

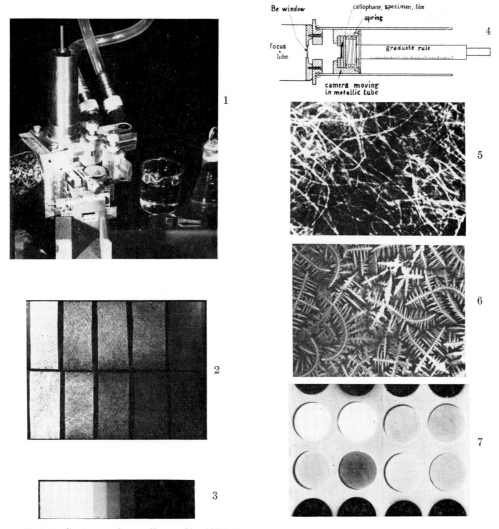

Pl. I—FIG. 1: Contact microradiography (CMR) equipment used for plant materials (1 to 20 kV). Technique is described in text as "Histological technique of MR".

FIG. 2: Reference papers impregnated with heavy ion salts of increasing concentration and macroradiographed, ×1

FIG. 3: Photographic film reference system (Kodak) for comparison of intensities of a microradiograph

FIG. 4: Arrangement of specimen to be radiographed and film inside camera moving in cylinder fixed to the x-ray tube

FIG. 5: Cigarette paper impregnated with heavy ion salt and microradiographed by contact before desiccation, ×50

FIG. 6: The same paper microradiographed after evaporation. Notice that crystallization is oriented by direction of fibers, ×50

FIG. 7: Another reference salt system composed by diverse concentrations of solutions put in small cylinders hollowed in Perspex block, ×1

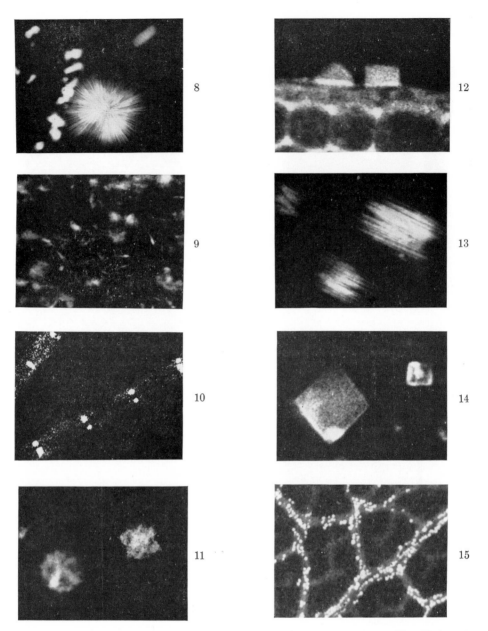

Pl. II—Fig. 8: Crystalline formation recently found in Virginia creeper stem, not identified, ×65

Fig. 9: Crystalline short stilettos shaped in cells of a bark rich in radio-opaque salts, ×260

Fig. 10: Groups of cells containing iodine in a filamentous red alga, ×250

Fig. 11: Sea urchins crystals of Ca oxalate in *Pelargonium* stem, ×260

Fig. 12: Extra-epidermic crystals recently observed on Virginia creeper stem rich in radio-opaque salts, ×260

Fig. 13: Raphids of Ca oxalate; these bundles of crystals are those of *Hyacinthus* bulb, ×98

Fig. 14: Quadrangular crystals, possibly weddellite, in Virginia creeper tissue, ×260

Fig. 15: Ribs of *Rosa* leaf with opaque crystals; parenchym shows numerous chlorophyllian spots quite transparent, ×50

cleus and nucleolus are particularly well visible with the usual microscope. This choice was very suitable to show biologists what they can hope of microradiography down to the scale of individual cells. From the description (1956) several results were given on resting phase and mitotic sequences of the nucleus. Each of them is perfectly recognizable by comparison with observations by the Feulgen staining technique. Evidently all chromosomes are seen on the same plan in microradiographs so that it is sufficient to localize dry weight inside nuclear structures; but the ordinary microscopic image remains necessary in order to count chromosomes with security. The size of the nucleolus is about 10 μ and diameters of the nucleus a few tens of microns. Enlargement of microradiographs in (17) reaches ×2000. This successful method permits the investigator to localize and measure chemical elements responsible for cell opaque spots. Also it permits experimentation with the help of solvents or enzymes as carried out by Brattgård and Hydén (1952) (19) on nerve cells.

Cytological Technique of Microradiography (MR): The physical characteristics of this contact method are utilization of soft X-rays (500 to 2000 V) and high vacuum. The window is a 1000 to 2000 A thick Al foil. Observable area is 12 mm². Film is a high resolution photographic emulsion: Eastman Kodak Spectroscopic Plate type 649 and Kodak Maximum Resolution Plate. Quantitative measurements can be made on the sample microradiographed. Material is fixed by Flemming or Allen's solutions or freeze-dried before embedding. As shown by Engström (20) isolated cells require a simple smearing technique. However, to be examined in vacuo they must be dried. Tissue blocks also after freezing are dehydrated at low temperature and low pressure, and impregnated with paraffin in vacuo. These thin sections have a thickness varying between 1 and 5 μ. They are deparaffined and floated onto the photographic emulsion or pressed on it. Microradiographs have 0.2 μ as a resolution, the same as an ordinary microscope. Shrinkages and artefacts must be considered in interpretation of microradiographs both in qualitative and quantitative methods, but this is true of any technique. The fixation effect is one of the constant cares of a cytologist; the desiccating effect must be added to it for a microradiologist.

The second example offered by literature on investigation of plants by the high resolution contact microradiography above described concerns pollen in *Tradescantia* (1957) (21) (Dahl, Rowley and co-workers). Diverse phases of development of mother cells of pollen were obtained. Here the soft-ray region used was 6 to 12 A. Specimens were transferred from the X-ray specimen holder to a microscope slide and Feulgen reagent. The reference system was made of narrow strips of nitrocellulose film. High absorption in the chromosomes was again observed and changes of opacity were studied in mature pollen.

Recently Dietrich (1959) (22) published results obtained with the same technique on pollenic material fixed by ethyl alcohol, embedded with paraffin, cut in 2 to 4 μ sections, floated on distilled water at 35°, coated with film of nitrocellulose, directly gathered on high resolution emulsion and dried during 6 hours; after the paraffin was taken off, sections were exposed to x-rays generated at 700 to 1000 V (= 10 to 20 A) with a copper target. Vacuum was maintained around the specimen and into the demountable tube. Al foil 1 μ protected film and specimen from light exposure. The purpose of this work was observation on changes of opacity inside pollen during formation of mature grains and new membranes between tetrads. Comparison with the colored Feulgen technique was used on microradiographed sections. Mitosis and cytoplasm particularly were observed before, during and after nuclear division.

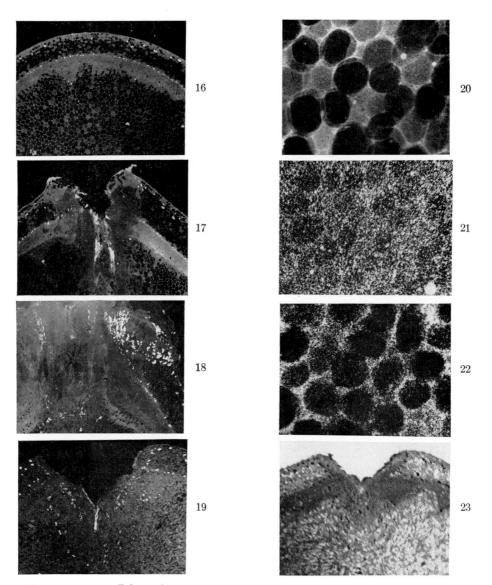

Pl. III—all figures concern *Pelargonium* stem

Fig. 16: Cross section through normal tissue by CMR histological technique, ×10

Fig. 17: Cross section through injury in tumoral tissue 10 days after infection with *Agrobacfaciens*, ×10

Fig. 18: Injury in tumoral tissue three weeks after infection, ×10

Fig. 19 and 23: Phenomenon of solarization by X-rays. Compare the two cross sections through stem. Fig. 19 shows the test microradiograph with white opaque crystals while ground is black outside of section. On Fig. 23 the phenomenon of solarization is shown after longer exposure time than for Fig. 19: an inversion shows black crystals and white ground outside of section, ×10

Fig. 20: This figure and the two following show a comparison of results obtained with different voltages on bark tissue and film; here 10 kV—20 mA—5 min.—Lippmann film. The figure outlines the best result compatible with a necessary short exposure time, ×165

Fig. 21: 10 kV—20 mA—1 min.—Kodalith film. With an identical voltage a coarser grained though more sensitive film is poor in comparison with the fine grained film in Fig. 20, ×165

Fig. 22: 4 kV—25 mA—4 min.—Kodalith film. Improvement of image is evident relative to fig. 21; it is due to increasing contrast determined by decreasing voltage, ×165

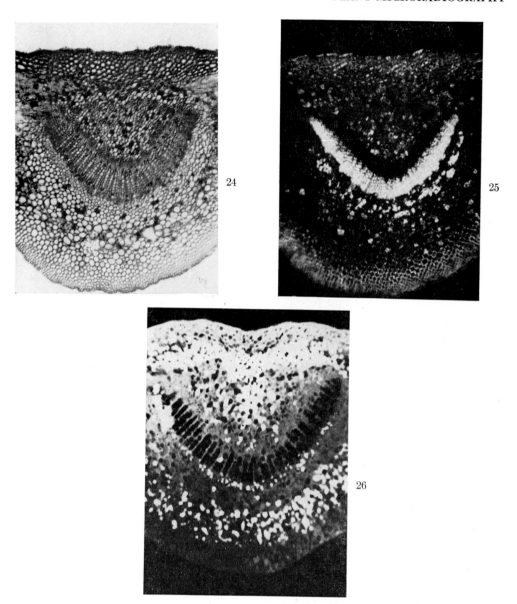

Pl. IV—Figs. 24, 25, 26: Comparison of different microscopic techniques on cross sections of *Nerium* leaf. Fig. 24: Normal light microscopy. Fig. 25, Polarizing microscopy.
Fig. 26: Microradiography. Diverse kinds of tissue or inclusions appear with the different techniques; in particular both lignin and Ca oxalate crystals are more evident with microradiography, ×50

Interpretation of Microradiographs: Exactness of interpretation is a function of previous plant knowledge, theoretical considerations and calculations. The worker must know possible artefacts from fixatives, injury of fresh section or complications arising from components such as sap or included bodies of tissue. Among main observations made on plant tissues, mention should be made of the largest diversity of mineral localization, either crystals (in rows surrounding vessels, superficial deposits or limiting physiologically different tissues) or absorbing zones and poles affecting flow especially of saline solutions. Salts found in higher plants are chiefly calcium ones (carbonate, tartrate, oxalate under various crystallized forms: styloids, raphids, sea urchins) and silicaceous formations. Iodine is a possible component of Algae; its high x-ray absorption distinguishes cells containing it. Often kinetics of disintegration of living matter and secretions present some interesting information. A remarkable variety of structures in plant tissue and the rapid progression of absorption coefficient with atomic number of plant chemical elements are quite able to be revealed by x-ray microscopy.

Interpretation of historadiographs is easier when some characteristics of the tissue are already known and problems otherwise studied. Theory and previous trials have indicated approximate radiotransparencies of some groups of substances (pigments, essences, glucids, proteids, some lipids) and radio-opacities of some other groups (tannins, resins, salts, some lipids). Living matter is mainly composed of complexes; these are either organic only or both mixed mineral and organic substances in various proportions. What contains the highest concentration of atoms of higher mass per unit area is the most absorbing and opaque. To know what components exist in this area it is possible to employ X-ray diffraction* in case of crystals, or usual chemical microanalysis. To determine what simple elements build the components, x-ray spectrometric microanalysis is employed.

Generally C, H and N present no problem because of high transparency; opacity appears with O in molecules when concentra-

---

* X-ray diffraction has been employed principally on membranes and fibers by Frey-Wyssling in higher plants, Preston on Algae and Kreger on coatings from plants. The textile industry uses this method extensively.

tion is sufficient. High atomic number elements are characterized by strong absorption distinctly visible in the microradiograph. Frequently crystalline structures assure an important contrast in most plant organs conveniently detected by high voltage (15 to 20 kV) x-rays in mass tissue, and are relatively easy to observe; but fineness of cell contrasts is so delicate to obtain at these voltages that only the use of soft x-rays permits detection of such order of details in tissue. Low voltages therefore are indispensable to interpret entirely plant structure tissue as it is now possible.

NOTES ON TECHNIQUES FOR INEXPERIENCED PLANT RESEARCH INVESTIGATORS

1. Microradiographic contrast increases as generator voltage decreases and wavelength increases.
2. Limit between hard and soft x-rays is considered to be 1 Å. Hard x-rays are below 1 Å; soft x-rays employed in biological microradiography are separated in two parts: soft x-rays properly so-called (1 to 10 Å) and ultrasoft x-rays (10 to 100 Å).
3. Quality of microradiography depends on two main factors: the resolution power which obtains accuracy, and contrast of image which assures the detail of information.
4. Time of exposure depends on intensity of the beam (this depends itself on focal spot size) and focus-specimen distance, therefore on the method used. It increases with thickness of specimen and decreasing grain-size of the film.
5. The notion of absorption is fundamental in radiography. Absorption by matter depends on x-ray wavelength, nature of elements traversed and their thickness.
6. Absorption is related to opacity: when a beam of such wavelength passes through the mass of varying chemical composition, an image is registered on film placed behind it relative to the

x-ray source. When beams of increasing wavelengths pass successively through the same chemical element, each giving a radiograph in constant exposure time, perhaps the first one will produce only blackness of the film matter being transparent to short wavelengths; the following will have a slight impression (but by virtue of differential opacity of matter a corresponding image appears on the film); the last beam will show only a white image, which means the object is quite opaque towards the corresponding wavelength used. What seems to be a progressive phenomenon of absorption is due to the quality of the chemical element. Another one of different atomic number would have an analogous behavior towards other wavelengths with a different threshold of opacity.

7. The image is formed by adjacent areas of several different simple elements differentially absorbing radiation as explained above. The diversity of phases each with its own opacity produces the contrast in the whole image. From the concept of opacity, therefore of absorption, results this one of contrast. This kind of image exists for alloys but practically never for living matter.

8. A simple element plays an important role in the constitution of plant tissue; living matter produces images composed by heterogeneous areas. Each of these is made of complex substances mixed with much water. When a simple element prevails in such a cell area, its presence is indicated by a notable opacity or notable transparency; this element can be identified and estimated in amount, but it represents only a more or less important fraction of the total substance from a given area. The mechanism of absorption, phenomenon of opacity and radiocontrast occur individually for each simple element of a complex tissue. The entire image is a summation of their individual effects and the smallest area always appears as a very small entire image. In fact final interpretation of biological structures is relative, but a biologist works always with the complexity of manifestations of life.

9. Highest enlargement obtained today in contact microradiography is ×1750 with a striated muscle of mouse, more than ×2000 with *Allium* root tip cells (Engström), which are an excellent performance in microradiography.

10. Limit of resolution of a projection microscope is actually the best one with 0.1 μ; that of the contact method depends on resolution power of light microscope with only 0.2 μ. These limits concern usual apparatus and no special experimental arrangements.

11. Total error of quantitative microanalysis from microradiographs is 2.5%, ten times less than some years ago. The reference system error is more important.

12. As pointed out above the two optical methods currently used with x-rays to observe microscopic structures are:

   (1) contact microradiography (CMR); specimen and film adhere to each other; x-ray image is further enlarged by photographic process;

   (2) projection microradiography (PMR); specimen and film are distant to each other; x-ray beam produces direct image enlarged.

Both are employed by authors in plant field; respective advantages and disadvantages decide choice of apparatus. Moreover a third method evolves from x-ray optical laws:

   (3) reflection microradiography (RMR); x-ray beam from specimen incident at grazing angles on mirrors is reflected to form an enlarged image (cf. p. 672). This

method is still in process of development at the present time. Besides the plant tissue artefacts mentioned above, artefacts inherent in these optical methods lower the quality of radiograms if they are not corrected.

Results drawn from medical or animal investigations can incite plant cell research to intensive application. It is known, among other examples, how mineral elements are distributed in calcified bone tissue, how lipids, pentose-nucleoproteins and proteins in nerve cells are quantitatively determined by x-rays. Perhaps most botanists ignore still these possibilities and also the limitations of microradiographic techniques.

The role of microradiography is primarily to detect or localize opaque substances. However it does not always take the place of other techniques. If MR is able to be a worthy auxiliary method in botanical research, it would be inadvisable to neglect information obtained by other methods such as crystallography, histology, cytology or microchemistry. Surely it is expedient to know the very interesting attempts to obtain precise knowledge of living matter by x-ray techniques, as did Zeitz and Baez (23) on Mn and Rb content of tea leaves; their physical work is necessary to future progress in microanalysis. But a botanist knows that spots in leaves generally are calcium salts and they will have to inquire with a crystallographic method as to precisely what kind of salt composes the crystals of spots. Microchemistry usually provides information about ions present in situ. In this way both chemical composition and localization will be correlated.

On the other hand there are advantages of microradiography relative to other techniques in some results recently acquired. It discloses in normal plant tissue interesting architectures as crystallized components, impregnations, intra- or extra-cell flow. Microradiographs, in which there is a summation of numerous elements of a formation in sections as thick as 80 μ, give statistical information of which other techniques are incapable. MR is able to distinguish two (or several) groups of substances both birefringent, in cases where they show different x-ray absorption (by example lignin from calcium oxalate crystals). Other results in plant field show great utility of MR in pathologic and trophic problems: this method discloses high absorption of tumoral meatus though these are not birefringent in polarized light, mineral matter being in an unusual amorphous state in them. As MR provides information on motion of heavy ions during nuclear division, it serves in the same way for a cell such as pollen and for tissue either normal or tumoral such as stem. Leaves fed with different nutrients have been distinguished only by MR.

If we compare now MR and electron microscopy, both evidently apply to two different scales of magnitude. The latter concerns purely descriptive cell morphology with a resolving power of the order of a few A, but it is closely dependent on the kind of fixation. MR is on a microscopic scale of complementary interest to the use of the ordinary optical microscope because the resolving powers of both are similar. Thus they contribute together in the solution of the same problems in the plant field.

Some typical examples are illustrated in the figures, each of which is described in a specific legend.

REFERENCES

I. Books and General Information about Microradiography*

Cosslett, V. E., Microscopy with X-rays, *Nature,* graphy, **183,** p. 1423–27 (1959).

Cosslett, V. E., Engström, A. and Pattee, H. H., X-ray Microscopy and Microradiography, Acad. Press, N. Y., 1957.

Engström, A., Biological Ultrastructure, 326 p., Acad. Press, N. Y., 1957.

Henke, B. L., High Resolution Microradiography,

---

* See also other articles on X-Ray Microscopy in this Encyclopedia.

Technical Report No. 2, Ultrasoft X-Ray Physics, Air Force Office of Scientific Research, 1958.

NIXON, W. C., in Modern Methods of Microscopy, Butterworths, London, 1956.

ONG SING POEN, Microprojection with X-rays, 132 p., Drukkerijen Hoogland en Waltman, Delft, 1959.

TRILLAT, J. J., Metallurgical aspects of Microradiography, Metallurgical Reviews, vol. 1, Part 1, 27 p., 1956.

II. Technical Articles Referred to in Text.

1. GOBY, P., *C.R. Ac. Sc.*, **156**, 686, 1913.
2. DAUVILLIER, A., *C.R. Ac. Sc.*, **190**, 1287, 1930.
3. BARCLAY, A. E., *Brit. J. Radiol.*, **20**, 394, 1947; **22**, 268, 1949. Microarteriography, Oxford, Blackwell Scientific Publications.
   BARCLAY AND LEATHERDALE, D., *Brit. J. Radiol.*, **21**, 544, 1948.
   LEATHERDALE, *Sci. News, Harmondsworth*, **19**, 61, 1951.
4. LAMARQUE, P., *Radiology*, **27**, 563, 1936.
5. CLEMMONS, J. J. AND APRISON, M. H., *The Review of Scientific Instruments*, **24**, No. 6, 444, 1953.
6. MITCHELL, G. A. G., *The J. of Photographic Science*, **2**, 113, 1954.
7. PELGROMS, J. D., *Paper Trade J.*, **4**, 25, 1952.
8. LEGRAND, C. AND SALMON, J., *J. des Recherches, CNRS*, **26**, 298, 1954; *Bull. de Microsc. Appl.*, **4**, No 1–2, 9, 1954.
9. SALMON, J., X-ray Microscopy and Microradiography, 465, Acad. Press, N. Y., 1957.
10. MANIGAULT, P. AND SALMON, J., *J. des Recherches, CNRS*, **37**, 319, 1956; SALMON, X-ray Microscopy and Microradiography, 484, Acad. Press, N. Y., 1957; MANIGAULT AND SALMON, *Bull. de Microsc. Appl.*, **8**, No 1, 14, 1958; SALMON, *Bull. Soc. bot. Fr.*, **101**, No 7–9, 429, 1954; SALMON, *C.R. Ac. Sc.*, **247**, 510, 1958; SALMON, *C.R. Ac. Sc.*, **248**, 734, 1959; MANIGAULT, SALMON AND ROUSSEAU, M., *Bull. de Microsc. Appl.*, **9**, 10, 1959.
11. CLARK, G. L., Applied X-Rays, 4th ed. McGraw-Hill, N. Y., 1955.
12. NIXON, W. C., X-ray Microscopy and Microradiography, 34, Acad. Press, N. Y., 1957.
13. JACKSON, C. K., X-ray Microscopy and Microradiography, 487, Acad. Press, N. Y., 1957.
14. ELY, R. V., X-ray Microscopy and Microradiography, 59, Acad. Press, N. Y., 1957.
15. ONG, S. P. AND LE POOLE, J. B., *Appl. Sci. Res.*, B, **7**, 233, 1958.
16. ENGSTRÖM, A., Historadiography, in Analytical Cytology, McGraw-Hill Book Co., Inc.,
N. Y., 1955; ENGSTRÖM, A., in OSTER G. AND POLLISTER, A. W., Physical Techniques in Biological Research, **3**, 489, Acad. Press, N. Y., 1956; ENGSTRÖM AND GREULICH, R. C., *J. Appl. Phys.*, **27**, 758, 1956; ENGSTRÖM, LUNDBERG, B. AND BERGENDAHL, G., *Ultrastr. Rev.*, **1**, No. 2, 147, 1957.
17. GREULICH, R. C., AND ENGSTRÖM, A., *Experim. Cell. Res.*, **10**, No. 1, 251, 1956.
18. ENGSTRÖM A., AND LUNDBERG, B., *Experim. Cell. Res.*, **12**, No. 1, 198, 1957.
19. BRATTGÅRD, S. O. AND HYDÉN, H., *Acta Radiol.*, suppl. **94**, 1952.
20. ENGSTRÖM, A., in OSTER AND POLLISTER (see 16).
21. DAHL, A. O., ROWLEY, J. R., STEIN, O. L. AND WEGSTEDT, L., *Experim. Cell Res.*, **13**, 31, 1957.
22. DIETRICH, J., Congress on X-ray Microscopy and Microradiography, Stockholm, 1959.
23. ZEITZ, L. AND BAEZ, A. V., *X-ray Microscopy and Microradiography*, p. 417, Acad. Press, N. Y., 1957.

J. SALMON

POINT PROJECTION X-RAY MICROSCOPY*
(*See also* p. 661)

The shadow projection method of x-ray microscopy is a recently devised technique for producing enlarged images with x-rays. This type has developed rapidly by following the methods of electron microscope design, leading to a resolution of 1 micron at an early stage, and 0.1 micron after further refinement. In this survey the fundamental principles are presented together with a few applications. Detailed recent results may be found in the four volumes on x-ray microscopy given as references.

Physical Basis of Projection X-Ray Microscopy

A comparison between the contact method of microradiography and projection microradiography is shown in Fig. 1. With contact microradiography (CMR) a normal type of x-ray tube can be used at low kilovoltage and

* Revised version of a chapter in a book entitled "X-ray Microscopy and Microradiography" published by Academic Press, New York, 1957.

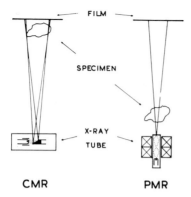

FIG. 1. Comparison of contact microradiography, CMR, and projection microradiography, PMR. (From V. E. Cosslett and W. C. Nixon, *The Times Science Review, London,* **18**, 10, 1955.)

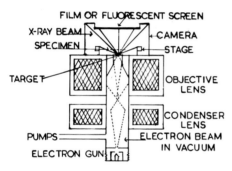

FIG. 2. Essential parts of a Projection X-ray Microscope.

the specimen is placed almost in contact with the photographic recording film. All of the enlargement is obtained optically with a light microscope from the original x-ray negative. This method is simple, quick and inexpensive and has been used by many workers, both in biology and metallurgy, since the original discovery of x-rays. With projection microradiography (PMR) the difficulty of focusing x-rays is circumvented by using a special x-ray tube to form a point source of radiation, and initial x-ray enlargement is produced by simple geometrical projection of the image of a specimen close to the source. The production of a magnified image using x-rays has encouraged the use of the term "x-ray microscope," qualified by

the word "projection," although no x-ray lenses or mirrors are needed.

This form of x-ray microscope is seen in detail in Fig. 2. An electron gun (hot tungsten filament, biasing cap and anode at earth potential) forms a narrow beam of electrons accelerated to 5 to 20 kV. The space traversed by the electrons is evacuated as in an electron microscope and the electron beam is focused by two magnetic lenses placed outside of the non-magnetic vacuum chamber. The objective lens with pole pieces reduces the size of the electron source and the condenser lens, although weaker, conveniently determines the amount of reduction over-all. The minute electron beam, from a few microns down to 0.1 micron or less, strikes the thin metal foil target that also forms the vacuum wall of the upper end of the x-ray tube. The x-rays generated in this way come from a spot similar to the electron beam size and are used to form an x-ray projected image of the specimen on the film or fluorescent screen. The specimen is held in a stage with three degrees of freedom for scanning the field of view in two directions and changing the magnification with the third. The camera for recording the x-ray image is merely a light tight box holding a cassette so that the plate can be exposed to the x-ray beam.

The x-ray target and electron beam are shown schematically in Fig. 3 to demonstrate the method of image formation in the projection x-ray microscope. The electron beam, coming from the left and focused by the objective lens, is enlarged by the lens aberrations to a size δ, even if the total reduction in beam size would be much smaller than this. The semi-angular aperture of the lens, α, determines the value of δ and also the total beam current striking the target. A strong lens with the lowest aberration is used for the final beam reduction although this means a short working distance and consequent placing of the target in the pole piece gap. The exact opposite arrangement is

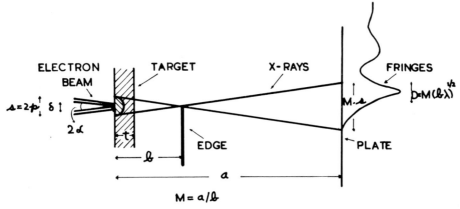

FIG. 3. Image formation by projecting x-ray microscopy. Unsharpness in the image plane = Ms. First Fresnel fringe half-width in the image plane = $M(b\lambda)^{\frac{1}{2}}$. (From W. C. Nixon, *Proc. Roy. Soc.* **A232:** 475, 1955.)

found in the double condenser lens systems of modern electron microscopes where a long working distance is needed from the lens to the specimen stage. In this case the second lens is weak and aberrations occur but the electron intensity (unlike the x-ray intensity) is sufficient for high magnification on the final screen.

The electron beam when striking the target will be scattered and diffused within the metal foil to give a source of x-rays approximately equal to s where $s = 2p$ and p is the penetration distance of the electrons at the kilovoltage applied to the electron gun. A specimen represented by a straight edge a distance b away will cast an enlarged x-ray image onto the screen or photographic plate at distance a with the magnification $M = a/b$. The blurring due to the source size is also enlarged by M and so the "resolution" in these terms in the object is similar to the x-ray source size.

This simple projective magnification means that a thick specimen is magnified by different amounts from front to back but the total specimen image is all in focus. This is easily demonstrated by using a point source of light, say a flashlight bulb and two batteries, and a coarse mesh grid. In a darkened room the projected image of the grid will be seen to vary in magnification as the grid is tilted but the image will remain sharp within the limits imposed by the size of the point source of light. There is no overlapping of out-of-focus layers of the specimen and stereographic techniques for qualitative viewing and quantitative measurement can be used even at the highest magnification hoped for in the future.

These x-rays have a wavelength of 1 to 10 A, very much shorter than the 4000 A of blue light in an optical microscope. This means that the diffraction limit on resolution is much less serious in x-ray microscopy at the present time but as the resolution improves this effect will join the geometrical limits discussed above.

The magnitude of the Fresnel diffraction fringes is shown in Fig. 3 and the width of the first fringe at the plate, i.e., in the image, is $D = M(b\lambda)^{1/2}$ or in terms of the specimen, $d = (b\lambda)^{1/2}$. In this case b is the distance shown in the figure and λ is the x-ray wavelength. The recognition of such fringes as a resolution limit is determined by the total magnification of the x-ray micrograph. This fringe width, d, in microns is plotted against the plate distance, a, in cm in Fig. 4. Various constants must be chosen for this equation, such as the optical magnification of the

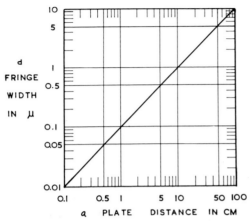

FIG. 4. Minimum plate distance from x-ray source to observe a fringe of width d, allowing 10× photographic enlargement. (From W. C. Nixon, *Proc. Roy. Soc.*, **A232**, 475, 1955.)

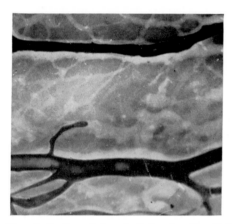

FIG. 5. Section of dog skull showing the diploe veins. (From C. G. Hewes, W. C. Nixon, A. V. Baez and O. F. Kampmeir, *Science*, **124**, 129, 1956.)

x-ray negative, and the actual values will determine the exact result. However, the values shown give the order of magnitude of the effect.

It is seen that for a fringe of one micron width, the plate must be 10 cm from the x-ray source for that fringe to be visible in the final image. This distance is longer than usually used and the exposure time would be longer as well. In fact, with one micron resolution no one micron fringes have been seen due to Fresnel diffraction for this reason. As the resolution improves to 0.1 micron the plate distance falls to 1 cm and this is the distance most used in practice and indeed fringes of this size have been seen.

These then are the main limitations on the performance of the projection x-ray microscope. All attempts at making an x-ray microscope of this type quickly lead to a resolution "less than one micron" and equal to the penetration limit for the kilovoltage and target metal used. The different types of lenses that focus and reduce the electron beam merely affect the number of electrons in the final spot and thus the exposure time, with the poorer lens giving a longer exposure but at the same resolution. This implies enough intensity on the fluorescent screen to focus the microscope in the first place. Performance can only be judged if all comparison figures are given such as spot size, beam current at the target, kV, exposure time, plate distance and specimen.

Results

An x-ray micrograph of a 5-mm section of dog skull is shown in Fig. 5, taken with Dr. Baez' x-ray microscope at the University of Redlands, California. The blood vessels within the bone have been injected with a blue vinyl plastic and detail of the *diploe* veins is shown. This single 5 minute exposure presents the same information as would be obtained after some 25 hours of normal optical sectioning and examination. A detailed examination would take several months by normal methods, but a few 5-minute exposures with the x-ray microscope.

Another example is the frozen-dried foot of a newborn mouse seen in Fig. 6, and taken by Mosley and Wyckoff at the National Institutes of Health, Bethesda, Maryland. In this case a study of developing bone and teeth is aided by the penetration possible with the x-ray microscope and freeze-drying is used both for fixation and removal of the water that would obscure the detail of the bone and tissue. Similar photographs of the mouse head, both new born and embryonic, show the developing tooth buds *in situ*, and the spatial arrangement is seen with a stereographic view.

Other metallurgical, mineralogical, chemical and industrial applications may be found in the publications listed at the end of the article.

Resolution

Electron penetration in the target varies roughly as the square of the kilovoltage of the electron beam and reducing the voltage from 10 kV to 2 kV would imply an improvement of 25× in resolution. In addition the x-rays generated at this lower voltage would be more easily absorbed by the thinner specimens and sufficient contrast would be expected even for much finer detail. However, the x-ray intensity falls off very rapidly as the kilovoltage is lowered due to less efficient electron gun operation, less efficient x-ray generation, more absorption in the target and in the x-ray path to the photographic plate. The ideal solution is some form of soft x-ray image intensifier but until that time it is necessary to use the higher kilovoltage and overcome the electron limit in some other way.

A thin layer of evaporated metal on a thicker beryllium backing will not give an improvement because x-rays are generated in the beryllium by the electrons that pass through the thin metal layer and this background fogging obscures the improved resolution. The alternative is to use a thin foil with no backing at all and this has been done for Figs. 7 and 8. In Fig. 7 the same type of test object as used previously by all three methods of x-ray microscopy is shown at a higher magnification and with a resolution that is estimated to be close to 0.1 micron. A faint white Fresnel diffraction fringe of this width can be seen around the grid bars. An actual specimen as opposed to a test object is shown in Fig. 8. This is a bean section, also taken

FIG. 6. Frozen dried new born mouse foot. (From V. M. Mosely and R. W. G. Wyckoff, unpublished.)

with a thin metal target and the same fringe can be seen around this specimen as well.

These photographs represent about the best that can be done with the static x-ray projection microscope until some means of increasing x-ray intensity is found by any or all of the possible approaches including image intensifiers, field emission electron sources and better electron lenses corrected for spherical aberration.

Other Methods of Point Source X-Ray Microscopy

The difficulty of finding x-ray fringes was shown in Fig. 4 and the small size even at high resolution is seen in Figs. 7 and 8. This makes the practice of Gabor diffraction microscopy with x-rays very difficult if not impossible since it is necessary to have many fringes in the hologram if there is to be any information in the reconstruction. Baez and El-Sum show other difficulties as well, such as monochromatizing the x-ray beam, using opaque specimens and producing a mathematical point source.

FIG. 7. Silver grid, 1500 mesh/inch, 3 micron bars, white Fresnel Fringe (From W. C. Nixon, *Nature*, **175**, 1078, 1955.) Magnification given by 2 micron bar.

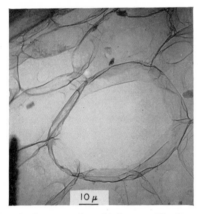

FIG. 8. Bean section, high magnification using thin target. Magnification given by 10 micron bar.

The ×2 method of Le Poole and Ong is another way of getting a slight gain in resolution if the film grain size and the x-ray source size are similar. The exact improvement is still arguable but the results they show are very good and the gold-shadowed and unshadowed bull spermatozoa taken in this way are superior to those obtained with the thin metal targets used for Figs. 7 and 8.

Other projection methods are outlined by Rovinsky where in one case a pin-hole produces the small x-ray source and in the other a fine tungsten point acts as the x-ray target. The resolution and exposure times are similar to the more standard methods and

these variations on the basic theme may lead to improvements in the future, although not offering better resolution at present.

Microanalysis

X-ray microscopy in common with other methods of microscopy is intended to supply information on the microscale. With the electron microscope the scattering of electrons to produce the contrast in the image does not bear a simple relationship to the elements of the specimen. Selected area micro electron diffraction must be employed to identify the crystalline components of the object, from an area of one micron square or slightly less. A similar method can be used with the projection x-ray microscope where selected area x-ray diffraction can be used for areas down to a few microns in size. Localization of the area is done from the x-ray image seen on the fluorescent screen; an aperture is brought into the beam so that a narrow pencil of rays strikes the specimen and the broader diffracted beam is recorded on fast x-ray film in place of the slower emulsions used for microscopy. This method allows the identification of complicated crystalline compounds containing many separate elements.

In addition to this method, analogous to electron diffraction, it is also possible to perform x-ray absorption and emission microanalysis in a manner that has no parallel in electron microscopy. For the absorption method the techniques developed by Prof. Engström and his colleagues can be applied to projection x-ray microscopy with the advantage of using an x-ray enlarged image for analysis. If this is recorded photographically the final accuracy with the present x-ray microscope resolution is similar to that of the contact method but it is more difficult to produce monochromatic radiation with the projection tube. The enlarged image does allow the use of radiation counter recording and this may speed up the whole process and make it more automatic. A more powerful approach is to use the x-ray fluorescent emission from the specimen when the primary x-ray beam has sufficient energy to excite the characteristic lines sought. This is the same method that is widely practiced on the macro scale for x-ray analysis of large amounts of material. The projection x-ray tube has a very high specific loading of the x-ray focal spot and this high brightness makes it specially suitable for micro-diffraction, as mentioned above, and for microfluorescent analysis. In this case the primary x-ray beam is collimated to a narrow beam and this strikes a very small area of the specimen. The emitted radiation is detected by a counter placed to one side of the main beam and for analysis a spectrometer is placed between the specimen and the counter.

A similar but perhaps more powerful variant of x-ray microanalysis is the use of the x-ray emission from the target itself. In this case the specimen replaces the normal x-ray target, is struck by the electron beam, and the emitted x-rays from an area equal to the size of the beam are analyzed by a spectrometer and counter. Point to point detection was achieved by mechanical scanning of the specimen in early models of this method with the position of the electron probe determined by means of an additional optical microscope focused on the same area. A recent more elegant approach is where the specimen is still moved for general viewing of the surface but the electron beam is scanned as well, as in a television raster, and the x-ray output modulates a cathode-ray tube that is scanned with the same speed. The resultant picture on the face of the tube represents the exact element analysis for each particular setting of the spectrometer detector. This method of scanning x-ray microanalysis seems to be the true strength of the scanning x-ray microscope and efforts are being made to extend the analysis to lower atomic numbers, lower concentrations and to determine the limit of detection. (See "Encyclopedia of Spectroscopy," pp. 745, 768.)

These analytical tools use the same beam forming systems as the static x-ray projection microscope and the combination of x-ray microscopy and x-ray analysis although not at the resolution of the electron microscope, should become a well established technique of microscopical investigaion.

REFERENCES

Nixon, W. C., *Research*, **8**, 473 (1955) (reprinted in "Modern Methods of Microscopy", p. 92, Butterworths, London, 1956 and Interscience, N. Y.)
Proceedings of the Cambridge Symposium "X-ray Microscopy and Microradiography", August 1956, Cambridge, England; editors, V. E. Cosslett, A. Engström and H. H. Pattee, Academic Press, N. Y., 1957.
Proceedings of the Stockholm Symposium "X-ray Microscopy and X-ray Microanalysis", June 1959, Stockholm, Sweden; editors, A. Engström, H. H. Pattee and V. E. Cosslett, Elsevier Press, Amsterdam, 1960.
Ong Sing Poen. "Microprojection with X-rays", Hoogland and Waltman, Delft, Netherlands, 1959.
Cosslett, V. E. and Nixon, W. C., "X-ray Microscopy", Cambridge University Press, 1960.

W. C. Nixon

PRODUCTION OF CONTINUOUS AND CHARACTERISTIC X-RADIATION FOR CONTACT AND PROJECTION MICRORADIOGRAPHY

When discussing the production of characteristic or continuous x-radiation, by bombarding a target with electrons, it is convenient to separate the elementary processes of bremsstrahlung and inner-shell ionization from the modifying effects of electron scattering and energy loss. The so-called 'ideally thin' target is one in which only a small fraction of the electrons undergo any encounter (radiative or otherwise) within the target so that the electrons are undeviated and are of full energy. This ensures that any encounter resulting in the production of x-radiation takes place when the bombarding electron has a known energy and direction. Targets satisfying this condition would be impracticably thin, but Von Borries (1949) and Lenz (1954) have calculated the distance in which an electron is expected to suffer 1 elastic collision*, and this is a convenient criterion for our purposes. At 10 kV it is approximately 2×10^{-6} gm/cm² for all elements, rising to about 8×10^{-6} gm/cm² at 40 kV. As the most probable angle of single scattering is only 0.01–0.1 radian, this criterion ensures that the electrons are usually deviated by only quite small amounts from their initial directions. The inelastic encounters cause even smaller deviations (for example 1.4×10^{-4} radian in carbon at 20 kV) and so can be neglected in this connection; and it can be readily shown (e.g., from the data of Lane and Zaffarano, 1954) that the amount of energy lost in this critical thickness if very small, being for example 0.04 kV for aluminum, for an incident electron energy of 10 keV. At 10 keV the full range is 0.26 mg/cm² for aluminum, or 130 times the Aufhellungsdicke. The range increases slowly with increasing atomic number, and from the Bethe-Bloch expression (e.g. Paul and Steinwedel, 1955) can be shown to be greater for gold than for aluminum by a factor of about 2.

It is clear that work with thin targets is more fundamental and can be compared more readily with theory, whereas thick targets are of more practical importance in that they provide maximum yields of x-rays. Thick targets can be subdivided into foils which are thin enough to transmit the x-radiation produced, as used in the projection x-ray microscope (e.g., Nixon (1955)), and the massive anticathode familiar in conventional x-ray tubes.

We shall consider the production of the continuous and characteristic spectra in thin and thick targets, in the energy region of interest in x-ray microscopy.

* Termed by them the 'Aufhellungsdicke', in connection with image formation in electron microscopy.

Continuous Spectrum from Thin Targets

Spectral Distribution. The spectral distribution from thin targets was first studied by Nicholas (1929) using an electron energy of 45 keV and targets of aluminum and gold. Measurements were made at angles of 40, 90 and 140 degrees to the forward direction. In general the data showed that the intensity per unit frequency interval I_ν was approximately constant up to the high frequency limit ν_0, and zero thereafter. A theoretical treatment by Kramers (1923) gave a similar relationship, of the form

$$I_\nu d\nu = \frac{KZ^2}{V} d\nu.$$

This expression is not in general true, although it is a good approximation when considering radiation emitted at right angles to the incident electron beam, using targets of high atomic number and electrons of low energy.

The more rigorous quantum mechanical theory of the continuous spectrum is due to Sommerfeld and has been put into numerical form by Kirkpatrick and Wiedmann (1945) who gave theoretical spectral distributions for a wide range of conditions. According to their data, the shape of the spectral distribution depends on the parameter Z^2/V, and not upon either of these two variables separately, except at the extreme low frequency end of the spectrum, where the screening effect of outer electrons, which reduces the x-ray intensity somewhat, depends on Z separately. The spectral shape depends markedly on the angle of observation. Fig. 1 (calculated from Kirkpatrick and Weidmann's data) illustrates the spectral distributions at 0° and 90°, and also averaged over all directions, for an electron energy of 10 keV, using targets for which $Z = 13$ (aluminum) and 58 (the highest available from their calculations, at this low energy). The simple expression of Kramers can be

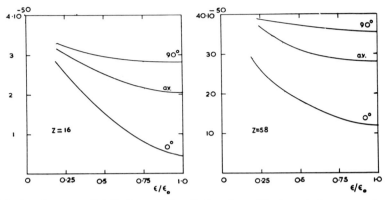

FIG. 1. Calculated energy distribution of X-radiation from thin targets for an accelerating voltage of 10 kV. The units are ergs/steradian/unit frequency interval/electron/atom-per-cm². (After Kirkpatrick and Wiedmann, 1945.)

seen to be a useful approximation of 90°, although is not applicable in the forward direction.

The intensity averaged over all angles, (but at the high energy limit only), is illustrated in Fig. 2, as a function of Z^2/V, again after Kirkpatrick and Wiedmann. The simple Kramer's theory predicts exact proportionality; and this is indeed very nearly so, over a wide range of the parameters.

Amrehn and Kuhlenkampff (1955) determined the spectral distribution at 90° from thin targets of aluminum, nickel and tin. The effective thicknesses of their targets ranged from 4×10^{-6} gm/cm² (tin) to 1.2×10^{-5} gm/cm² (aluminum). By comparing this with the Aufhellungsdicke of $5–8 \times 10^{-6}$ gm/cm² (for the electron energies of 25 to 40 keV used by these authors) it can be seen these represent a real approach to the condition of ideal thinness. It is perhaps more important to note that the energy loss in these targets would not exceed about 0.15 keV, a small fraction of the incident energy. The intensity from such targets is low, but by using a proportional counter and pulse height analyzer it was possible to obtain data of good statistical accuracy in reasonable times (30 seconds for each observation). Fig. 3 shows the spectral distribution obtained at right angles to the direction of the

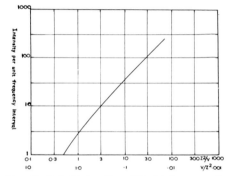

FIG. 2. Total intensity at the high energy limit as a function of Z^2/V (After Kirkpatrick and Wiedmann, 1945). The units are as in Fig. 1.

electron beam, using an accelerating voltage of 34 kV, and a target of aluminum. The corresponding theoretical curve is given (normalized to give the best fit with the experimental data) and it is seen that the agreement in shape is very good indeed. When comparing aluminum and nickel, the total intensity was found to be closely proportional to Z^2, (for equal atoms/cm²), although with tin the agreement was somewhat less good.

Angular Distribution. The angular distribution of the continuous spectrum from thin targets has been investigated by several workers. The radiation from targets of aluminum 6000 A in thickness was examined by Kulenkampff (1928) using electron energies from 16 to 38 keV. It was observed that the

655

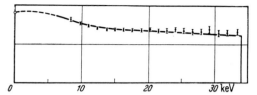

FIG. 3. Spectral distribution form a thin aluminum target (accelerating voltage 34 kV) at 90° to the electron beam (Amrehn and Kuhlenkampff, 1955).

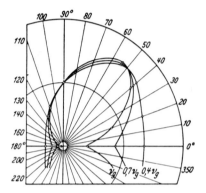

FIG. 4. Angular distribution from a thin aluminum target (accelerating voltage 34 kV) (Kerscher and Kuhlenkampff, 1955).

intensity (i.e., energy flux per unit solid angle) in the forward direction is minimal and that the intensity passes through a maximum at an angle dependent upon the electron energy and the quantum energy. Bohm (1937–8) and Honerjager (1940) carried out more detailed measurements (in the same region of electron energy) on targets of aluminum and magnesium and confirmed the essential aspects of the earlier investigations. The maximum occurs at smaller angles as the electron energy is increased; but for a fixed electron energy, it is the softer components of the spectrum which have the smallest angle of maximum intensity. Bohm and Honerjager observed additionally that, with decreasing target thickness, the forward minimum became more marked, because of the decreasing effect of electron scattering and diffusion.

It was noted that even at the high energy limit there was some emission in the forward

direction but this was attributed to the effect of electron diffusion, even in the thinnest targets used. The theory of Scherzer (1932) predicted that there would be no forward emission, but this involved the assumption of small atomic numbers and high electron energies, and the more general calculations of Scheer and Zeitler (1955) show that there is expected to be some forward emission.

The finite intensity observed by Honerjager in the forward direction using his thinnest (100 A) target affords evidence of this, because this thickness is only one half of the "Aufhellungsdicke" at this energy. Electron scattering would not be expected to affect the original distribution to any observable extent.

Kerscher and Kuhlenkampff (1955) have used targets 250 A in thickness, and have established accurately the shape of the angular distributions for several different photon energies within the continuous spectrum excited in aluminum at 34 kV (Fig. 4). These workers used a proportional counter and single channel pulse analyzer to select particular bands of photon energies. This method suffers from the disadvantage that the boundaries of the selected channels are ill-defined (because of the finite 'spread' in the heights of pulses produced by photons of a given energy) and Doffin and Kuhlenkampff (1957) have recently avoided this difficulty by using balanced filters, to select a well defined energy band.

Massey and Burhop (1952) have given a comparison between the theoretical angle of maximum emission (at the high energy limit) and the experimental data of Kuhlenkampff and of Bohm. The agreement is very good, and the more recent data also fit well.

X-ray Production in Electron-opaque Targets

Spectral Distribution. When the x-ray target is thick enough to bring the electrons to rest, the observed spectral distribution is a superimposition of thin target spectra for all electron energies up to the incident energy. The form of the thick target distribution can be calculated only if the range-energy relationship is known. The scattering of the electrons causes a further modification of the spectral distribution in a given direction, because the electrons in the beam are no longer travelling in a defined direction with respect to the point of observation. The problem is not amenable to exact calculation but it is clear that the spectral distributions will contain a greater proportion of soft radiation than is observed from thin targets.

Using the spectral distribution $I_\nu = \text{const.}$, together with the then accepted Thomson-Whiddington law of energy loss, Kramers obtained a thick target distribution of the form $I_\nu = KZ(\nu_0 - \nu)$ which is in fact very closely obeyed in practice, as will be shown below. The intensity per unit frequency interval is related to the intensity per unit energy interval, and to the somewhat more familiar intensity per unit wavelength interval, by the relations

$$I_\nu = hI_\epsilon = \frac{\lambda^2}{c} I_\lambda.$$

The continuous spectrum from massive targets of several elements was investigated by Kuhlenkampff (1922), at an angle of approximately 90° to the electron beam, using accelerating voltages between 7 and 12 kV. It was established that the Kramers relationship was closely applicable down to about $0.4\,\nu_0$. A small additional term, independent of kilovoltage and photon energy but proportional to Z^2, was found to be necessary. This second term is important only in the immediate vicinity of the high energy limit. These measurements were extended to higher accelerating voltages (20–50 kV) by Kuhlenkampff and Schmidt (1943), and to lower voltages (1–2 kV) by Neff (1951). Some of the latter data are reproduced in Fig. 5.

The spectral distribution in the forward direction from electron-opaque targets con-

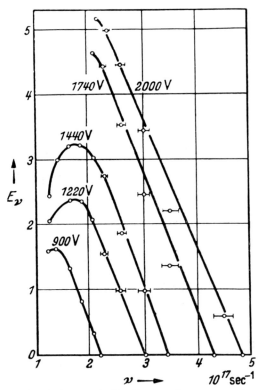

FIG. 5. Spectral distribution from a massive target of platinum (Neff, 1951).

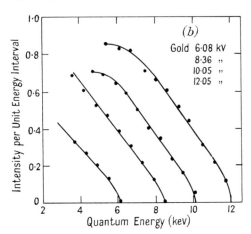

FIG. 6. Spectral distribution in the forward direction from an electron-opaque gold target (Dyson, 1959a).

sisting of foils in the region of 1 mg/cm² in thickness has been investigated recently (Cosslett and Dyson (1957); Dyson (1959a))

657

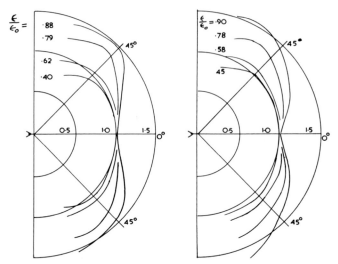

FIG. 7. Angular distributions in the forward hemisphere from an electron-opaque aluminum target, for electron energies of 10.05 and 12.05 keV respectively. The curves in the upper quadrant represent observed data. Those in the lower quadrant have been corrected for self-absorption within the target. (Cosslett and Dyson, 1957).

in the region of 6–12 kV. The data resemble very closely that obtained by Kuhlenkampff at 90°. Fig. 6 shows the spectral distribution in the forward direction from a gold target for four different accelerating voltages.

Angular Distribution. The angular distribution of the total radiation from an electron-opaque target of gold was measured at 10 and 25 kV by Oosterkamp and Proper (reported by Botden *et al.* (1952)). At the higher electron energy there was a slight rise in intensity at increasing angles to a maximum at 15° from the forward direction, showing that electron scattering does not quite obliterate the type of distribution observed with electron-transparent films. At 10 kV there was no rise (i.e., no minimum in the forward direction), and it was considered that this was due to absorption in the target, the effect of which would increase with increasing angle. Their measurements were made with an ionization chamber, for dosimetric purposes; this would in fact accentuate the lower photon energies which show little anisotropy even when an electron-transparent target is used.

In the work just referred to no attempt was made to discriminate between the different energies within the continuous spectrum, but a series of measurements using targets of aluminum, copper and gold has been described by Cosslett and the writer (1957, 1959a), in which a proportional counter was used for energy discrimination. Near the high energy limit the radiation is pronouncedly anistropic, although much less so than in the case of ideally thin targets. For example, for aluminum at 10 kV, at a quantum energy of 9 keV, the anisotropy (defined as the intensity per unit solid angle in the direction of maximum emission divided by that in the forward direction) is calculated to be 4.1, for an ideally thin target, whereas the "thick target" value observed in these measurements was 1.6 (see Fig. 7). At lower quantum energies the anisotropy is even less and below about 0.5 of the high energy limit the radiation is virtually isotropic.

Comparison with theory is difficult, but in principle it is possible to deduce the extent of electron scattering by comparing the anisotropies for thick and thin targets. It appears in fact that multiple scattering and diffusion prevail even when the electrons have lost only a small fraction (one tenth in this example) of their initial energy. This implies that virtually all the x-ray output from a thick aluminum target for an incident electron energy of 10 keV is produced from electrons which are fully diffused. "Full diffusion" and its relation to multiple scattering is discussed by Bothe (1932) and Paul and Steinwedel (1955).

Efficiency of Production of Continuous X-radiation

The main source of theoretical information regarding the efficiency of production in thin targets is the data of Kirkpatrick and Wiedmann (1945), and for comparison some experimental data are available.

Massey and Burhop (1952) have considered the data of Smick and Kirkpatrick (1941) and Clark and Kelly (1941), converting it into absolute units where necessary, and drawing upon Kirkpatrick and Wiedmann's data in preference to the earlier calculations used by the experimenters. Smick and Kirkpatrick measured the radiation from a thin nickel target bombarded by 15 keV electrons, using balanced filters to select a band of radiation of quantum energy about 8 keV or 0.575 of the high energy limit. At 88 degrees to the forward direction the intensity was 2.2×10^{-50} ergs/steradian/unit frequency interval/electron/atom per cm^2. The data of Kirkpatrick and Wiedmann yield a value of 6×10^{-50} in the above units, although Smick and Kirkpatrick give a calculated value (after Sauter (1934)) of 2.9×10^{-50}. Clark and Kelly made a similar measurement using aluminum at a bombarding energy of 31.7 kV and a quantum energy of 0.82 of the high energy limit; at 60 degrees they found the intensity to be 6.2×10^{-51} ergs, etc., ($\pm 33\%$), as compared with 4.23×10^{-51} from Kirkpatrick and Wied-

mann's data. The agreement is in this case within the experimental error.

More recently the theory has been subjected to a relatively comprehensive test by the work of Amrehn and Kuhlenkampff (1955) and Amrehn (1956). The latter author has made a detailed absolute comparison between his experimental energy distributions for five elements and the calculations of Kirkpatrick and Wiedmann. Agreement is often better than 10 % and nearly always better than 20 %. The general impression is that the theory is now well verified for bombardment energies in the region of 20–40 KeV.

Kirkpatrick and Wiedmann extended their calculations to give an expression for the thin target efficiency of production of x-radiation, by integrating their energy distribution curves over all energies and directions, and by comparing this with the energy loss suffered by the bombarding electrons. The thin target efficiency is given approximately by

$$\eta = 2.8 \times 10^{-9} ZV \ (V \text{ in volts}),$$

although the calculations show that it is not strictly a function of ZV, but depends upon these two variables separately to some small extent.

Turning now to thick targets, the experimental data were reviewed by Compton and Allison (1935), and the expression

$$\eta = 1.1 \times 10^{-9} ZV \ (V \text{ in volts})$$

was considered to be accurate to about 20 %. This confirmed the calculation of Kramers who obtained the result

$$\eta = 0.92 \times 10^{-9} ZV$$

from his theoretical expression for the energy distribution from thick targets. Kirkpatrick and Wiedmann calculated the efficiency by integrating their thin target data over all angles and energies and found the efficiency to be proportional to voltage and atomic number to quite a high degree of accuracy,

659

with a constant of proportionality of 1.3×10^{-9}.

The absolute intensity of production in thick targets in the forward direction has been measured by the writer (1959a) for targets of aluminum, copper and gold. The measurements extend from the high energy limit ϵ_0 down to about $5.4 \epsilon_0$. From these data the absolute efficiency can be estimated by extrapolation to zero energy and integration over the whole energy range. Such an extrapolation is subject to some uncertainty but within this limitation the efficiencies in the forward direction were found to be accurately proportional to the accelerating voltage, and approximately proportional to the atomic number. The constant of proportionality was found to be 1.3×10^9 which is slightly in excess of Compton and Allison's estimate but in good agreement with the calculations of Kirkpatrick and Wiedmann.

Characteristic Radiation

When discussing the production of characteristic x-radiation by electron bombardment it is convenient to define a cross-section $Q_{K,L} \cdots$ for $K,L \cdots$ ionization and to express it as a function of the electron energy and of $V_{K,L} \cdots$ the $K,L \cdots$ excitation energy. The problem of finding a suitable expression has been discussed by Worthington and Tomlin (1956) who express Q_K in the form

$$Q_K V_K^2 =$$

$$0.7 \pi e^2 \frac{1}{U} \log_e [4U/(1.65 + 2.65 \exp (1 - U))],$$

where

$U = V/V_K$ and V is the electron energy.

The essential aspects of this expression are the inverse relation between Q_K and V_K^2 (implying a strong inverse relation between Q_K and Z), and a rapid rise in Q_K as U is increased from 1, to a maximum value at $U =$ approximately 2.5, followed by a slow fall in Q_K as U is further increased. $Q_K V_K^2$ is the same function of U for all elements, and is illustrated in their paper. The actual output of x-radiation is obtained by multiplying Q_K by w_K, the fluorescence yield, and by ad hoc additional terms depending upon geometry, self-absorption within the target, etc.

Little absolute data are available for thin targets but the existing information for silver and nickel targets has been summarized and discussed by Worthington and Tomlin (1956), following Massey and Burhop (1952). The experimental and theoretical results do not fit well, although the curves agree in general shape.

The output from thick targets has been calculated by Worthington and Tomlin, but direct experimental observation by these authors and by the writer (1959b) on copper, and by Dolby (1960) on aluminum suggest that their calculations yield values which are high by factors of approximately 2 and 4, respectively.

The experimental data and the theoretical expressions show that the efficiency and the intensity vary with kilovoltage in a somewhat complex manner. For the intensity, empirical relations of the form

$$I = k(V_0 - V_k)^q$$

have frequently been observed to be of use over a restricted range of the variables, where q equals, for example, 1.6 (Worthington and Tomlin 1956) or 1.65 (Compton and Allison 1935). But formulas of wide applicability and methods of calculating the absolute yields on a systematic basis have yet to be found.

REFERENCES

1. AMREHN, H., Z. Phys., **144**, 529 (1956).
2. AMREHN, H., AND KUHLENKAMPFF, H., Z. Phys., **140**, 452 (1955).
3. BOHM, K., Physik. Z., **38**, 334 (1937).
4. BOHM, K., Ann. Physik, **33**, 315 (1938).
5. BORRIES, B. v., "Die Ubermikroscopie", Saenger: Berlin (1949).
6. BOTDEN, P. J. M., COMBEE, B., AND HOUTMAN, J., Philips Tech. Rev., **14**, 165 (1952).

7. Bothe, W., Handb. Phys. XXII, **2**, Springer: Berlin 2nd Edit. 1932.

8. Clark, J. C., and Kelly, H. R., *Phys. Rev.*, **59**, 220 (1941).

9. Compton, A. H., and Allison, S. K., "X-rays in theory and experiment", Van Nostrand, New York, 1935.

10. Cosslett, V. E., (1959) Unpublished.

11. Cosslett, V. E., and Dyson, N. A., contribution to "X-Ray Microscopy and Microradiography" Academic Press, New York, 1957.

12. Doffin, H., and Kuhlenkampff, H., *Z. Phys.*, **148**, 496 (1957).

13. Dolby, R. M., *Brit. J. Appl. Phys.* (1960). (in press).

14. Dyson, N. A., *Proc. Phys. Soc.*, **73**, 924 (1959a).

15. Dyson, N. A., *Brit. J. App. Phys.*, **10**, 505 (1959b).

16. Honerjager, R., *Ann. der Phys.*, **38**, 33 (1940).

17. Kerscher, R. and Kuhlenkampff, H., *Z. Phys.*, **140**, 632 (1955).

18. Kirkpatrick, P., and Wiedmann, L., *Phys. Rev.*, **67**, 321 (1945).

19. Kramers, H. A., *Phil. Mag.*, **46**, 836 (1923).

20. Kuhlenkampff, H., *Ann. Physik*, **69**, 548 (1922).

21. Kuhlenkampff, H., *Ann. Physik*, **87**, 597 (1928).

22. Kulenkampff, H., and Schmidt, L., *Ann. Physik*, **43**, 494 (1943).

23. Lane, R. O. and Zaffarano, D. J., *Phys. Rev.*, **94**, 960 (1954).

24. Lenz, F., *Zeit. Naturforsch.*, **9a**, 185 (1954).

25. Massey, H. S. W., and Burhop, E. H. S., "Electronic and Ionic Impact Phenomena" Oxford, 1952.

26. Neff, H., *Zeit. Phys.*, **131**, 1 (1951).

27. Nicholas, W. W., *Bur. of Stand. J. of Res.*, **2**, 837 (1929).

28. Nixon, W. C., *Proc. Roy. Soc.*, **A232**, 475 (1955).

29. Paul, W., and Steinwedel, H., (Article in "β- and γ-ray Spectroscopy", ed. K. Siegbahn, North Holland Publishing Co. Amsterdam), 1955.

30. Sauter, F., *Ann. d. Physik.*, **20**, 404 (1934).

31. Scheer, M., and Zeitler, E., *Z. Phys.*, **140**, 642 (1955).

32. Scherzer, O., *Ann. Physik*, **13**, 137 (1932).

33. Smick, A. E., and Kirkpatrick, P., *Phys. Rev.*, **60**, 162 (1941).

34. Worthington, C. R., and Tomlin, S. J., *Proc. Phys. Soc.*, **69A**, 401 (1956).

N. A. Dyson

PROJECTION MICROSCOPY (See also p. 647)

The idea of using a small x-ray source for projecting enlarged images was mentioned by Sievert (1) in 1936. In order to limit the effective emitting area, the use of a pinhole aperture was proposed. This method usually called the camera obscura or pinhole camera, was re-introduced by Avdeyenko, Lutsau and Rovinsky (2) at the Cambridge Symposium on x-ray microscopy and microanalyses. It is equally suitable for both transmission and emission microscopy.

In 1939, von Ardenne (3) proposed use of an electron optical system to make an x-ray source of very small dimension and high specific load. This type of microscope (which was successfully realized by Cosslett and Nixon (4) in 1951) is usually called the projection microscope.

Since 1951, the problems of obtaining better resolution and more reliable instrumentation have been studied by Cosslett, Nixon and Pearson (5) (England), Le Poole and Ong (6) (Holland), Newberry and Summers (7) (USA) and Bessen (8) (USA), among others.

The Projection Microscope

Principle. The projection microscope is a microfocus x-ray tube, consisting essentially of an electron source, an electron optical system, and a transmission type target (Fig. 1).

The electrons which have an energy of some 5–15 keV are focused onto a 1–0.1 μ spot. In most cases the target acts as a vacuum seal, allowing the specimen to remain in air. The electron optical system consists of a very strong lens, usually called the objective, and a weak one, the condenser. The function of the latter is to regulate the rate of demagnification of the lens system. As the current density of the electron spot largely depends on its size, the use of the condenser is indispensable for optimum working conditions. Due to the short lifetime of both target and cathode filament,

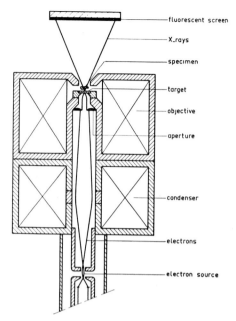

FIG. 1. Principle of the projection microscope.

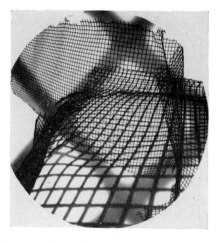

FIG. 2. 1500 mesh per inch silver grid, demonstrating the large depth of field. (Experimental Delft microscope.)

these elements are replaceable. Thus, the projection microscope is a demountable system continuously evacuated to maintain the required vacuum.

Properties. The advantage of using x-rays for microscopy is discussed elsewhere in this volume. This section will deal primarily with the specific aspects of the projection microscope as compared with the widely used contact method. (See B. L. Henke, p. 675.) These are:

(1) The resolution is not limited by the resolution of either the recording material or the optical microscope. As the initial magnification can be adapted to the recording material, the choice of the film is more a matter of working convenience. Usually such a film is chosen to allow some 10× optical magnification. For printing at this magnification a normal enlarger may be used. Le Poole and Ong (9) show that the use of ultra-fine film (of the Lippmann type) for projection microscopy has some advantages.

(2) The resolution is determined by the source size and the diffraction phenomena exclusively. In the region where diffraction does not affect the resolution, the unsharpness is the product of source size and magnification. As a result, the depth of field is very large. (For diffraction error, see B. L. Henke, p. 677.) The magnification varies with the source to specimen distance resulting in a perfect perspective of the specimen. See figs. 2 and 3. This fact is particularly important for stereo microscopy.

(3) The specimen and film are spatially separated. This fact allows us to: (a) study specimens at high temperature; (b) study

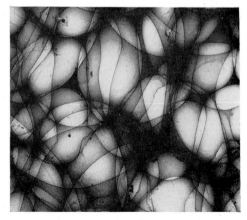

FIG. 3. Plastic sponge, ca. 50×. (Experimental Delft microscope.)

specimens which fluoresce under x-ray radiation; (c) eliminate the effect of electron emission and x-ray fluorescent radiation on the recording material when using hard radiation; (d) study specimens which may influence the properties of the photographic emulsion.

The specimen lies very close to the target of the projection microscope and great care must be taken to avoid reaction between specimen and target. The author notices, for example, that a Mercurichrome-stained specimen may give trouble, if it is used in connection with an aluminum target.

(4) To reduce spherical and chromatic errors, the lens must have a short focal length (10, 11). As both the specimen and target lie almost in the focal plane of the lens, the specimen is in the active region of the lens field. If the specimen consists of ferromagnetic material it may introduce lens errors and change the focal condition. If the specimen is symmetrically aligned with respect to the optical axis and focusing is performed with the specimen in position, these errors can be minimized. Experiments, performed with the commercial T.P.D. microscope show that thin magnetic tape does not appreciably change the focal condition.

Limitations: *The Intensity Problem.* As a microscope is aimed to reveal small details, it must have a good resolution. The resolution, however, is among other things proportional to the image contrast (12), so the use of long wavelength radiation is imperative in connection with low absorbing specimen. Both the source size and the anode voltage are limited in their lowest values. This is caused by the relatively low specific emission of the cathode, resulting in a very low current density of the electron spot at the target. Although it may be possible in principle to obtain an electron focus of less than 100 A with a 1 kV anode voltage, this is not practicable because of the low intensity.

The current density of the electron spot is directly proportional to the brightness of

the electron source and the square of the aperture of the objective lens. The latter is determined by lens errors, especially the spherical aberration. Calculations show that for white radiation, the x-ray energy flux at screen level is:

$$\rho_x \propto J V^3 d^{8/3} C_s^{-2/3} b^{-2} \qquad (1)$$

in which J is the specific emission of the cathode; V, the anode voltage; d, the diameter of the electron spot; C_s, the spherical aberration constant, and b, the target to screen distance.

Focusing of the electron spot. The energy flux ρ_x determines the brightness of the fluorescent image and the exposure time of the film. At the expense of this figure, either the anode voltage V or the source size d can be decreased. The limit will be determined by the impossibility of visual focusing on the fluorescent image rather than by excessively long exposure. An image intensifier will not give considerable improvement as the contrast and thus the visibility of detail will be limited by the number of x-ray quanta used for building an image element. This number is proportional among other things to the x-ray energy flux at screen level and the storage time of the eye or screen. By decreasing the target-to-screen distance b, the brightness of the fluorescent image can be increased considerably at the expense of the field during focusing. The limited field of view is not serious in this case; as in fact, for focusing, one image element is sufficient.

The condition that the magnification on the screen must be sufficiently high to insure proper focusing sets a limit on the smallest screen-to-target distance. A better approach to the "focusing on one image element" method is realized by Ong and Le Poole (14). Instead of x-rays, they used the electrons which are reflected from the target. The reflection coefficient of the order of 2 to 5 % is greater than the x-ray efficiency. The electrons which have the same energy as the incident ones pass the lenses in oppo-

663

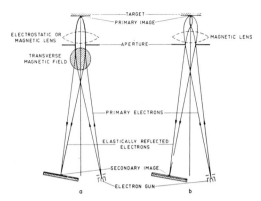

FIG. 4. Principle of the focusing method, using reflected electrons.

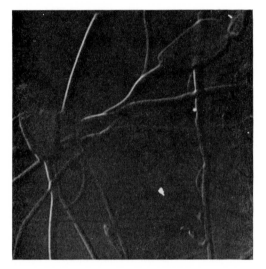

FIG. 5. Gold shadowed bull sperms, ca 2000×. (Experimental Delft microscope.)

site direction (see Fig. 4) and give an enlarged electron image of the spot. For symmetry reasons it can easily be recognized that this image lies in the electron source and has the same size and shape when the target is in focus. By using a transverse magnetic field or by slightly tilting the lens, if it is of the magnetic type, this secondary image can be separated from the primary electron path and caught on a fluorescent screen.

Calculations (14) show that the brightness of this image is some 10^4 higher than that

of the x-ray fluorescent screen under normal focusing condition. So, when using this focusing method, the limit will be set by insufficient stability during long exposure. An important advantage of this focusing method is that it works with the real specimen in position and that the focus can be checked during exposure.

The resolution, obtained by using this focusing method is demonstrated in figs. 5 and 6.

Stability. While the problem of focusing is solved, the intensity problem still remains. Thus long exposure times are required and during this time, the microscope must be stable. The stability concerns:

(a) *Electrical stability.* Changes in both anode voltage and lens current cause a broadening of the electron spot. If the electron optical system is not well aligned, there will be an associated image shift. Although electrical stability can be achieved to a very high degree for a short time, it becomes more difficult to obtain the same stability over long periods. The use of electrostatic lenses will not solve this problem because they give more spherical aberration, resulting in a

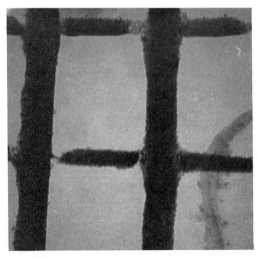

FIG. 6. 1500 mesh per inch silver grid, showing the resolution of the projection microscope. (Experimental Delft microscope.)

lower x-ray intensity and thus necessitating a longer exposure time. And the combined electron optical and thermal effect is more serious.

(b) *Thermal stability*. The electron spot on the target is not the image of the cathode, but that of the crossover which has a more uniform intensity distribution and a smaller size. The apparent position of this crossover depends greatly on the geometry of the cathode, Wehnelt cylinder and anode as these elements act as an immersion lens.

Temperature changes effect the optical properties and thus the position of the crossover. This effect is especially serious when it is accompanied with a disalignment of the immersion lens. Bearing in mind that the cathode is at a high temperature and the surroundings have a relatively large mass, the temperature may still change considerably during an exposure of more than 20 minutes. For high-resolution work, refocusing before each exposure is necessary, even after several hours of continuous use. Preheating the surrounding parts may reduce this effect. A more effective solution will be to use an illuminated pinhole aperture as the electron source. This will, however, need one extra lens.

(c) *Mechanical stability*. Mechanical stability may be achieved by appropriately constructing and mounting the different parts. The most serious error results from relative movement between x-ray source and specimen during exposure, therefore, these parts need special attention.

Other limitations. The resolution limitation due to diffraction is discussed by Henke in this volume (p. 677). Another limitation of the resolution may be due to the depth of penetration and diffusion of the electron in the target. This effect can be reduced either by using a lower voltage or a very thin target (13). The effect of carbon contamination proves to be negligible when the specific load is high enough (14).

In contrast to conventional x-ray tubes,

heat dissipation in the target is not a problem (15). As the source size becomes smaller, the heat flow becomes more favorable. The admissible specific load may be increased proportionally with the reciprocal value of the spot diameter. So, in a spot size of 1 μ, a load as high as 10^7 W/cm² can be tolerated. However, with the conventional hot cathode this is hardly realizable when low voltages are used.

Description of a Commercial Projection X-ray Microscope

In comparison with the contact tube, the projection x-ray unit is a rather complicated electron optical and mechanical device. First it must be continuously pumped to maintain the required vacuum. (For ultrasoft x-ray work, the contact tube cannot be made as a sealed off tube either.) Furthermore, it must contain a highly stabilized anode voltage and lens current supply and an accurately machined specimen and target stage. As the requirements are similar to those of an electron microscope some manufacturers provide adaptors which allow the use of the electron microscope as an x-ray microscope. It is encouraging to notice that complete commercial projection units are also available now.

Recently the Electron Microscope Division of the Technical Physics Department, T.N.O. and T.H. at Delft, Holland, introduced its commercial microscope, which has some special features. This instrument, a picture of which is shown in Fig. 7 and a simplified cross section in Fig. 8, will briefly be described. The principal parts, i.e., the electron source, electron lenses, target and specimen stage and the camera may easily be recognized. The electron reflection focussing method, mentioned previously, is used here. A simple but effective mirror optic in combination with a concentric corrective lens and a 5× ocular are used for observing the focusing screen. The total magnification of this viewer system is 25×.

FIG. 7. Commercial X-ray projection microscope, manufactured by the electron microscope division of the T(echnical) P(hysics) D(epartment), T.N.O. and T.H., Delft, Holland.

The magnetic objective has a focal length of about 1.8 mm. It consumes 90 W and is water-cooled. As the specimen and target are inserted sidewards, the gap between the pole pieces is made relatively large (ca. 7 mm). The specimen carrier can be moved independently in three directions, the magnification on the film is variable between $150\times$ and $10\times$. The admissible optical magnification of the film is approximately $10\times$. To realize the two extreme values of the magnification the specimen must be put very close to the target in the first case and almost at the upper pole piece in the second case. As a result the magnification cannot be varied continuously over the whole range. Without breaking the vacuum, the specimen holder can be turned over 180° after a small outward movement. For a magnification greater than $150\times$ either the specimen must be fixed on the target carrier or the target fixed on the specimen carrier. To accomplish this the target holder can be completely moved outward. Furthermore, it can be moved in a plane perpendicular to the optical axis, thus allowing the use of a clean part of the target for each exposure (See Fig. 9). The target holder can contain up to four different materials in the form of thin, evaporated or rolled metal films.

The x-ray fluorescent screen is fixed on an aplanat and viewed with a binocular (two separate objectives) viewer (16). As focusing is carried out with the reflected electrons and the fluorescent image is inadequate for visual observing, this part of the microscope should be considered as a view-finder. Hence, the image brightness is more important than the magnification. Thus the former is increased at the expense of the latter. The total optical magnification of this finder system is some $20\times$. The screen and aplanat can be moved away so that the specimen can be viewed with the binocular for preliminary positioning.

In contrast with other projection units, the specimen as well as the camera is in vacuum for the following reasons. By using either very high or very low voltages, the target thickness must be equal to or less than the resolution. This is necessary to reduce the effect of electron diffusion in the target in the first case and to avoid too much absorption of the x-rays in the second case. Such a target is inadequate as a vacuum seal unless its area is very much restricted. Furthermore, the air between source and film would absorb too much soft radiation. A direct advantage of a non-sealing target is that it can be easily exchanged during operation and that a clean part can be used for each exposure. The restriction that only dry specimens can be used is not considered to be a serious one. The new instrument, however, is designed in such a way so as to allow the target and specimen stage to be exchanged for another one with a vacuum sealing target. The author has no information yet about the design and execution of this particular part.

The camera is designed for 20 exposures on 35 mm film. The film is transported automatically by moving the camera back and forth. A shutter is provided, which opens in exposure position. For short exposure, the intermediate target, which lies between objective and condenser may be used to inter-

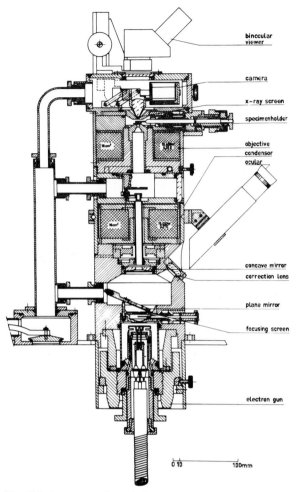

Labels on figure:
binocular viewer
camera
x-ray screen
specimenholder
objective
condensor
ocular
concave mirror
correction lens
plane mirror
focusing screen
electron gun

0 10   100mm

FIG. 8. Simplified cross section of the microscope shown in Fig. 7.

rupt the electron beam. The image field is about 25 mm on the film. (Angular field approx. 36°.)

The anode voltage is variable in four steps from 5 to 20 kV. In each position the lens current is automatically adjusted so that the lenses maintain the same strength.

The desk model housing contains the mechanical and diffusion pumps, the high voltage and lens current supply, and the electronic stabilizer.

Practical X-ray Microscopy

In general, the brightness of the fluorescence images is so low that they are not suitable for visual observation. Another consequence of this low intensity is the poor contrast. As the visibility of a detail will be limited by quantum noise, a considerable gain cannot be expected from an image intensifier unless it has a large storage time, preferably with a contrast correction. Admittedly, such a device would bring the screen brightness to a convenient level, eye adaptation not being necessary, but an image intensifier is a much too complicated instrument to use it for this purpose only. The use of fluorescent screens with better resolution in combination with a high-aperture microscope objective may do the same.

667

FIG. 9. Close up of the target-, aperture- and specimen holder.

The required storage time can easily be achieved by using a photographic film. In the wavelength region normally used for projection microscopy, the quantum yield, i.e., the number of developed silver grains per absorbed x-ray quantum, is very close to 1. This results in a linear relation between film density and exposure. Contrast is proportional to the density, so for full visual information transfer a contrast correction may be necessary (17).

Although the depth of field of the projection microscope is large, a thick specimen may obscure important detail and furthermore it needs a longer exposure time. So the thickness will be determined by the fact whether we want to see the absorption distribution in a plane or in a volume. The last one is made possible by stereomicroscopy.

As the anode voltage and target material determine the spectral distribution of the x-ray source, they must be adapted to the specimen to give an adequate contrast. When using monochromatic radiations of different wavelengths a qualitative chemical analysis can be carried out (18). The fact that the specimen is spatially separated from both film and target allows us to make a series of exposures with different wavelengths while still projecting the specimen at exactly the same angle. This fixed source-to-specimen position is necessary to get an unambiguous relation between the specimen and its projected image.

A direct consequence of the large depth of field is the fact that the magnification of the image is not well defined. It may vary widely over the different parts of the specimen, especially when the thickness of the specimen is comparable with its distance to the source (see Fig. 2).

For thin specimens, the magnification can be determined in different ways similar to those used in light microscopy. A method to determine the magnification of the various parts of a thick specimen will be discussed in the next section about stereomicroscopy. As in projection x-ray microscopy the use of long wavelengths is very limited by the intensity, the contrast for thin organic samples is very poor. If the special features of this type of microscope are desirable for such specimen, contrast can be improved by an appropriate treatment. In many cases this kind of preparation and staining technique can be a modification of existing techniques used in light and electron microscopy and x-ray medical diagnostic. For example, I_2 or $I_2 \cdot KI$ solutions will stain cellulose, and OsO_4 will stain unsaturated fatty acids (see Fig. 10). $BaSO_4$-sugar mixture can be fed to small insects (19). Shadowcasting with a heavy metal will reveal surface structure (see Fig. 5 and Fig. 11). Replicating allows study of the coarse surface of thick heavily absorbing specimens. For relatively thick specimens such as fabric, (Fig. 12), wood particles (Fig. 13), small insects (Figs. 14, 15) etc., an anode voltage of 10–12 kV can successfully be used.

The technique of selective staining, like fat particles by OsO_4, is still in its initial stage. Using different staining agents and radiating with x-rays of different wavelengths may show the distribution of the concentration of some chemical compounds in the specimen. The different pictures obtained in this way may be superimposed after suitable coloring, and thus a color picture can be obtained.

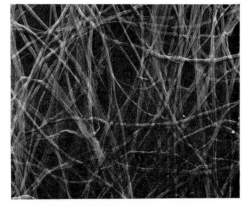

FIG. 11. Tissue paper, gold shadowed, ca 63×. (Experimental Delft microscope.)

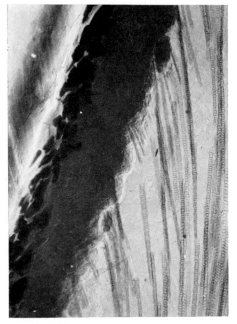

FIG. 10. A section of mouse skin, stained with OsO_4. (Experimental Delft microscope.)

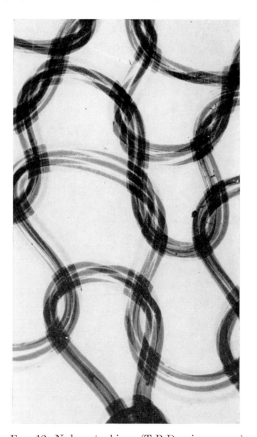

FIG. 12. Nylon stocking. (T.P.D. microscope.)

Stereomicroscopy

As a result of the large depth of field, it is often very difficult to get an idea of the

FIG. 13. Wood splinters. (T.P.D. microscope.)

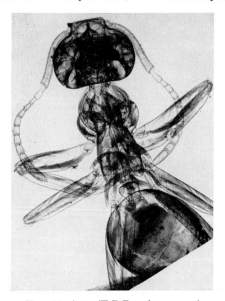

FIG. 14. Ant. (T.P.D. microscope.)

spatial distribution of the specimen out of a
print. This is clearly illustrated in Fig. 3.

The large depth of field, however, is especially important for stereomicroscopy in
which the specimen is seen in its right proportion, but on a larger scale. The geometrical conditions for this can easily be deducted
from Fig. 16. Assume that the M times magnified specimen is placed at a distance l from
the observer (Fig. 16a). Let the maximum
angle of convergence be φ. Thus $\tan \varphi =
e/2l$, in which e is the interocular distance.

FIG. 15. Posterior end of a mosquito.

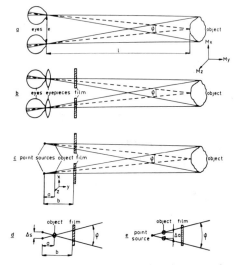

FIG. 16. Condition for making stereographs.

In Fig. 16b, the specimen can be thought of as being replaced by two film images, obtained by projecting the various points with each of the eye pupils as a projecting center. Fig. 16c shows that the same images can also be the result of two equal objects which are M times smaller (and thus have the dimension of the real specimen under study). As the two objects are exactly identical, the two film images are the projections of one object, with the projection center shifted over a distance Δs (Fig. 16d). Fig. 16e shows that instead of moving the projection center, the specimen itself may be shifted over a distance $\Delta a = \Delta s$. The geometrical condition for making stereographs will be:

$$\Delta s = \Delta a = ae/l \qquad (2)$$

in which a is the source to specimen distance. In general, the value of a cannot easily be measured, especially for high magnification. The source to film distance b, however, is in most cases a constant of the instrument. So, introducing the magnification on the film, or primary magnification

$$M_p = b/a \qquad (3)$$

equation (2) can be transformed to

$$M_p\Delta s = M_q\Delta a = be/l \qquad (4)$$

in which the second member is a constant.

The antecedent is the image displacement on the film or screen. So to satisfy this condition, neither the magnification nor the specimen displacement need be known. If, however, Δa is known, by means of a calibrated specimen shift, M_p can be calculated from the relative displacement on a stereoscopic pair of negatives. As this method of measuring the magnification is the only generally reliable one, all projection microscopes should be provided with a calibrated specimen shift.

The source-to-specimen distance is related to the magnification by the following equation:

$$a = l/M \qquad (5)$$

This relation gives the order of magnitude of a. As the viewing distance l is not very critical, it is not necessary to know a accurately. Note that in equation (5) M is the final magnification. Inserting $l = 300$ mm and $M = 1000$ gives $a = 0.3$ mm. So this

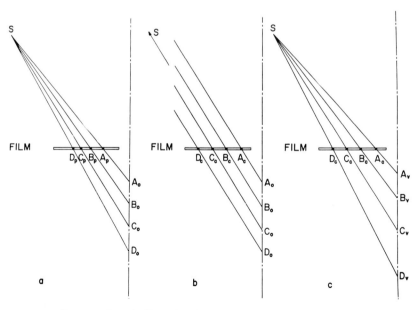

FIG. 17. Depth distortion in contact stereomicroscopy.

condition cannot be fulfilled by the contact method where a is larger by at least two orders of magnitude. If equation (5) is not fulfilled, a distortion in the depth dimension occurs. This can easily be shown in Fig. 13.

Let A_0, B_0, C_0, and D_0 be four points equally spaced along a line. Let, furthermore, S be the projection center (x-ray source), F be the film and A_p, B_p, C_p, and D_p the projected points. If A_0D_0 is a reasonable fraction of A_0S, (Fig. 17a), then $A_pB_p \neq B_pC_p \neq C_pD_p$. If, however, $AS \gg A_0D_0$ (See Fig. 13b), the rays $A_0A_c \parallel B_0B_c \parallel C_0C_c \parallel D_0D_c$ thus $A_cB_c = B_cC_c = C_cD_c$. When after processing and magnifying, the film is viewed, the resulting points seem to come from A_v, B_v, C_v, and D_v; now $A_vB_v \neq B_vC_v \neq C_vD_v$. For depth measurements, however, the last method is preferable because the ratio of the distances on the film and depth dimension of the specimen remain the same. This results in better accuracy.

The depth of field must be a reasonable fraction of the source-to-specimen distance. An object with a depth dimension of some 15 cm and placed with the shortest distance to the observer of 30 cm can still be surveyed. In terms of our considerations, this means that the depth of focus of the microscope must be a reasonable fraction of the distance a. For microscopes using an optical system, the focal length f should be used instead of a. So this condition cannot be fulfilled. The only microscopes where all these conditions can be met are the camera obscura and the projection microscope.

The use of x-rays for stereoscopic examination has many advantages over using ordinary light. Besides the possibility of observing opaque parts, the negligible refraction, and reflection make any part of the specimen observable. (Compare the visibility of a specimen behind a ground glass screen.)

(The pictures shown in this article were kindly supplied by the Electron Microscope Division of the Technical Physics Department, T.N.O. and T.H., Delft, Holland.)

REFERENCES

1. Sievert, R., *Acta Rad.*, **17**, 299 (1936).
2. Rovinsky, B. M., Lutsau, V. G., and Avdeyenko, A. I. "X-ray Microscopy and Microradiography," Academic Press, p. 269, New York, 1957.
3. Ardenne, M. von, *Naturwiss.*, **27**, 485 (1939).
4. Cosslett, V. E., and Nixon, W. C., *Natl. Bur. Stand. Symposium* (1951), Circular 527, p. 257.
5. Cosslett, V. E., Nixon, W. C., and Pearson, H. E., "X-ray Microscopy and Microradiography," Academic Press, p. 96, New York, 1957.
6. Le Poole, J. B. and Ong Sing Poen, *Ibid.*, p. 91.
7. Newberry, S. P. and Summers, S. E., *Ibid.*, p. 116.
8. Bessen, I. I., Philips Electronic Inc., Engineering report #66, (1958).
9. Ong Sing Poen and Le Poole, J. B., Proc. 4th Int. Conf. Elec. Mic., Berlin, (1958).
10. Liebmann, G. and Grad, E. M., *Proc. Phys. Soc.*, **B64**, 56 (1951).
11. Dorsten, A. C. van and Le Poole, J. B., *Phil. Tech. Rev.*, **17**, 47 (1955).
12. Ong Sing Poen, "Microprojection with X-rays," p. 71, Martinus Nijhoff, The Hague, 1959.
13. Nixon, W. C., *Proc. Roy. Soc.*, **A232**, 475 (1955).
14. Ong Sing Poen and Le Poole, J. B., *Appl. Sci. Res. B*, **7**, 233 (1958).
15. Cosslett, V. E., *Proc. Phys. Soc. B*, **BXV** 782 (1952).
16. Ong Sing Poen, "Microprojection with X-rays," p. 31 Martinus Nijhoff, The Hague, 1959.
17. Ong Sing Poen, *Ibid.*, p. 74.
18. Mosley, V. M. and Wyckoff, W. G., *J. Ultracelstructure Res.*, **1**, 337 (1958).
19. Botden, P. J. M., Combée, B., and Houtman, J., *Phil. Tech. Rev.*, **14**, 114 (1952).

Ong Sing Poen

REFLECTION MICROSCOPY (KIRKPATRICK)

Since Röntgen's first unsuccessful experiments in attempting to concentrate x-rays by lenses and mirrors, many similar efforts have been made and the failures recorded in the literature. It has been evident always that a successful x-ray microscopy would open up fields of investigation closed to optical microscopy because of limited resolution and to electron microscopy because of the very limited penetration of electrons, thus necessitating extremely thin specimens. All such attempts until the one announced in September, 1948, were unsuccessful, so that focusing and image formation in a microscope were generally considered to be impossible. Accepting the known fact of total reflection of x-rays from mirrors at extremely

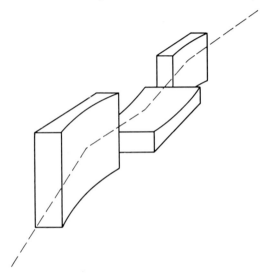

FIG. 1. Arrangement of reflecting mirrors.

small grazing angles of incidence, Prof. Paul Kirkpatrick of Stanford University has taken a great step forward toward a successful solution of a seemingly impossible problem.

A concave spherical mirror receiving x-rays at grazing incidence images a point into a line in accordance with a focal length $f = Ri/2$, where R is the radius of curvature and i the grazing angle. The image is subject to an aberration such that a ray reflected at the periphery of the mirror misses the focal point of central rays by a distance given by $S = 1.5Mr^2/R$, where M is the magnification of the image and r is the radius of the mirror face. The possible resolving power is such as to resolve points separated by 70 A, independent of wavelength. Point images of points and, therefore, extended images of extended objects may be produced by causing the x-rays to reflect from two concave mirrors in series, particularly when crossed at right angles to each other. Figure 1 gives a schematic idea of the arrangement of the mirrors of the apparatus, Fig. 2 reproduces photographs of the microscope, Fig. 3 is a reproduction of the photographed enlarged images from a 350-mesh screen. This figure shows, besides the full image from both mirrors (upper left), partial images from each mirror separately (H, upper right, V, lower

| A | B |

FIG. 2. Reflection microscope: (a) end showing x-ray tube (right) specimen, specimen holder and mirror mount; (b) film end showing window for observing fluorescent screen.

Fig. 3. Enlarged images of 350-mesh screen in x-ray microscope. (Kirkpatrick.) Upper left, full image from two mirrors; upper right, partial image from horizontal mirror; lower left, partial image from vertical mirror; lower right, direct radiation.

left, and the large spot, lower right, caused by direct radiation).

While this development is still in its early stages both in theory and in practice, it is evident that there is every prospect of a successful x-ray microscope. Elliptical surfaces already have been found to be superior to spherical or cylindrical ones in tests with mirrors made by coating a spherical mirror with a continuously variable amount of gold. Magnifications of 70 diameters already obtained are bound to be exceeded. The optical system is also suitable for focusing of very soft x-rays with wavelengths up to 45 A used for diffraction analysis of structures of materials with very large d spacings and microradiography of single cells (cf. article on Ultrasoft X-ray Microscopy, by B. Henke); and for focusing of neutrons. As the very newest development is the use of a system of cross-reflecting mirrors to focus *solar x-rays* in an *X-Ray Telescope*, as described by A. V. Baez in the Encyclopedia of Spectroscopy (q.v.).

REFERENCES

1. Clark, G. L., "Applied X-rays," 4th ed., Mc-Graw-Hill Book Company, N. Y., pp. 105–106, 1955.

2. *J. Opt. Soc. Amer.*, 38, 766 (September, 1948); also a manual prepared by A. V. Baez.

G. L. Clark

TWO-WAVE (BUERGER) MICROSCOPE

In the final analysis of ultimate crystal structures in terms of the motif, or complete configuration of a molecule serving as a point which is translated according to a definite repeating plan, a Fourier series is summed up. This is the same process as the superposition of many sets of interference fringes in a microscopic image. Hence optics provides several methods of Fourier synthesis in place of mathematical calculations.

The ultimate extension of the optical-analogue method is the two-wavelength microscope. Since x-rays cannot be focused as conveniently as visible light (cf. article on Reflection Microscopy (X-Rays)) it is possible only to collect a diffraction pattern. But W. L. Bragg also conceived the idea that, if visible light could be made to continue in the paths of the x-ray diffracted beams, it could be focused to give an image of the crystal. Such a two-wavelength microscope (Fig. 1) has been successfully constructed by Buerger at MIT, starting with a diffraction pattern photographed in his precession camera (an undistorted reciprocal-lattice photograph) which is equivalent to the interference pattern that would be formed by visible light and photographed by a lens. A replica of the x-ray pattern is made by boring holes in a brass plate and is placed in an optical system that produces an interference pattern which is the image of the original crystal. The most complex part of the apparatus involves the use of mica plates behind the holes in the brass plate capable of being tilted to produce phase shifts by varying the length of optical path. Individual rows of holes produce optical patterns as lines at right angles to the rows similar to the Bragg-Huggins fringes. The total effect is optical summation of all

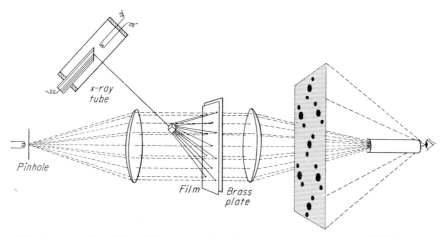

FIG. 1. The Buerger Two-Wave Microscope showing atomic arrangement of FeS_2, marcasite, on the screen.

patterns to give the structure pattern. The result for marcasite, FeS_2, is shown in Fig. 1.

Thus the good features of x-rays, with wavelengths short enough to be compatible with atomic dimensions, are combined with the scaling up by substitution of visible light of the whole optical image-forming process, so that the image is magnified by a factor of the quotient of the wavelength of visible light to that of x-rays, or 10^7 diameters.

REFERENCES

1. BUERGER, M. J., *J. Appl. Phys.*, **21,** 909 (1950).
2. CLARK, G. L., "Applied X-rays," 4th ed., Mc-Graw-Hill Book Company, N. Y., pp. 460–462, 1955.

G. L. CLARK

ULTRASOFT X-RAY MICROSCOPY

X-ray microscopy has essentially the same resolution limit as does light microscopy and it is usually the slower and less convenient of the two methods. Nevertheless there are important possible advantages of x-ray microscopy which arise mainly through the basic differences in the optics of image formation and in the image contrast mechanism.

The simple method utilized in the projec-tion of x-ray images is illustrated in Fig. 1. Here it is seen that all planes of the three-dimensional object are imaged, with equal sharpness, into an essentially two dimensional plane—usually a thin photographic emulsion which becomes the "microradiogram." Such complete depth of field can only be approximately realized with light microscopy through the use of very small objective apertures and with a consequent sacrifice of resolution due to diffraction. Sharp projection images, relatively free of Fresnel diffraction blurring, are possible only with the shorter wavelength x-radiations. This two dimensional microradiogram "model" of the object is often more amenable to high resolution measurement of structural detail and to quantitative stereographic analysis of thickness or depth dimensions.

Unlike light images, x-ray images have contrast which is due mainly to photo-electric absorption of the x-radiation by the sample; the complicating effects of refraction, diffraction and reflection are either small or completely negligible. This leads to a relatively unambiguous interpretation of contrast and often permits quantitative microabsorption analysis. X-ray absorption analysis complements that by light absorp-

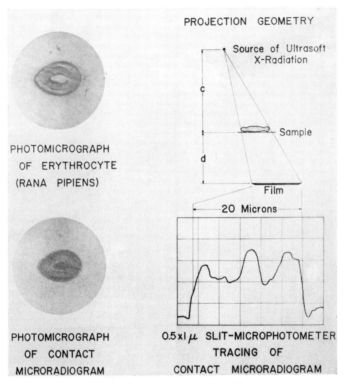

PROJECTION GEOMETRY

PHOTOMICROGRAPH
OF ERYTHROCYTE
(RANA PIPIENS)

PHOTOMICROGRAPH
OF CONTACT
MICRORADIOGRAM

0.5 x 1 μ SLIT-MICROPHOTOMETER
TRACING OF
CONTACT MICRORADIOGRAM

FIG. 1. Illustrating the point of projection geometry utilized in x-ray microscopy. Interpretation of the structure of the biological cell from the light microscope micrograph is made difficult because of such effects as refraction and a very short depth of field. Contrast in the x-ray microscope picture is simply and directly related to the chemistry and mass-thickness of the cell.

tion since it measures the mass and elementary chemistry of the sample only, and it is not sensitive to the effects of molecular combination of the elements as is light absorption analysis. It is also of importance to note that a wide range of x-ray wavelengths are available for microscopy, e.g., 1 to 100 A, with an associated range of absorption coefficients which vary by a factor of 100,000.

A considerable amount of research has been reported since the time of the discovery of x-rays on contact microradiography with radiation in the 1 to 10 A region. In this kind of x-ray microscopy, conventional x-ray sources are used and the samples are placed in contact with the photographic emulsion. In 1951 Cosslett and Nixon introduced projection microradiography in which the samples are placed very near a point source of

x-rays of micron dimensions and generated by precisely focusing a demagnified electron image of an electron source onto the target material using magnetic lenses (see paper by Ong Sing Poen, this volume). For nearly all of this work with the soft x-rays (1 to 10 A) the relatively thick samples required for contrast limits the useful magnification to about 300×. However, for dense materials of the heavier elements, resolutions have been obtained with these radiations which have permitted magnifications of the order of 1000×. Quantitative x-ray microscopic analysis for both the mass and the elementary chemistry of biological materials was first introduced by Engstrom in 1946. He was also one of the first to recognize the feasibility of using the ultrasoft x-radiations for high resolution microradiographic analysis. References to most of the work accomplished to date in x-ray microscopy may be found in the several that are listed at the end of this paper (1).

The wavelengths in the 10 to 50 A region are of particular value for the quantitative analysis of micron-size systems of organic and light element inorganic composition— i.e. for elements up through Ge 32. This follows from the fact (to be established in a later section) that at least 60% absorption is required for precisions in the one to five percent region in the measurement of the parameter μm, where m is the sample mass-per-unit-area "thickness" and μ is the mass absorption coefficient as defined by the expression for the ratio of transmitted to incident monochromatic x-radiation

$$t = I/I_0 = e^{-\mu m} \qquad (1)$$

It is shown in Fig. 2 that in order to have 60% absorption for either light element inorganic or organic materials with thicknesses of the order of one micron, wavelengths in the 10 to 50 A region should be employed. The discontinuities in these curves are due to the presence of critical K or L absorption edges. Ultrasoft radiations are of very great value for the microanalysis of this highly important problem area of the lighter element samples not only because optimum absorption signal may be gained, but also because either the K or the L absorption edges for the elements of atomic number 6 to 32 lie in this 10 to 50 A x-ray region. These absorption edges form the bases for sensitive, differential absorption analysis.

In the sections that follow, analysis and experimental results are presented in order to illustrate optimum methods and instrumentation and application of high resolution, ultrasoft x-ray microscopy for quantitative analysis.

Resolution Limit for X-Ray Microscopy

As stated above, the first requirement for resolving microscopic detail of fractional

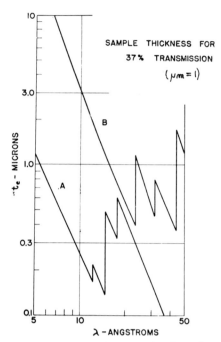

FIG. 2. Indicating the necessity for using the ultrasoft wavelength in order to gain the sufficient absorption in micron-size systems for quantitative measurement.

micron dimensions is sufficient contrast for detection and measurement. This must be met, for samples comprised of elements from the lower half of the periodic table, by the use of the ultrasoft wavelengths (10 to 100 A). It is important to note, however, that as the wavelength is increased in order to gain contrast, the diffraction blurring of the image also increases. The resolution limit is reached when this diffraction error becomes comparable with the object dimensions which are required for minimum absorption contrast.

The characteristics of the diffraction error for an image formed by monochromatic radiation from a point source is illustrated in Fig. 3. The effect of having a finite source size and perhaps polychromatic radiation is simply the superposition and addition of many such intensity patterns so as to blur the edge of the image. The minimum error may be measured by the distance, f, from

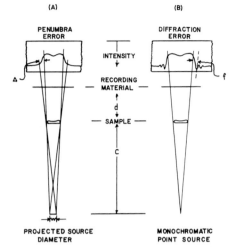

(A) PENUMBRA ERROR (B) DIFFRACTION ERROR

FIG. 3. Defining the two major causes for image unsharpness in ultrasoft x-ray microscopy due to (a) finite source size and (b) Fresnel diffraction.

the ideal image edge position, formed without diffraction, to the position of the first intensity maximum. This may be shown from diffraction theory to be given by the relation

$$f = (\lambda L)^{1/2} x^{1/2}/(1 + x) \text{ microns} \qquad (2)$$

with L measured in cm and λ in angstroms. L is the source to image distance and x is the ratio of sample-to-image distance to sample-to-source distance, d/c. It is evident from this relation, as plotted in Fig. 4, that the diffraction error is maximum for x equal to unity and primary magnification equal to $2X$ ($M = 1 + x$), assuming the camera length, L, to be constant. As has been [2] pointed out, the diffraction limit for $2X$ magnification is actually 70 % of that for high magnification projection microscopy for dimension c held constant, i.e., for constant sample field. In order to reduce this error one must use either unit primary magnification (contact method) or high primary magnification. For contact microradiography Eq. (2) may be written as

$$f = (\lambda d)^{1/2} \qquad (3)$$

and for projection microradiography ($x \gg 1$)

$$f = (\lambda c)^{1/2} \qquad (4)$$

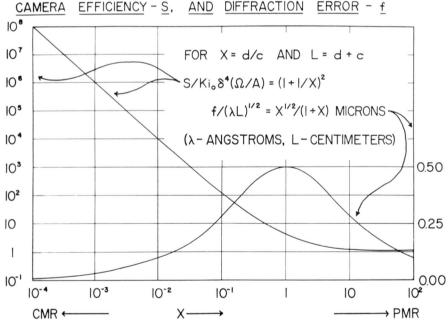

CAMERA EFFICIENCY – S, AND DIFFRACTION ERROR – f

FOR X = d/c AND L = d + c

$$S/K_{i_o}\delta^4(\Omega/A) = (1 + 1/X)^2$$

$$f/(\lambda L)^{1/2} = X^{1/2}/(1 + X) \text{ MICRONS}$$

(λ – ANGSTROMS, L – CENTIMETERS)

CMR ←——— X ——→ ——→ PMR

FIG. 4. Illustrating the very high efficiency and relative freedom from Fresnel diffraction error for contact microradiography.

In order to compare the two methods, let us consider the error associated with an object of one micron dimensions and of composition (organic or of the lighter elements) requiring typically about 25 A for measurable contrast. For contact microradiography the effective emulsion thickness is a fraction of a micron so that d is of the order of one micron and the error becomes from (3) about 0.05 micron. This is appreciably less than the diffraction error resulting from the light microscope used to measure the microradiogram which, for high resolution measurement, is about 0.2 μ and which is consequently the limit of resolution for contact microradiography. To minimize diffraction error in projection microscopy the sample must be placed as close to the x-ray point source as is practical. For this distance equal to 0.1 mm the error is equal to 0.5 μ and for the sample to source distance equal to 25 microns or 0.001″, the error becomes 0.25 μ. It should be noted that even if the wavelength could be reduced to one fourth (6A) as permitted by heavy element samples, this error is reduced by only one half. It is therefore concluded that *projection microscopy has a resolution limit comparable to that of light microscopy and contact microradiography.*

Relative Efficiency of X-Ray Microscope Methods

At present, the most serious practical limitation on x-ray microscopy is the very low efficiency of production of the required low-voltage x-radiations. With three or four kilovolts and maximum beam current, present day projection microscopes yield barely enough intensity for the required fluorescent screen focusing of the point source as generated by magnetic lens demagnification of a point source of electrons. Exposure times are often longer than can be tolerated because of the instability of the focal spot position. To date no projection microscopes have been developed for the ultrasoft wavelengths.

There is a possibility of successfully meeting the intensity problem by operating the present projection microscopes at normally high voltages with transmission targets of such thickness and composition that a sufficient amount of the desired ultrasoft radiation is generated along with the shorter wavelengths. The harder radiations would permit precise adjustment for high resolution work and might then be rejected in the microradiographic measurement by a recording material sensitive only to the ultrasoft component, e.g., the usual, very thin concentrated Lippmann emulsion mounted upon a thin plastic film, the combination being transparent to the harder radiation.

The relative efficiency of the two methods, defined as the reciprocal of the exposure time required per unit sample area, may be established as follows:

The camera speed, S, defined as the reciprocal of the time required to record a given sample, is equal to the product of i_0, the radiant flux per unit solid angle and per unit projected source area; of Ω, the solid angle of the x-radiation which is utilized; of the projected source area, which is proportional to the source diameter, w, squared; of the sensitivity of the recording material which is assumed proportional to the square of its resolution error, Δ_r; and divided by the area of the irradiated recording material, M^2A, where M is the primary magnification and A is the sample area. Thus,

$$S = \frac{Ki_0\Omega w^2\Delta_r^2}{M^2A} \qquad (5)$$

For an optimum condition of operation, the penumbra error, Δ, is equated to the recording error, Δ_r. Also, from Fig. 3 it is noted that

$$\Delta = wx = M\delta = (1 + x)\delta \qquad (6)$$

where $x = d/c$ and δ is the error, Δ, as measured at the sample. The maximum camera speed may then be written as

$$S = Ki_0\delta^4(\Omega/A)(1 + 1/x)^2. \qquad (7)$$

679

Two important facts are immediately evident from this result: (1) In order to gain maximum speed and because of the dependence upon δ^4, it is very essential that the recording material and the source size be "matched" to the particular resolution problem as required by Eq. (*6*). (2) The microscope efficiency, which is equal to SA, is very much greater for the contact method than for the projection method as illustrated in Fig. 4.

For high-resolution projection microscopy ($x \gg 1$) the camera speed, S, is equal to $Ki_0\delta^4/c^2$ and the efficiency, SA, is a constant equal to $Ki_0\delta^4\Omega$. For contact microradiography, the camera speed is essentially constant for a given sample thickness, d, and equal to $Ki_0\delta^4/d^2$ and the efficiency is equal $Ki_0\delta^4\Omega/x^2$. (In the expressions for S, Ω has been equated to A/c^2.) It should be noted that the maximum speed, S, for contact microradiography is higher than that for projection microscopy if the same source or source brightness, i_0, is used since the sample-to-film distance, d, for contact microradiography is usually less than the sample to source distance, c, in projection microscopy.

The specific intensity, i_0, is limited by the rate of heat dissipation in the conventional large focal spot tubes. For the microfocus source, however, the efficiency of heat transfer is much higher for geometrical reasons and i_0 is not set by the target loading limit but rather it is set by the maximum beam current as allowed for a given resolution required for the electron optical system. In practice i_0 may be as much as fifty times higher for the microfocus tubes. This fact is often utilized in order to reduce exposure time in contact microradiography, at the sacrifice of sample field, by placing the sample and film very close to the microfocus source.

Contact Method or Projection Method?

From the foregoing discussion, certain conclusions may now be summarized: (1) The resolution limit of both contact and projection microscopy are essentially the same and equal to that of light microscopy, viz. about 0.2 μ. The present practical limit of resolution of both methods is dependent somewhat upon the resolving power of present day concentrated Lippmann emulsions and other recording materials for contact microradiography and upon the intensity problem and consequent instability problem for high-resolution projection microscopy. For dense, heavy element samples, and with shorter wavelength x-rays, resolutions of about 0.1 μ might be achieved with the projection method as demonstrated by Nixon using a silver grid (3). (2) The contact method can yield shorter exposure times (higher speed) and shorter exposure-times-per-unit-sample-area (higher efficiency) than are possible with the projection method—this fact is of utmost importance in the ultrasoft x-ray analysis. (3) Inasmuch as intense, sharply focused sources are required for projection microscopy, and are not needed for contact microscopy, the instrumentation for the contact method is much simpler and is easier to operate for high resolution work.

It should be emphasized here, nevertheless, that the projection microscope becomes of considerable advantage for certain special problems (see paper of Ong Sing Poen) and also that the excellent electron-optical systems which have been developed for projection microscopy are of very great and unique value as tools in other kinds of microanalysis.

Ultrasoft X-Ray Absorption Measurement

Most of the ultrasoft x-ray interaction is by photoelectric absorption, and, in general, the relatively small amount of the incident energy that is scattered is coherent and in the forward direction (low-angle scattering and diffraction) (4). The energy which is photoelectrically absorbed is re-emitted first as a photoelectron and subsequently, as the atom returns to its normal state, as fluorescent radiation and Auger electrons. Because of the extremely low fluorescent yield for ultrasoft x-ray interactions the fraction of this energy which reaches the recording material in either projection or contact microscopy is negligible. Because of the extremely short range of the emitted electrons within the sample and its supporting membrane, this component of the transmitted energy is also negligible.

It is thus evident that projection microscopy measures the amount of energy which is photoelectrically absorbed and low-angle scattered out of the direct beam. It is important to note that contact microscopy, with ultrasoft radiations, measures only the amount of energy which is photoelectrically absorbed since low-angle scattered energy remains effectively in the direct beam within the short distance to the recording material. Because the amount of energy that is not scattered at the very low angles is so small, the contrast, or absorption signal, in contact microradiograms may be considered as resulting purely from photoelectric absorption.

The measured sample transmission by Eq. (1) depends only upon the mass photoelectric absorption coefficient, μ, and the mass-per-unit-area-thickness, m, of the sample. The photoelectric absorption cross-section is a function only of the x-ray wavelength and the atomic number of the absorbing element; it is not sensitive to the molecular combination of the elements, and, unlike the scattering cross section, it is not a function of the physical structure of the sample. *This simple and direct connection between the mass-and-elementary-chemistry of the sample and the x-ray transmission as easily measured from the microradiogram is probably the greatest and most distinctive advantage of this form of microscopy.*

It is for this reason the writer has felt that it is important that work be carried out on the measurement and tabulation of photoelectric absorption coefficients for the ultrasoft x-ray region and on the development of efficient ultrasoft x-ray sources of monochro-

matic radiation. A tentative tabulation (see Table 1) of light element mass absorption coefficients has been established (5) based upon a semiempirical method of interpolation from the best available absorption data and listed here for the several monochromatic ultrasoft wavelengths which have been found to be useful in this laboratory for quantitative microradiographic analysis.

Example of an Ultrasoft X-Ray Source and Camera for Contact Microradiography

There are three basic types of x-ray sources for contact microradiography: The first is a microfocus source used for maximum speed contact microradiography, as mentioned above, in which the sample and film are placed very near the source. The high speed is at the expense of sample field which is of the order of size equal to the source-to-sample distance. The second type is a source of conventional focal spot size, a few mm or less, and it permits sample fields of the order of one to two cm in diameter at the minimum working distance for high resolution. There are many such sources described in the literature (1) and these have been applied primarily for polychromatic radiation. The third type, which has been under development in this laboratory, utilizes a large focal spot area and consequently requires relatively large anode power; but it is designed for quantitative, microradiographic analysis, presenting monochromatic radiation and a relatively large, uniform field. It is described below.

Monochromatic ultrasoft radiation is gained by utilizing the K or L characteristic radiation from an appropriate target material. This radiation is isolated from the relatively low intensity background radiation by a proper choice of filter and excitation voltage. In order to obtain such radiation it is extremely important that the target be kept free from tungsten and carbonaceous contamination otherwise the low-voltage elec-

TABLE 1. MASS ABSORPTION COEFFICIENTS FOR SOME USEFUL ULTRASOFT WAVELENGTHS DERIVED SEMIEMPIRICALLY[1] WITH A PROBABLE ERROR OF ABOUT ±2%

Absorber	Atomic Number	Al Kα_{12} 8.34 A	Cu Lα_{12} 13.3 A	Fe Lα_{12} 17.6 A	Cr Lα_{12} 21.7 A	O Kα_{12} 23.7 A	Ti Lα_{12} 27.4 A	C Kα_{12} 44. A
H	1	7.5	30	70	130	170	260	1100
He	2	30	120	275	500	660	1000	4300
Li	3	78	280	640	1200	1450	2300	9400
Be	4	151.7	581	1288	2292	2965	4532	17430
B	5	323.7	1233	2711	4784	6130	9200	32540
C	6	605	2290	4912	8440	10730	15760	
N	7	1047	3795	7910	13120	16270	22590	3647
O	8	1560	5430	10740	16610	983	1473	5470
F	9	1913	6340	11600	1015	1301	1949	7280
Ne	10	2763	8240	1079	1863	2379	3575	13180
Na	11	3129	661	1402	2429	3100	4651	16650
Mg	12	3797	981	2085	3601	4592	6830	22850
Al	13	322.6	1146	2441	4189	5310	7840	24910
Si	14	510	1813	3812	6420	8040	11510	33840
P	15	640	2259	4661	7670	9470	13280	38610
S	16	814	2839	5710	9160	11190	15520	45230
Cl	17	990	3364	6530	10210	12450	17330	50100
A	18	1163	3795	7110	11070	13540	18820	
K	19	1429	4504	8310	12960	15820	22030	
Ca	20	1706	5150	9450	14800	18030	24910	
Zapon		998	3571	7270	11690	6500	9470	
Parlodion		1177	4167	8390	13320	5450	7870	
Animal proteins		854	3095	6391	10480	8719	12584	
H$_2$O		1388	4830	9554	14779	893	1338	4984

Zapon (H 5.3%, C 46.7%, N 6.6%, O 41.4%), Parlodion (H 3.6%, C 28.1%, N 11.5%, O 56.8%), Animal Proteins (H 7%, C 52.5%, N 16.5%, O 22.5%, S 1.5%)

tron beam will be prevented from ever reaching the target and exciting the desired characteristic radiation. This primary requirement has been met in two ways, as is illustrated in Fig. 5.

Tungsten contamination has been eliminated by placing the tungsten coil emitter below the target and by electrostatically focusing the electron beam along a circular path to the target surface. In order to avoid the space charge limiting of the beam current which usually accompanies the "hiding" of the anode from the emitter, a special grid at anode potential has been employed.

The carbonaceous depositing under the interaction of the electron beam and hydrocarbon vapors at the target has been minimized by maintaining a vacuum of about 10^{-6} mm pressure, using water-cooled baffles and a charcoal trap between the oil diffusion pump and the x-ray source. A sample may be introduced without contaminating the x-ray source by using a separately evacuated camera and a vacuum isolation gate which is used to introduce a thin filter-window to the

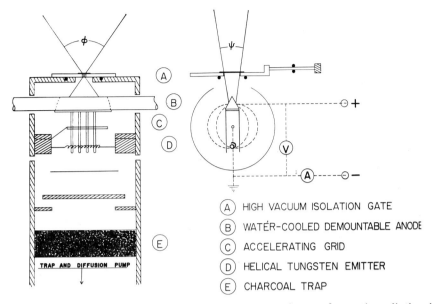

(A) HIGH VACUUM ISOLATION GATE

(B) WATER-COOLED DEMOUNTABLE ANODE

(C) ACCELERATING GRID

(D) HELICAL TUNGSTEN EMITTER

(E) CHARCOAL TRAP

FIG. 5. The schematic design of an ultrasoft x-ray source of monochromatic radiation in which tungsten contamination of the target has been eliminated by placing the emitter below the anode.

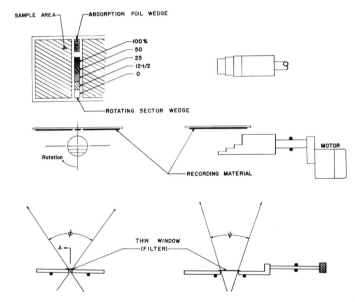

FIG. 6. Illustrating the method used for generating an exposure wedge for the precise calibration of a large-field microradiographic plate for quantitative analysis.

source when the camera has been pumped down.

In order to carry out precise quantitative microradiographic analysis, it is necessary to have a sufficient area of uniform field on the microradiogram plate for an accurate exposure wedge. Such a wedge, as shown in Fig. 6, generated simultaneously with the sample exposure, permits an accurate calibration of the emulsion, without the extreme

683

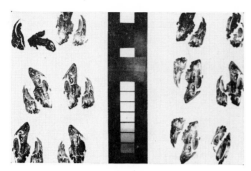

FIG. 7. A print taken directly from a micro-radiogram of 24 embryonic rat head sections illustrating the relatively large uniform field available for an exposure wedge, multiple samples and controls.

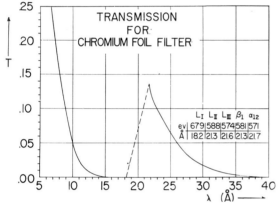

	L_I	L_II	L_III	β_1	α_12
ev	679	588	574	581	571
Å	182	213	216	213	21.7

FIG. 8. The transmission characteristic for a typical filter as used for isolating the Cr-L(21.7 A) and O-K(23.7 A) radiations. One kilovolt excitation of these characteristic wavelengths places the relatively sharp peak of the continuous radiation within the absorption band, 12 to 18 A.

normal to the direction of the anode so that effectively a "point" area of the anode is "seen" at any given position on the micro-radiographic plate. With the instrument described here, 2 by 3 inch glass microradiographic plates are exposed with a good uniformity of field area for the exposure wedge and with four square inches of area for the mounting of multiple samples and controls (see Fig. 7).

In order to gain high specific intensity from the target, the tube has been designed for large anode power—up to about 1000 ma beam currents for anode voltages in the range of 500 to 2000 volts.

Aluminum, copper and iron anode tubes are used for Al–K (8.3A) Cu-L(13.3 A) and Fe-L(17.6 A) respectively, using filter materials of the same metal as the target. A copper anode is used, plated with chromium for Cr-L(21.7 A), oxidized for O–K(23.7 A), vacuum evaporation coated with titanium for Ti-L(27.4 A), and painted with aquadag for C-K(44 A).

In general, relatively heavy filtering and low-excitation voltages are used in order to insure monochromaticity. For example a typical transmission curve for a chromium filter is as shown in Fig. 8. For chromium radiation, one kilovolt excitation is used, placing the relatively sharp peak of the continuous radiation well within the 12 to 18 angstrom absorption band which is illustrated here. The Lβ radiation is repressed by the effect of its wavelength lying between those of the critical L II and L III absorption edges. To estimate the effectiveness of a given filter and to determine the maximum tube voltage permissible, it has been convenient to observe the pulse height distribution appropriately displayed on an oscilloscope which is connected directly to the preamplifier of a flow-type proportional counter. A pulse height distribution curve for the O–K radiation from a copper oxide target at 1 kV potential and filtered by a chromium foil filter is illustrated in Fig. 9.

care and control in photographic development as required by separate emulsion calibration exposures. (This same requirement for a large uniform field obtains also for the conventional step-wedge of foils of a material of known thickness and of similar absorption characteristics as that of the sample.) In order to achieve this large angular field for the x-ray source without the use of excessively large, thin-foil window areas, a "line" source is employed as shown in Fig. 5, consisting of a water-cooled anode tube. The window is of slit geometry, the long dimension being

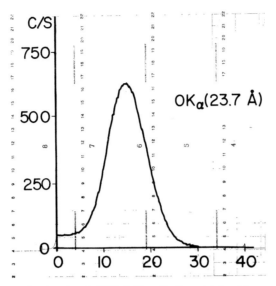

FIG. 9. Pulse height distribution for O-K(23.7 A) radiation obtained from an oxidized copper anode at one kilovolt excitation and with a chromium filter as described in Fig. 8.

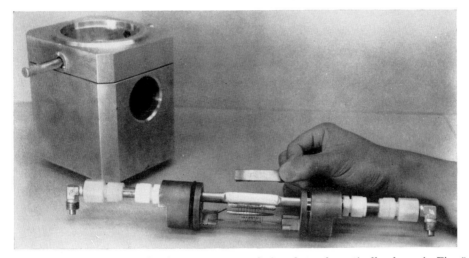

FIG. 10. Photograph of a "plug-in" x-ray source designed as schematically shown in Fig. 5.

In Figs. 10 and 11 are shown photographs of the source and the camera, and in Fig. 12 is shown the complete instrument mounted with its power supply.

Measurement of the Microradiographic Image

The photographic method has been the most successful of those proposed to date for quantitative ultrasoft x-ray microradiographic analysis. It would be ideal if the transmitted intensity could be measured directly, as, for example, by a proportional counter, by microphotometry from a fluorescent screen image, or by the direct measurement of the photo and Auger electrons emitted by the sample by electron multiplier techniques. However, a very high image in-

FIG. 11. Showing the three sections, the baffle and trap, the x-ray source, and the camera.

the contrast and density of the image. The resolution for line gratings or grids (lines per mm resolution of black and white areas) is equal to or better than that for the light microscope itself. However the spatial resolution needed, for example, in the measurement of the variation of mass thickness, as measured across an image of a biological cell, is limited to about 0.5 μ so that the recording material and not the light optical measurement becomes the limiting factor.

The writer has made some preliminary measurements on very thin "grainless" phosphors used as recording material, photomicrographing the fluorescent image during the x-ray exposure. These were made by the evaporation of Mn-activated Zn_2SiO_4 (obtained from General Electric) according to the method developed by Feldman and O'Hara (6). It was hoped that, at the expense of sensitivity, higher resolution might be gained. Measurements from thin layers of this phosphor evaporated upon quartz cover-slips have indicated comparable granu-

tensity is required for precise measurements to be made within one square micron of area or less—this fact is clearly evidenced by the requirement for very high-intensity light sources in ordinary microphotometry of such resolution. And, as indicated earlier, because of the very low efficiency of production of ultrasoft radiations, such high image intensities are extremely difficult to realize. The amplification of the x-ray "signal," resulting from the development of the photographic image, has made this method highly efficient.

The resolution of the finest grain photographic emulsions which are currently available, e.g., Eastman Spectroscopic-649, is between 0.1 and 1.0 micron, depending upon

FIG. 12. The complete ultrasoft x-ray microradiographic analysis system with power supply and vacuum gage circuit.

larity to that of Lippmann emulsions and lower contrast. Pattee has carried this work (7) much further and has developed an instrument, called the microfluoroscope (p. 563), which permits direct viewing of the image from such a phosphor recording material, gaining the necessary maximum intensity by placing the sample within 0.1 mm or less of a microfocus source. He has reported that adequate intensity has been obtained for direct viewing, using a 3 micron aluminum target foil, at 9 kilovolt excitation. At the Stockholm Symposium on X-Ray Microscopy in 1959, Auld and McNeil reported that xerography (8), with liquid developers, will also yield resolution comparable to that of the concentrated Lippmann emulsions. To date none of the non-photographic recording materials has been demonstrated as being superior to the photographic method for quantitative measurements in ultrasoft microradiographic analysis.

The following analysis is given in order to establish an optimum procedure in photographic measurement for microradiography. Let us consider first the determination of the absorption parameter μm (μ the mass absorption coefficient and m the mass-per-unit-area-thickness) *for a small object* which has caused only a relatively small variation in the density of the microradiogram. The photographic blackening or density will be defined as D_s in the region originally under the sample object, and as D_b in the immediate surrounding. The corresponding x-ray exposures which resulted in these densities will be defined as E_s and E_b. The photographic densities are related to the photometer readings on the microradiogram, (p_2 in the sample region, p_1 in the immediate surrounding, and p_0 in the clear emulsion) by the defining equations

$$D_s = \log (p_0/p_2) \text{ and } D_b = \log (p_0/p_1) \quad (8)$$

The ratio of the x-ray exposures for the sample and surroundings is equal to the ratio of the corresponding intensities (reciprocity law obtaining for these wavelengths) and therefore given, from (1), as

$$E_s/E_b = e^{-\mu m} \quad (9)$$

so that

$$\log E_b - \log E_s = \mu m \log e = \Delta(\log E) \quad (10)$$

Since the parameter μm is measured by the value $\Delta(\log E)$, it is convenient to present the emulsion characteristics as

$$D = f(\log E) \quad (11)$$

as is conventional for light photography. Then from (8), (10) and (11) and for relatively small differences between E_b and E_s, we may write

$$\Delta D/\Delta(\log E) = df/d(\log E)$$

$$\gamma = \log (p_2/p_1)/\mu m \log e$$

giving finally

$$\gamma\mu m = \ln (p_2/p_1) \quad (12)$$

where γ is the slope of the D vs log E characteristic, conventionally designating emulsion contrast, and $\log(p_2/p_1)/\log e$ has been replaced by the logarithm to the natural base, e, viz. $\ln(p_2/p_1)$.

We may now determine the effect of the measurement errors upon the determination of μm. By differentiating (12) we obtain

$$d(\mu m)/\mu m = \frac{\mp(dp_2/p_2) \mp (dp_1/p_1)}{\gamma\mu m}$$

$$= \frac{\sqrt{(dp_1/p_1)^2 + (dp_2/p_2)^2}}{(\gamma\mu m)} \quad (13)$$

in which we have added ($\mp$) errors in the usual manner.

In order to define the conditions required for minimum error it is necessary to define the type of photometric error, (dp/p), involved in a given measurement. For *low magnification* work in which emulsion granularity is *not* the dominant source of error, we may often have $dp_1 \approx dp_2 \approx$ a constant over the entire range of the photometer scale. For this case, (13) may be rewritten as

$$d(\mu m)/\mu m = \left\{ \frac{\sqrt{1 + (p_2/p_1)^2}}{\ln (p_2 p_1)} \right\} (dp_2/p_2) \quad (14)$$

(Low Magnification)

where (dp_2/p_2) is the relative error of the higher photometer reading. The low magnification error function, presented in brackets in (14) has a minimum value as illustrated in Fig. 13. In order to minimize such error, p_2 should be set at full photometer scale reading and p_2 should lie between about $1/7$ and $1/2$ of this p_2 reading. This requires a corresponding values of $\gamma \mu m$ in the range 0.7 to 2.0. *It is important to note the rapid increase of the error in μm for lower values of $\gamma \mu m$.*

To measure relatively small values of μm, it is clearly evident that the exposure time be such as to gain a maximum value for the contrast, γ. As may be deduced from the characteristic curves, D vs log E, as plotted in Fig. 14, this requires exposures for relatively high densities, contrary to conventional x-ray practice. It is convenient that this high-γ region also produces optimum

visual contrast—a fact which has been long recognized. And finally since γ is constant in this high-density region, the relation given in (12) need not apply only for small values of μm, as assumed at the outset of this analysis.

For high magnification work, the dominant source of photometric error is emulsion granularity. It has been found that for such errors, $(dp_1/p_1) = (dp_2/p_2) = $ a constant for a given high magnification measurement (500 to 1000$\times$). For this case we rewrite (13) as

$$d(\mu m)/\mu m = \sqrt{2}(dp/p)/\gamma \mu m = \sqrt{2}/\mu m(\gamma/N) \quad (15)$$

The value of (dp/p), as due mainly to photographic noise and designated by the symbol N, has been measured as the average value of the relative variation in the photometer signal as read from microphotometer tracings at various microradiogram densities using a 0.5 by 1.0 micron slit. The results of such measurements are also illustrated in Fig. 14.

It should be noted that μm increases more

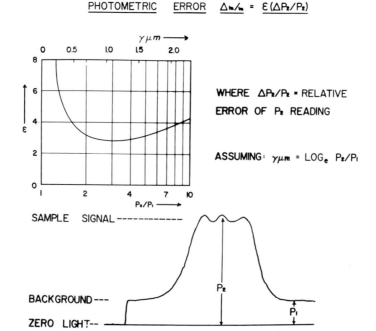

FIG. 13. The prediction of error for a measurement for the case of constant absolute photometric error, $dp_1 \approx dp_2$, as typical in low-magnification work.

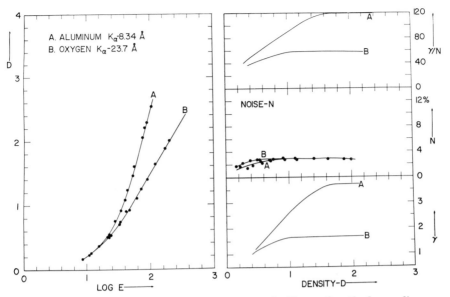

Fig. 14. The D vs log E characteristic for two wavelengths illustrating the longer linear region at the higher densities for the ultrasoft wavelength and the associated concontrast values, γ, and relative granularity noise, dp/p, measured with 0.5×1.0 micro slit microphotometry.

rapidly with wavelength than does (γ/N), indicating the value of the longer wavelengths in reducing measurement error. For a given wavelength, the value of (γ/N) may be considered a "figure of merit" for microradiographic emulsions. The value of (γ/N) is a maximum in the linear high density region is thus the optimum working region for both low and high magnification microradiographic measurement.

(γ/N) has been measured in a recent investigation (9) as a function of the type and time of photographic development which has indicated that a "soft" development such as 2 to 3 minutes in D158 (Eastman) seems optimum.

We may now summarize, from the foregoing discussion, the procedures for an optimum photographic measurement in microradiographic analysis: The absorption parameter, μm, may be simply determined for either high or low magnification through the relation

$$\mu m = (1/\gamma) \ln (p_2/p_1)$$

providing the exposure is for the linear high-

density region ($D > 1.0$ for ultrasoft radiations and spectrographic-649 emulsion) for which γ is a constant and of maximum value. The minimum wavelength permissible for low magnification ($dp_1 \approx dp_2$) is set by the requirement that $\gamma \mu m$ should lie within the range 0.7 to 2.0. The measurement errors become very large in this case for $\gamma \mu m < 0.5$. The minimum wavelength is set for high magnification ($dp_1/p_1 \approx dp_2/p_2$) by the requirement that μm satisfies the relation (15) for a given required measurement precision, $d(\mu m)/\mu m$, (or for dm/m-uniform chemistry) and for a given emulsion and hence (γ/N) value. The minimum wavelength and exposure time are thus fixed for each microradiographic measurement.

As shown, for example, in Fig. 14, the (γ/N) value for Spectroscopic-649 plate for 23.7 A radiation is about 60. Therefore, from (15), for a minimum error 2%, the x-ray wavelength should be chosen so that μm is at least equal to unity, corresponding to approximately 60% absorption.

To measure high densities on microradiogram areas of about one square micron or

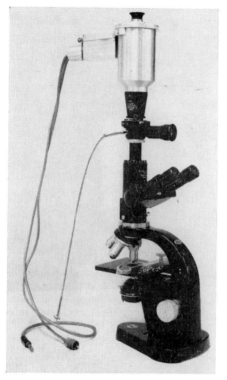

FIG. 15. The utilization of standard light microscope optics for high resolution microphotometry.

less presents a relatively difficult problem in microdensitometry which has been solved in the following manner: A very intense, concentrated light source is necessary, such as the high pressure mercury arc (AH-6 of General Electric for example). A trinocular microscope with a Leitz photomicrographic attachment has been found to be most convenient for the optical system, as shown in Fig. 15. The light is diverted to the binocular section only when surveying the microradiogram and centering the object area to be measured. For densitometric measurement the first image, as formed by the objective just below the projector lens in the photo-attachment, falls upon a stop with a 0.5 mm hole at its center. Only light from this central portion of the image proceeds directly to the top of a camera chamber which has been added to the Leitz attachment. Here 2″ x 2″

lantern slide plates can be exposed for convenient photomicrography, at 500× or less.

A low-power eyepiece is placed here for critical, direct focusing on the enlarged field. Also, at this final image plane, a "light pipe" may be slid into place consisting of a thin piece of glass with a 45° polished end and masked so that light from a 0.25 × 0.5 mm central field area may be internally and totally reflected at its tip, and channeled down the long glass section to a 1P21 (RCA) photomultiplier tube. The precise position of the equivalent 0.5 by 1.0 micron object field which is being measured may be simultaneously viewed by the upper eyepiece. The phototube output is "matched" to a ten millivolt chart recorder by connecting it directly to the 1.5 volt input of a standard vacuum tube voltmeter. The recorder is attached to the meter circuit of the VTVM. The sensitivity of the system is set by varying the multiplier tube voltage in the range 450–900 volts.

When a profile rather than point measurement is desired, the microradiogram is translated by means of a simple mechanical linkage between the stage screw and a synchronous motor. The latter is geared down to effect a 40 micron motion of the stage in about 3 minutes.

A 95× oil immersion apochromat objective is used. Monochromatic light, effectively the mercury 4360 A blue light, is obtained by a filter—it has been found that the (γ/N) ratio for blue light is 30 % higher than that for the green light (5461 A) because of the higher scattering efficiency of the Lippmann grains for the shorter wavelengths. The monochromatic light yields a significant improvement in image quality also.

Once the image field to be measured is located in the central hole at the stop in the projector lens, the prisms for side viewing are thrown out of the beam so that there are a minimum number of glass surfaces involved, and only the light forming the central image area which closely surrounds that being measured is allowed to pass through the projector lens to the phototube window. In this manner stray light scatter is effectively eliminated. In Fig. 16, the resolution of this system is demonstrated by the resolving of the Fresnel fringes associated with the imaging of a diffraction grating of 10 micron spacing; the freedom from stray light scattering or "spill-over" is shown by the relatively sharp corners of the shadow produced by a 25 micron wire.

Application of Contact Microradiography to Micromass Measurement

A standard test object which has been used in this study for quantitative microradiographic analysis has been the human red blood cell (erythrocyte) which was chosen not only because of its importance to certain medical research, but in particular here because it is of such material and size as to make its precise measurement approach the

MICROPHOTOMETER RESOLUTION

(0.5μ × 10μ SLIT)

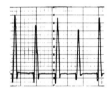

10μ - ZEISS CALIBRATION GRATING

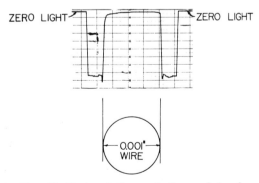

FIG. 16. Tests of the resolution and freedom from stray light scatter for the microphotometer shown in Fig. 14.

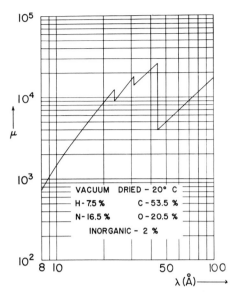

FIG. 17. Absorption characteristics for ultrasoft x-radiations of essentially the hemoglobin composition of human red blood cells (as determined for one test sample).

limit of present day x-ray microscopy and appreciably beyond the capability of other types of microscopy, e.g., interferometric microscopy. Sample smears of these cells are easy to prepare in a standard, reproducible manner. The single vacuum dried cell is approximately 8 microns in diameter, 2 microns in depth, biconcave, of total mass 30×10^{-12} g and of mass density of about 0.4 g/cm³. Its chemical composition is almost entirely hemoglobin.

In a recent study (10) a sample of normal blood was centrifuged and washed in physiological saline five times. 2″ x 3″ Spectroscopic-649 plates were coated with a thin protective film of Parlodion by dipping into a 1 % solution of Parlodion in amyl acetate, and then smeared in the usual clinical manner. A portion of the same sample was chemically analysed for its effective absorption components, C, N, O and H. The analysis for this sample and the corresponding ultrasoft x-ray absorption curve is shown in Fig. 17.

A typical microradiographic field of the

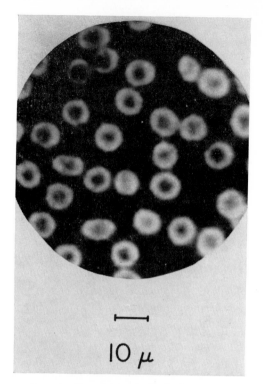

FIG. 18. Photomicrographed from a contact microradiogram of human erythrocyte.

CELL MASS MEASUREMENT

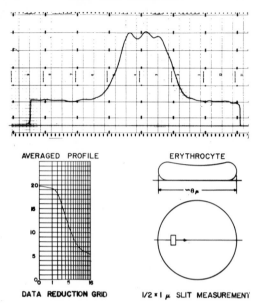

AVERAGED PROFILE

DATA REDUCTION GRID

ERYTHROCYTE

1/2 × 1 μ SLIT MEASUREMENT

FIG. 19. Photometer readings, p_2 and p_1, are taken from an average profile, assuming radial symmetry, at sixteen points at radial positions of such interval as to yield equal effect upon the total mass measurement. The reduction of such data to mass per unit area, m, and subsequent numerical integration for total mass was carried out with a digital computer.

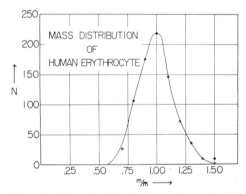

FIG. 20. The calculated values of $\gamma\mu m$ for eight hundred single cell measurements were divided by the average value to obtain a corresponding number of $m/\bar{m}$ values which are thus independent of γ and μ and their respective errors. These data were counted in intervals of 0.1. The precision (average deviation) of a single measurement is of the order 0.03.

smeared sample is shown in Fig. 18. The microradiogram, after exposure, was washed in acetone to remove the sample and Parlodion film and was developed for three minutes in D-158. O–K(23.7 A) radiation was used as obtained from an oxidized copper anode target excited at one kilovolt and with a chromium filter of transmission as shown in Fig. 8.

This ultrasoft radiation yields a value for $\gamma\mu m$ of about 1.2, and with γ equal to 1.72, μm is about 0.7. From (15) and for (γ/N) equal to about 60 for this measurement, the predicted average relative error is 3 % in a mass per unit area, m, determination.

The total cell mass was determined as illustrated in Fig. 19. Radial symmetry was assumed in these measurements and sixteen photometer readings, p_2, and the associated background reading, p_1, were taken from an averaged profile as determined from the mi-